Baylands Ecosystem

Species and Community Profiles

Life Histories and Environmental Requirements of Key Plants, Fish and Wildlife

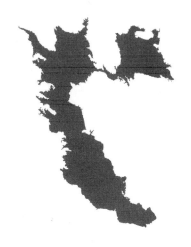

Prepared by the San Francisco Bay Area Wetlands Ecosystem Goals Project

To order additional copies of this report ($25.00 each), please contact:
San Francisco Estuary Project
c/o S.F. Bay Regional Water Quality Control Board
1515 Clay Street, Suite 1400
Oakland, CA 94612
(510) 622-2465

Please cite this report as:
Goals Project. 2000. Baylands Ecosystem Species and Community Profiles: Life histories and
environmental requirements of key plants, fish and wildlife. Prepared by the San Francisco Bay Area
Wetlands Ecosystem Goals Project. P.R. Olofson, editor. San Francisco Bay Regional Water Quality
Control Board, Oakland, Calif.

Also available from the Goals Project:
Baylands Ecosystem Habitat Goals: A report of habitat recommendations. March 1999. Reprint
with minor corrections, June 2000.

Printing of the Species Profiles was made possible, in part, by a grant from the CALFED Bay-Delta Program through
the U.S. Bureau of Reclamation to Friends of the Estuary:
CALFED Project #99-B10
U.S. Department of the Interior
Bureau of Reclamation Grant #00FC200183

On behalf of the Resource Managers Group and all of the other Goals Project participants, we offer our sincere thanks and appreciation to the authors of these profiles. The authors willingly volunteered their time to construct a good part of the biological foundation of the Habitat Goals. Little did they know when they started that their work eventually would comprise this fine report.

We also want to recognize the role of the San Francisco Bay Regional Water Quality Control Board in the preparation of this document. Without the support of the Regional Board's top managers—Loretta Barsamian, Larry Kolb, and Bruce Wolf—the profiles would likely still be a pile of interesting papers on the flora and fauna of the San Francisco Bay area, rather than a unified compendium. By encouraging their staff to compile and polish the profiles, they helped provide the public with a scientific document that will lead to the improvement of habitat conditions and water quality throughout the Bay and along its tributaries.

Above all, we would like to extend a special thanks to Peggy Olofson of the Regional Board. Peggy not only helped to manage the Goals Project through its four-year life, but she spent the better part of the past year preparing this document for press. Her work far exceeded merely editing the draft profiles. Rather, she collaborated with many of the report authors in acquiring data and expanding sections of text, cajoled authors into clarifying certain points, obtained photographs, hunted down references, created the report design, and laid out each page. And she did all this while attending to her regular duties as a Water Resources Engineer. We all owe Peggy our gratitude for a job well done.

Michael Monroe
Carl Wilcox

Resource Managers Group Co-Chairs
San Francisco Bay Area Wetlands
Ecosystem Goals Project

Credits

Editor

Peggy R. Olofson — San Francisco Bay Regional Water Quality Control Board

Authors

David G. Ainley
Joy D. Albertson
Janice M. Alexander
Peter R. Baye
Dennis R Becker
William G. Bousman
Andrée M Breaux
Michael L Casazza
Steven C. Chappell
Howard L. Cogswell
Ron Duke
Jules G. Evens
Phyllis M. Faber

Leora Feeney
Steve Foreman
Stephen L. Granholm
Brenda J. Grewell
Janet T. Hanson
Laura A. Hanson
Elaine K. Harding
Bruce Herbold
Catherine M. Hickey
Kathryn A. Hieb
Glen Holstein
Mark R. Jennings
Michael L. Johnson

Robert E. Jones
Kurt F. Kline
Brita C. Larsson
Robert A. Leidy
William Z. Lidicker, Jr.
Kevin MacKay
Wesley A. Maffei
Lt. Dante B. Maragni
Carolyn M. Marn
Michael F. McGowan
A. Keith Miles
Michael R. Miller
Gary W. Page

Thomas P. Ryan
Michael K. Saiki
Howard S. Shellhammer
Ted R. Sommer
Lynne E. Stenzel
John Y. Takekawa
Robert N. Tasto
Scott Terrill
Lynne A. Trulio
David C. VanBaren
Nils Warnock
Sarah E. Warnock
Frank G. Wernette

Report Production

Report Design & Layout: Peggy Olofson

Cover Design: Nina Lisowski

Computer & GIS Support: Jeff Kapellas

Text & Copy Editing: Cristina Grosso (lead)
Elisa Gill
Terra Hendrich
Harini Madhavan
Michael Monroe
Dewey Schwarzenberg
Jill Sunahara

Additional Assistance

In addition to the authors and production staff, we also thank the many people who provided support and assistance to make this publication possible.

We thank Marcia Brockbank and her staff at the San Francisco Estuary Project for ongoing help with funding and coordination, and the staff at CALFED and the Bureau of Reclamation for funding assistance. For generous and timely support for preliminary editing and document design, we thank the California Coastal Conservancy, and particularly Nadine Hitchcock.

Special thanks to Kathy Hieb, who provided extensive organizational and editing assistance with the fish profiles, in addition to authoring several of them herself. Several other authors, including Peter Baye, Bill Bousman, Howard Cogswell, Jules Evens, and Glen Holstein worked patiently with the editor over many months to provide additional tables and figures for the report.

For their guidance in publication planning and preparation, we thank Michelle Yang, Mark Rodgers, and the rest of the staff at Alonzo Environmental. Also, we thank Debbi Nichols for helping to keep things together when it was needed most.

Photography and Artwork

We would especially like to thank the photographers and artists who so graciously donated the use of their images for this publication:

Peter Baye

Berkeley Digital Library

Nancy Black, Monterey Bay Whale Watch
www.gowhales.com

Ted Brown, California Acadamy of Sciences

Mia Bruksman

California Dept. of Fish and Game (CDFG)

Les Chibana *les@auc.com*

Citizens' Committee to Complete the Refuge

Jack Kelly Clark, Statewide IPM Project. Permission by the Regents of the University of California

Howard L. Cogswell

Josh Collins

Don DesJardin
www.camacdonald.com/birding/DesJardin

Joe DiDonato, bioQuest Wildlife Photography and Consulting (510)769-9209

Dr. Richard B. Forbes

Dr. Allan Francis *garter.snake@virgin.net*

Rick A. Fridell *nrdwr.rfridell@state.ut.us*

S.H. Hinshaw

Dan Holland

Jimmy Hu
www.silcom.com/~njhua/otter/otter.html

Marshall Iliff *miliff@aol.com*

Dr. J.L. King

Peter LaTourrette *www.birdphotography.com*

Denise Loving *snakelady@home.com*

Wesley Maffei *midge@lanminds.com*

Peter Moyle, from *Inland Fishes of California*, copyright 1976. Permission by the Regents of the University of California

Ruth Pratt

T. Douglas Rodda *sawwhet@ix.netcom.com*

M. Roper, Aquatic Research Organisms, Hampton, NH (1991)

Tom Rountree

Brad Shaffer

Ted Sommer

Rick Stallcup

Dr. Daniel Sudia *dan.sudia@mindspring.com*

U.S. Fish and Wildlife Service (USFWS)

U.S. Geological Survey, National Biological Service (USGS/NBS)

Staffan Vilcans

Jens V. Vindum, California Acadamy of Sciences

Bob Walker

Peter S. Weber *www.wildbirdphotos.com*

Zoological Society of Milwaukee County, Wisconsin *www.zoosociety.org*

Contents

1. Plant Communities

2. Estuarine Fish and Associated Invertebrates

7. Bayland Birds Other than Shorebirds and Waterfowl

List of Tables

5. Mammals

6. Waterfowl and Shorebirds

7. Other Birds of the Baylands Ecosystem

List of Figures

4. Anphibians and Reptiles

5. Mammals

6. Waterfowl and Shorebirds

7. Other Birds of the Baylands Ecosystem

Introduction

The San Francisco Bay Area Wetlands Ecosystem Goals Project began in 1995 as a cooperative effort among nine state and federal agencies and nearly 100 Bay Area scientists. The Project's purpose was to develop a vision of the kinds, amounts, and distribution of habitats needed to sustain healthy populations of fish and wildlife in and around San Francisco Bay (**Figure 1**). This vision was presented to the public in the Goals Project's final report, the *Baylands Ecosystem Habitat Goals*[1].

Developing the Habitat Goals involved several steps, many of which were carried out by teams of scientists. First, each team selected "key" animal species (or plant communities, in the case of the Plants Focus Team). Then they compiled available information regarding each species' historic and modern distribution, use of habitats, migration, relationship and interaction with other species, conservation and management issues, and research needs. When time and data were available, some team members compiled additional information on life history and other relevant topics. The teams then discussed the habitat needs of their species and developed initial habitat recommendations. Ultimately, the habitat recommendations of all the teams were integrated to form the Project's final recommendations.

Compiling the information on key species and plant communities into "profiles" was a crucial step in developing the Habitat Goals. Sharing these profiles enabled team members to better understand the habitat needs of a large proportion of the bayland's flora and fauna. It also facilitated the development of more balanced and diverse habitat recommendations.

When Project participants began sharing the profiles, they realized that much of the information had never before been compiled They also recognized that, although some of the profiles were not comprehensive, other researchers interested in the Bay and its watersheds might find them useful.

The intent of this report is to provide useful information to those working to restore the baylands ecosystem. However, because the profiles were compiled to inform a specific process, this report should not be considered a complete treatise. Rather, it should be seen as a reference and a starting point. Contact information for the profile authors is included in **Appendix A** for the reader who would like additional information or clarification, or who would just like to continue the process of scientific discussion and discovery.

---

[1] Copies of the Baylands Ecosystem Habitat Goals report may be obtained from the San Francisco Estuary Project at the address indicated in the front of this report.

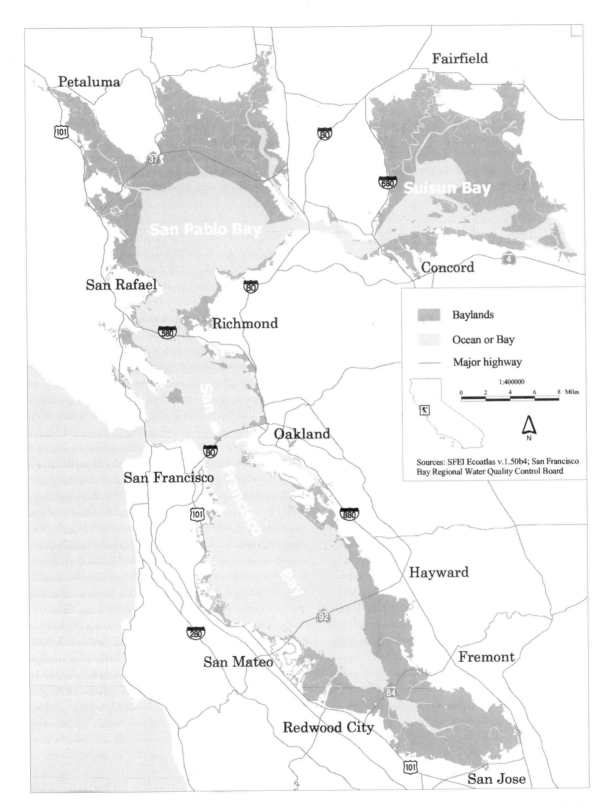

Figure 1. The Project Area of the San Francisco Bay Area Wetlands Ecosystem Goals Project – The baylands and adjacent and associated habitats of the San Francisco Bay-Delta Estuary, downstream of the Sacramento-San Joaquin Delta

1

Plant Communities

Plants of Shallow Subtidal Habitat and Tidal Flats
(with an emphasis on eelgrass)

Laura A. Hanson

Introduction

There are about 200,000 acres of shallow subtidal habitat and tidal flats in San Francisco Bay, San Pablo Bay, and Suisun Bay. Of this area, approximately 171,000 acres are subtidal habitat and about 29,000 acres are tidal flats. While relatively simple in terms of species diversity, the plant communities that occur in these areas are important components of the estuarine ecosystem.

Although this paper describes the plant communities of shallow subtidal habitat and tidal flats, it focuses on the eelgrass (*Zostera marina*) community. For more detailed information on the other plant communities (primarily microalgae and macroalgae) that occur in the shallow subtidal areas and on tidal flats of the San Francisco Bay Estuary, please refer to Silva (1979), Nichols and Pamatmat (1988), Meiorin et al. (1991), and Herbold et al. (1992).

Environmental Setting

Shallow subtidal areas and tidal flats are defined by their elevation in relation to tidal height. The shallow subtidal range includes the areas between mean lower low water (MLLW) and the approximate bathymetric contour 18 feet below MLLW. Tidal flats generally occur between the mean tide level (MTL), or the lower elevation limit of *Spartina* (cordgrass) flats, to about 2.5 feet below MLLW. Tidal flat composition can include various combinations of clay, silt, sand, shell fragments, and organic debris. Daily tidal cycles submerge and expose tidal flat surfaces twice every 24.8 hours. During each tidal cycle, tidal flats are also exposed to fluctuating wave action, current velocities, and nutrient supply. Where tidal marshes still exist, incoming tides flood into the upper marsh areas. As these tidal waters recede, organic materials are transported downslope to tidal flats where they become food sources for millions of detritus-feeding invertebrates.

The environmental conditions of shallow subtidal areas and tidal flats are stongly influenced by suspended sediments. In general, the San Francisco Bay Estuary has high concentrations of suspended sediments (Hanson and Walton 1988). This suspended particulate matter is comprised of 70 - 97% non-organic sediment made up of silty clay; the remaining content is comprised of living and other organic matter (Conomos and Peterson 1977). Suspended sediment concentrations are influenced by wind speed, substrate, particle size, wave action, current velocity, tidal action, water depth and seasonal runoff (Cyrus and Blaber 1987). Human activities such as type of land use (Kemp et al. 1983), channel dredging (LaSalle 1988, Hanson and Walton 1988), construction and use of marinas and ferry terminals, and propeller wash (Walker et al. 1989, Thom and Shreffler 1995) can also affect water clarity.

Total suspended solids (TSS) in Suisun and San Pablo bays average between 50 mg/l in the summer to 200 mg/l in the winter (Nichols and Pamatmat 1988). In North Bay and Central Bay, tides can have a significant influence on sediment resuspension, particularly during spring tides and during the ebbs preceding lower low water when the current speeds are highest. Central Bay – characterized by cold, saline, and relatively clear ocean water – has the lowest TSS concentrations, at 10 to 60 mg/l. South San Francisco Bay has slightly higher TSS concentrations than Central Bay (O'Connor 1991).

Salinity levels vary depending on season, weather, amount of diverted fresh water, and location in the Bay. In general, salinity levels within the water column and within tidal flats increase along a gradient from the Delta to the Golden Gate. For example, the salinity in Suisun Bay averages about seven parts per thousand (ppt), and in Central Bay it averages about 30 ppt (Fox et al. 1991). During dry years, South Bay averages salinity levels up to 35 ppt.

Intertidal and Subtidal Plant Communities

The shallow subtidal areas and tidal flats of the San Francisco Bay Estuary support relatively few plant communities. These communities include diatoms and other microalgae, macroalgae, and eelgrass.

Microalgae form the basis for the estuarine food web. These algae, consisting of diatoms and blue-green algae, often form dense patches on tidal flats, creating a brown hue to the substrate surface during low tide. Microalgae and settled phytoplankton represent a readily available food source for creatures, such as worms and clams, within the mudflats (Nichols and Pamatmat 1988). Shorebirds and waterfowl then consume these creatures.

Macroalgae (seaweeds) are also found throughout the Estuary, particularly in the more saline areas. Few macroalgae can make the necessary adjustments in internal water and mineral content to survive at low salinity levels. The exceptions include *Gracilaria sjoestedtii*, *Enteromorpha* spp. and the closely related *Ulva* spp. *G. sjoestedtii* is usually found from the mid-intertidal to the shallow subtidal zone attached to rocks partially buried in coarse sand. It also grows attached to small bits of clam and oyster shell in muddy portions of the Bay. In such situations, the plants and associated substrata are easily moved by currents and wave action. *Enteromorpha* and *Ulva* form bright green patches and can occur in great abundance throughout the intertidal zone, often growing on any available hard substrate. *Enteromorpha* can be found occupying higher tidal zones where shade is available. It is especially prevalent on boat hulls, buoys, docks, and woodwork. *Ulva* occupies the lower tidal zones, completing its life cycle in a few weeks and varying its distribution over a short time period. These kinds of macroalgae often undergo seasonal cycles of abundance, becoming common in the warmer months and virtually disappearing in colder months. Maximum abundance occurs in late summer and early fall (Jones and Stokes Associates, Inc. 1981). Many species of *Ulva* are often common in heavily polluted areas because they can use ammonia as a nitrogen source and are generally tolerant of organic and metal pollution (Dawson and Foster 1982). In the absence of eelgrass, *Ulva* can provide a preferred habitat for several invertebrate species (Sogard and Able 1991).

Eelgrass (*Zostera marina*) is currently the only seagrass found in San Francisco Bay. Belying its common name, it is not a grass but is a flowering plant that has adapted to living submerged in the shallow waters of protected bays and estuaries in temperate regions of the world (Den Hartog 1970, Phillips and Menez 1988). *Z. marina* reproduces both sexually through pollination of seeds, and asexually through a rhizome meristem that extends through the sediments (Setchell 1929). Where abundant, *Z. marina's* dense, matted root and rhizome

Uprooted *Zostera marina* from intertidal zone off of Alameda shroreline. Leaves may be 1.5–12 mm wide and up to 15 meters in length.

system functions to stabilize the soft bottom. Its leaves slow currents and dampen wave action, causing sediment and organic material to accumulate. *Z. marina* is found in intertidal areas, becoming exposed during the lower spring tides; it also occurs in subtidal areas at depths less than one to two meters below MLW (Kitting 1994).

Historic and Modern Distribution (of Eelgrass)

Information on historic distribution of *Zostera marina* in the San Francisco Bay Estuary is very limited. San Francisco Bay may have supported extensive *Z. marina* meadows in the past. (Setchell 1929, Wyllie-Echeverria and Rutten 1989). Low light availability within the water column has been found to limit the development of extensive eelgrass meadows and may be the principal cause of eelgrass decline in San Francisco Bay (Alpine and Cloern 1988, Zimmerman et al. 1991).

In 1989, Wyllie-Echeverria and Rutten published the first survey on the distribution of *Zostera marina* in San Francisco Bay (including San Pablo Bay) and mapped a total of 316 acres (**Table 1.1**). As **Table 1.2** and **Figure 1.1** show, the per area abundance of eelgrass within San Francisco Bay is much less than that of Humboldt Bay or Tomales Bay, two other northern California estuaries.

The 1989 Wyllie-Echeverria and Rutten survey described the *Zostera marina* populations as "patchy" and some as "stressed." Since that time a few of these beds have increased in size, and new patches have been sited (Kitting 1993 and pers. comm.).

Table 1.1 Acreage of Individual Eelgrass Beds in San Francisco/San Pablo Bay in 1989

Location	Acres
San Pablo Bay	124
Point Orient	3
Naval Supply Depot	12
Point Molate Beach	26
Toll Plaza, East	0.5
Toll Plaza, West	0.5
Point Richmond, North	7
Point Richmond, South	4
Richmond Breakwater, North	18
Richmond Breakwater, South	7
Emeryville	13
Alameda	55
Bay Farm, North	2
Bay Farm, South	4
Coyote Point	1
Richardson Bay	13
Angel Island	3
Belvedere Cove	5
Point Tiburon	1
Keil Cove	10
Paradise Cove, North	4
Paradise Cove, South	3
TOTAL ACRES	**316**

Table from NMFS SW Region. Wyllie-Echeverria and Rutten 1989 Administrative Report SWE-89-05

Associated Fauna Including Rare and Sensitive Species

Tidal flats include a living system of diatoms, microalgae, and protozoa that are fed upon by suspension or surface deposit feeding invertebrates. The bottom invertebrates are in turn fed upon by larger consumers such as fish, shrimp, and crabs. During low tide, these primary and secondary consumers are exploited by millions of migratory shorebirds. The extensive intertidal mudflats of San Francisco Bay are considered a key migratory staging and refueling area for over-wintering shorebirds of the Pacific Flyway (Harvey et al. 1992).

Macroalgae and eelgrass provide food, shelter, and spawning grounds for many Bay fish and invertebrates. The major subtidal spawning areas for *Clupea harengus* (Pacific herring), recently the most valuable fishery in California, are Richardson Bay and the large shallow area between Richmond and Oakland. In these areas, spawning occurs predominantly on *Gracilaria* ssp. and small patches of *Zostera marina* (Spratt 1981). When available, *C. harengus* preferentially uses *Z. marina* habitats for spawning (Taylor 1964, Spratt 1981).

Zostera marina beds support a variety of organisms, more than that of non-vegetated areas (van Montfrans et al. 1984, Kitting 1993, Hanson 1997). *Z. marina* roots and leaves provide habitat for many plants and animals. For example, the long blade-like shoots provide shelter and serve as a nursery ground for many fish species. Small plants (epiphytes) and animals (epizoites) attach to the leaves, motile animals find cover between the leaves, and burrowing animals live among the roots. Epiphytes are an important part of the eelgrass community, contributing up to 22% of the total primary productivity (Jones 1968, Marshal 1970, Penhale 1977). They, in turn, provide food for resident invertebrate grazers (Kitting et al. 1984). Within the rich organic sediment, anaerobic processes of microorganisms regenerate and recycle nutrients and carbon (Kenworthy et al. 1982).

Because *Zostera marina* contains noxious sulfated phenolic compounds that can inhibit bacterial degradation and animal grazing, few animals consume it (Tenore 1977, Harrison and Chan 1980, McMillan et al. 1980). Notable exceptions include several species of waterfowl such as *Anas americana* (wigeon), *Anas strepera* (gadwall), *Anas acuta* (pintail), *Branta canadensis* (Canada goose), and *Branta nigricans* (black brant) (Phillips 1984). *Z. marina* has been an obligate food for black brant along its flyway (Einarsen 1965). Black brant populations are in great decline along the Pacific Flyway, possibly due to this species' dependence on dwindling eelgrass resources (Einarsen 1965).

Some bird species also forage on the fauna associated with *Zostera marina*. An example is the *Sterna albifrons browni* (California least tern) that was listed as an endangered species in 1970. Least terns are known to forage on juvenile and small fishes (Magenheim and Rubissow 1993) that inhabit *Z. marina* beds, particu-

Table 1.2 Comparison of Three Northern California Estuaries Relative to Size of Estuary and Total Acres of Eelgrass (*Zostera marina*)

Location	(km²)	Extent of Eelgrass (Bottom coverage, acres)	Reference
Humbolt Bay	62.4	3,053	Phillips 1984
Tomales Bay	30.0	965	Spratt 1985
San Francisco Bay	1,140.0	316	Wyllie-Echeverria 1990

Table from NMFS SW Region. Wyllie-Echeverria (1990)

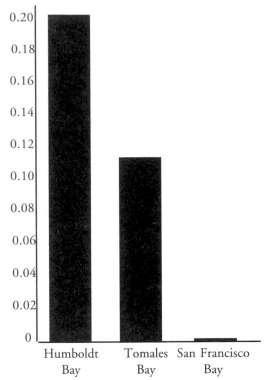

Figure 1.1 Comparison of Percent Eelgrass Coverage in Three West Coast Estuaries (Based on Wyllie-Echeverria (1990))

larly at a major nesting site near the Oakland International Airport and the Alameda Naval Air Station (Collins and Feeney 1983-6, Feeney 1988 and 1989, Harvey et al. 1992).

Invertebrates such as juvenile *Cancer magister* (Dungeness crab) appear to grow up most successfully in the nursery-like habitat that *Zostera marina* provides, particularly in the northern reaches of the Bay. The isopod, *Synidotea laticauda* is periodically found in high numbers (up to 200/m²) among *Z. marina* beds in Central San Francisco Bay (Hanson 1998). They are an important food item for economically valuable sport fishes such as young striped bass, starry flounder, steelhead trout, king salmon, white sturgeon, plus other fishes in San Francisco Bay (Morris et al. 1980)

The transport of *Zostera marina* fragments acts as a vector for animal dispersal (Highsmith 1985, Worcester 1994). Kitting (1993) found several fish species and a variety of invertebrates usually associated with *Z. marina* on dead blades found at depths greater than four meters below MLW.

Conservation Issues

Exotic Plants – There is some potential for two exotic *Zostera* species to invade San Francisco Bay. The Asian seagrass, *Zostera japonica*, introduced to British Columbia, Washington, and Oregon has not yet been reported in San Francisco Bay. *Z. japonica* has a differ-

ent life history, morphology, and preferred habitat than *Z. marina* (Harrison and Bigley 1982). Culture experiments determined that *Z. japonica* is not likely to displace existing *Z. marina* beds (Harrison 1982). This may not be the case in San Francisco Bay. *Z. japonica* favors the intertidal zones, the areas where *Z. marina* has been limited to in San Francisco Bay. Thus far, *Z.japonica* occupies only a small fraction of its potential habitat in North America, threatening significant changes in the ecology of the intertidal sediments as this seagrass spreads (Harrison and Bigley 1982).

Zostera asiatica is found from Tomales Bay in the north, to Santa Monica Bay in the south. Phillips and Wyllie-Echeverria (1990) published the first record of this species in the Eastern Pacific. It is a wide bladed *Zostera* that occurs sub-tidally from five meters below MLLW to 17 meters below MLLW. *Z. asiatica* has not yet been identified in San Francisco Bay. This is probably due to its deeper water distribution where photosynthetic processes could be limited in San Francisco Bay.

Factors Limiting Eelgrass Distribution – Under suitable conditions, *Zostera marina* can form dense, continuous, and extensive carpets as seen in Tomales and Humboldt bays. Light, temperature, salinity, tidal range and water motion all affect growth and productivity of *Z. marina* (Thayer et al. 1984, Fonseca et al. 1985, Fonseca and Kenworthy 1987). The amount of time it is exposed to air during low tides determines the upper limits of *Z. marina,* and the amount of available light determines the lower limits (Backman and Barilotti 1976; Dennison and Alberte 1982, 1985, 1986; Bulthuis 1983; Bulthuis and Woelkerling 1983; Wetzel and Penhale 1983; Lewis et al. 1985; Josselyn et al. 1986; Duarte 1991). The primary factor responsible for a worldwide decline in *Z. marina* and other submerged aquatic vegetation is reduced light availability (Giesen et al. 1990, Dennison et al. 1993).

In San Francisco Bay, *Zostera marina* requires somewhere between three and five hours of H_{sat} (length of irradiance-saturated photosynthesis) each day (Zimmerman et al. 1991). In areas with favorable light conditions, *Z. marina* plants have adequate carbon reserves to withstand at least 30 days of light limitation (Zimmerman et al. 1991); however, due to frequent and persistent periods of high turbidity, it is unlikely that plants at the deeper edge of eelgrass meadows in San Francisco Bay can accumulate large carbon reserves (Zimmerman et al. 1991). Average turbidity of the Bay and, more critically, brief periods of high turbidity limit *Z. marina* distribution in deeper water and limit establishment of seedlings and vegetative propagules (Zimmerman et al. 1991). If daily, monthly, and seasonal H_{sat} requirements are not met, long-term survival of the plants may be limited (Zimmerman et al. 1991). Any activities that increase turbidity within Bay waters, whether natural or

Zostera marina plants, discernable as dark blotches in the foreground, near Belvedere Cove, Marin County.

anthropogenic, have detrimental effects on existing eel-grass populations and associated food webs.

Current Restoration Success – The technology for successfully establishing seagrass beds has been un-reliable (Phillips 1974, 1980; Lewis 1987), although, in 1989 Zimmerman et al. (1995) successfully transplanted *Zostera marina* at two locations in San Francisco Bay. According to Fonseca et al. (1988), waning interest in *Z. marina* restoration was due to a net loss of habitat through seagrass mitigation projects. Planting projects have often failed as a result of poor selection of planting sites or plant material and incorrect use of planting meth-ods. Factors that limited success include a general lack of knowledge of physiological requirements and un-known local environmental factors controlling *Z. marina* growth (Lewis 1987, Merkel 1990). For example, in 1984, an eelgrass transplant was initiated in San Fran-cisco Bay. Limited transplant success was attributed to a lack of data on local eelgrass autecology coupled with nearby dredging operations and diminished water qual-ity (Fredette et al. 1988).

Conclusions and Recommendations

There has been considerable interest in protecting and expanding existing *Zostera marina* beds in San Francisco and San Pablo bays (Fredette et al. 1988). Since the 1989 survey, sitings have indicated a marked change in the distribution and abundance of this species. Better con-serving this species in the Estuary will require more fre-quent monitoring of individual populations.

It also is imperative to protect the current eelgrass beds from further decline. Because of the inherent dif-ficulties in establishing eelgrass, plantings conducted in exchange for permitted losses (mitigation projects) could result in a greater loss of habitat and should not be allowed. The current *Zostera marina* populations may be the last remnants in San Francisco Bay and are extremely vulnerable to local extinction (Kitting and Wyllie-Echeverria 1991); therefore, plantings should be used to enhance current beds or to create new beds.

There are several actions that should be undertaken when designing potential restoration or enhancement projects:
1. Conduct a thorough survey to assess physical conditions of the site. Collect and evaluate environmental data and/or pilot test the planting at a particular site before commitment of a full restoration project. The success of any seagrass re-vegetation effort, including long-term plant growth, is strictly dependent upon a physical environment suitable for initial establishment (Zimmerman et al. 1991).
2. Carefully evaluate light availability before proceed-ing with any major transplant effort. Water column turbidity is sufficiently high throughout much of the Central Bay, limiting the euphotic zone (depth where irradiance falls to 1% of surface irradiance) to less than 1 m (Alpine and Cloern 1988).
3. Use stocks for planting from a site with conditions as similar as possible to the planting site. There should be similar or equal water depths, salinity, temperature, tidal currents, wave exposure, and sediment composition (Fonseca 1994). Until we learn more about the genetic structure of this species, matching of phenotypes among restoration and donor sites remains the best guide for stock selection.
4. Limit planting to areas with small tidal ranges rather than high tidal ranges to provide greater light availability (Koch and Beer 1996), thus increasing survival success.
5. Plant in areas where parameters for deeper vertical distribution are available make the bed less vulnerable to adverse conditions (such as storm events or desiccation) due to availability of energy from the neighboring deeper shoots (Tomasko and Dawes 1989).
6. Plant in late spring and summer. Periods of high *Z. marina* growth and production coincide with warmer temperatures and greater light availability (Ewanchuk and Williams 1996).

References

Alpine, A.E. and J.E. Cloern. 1988. Phytoplankton growth rates in a light limited environment, San Francisco Bay. Mar. Ecol. Prog. Ser. 44: 167-173.

Backman, T.W. and D.C. Barilotti. 1976. Irradiance reduction: effects on standing crops of the eelgrass *Zostera marina* in a coastal lagoon. Mar. Biol. 34: 33-40.

Bulthuis, D.A. 1983. Effects of in situ light reduction on density and growth of the seagrass *Heterozostera tasmanica* (Martens ex Aschers.) den Hartog in Western Port, Victoria, Australia. J. Exp. Mar. Biol. Ecol. 67: 91-103.

Bulthuis, D.A. and W.J. Woelkerling. 1983. Seasonal variations in standing crop, density and leaf growth of the seagrass *Heterozostera tasmanica*, in Western Port, Victoria, Australia. Aquat. Bot. 16:111-136.

Collins, L.D. and L.R. Feeney. 1983-6. California least tern nesting season at the Oakland Airport. Port of Oakland.

Conomos, T.J. and D.H. Peterson. 1977. Suspended-particle transport and circulation in San Francisco Bay: An Overview. *In:* M. Wiley (ed). Estuarine processes. Vol. 2. Academic Press, New York. pp 82-97.

Cyrus, D.P. and S.J.M. Blaber. 1987. The influence of turbidity on juvenile marine fishes in estuaries. J Exp. Mar. Biol. Ecol. 109(1): 53-70.

Dawson, E.Y. and M.S. Foster. 1982. Seashore Plants of California. Univ. of Ca Press. Berkeley, Calif. 226 pp.

Den Hartog, C. 1970. Seagrasses of the World. North-Holland, Amsterdam. 275 pp.

Dennison, W.C. and R.S. Alberte. 1982. Photosynthetic response of *Zostera marina* L. (eelgrass) to in situ manipulations of light intensity. Oecologia. 55: 137-144.

_____. 1985. Role of daily light period in the depth distribution of Zostera marina (eelgrass). Mar. Ecol. Prog. Ser. 25: 51-61.

_____. 1986. Photoadaptation and growth of *Zostera marina* L. (eelgrass) transplants along a depth gradient. J. Exp. Mar. Biol. Ecol. 98: 265-282.

Duarte, C.M. 1991. Seagrass depth limits. Aquatic Botany. 40:363-377.

Einarsen, A.R. 1965. Black brandt: sea goose of the Pacific Coast. Seattle, WA. Univ. of Washington Press.

Ewanchuk, P.J. and S.L. Williams. 1996. Survival and re-establishment of vegetative fragments of eelgrass (*Zostera marina*). Can. J. Bot. 74:1584-1590.

Feeney, L.R. 1988. California least tern breeding season at the Metropolitan Oakland International Airport. Port of Oakland.

_____. 1989. California least tern breeding season at the Metropolitan Oakland International Airport. Port of Oakland.

Fonseca, M.S. 1994. A guide to planting seagrass in the Gulf of Mexico. Publ no. TAMU-SG-94-601 Sea Grant College. 25 pp.

Fonseca, M.S., W.J. Kenworthy, G.W. Thayer, D.Y. Heller and K.M. Cheap. 1985. Transplanting of the seagrass *Zostera marina* and *Halodule wrightii* for sediment stabilization and habitat development on the east coast of the United States. U.S. Army Corps of Engineers Tech. Rep. EL-85-9, 49 pp.

Fonseca, M.S. and W.J. Kenworthy. 1987. Effects of current on photosynthesis and distribution of seagrasses. Aquat. Bot. 27: 59-78.

Fonseca, M.S., W.J. Kenworthy and G.W. Thayer. 1988. Restoration and management of seagrass systems: a review. Chapter 38 pp 353-368. *In:* D.D. Hook et al. (eds). The ecology and management of wetlands, Vol. 2. Management, use and value of wetlands. Portland, OR. Timber Press.

Fox, J.P., T.R. Mongan and W.J. Miller. 1991. Long-term annual and seasonal trends in surface salinity of San Francisco Bay. Journal of Hydrology. 122: 93-117.

Fredette, T.J., M.S. Fonseca, W.J. Kenworthy and G.W. Thayer. 1985. Seagrass transplanting: 10 years of Army Corps of Engineers Research. P. 121-134 *In:* F.J. Webb (ed). Proc. of the 12th Ann. Conf. on Wetlands Restoration and Creation. Hillsborough Comm. Coll., Tampa Fl.

Fredette, T.J., M.S. Fonseca, W.J. Kenworthy and S. Wyllie-Echeverria. 1988. An investigation of eelgrass (*Zostera marina*) transplant feasibility in San Francisco Bay, CA COE Report EL-88-2. Army Engineer Waterways Experiment Station, Vicksburg, MS. 33 pp.

Hanson, C.H. and C.P. Walton. 1988. Potential effects of dredging on early life stages of striped bass (*Morone sasatilis*) in the San Francisco Bay Area: An overview. pp 38-56 *In:* C.A. Simenstad (ed). Effects of dredging on anadromous Pacific Coast fishes. Workshop proceedings. Seattle, Wa.

Hanson, L.A. 1998. Effects of suspended sediments on animals in a San Francisco Bay eelgrass habitat. MS Thesis. Calif. State Univ., Hayward. 72 pp.

Harrison, P.G. 1982. Comparative growth of *Zostera japonica* Asher. and Graebn. and *Z. marina* L. under simulated intertidal and subtidal conditions. Aquatic Botany. 14: In Press.

Harrison, P.G. and R.E. Bigley. 1982. The recent introduction of the seagrass *Zostera japonica* Aschers. and Graebn. To the Pacific Coast of North America. Can. J. Fish. Aquatic. Sci. 19: 1642-1648.

Harrison, P.G. and A.T. Chan. 1980. Inhibition of the growth of microalgae and bacteria by extracts of eelgrass (*Zostera marina*) leaves. Mar. Biol. 61: 21-26.

Harvey, T.E., K.J. Miller, R.L. Hotham, M.J. Rauzon, G.W. Page and R.A. Keck. 1992. Status and Trends Report on Wildlife of the San Francisco Estuary. Prepard by the U.S. Fish and Wildlife Service for the San Francisco Estuary Project, U.S. Environmental Protection Agency. January. San Francisco, Calif. 283 pp and appendices.

Herbold, B., A.D. Jassby and P.B. Moyle. (1992) Status and trends report on aquatic resources in the San Francisco Estuary. San Francisco Estuary Project, US Env. Prot. Agency.

Highsmith, R.C. 1985. Floating and algal rafting as potential dispersal mechanisms in brooding invertebrates. Mar. Ecol. Prog. Ser. 25: 169-179.

Plants

Jones and Stokes Associates, Inc. 1981. An ecological characterization of the central and northern California coastal region. Vol. III, Part 1, Habitats. Rep. No. FWS/OBS-80/47.1 for Bur. Land Manage., Pacific Outer Continental Shelf Off., and US Fish and Wildl. Serv., Off. Biol. Serv., Washington, D.C.

Jones, J.A. 1968. Primary productivity of the tropical marine turtle grass, *Thalassia testudinum* König and its epiphytes. Thesis, Univ. of Miami, Coral Gables, FL, 196 pp.

Josselyn, M.N., M.S. Fonseca, T. Nieeson and R. Larson. 1986. The ecology of *Halphila decipens*: distribution and production. Aquat. Bot. 25: 47-61.

Kemp, W.M., W.R. Boynton, R.R. Twilley, J.C. Stevenson and J.C. Means. 1983. The decline of submerged vascular plants in Upper Chesapeake Bay: Summary of results concerning possible causes. Mar. Technol. Soc. J. 17(2): 78-89.

Kenworthy, W.J., J.C. Zieman, and G.W. Thayer. 1982. Evidence for the influence of seagrass on the benthic nitrogen cycle in a coastal plain estuary near Beaufort, North Carolina. Oecologia 54: 152-158.

Kitting, C.L. B. Fry and M.D. Morgan. 1984. Detection of inconspicuous epiphytic algae supporting food webs in seagrass meadows. Oecologia. 62: 145-149.

Kitting, C.L. and S. Wyllie-Echeverria. 1991. Eelgrass meadow communities of San Francisco Bay. *In:* Proceedings of the 1990 Natural Areas Conference, Yosemite Centennial. Natural Areas Association.

Kitting, C.L. 1993. Investigation of San Francisco Bay shallow-water habitats adjacent to the Bay Farm Island underwater excavation. A Report for US Dept. Commerce/NOAA, National Marine Fisheries Service, Long Beach and Santa Rosa, CA. 41 pp.

_____. 1994. Shallow populations of small fishes in local eelgrass meadow food webs. *In:* Alameda Naval Air Station's Natural Resources and Bas Closure: The Proceedings. Golden Gate Audubon Society. pp 65-83.

Koch, E.W. and S. Beer. 1996. Tides, light and the distribution of *Zostera marina* in Long Island Sound, USA. Aquatic Botany 53: 97-107.

LaSalle, M.W. 1988. Physical and chemical alterations associated with dredging: an overview. pp 1-12 *In:* C.A. Simenstad (ed). Effects of dredging on anadromous Pacific Coast fishes. Workshop proceedings. Seattle, Wa.

Lewis, R.R., M.J. Duarko, M.D. Moffler and R.C. Phillips. 1985. Seagrass meadows of Tampa-Bay — a review. *In:* S.F. Treat, J.L. Simon, R.R. Lewis and R.L. Whitman (eds.), Proc. Tampa Bay Area Scientific Information Symposium, May 1982, Florida Sea Grant Publ. 65, Burges, Minneapolis, pp. 210-246.

Lewis III, R.R. 1987. The restoration and creation of seagrass meadows in the southeast United States.

In: M.J. Durako, R.C. Phillips and R.R. Lewis III (Eds). Proceedings of the Symposium on Subtropical Seagrasses of the Southeastern U.S. Florida Marine Research Publications, Fla. Dept. Natural Resources. pp 153-173.

Magenheim, E. and A. Rubissow. 1993. Grass weathers wake. Estuary, your Bay-Delta News Clearinghouse. 2(4): 5.

Marshall, N. 1970. Food transfers through the lower trophic levels of the benthic environment, *In:* J.H. Steel (Ed). The Biology of Diatoms. Blackwell, Oxford, pp. 333-371.

McMillan, C. P.L. Parker and B. Fry. 1980. $^{13}C/^{12}C$ ratios in seagrasses. Aquat. Bot. 9: 237-249.

Meorin, E.C., M.N. Josselyn, R. Crawford, J. Calloway, K. Miller, R. Pratt, T. Richardson and R. Leidy. 1991. Status and trends report on wetlands and related habitats in the San Francisco Estuary. Prepared for the San Francisco Estuary Project, U.S. Environmental Protection Agency, San Francisco, Calif. 209 pp and appendices.

Merkel, F.W. 1990. Eelgrass transplanting in south San Diego Bay, California. *In:* K.W. Merkel and R.S. Hoffman (eds). Proceedings of the California Eelgrass Symposium. Chula Vista California. Sweetwater River Press. National City, Calif. pp 28-42.

Morris R.H., D.P. Abbot and E.C. Haderlie. 1980. Intertidal Invertebrates of California. Stanford Univ. Press, Stanford, Calif. 550 pp.

Nichols F. and M.M. Pamatmat. 1988. The ecology of the soft-bottom benthos of San Francisco Bay: a community profile. US Fish and Wildlife Service Biological Report 85 (7.19). 73 pp.

O'Connor, J.M. 1991. Evaluation of turbidity and turbidity-related effects on the biota of the San Francisco Bay-Delta Estuary. U.S. Army Engineers Report. 84 pp.

Penhale, P.A. 1977. Macrophyte-epiphyte biomass and productivity in an eelgrass (*Zostera marina* L.) community. J. Exp. Mar. Biol. Ecol. 26: 211-224.

Phillips, R.C. 1974. Transplantation of seagrasses, with specific emphasis on eelgrass, *Zostera marina* L. Aquaculture. 4: 161-176.

_____. 1980. Creation of seagrass beds. *In* J.C. Lewis and E.W. Bunce (eds). Rehabilitation and creation of selected coastal habitats: proceedings of a workshop. US Fish Wildl. Serv., Washington, DC. pp 91-104.

_____. 1984. The ecology of eelgrass meadows in the Pacific Northwest: A community profile. U.S. Fish Wildl. Serv. FWS/OBS-84/24. 85 pp.

Phillips, R.C. and E. G. Menez. 1988. Seagrasses. Smithsonian Institute Press, Washington DC. 104 pp.

Phillips, R.C. and S. Wyllie-Echeverria. 1990. *Zostera asiatica* Miki on the Pacific Coast of North America. Pacific Science. 44 (2): 130-134.

Setchell, W.A. 1929. Morphological and phenological notes on *Zostera marina*. Univ. Calif. Pub. Botany. 14: 389-452.

Silva, P.C. 1979. The benthic algal flora of central San Francisco Bay. *In:* T.J.Conomos (ed). San Francisco Bay: the urbanized estuary. Pacific Division, Amer. Assoc. for the Advancement of Science, San Francisco, Calif. pp 287-311.

Sogard, S.M. and K.W. Able. 1991. A comparison of eelgrass, sea lettuce macroalgae, and marsh creeks as habitats for epibenthic fishes and decapods. Estuarine, Coastal and Shelf Science. 33: 501-519.

Spratt, J.D. 1981. Status of the Pacific herring, *Clupea harengus pallasii*, resource in California 1972 to 1980. Fish Bulletin 171. Calif. Dept. Fish and Game.

Taylor, F.H.C. 1964. Life history and present status of Columbia herring stocks. Fish. Res. Board Can. Bull. 81 pp.

Tenore, K.R. 1977. Growth of the polychaete, *Capitella capitata*, cultured on different levels of detritus derived from various sources. Limnol. Oceanogr. 22: 936-941.

Thayer, G.W., W.J. Kenworthy and M.F. Fonseca. 1984. The ecology of eelgrass meadows of the Atlantic Coast: A community profile. U.S. Fish Wildl. Serv. FWS/OBS 84/02, 147 pp.

Thom, R. and D. Shreffler. 1995. Mitigating impacts of ferry terminals on eelgrass in Puget Sound. Abstract *In:* Estuaries: Bridges from Watershed to Coastal Seas. 1995 Texas A and M Univ. Sea Grant College Program.

Tomasko, D.A. and C.J. Dawes. 1989. Evidence for physiological integration between shaded and unshaded short-shoots of *Thalassia testudinum*. Mar. Ecol. Progr. Ser. 54: 299-305.

Van Montfrans, J., R.L. Wetzel and R.J Orth. 1984. Epiphyte-grazer relationships in seagrass meadows: Consequences for seagrass growth and production. Estuaries. 7: 289-309.

Walker, D.I., R.J. Lukatelich, G. Bastyan and A.J. McComb. 1989. Effect of boat moorings on seagrass beds near Perth, Western Australia. Aquatic Bot. 36: 69-77.

Wetzel, R.G. and P. Penhale. 1983. Production ecology of seagrass communities in the lower Chesapeake Bay. Mar. Technol. Soc. J. 17(2): 22-31.

Worcester, S.E. 1994. Adult rafting versus larval swimming: dispersal and recruitment of a botryliid ascidian on eelgrass. Mar. Biol. (Berlin), 121: 309: 317.

Wyllie-Echeverria, S. and P.J. Rutten. 1989. Inventory of eelgrass (*Zostera marina* L.) *In:* San Francisco/San Pablo Bay. Administrative Report, Southwest Regional NOAA, National Marine Fisheries Service, Terminal Island, CA 18 pp.

Wyllie-Echeverria, S. 1990. Distribution and geographic range of *Zostera marina*, eelgrass in San Francisco Bay, California. *In:* K.W. Merkel and R.S. Hoffman (eds). Proceedings of the Calif. Eelgrass Symposium. Chula Vista Calif. Sweetwater River Press. National City, Calif. pp 65-69.

Zimmerman, R.C., J.L. Reguzzoni, S. Wyllie-Echeverria, M. Josselyn and R.S. Alberte. 1991. Assessment of environmental suitability for growth of *Zostera marina* L. (eelgrass) in San Francisco Bay. Aquatic Botany. 39: 353-366.

Zimmerman, R.C., J.R. Reguzzoni and R.S. Alberte. 1995. Eelgrass (*Zostera marina* L.) transplants in San Francisco Bay: Role of light availability on metabolism, growth and survival. Aquat. Bot. 51: 37-86.

Tidal Marsh Plants of the San Francisco Estuary

Peter R. Baye
Phyllis M. Faber
Brenda Grewell

Introduction

The general ecology San Francisco Bay has been reviewed by Josselyn (1983), who included a brief treatment of its tidal marsh plant community composition and structure. Macdonald (1977, 1988) reviewed the vegetation of California salt marshes, including San Francisco Bay, with emphasis on sedimentation, drainage, topography, salinity, flooding, community structure, and summaries of autecology of selected dominant species. Newcombe and Mason (1972) made descriptive accounts of the Suisun Marsh area vegetation. Atwater et al. (1979) summarized and interpreted the relationships between tidal marsh vegetation of the San Francisco Estuary and its landforms and geomorphic processes. Wells and Goman (1994) reviewed and expanded the quaternary history of the San Francisco Estuary. The purpose of this plant community profile is to supplement previous reviews, and provide additional information on historic changes in the composition, distribution, and abundance of tidal marsh plants of the Estuary.

Environmental Setting

Prehistoric Tidal Marsh Development – Tidal marshes of the modern San Francisco Estuary formed around 10,000 years ago during the Holocene submergence when the rate of sea-level rise slowed sufficiently for tidal marsh sediments to accrete near sea-level (Atwater et al. 1979). Prior to that time, during the Pleis-

tocene epoch, the site of the modern Estuary consisted of broad stream valleys far above glacial low sea level. Pleistocene tidal marsh plant communities were probably associated with either stream mouths or backbarrier lagoons at the edge of an emergent broad coastal plain, now submerged and eroded or buried offshore from the modern Golden Gate. Tidal marsh plant species probably migrated upstream in valleys and embayments as sea level rose. Ancestral Pleistocene populations of tidal marsh plant species in today's estuaries may not have been as discontinuously distributed as they are today: coastal plain shorelines (e.g., East Coast of North America) often provide widespread tidal inlets and tidal marsh (Davies 1980). Holocene fragmentation of salt marshes from more extensive or continuous Pleistocene coastal plain salt marsh distributions may account for historic disjunct, relict populations of species in San Francisco Bay which are now found only in south-central or southern California tidal marshes (e.g., *Solidago confinis* (southern goldenrod), *Suaeda californica* (California sea-blite)).

Tidal marshes of the Estuary fluctuated in vegetation composition during the Holocene epoch, apparently in relation to changes in long-term climate. This is indicated by stratified deposits of fossil pollen and plant fragments which indicate periods of accumulation of plants associated with near-freshwater marsh conditions with species associated the more saline (brackish) conditions (Wells and Goman 1994). These findings are consistent with independent evidence on climate changes during the last 6,000 years which show prolonged periods of drought and high rainfall compared with historic conditions (Ingram et al. 1996, Peterson et al. 1989). The tidal marshes in San Francisco Bay were also not static prior to European influence. Some marsh shoreline configurations indicate long-term scarp retreat across marshes with large sinuous tidal creeks and growth of berms and sand spits (Atwater et al. 1979). Areas of rapid marsh growth in some parts of south San Francisco Bay,

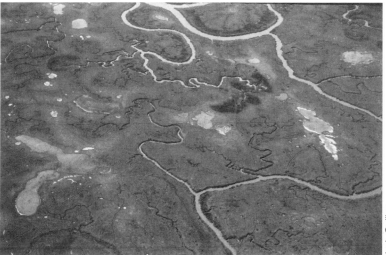

Tidal Marsh along Petaluma River shows complex channels and natural salt pans.

Josh Collins

outside the influence of Sierran gold mining and prior to extensive diking, were evident in maps of the Bay prepared in the 1870s (U.S. Coast Survey maps).

Marsh Sediments and Plants – Depositional environments of tidal marshes in the San Francisco Estuary are variable and are significant for the distribution of uncommon plant species. In most of the San Francisco Estuary, the sediments of the middle-marsh marsh plain consists of bay mud (fine silt and clay) with significant percentage of organic matter in mature marshes. Local coarse sediment deposits, often beach ridges (marsh berms, or marsh-beach ecotones) composed of sand, shell fragments, organic debris, or mixtures, create physically mobile (periodically eroded and redeposited), well-drained high marsh habitats with affinity for some common high marsh species (e.g., *Grindelia stricta* var. *angustifolia*, gumplant) and probably also species now locally extinct or rare, such as *Suaeda californica*, *Atriplex californica* (California saltbush), and *Castilleja ambigua* (salt marsh owl's clover or Johny-nip). Marsh berms are associated with relatively high wave energy environments in the Estuary, located near coarse sediment sources such as eroding bluffs, submerged fossil sand and shell deposits, stream mouths, and eroding marsh edges. Such features were commonly represented on U.S. Coast Survey maps of the mid-1800s, but persist today in very few localities of the Estuary (e.g., Point Pinole, Redwood City area, San Leandro area, and northern San Francisco peninsula). Similar coarse-sediment features probably occurred as natural levees of upstream reaches of large tidal sloughs with significant coarse sediment loads, as is observed today in Morro Bay. Alluvial fans also create gradually sloping ecotones with uplands, with variably textured sediments and freshwater runoff and seeps. Few small alluvial fans exist at tidal marsh edges of the Estuary today (e.g., Point Pinole, Whittell Marsh), but were historically abundant in parts of the Estuary, supporting diverse ecotonal plant communities (Cooper 1926). Analogous alluvial fan-tidal marsh ecotones occur in maritime salt marshes of Point Reyes and Tomales Bay areas, where they support distinctive local plant assemblages, including uncommon to rare species.

Regionall rare salt marsh owl's clover, or Johnny-nip (*Castilleja ambigua* ssp. *ambigua*). (Tidal marsh, Whittell Marsh, Point Pinole)

Comparison With Other Estuaries – The tidal marshes of the San Francisco Estuary are the most extensive on the central coast of California, and their plant communities are distinct from other central coast tidal marshes in many respects. Most other large central coast tidal marshes are associated with shallow embayments with large open tidal inlets (e.g., Tomales Bay, Drakes Estero and Bolinas Lagoon in Marin County; Bodega Bay in Sonoma County; Elkhorn Slough in Monterey County; Morro Bay in San Luis Obispo County) which impose strong marine influence on the character of their sediments, salinities, and vegetation. Central coast tidal marshes tend to be isolated and few because of the steep modern shoreline with few valleys or wave-sheltered bays. These tidal marshes have extensive sandy substrates, relatively small, local inputs of fine sediment and freshwater discharges and brackish (mesohaline) conditions, and are inundated by water approaching marine salinity (34 ppt) during most of the growing season. Some tidal marshes associated with stream mouths have relatively more freshwater influence and brackish marsh vegetation (e.g., pre-historic Elkhorn Slough and Salinas River, Monterey County; Russian River estuary, Sonoma County), but in association with seasonal reduction in tidal influence because of partial or complete closure of coastal inlets at river mouths (dammed by sand beach ridges during periods of relatively low river discharge). In contrast, the tidal marsh plant communities of the San Francisco Bay Estuary developed under conditions of abundant and predominantly fine sediment (bay mud, clayey silts and silty clays with high nutrient-holding capacity), relatively large tidal range, and extensive brackish marshes associated with relatively large freshwater discharges, distributed over broad, fluctuating salinity gradients (Atwater et al. 1979)

Historically, salt pans (unvegetated, seasonally inundated depressions or flats within the tidal marsh) and local salt ponds (perennial deposits of crystalline salt in hypersaline ponds) were well-developed in San Francisco Bay tidal marshes (U.S. Coast Survey T-charts, 1850s), supporting distinctive vegetation (widgeongrass, *Ruppia maritima*, in some pans) or microalgal floras (in salt ponds). Pans are relatively infrequent in other central coast tidal marshes compared with the historic conditions of the San Francisco Estuary, and natural salt ponds were not known to occur in other central coast tidal marshes. Today, edges of high marsh pans are associated with at least two regionally rare species (*Cordylanthus maritimus* ssp. *palustris* and *Castilleja ambigua* ssp. *ambigua*), and may have been associated with many others in the past (e.g., *Lepidium latipes*, *L. oxycarpum*; **Table 1.3**)

Tidal Marsh Plant Communities

The distribution of tidal marsh plants is strongly (but not exclusively) influenced by tidal elevation and salin-

Pickleweed (*Salicornia virginica*), a dominant within the salt marsh middle marsh zone, shown enshrouded by parasitic dodder (*Cuscuta salina*).

ity (Hinde 1954, Atwater and Hedel 1976). Following Peinado et al. (1994), three elevation "zones" of the tidal marsh can be objectively distinguished (and are visually conspicuous): (1) the low marsh zone, occurs from approximately mean sea level to mean high water; (2) the middle marsh zone, occurs from approximately mean high water to mean higher high water; and (3) the high marsh zone (colloquially also called the "upland transition" or "peripheral halophyte" zone; "upper salt marsh zone" of Peinado et al. 1994), occurs near and above mean higher high water up to several meters above extreme high water line (Peinado et al. 1994). The typical species composition of these zones is described below for tidal salt marsh and tidal brackish marsh. Unlike beach, dune, and bluff communities (Barbour and Johnson 1977, Barbour et al. 1973), there is no empirical evidence of salt marsh zonation attributable to salt spray; estuaries and embayments are relatively low-energy wave environments (Davies 1980, Carter 1988). Other potentially significant influencing factors have not yet been well studied.

There are significant floristic differences between the tidal marshes of San Francisco Estuary and other central coast tidal marsh systems. These include:

1. The dominance of *Spartina foliosa* (Pacific cordgrass), either absent today or historically absent from most or all other central coast tidal marshes (Macdonald 1977);

2. The presence of rare species of disjunct distribution, such as *Suaeda californica* (native only to Morro Bay and San Francisco Bay); and

3. The presence of local endemic species such as soft bird's-beak (*Cordylanthus mollis* ssp. *mollis*) and Suisun thistle (*Cirsium hydrophilum* var. *hydrophilum*).

Conversely, some uncommon tidal marsh species which have either declined severely or become extirpated in the San Francisco Estuary still occur in local abundance in some maritime salt marshes of the region (e.g., *Atriplex californica*, *Castilleja ambigua*, *Puccinellia nutkanensis*). Few species associated with high marsh zones of maritime salt marshes in the region were historically absent from the San Francisco Estuary (e.g., *Astragalus pycnostachyus* var. *pycnostachyus* (coastal marsh milkvetch), *Castilleja ambigua* ssp. *humboldtiensis* (Humboldt Bay owl's clover), *Leymus* x *vancouveriensis* (Vancouver's ryegrass), and *Grindelia stricta* var. *stricta* (gumplant)).

Differences exist also between the structure of vegetation found in predominantly marine-influenced salt marshes of the central coast and tidal marshes of the San Francisco Estuary. Although the middle marsh zone of San Francisco Bay salt marshes has been described as supporting "prostrate" growth forms of pickleweed (Macdonald 1977), the middle marsh plains of sandy or sandy peat salt marshes of Bolinas Lagoon (Allison 1992), Point Reyes, Tomales Bay, and Morro Bay often support very thin, low (< 10 cm) turf-like vegetation mosaics with extremely short, sparse, or prostrate pickleweed as a relatively minor component, or at most co-dominant with species such as *Triglochin concinna* (slender sea arrowgrass; uncommon to rare in San Francisco Estuary). These salt marsh turfs often support high plant species diversity compared with San Francisco Bay salt marsh plains, which tend to be dominated by pickleweed, which often grows in dense stands (usually over 20 cm thick; up to 50-60 cm in some fringing marshes of San Pablo Bay). Low, turf-like middle marsh vegetation is very uncommon in San Francisco Bay, both in brackish and salt marshes.

Salt Marsh Plants and Their Associations – Salt marsh here refers to tidal marsh plant associations that approximate the species composition typical of near-marine salinity during the growing season (34 ppt). Few if any salt marshes in the San Francisco Estuary are ac-

Soft bird's-beak (*Cordylanthus mollis* ssp. *mollis*). The hairy bracts of the flowering stems are jeweled with salt-encrusted glands. (Brackish tidal marsh, Southampton Marsh, Benecia)

tually regularly exposed to near-marine salinity, but in the upper estuarine salinity range (roughly 20 ppt and above), they are effectively salt marsh in vegetation character. The salt marsh plant community is typical of San Francisco Bay and the outer marshes of most of San Pablo Bay.

The <u>low salt marsh zone</u> in San Francisco Bay is usually dominated by a single species, *Spartina foliosa* (Pacific cordgrass), but is increasingly becoming dominated by the invasive introduced Atlantic species, *Spartina alterniflora* and its highly variable hybrids and novel "ecotypes" (Callaway and Josselyn 1992; Daehler and Strong 1994, 1997; Daehler et al. 1999). *S. foliosa* stands occur as uniform fringes along tidal creek banks or as broad uniform plains on prograding marshes at the edges of broad tidal mudflats. They extend from approximately mean high water to mean sea level (Hinde 1954, Atwater et al. 1979). On gentle elevation gradients, they intergrade with middle marsh plains in mixed stands of *Salicornia virginica* (pickleweed), as at Dumbarton-Mowry marsh and eastern San Pablo Bay fringe marshes. They may also occur as abrupt zones at the edge between tidal mudflats and wave-cut peat scarps. Pioneer colonies of Pacific and smooth cordgrasses on mudflats are abundant in some years, particularly in years of high or late rainfall. They apparently establish by seedlings and regenerated rhizome fragments, but the relative proportion of these of propagule types is unknown. Pioneer colonies of *S. alterniflora* were observed on open mudflats of the San Lorenzo Creek delta in 1991, and are visible in aerial photographs of the Alameda Creek area around 1980. Seedlings and pioneer colonies of *S. foliosa* were common on high mudflats of San Pablo Bay and its tributaries in the late 1990s. The taller *S. alterniflora* appears to be able to spread clonally below mean sea level, but long-term comparisons of colonial spread between

Annual pickleweed (*Salicornia europaea*)— Occasionally found in conspicuous colonies on higher mudflats between upper cordgrass and lower pickleweed zones, it more commonly grows as a short, dense single plant. It turns brilliant crimson in fall, in contrast with the dominant dull green-brown *Salicornia virginica.*

native and introduced cordgrasses have not yet been conducted. The only other species of the low marsh is *Salicornia europaea* (annual pickleweed), which occasionally occurs in the upper edge of the zone, often in accreting high mudflats in transition between low and middle marsh zones.

The <u>middle salt marsh zone</u> composes the extensive salt marsh plains of San Francisco Bay (Hinde 1954, Atwater et al. 1979). Younger marshes tend to be characterized by low-diversity vegetation dominated by *Salicornia virginica* (Cuneo 1987), but some older marsh remnants (e.g., Greenbrae and Heerdt Marsh; upper Newark slough marsh) may comprise complex and annually variable mosaics of *S. virginica, Distichlis spicata* (saltgrass), *Cuscuta salina* (salt marsh dodder), *Jaumea carnosa* (fleshy jaumea), *Frankenia salina* (alkali-heath) and *Atriplex triangularis* (spearscale or fat-hen). Species diversity in the middle salt marsh is not necessarily correlated with marsh age: old marshes at China Camp and Whittell Marsh (Point Pinole) also support relatively low-diversity vegetation dominated by *S. virginica*. The parasitic *Cuscuta salina* (dodder) can become conspicuously co-dominant or even dominant in the middle marsh zone by mid-summer in some marshes in some years, turning the middle marsh into an orange and green mosaic visible at great distances (Dumbarton-Mowry marsh, San Pablo Bay fringe marshes). Colonization and species recovery dynamics associated with dodder-induced dieback of marsh vegetation have not been investigated.

Relatively uncommon species of the middle marsh zone of San Francisco Bay include *Triglochin maritima* (sea arrow-grass), *Limonium californicum* (sea-lavender), and *Polygonum prolificum* and *P. patulum* (non-native knotweeds). Reports of the rare Point Reyes endemic *Polygonum marinense* (Marin knotweed) in San Francisco Bay require taxonomic verification. Species which sel-

Locally rare Point Reyes bird's-beak (*Cordylanthus maritimus ssp. palustris*), is abundant in salt marshes of Tomales Bay, Bolinas Lagoon, and Limantour Estero. (Salt marsh, Marin City shoreline)

dom occur in the middle salt marsh zone of San Francisco Bay include *Cordylanthus maritimus* ssp. *palustris* (Pt. Reyes bird's-beak; Richardson Bay, Heerdt Marsh), *Puccinelia nutkaensis* (Pacific alkali grass; Ravenswood fringe marshes and Newark), *Plantago maritima* (sea-plantain) and *Triglochin concinna* (slender arrow-grass). These latter species are locally abundant in maritime salt marshes of Marin County. Invasive exotic species of the middle salt marsh include *Spartina densiflora* (Chilean cordgrass; Richardson Bay and Point Pinole), *Spartina patens* (saltmeadow cordgrass; near Burlingame and in brackish middle marsh at Southhampton Bay) and *Cotula coronopifolia* (brass buttons; early introduction, widespread but never persistent as a dominant in tidal marsh). The invasive exotic *Salsola soda* (Mediterranean saltwort) also is spreading from high salt marsh to the middle marsh zone (Dumbarton-Mowry marsh).

<u>High or upper salt marsh</u> may occur as topographic highs within the marsh plain (e.g., channel bank levees, wave-deposited ridges or mounds) or along the upland or alluvial edges of the marsh. This zone today commonly includes natives such as *Grindelia stricta* var. *angustifolia* (frequently a dominant in this zone), *Distichlis spicata*, erect-ascending phenotypes of *Salicornia virginica*, *Cuscuta salina*, *Frankenia salina*, *Limonium californicum* (sea-lavender), and *Atriplex triangularis* (spearscale, fat-hen). Where the upper marsh intergrades with low-lying alluvial soils and high groundwater (a condition today very rare in San Francisco Bay), the high marsh zone is dominated by dense stands of *Leymus triti-*

Tiidal salt marsh low marsh zone dominated by Pacific cordgrass *(Spartina foliosa)*.

Josh Collins

coides or *L. x multiflorus* (creeping wildrye), or *Juncus lesueurii* (salt rush, wire rush), as still occurs commonly in maritime salt marshes of the region.

Cooper (1926) described a broad high salt marsh zone along the Palo Alto shoreline dominated by *Distichlis spicata* and *Grindelia stricta* var. *angustifolia* (an association still evident in reduced extent today), and a high salt marsh - alluvial transition zone which no longer exists. Cooper's reconstructed high salt marsh ecotone community was dominated by native composites— *Hemizonia pungens* ssp. *maritima*, *H. congesta* (tarweeds), *Helianthus bolanderi* (Bolander's sunflower), *Aster subulatus* (as "*A. exilis*"; slim or salt marsh aster), *Aster chilensis* (Chilean aster; possibly also including the rare *A. lentus*), *Baccharis douglasii* (salt marsh baccharis), *Euthamia occidentalis* (western goldenrod), and *Iva axillaris* (poverty weed). Of these, *I. axillaris*, *A. chilensis*, *H. pungens*, *B. douglasii*, and *E. occidentalis* still occur in high tidal brackish marsh of San Pablo Bay and Suisun Marsh. It therefore appears likely that historic upper edges of some salt marshes were at least locally brackish or subsaline rather than hypersaline in character, influenced by surface and subsurface freshwater discharges. This is also indicated by Cooper's description of water table-dependent, salt-intolerant tall (to 9 m) thickets of willow, cottonwood, box-elder, ash, blackberry, ninebark, and California rose at the high marsh edge (*Salix lasiolepis*, *Populus trichocarpa*, *Acer negundo*, *Fraxinus oregona*, *Rubus ursinus*, *Physocarpus capitatus*, *Rosa californica*). Cooper (1926) interpreted this community from isolated remnants of what he assumed was undisturbed vegetation, but the disturbance history of the South Bay marsh edge at the time of his observations, and older reports he collected, is uncertain.

The high salt marsh zone also historically included many other native species, which are now uncommon, rare, or extirpated in San Francisco Bay (**Table 1.3**). Most of these still persist at other California salt marsh localities. Most high salt marsh zones in San Francisco Bay today occur on artificial slopes and substrates at the upper marsh edge, and include many non-native species that sometimes dominate the zone. Common non-native plants of the high salt marsh zone include *Lepidium latifolium* (broadleaf peppercress, perennial peppergrass), *Bassia hyssopifolia* (bassia), *Salsola soda* (saltwort), *Beta vulgaris* (wild beet), *Mesembryanthemum nodiflorum (annual iceplant)*, *Carpobrotus edulis* and its hybrids (iceplant), *Atriplex semibaccata* (Australian saltbush), *Bromus diandrus* (ripgut brome), *Hainardia cylindrica* and *Parapholis incurva* (sicklegrasses), and *Polypogon monspeliensis* (rabbit's-foot grass).

Brackish Marsh Plants and Their Associations – Brackish tidal marshes prevail over northern San Pablo Bay (slough systems of the Petaluma River, Tolay Creek, Sonoma Creek, and Napa River), the Suisun Marsh area, and the Contra Costa marshes (North Bay marshes).

They also occur in transition with San Francisco Bay salt marshes where significant freshwater discharges occur (e.g., fringing marshes of Mud Slough, Coyote Creek, Artesian Slough, Alviso Slough, and Guadalupe Slough). The distinction between "salt marsh" and "brackish marsh" is a recent convention in descriptions of San Francisco Bay Area tidal marshes: brackish marshes were indiscriminately described as "salt marshes" by early California botanists, making it difficult to separate distinct elements of "salt" and "brackish" marsh associations. The description and demarcation of brackish marsh plant communities is essentially a matter of convenience and convention: there is no precise, stable salinity threshold at which tidal marshes are known to switch from one "type" to another (Adam 1990). Instead, brackish marsh vegetation in the San Francisco Estuary is typically a dynamic continuum between salt marshes of San Francisco Bay and freshwater tidal marshes of its major tributary rivers, fluctuating with variable influence of rainfall and freshwater discharges which alter marsh salinity and vegetation gradients geographically and over time. Associated changes in local tidal elevations (related to freshwater discharges) may also possibly interact with salinity variations in altering the character of brackish marsh vegetation. Changes in brackish marsh vegetation between dry and wet years at the same location may be dramatic: cover can change from that typical of San Francisco Bay salt marsh (dominant pickleweed) to that typical of Suisun Marsh (mosaic of rushes, bulrushes, alkali-bulrush, cattails, saltgrass, and many broad-leaved herbaceous species) in very few years. The causes of these dramatic changes in brackish tidal marsh vegetation are presumably related to plant interactions (competition, facilitation, and parasitism) which are influenced by seasonal and annual variation in salinity and drainage (Pearcy and Ustin 1984), but are poorly understood beyond descriptive observation.

The most extensive tidal brackish marshes occur in the Petaluma Marsh, but relatively large relict tidal brackish marshes also occur along the Napa River (Fagan Slough marsh) and in the Hill Slough/Rush Ranch area in Suisun Marsh. Relatively young but large and well-developed brackish marshes also occur bayward of dikes constructed after the 1870s, particularly in the Napa-Sonoma marsh complex and Suisun Marsh, including marsh islands of Suisun Bay. The Contra Costa marshes are predominantly intermediate between fully tidal marsh and diked (reduced tidal range) brackish marshes. The extensive wave-influenced, prograded pickleweed-dominated marsh plain and low natural marsh levee along northern San Pablo Bay are transitional between salt marsh and brackish marsh, exhibiting increases in brackish-associated species (particularly *Scirpus maritimus* at the east end of the Bay) in series of wet years.

Plant species richness and diversity markedly increase in brackish marshes of the San Francisco Estuary

Sea-milkwort (*Glaux maritima*) is found in tidal marshes on the northern Pacific Coast, and on the Arctic, American, and European Atlantic coasts. (Tidal marsh, Rush Ranch, Suisun Marsh)

compared with salt marsh. Grewell (1993 *et seq.*) compiled extensive vascular plant species lists of the Suisun Marsh (including uplands of dikes and artificial uplands), and presented the only comprehensive and contemporary synthesis of Suisun Marsh plant ecology and its history (Grewell et al. 1999). Mason (Newcombe and Mason 1972) described plant community composition of brackish tidal marshes extending into the Sacramento-San Joaquin Delta.

The low brackish marsh zone differs from the corresponding zone in the San Francisco Estuary salt marshes in several respects: it supports multiple dominant species in variable mixtures or monospecific stands; it extends to the low end of intertidal zone, and it regularly develops tall, dense vegetation. In San Pablo Bay and western Suisun Marsh, alkali-bulrush (predominantly *Scirpus maritimus* around San Francisco and San Pablo bays and western Suisun Marsh, but also including *S. robustus*, a taxon formerly misapplied to *S. maritimus* in floras of the region) occurs in the upper portion of the low marsh, often dominant in the saline end of the brackish marsh gradient. The tallest graminoid species, tules and cattails, dominate where freshwater influence is relatively strong; these include *Typha angustifolia*, *T. latifolia*, *T. dominguensis* and hybrids; *Scirpus californicus* (California tule), *S. acutus* (hardstem tule) and hybrids. These graminoid species can also establish within poorly drained portions of the middle marsh plain.

The middle brackish marsh zone was historically dominated by *Distichlis spicata* (saltgrass), as it commonly is today (Newcombe and Mason 1972). Other native species of the high marsh which occur in variable abundance (common to co-dominant) include *Salicornia virginica*, *Atriplex triangularis*, the *Juncus balticus-lesueurii* complex, *Jaumea carnosa*, *Frankenia salina* and *Cuscuta salina*. Locally common natives include *Limonium californicum* (sea-lavender), *Glaux maritima* (sea-milkwort), and *Scirpus koilolepis cernuus* and *S. cernuus* (clubrush; also in high brackish marsh), *Eleocharis macrostachya* (creeping spikerush), *Helenium bigelovii* (Bigelow's sneezeweed), and *Deschampsia cespitosa* ssp. *holciformis* (tufted hairgrass; especially eastern Suisun Marsh). Infrequent to rare species of this zone include *Lilaeopsis masonii* and *L. occidentalis* (Mason's and western lilaeopsis; on exposed eroding channel bank edges as far west as Tolay Creek), *Triglochin maritima* (locally common), *T. concinna*, *T. striata*, *Sium suave* (water parsnip), *Oenanthe sarmentosa* (ditch-carrot), *Cicuta maculata* ssp. *bolanderi* (water hemlock), *Eleocharis parvula* (slender spikerush), *Pluchea odorata* (salt marsh fleabane), and *Lythrum californicum* (California loosestrife; eastern Suisun Marsh and Delta). In wet years, depressions in the middle marsh plain support increased abundance of *Scirpus americanus* (Olney's bulrush) or *S. maritimus* (alkali-bulrush; western Suisun and San Pablo Bay) and *Phragmites australis* (common reed; eastern Suisun Marsh, also in the low-middle marsh zone). The dominant non-native species of the middle brackish marsh is again *Lepidium latifolium*, which rapidly forms dense monotypic clonal populations, spreading into the marsh plain. Other exotic species which have established in the brackish middle marsh zone include *Apium graveolens* (wild celery, widespread and abundant in Suisun Marsh), *Lythrum hyssopifolium* (annual loosestrife), *Cotula coronopifolia* (brass-buttons) and *Chenopodium chenopodioides* (fleshy goosefoot; Napa-Sonoma marshes).

The high brackish marsh zone is today typically altered by artificial dikes and invasive plants (particularly *Lepidium latifolium* (perennial or broadleaf peppercress), *Conium maculatum* (poison hemlock), *Foeniculum vulgare* (fennel), and Mediterranean grasses. However, many native remnants of the brackish high marsh community have regenerated on old, stable, relatively undisturbed levees, or have persisted locally along undiked tidal marsh edges. They include *Achillea millefolium* (yarrow), *Baccharis douglasii* (salt marsh baccharis), *B. pilularis* (coyote-brush), *Leymus triticoides* and *L. x multiflorus* (creeping wildrye), *Scrophularia californica* (California bee-plant), *Rubus ursinus* (blackberry, in the upland ecotone) *Rosa californica* (California rose, also in the upland ecotone), *Iva axillaris* (poverty-weed), *Atriplex triangularis* (fat-hen or spearscale), *Grindelia stricta* var. *angustifolia* (and intermediates with *G. camporum*), *Calystegia sepium* ssp. *limnophila* (morning-glory), *Cressa truxillensis* (alkali-weed), *Frankenia salina* (alkali-heath), *Lathyrus jepsonii* var. *californicus* (California tule pea), *Juncus balticus - lesueurii* complex (salt or wire rush), *Juncus mexicanus* (Mexican rush), *J. bufonius* (toad rush),

Ambrosia psilostachya (western ragweed), *Euthamia occidentalis* (western goldenrod), *Epilobium brachycarpum*, *E. ciliatum* (willow-herbs), *Polygonum* spp. (smartweeds, knotweeds), *Triglochin maritima* (sea arrow-grass) and *Eryngium articulatum* (coyote-thistle). Uncommon to rare species such as *Lathyrus jepsonii* var. *jepsonii* (Delta tule pea), *Aster lentus* (Suisun aster), *A. subulatus* var. *ligulatus* (slim aster), *Plantago elongata* (dwarf plaintain), *Rumex occidentalis* (western dock), *Eleocharis parvula* (spikerush), and endangered *Cordylanthus mollis* ssp. *mollis* (soft bird's beak) and *Cirsium hydrophilum* var. *hydrophilum* (Suisun thistle) typically occur locally in the lower end of well-drained high marsh gradient, often on slight topographic relief above the marsh plain. *Salicornia virginica* (common pickleweed) and occasionally *S. subterminalis* (Parish's glasswort) can also be abundant elements of high brackish marsh near Suisun. The composition of high brackish marsh vegetation appears to vary with slope, drainage, and local surface or subsurface freshwater influence, but no studies have yet analyzed vegetation patterns or related environmental factors in brackish marshes of the region.

Invasive non-native species (weeds of mesic and wetland habitats with slight salt tolerance) of the high brackish marsh zone are numerous, particularly in years of high rainfall, but the most aggressive and successful is again *Lepidium latifolium*. *Lotus corniculatus* (bird's-foot trefoil) and *Lolium multiflorum* (ryegrass) are other exotics which are locally abundant along portions of the upper brackish marsh edge some years. *Elytrigia pontica* ssp. *pontica* (tall wheatgrass, currently local around Alameda Creek and Mare Island), *Rumex crispus* and *R. pulcher* (curly and fiddle docks), *Asparagus officinalis* (locally abundant near Napa-Sonoma marshes) have also naturalized along brackish marsh edges, but are seldom invasive.

Ditch-carrot (*Oenanthe sarmentosa*), a common freshwater marsh plant, also occurs in fresher phases of brackish tidal marshes. (Southhampton Marsh, Benicia)

Tidal Marsh Pans and Vegetation – Poorly drained flats, depressions, and barrier-impounded areas of tidal marsh lacking emergent vascular vegetation, called pans (alternatively spelled "pannes"), range from nearly planar unvegetated marsh areas subject to shallow periodic ponding, to steep-sided or cliff-edged shallow ponds which are persistently inundated (Pestrong 1965, Pethick 1974, Atwater et al. 1979). Pans have various modes of origin and development, which have not been completely clarified (Adam 1990, Carter 1988, Pethick 1974, Chapman 1960). In San Francisco Bay Area marshes, pan variation includes nearly circular ponds between drainage channels (Pestrong 1965), historic long ponds parallel with impounding bayfront marsh berms (Atwater et al. 1979), shore-parallel pans historically present along portions of the back edge (upland or lowland margin) of tidal marsh (depicted in 1880s U.S. Coast Survey Maps), and natural historic salt ponds impounded by low estuarine ridges (Atwater et al. 1979). Some sloped to planar pans in the high marsh (bare flats, rarely submerged) may be related to wrack deposition and smothering, or local substrate conditions. Little is known of the ecology of pan types that are no longer represented in the altered modern Estuary.

Many pans are reported to become seasonally hypersaline (Pestrong 1965) or even salt-crystallizing (Atwater et al. 1979; see also salt pond profile, this volume) and lack vascular plants, but some pans along the landward edge of the tidal marsh develop marginal vegetation typical of brackish or fresh marshes (e.g., China Camp). Ponded pans within the marsh plain have been described as "unvegetated" (Pestrong 1965), but they often support a dense submerged mixed vascular and non-vascular vegetation variously composed of widgeongrass (*Ruppia maritima*) and membranous green algae

(particularly *Enteromorpha* and *Ulva* spp.). According to Mason (Newcomb and Mason 1972), brackish ponds in Suisun Marsh also support *Zannichellia palustris* and *Potamogeton pectinatus*, submerged species typical of freshwater ponds. The halophilic microflora of salt ponds is discussed in the salt pond profile(this volume). Shallow, relatively planar and ephemeral pans in San Pablo Bay are either periodically or marginally colonized by pickleweed, which dies back during years of frequent flooding or high rainfall. The steep-sided edges of well-defined, nearly circular old pans sometimes develop small natural levees of locally improved drainage, and sometimes support certain species at frequencies more typical of high marsh vegetation. In the high marsh, on gently sloping alluvial fans, "dry pans" (small playa-like flats with very short flooding periods and superficial salt films) also develop, often on relatively coarse (sandy, silty, or even gravel-silt mixtures) sediments. These features are very rare today because of diking, but fine examples persist at Point Pinole (Whittell Marsh). Here, as at similar pans on alluvial fans at tidal marsh edges in maritime Marin County, the pan-marsh edges are associated with local abundance of the regionally rare salt marsh owl's clover (*Castilleja ambigua* ssp. *ambigua*; salt-tolerant ecotypes). Salt marsh bird's-beak (*Cordylanthus maritimus* ssp. *palustris*) also exhibits a pan-margin local distribution pattern in western San Pablo Bay (e.g., JEPS83457). Analogous artificial features (gently sloping, formerly disturbed silty to sandy high marsh fills with residual vegetation gaps) elsewhere in the Estuary have also become colonized with rare plants such as *Cordylanthus mollis* (Hill Slough near Lawler Ranch; B. Grewell, pers. obs.) and *Cordylanthus maritimus* (near Marin City). Natural and artificial high marsh pans of this type, associated with alluvial or deltaic deposition

High marsh pan in Whittell Marsh (Point Pinole, Contra Costa County), fringed with salt-marsh owl's clover (*Castilleja ambigua*). Whittell Marsh is the last known tidal marsh locality of this species in the San Francisco Estuary.

Peter Baye

Peter Baye

Regionally rare smooth goldfields (*Lasthenia glabrata*). (Whittell Marsh, Point Pinole, Contra Costa County)

or erosion, have not been identified in the regional literature on salt marsh ecology, and require study.

The number of species from former alkali-subsaline vernal pools around San Francisco Bay which were historically reported from local salt marshes as well (see diked wetlands profile, this volume) suggests that ecologically equivalent habitat occurred in both ecosystems. Although there are very few intact remnants of the elongate pans which occurred along tidal marsh edges (represented clearly in historic U.S. Coast Survey maps of the 1850s), it is possible that some of these seasonally ponded depressions in the upper marsh ecotone were partial ecological equivalents of subsaline vernal pools. Strong historic evidence for this conclusion is found in Jepson's (1911) range and habitat descriptions for the typical vernal pool species, *Downingia pulchella*, which he described as "abundant and of rank growth in the salt marshes near Alvarado" [now Union City]. Other species indicative of vernal pools and similar seasonally ponded/desiccated alkaline/subsaline environments, such as *Lasthenia conjugens* (JEPS25099), *L. platycarpha* (DS695549, Greene 1894) and *L. glabrata* (CAS897444, DS73122, DS286573) have been collected from the edges of San Francisco Bay.

Although pans are often presumed to be generally hypersaline, some appear to have occurred historically in alluvial lowlands with probable groundwater or surface discharges that could maintain brackish conditions in pans along tidal marsh edges. A number of characteristic freshwater marsh species were reported by Jepson (1911) and others from historic salt marsh habitat (e.g., *Agrostis exarata, Carex aquatilis, C. densa, Lycopus asper*), suggesting that freshwater sub-habitats occurred marginally along tidal salt marshes. Unpublished historic writings of southeastern San Francisco Bay marsh borders by 19th century botanist Joseph Burtt-Davy, archived at the Jepson Herbarium, University of California, describe extensive colorful wildflower meadows with spe-

cies typical of vernal pools and wet grassland (R. Grossinger, pers. comm. 1999). Examples of brackish and even freshwater vegetation at edges of salt marsh with pans near zones of groundwater discharge can be observed today at China Camp (Marin County) and Point Pinole (Contra Costa County), and in maritime Marin County tidal marshes. Diked seasonal wetlands in historic tidal marsh (this volume) may also approximate this type of lost habitat, since numerous seasonal wetland species of vernal pools and alkali basins have colonized diked Baylands.

Uncommon, Rare, Declining, and Extirpated Plant Species

There is a widespread impression, even among ecologists familiar with the San Francisco Estuary, that native plant species richness of tidal marshes (particularly salt marsh) is relatively low, and that rare species in the Estuary are principally wildlife taxa, not plants. This impression is due in part to reviews of species richness in tidal marshes based solely on modern surveys: for example, Atwater et al. (1979) reported only 15 vascular plant species for San Francisco Bay, based on modern reports. Josselyn (1983) discussed only a small representation of the San Francisco Estuary flora, and did not address either its historic or modern species richness. In addition, very few plants native to the San Francisco Estuary are federally listed as endangered or threatened, and only two of these (soft bird's-beak, *Cordylanthus mollis* ssp. *mollis*, and Suisun thistle, *Cirsium hydrophilum* var. *hydrophilum*) currently inhabit this Estuary. The modern lack of attention to rare plants in the Estuary is probably due to unfamiliarity with plant species which were known only to early botanists, but are either now entirely extinct (or even extirpated) in the Estuary. Plant species that were historically recorded in the tidal marshes of the Estuary, or along its edges (high marsh), but have become uncommon, rare, regionally extirpated, or extinct, are summarized in **Table 1.3**. Most of these species were known from tidal marsh edges, transitional habitats of high ecological diversity. This is significant, because original remnants of this ecotone are almost completely eliminated from the Estuary, and their modern counterparts are mostly weedy, disturbed habitats like dikes.

Extinct species of the Estuary include California sea-blite, *Suaeda californica*, a federally endangered shrubby true halophyte (salt-tolerant plant) which today inhabits relatively well-drained marshy beach ridges along relatively high-energy shorelines with coarse sediment in Morro Bay. According to Jepson (1911) and Greene (1894), it was never abundant in San Francisco Bay even in the late 19th century. The distribution of its sandy marsh habitats was unfortunately in areas of the greatest urbanization: San Francisco, Oakland, Alameda, and San Leandro were its core populations,

although it was also collected in Palo Alto (where shell hash beaches today occur) and at the former San Pablo Landing (Richmond, where local sand beaches still persist). The species today is restricted to sandy salt marsh edges of Morro Bay, San Luis Obispo County, and also exists in cultivation. It was last collected in San Francisco Bay in 1958 in San Leandro (JEPS25020) More recent local reports are based on misidentification of the similar species, *S. moquinii*, in diked Baylands.

Many other salt marsh species that have affinity for high sandy salt marsh were also reported from San Francisco Bay, but are now extinct or rare in the Bay (Jepson 1911, Greene 1894). They include California saltbush (*Atriplex californica*), still found in Tomales Bay and Point Reyes sandy salt marshes, but extinct in the Bay, and *Plantago maritima*, common in sandy maritime salt marshes, uncommon to rare in the Bay. The sea-pink (*Armeria maritima*) a showy pink spring wildflower which still occurs locally along sandy edges of Point Reyes salt marshes, was cited by Jepson (1911) to range within San Francisco Bay. (This may possibly have been along former sandy beaches, sandy salt marsh, or stabilized former bayside dunes. There are no historic herbarium specimens from San Francisco Bay salt marshes to corroborate Jepson's report, however.) Other rare species, such as *Cordylanthus maritimus* ssp. *palustris* and *Castilleja ambigua* ssp. *ambigua*, are less uncommon in sandy maritime salt marshes, but are rare in San Francisco Bay. The decline or demise of these species in the Bay is very likely a result of the near-complete elimination of its sandy estuarine barrier beaches.

Two other species which are probably extinct in San Francisco Bay, but occur elsewhere, include two members of the Aster family: southern goldenrod (*Solidago confinis*) and *Pyrrocoma racemosa* (=*Haplopappus racemosa*). Southern goldenrod was formerly reported as rare only by Henry Bolander in 1863 (Jepson 1911),

when it was misidentified as seaside goldenrod (*S. sempervirens*). In California tidal marshes today, *S. confinis* is known only locally from the high brackish marsh zone of southern Morro Bay. *P. racemosa* was formerly reported from the edges of salt marshes and saline soils at Cooley's Landing and near Alviso (Thomas 1961), but has not been reported from salt marsh edges in recent decades. Another species, Adobe sanicle (*Sanicula maritima*), was found locally in lowlands adjacent to salt marshes at Alameda (Behr 1888, Greene 1894, Jepson 1911) and in San Francisco (Brandegee 1892). It is now extinct in the Bay Area, and is very rare elsewhere (known from fewer than 10 sites in Monterey and San Luis Obispo Counties today; Skinner and Pavlick 1994).

Two popcornflower species (genus *Plagiobothrys*, well represented in vernal pools) that were found in saline soils near the edge of the Estuary are now presumed to be extinct (although it is possible that buried dormant seed may persist somewhere in diked Baylands, awaiting resurrection). They include Petaluma popcornflower (*Plagiobothrys mollis* var. *vestitus*), which was probably distributed in alkaline or subsaline seasonally wet depressions (vernal pools) in grasslands and lowlands adjacent to tidal marsh in the Petaluma Valley, and Hairless popcornflower (*P. glaber*), a species of seasonally wet alkaline/subsaline soils of tidal marshes of the south San Francisco Bay (reported by Jepson (1911) from Alvarado [now Union City]), as well as some interior valleys. Almost nothing is known of the ecology of these species because of their early historic extinction.

Other species that are known to occur in subsaline to alkaline vernal pools, and which historically occurred in salt marshes (presumably along lowland edges), include several species of goldfields (*Lasthenia* spp.). Fleshy goldfields, *Lasthenia platycarpha* (presumed extinct in the Estuary) was known from salt marshes near Vallejo (Greene 1894), and smooth goldfields (*L. glabrata* ssp. *glabrata*) was reported from edges of salt marshes (Thomas 1961, Jepson 1911, Greene 1894). *L. glabrata* was recently confirmed to occur naturally at Whittell Marsh, Point Pinole, and a population of undetermined origin occured briefly in 1998 on a hydroseeded levee at the Sonoma Baylands tidal marsh restoration project's pilot unit. Behr (1888) listed *L. glabberima* as a species occurring "near salt marshes," but is not otherwise reported from tidal marshes in the region. The federally endangered vernal pool goldfields species, Contra Costa goldfields (*L. conjugens*) was reported by Jepson (1911) from "subsaline soils" near Antioch and Newark, and was recently discovered in subsaline vernal pools in Fremont near the diked edge of the at the Warm Springs Unit of the National Wildlife Refuge in Fremont and adjacent derelict fields. *L. conjugens* was also observed along high tidal marsh edges of Hill Slough in the early 1990s. Another well-known vernal pool species, the showy *Down-*

Federally listed as endangered, California sea-blite (*Suaeda Californica*) is extinct in San Francisco Bay. (Morro Bay)

Peter Baye

Peter Baye

The southern-most population of Point Reyes bird's-beak (*Cordylanthus maritimus* ssp. *palustris*), in a small marsh on the Marin City shoreline.

ingia pulchella (producing spring masses of blue, white, and yellow flowers resembling lobelias) was described by Jepson (1911) to occur abundantly in South Bay salt marshes. It still occurs in the subsaline vernal pools adjacent to tidal marsh at the Warm Springs Unit of the Refuge in Fremont, and in diked agricultural Baylands (former tidal marsh) near Fairfield. The rare annual milkvetch (locoweed), *Astragalus tener* var. *tener,* was formerly collected from "saline areas along San Francisco Bay" as far south as Mayfield (Mountain View area; Thomas 1961). Once found in alkali vernal pools, it was collected in the Bay Area in 1959 (Skinner and Pavlick 1994) and was recently rediscovered near the historic Bay edge in Fremont (G. Holstein, pers. comm. 1999).

Two hemiparasitic annual snapdragon family herbs are extinct in the salt marshes of south San Francisco Bay, but occur elsewhere in the Estuary or region. The Point Reyes bird's-beak (*Cordylanthus maritimus* ssp. *palustris*), a close relative of the endangered salt marsh bird's beak of Southern California (*C. m.* ssp. *maritimus*), was formerly found almost throughout San Francisco Bay. It is now restricted to very few populations in the Central Bay, with small remnant populations probably persisting in Petaluma Marsh and near Gallinas Creek, Marin County. The remaining San Francisco Bay populations of Marin County are typically showier (usually more conspicuous, rosy purple flowers and purplish herbage) than most of the core populations of Point Reyes, which typically have gray-green foliage and white-and-maroon flowers. Another annual Snapdragon family herb, Johnny-nip or salt marsh owl's clover (*Castilleja ambigua* ssp. *ambigua*) was formerly found in the salt marshes of San Francisco Bay (Berkeley, Oakland, Alameda, Bay Farm Island, Burlingame), but is nearly extinct there now. The only salt marsh population of this colorful annual herb in the San Francisco Estuary is from Point Pinole, which supports a form with purple-tinged foliage, bracts, and flowers (atypical of the subspecies

ambigua, but typical of ssp. *insalutata* of Monterey County). Salt-tolerant locally adapted populations of this subspecies also occur at Rodeo Lagoon and Bolinas Lagoon, but are otherwise rare in central coast tidal marshes (very local in Limantour estero and Tomales Bay). A related salt marsh endemic subspecies, *C. a.* ssp. *humboldtiensis*, occurs only in Humboldt Bay and Tomales Bay. Non-halophyte populations of *C. a.* ssp. *ambigua* occur somewhat more widely in coastal grasslands, headlands, and bluffs.

Still surviving but rare within its historic range in brackish tidal marshes from Petaluma Marsh to Antioch is another annual Snapdragon family herb, soft bird's-beak (*Cordylanthus mollis* ssp. *mollis*). This white-yellow flowered herb is covered with salt-encrusted secretory glands. It is listed as federally endangered, and is restricted mostly to the Suisun Marsh area, especially in old relict tidal brackish marsh. It formerly ranged as far west as Petaluma Marsh (Howell 1949). Like the other annual hemiparasitic salt marsh Snapdragon relatives, its numbers fluctuate tremendously from year to year (Rugyt 1994), sometimes disappearing for a year or more before regenerating from dormant seed banks.

Numerous other species, particularly grasses and sedge species, were cited by early California botanists as commonly occurring in salt marshes, but are scarce or absent today in the San Francisco Bay Area. By analogy with relatively intact tidal marshes of Point Reyes to the north and Elkhorn Slough to the south, it appears very likely that these "missing" salt marsh species occurred along upland or lowland (alluvial) margins of tidal marshes. Some, like *Agrostis exarata* (= *A. asperifolia*), *Juncus xiphioides, J. lesueurii,* and *J. effusus* var. *brunneus* were described as common in Bay Area salt marshes (Jepson 1911, Brewer et al. 1880, Howell 1949), although they occur only very locally in Bay Area tidal marshes today. Other grass species, like *Leymus triticoides* (including *L. x multiflorus*), are presumed to be former marsh edge dominants based on relict occurrences at intact lowland tidal marsh edges (e.g., Rush Ranch, Point Pinole) and colonizing behavior on levees which have not been maintained (Dutchman Slough and Mare Island, San Pablo Bay). The salt marsh grass *Puccinelia nutkaensis*, in contrast, occurred in periodically inundated middle salt marsh zones in the South Bay as well as on levees (Thomas 1961). It is rarely found in San Francisco Bay today, such as near Ravenswood, Palo Alto and Newark. Other grasslike plants, such as *Plantago elongata*, were reported as common in Bay Area tidal salt marshes (Brewer *et al* 1880, Greene 1894) but have become uncommon or rare here. Other grasslike plants of uncertain former abundance in tidal marshes, which are scarce or absent in Bay Area tidal marshes today, include *Carex aquatilis* var. *dives*, *C. densa*, and *C. praegracilis* (Thomas 1961, Jepson 1911); *C. praegracilis* occurs infrequently in tidal brackish marshes of the Suisun Marsh area. Sedges such as *Carex subbracteata*, and *C. obnupta* would also be expected to have occurred in former salt marsh edges, as they do in other estuaries of the Central Coast, especially northward.

Many broadleaved herbs were also more plentiful along tidal marsh edges, but have become localized or rare today. They include *Aster lentus* (Greene 1984, Jepson 1911), a species now generally rare in any estuarine habitat; Chilean aster (*Aster chilensis*) (Howell 1949, Thomas 1961), a common species of non-saline habitats which has nearly disappeared from salt marsh edges but persists occasionally in Suisun, Petaluma, and Napa-Sonoma marshes. Salt marsh baccharis (*Baccharis douglasii*) was formerly abundant in salt marshes (Jepson 1911) but is now uncommon to rare in brackish marshes, mostly in the North Bay (Best et al. 1996, Thomas 1961). Two species which were inferred by Cooper (1926) to be major elements of his reconstructed "willow-composite" community at South Bay salt marsh edges, slim aster (*Aster subulatus* var. *ligulatus*), and spikeweed (*Hemizonia pungens* var. *maritima*) are now scarce in tidal marshes, and occur mainly in the North Bay (Best et al. 1961; B. Grewell, pers. obs. 1997). Other spikeweeds, *H. parryi* sspp. *parryi* and *congdonii,* were locally common in the South Bay salt marshes (Munz 1959), but are generally rare today. Species that were formerly frequent in North Bay brackish and salt marshes (Greene 1894) include morning-glory (*Calystegia sepium* var. *limnophila*) and sea-milkwort (*Glaux maritima*), which are now uncommon to rare. Other herbs which have historically declined to a significant extent in frequency, distribution, and abundance in Bay Area tidal marshes and their edges include *Hutchinsia procumbens* (Greene 1894, Thomas 1961), tidy-tips, *Layia chrysanthemoides* (Howell 1949, Thomas 1961), native annual peppercress species *Lepidium dictyotum, L. latipes,* and *L. oxycarpum* (Thomas 1961, Munz 1959, Howell 1949, Greene 1894), salt marsh fleabane, *Pluchea odorata* (Jepson 1911), and butterweed, *Senecio hydrophilus* (Greene 1894, Jepson 1911).

Conservation Issues

Exotic Plants – There are many exotic plants that have become established within, or along the edges of, the San Francisco Estuary, but only a few are aggressive invaders that have become widespread and dominant, or threaten to do so (Grossinger et al. 1998). Of these, *Lepidium latifolium, Spartina alterniflora* (and hybrids), and *Salsola soda* have demonstrated ability for rapid, extensive invasion and development of monodominant stands in the San Francisco Estuary. *Spartina densiflora*, an exotic cordgrass from Chile with a bunchgrass growth habit, has become a dominant species in Humboldt Bay, and is expected to be able to achieve the same dominance if its spread is unchecked in San Francisco Bay. The taller stature of *S. alterniflora* enables it to endure high tides with relatively little submersion of its foliage, even when rooted below mean sea level. Turf-forming *S. patens* (salt meadow cordgrass) and dwarf strains of *S. alterniflora* (Daehler et al. 1999) present in the Bay may be latent invaders of salt marsh plains. The tendency for *S. alterniflora* pollen to swamp the pollen of the native *S. foliosa* and produce hybrids and introgressants threatens to genetically assimilate the native Pacific cordgrass over a significant portion of its geographic range (D. Ayers and D. Strong, pers. comm. 1999). The higher densities, larger plant size, and greater colonizing ability of *S. alterniflora* at lower tidal elevations also suggest that its spread may have significant geomorphic impacts on the Estuary, particularly on channel stability, sedimentation, and mudflat colonization, and their indirect effect on wildlife habitat (Grossinger et al. 1998).

Lepidium latifolium invasion is particularly a concern for the conservation and recovery of rare or endangered plant species of the San Francisco Estuary, most of which occur in the high marsh zone where *L. latifolium* is dominant. *L. latifolium* actively encroaches on populations of endangered *Cordylanthus mollis* ssp. *mollis* and *Cirsium hydrophilum* var. *hydrophilum* in Suisun Marsh (B. Grewell, pers. obs. 1998) and Southhampton Bay (P. Baye, pers. obs. 1998). The impact of exotic plant invasions in the high marsh zone is magnified by the truncation and degradation of this habitat by widespread diking, which compresses the high marsh zone into a relatively invariant, steep slope of disturbed Bay mud.

Tidal Marsh Restoration Design – Tidal marsh restoration in the San Francisco Estuary has convention-

Invasive exotic *Lepidium latifolium* (background) looms over the endangered *Cordylanthus mollis* ssp. *mollis* at the high marsh edge. (brackish tidal marsh, Southampton Marsh, Benecia.)

ally been designed for wildlife species, treating plants only as habitat for wildlife species rather than as the subject of restoration aims. Restoration designs have generally afforded little or no consideration for soils or slopes of the high marsh zone, variations in sediment texture, surface or subsurface freshwater flows, and variation in incident wave energy that influence the microenvironmental variables which are significant for plant diversity. Highly managed estuarine wetlands (e.g., artificial salt ponds, extremely microtidal or non-tidal salt marshes) generally support an artificially low diversity of native tidal marsh plant species. Plans for rare tidal marsh plant reintroduction have only recently been proposed (e.g., Pier 98, Port of San Francisco; Crissy Field, Presidio/Golden Gate National Recreation Area), and none has yet been implemented. Of the rare plant refugia in relict tidal marshes of the Estuary (e.g., Hill Slough, Fagan Marsh, Rush Ranch, Peytonia Slough, and Whittell Marsh), none has site-specific rare plant management plans or programs, despite imminent threats by invasive species. There is no Estuary-wide program to survey and map rare plant species populations; plant inventories are biased towards species with special legal status, and are typically driven by environmental impact assessment for projects rather than regional conservation. Other surveys consist of voluntary and opportunistic reports. Conservation of plant diversity in the Estuary will require both active protection of remnant rare plant refugia, active management of conserved areas, systematic inventory of the Estuary's botanical resources, and large-scale, scientifically sound tidal marsh restoration and reintroduction projects.

Many natural resource agencies are cautious about restoration and reintroduction of rare plants, probably because this has conventionally been considered in a mitigation context (Berg 1996). Restrictive generalized policies on geographic specificity of reintroduction to documented historic localities, regardless of natural temporal and spatial scales of plant population dynamics and ecosystem processes, in some cases has narrowed opportunities for re-establishment of rare plants (White 1996). In situations where the range of rare plants is extremly reduced, historic collection data are sparse and vague (which is generally the case), and relatively few potential source populations for founders exist, an experimental approach may be most appropriate for reintroduction planning. Successful reintroduction will likely require much replication over years (variable climate conditions) and at many localities. Caution is appropriate, however, when the taxonomic interpretation or population variability is at issue when determining suitable populations for reintroduction.

Artificial Salinity Manipulation – In Suisun Marsh, salinity control gates on Montezuma Slough were installed to enforce standards for salinity based on the perceived needs of waterfowl marsh management in diked wetlands, aimed at maintaining low channel water salinity. The impacts of sustained low marsh salinity on the progression of exotic plant invasions and the natural dynamics of brackish tidal marsh vegetation (particularly rare and endangered species) were not considered in the design and operation of the salinity control gates, and no long-term monitoring of rare plant populations during gate operation was authorized. The reduction of periodic high salinity events during drought cycles, and

Pioneer plants (1st year seedling) of native *Spartina foliosa* and *Salicornia virginica* colonize the well-consolidated upper mudflats bayward of the marsh edge at Mare Island, eastern San Pablo Bay. The erosional scour pools and drainages adjacent to the plants indicate the relatively hight wave energy estuarine environment in which they are able to establish, given stable microhabitats.

Peter Baye

the subtle changes in tide elevations caused by gate operation, could potentially have significant adverse long-term impacts on rare plant persistence. Scientific investigations of the effects of gate operation on plant communities and rare plant populations of Suisun tidal marshes are urgently needed, as recommended by the Brackish Marsh Subcommittee of the Suisun Ecological Workshop (CWRCB 1999).

In the South Bay, perennial urban wastewater discharges in confined, diked tidal sloughs have caused conversion of salt marsh to brackish marsh (Harvey and Associates 1997). The Alviso and Milpitas area marshes were the sites of historic rare plant populations (**Table 1.3**) which could not be re-establish naturally or be reintroduced in marsh vegetation dominated by perennial pepperweed, bulrushes and tules which are stimulated by augmented and confined freshwater flows and elevated nutrient concentrations throughout the growing season.

Loss of Restorable Habitat – Economic pressure to convert diked Baylands to land uses that are incompatible with potential tidal marsh restoration over large contiguous tracts (particularly in connection with uplands and alluvial areas) remains high today. Developments in diked Baylands for extensive housing (Redwood Shores, San Mateo County), golf courses (Black Point, Marin County), business parks (old Fremont Airport, Alameda County) have proceeded into the 1990s, and other large scale land use conversions for dredged material disposal and rehandling (Napa salt crystallizers) have been considered. The largest tracts of undeveloped diked Baylands are in San Pablo Bay, where vineyard expansion threatens to encroach into restorable former tidal marsh sites. Single-purpose management of other diked wetland types at large scales (salt production, waterfowl production) also restricts opportunities for tidal marsh plant community restoration. Large-scale tidal marsh restoration near centers of relict tidal marsh plant populations (e.g., Cullinan Ranch, Hamilton Airfield, Redwood Landfill, and Skaggs Island) offer some hope for long-term recovery of tidal marsh plant species in decline.

Conclusions and Recommendations

The San Francisco Estuary tidal marshes are poorly understood in terms of modern and historic plant species composition, the dynamics of the vegetation, and the interaction between vegetation and geomorphic and hydrologic processes. Many plant species have become extirpated or nearly so with little or no attention from botanists or ecologists, and many more species have declined significantly. The Estuary's historic and modern flora is considerably richer than has been generally recognized. Further attrition of native plant diversity in the Estuary is likely because of the uncontrolled spread of invasive exotic plants, and insufficient planning, management, and restoration of the Estuary's plant community. Carefully designed tidal marsh restoration projects that promote native plant species diversity and recovery are needed to conserve the Estuary's flora. Recommendations for the conservation of the Estuary's plant communities are presented in the Baylands Ecosystem Habitat Goals Report (Goals Project 1999, Appendix A).

Peter Baye

An example of marsh progradation — Seedling plants of *Salicornia virginica* and *Spartina foliosa* are frequently comingled without clear zonation, as in these exceptionally firm upper mudflats in eastern San Pablo Bay. (Mare Island, north of the jetty)

Table 1.3 Historic Changes in the Distribution and Abundance of Selected Native Vascular Plant Species Occurring in Tidal Marshes of the San Francisco Estuary

Taxon	Historic References	Contemporary Distribution
Agrostis exarata Trin. (*A. asperifolia* Trin.)	**Jepson 1911**: Common in the San Francisco Bay region in salt marshes and other wet places: Berkeley…San Francisco; Martinez."	Not currently reported from tidal marsh ecotone in San Francisco Bay Estuary, but common and widespread in non-tidal moist habitats (Hickman et al. 1993).
Armeria maritima (Miller) Willd. ssp. ***californica*** (Boiss.) Pors. (*Armeria vulgaris* Willd.) (*Statice armeria* L.)	**Greene 1894**: "Along sandy beaches in wet ground…" **Jepson 1911**: "common on the sandy beaches or fields near the sea…or about San Francisco Bay."	Apparently extirpated in San Francisco Bay Estuary; otherwise restricted to maritime coastal salt marshes, dunes, bluffs.
Aster chilensis Nees.	**Cooper 1926**: (presumed species of reconstructed "willow-composite" community at salt marsh edges, Palo Alto vicinity) **Howell 1949**: (Marin Co.) Common and widespread from salt marshes and coastal swales to low valleys…" **Thomas 1961**: "…edges of salt marshes…"	Few current reports known from edges of San Francisco Bay or San Pablo Bay tidal marshes; local in Suisun Marsh edges. Presumed rare from tidal marshes.
Aster lentus E. Greene (*A. chilensis* Nees. var. *lentus* Jepson) (*A. chilensis* var. *sonomensis* (E. Greene) Jepson)	**Greene 1894**: (*A.c.* var. *lentus*) "Plentiful along tidal streams in the western part of the Suisun Marsh…" (*A. c.* var. *sonomensis*) "In open plains of the Sonoma Valley, in low subsaline ground." **Jepson 1911**: (*A.c.* var. *lentus*) " very common and conspicuous in the Suisun Marshes." (*A. c.* var. *sonomensis*) "subsaline lands: Petaluma, Napa" **Munz 1959**: (*A.c.* var. *sonomensis*): Coastal Salt Marsh; saline ground around San Francisco Bay. Sonoma, Napa…"	Rare; restricted primarily to Suisun Marsh. Some herbarium collections known from San Francisco Estuary prior to 1960 (Berkeley, Alviso, Napa). Recent status uncertain in San Pablo Bay area tidal marshes.
Aster subulatus Michaux var. ***ligulatus*** Shinn. (*Aster exilis* Ell.) (*Aster divaricatus* Nutt.)	**Behr 1888**: (*A. divaricatus*) "Salt marshes." **Greene 1894**: "Borders of Suisun Marshes and elsewhere on subsaline land" **Jepson 1911**: "Saline soil, not common ….Alvarado." **Cooper 1926**: (presumed species of reconstructed "willow-composite" community at salt marsh edges, Palo Alto vicinity) **Thomas 1961**: "Salt marshes along San Francisco Bay and occasionally elsewhere. San Francisco, Palo Alto, Alviso…"	No current reports known from edges of San Francisco Bay . Uncommon to rare in San Pablo Bay and Suisun tidal marshes.
Astragalus tener Gray var. ***tener***	**Jepson 1911**: "Alkaline fields, mostly in moist places." **Thomas 1961**: Known locally only from saline areas along San Francisco Bay. San Francisco and Mayfield."	Recently rediscovered near historic Bay edge in Fremont, Alameda County. Known in region from alkali vernal pools, Solano County.

Taxon	Historic References	Contemporary Distribution
Atriplex californica Moq.	**Greene 1894**: "…along the edges of salt marshes, from near San Francisco and Alameda, southward." **Jepson 1911**: "Sandy beaches along the ocean and about San Francisco Bay."	Extirpated in San Francisco Bay Estuary margins. Small relict populations occur on bluffs of Golden Gate in San Francisco. Maritime salt marsh populations occur at Limantour Estero and Tomales Bay (Marin Co.).
Baccharis douglasii DC.	**Jepson 1911**: "…abundant in the salt marshes about San Francisco Bay." **Thomas 1961**: (SW San Francisco Bay) "…occasionally along the edges of salt marshes…Alviso…" **Best** et al. **1996**: "Uncommon. Damp thickets, salt marshes."	Now uncommon to rare in alluvial high marsh and upland ecotone, San Pablo Bay area and and Suisun Marsh; one colony occurs along salt pond edge at a seep in Coyote Hills, Alameda Co., possibly rare elsewhere in San Francisco Bay.
Carex aquatilis Wahlenb. var. ***dives*** (Holm) (*C. sitchensis* Prescott)	**Brewer** et al. **1880**: "In salt marshes, about San Francisco Bay (*Bolander*)…" **Jepson 1911**: "Salt-marshes about San Francisco Bay and northward along the coast". **Munz 1959**: "Rare, swampy places, usually near the coast…"	No current reports known from edges of San Francisco Bay or San Pablo Bay tidal marshes. Presumed rare or extirpated from tidal marshes.
Carex densa Bailey (*C. brogniartii* Kunth. var. *densa* Bailey)	**Jepson 1911**: (*C. b.* var. *densa*) "Salt marshes near San Francisco…"	No current reports known from edges of San Francisco Bay or San Pablo Bay tidal marshes. Presumed rare or extirpated from tidal marshes.
Carex praegracilis W. Boott (*Carex Douglasii* var. *brunnea* Olney) (*C. usta* Bailey)	**Thomas 1961**: " Boggy areas along the edges of salt marshes; San Francisco, Woodside, Mayfield…"	Rare in Suisun area tidal marshes, west to Southampton Bay. Common in alkaline, moist places in California floristic province.
Castilleja ambigua Hook and Arn. (*Orthocarpus castillejoides* Benth.)	**Behr 1888**: "Marsh near Tamalpais." **Greene 1894**: "Common along the borders of salt marshes." **Jepson 1911**: "Marshy ground near the coast. Alameda; W. Berkeley; Napa Valley; Sonoma Co." **Howell 1949**: "low ground along the upper reaches of the salt marshes, occasional:..Mount Tamalpais; Greenbrae Marshes; Hamilton Field…"	Currently reported only from Point Pinole salt marsh and pan edges; other historic records at Greenbrae, Tamalpais (Mill Valley), Hamilton Field, Burlingame, Oakland. Halophytic populations rarely occur in brackish marsh and salt marsh at Rodeo Lagoon, Tomales Bay, Drakes Estero, Limantour Estero (maritime Marin Co. marshes)
Centaurium trichanthum (Griseb.) Robinson (*Erythrea trichantha* (Griseb.))	**Howell 1949**: "in typical form…known in Marin only from low ground bordering the salt marsh near Burdell Station". **Munz 1959**: "Moist often saline places…edge of Coastal Salt Marsh… San Mateo Co. to Siskyo Co."	No current reports known from edges of estuarine tidal marshes. Similar species *C. muehlenbergii* occurs in subsaline diked wetlands, Napa-Sonoma marsh, and tidal marsh edge at China Camp.

Taxon	Historic References	Contemporary Distribution
Calystegia sepium (L.) R.Br. ssp. **limnophila** (E. Greene) Brummit (*Convolvulus sepium* L.)	**Greene 1894**: "Plentiful in brackish marshes toward the mouth of the Napa River and about Suisun Bay; its roots within reach of tide water; its stems twining upon rushes and sedges. **Munz 1959**: "Occasional in swampy saline places; Coastal Salt Marsh; Marin, Solano and Contra Costa Cos."	Occasional In Suisun Marsh area west to Southhampton Bay; rare in San Pablo Bay edges.
Cicuta maculata L. var. **bolanderi** (S. Watson) Mulligan (*Cicuta bolanderi* Watson)	**Jepson 1911**: "Suisun marshes, abundant and conspicuous." **Munz 1959**: "Salt marshes, Marin to Solano and Contra Costa cos."	Uncommon to rare in Suisun Marsh; not currently reported elsewhere in the Estuary.
Cirsium hydrophilum (E. Greene) Jepson var. **hydrophilum** (*Carduus hydrophilus* Greene)	**Jepson 1911**: "Suisun marshes" **Munz 1959**: "Brackish marshes about Suisun Bay".	Extremely rare (federally endangered) in Suisun Marsh.
Cordylanthus maritimus Benth. ssp. **palustris** (Behr) Chuang and Heckard (*Cordylanthus maritimus* Nutt.) (*Adenostegia maritima* (Nutt.) Greene)	**Brewer** et al. 1880: "Sandy salt-marshes along the coast, from San Francisco Bay to San Diego." **Behr 1888**: "Salt marshes, San Francisco." **Greene 1894**: "Sandy salt marshes from near San Francisco southward." **Jepson 1911**: 'Salt marshes near the coast from San Francisco Bay south…" **Howell 1949**: "*Salicornia* flats in salt marshes along the bay..:.Almonte, Greenbrae…" **Thomas 1961**: "Salt marshes along the borders of San Francisco Bay; San Francisco, Redwood City, Palo Alto, and near Alviso."	Currently reported only from Richardson Bay, Greenbrae, and Petaluma marsh (Marin Co.). Recently reported from Gallinas Creek area marsh. Extirpated in central and southern San Francisco Bay. Major populations occur In maritime tidal salt marshes of Tomales Bay, Bolinas Lagoon, and Limantour Estero (Marin Co.). San Francisco Estuary populations have purplish foliage, and rosy, well-exerted inflated flowers.
Cordylanthus mollis Gray ssp. **mollis**	**Brewer** et al. 1880. "Salt-marshes of San Francisco Bay, at Mare Island and Vallejo, C. Wright, E.L. Greene." **Behr 1888**: "Salt marshes. Vallejo." **Greene 1894**: "Brackish marshes about Vallejo and Suisun." **Howell 1949**: (Marin Co.) "…San Rafael, acc. Ferris; Burdell Station, San Antonio Creek…." **Best** et al. 1996: (Sonoma Co.): Rare, estuarine…Petaluma Marsh between San Antonio and Mudhen Slough…(1978)…"	Rare (federally endangered): local in tidal brackish marsh around Napa River, Carquinez Straits tidal marsh, Suisun Marsh area. Presumed extirpated in Petaluma River marshes. Putative San Francisco (city) record is erroneous interpretation of early San Francisco Bay Area collection acc. L. Heckard.
Downingia pulchella (Lindley) Torrey (*Bolelia pulchella* E. Greene)	**Jepson 1901**: "…Abundant and of rank growth in salt marshes near Alvarado (Union City)". **Munz 1959**: "…Coastal Salt Marsh."	Extirpated in Union City. Occurs in alkaline/saline vernal pools at Warm Springs, Fremont, Alameda Co., and in some diked baylands near Fairfield, Solano Co.

Table 1.3 (continued) Historic Changes in the Distribution and Abundance of Selected Native Vascular Plant Species Occurring in Tidal Marshes of the San Francisco Estuary

Taxon	Historic References	Contemporary Distribution
Eleocharis parvula (Roemer and Shultes) Link	(not reported in early floras; Munz 1959 reported only from coastal salt marshes of San Luis Obispo and Humboldt Cos.)	Rare in brackish tidal marshes of San Pablo and Suisun Bay area. Local in diked baylands, lower Napa River.
Festuca rubra L.	(reported only from generalized habitats in early floras; halophytic populations not distinguished. Speculative likely component of historic sandy salt marsh edges of Central Bay.)	Not currently reported from San Francisco Bay estuarine tidal marsh edges; halophytic populations presumed extirpated. Halophytic populations occur along edges of maritime salt marsh and brackish marsh at Rodeo Lagoon, Limantour Estero, Tomales Bay (Marin Co).)
Glaux maritima L.	**Behr 1888**: "Salt marshes." **Greene 1894**: "Frequent both along the seabord and in subsaline soils in the interior" **Jepson 1911**: "Marshy shores of … San Francisco and Suisun bays." **Howell 1949**: (Marin Co.) "salt marshes… Burdell…" **Thomas 1961**: "…Palo Alto, but expected elsewhere in salt marshes" **Atwater** et al. **1979**: (recorded as present in San Pablo Bay) **Best** et al. **1996**: (Sonoma Co.) "Rare, salt marshes: Petaluma, *Davy* (1893 UC)."	Few recent reports known from San Francisco Bay or San Pablo Bay salt marshes; reported as infrequent in Petaluma Marsh; local in tidal marsh near mouth of Tolay Creek, Sonoma Co.; occasional to locally frequent in Suisun Marsh area and Fagan Slough (Napa River).
Heliotropium curassavicum L.	**Howell** et al. **1958**: "salt marsh near Visitacion Valley (southeastern San Francisco)."	No current reports known from San Francisco Bay. Recently reported from Suisun Marsh area.
Hemizonia pungens (Hook and Arn.) Torrey and A. Gray ssp. ***maritima*** (E. Greene) (*Centromadia maritima* Greene)	**Greene 1894**: "Borders of salt marshes about San Francisco Bay." **Cooper 1926**: (dominant species of reconstructed "willow-composite" community at salt marsh edges, Palo Alto vicinity.)	Local, infrequent species along tidal marsh edge around the San Francisco Estuary.
Hemizonia parryi E. Greene ssp. ***parryi***, ssp. ***congdonii*** (Robinson and Greenman) Keck	**Munz 1959**: (ssp. *congdonii*) "Locally common…s. end of San Francisco Bay, mostly Alameda Co." (ssp. *parryi*) "Coastal Salt Marsh…to N. San Mateo Co…" (not reported from salt marsh in Jepson 1901, Greene 1894)	No current reports known from San Francisco Bay Estuary tidal marsh edges. Rare.
Hutchinsia procumbens (L.) Desv. (*Bursa divaricata* (O. Ktze) Nutt.) (*Capsella divaricata* Walp.) (*Capsella procumbens* Fries.) (*Capsella elliptica* C.A. Mey.) (*Lepidium procumbens* L.) (*Hutchinsia californica, H. desertorum* A. Davids)	**Greene 1894**: "Borders of salt marshes." **Jepson 1911**: Alkaline soil from Vallejo (acc. Bot. Cal.), Alameda…" **Thomas 1961**: Known locally from saline areas along San Francisco Bay; Palo Alto and Mayfield."	No current reports known from San Francisco Bay Estuary tidal marsh edges. Occurs in high marsh ecotone of central CA coast salt marsh, and in other alkaline or subsaline habitats in California floristic province.

Taxon	Historic References	Contemporary Distribution
Juncus effusus L. var. ***brunneus*** Engelm.	**Brewer** et al. **1880**: "...common in the salt-marshes about San Francisco Bay..." **Brandegee 1892**: "Salt marshes about the bay shore." **Jepson 1911**: "Common in marshy ground: Monterey to San Francisco and Bolinas Bays and northward." **Howell 1949**: "Swamps and swales generally near the ocean...Tiburon; Sausalito..." **Thomas 1961**: "Usually along or near the coast...Palo Alto, near Alviso..."	Rare, local at edges of salt marsh and brackish marsh ecotones in San Pablo Bay (China Camp). No known reports from San Francisco Bay tidal marshes.
Juncus lesueurii Boland.	**Brandegee 1892**: "Salt marshes at Visitacion Bay. South San Francisco." **Howell 1949**. "Common along the upper reaches of salt marshes... Tiburon; Tamalpais Valley.... In Marin County,... (*J. balticus*) is not readily distinguished from *J. Leseurii*...)"	Apparently associated with sandy salt marsh edges of maritime coast. Intermediates with *J. balticus* not uncommon in San Francisco Bay Area tidal marshes; difficult to separate. Rare in south San Francisco Bay tidal marshes; one colony in seep at salt pond edge, Coyote Hills.
Juncus xiphioides E. Meyer	**Jepson 1901**: "A common species of salt marshes... Berkeley; Belmont... Suisun Marshes..." **Thomas 1961**: "Occasional in sloughs ... Palo Alto, nr. Alviso..."	Not recently reported; presumed rare or possibly extirpated in most tidal salt marshes of San Francisco Estuary.
Lasthenia glaberrima D.C.	**Behr 1888**: "Near salt marshes."	No other reports, historic or current, are known from San Francisco Bay estuarine marshes.
Lasthenia conjugens E. Greene (*Baeria fremontii* (Torr.) A. Gray in part)	**Greene 1894**: "Subsaline soil near Antioch..." **Jepson 1911**: "Subsaline fields in the Bay region; Antioch; Newark, etc."	Occurs in alkaline/saline vernal pools bordering salt pond 22 in Fremont, Alameda Co., and in diked baylands at upper end of Hill Slough (Potrero Hills), Solano Co. Historic localities near Mt. Eden along bay shore and near Newark. Rare; federally endangered.
Lasthenia platycarpha (A. Gray) E. Greene (*Baeria carnosa* E. Greene) (*B. platycarpha* A. Gray)	**Greene 1894**: "Border of salt marsh north of Vallejo: rare or local." **Jepson 1911**: "Salt marshes at Vallejo (Greene)."	Historic locality at Redwood City shoreline. Apparently extirpated from San Francisco Bay estuarine marshes. Occurs infrequently in alkaline vernal pools, Solano Co.
Lasthenia glabrata Lindley ssp. ***glabrata***	**Behr 1888**: "Common." **Greene 1894**: "Borders of salt marshes only; not common." **Jepson 1911**: "Borders of salt marshes." **Thomas 1961**: Edges of salt marshes along San Francisco Bay...Millbrae... Belmont, Redwood City, Mayfield."	Currently reported within San Francisco Bay Estuary only from Point Pinole (Whittell marsh) salt marsh and new seeded levee slope at Sonoma Baylands. Many historic salt marsh collections known from Burdell, Alvarado, Mt. Eden, Alameda, Mowry's Landing, Denverton. Maritime salt marsh population occurs in Limantour Estero, Marin Co.

Taxon	Historic References	Contemporary Distribution
Lasthenia minor (DC.) Ornd. (*Baeria minor* (DC.) Ferris (*Baeria uliginosa* Nutt.) (*Lasthenia uliginosa* (Nutt.) E. Greene)	**Brandegee 1891**: "About the borders of marshes, Islais Creek, Visitacion Valley, Presidio, South San Francisco."	Apparently extirpated from San Francisco Bay estuarine marshes.
Lathyrus jepsonii E. Greene var. **jepsonii** Jepson	**Greene 1894**: "Suisun marshes." **Jepson 1911**: "Suisun marshes."	Occasional to rare in Suisun Marsh. Also occurs locally in tidal brackish marshes along Napa River (Dutchman Slough). May be under-reported in drought years.
Layia chrysanthemoides (DC.) A. Gray (*Blepharipappus chrysanthemoides* Greene)	**Howell 1949**: "Locally common on flats bordering the salt marshes: Ignacio;…Chileno Valley." **Thomas 1961**: "occasionally in low alkaline soils of San FranciscoBay… Millbrae, Redwood City."	No current reports known from San Francisco Estuary tidal marsh edges.
Leymus triticoides (Buckley) Pilger (incl. *Leymus X multiflorus* (Gould) Barkworth and D.R. Dewey (*Elymus triticoides* Buckley)	(general grassland habitats reported historically. Presumed abundant or dominant species of historic tidal marsh edges.)	Occurs locally (abundant) at salt marsh edges at Newark, Alameda Co.; Rush Ranch, Solano Co; Petaluma Marsh, Marin Co.; China Camp, Marin Co.; Dutchman Slough, Solano Co.
Lepidium dictyotum A. Gray	**Greene 1894**: "Along the borders of marshes at Alameda."	No current reports known from San Francisco Bay tidal marsh edges. Presumed extirpated or rare in Estuary.
Lepidium latipes Hook.	**Greene 1894**: "in saline soil at Martinez, Alameda, etc." Jepson 1901: "…alkali flats…Martinez…"	No current reports known from San Francisco Bay tidal marsh edges. Reported rarely in diked baylands and tidal marsh edges, Solano Co. (Suisun Marsh area).
Lepidium oxycarpum Torrey and A. Gray	**Greene 1894**: "Borders of salt marshes at Vallejo…also in subsaline soils… near Alameda." **Howell 1949**: "A rare peppercress of alkaline valley floors and of saline flats adjacent to coastal salt marshes, in Marin Co. known only from low pastures bordering San Francisco Bay near Novato." **Munz 1959**: "V. Grassland and edge of Coastal Salt Marsh; largely about San Francisco Bay…" **Thomas 1961**: "Saline and alkaline flats along San Francisco Bay and Santa Clara Valley: Redwood City, Cooley's Landing, Palo Alto, Mayfield…"	No current reports known from San Francisco Bay tidal marsh edges. Rare, Suisun Marsh edges.
Lilaeopsis masonii Mathias and Constance (*Lilaeopsis lineata* (Michx.) Greene, in part	**Jepson 1911**: (as *L. lineata*, in part) "Salt marshes or brackish mud flats:… Port Costa to Antioch; Robert's Island".	Rare in tidal brackish tidal marshes, Napa Marsh, Suisun Marsh area, to Tolay Creek, San Pablo Bay. Uncommon in western Sacramento river delta fresh-brackish marshes.

Table 1.3 (continued) Historic Changes in the Distribution and Abundance of Selected Native Vascular Plant Species Occurring in Tidal Marshes of the San Francisco Estuary

Taxon	Historic References	Contemporary Distribution
Lycopus asper E. Greene (*Lycopus lucidus* Turcz.) (*L. lucidus* Benth. misapplied)	**Jepson 1911**: "Salt marshes: Suisun; Benicia; San Francisco." **Hickman** et al. **1993**: Uncommon. Moist areas, marsehs, streambanks… Deltaic GV, SnFrB, GB; to w Can, Great Plains.	No current reports known from San Francisco tidal marsh edges; presumed rare or extirpated in Estuary there.
Plagiobothrys glaber (A. Gray) I.M. Johnston (*Allocarya salina* Jepson) (*Allocarya glabra* Macbr.)	**Jepson 1911**: "Alvarado (Union City), margin of salt marshes." **Munz 1959**: "Coastal Salt Marsh; s. shore of San Francisco Bay…"	**Hickman 1993**: "PRESUMED EXTINCT. Wet, alkaline soils in valleys, coastal marshes…CCo, s SnFrB… Perhaps a var. of *P. stipitatus.*"
Plagiobothrys mollis (A. Gray) I.M. Johnston var. **vestitus** (E. Greene) I.M. Johnston (*Allocarya mollis* A. Gray var. *vestita* E. Greene (*A. vestita* E. Greene)	**Jepson 1911**: Petaluma, *Congdon, 1880*; not since collected.	**Hickman 1993**: "PRESUMED EXTINCT. Wet sites in grassland, possibly coastal marsh margins…"
Plagiobothrys stipitatus (E. Greene) var. **stipitatus**	**Best** et al. **1996**: "salt marsh near Sears Point, Keck 1935"	Reported at Sonoma Baylands, high tide line, 1996. Otherwise no current reports known from San Francisco Estuary tidal marsh edges
Plantago elongata Pursh (*Plantago bigelovii* Gray)	**Brewer** et al. **1880**: "Salt-marshes, San Pablo Bay, at Benicia and Vallejo, *Bigelow, E.L. Greene.*" **Greene 1894**: "Borders of saline or brackish marshes; quite common about the Bay…" **Howell 1949**: (Marin Co.; not reported from estuarine stations) **Thomas 1961**: (SW San Francisco Bay) "…edges of salt marshes…Mayfield, Alviso…) **Best** et al. **1996**: (Sonoma Co.) "uncommon, salt marshes…Petaluma, *Congdon* (1880); 5 mi. n. of Sear's Point, *Rubzoff* (1970).	Rarely reported from San Francisco Bay Area high tidal marshes (Suisun Marsh). No recent localities in tidal marsh edges confirmed.
Plantago maritima L. (*P. maritima* L. ssp. *juncoides* (Lamk.) Hulten, *P. juncoides* Lamk. var. *juncoides*)	**Greene 1894**: "…sandy salt marshes" **Jepson 1911**: "…West Berkeley…" **Howell 1949**: (Marin Co.) "occasional in salt marshes bordering the bay or ocean: Almonte…" **Thomas 1961**: "occasional in salt marshes and on coastal bluffs as far south as San Mateo County: San Francisco, Redwood City, and Mayfield." **Best** et al. **1996**: *(Not reported from estuarine Sonoma Co. stations.)*	Infrequent to rare in San Francisco Bay tidal marshes, mostly Richardson Bay. Relatively common in maritime salt marshes, and occaisional in Suisun Marsh (Hill Slough).

Taxon	Historic References	Contemporary Distribution
Pluchea odorata (L.) Cass. (*P. camphorata* (L.) DC. and *P. purpurascens* (Sw.) DC. misapplied)	**Behr 1888**: Salt marshes. **Greene 1894**: "Borders of brackish marshes about Suisun Bay, etc." **Jepson 1911**: "Common in the salt marshes about Suisun and San Francisco Bays…" **Howell 1949**: (Marin Co.; not cited) **Thomas 1961**: (SW San Francisco Bay; not cited)	No current reports known from San Francisco or San Pablo Bays; uncommon in Suisun marshes.
Puccinelia nutkaensis (J.S. Presl.) Fern. and Weath. (*P. grandis* Swallen)	**Thomas 1961**: "levees and salt marsh along San Francisco Bay".	Rare, local, south San Francisco Bay. No records of San Pablo Bay collections in Howell 1949, Best et al. 1996.
Pyrrocoma racemosa (Nutt.) Torrey and A. Gray var. ***racemosa*** (*Haplopappus racemosa* (Nutt.) Torr.; *P. elata* E. Greene)	**Greene 1894**: "A somewhat rare plant of subsaline soils at Calistoga and near San Jose." **Thomas 1961**: "edges of salt marshes, saline soils, and occasionaly disturbed areas. Cooley's Landing, Near Alviso, Agnews, and San Jose."	No current reports known from San Francisco Bay high tidal marsh. Presumed extirpated in San Francisco Bay.
Rumex occidentalis S. Watson (*R. fenestratus* E. Greene)	**Greene 1894**: "Frequent in marshy places." **Jepson 1911**: "Marshes bordering San Francisco Bay." **Munz 1959**: "Coastal, often brackish marshes, San Francisco Bay…" **Hickman** et al. **1993**: "Uncommon. wet +/- salty places."	Infrequent to rare in North Bay, Suisun Marsh area brackish tidal marshes.
Salicornia subterminalis Parish (*Arthrocnemum subterminale* (Parish) Standley)	(Not reported from estuarine stations in early floras.)	Local, rare in South Bay, south Fremont, Milpitas (in diked wetlands, former Fremont Airport), and at Hill Slough, Suisun Marsh.
Sanicula maritima Wats. (*S. maritima* Kellogg)	**Behr 1888**: "Alameda marshes." **Greene 1894**: "In lowlands adjacent to salt marshes near Alameda, San Francisco, etc." **Jepson 1911**: "Local species of low and wet adobe lands in the vicinity of salt marshes bordering San Francisco Bay; near Alameda…and Potrero Hills, San Francisco, the only recorded localities."	Extinct in San Francisco Bay; known from fewer than 10 stations in 1988, Monterey and San Luis Obispo Counties.
Senecio hydrophilus Nutt.	**Brewer** et al. **1880**: "…salt marsh at Vallejo (*Greene*)…" **Greene 1894**: "Brackish marshes; formerly plentiful at West Berkeley, and on the lower Napa River; still abundant in the Suisun marshes." **Jepson 1911**: Abundant in the Suisun Marshes and found in other marshes about San Francisco Bay"	Apparently extirpated in San Francisco, San Pablo Bay (incl. Petaluma R.); infrequent but locally common in Suisun Marsh area and Carquinez Strait tidal marshes; possibly Napa R.." **Hickman 1993**: "Reduced from wetland development."

Table 1.3 (continued) Historic Changes in the Distribution and Abundance of Selected Native Vascular Plant Species Occurring in Tidal Marshes of the San Francisco Estuary

Taxon	Historic References	Contemporary Distribution
Sium suave Walter (*Sium cicutaefolium* Gmel. var. *heterophyllum* Jepson)	**Jepson 1911**: "Suisun marshes; Stockton"	Rare in Suisun Marsh, primarily in wet years. Recently observed near Rush Ranch, Hill Slough, and Brown's Island.
Suaeda californica Wats.	**Brewer** et al. **1880**: "In salt-marshes on the coast, about San Francisco." **Behr 1888**: "Salt marshes on an island near Alameda." **Greene 1894**: "Vicinity of sand beaches about San Francisco Bay, but seldom seen." **Jepson 1911**: "Sandy beaches bordering San Francisco Bay, the known stations few: San Pablo Landing; Bay Farm Island." **Thomas 1961**: "Occasional in salt marshes along San Francisco Bay; San Francisco and Palo Alto."	Extinct in San Francisco Bay Estuary, probably since ca. 1950. Restricted to one large population at Morro Bay, where it occurs primarily along sandy high marsh edges. Planned for reintroduction. Misreported occurrences often due to confusion with *Suaeda calceoliformis, S. moquinii, Salsola soda,* and *Bassia hyssopifolia.*
Solidago confinis Nutt. (*S. sempervirens* L. misapplied) (*S. confinis* var. *luxurians* Jepson)	**Jepson 1911**: "Salt marshes, San Francisco Bay, *Bolander* (1863). Rarely collected.	Apparently long extirpated in San Francisco Bay Area. Occurs in brackish tidal marsh edges of Morro bay, San Luis Obispo co.

References

Adam, P. 1990. Salt marsh ecology. Cambridge Univ. Press. 461 pp.

Allison, S.K. 1992. The influence of rainfall variability on the species composition of a northern California salt marsh plant assemblage. Vegetation 101: 145-160.

Atwater B.F. and C.H. Hedel. 1976. Distribution of seed plants with respect to tide levels and water salinity in the natural tidal marshes of the northern San Francisco Bay Estuary, California. US Geolog. Survey, Menlo Park, Calif. Open File Report 76-389. 41 pp.

Atwater, B.F., S.G. Conard, J.N. Dowden, C.H. Hedel, R.L. MacDonald and W. Savage. 1979. History, landforms and vegetation of the estuary's tidal marshes. *In*: T.J. (ed). San Francisco Bay: the urbanized estuary. Proc. 58th Ann. Mtg. Pacific Div. of the American Association of the Advancement of Science. Calif. Academy of Sciences.

Barbour, M.G., R.B. Craig, F.R. Drysdale and M.T. Ghiselin. 1973. Coastal Ecology: Bodega Head. Univ. of Calif. Publications. 338 pp.

Barbour, M.G. and A.F. Johnson. 1977. Beach and dune. *In*: M.G. Barbour and J. Major (eds). 1988. Terrestrial Vegetation of California. Calif. Native Plant Society Publication No. 9, 1030 pp.

Behr, H.H. 1888. Flora of the Vicinity of San Francisco. San Francisco, Calif.

_____. 1892. Botanical Reminiscences. Zoe 2: 2-6.

Berg, K.S. 1996. Rare plant mitigation: a policy perspective.pp. 279-292. *In*: D. Falk, C. I. Millar, and M. Olwell (eds). Restoring diversity: strategies for reintroduction of endangered plants. Island Press. 505 pp.

Best, C., J.T. Howell, W.I. Knight and M. Wells. 1994. A flora of Sonoma County. 347 pp. Calif. Native Plant Society.

Brandegee, K. 1892. Catalogue of the flowering plants and ferns growing spontaneously in the city of San Francisco. Zoe 2: 334-383.

Brewer, W.H., S. Watson and A. Gray. 1880. Geological survey of California. Botany. John Wilson and Son, Cambridge, Mass. Second Edition.

Callaway, J. and M. Josselyn. 1992. The introduction and spread of smooth cordgrass (*Spartina alterniflora*) in South San Francisco Bay. Estuaries 15: 218-226.

California Water Resources Control Board (CWRCB). 1999. Suisun Ecological Workgroup Report to the Calif. State Water Resources Control Board. Sacramento, Calif.

Carter, R.W.G. 1988. Coastal environments. New York: Academic Press. 617 pp.

Chapman, V.J. 1960. Salt marshes and salt deserts of the world. Leonard Hill - Interscience Publishers. 392 pp.

Cooper, W.S. 1926. Vegetational development of alluvial fans in the vicinity of Palo Alto, California. Ecology 7: 1-30.

Cuneo, K. 1987. San Francisco Bay salt marsh vegetation, geography, and ecology: A baseline for use in impact assessment and restoration planning. Ph.D. dissertation, Univ. of Calif., Berkeley.

Daehler, K. and D. R. Strong. 1994. Variable reproductive output among clones of *Spartina alterniflora* (Poaceae) invading San Francisco Bay, California: the influence of herbivory, pollination, and establishment site. Amer. J. Bot. 81: 307-313.

Daehler, K., C.K Antilla, D. R. Ayres, D.R. Strong and J.P. Bailey. 1999. Evolution of a new ecotype of *Spartina alterniflora* (Poaceae) in San Francisco Bay, California, USA. Amer. J. Bot. 86: 543-546.

Davies, J.L. 1980. Geographical variation in coastal development, 2nd edition. Longman, New York. 212 pp.

Goals Project. 1999. Baylands Ecosystem Habitat Goals. A report of habitat recommendations prepared by the San Francisco Bay Area Wetlands Ecosystems Goals Project. Joint publication of the U.S. Environmental Protection Agency, San Francisco, California and San Francisco Bay Regional Water Quality Control Board, Oakland, Calif. 210 pp.

Grossinger, R., J. Alexander, A. Cohen and J. Collins. 1998. Introduced tidal marsh plants in the San Francisco estuary: regional distribution and priorities for control. San Francisco Estuary Institute, Richmond, Calif. 52 pp.

Greene, E.L. 1894. Manual of the botany of the region of San Francisco Bay. Cubery and Company, San Francisco.

Grewell, B. 1993 (*et seq.*). Unpublished vascular plant species list, Suisun Marsh.

[References continued on page 29]

Grewell, B., D. Hickson and P. Baye. 1999. SEW (Suisun Ecological Workgroup) Brackish marsh vegetation subcommittee report. Report to the California State Water Resources Control Board. Sacramento, Calif.

Harvey and Associates. 1997. Marsh plant associations of south San Francisco Bay: 1997 comparative study. Unpublished report to the City of San Jose. H.T. Harvey and Associates, Alviso, Calif.

Hinde, H. 1954. The vertical distribution of salt marsh phanerogams in relation to tide levels. Ecol. Monogr. 24: 209-225.

Howell, J.T. 1949. Marin Flora. Univ. of Calif. Press. 319 pp.

_____. 1969. Marin Flora Supplement. Univ. of Calif. Press.

Howell, J.T., P.H. Raven and P.R. Rubtzoff. 1958. A flora of San Francisco, California. Wasmann J. of Biol. 16: 1-157.

Ingram, B.L., J.C. Ingle and M.E. Conrad. 1996. A 2000 year record of Sacramento-San Joaquin river inflow to San Francisco Bay Estuary, California. Geology 24: 331-334.

Jepson, W.L. 1911. A Flora of middle western California. Cunningham, Curtiss and Welch, San Francisco. (Revised edition of 1901). 515 pp.

_____. 1925. Manual of the flowering plants of California. Univ. of Calif. Press. 1238 pp.

Josselyn, M. 1983. The ecology of San Francisco Bay tidal marshes: A Community Profile. US Fish Wildl. Serv. OBS-83/23, Oct. 1983. 102 pp.

Macdonald K.B. 1977. Coastal salt marsh. *In*: M.G. Barbour and J. Major (eds). 1988. Terrestrial vegetation of California. Calif. Native Plant Society Publ. No. 9, 1030 pp.

_____. 1988. Supplement: coastal salt marsh. *In*: M.G. Barbour and J. Major (eds). 1988. Terrestrial vegetation of California. Calif. Native Plant Society Publ. No. 9, 1030 pp.

Munz, P.A. 1959. A California flora. Univ. of Calif. Press. 1681 pp.

_____. 1968. Supplement to a California flora. Univ. of Calif. Press. 224 pp.

Newcombe, C.L. and H. Mason. 1972. An environmental inventory of the North Bay-Stockton ship channel area. San Francisco Bay Marine Research Center. 2 vols.

Pearcy R. W. and S. L. Ustin. 1984. Effects of salinity on growth and photosynthesis of three California tidal marsh species. Oecologia 62: 68-73.

Peinado, M., F. Alcaraz, J. Delgadillo, M. De La Cruz, J. Alvarez and J.L. Aguirre. 1994. The coastal salt marshes of California and Baja California: phytosociological typology and zonation. Vegetatio 110: 55-66.

Pestrong, R. 1965. The development of drainage patterns of tidal marshes. Stanford Univ. Publications in Geolog. Sciences 10: 1-87.

Pethick, J.S. 1974. The distribution of salt pans on tidal salt marshes. J. Biogeog. 1: 57-62.

Peterson, D.H., D.R. Cayan, J.F. Festa, F.H. Nichols, R. A. Walters, J.V. Slack, S.E. Hager and L.E. Shemel. 1989. Climate variability in an estuary: effects of riverflow on San Francisco Bay. *In*: D.H. Peterson (ed). Aspects of climate variability in the Pacific and the western Americas. Geophys. Union. Geophys. Monogr. 55: 41-442.

Rugyt, J. 1994. Ecological studies and demographic monitoring of soft bird's-beak (*Cordylanthus mollis* ssp. *mollis*), a California listed rare plant species (and habitat recommendations). Report to Calif. Dept. Fish and Game, Natural Heritage Div., Sacramento, Calif. 173 pp.

Skinner, M.W. and B.M. Pavlick. 1994. California Native Plant Society's inventory of rare and endangered vascular plants of California, 5th edition. CNPS Publications, Sacramento, Calif. 338 pp.

Thomas, J.H. 1961. Flora of the Santa Cruz Mountains of California. Stanford Univ. Press. 434 pp.

Wells, L.E. and M. Goman. 1994. Late Holocene environmental variability in the upper San Francisco Estuary as reconstructed from tidal marsh sediments. *In*: C.M. Isaacs and V.L. Tharp (eds). Proc. 11th Ann. Pacific Climate Workshop, Technical Report 40, Calif. Dept. Water Resources, Sacramento, Calif.

White, P. S. 1996. Spatial and biological scales in reintroduction. pp. 49-86 *In*: D. Falk, C. I. Millar, and M. Olwell (eds). 1996. Restoring diversity: strategies for reintroduction of endangered plants. Island Press. 505 pp.

Plants and Environments of Diked Baylands

Peter R. Baye

Introduction

This report focuses on wetland areas within historic tidal marshes that have been isolated from tidal action by dikes (levees) and converted to non-tidal salt marsh, non-tidal brackish marsh, or subsaline to freshwater seasonal wetlands. These areas are referred to herein interchangebly as "diked wetlands" or "diked Baylands." Because instantaneous salinity (or even average annual salinity) of diked wetland soils does not consistently correspond with plant community composition, and varies over time, these salinity categories are intended to be broadly descriptive of plant associations rather than quantitative threshold values of soil salinity. Accordingly, the marsh types described are not discrete, but intergrade continuously and may vary over time at any site. Diked wetlands as treated below do not include artificial salt ponds (treated separately) or "muted tidal" managed marshes (marshes with reduced tidal range controlled by tidegates), and cover only wetlands with non-tidal hydrologic inputs (rainfall, groundwater, surface runoff, streamflow, engineered water control structures, or very infrequent overtopping of dikes by extreme tides).

Published and unpublished sources of useful, precise data and other information on the vegetation and flora of diked Baylands are very scarce. Most usually are limited to short-term observations and coarse descriptive accounts (such as lists of dominant species) at a particular time of year, or generalized accounts of resource management plans (e.g., Eicher 1988, Hudson 1980). Vegetation was usually described for wildlife habitat evaluation, rather than for floristic analysis or quantative plant community description. Relatively more detailed information about some individual diked Bayland sites is sometimes available for sites which are proposed for major development projects, and become the subject of detailed wetland delineations and field studies for environmental evaluations (e.g., Rugyt 1991, Kaufman and Harvey 1987). The level of detail in vegetation analysis of diked Baylands even for site-specific studies was still low until the mid 1980s when technical vegetation criteria for wetland jurisdictional delineations were promulgated (WES 1997). There are no long-term studies of changes in vegetation in diked Baylands. Some coarse information about vegetation change in diked wetlands is available through inspection of historic aerial photographs, particularly color infrared photos from the 1980s to the present. Based on recent information from some of the more intensively surveyed diked wetlands (e.g., Montezuma Wetlands, Solano County; Cullinan Ranch,

Solano County; Renaissance Faire site, Marin County), it appears that the diversity and dynamics of diked wetland vegetation have been substantially underestimated in past assessments.

Historic information on the diking of San Francisco Bay tidal marshes is based on numerous sources, particularly U.S. Coast Survey maps (multiple series); historic accounts of salt pond levee development (Ver Planck 1958); and field observations of modern levee maintenance and repair methods and agricultural drain systems.

Environmental Setting

The physical origins of diked wetlands are similar throughout the San Francisco Estuary. Most of the tidal marshes were reclaimed for agricultural use in the late 19th century when the use of mechanical dredges became commercially available to landowners (after *ca.* 1870), although many dikes were constructed manually (Madrone Associates 1977). Tidal marshes were diked for reclamation either as pasture, hayfields, salt ponds, or (rarely) cropland. Reclamation involved construction of dikes (earthen levees made of locally excavated Bay mud) along the margins of marsh plains (middle marsh between approximately MWH and MHHW) where they bordered mudflats or major tidal creeks. The borrow ditches for dike construction were typically located inside of the dike, creating narrow canals about 20 ft from the foot of the dikes. Enclosure of tidal marshes by dikes, and resulting fluctuation between winter flooding and summer desiccation of saline basins, would have rapidly killed most standing tidal marsh vegetation. When levees were stabilized after several lifts (sequential layers of dewatered dredged Bay muds) tidegates were installed to enable the enclosed basins to drain on low tides. After stabilization, dikes typically stood about 3 (to 4) ft above the marsh plain (Ver-Planck 1958).

Environmental Changes From Diking – Following the initial phase of dike construction, several changes occurred. Mature tidal marsh soils accumulated peaty organic matter under anaerobic conditions, which minimizes decomposition. Drained marsh soils high in peaty organic material underwent aerobic decomposition and dewatering, causing land elevations to subside. Dikes also caused compression of underlying plastic clayey silts and peats, and subsided (Madrone Associates et al. 1983). Differential subsidence of the marsh surface tended to exaggerate relict marsh topographic relief, causing natural levees (containing coarser silts) to stand out against isolated depressions where peat content was relatively great, and the effects of aerobic peat decomposition were greatest. Tidal creek topography typically persisted as depressional sinuous swales. Early-succession diked marsh plant communities, typically dominated by perennial pickleweed (*Salicornia virginica*; drier, more saline conditions) or alkali bulrush (*Scirpus maritimus*), bulrush (*Scirpus californicus*; less often *S. acutus*) or cattails (mostly *Typha angustifolia*; wetter brackish to subsaline ditches) tend to be best developed in relict swales and depressions. As salts were drained from the diked basins and lands were managed for agriculture, these pioneer diked salt marsh communities were reduced or eliminated (Madrone Associates et al. 1983, Harvey 1987).

Marsh Progradation and "Second Generation" Diked Wetlands – The strong reduction in tidal flows caused by diking all but the largest tidal creeks in the marsh system caused significant increases in sedimentation outside of diked marshes, causing rapid marsh progradation on sloping mudflats. In addition, slow migration of the pulse of hydraulic mining outwash from the Sacramento River contributed to marsh progradation in San Pablo and Suisun Bays (Doane 1999, Jaffe et al. 1998). In some areas (e.g., south of Novato Creek), marsh progradation was so extensive that a second phase of diking occurred in the newly accreted marshes. These progradational marshes are typically broad pickleweed-

Agricultural areas within the diked historic Baylands can pond water and exhibit seasonal wetland plant associations. (North San Pablo Bay diked Baylands after a storm event)

Ruth Pratt

dominated plains with fringes of cordgrass, cordgrass/alkali bulrush mixtures, or erosional scarps in pickleweed peats. Like early-succession diked salt marsh, they support relatively low salt marsh species diversity, and low densities of narrow, sparsely branched shore-perpendicular tidal creeks. Because of the influence of wave deposition of sediment and coarse organic debris, the tidal elevations of these dike-fringing salt marshes is often above MHHW in some areas, particularly where incipient natural levees form at the edge of mudflats. These secondary prograded high marshes with little antecedent topography were readily converted to diked agricultural land, as in the Baylands of Novato (Hamilton, Bel Marin Keys).

Dike Disturbance Cycle and Vegetation – Subsidence of dikes themselves caused a need to maintain dike crest elevations by dredging borrow ditches to resupply material. This established a periodic disturbance regime to dike vegetation and adjacent ditches. In areas of high wave energy (long fetch distance, narrow mudflats), maintenance by topping dikes with dredged muds and repairing erosional slopes may occur in cycles as short as five years or less. Many bayfront dikes unsheltered by fringing marsh require armoring by placement of rock or concrete fragments. Well-protected dikes behind extensive salt marsh on firmer peats may have maintenance cycles longer than a decade or two. Repaired dike slopes provide bare mineral substrate which is gradually leached of salts and open to colonization by upland weeds.

The dike disturbance cycle has favored a ruderal flora along the upper slopes and crests of dikes (including many native and exotic halophytic weeds as well as glycophytes; e.g., mustard *(Hirschfeldia incana, Brassica* spp.), radish *(Raphanus sativus)*, fennel *(Foeniculum vulgare)*, plantain *(Plantago coronopus, P. major, P. lanceolata)*, annual ice-plant *(Mesembryanthemum nodiflorum;* mostly South Bay), sea-fig *(Carpobrotus chilense)*, hottentot fig *(Carpobrotus edulis* and hybrids with *C. chilense)*, poison hemlock *(Conium maculatum)*, Mediterranean brome species *(Bromus* spp.), wild barley *(Hordeum murinum* ssp. *gussonianum,)*, ryegrass *(Lolium multiflorum, L. perenne)*. Lower portions of disturbed outboard (bayward) dike slopes are typically more saline and wetter, and support brackish marsh or salt marsh species, often with an exaggerated proportion of weedy halophytes (e.g., spearscale, *Atriplex triangularis;* perennial peppercress, *Lepidium latifolium,* sicklegrasses *Parapholis incurva, Hainardia cylindrica;* bassia, *Bassia hyssopifolia;* saltwort, *Salsola soda;* wild beet, *Beta vulgaris)*. Interior slopes of dikes which face salt ponds, and contiguous fringing nontidal saltmarsh, are either bare or vegetated with saltgrass *(Distichlis spicata), Salicornia virginica,* dodder *(Cuscuta salina),* and alkali-heath *(Frankenia salina)*. Dikes with very infrequent maintenance tend to become dominated by dense stands of coyote brush *(Baccharis pilularis;* South Bay) or mixed coyote brush and bee-plant *(Scrophularia californica;* North Bay), often with sub-dominant mustard, poison-hemlock, and radish. High marsh halophytes (pickleweed, alkali-heath, gumplant, spearscale) tend to dominate the lower portion of the outboard dike slopes adjacent to salt marshes, although weedy species can persist for many years after a levee has been disturbed by maintenance and repair activities.

The ecological significance of the dike disturbance cycle for wetland plants is that it has provided corridors through tidal marshes and diked marshes for a weedy flora (both exotic halophytes and glycophytes) to disperse, and places weed seed sources along a topographically superior location for dispersal into adjacent diked and tidal wetlands. The rapid local spread of weedy halophytes on dredge spoils along recently maintained/repaired dikes (especially *Salsola soda, Lepidium latifolium, Mesembryanthemum nodiflorum)* can be observed throughout the Bay. Similar halophyte weed dispersal occurs along side-cast spoils in diked marshes where drainage ditches are created or maintained. Dike disturbance corridors may accelerate the spread of exotic halophyte population outposts into uninvaded wetland habitats. In particular, *Lepidium latifolium's* invasion of brackish marshes appears to have tracked patterns of dike disturbance, invading first along dredge spoil at levee edges, subsequently spreading into diked and tidal wetlands.

Hydrologic Changes in Diked Wetlands – Patterns of soil waterlogging and inundation in diked conditions differ fundamentally from tidal marsh. They depend principally on the efficiency of artificial drainage, the permeability of substrate (related to soil clay content), and the amount and seasonal distribution of rainfall. The efficiency of the early drainage systems in diked marshes was based on the amount of ditching and the pattern of ditching in relation to subsided marsh topography. Because of the great extent of the areas diked, density of drainage ditches was relatively low. Ditches were mostly confined to the borders of farmed parcels, but sometimes

Josh Collins

Diked wetlands in Suisun are managed primarily for waterfowl production.

reached across extensive marsh depressions. The drains were originally driven by gravity, drawing drainage water downslope to one-way flapgates which discharged to adjacent tidal marshes at low tide. This original gravity-driven drainage system had limited efficiency. Topographic lows in the diked basins (swales of relict tidal creeks, relict marsh pans) remained poorly drained into the crop growing season, while relict creek levees and higher relict tidal marsh became better drained. Relictual tidal marsh patterns of wetland and upland are evident in black and white photographs of diked hayfields in the mid-20th century. Even with modern pump-driven drainage systems, persistent soil waterlogging and inundation in depressions occurs following rainstorms (Granholm 1986, Madrone Associates et al. 1983).

The proportions of poorly drained (waterlogged or inundated in spring) and well-drained (aerobic soils in spring) soils in diked Baylands vary with precipitation amounts and patterns. Years of normal or above normal rainfall, particularly those with large storms late in the precipitation season, cause expansion of wetland areas in diked conditions. These contract during years of below-normal precipitation, especially with a lack of spring storms. The proportions of effective wetland and upland also vary with drainage efficiency and the degree of subsidence.

Long-term Drainage of Diked Wetlands –
As subsidence increased, wetland areas increased behind dikes, particularly in peaty soils. In the early 20th century, many diked farmlands failed because the costs of compensating for increased subsidence and dike degeneration at times exceeded the return on agricultural benefits. Many derelict agricultural parcels with degenerated dikes are evident in aerial photographs of San Pablo Bay in the 1940s. After abandonment of diked farmlands, partial levee and drain failures increased, causing reversion of agricultural lands to brackish or salt marsh conditions. For example, prior to conversion to salt ponds, many of the Napa Marsh area's derelict hayfields in the 1940s had partially reverted to wetland (Madrone Associates 1977).

Contemporary Drainage of Diked Wetlands –
Today, subsidence of diked active agricultural lands has increased to the point at which it cannot be compensated by passive gravity drainage through flapgates alone; drainage sufficient for oat hay farming depends primarily on active pumping of water in ditches for discharge to the Bay. It is common for elevations in diked Baylands of San Pablo Bay to average as low as 0 - 1.0 ft N.G.V.D, and some average below -3.0 ft or more over extensive areas, as at Bel Marin Keys and Hamilton Field (USACE 1988). In south San Francisco Bay, which was affected by past subsidence due to long-term groundwater extraction, diked wetland elevations may be even lower (Moffett and Nichols and Phil Williams Associates 1988). These subsided diked marsh surfaces are often

very close to the groundwater surface. Accordingly, the proportion of wetland and upland in contemporary conditions depends on the intensity of pumping and ditch maintenance. These conditions vary significantly among diked parcels under different ownership and management. Therefore, the mosaic of wetland and upland in diked agricultural lands is relatively variable and unpredictable among years and between parcels.

Variability of Artificial Hydrologic Conditions –
The patchiness and instability of diked wetlands is evident, for example, in recent land-use changes in San Pablo Bay. Cullinan Ranch, actively drained and farmed oat hayfield until the early 1990s, supported a matrix of upland cropland and many seasonally wet depressions with wetland weeds. After cessation of pumping by the mid-1990s (a period of above average rainfall), the Ranch rapidly (within 2 years) and spontaneously converted to a seasonal freshwater marsh dominated by cattails and flats of *Eleocharis parvula* (Takekawa et al. 1999). Nearby, between Tolay Creek and the Petaluma River, adjacent hayfields with differing schedules of ditch maintenance changed from very similar extensive winter-ponded swale patterns to striking contrasts of ponded and drained fields. At another location near Sears Point, San Pablo Bay, cessation of pumping in relict hayfields caused conversion to seasonal wetlands dominated by annual plant species typical of vernal pool communities (many of which are present in the ephemeral weed floras of depressions within hayfields; *Downingia pulchella, Plagiobothrys bracteatus, Eryngium aristulatum, Callitriche* spp., *Eleocharis macrostachya*). Thus, the extent of diked wetlands and their character today are very much artifacts of drainage pump activity.

Similar artificial drainage controls wetland plant communities in the diked basins of the Suisun Marsh, which is managed mostly for waterfowl production. There, relatively low-salinity tidewaters are admitted to the basins selectively to sustain fresh-brackish perennial and seasonal marshes (Jones and Stokes 1976, Mall 1969, Meiorin et al. 1991). The proportion of ponded to vegetated marsh may be controlled by modifying managed hydroperiods, so that prolonged flooding causes dieback of vegetation in areas of relatively lower substrate elevation. The seasonal variations in tidewater salinity enable the timing of flooding to control substrate salinity, also. Managed marsh hydroperiods are usually designed to favor mixtures of shallow submerged mud, bulrushes (*Scirpus maritimus, S. americanus, S. pungens*), tules (*S. californica, S. acutus*), cattail (*Typha* spp.) and brass-buttons (*Cotula coronopifolia*), and some non-native annual grasses (*Echinochloa crus-gallii, Polypogon monspeliensis*). Also common in diked brackish marshes are baltic rush (*Juncus balticus*), saltgrass (*Distichlis spicata*) and pickleweed (*Salicornia virginica*). Other species have colonized these brackish managed wetlands, including goosefoot (*Chenopodium chenopodioides*), docks (*Rumex crispus, R.*

pulcher), purslane (*Sesuvium verrucosum*, a recent invader native to the Great Basin), celery, *(Apium graveolens), Lepidium latifolium,* and *Conium maculatum.* Some diked brackish marsh communities are essentially artificial, in contrast with the incidental nature of wetland communities in diked Baylands which are either derelict or managed for hay production, pasture, or salt production.

Salinity in Diked Wetlands – The substrate salinity conditions in the diked, drained marshes were modified by leaching the silty clay Bay muds with precipitation, eliminating leached salts through drainage ditches and tidegates, and excluding tidal inundation by dikes. This caused rapid desalinization of the substrate, enabling glycophytes with relatively low salt tolerance (compared with the salt marsh flora), such as oats and agricultural weeds, to dominate the converted tidal marsh soils (Harvey 1987, Madrone Associates et al. 1983, Meiorin et al. 1991). The desalinized conditions of the substrate were maintained by drainage through ditches and tidegates. Subsidence caused (and continues to cause today) decreased efficiency of drainage, and therefore also decreased flushing of residual or reintroduced salts.

Diked wetlands which have been effectively desalinized for agricultural production do not remain so unless substantial maintenance efforts are applied to drainage and dikes. Diked wetlands become resalinized by partial failure of tidegates and levees (Madrone Associates et al. 1983). Leaking or ruptured tidegates allow influx of saline tidal waters in drainage ditches. Saline or brackish ditch water can recharge salts locally in groundwater, and move into the soil through evapotranspiration and capillary movement. In derelict cattail-lined ditches of abandoned diked hayfields, late summer ditch water salinity can reach 15 ppt, due to salt leaching and evaporation. In addition, seepage through dikes (particularly where Bay mud is silty) introduces salts locally. Overtopping (cresting) of dikes during storm surges floods reclaimed salt marsh soils with brackish or saline water. All these processes recharge soil salinity in diked wetlands. Overtopping typically occurs in winter, and is not a rare event, particularly in south San Francisco Bay (USACE 1988). If poor drainage conditions prevail following a substantial tidal flooding event in a diked basin, wetlands rapidly become recolonized by salt-tolerant vegetation. High salinity in diked Baylands is often maintained by episodic tidal flooding events which are not often observed. Residual salinity tends to decline very rapidly except where drainage is very poor.

Acidification of Diked Wetlands – Soil acidity affects plant growth primarily by altering the availability of soil nutrients, or liberating excessive amounts of otherwise low-solubility ions into the soil solution, creating toxicity problems for roots. Acid-related toxicity occurs only at very low pH (Reuss and Johnson 1986).

Soil acidity is normally not highly variable in tidal salt marshes, which are buffered by cations of estuarine water and relatively stable reduction-oxidation conditions established by groundwater surface position in the marsh soil profile (Adam 1990). In diked conditions, extreme seasonal fluctuations in the soil saturation levels may occur, causing release of sulfides and free metals in marsh soils with high sulfur contents. Some depressions in diked wetlands develop very low pH (pH 4 and occasionally lower) and high concentrations of iron oxide precipitates (Madrone Associates et al. 1983, Madrone Associates 1977). These areas are often barren of vegetation, or develop sparse, low diversity vegetation. Less extreme but low pH in diked wetlands may inhibit plant production, but the abundant phytomass of many diked wetlands (e.g., rank growth of pickleweed, cattails, peppercress) suggests that the seasonal drainage and aeration of diked wetland soils commonly has a stronger overall effect on vegetation production than low pH. Extremely low redox potential and sulfite toxicity, which often accompany low pH, are highly significant inhibitors of plant growth (Russell 1973). Soil acidity is highly variable in diked wetlands and depends on local soil conditions and prevailing hydroperiods.

Disturbance in Diked Wetlands – The disturbance regimes of diked wetlands are influenced primarily by discing and flooding. Discing is performed for agriculture, suppression of weed biomass, and suppression of mosquito production. Episodes of discing have maintained a significant ruderal (weedy) element to the diked wetland flora of San Francisco Bay, creating large vegetation gaps suitable for invasion by non-native plants, particularly annuals. Extreme flooding events which are possible in non-tidal diked marshes also cause disturbances: deep, prolonged flooding causes mass dieback of most standing perennial vegetation. Following dieback events, similar or very dissimilar plant associations may establish.

Diked Bayland Plant Communities

The plant communities present in the diked Baylands can resemble those of local tidal salt marshes, tidal brackish marshes, non-tidal perennial freshwater marshes, or seasonally wet grasslands. Some also have characteristics similar to components of tidal marshes which are now regionally scarce or extirpated, such as high marsh pans and alluvial high marsh ecotones. Diked wetlands usually have lower native species richness than their analogous natural plant communities, and often a larger component of exotic plant species. The typical "weediness" of many diked wetlands is probably more a result of past land uses rather than an intrinsic susceptibility to invasion by exotic vegetation. Some diked wetlands are managed actively to maintain community dominance by marsh plant species favored by wildlife or game managers (Mall 1969). Most are either managed for purposes other than wildlife conservation (hayfields, grazed pasture, flood detention basins, salt evaporation ponds) or are derelict (i.e., pending conversion to urban development), but may still support significant marsh plant communities.

Plant community composition in diked wetlands is strongly influenced by the degree of residual soil salinity or salt recharge of soils, the efficacy of artificial drainage, and the relictual factors of land use history. These factors vary extremely in diked Baylands: some exhibit insignificant salinity, maximal drainage and disturbance in some intensively cropped oat hayfields in San Pablo Bay; others exhibit high salinity, poor drainage and little disturbance in diked pickleweed marshes in south San Francisco Bay. Other modifications persisting from past land uses which affect plant community composition include importation of soils or fill (e.g., former airport landing strips, derelict building pads), abandoned berms and ponds of gun clubs, residual effects of past fertilizer applications; industrial waste disposal, and soil contamination.

Relict Halophytic Vegetation – The majority of derelict diked wetlands in central and southern San Francisco Bay are dominated by species native to local tidal salt marshes and brackish marshes, such as *Distichlis spicata* and *Salicornia virginica* (BCDC and Harvey 1983, Madrone Associates et al. 1983). Salt-tolerant glycophyte species have very low physiological nutritional requirements for salt, and flourish in non-saline and subsaline soils (Waisel 1972). They often co-exist with species with little affinity for saline soil, such as *Polypogon monspeliensis* and *Lolium multiflorum* (Harvey 1987, Kaufman and Harvey 1987). *S. virginica* and *D. spicata* have a significant competitive advantage over salt-intolerant plant species when substrate salinities are in the range of halophytes (over 5 ppt soil salinity), and rapidly establish dominance during episodes of high salinity conditions. Some halophytes like *S. virginica* are efficient colonizers of bare wet mud even when salinity is low if seed rain intensity is high. Pioneer halophytes do not necessarily decline in abundance, however, when substrate salinities decline as a result of progressive leaching and drainage of salts. Many apparent diked "salt marshes" are composed of relict vegetation halophyte vegetation which persists in relatively low salinity conditions. This condition is indicated by the presence of a minor to subdominant component of species with relatively low salt-tolerance (e.g., ruderal composites, bedstraws, mustards), growing vigorously among halophytes without indications of salt stress (stunted growth, leaf tip burn, pale leaves) in diked "salt marshes." Examples are sometimes found in abandoned dredge disposal sites (Zentner and Zentner 1995, Huffman and Associates 1996). Some mixed halophyte-glycophyte associations may also occur where stratification of rooting zones occurs in distinct salinity horizons, caused by near-surface leaching of salts and accumulation in deeper portions of the soil profile.

Thus, apparent salt marsh vegetation in diked Baylands may indicate either current high salinity or former high salinity, and does not necessarily indicate sustained high residual salinity. It often represents inertia in plant community structure after relaxation of salinity stress. The term "non-tidal salt marsh" in the context of the San Francisco Bay Estuary should be interpreted narrowly in floristic rather than physiological terms, because dominance of halophytes in the unstable substrate salinity conditions in diked wetlands is an unreliable indicator of current substrate salinity. Some diked salt marshes are truly saline and tend to remain so because of chronically poor drainage or frequent partial dike failures. Others are in gradual succession to other vegetation types. Some diked salt marshes with low residual substrate salinity are subject to rapid conversion to other vegetation types following disturbances (e.g., discing or flooding).

Species Richness and Composition – The species richness and composition of diked marshes is highly variable among sites, and among different marsh types. High salinity and hypersalinity in diked marshes tend to promote low species diversity, selecting for a few tolerant species. Other extreme soil conditions, such as strong acid production and mass release of free iron (often associated with prolonged inundation followed by summer drought) minimize plant species diversity. Truly hypersaline seasonal wetlands in the Bay usually support only sparse *Salicornia virginica, Distichlis spicata,* and *Salsola soda,* with a minor component of *Frankenia salina.* Hypersaline seasonal wetlands are now scarce in the Bay Area, mostly scattered around South Bay salt ponds and adjacent lands. A few occur in the North Bay (e.g., parts of Gallinas Creek diked salt marshes, peripheral portions of the Napa salt ponds). Many former hypersaline diked wetlands have been altered by water management for mosquito abatement and wildlife habitat enhancement, and are now muted tidal marshes (e.g., New Chicago Marsh in Alviso, Oro Loma Marsh in Hayward).

Species diversity in nontidal diked brackish and salt marshes is generally much higher than in hypersaline basins, but this does not reflect relatively greater overall diversity of native plant species. Diked brackish to saline nontidal wetlands support a number of common native tidal brackish and salt marsh species (*Salicornia virginica, Distichlis spicata, Frankenia salina, Cuscuta salina, Atriplex triangularis*) and sometimes support relatively infrequent native species typical of the natural high tidal marsh and upland ecotone (*Iva axillaris, Leymus triticoides, Baccharis douglasii*). The native perennial grass *Leymus triticoides,* historically a dominant species of the upper transition zone of tidal salt and brackish marshes, is infrequently found in some diked brackish marshes, particularly where disturbance has been infrequent. A relatively rare historic component of subsaline tidal marsh ecotones, *Centaurium muehlenbergii* is found in diked subsaline wetlands at Cullinan Ranch. It is currently reported known from only one tidal marsh/upland ecotone (China Camp). The sedge *Scirpus maritimus*, a dominant native component of tidal brackish marshes, is often abundant or dominant in brackish to saline ditches or deep, wet depressions in diked marshes ((Madrone Associates et. al. 1983, Mall 1969).

Conversely, diked salt and brackish marshes generally fail to support some important species of corresponding tidal marsh communities; *Spartina foliosa* is excluded from nontidal conditions, and *Jaumea carnosa*, *Plantago maritima*, *Triglochin* spp. and *Limonium californicum* are absent or very infrequent in nontidal salt marsh; *Grindelia stricta* is generally less abundant in nontidal salt marsh than tidal marsh. Diked salt marshes typically lack rare tidal marsh species (e.g., *Cordylanthus* spp., *Castilleja ambigua*, *Lasthenia glabrata*, *Lilaeopsis masonii*, *Cirsium hydrophilum*, *Aster lentus*), and also usually lack most infrequent tidal marsh species (e.g., *Pluchea odorata*, *Senecio hydrophilus*, *Glaux maritima*). The failure of these tidal marsh species in diked conditions is probably due to the relatively greater competition by robust "generalist" species with broad ecological amplitude, and physiological intolerance of extremes of inundation and dryness in diked wetlands. Diked salt and brackish marshes in some cases, however, provide refugia for tidal marsh plants of the high tidal marsh which have become (or in some cases have always been) regionally rare or infrequent in the modern tidal marsh ecosystem, such as *Suaeda moquinii*, *Hemizonia pungens* ssp. *maritima*, *Salicornia subterminalis*, *Downingia pulchella*, *Juncus mexicanus*). As such, they may serve to maintain genetically differentiated salt-tolerant populations of species displaced from modern tidal marshes.

Diked brackish and salt marshes are subject to invasion by many non-native species and species which are not typical of tidal marshes, or are typically restricted to marginal conditions in tidal marshes. Non-native pasture grasses with moderate salinity tolerance, such as *Lolium multiflorum* (and hybrids), *Polypogon monspeliensis*, *Lotus corniculatus* and *Hordeum marinum* ssp. *gussoneanum*, and even *Rumex crispus* are also major components of diked salt and brackish marshes, often locally dominating either depressions (*Polypogon, Hordeum)* or mounds (*Lolium*). Exotic halophytic grasses *Parapholis incurva* and *Hainardia cylindrica* are also locally common in diked salt or brackish marsh. *Cotula coronopifolia* is usually only a minor component of tidal salt and brackish marsh, colonizing depressions and marsh pan edges, but is often a major component of diked brackish marshes, particularly in disturbed or winter-ponded brackish depressions where other vegetation has died

back after prolonged deep flooding. Other common herbaceous non-native plant species of diked brackish and saline marshes include *Lepidium latifolium*, *Bassia hyssopifolia*, *Beta vulgaris*, *Salsola kali*, and *Salsola soda*. *Lepidium latifolium* is especially invasive in brackish diked marshes, particularly where the soil has been disturbed, but also in areas of marsh with thin or discontinuous vegetative cover.

Diked subsaline and nonsaline Baylands are very seldom the subject of careful floristic surveys (e.g., Rugt 1991, Madrone Associates 1977); vegetation descriptions usually focus on visually dominant ruderal species, often based on summer survey dates when native annual species are not identifiable (Jones and Stokes 1977, Hudson 1980, Werminski 1973). Consequently, the floristic diversity and affinities of diked subsaline to fresh seasonal wetlands has probably in many (perhaps most) cases been underestimated. Diked subsaline and nonsaline wetlands are mixtures of exotic species of ruderal seasonal wetlands and native species typical of vernal pools and swales. Diked wetlands which are mostly subsaline to nonsaline after years of agricultural drainage support a range of marsh plant associations. These are most common around San Pablo Bay and Suisun Bay, where grazing pasture and oat hayfields have been maintained for many decades in diked former tidal brackish marshes. They may have inclusions of relatively brackish indicator species where soil salinity and acidity are locally elevated (e.g., mixtures of *Atriplex triangularis*, *Polypogon monspeliensis*, *Distichlis spicata*) but are dominated by glycophytic wetland plant species, both native and non-native. Composition of the fresh/subsaline diked wetland flora is influenced by disturbance. Annually disked hayfields support wetland "weeds" which are a mixture of native annuals (e.g., *Plagiobothrys* spp., esp. *P. stipitatus*, *P. leptocladus*), *Juncus bufonius*, *Lilaea scilloides*, *Callitriche marginata*, *C.* spp. *Cicendia quadrangularis*, *Elatine brachysperma*, *Eryngium* spp., *Cressa truxillensis*; locally, *Downingia* spp.; non-native annuals (*Lythrum hyssopifolium*, *Cotula coronopifolia*, *Polygonum aviculare*, *Hordeum marinum ssp. gussoneanum*, *Polypogon monspeliensis*,) and non-native perennials (*Lotus corniculatus*, *Agrostis avenacea*) Grazed pasture land in diked Baylands in San Pablo Bay may also support native annuals found in diked disked hayfields, as well as native perennials (*Eleocharis machrostachya*, *Glyceria* spp. *Juncus effusus*, *J. patens*) and naturalized non-native perennials (*Rumex crispus*, *R. pulcher*, *Cirsium arvense*, *Lolium multiflorum*). The relative abundance of these species in diked pasture and hayfield wetlands is variable and unstable. Some diked wetlands, after relaxation of intensive agricultural manipulation, develop seasonal wetlands with plant species composition highly similar to that of regional vernal pools and swales (locally dominated by *Downingia* spp., *Eryngium* spp. *Eleocharis macrostachya*, *Callitriche* spp. *Lilaea scilloides*, *Plagiobothrys* spp., etc.)

Reference Sites

Reference sites for different types of diked wetlands would generally not be long-lived because of the prevalence of unstable vegetation conditions in diked Baylands. Droughts, wet years, changes in drainage and pumping, disturbances from agricultural practices, and succession can cause profound changes in vegetation in short periods of time. The following reference sites reflect conditions observed in the mid-late 1990s.

1. Diked non-tidal salt marsh (dominant *Salicornia virginica*)
   * Fremont Airport (King and Lyons site; proposed for phased tidal restoration), Alameda Co.
   * Gallinas Creek diked wetlands, Marin Co.
   * Western Marsh and Central Lowlands, Bahia Site, Novato, Marin Co.
   * Dredge pond 3E, Mare Island, Solano Co.
   * Area H, Redwood Shores, San Mateo Co.
2. Diked non-tidal brackish marsh
   * Cullinan Ranch, Solano Co.
   * Suisun Marsh managed marshes, Solano Co.
   * Huichica Unit, CDFG Napa-Sonoma Marsh, Sonoma Co.
3. Diked subsaline to nonsaline seasonal wetlands
   * Black Point/Renaissance Faire site, Novato, Marin Co. (extirpated 1999)
   * Twin House Ranch Site, Lower Petaluma River, Sonoma Co.
   * Leonard Ranch, North Point, Dixon parcels, Sonoma Co., along Hwy 37

Historic and Modern Distribution

Wetlands of diked Baylands are relatively recent historic artifacts. The plant associations they support are analogous to, but distinct from, wetlands along the margins of historic tidal marshes. Brackish non-tidal marshes somewhat similar to diked brackish marshes probably occurred within alluvial deposits at mouths of small streams which discharged into tidal marshes with locally poor drainage, such as near Ignacio (Novato), where riparian areas converged with dense marsh ponds and few or no tidal creeks. Analogous examples of brackish or subsaline marshes with marginal tidal flooding are found today along Drakes Estero and Tomales Bay, particularly near shallow backbarrier lagoons. Salt marsh with restricted tidal influence probably occurred along portions of the Bay where local sand beach ridges were likely to obstruct tidal flows. One modern example exists at Pinole Point (Whittell Marsh), where the proximal end of a sand spit episodically dams small tidal channels, causing seasonal ponding in a small salt marsh cut off from regular tidal flows. Prehistoric examples of "pocket" nontidal salt marsh probably occurred in the vicinity of Richardson Bay, Alameda, Oakland, and the San Francisco Peninsula, where sand beach ridges occurred.

Seasonal freshwater wetlands (vernal pools and swales, springs) occurred within grasslands peripheral to the Bay, particularly in the Petaluma River valley, on alluvial terraces near Fremont, portions of Richmond and Berkeley, and along much of the Suisun Marsh area. Their distribution and abundance, as suggested by soil surveys, were probably not limited to areas mapped as poorly drained; seasonal freshwater wetlands often occur as local inclusions within soil series in which wetlands are not indicated as prevalent. This is indicated by records of vernal pool endemics in locations like San Francisco, where "vernal pool" soil types are not mapped, but winter pools with typical endemic annuals were found.

The historical abundance and distribution of these wetland types is extremely difficult to quantify in terms of area. Quantitative estimates of historic abundance of seasonal wetlands displaced by urbanization depends heavily on interpretation and assumptions about early soil surveys (which were not intended to function as maps of actual or potential native vegetation), historical accounts, and fragmentary information on species occurrences in old floras. The qualitative differences in natural non-tidal wetland types and their diked Bayland analogues further obscures the relevance of quantitative comparisons between historic losses of natural seasonal wetland plant communities and their partial replacement with wetlands of diked Baylands.

Conservation Issues

Plant conservation needs for diked wetlands are dependent on larger-scale wetland management and restoration plans. Diked wetlands usually support less native plant species diversity than mature tidal marshes at equivalent locations, but may in some cases still provide important plant conservation functions. For example, in San Pablo Bay, agriculture and development have eliminated most historic natural seasonal wetlands in supratidal grasslands peripheral to the Bay. The original vernal pool flora which occurred in subsaline to alkaline depressions around the historic edge of the Bay (as in parts of northeastern Suisun Marsh today) has been largely extirpated in its original location, but persists in artificial equivalent topography and edaphic conditions in some diked seasonal wetlands. These populations maintained in subsaline conditions may provide important founder populations for opportunities to restore vernal pool and swale systems in the original soil types and topography along the margins of the Bay, in coordination with tidal restoration. Similarly, one diked salt marsh in the South Bay (former Fremont Airport) provides refugia for *Suaeda moquinii*, otherwise found around the Bay only in remnant alkali vernal pools adjacent to the Bay at one site (Zentner and Zentner 1996). Partial vernal pool floras have also been generated spontaneously after cessation or relaxation of agricultural manipulation at Montezuma Wetlands (Solano County), Sears Point (Sonoma County), and a construction site in Alviso (Santa Clara County). Most diked wetlands are poorly surveyed, and may act as refugia for many populations of plants of conservation significance.

Diked wetlands are also conservation threats to plant species diversity when they provide outposts, reservoirs, or dispersal corridors for invasive wetland weeds, such as *Lepidium latifolium* and *Salsola soda*. By increasing seed rain pressures on adjacent tidal marshes, or adjacent marsh restoration sites, diked wetlands may also cause degradation of tidal marshes.

Sea level rise makes long-term conservation of diked wetlands problematic. In addition to inherent tendencies of diked systems to suffer levee subsidence and erosion, sea level rise imposes increasing risks of levee failure and tidal flooding. Breached diked wetlands spontaneously revert to tidal wetlands, but usually only as low mudflat or marsh to lower middle marsh after even two decades (e.g., White Slough, Vallejo, Solano County) In addition, some high-sulfur diked marsh soils undergo long-term changes in soil chemistry which make them unsustainable for any valuable natural or artificial vegetation.

Dike maintenance and repair may cause degradation to diked and tidal marsh plant communities by favoring spread and dominance of exotic invasive marsh plant species. Dike maintenance practices currently lack any elements which facilitate recolonization by native species.

Restoration of diked marshes is somewhat self-contradictory, since true restoration would entail conversion to the original tidal marsh condition. However, diked wetlands can be significantly enhanced as non-tidal marshes by reducing or eliminating adverse land use practices. Reduction of intensive drainage efforts and elimination of high-frequency disking can enable diked fresh/subsaline wetland plant communities to mature and accumulate greater native species. Pasture management that tolerates some winter inundation in depressions, for example, is more compatible with native wetland plant species diversity than oat crop management.

Conclusions and Recommendations

Diked wetlands considered for conversion to other marsh types, such as tidal wetlands, should be studied individually for site-specific floristic values, particularly for potential functions as refugia for species displaced from historic seasonal wetlands and tidal marsh ecotones. Diked wetlands should not be assumed to have uniformly low native wetland plant species diversity or "ruderal" status. In areas where restoration of seasonal fresh wetland

systems (e.g., vernal pools, alkali basins, alluvial *Juncus/ Scirpus* marsh, etc.) is precluded by development, some diked wetlands should be considered for modification and management to maintain regionally scarce plant communities. Generally, however, priority should be assigned to restore peripheral estuarine plant communities in their proper original soils and topographic position. Where diked wetlands support regionally rare plant populations, they should be given interim conservation priority until suitable population restoration sites are established in more natural or restored habitats. Existing diked marshes should be managed to minimize impacts of exotic invasive plants on adjacent managed or natural tidal marshes. Dike maintenance should include best management practices which favor recolonization of disturbed dike surfaces by native vegetation and suppress re-invasion by exotic species.

References

Adam, P. 1990. Saltmarsh ecology. Cambridge Univ. Press.

BCDC (San Francisco Bay Conservation and Development Commission) and H.T. Harvey. 1983. Aquatic and wildlife resources of Richardson Bay. Unpublished report prepared for the Richardson Bay Special Area Plan Study.

Doane, S. N. 1999. Shoreline changes in San Pablo Bay, California. M.Sc. thesis, Vanderbilt Univ. 116 pp.

Eicher, A. L. 1988. Soil-vegetation correlations in wetlands and adjacent uplands of the San Francisco Bay estuary, California. U.S. Fish and Wildlife Service Biological Report 88 (21), contract no. 14-16-0009-85-001. August 1988

Granholm, S.L. 1989. Endangered habitat: a report on the status of seasonal wetlands in San Francisco Bay. Report sponsored by National Audubon Society, San Francisco Bay Area Audubon Society chapters, Save San Francisco Bay Association, Sierra Club Bay Chapter.

Harvey, T.E. 1987. Fish, wildlife, and habitat management plan for Naval Security Group Activity - Skaggs Island, California. U.S. Fish and Wildlife Service, San Francisco Bay National Wildlife Refuge, Newark, Calif.

Hudson, J. 1980. Bird census of diked-marshland habitat. *In*: D.S. Sloan (ed). San Pablo Bay: an environmental perspective. Environmental Studies Group, Univ. of Calif., Berkeley.

Huffman and Associates 1996. Proposed Section 404 wetland delineation for the Bahia Master Plan, Novato, California. U.S. Army Corps of Engineers, San Francisco District, file no. 148831.

Jaffee, B., R.E. Smith and L.Z. Torressan. Sedimentation changes in San Pablo Bay. U.S. Geological Survey open-file report 98-759.

Jones and Stokes. 1976. Suisun Marsh Protection Plan. Calif. Dept. Fish and Game, Sacramento, Calif.

Kaufman, S. and H.T. Harvey. 1987. Plant list: Army Corps of Engineers; Leslie Salt Site. File no. 309-01. Harvey and Associates, Alviso, Calif.

Madrone Associates. 1977. The natural resources of Napa Marsh. Report prepared for the Calif. Dept. Fish and Game, Coastal Wetland Series # 19. Sacramento, Calif.

Madrone Associates, Philip William and Associates, J.R. Cherniss and N. Wakeman. 1983. Ecological values of diked historic baylands. A technical report prepared for the San Francisco Bay Conservation and Development Commission, April 1992 (revised 1983).

Mall, R.E. 1969. Soil-water-salt relationships of waterfowl food plants in Suisun Marsh of California. State of Calif. Dept. Fish and Game Wildlife Bulletin No. 1. Sacramento, Calif.

Meiorin, E.C., M.N. Josselyn, R. Crawford, J. Calloway, K. Miller, R. Pratt, T. Richardson and R. Leidy 1991. San Francisco Estuary Project status and trends report on wetlands and related habitats in the San Francisco Estuary. Public Report prepared under cooperative agreement #815406-01-0 with the U.S. Environmental Protection Agency by the Association of Bay Area Governments, Oakland California; Romberg Tiburon Centers of San Francisco State Univ., and the U.S. Fish and Wildlife Service, Sacramento Calif.

Moffatt and Nichol and Wetland Research Associates 1988. Future sea level rise: predictions and implications for San Francisco Bay. Report prepared for the San Francisco Bay Conservation and Development Commission, San Francisco, Calif. Revised edition.

Reuss J.O. and D.W. Johnson. 1986. Acid Deposition and Acidification of Soils and Waters. Springer-Verlag, New York.

Rugyt, J. 1991. Checklist of vascular plant species at the Montezuma Wetlands Project site. Appendix to Montezuma Wetlands Project Technical Report, Levine-Fricke Restoration Corp., Emeryville, Calif.

Russell, E.W. 1973. Soil conditions and plant growth. 10th ed., Longman, London and New York.

Takekawa, J., M. Eagan and R. Laird. 1999. Monitoring tidal wetland restoration projects in the San Pablo Bay National Wildlife Refuge. Progress Report, May 1999. U.S. Geological Survey Biological Resources Division, Mare Island Field Office, Calif.

U.S. Army Corps of Engineers (USACE). 1988. San Francisco Bay Shoreline Study: Southern Alameda and Santa Clara Counties, Interim Office Report. U.S. Army Corps of Engineers, San Francisco District.

Ver Planck, W.E. 1958. Salt in California. State of Calif. Dept. Natural Resources, Division of Mines, Bulletin 175. 168 pp.

Wermunski, J. 1973. Ecological attributes of the Hayward Area Shoreline: a habitat survey with recommendations. Unpublished background technical report prepared for the Hayward Area Shoreline Planning Agency, Hayward, Calif.

Waisel, Y. 1972. The biology of halophytes. New York: Academic Press.

Waterways Experimental Station, U.S. Army Corps of Engineers (WES). 1987. Corps of Engineers Wetlands Delineation Manual. U.S. Army Corps of Engineers Wetlands Research Program Technical Report Y-87-1, January 1987.

Zentner and Zentner. 1995. Section 404 wetland delineation for the Bayside Business Park Phase II, Fremont, California. U.S. Army Corps of Engineers, San Francisco District.

Plants

Plants of San Francisco Bay Salt Ponds

Peter R. Baye

Introduction

The term "salt pond," as treated in this discussion, includes both natural and artificial large-scale persistent hypersaline ponds that are intermittently flooded with Bay water, and which occur within tidal salt marsh systems of San Francisco Bay and San Pablo Bay. Historic natural salt ponds were characterized by persistent thick accumulation of salt inundated with concentrated seawater brines. They were restricted to a relatively narrow reach of San Francisco Bay near San Lorenzo Creek. They are distinguished here from related salt marsh features such as pans and which occur at smaller spatial scales, have distinctive physiographic traits, and lack strong persistent (perennial) brines and precipitated crystaline salt deposits. Artificial salt ponds (solar salterns) are diked salt marshes which are managed for the production of concentrated brine and fractional crystallization of sea salts. Natural and artificial salt ponds are presumed to share the same narrowly adapted hypersaline biota.

Information on modern artificially engineered salt pond systems is derived principally from the biological literature on solar salterns and hypersaline environments (Javor 1989, and references within), historic documentation on the salt industry in California from the State Division of Mines (Ver Planck 1958, 1951; Dobkin and Anderson 1994) and regional documentation produced by the local salt industry and government regulatory agencies (Corps of Engineers, San Francisco District, Regulatory Branch permit and compliance files; Office of Counsel files, and references within). Information on historic salt pond systems is limited to descriptive historic accounts and descriptions, detailed topographic maps of natural salt ponds prior to extensive dike construction (U.S. Coast Survey T-charts, 1956), and field investigations by the author comparing modern salt pans, marsh ponds, and artificial salt ponds.

Environmental Setting

Salt ponds are large, shallow, hypersaline impoundments or depressions in tidal salt marsh systems which undergo a sequence of infrequent flooding with saline or brackish Bay water, evaporative concentration, and formation of strong hypersaline brines and deposits of gypsum, calcium carbonate, and crystalline salt (halite; sodium chloride).

Historic salt ponds were mapped with a high degree of resolution in the 1856 U.S. Coast Survey. They were nested within particular portions of the salt marshes along the Alameda shoreline in the vicinity of San Lorenzo Creek and Mount Eden Slough. This reach of salt marsh was distinguished by a relatively straight-edge erosional marsh shoreline, little tidal drainage at the edge of the mudflats, and evidence of drowned marsh topography (mapped as emergent sinuous tidal creek levees). The upland edge was an extensive alluvial lowland, presumably with significant subsurface groundwater discharge. No major freshwater creeks were directly associated with the salt ponds. Atwater et al. (1979) suggested that natural estuarine beach ridges along outer marsh edge were responsible for the impoundments of salt marsh that created salt ponds near San Lorenzo. Some salt ponds at the northern end of the local San Lorenzo distribution were certainly associated with well-defined barrier sand spits (U.S. Coast Survey T-charts, 1850s), which were probably nourished by sand eroded from submerged Merritt sand deposits (Pleistocene marine beach and dune). Less well-defined transgressive berms of sand and coarse organic detritus may have been deposited on top of the erosional marsh edge south of the sand spits themselves. Similar transgressive beach-marsh berms today act as dams enclosing freshwater to brackish ponds and marshes in Drake's Estero, Point Reyes and at one location in San Francisco Bay (Whittell Marsh, Point Pinole, Contra Costa County). U.S. Coast Survey T-charts also indicate numerous sandy barrier beaches which dammed (either permanently or intermittently) lagoons. The impoundment of Crystal Salt Pond by a wave-constructed swash bar or beach ridge would distinguish it morphologically, hydrologically, and topographically from more common salt marsh ponds (pans) which occurred as depressions, sometimes extensive, between tidal creeks. These were widely distributed in salt marshes in the South Bay. Extensive, elongate pans also occurred near and below the upland borders of salt marshes; these have been termed "transitional" pans, although their position and form do not necessarily indicate a gradual ecotonal relationship with alluvial or upland habitats.

Salt ponds today (solar salterns) are artificially managed and engineered diked Baylands converted from tidal salt marsh. The first artificial salt ponds began as extensions and improvements of natural salt ponds which occurred near Hayward (Crystal Salt Pond), but most of the contemporary man-made salt pond system is established in former tidal marsh that included few or no perennial hypersaline ponds. Artificial salt ponds have entirely displaced their natural forerunners; no natural true salt-crystallizing ponds remain in San Francisco Bay today, although related smaller salt pans and marsh ponds containing weak brines in summer and fall do occur.

Classification of Salt Ponds – Javor (1989) placed marine-derived hypersaline aquatic environments in four ecological salinity classes:

The first salinity class (*ca.* 60 - 100 ppt) contains a highly diverse, productive biota dominated by marine species. This class would correspond to "low salinity" ponds (a misnomer, since salinity exceeds seawater concentration), from intake ponds to the next one or two stages that support abundant macroalgae and fish.

The second class (*ca.* 100 - 140 ppt) is dominated by specially adapted halophilic species which are related to freshwater taxa, not marine taxa. The organisms include abundant cyanobacteria, unicellular green algae, brine shrimp, and various halobacteria.

The third class (*ca.* 140 - 300 ppt) is distinguished by marked reduction of species diversity (loss of cyanobacteria, most invertebrates other than brine shrimp), and dominance of *Dunaliella* and brine shrimp.

The fourth class (300 ppt to salt saturation, near 360 ppt) contains only *Dunaliella* and bacteria at low productivity.

The first class predominates in modern marsh ponds. The historic natural salt pond complex probably varied seasonally between Javor's second to fourth hypersaline classes. Other natural marsh pans were most likely predominantly in the first class only, becoming seasonally hypersaline, and supporting relatively weak brines and macroalgal cover. Natural historic salt ponds were distinguished from other types of inundated depressions in salt marshes by the persistent thick halite deposits, indicating perennial hypersaline conditions, and their large lake-like size. In these aspects, they differ from shallow marsh ponds and marsh pans, which are regularly flooded during higher spring tides, and either remain persistently ponded or develop thick algal mats which desiccate in summer (bleaching white in the sun, resembling salt deposits in aerial photographs), or only develop thin, temporary salt films on unvegetated mud and peat.

Various marsh pan features are represented in U.S. Coast Survey maps of the mid-19th century, but only a few have persisted in modern rare remnant tidal marshes, such as Petaluma Marsh, Rush Ranch and Hill Slough (Solano County). Elongate marsh ponds are evident along the upland edge of historic marshes, particularly in eastern and southern parts of San Francisco Bay. Some of these may have been influenced by surface runoff and groundwater seepage from adjacent alluvial uplands, and could have been less saline than other marsh depressions most of the year. Some historic elongate marsh edge pans may also have been the unvegetated upper intertidal surface of alluvial fans and terraces, consistent with small modern "transitional pans" observed at Hill Slough, Solano County. These also lack brine and halite development. Modern elongate marsh pans have formed in recently (100 year) prograded marshes adjacent to Mare Island dredge ponds. These ponds are about 0.3 m deep in winter and spring, and range from brackish (nearly fresh) in winter to hypersaline when ponded areas are highly reduced in summer, but no significant halite precipitation is evident in them. These and similar pans may appear white with sun-bleached dried algal mats, which resemble salt flats. High densities of true natural marsh ponds, also termed "drainage divide ponds" (owing to their position in poorly drained marsh areas between tidal creeks), also occur in the Petaluma Marsh. Marsh ponds are a variation of salt pans which are topographic depressions flooded by spring tides, and support submergent vegetation, typically macroalgae (such as *Enteromorpha* spp.) and beds of widgeon-grass (*Ruppia maritima*), indicating brackish to near-marine salinity. The beds of marsh ponds are usually a soft organic oil-like black muck composed of decayed, waterlogged organic matter.

In contrast with salt ponds in estuaries with strong marine influence, such as San Diego Bay, San Francisco Bay salt ponds are relatively nutrient-rich and sustain high primary productivity (Javor 1989). Nutrient-poor salt pond conditions promote microbial mats, while planktonic microalgae tend to dominate nutrient-rich salt pond systems (Javor 1989). Most salt ponds in San Francisco Bay support richly pigmented and somewhat turbid organic "soups" of *Dunaliella*, halobacteria, cyanobacteria, dissolved organics and organic particulates and, often in ponds between approximately 120 - 200 ppt salinity, large "blooms" of brine shrimp which graze primarily on *Dunaliella*.

Historic natural salt ponds were unlike modern artificial salt ponds in that they were not differentiated geographically into stable hypersaline classes, but varied only seasonally in salinity. Natural salt ponds went through a seasonal "intake" phase during extreme high spring tides (December-January and June-July), when Bay water flooded them and diluted them with brackish to saline Bay water, seldom exceeding 20 ppt, and typically between 2 - 10 ppt in winter. During summer-fall evaporation periods, brines formed *in situ*, ranging in salinity over time up to crystallization (saturation) near 360 ppt. In contrast, the modern engineered salt pond system is based on timed transfers of brines between ponds, resulting in spatial separation of brines at different stages of concentration, and fractional crystallization of various seawater salts (other than sodium chloride, halite), such as magnesium and potassium salts (bitterns), gypsum (calcium sulfate) and lime (calcium chloride) in different ponds. In this system, crystallization is restricted to relatively few ponds engineered to facilitate harvest of halite deposits, and relatively stable hypersalinity regimes are established for individual evaporator ponds in the system (Ver Planck 1958).

The sequential and spatial separation of brines in artificial salt pond systems also produces salt pond "types" which are not fully analogous to natural systems. The late stages of brine production near sodium chloride crystallization produce strong non-sodium brines called "bittern." Bittern brines (or bittern) are a concentrated solution of sodium chloride, magnesium chloride and sulfate, and potassium chloride and sulfate. The ionic balance of highly concentrated bittern is toxic even to bacteria, and saturated bittern is considered sterile (Javor 1989). During winter rains, dilute bittern stratifies on top of the concentrated bittern, and brine shrimp may appear seasonally, indicating algal production (Jim Swanson, Rick Coleman, pers. comm.). Natural salt pond brines did include bittern salts; in fact, the "low quality" of early California solar salt was due to bittern, and the modern solar saltern system is principally devised as a method to fractionate sodium and bittern salts. Crystallizer ponds, which are used to precipitate halite, are also maintained near the limits of halotolerance of *Dunaliella* (which can nonetheless fix carbon up to salt saturation; Javor 1989), but undergo seasonal dilution during winter rains.

Salt Pond Plant Community

Salt ponds support a distinctive and highly specialized halotolerant to halophilic biota consisting of microalgae, photosynthetic bacteria, and invertebrates, but no vascular plants (except along the edges of artificial salt pond levees). The dominant photosynthetic organisms of most hypersaline San Francisco Bay salt ponds are a single-celled green algal species, *Dunaliella salina* (Chlorophycophyta) and numerous species of blue-green bacteria (Cyanobacteria), halobacteria, and purple sulfur-reducing bacteria. The proportions of these organisms vary with salinity. Artificial eutrophic salt ponds with salinities closer to marine concentrations (near 35 ppt; "intake ponds") are dominated by marine macroalgae such as sea-lettuce (*Ulva* spp.), *Enteromorpha* spp., *Cladophora* spp., and also sometimes support *Fucus* spp. and *Codium* spp. where substrate is stable and firm. They also include marine diatoms, dinoflagellates, and cryptomonads. There are no detailed studies of the species diversity, distribution or geographic variation of the halophilic microflora communities of San Francisco Bay.

Managed and engineered contemporary salt ponds are ecologically similar in many respects to their natural precursor salt ponds, and presumably share the same algal and bacterial microflora.

Indicator Species – There are no detailed classifications or analytic studies of salt pond algal communities. Following Javor's (1989) classification of hypersaline environments (see Classification of Salt Ponds, above), two broad hypersaline algal communities may be identified: communities dominated by free-floating marine macroalgae typical of upper tidepools near marine salinities to low-hypersaline conditions, corresponding to intake ponds and young brines in a saltern series (e.g., *Ulva* spp., *Enteromorpha* spp., *Cladophora* spp.; also bottom-mat forming cyanobacterial colonies); and communities dominated by motile unicellular halophilic phyto-

Modern salt ponds are artificially managed and engineered diked baylands converted from tidal salt marsh. (South San Francisco Bay)

plankton (principally *Dunaliella salina*), which characterize moderate to high hypersaline conditions. Macroalgal salt pond communities also correspond with fish-dominated animal communities, while phytoplankton-dominated brines are associated with brine shrimp abundance.

Dunaliella spp. is ubiquitous in salt ponds in San Francisco Bay. It is reported to survive, and can be photosynthetically active, in brines which are close to saturated (near 350 ppt), but may be absent in some extremely concentrated brines and bittern (potash-phase, or potassium-magnesium) brines (Javor 1989, Brock 1975). Its optimum salinity for growth is near 120 ppt, about four times the concentration of seawater. *Dunaliella salina* concentrates carotenoid and other pigments in response to various forms of physiological stress, including salinity. It can be used as a crude color-indicator of brine salinity: cells growing in 50-100 ppt are greenish, and turn yellowish-green in 150 ppt brine. Reddish hues occur in brines 200-250 ppt (Javor 1989). Purplish-red hues in brines over 200 ppt may be contributed by halophilic bacteria. A conspicuous mosaic of salt pond hues are readily visible from aerial views of San Francisco Bay, particularly in summer and fall. *Dunaliella* osmoregulates in hypersaline brines by concentrating glycerol as a compatible osmotic solute in its cytoplasm (Javor 1989).

Reference sites

There are currently no reference sites in the San Francisco Bay Estuary for true natural salt ponds (ponds which periodically or chronically produce crystalline salt deposits). The historic salt pond system near San Lorenzo Creek in Alameda was eliminated by diking in the 1850s and 1860s. All modern salt pans and marsh ponds in the Bay Area differ from these historic salt ponds. Most existing marsh ponds are only slightly hypersaline, or briefly hypersaline in late summer, and support algal mats rather than brines and halite beds. Most existing salt pans within small modern Bay Area salt marshes are comparatively small and produce sparse and thin (few mm) salt crusts in summer and fall. In contrast, reference sites for artificial salt ponds are abundant. Examples of (relatively) low salinity intake ponds, which are saline or slightly hypersaline, are found at Pond B1/B2 in Mountain View, Pond 1 near Mowry Slough, and Pond A9 in Alviso. Examples of intermediate hypersaline ponds (known as concentrators or evaporators) are found in ponds A10-14 in Alviso, ponds 2-8 near Coyote Hills, and ponds 2-6 between Mowry Slough and Coyote Creek. High hypersaline ponds (strong brines approaching or reaching salt saturation, "pickle") are found in extensive crystallizer beds near Newark and Redwood City, ponds 10 and 26 near Newark, and periodically in drained evaporators before they are re-filled.

Modern salt marsh (and brackish marsh) pans may be found in few remnant pre-historic tidal marshes at Petaluma Marsh (abundant), China Camp (scarce) and Point Pinole (Whittell Marsh; scarce). Pans vary in topography. Some upper marsh pans are similar to patches of salt flats, while pans in middle marsh zone depressions are normally shallow ponds 10-20 cm deep. Pans which become ponded, either because of depressional topography or marsh surface drainage barriers, develop algae or widgeon-grass. Salt marsh pans also occur in historically accreted marshes at Mowry Marsh. Elongate marsh pans fringing uplands ("transitional" pans) have also formed in the relatively young (20th century) salt marsh at Emeryville Crescent and adjacent to Mare Island dredge ponds. Elongate but diffuse shore-parallel marsh pans, perhaps best regarded as incipient pans, are found along the east end of the fringing salt marsh at Highway 37. Small but well-differentiated semi-circular to semi-linear salt marsh pans occur in peaty coastal salt marshes at Limatour Spit, Point Reyes; Bolinas Lagoon; Morro Bay; Elkhorn Slough; and along Tomales Bay. Morro Bay, Bodega Bay, and Bolinas Lagoon also have elongate shallow salt marsh pans fringing alluvial deposits. Most of these salt marsh pans are brackish in winter and spring, but become moderately hypersaline (usually 40-60 ppt, rarely > 90 ppt) in summer (Baye, unpub. data) when inundated.

Historic and Modern Distribution

The historic (pre-1860) location of natural salt ponds within San Francisco Bay was probably restricted to the Alameda shoreline in the vicinity of San Lorenzo Creek (between the historic Thompsons's Landing and Union City Creek). This area included an extensive complex of both connected and isolated large ponds in a matrix of salt marsh. The complex was labelled as "Crystal Salt Pond" on the 1856 U.S. Coast Survey T-chart of the area. The San Francisco Estuary Institute estimates the acreage of Crystal Salt Pond to be approximately 1660

acres, based on the precise pond outline represented on the 1856 T-chart (R. Grossinger, personal communication). If, however, the pond size fluctuated seasonally (as expected from winter rainfall and tidal flooding), the ponded area may have been several thousand acres from late fall to spring. Two smaller ponds with similar configuration occurred north of San Lorenzo Creek, and were clearly associated with sandy barrier beach deposits at the bayward edge of the marsh. (It is not clear whether these northern satellite ponds produced high concentration brine and halite, or were merely intermittently hypersaline lagoons). Crystal salt pond was used as a salt source by aboriginal inhabitants of the Alameda shoreline, and was exploited by early Mexican, Spanish and U.S. settlers (Ver Planck 1951, 1958). Early descriptions of Crystal Salt Pond indicate that it contained a persistent crust of crystalline salt up to eight inches thick, and the brines and salt contained "impurities" of concentrated non-sodium salts ("bittern" salts, principally magnesium chloride and sulfate; Ver Planck 1958).

The natural halite deposits of Crystal Salt Pond were exhausted rapidly by the infant salt collecting industry; by 1860 they were largely depleted. Artificial enhancement of solar evaporation of brines was initiated around 1853, when salt harvesters (farmers who used salt for tanning leather and curing meats, and expanded into the salt industry) began manual construction of low berms around natural salt ponds to enhance their capacity to retain saline floodwaters and capture and precipitate their salt loads. These artificially enhanced natural salt ponds became the nucleus of the solar salt industry.

By the end of the 19th century, the salt ponds of San Francisco Bay were still confined to the northern portion of the Alameda shoreline, from San Leandro Creek to Alvarado (Union City). They did not comprise a salt pond "system," but were an aggregation of many independently owned and operated enterprises. Extensive conversion of salt marsh to salt ponds in south San Francisco Bay did not occur until the 20th century. This was facilitated by the consolidation of almost all the independent salt operations to a few (dominated by Leslie Salt Company) in the 1930s. Permit requests to the Corps of Engineers to dam numerous sloughs and marshes in the South Bay were not filed until the early 1920s. Actual levee construction would have taken at least several years, and new ponds take about 5 - 7 years to "seal" (become impermeable after gypsum and carbonate precipitation; Ver Planck 1958, Dobkin and Anderson 1994); therefore, the 1920s ponds were probably not fully functional salterns until around 1930. The last extensive marshes in the Alviso and Sunnyvale areas were not diked for conversion to salt ponds until the early 1950s (Pacific Aerial Photo archives). Bair Island was not converted to salt pond until the 1950s, although it had previously been diked for agricultural use. The modern extent of salt ponds in the southern reaches of South Bay, therefore, is relatively recent compared with the northern Alameda salt ponds. The Napa salt ponds are even more recent: the diked Baylands of the Napa marshes were converted from derelict agriculture (seasonal subsaline to brackish wetlands) to salt ponds between 1953 and 1959. Salt production ceased there in the mid-1990s, but most of the system remains hypersaline.

Relative change – The minimum acreage of true natural salt pond in San Francisco Bay was less than 2,000 acres (SFEI 1998); the maximum acreage (assuming seasonal expansion of Crystal Salt Pond by flooding, and assuming that northern satellite ponds were brine/halite ponds) could have been on the order of 3,000 - 4,000 acres. Other marsh pan habitats were not likely to support persistent hypersaline algal communities and were presumably dominated by marine-related macroalgae or *Ruppia*, as are most salt marsh pans today. However, if a significant proportion of the historic extensive elongate lake-size marsh ponds fringing uplands (Redwood City to Palo Alto, and in the Newark vicinity) were seasonally or perennially hypersaline, the total acreage of salt pond habitat could have been on the order of 5,000 - 10,000 acres. There is very weak indication that elongate upland-fringing salt marsh pans ever contained persistent strong brines supporting the narrow hypersaline algal/bacterial community, however. Today, approximately 9,500 acres of derelict salt ponds remain in San Pablo Bay, and over 29,000 acres of artificial salt pond are actively maintained in San Francisco Bay.

Conservation Issues

Exotic Species – Salt pond microbial taxa are widespread geographically, but narrowly distributed ecologically. They are probably subject to dispersal by waterfowl and marine transport. There are no currently recognized exotic species "threats" to salt ponds as there are with vascular plants in salt marshes.

Restoration – The crude technology for creating artificial salt ponds (levee construction, wind-driven pumps, tidegates) has been well developed for over a century. There is little doubt that complete artificial salt pond systems can be created and maintained at a wide range of sizes, from as little as 20 - 50 acre historic "family size" or one-man operations (Ver Planck 1958), to the modern systems in the tens of thousands of acres. Low-salinity "intake" ponds can also be maintained independently, in the absence of a salt-producing system, by balancing influx of Bay water, residence time and redischarge at near-marine salinity. No new salt ponds have been constructed since the 1950s, although ponds have been interconverted from one type to another since then (evaporator ponds to bittern disposal/"storage"). Small and autonomous salt pond systems could be modified

to be less "productive" of salt, and more biologically "productive," by reducing the efficiency of brine and salt production. This could be achieved by increasing the flux in intake ponds, and reducing the residence time of brines in each pond transfer. In winter, when brines are diluted by rainwater, they could also be re-mixed with intake Bay water and redischarged to the Bay at near-marine salinities.

There have been recent tidal marsh restoration designs for artificial but naturalistic ponds and pans, but no marsh restoration designs have included equivalents of salt ponds. In principle, naturalistic salt ponds could be artificially created and naturally maintained by replicating the hypothetical historic conditions of Crystal Salt Pond (as inferred by Atwater 1979). This would entail deposition of coarse sediments (sand or shell hash) at the edge of a high-energy marsh shoreline, to be reworked as beach ridges which restrict marsh drainage. In theory, beach ridges would maintain form and size as they retreat with the eroding marsh edge, given ample sediment supply and overwash processes. Under less natural geomorphic settings for salt ponds, artificial naturalistic salt ponds could be created by constructing low, broad berms made of bay mud or sand that would be set at elevations enabling highest spring tides to overtop them. Low, wide berms would be less prone to gullying and breaching than steep levees, but would require some degree of maintenance. Maintenance would be minimized by setting salt pond levees within restored marshes which would shelter them from wave erosion of the open Bay. Restored naturalistic salt ponds would undergo extreme variation of salinity within and between years, depending on rainfall variation, evaporation conditions, and storm surges.

Sea Level Change and Levee Maintenance – The modern salt pond levee system requires periodic maintenance, and levees bordering the open Bay (not sheltered by fringing salt marsh) require frequent maintenance, armoring, or both. The need for levee maintenance (topping with fresh dredged sediment) is likely to become more frequent if storm frequency increases or sea level rises, as would be expected with global warming (Moffatt and Nichol and WRA 1988). Borrow pits along the interior side of salt pond levees become depleted over time, and some old borrow ditches have been widened so much that dredges need to re-handle material to bring it within reach of levees. Dredging tidal marshes as an alternative source of sediment is unlikely, since it causes conflicts with endangered species habitat. Therefore, sea level rise is likely to cause long-term increases in costs and risk of levee failure of the existing salt pond system. Sea level rise could also make naturalistic salt pond restoration more difficult, since beach ridges or low levees are more likely to breach and allow excessive (though restricted) tidal exchange to impounded areas.

Conclusions and Recommendations

The commercial salt pond operations of San Francisco Bay are unlikely to continue indefinitely because of economic changes in the Bay region and in the salt industry, and due to physical changes in the levee and borrow ditch system. Salt ponds are not likely to regenerate spontaneously as a result of natural geomorphic processes when salt marshes are restored. Other more common types of pans and ponds are unlikely to establish in young salt marshes; they are mature marsh features, associated with well-differentiated marsh topography. The environmental setting associated with salt ponds has been radically altered; the combination of steep and relatively high-energy Bay shorelines, coarse sediment supply, and extensive high salt marsh with impeded tidal drainage no longer exists. It is also likely that the feasibility of maintaining the erosion-prone levee system of the artificial salt ponds will decrease over time, as borrow ditches (sources of mud for levee repair) are depleted. Therefore, new and artificial measures will be required to conserve at least historic amounts of salt pond habitats within the Estuary in the long term. The highest priority setting for salt pond restoration of some type would be on the Alameda County shoreline, from approximately San Leandro to the Dumbarton Bridge, where the Bay shoreline profile and wave fetch may be conducive for formation of beach ridges (marsh berms), given appropriate sediment size and supply.

There is no minimal ecosystem size for salt ponds. The basic grazer food chain between *Dunaliella* and *Artemia* can be maintained in extremely small systems. However, the full microbial diversity of San Francisco Bay salt ponds, which has not been analyzed in detail, would probably not persist in small ponds. Also, since the stability of natural salt ponds is inherently low (subject to ordinary natural fluctuations as well as catastrophic changes), microbial diversity would be better conserved with a large system of semi-independent salt ponds. Pre-historic salt pond acreage was probably on the order of 2,000 acres. Aiming at this minimal acreage, in the absence of any experience at restoration of naturalistic salt ponds or "alternative" management of solar salterns, would probably be insufficient to conserve a diverse halophilic microflora.

We therefore recommend that long-term conservation of salt ponds entail the following actions:

1. Pilot projects should be undertaken that incorporate naturalistic salt pond designs as integral components of large-scale tidal marsh restoration on the northern Alameda shoreline;
2. Some existing salt ponds should be divided into smaller, autonomous units away from the open bay, preferably nested in the landward reaches of restored salt marsh areas, and managed to maintain intermediate strength brines rather than salt production;
3. Salt pond restoration and alternative management should aim for temporally variable as well as spatially variable salinity and brine depths;
4. Both artificial and naturalistic salt pond restoration should aim for designs which minimize maintenance requirements; and
5. An initial target acreage for salt ponds should reflect the uncertainty of restoring sustainable salt pond environments after commercial salt production ceases. We suggest that an initial target of approximately 10,000 acres (equivalent to late 19th century acreage) be stipulated and modified based on the results of salt pond restoration and alternative pond management.

References

Atwater, B., S.G. Conard, J.N. Dowden, C.W. Hedel, R. L. MacDonald and W. Savage. 1979. History, landforms, and vegetation of the Estuary's tidal marshes. *In*: T.J. Conomos (ed). San Francisco Bay: The Urbanized Estuary. American Association for the Advancement of Science, Pacific Division, Proc. of the 58th Annual Meeting.

Brock, T.D. 1975. Salinity and ecology of *Dunaliella* from Great Salt Lake. J. General Microbiol. 89:285-282.

Dobkin, M. and R.B. Anderson 1994. Oliver Bros. Salt Co. Alameda County, California: Historic Resource Evaluation Report. Contract 04F828-EP, Task Order #1, ALA-2, P.M. R0.0/R6.4, EA # 003050, prepared for Calif. Dept. Transportation, District 4 (Oakland).

Javor, B. 1989. Hypersaline Environments. Springer-Verlag.

Moffatt and Nichol and Wetlands Research Associates. 1988. Future sea level rise: predictions and implications for San Francisco Bay. Report prepared for BCDC (San Francisco Bay Conservation and Development Commission).

San Francisco Estuary Institute (SFEI). 1998. Draft spatial analysis of the Baylands ecosystem. San Francisco Estuary Institute, Richmond, Calif.

Ver Planck, W.E. 1951. Salines in the Bay Area. *In*: Geologic Guidebook of the San Francisco Bay Counties, Bulletin 154, State of Calif. Dept. Natural Resources, Division of Mines.

_____. 1958. Salt In California. Bulletin 175, State of Calif. Dept. Natural Resources, Division of Mines. 168 pp.

Plant Communities Ecotonal to the Baylands

Glen Holstein

Introduction

The San Francisco Bay estuary wetlands ecosystem historically included vegetated and non-vegetated areas. Dominant among physical factors influencing estuarine vegetation was the semi-diurnal tidal cycle. As a consequence, vegetation exposed to tides differed dramatically from plant communities that existed above the tides. For non-estuarine vegetation diurnal factors were relatively insignificant; annual climate cycles and non-cyclic geological factors were the dominant influences. Substrates in vegetated parts of the Estuary consisted almost entirely of Bay mud (Louderback 1951, Wahrhaftig et al. 1993). Beyond it they were much more heterogenous.

Environmental Setting

Vegetation increases in structural diversity and species richness beyond the estuarine ecosystem boundary in a complex pattern caused by interactions between the physical factors of climate, geology, and hydrology.

Climate – The San Francisco Bay Area, like all the California Floristic Province (Hickman 1993), has a climate characterized by wet winters and dry summers. Such climates are called "Mediterranean" because similar climatic conditions occur in the Mediterranean Basin, but the San Francisco Bay Area's Mediterranean climate is more extreme than much of its namesake since it rarely receives any significant rainfall during the years's warmest five months (Wernstedt 1972). Despite ample water, plant growth is retarded in winter by low temperatures and short days. Growth is maximal in spring when temperature and day length significantly increase and reserves of soil water from winter rains are still abundant (Walter 1979).

The diversity of the San Francisco Bay Area climate is explained, to a great extent, by variation in two factors; winter precipitation and summer marine air flow. Both cause local climates to be relatively mesic, but their maxima rarely coincide and do not identically affect vegetation. High winter precipitation makes abundant soil moisture reserves available for rapid spring and early summer plant growth where low temperatures and fog brought by marine air flow do not limit it. Since rapid plant growth increases biomass, high biomass vegetation types like redwood and mixed evergreen forests are frequently dominant in the Bay Area where rainfall is highest. A popular myth contends redwoods (*Sequoia sempervirens*) require summer fog. What they actually require (and are limited to) are places with high precipi-

tation that are protected from summer marine air flow and fog. By leaching mineral nutrients from surface soils, high rainfall also retards growth of herbaceous vegetation that could otherwise compete with forest tree seedlings (Holstein 1984a).

Bay Area mean annual precipitation varies from 13 inches at San Jose and Antioch to 47 inches at Kentfield in Marin County (Felton 1965). Not surprisingly, relatively undisturbed upland vegetation consists of redwood and mixed evergreen forests near Kentfield (Shuford 1993) and of grassland near Antioch and San Jose (Critchfield 1971). The Bay Area receives its precipitation from cyclonic storms with predominantly southwest winds arriving from the Pacific Ocean. Consequently stations with large mountains to the southwest lie in rain shadows with reduced precipitation. Antioch, for example, is in the lee of Mount Diablo, and San Jose is in the lee of the Santa Cruz Mountains. Kentfield, paradoxically, is also in the lee of a mountain, Mt. Tamalpais, but is close enough to receive an increase in rainfall caused by its orographic lifting. In most of the bay area, however, mean annual rainfall is between 15 and 25 inches (Gilliam 1962). Within this range, vegetation is controlled more by geologic substrate and slope exposure than relatively minor local differences in mean annual rainfall (Critchfield 1971).

In the San Francisco Bay Area, fog and associated marine air chilled by offshore upwelling reduce summer evapotranspiration and cause local climates to be mesic, where summer marine air flow is strongest and fogs most frequent. Such conditions reduce plant growth and resultant biomass, however, since they limit light and warmth. High biomass forest vegetation also seldom occurs in areas directly exposed to salt-laden winds associated with marine air flow (Holstein 1984a).

Summer water stress causes incomplete cover and much bare ground in most Mediterranean climate vegetation. In parts of the San Francisco Bay Area, however, marine air flow and fog mitigate summer drought sufficiently for occurrence of vegetation types like coastal scrub and prairie characterized by very complete cover and little bare ground despite relatively low biomass (Holstein 1984a).

Summer marine air flow and fog arrive at the Pacific Coast predominantly from the northwest because of anticyclonic origins, but a shallow semi-permanent temperature inversion confines their movement into and through the San Francisco Bay estuary to just a few low altitude gaps in the Coast Range. By far, the most important of these is the Golden Gate (Gilliam 1962).

Since marine air flow and fog suppress summer temperatures, mean July temperature is a reliable indicator of their relative presence or absence in the San Francisco Bay Area. Not surprisingly, San Francisco's July mean of 58.8°F is the lowest around the Estuary because of its location at the Golden Gate. Antioch's July mean of 74.0°F is the highest of any Estuary station since the low hills of northern Contra Costa County protect it from marine air flowing into the Central Valley through the Carquinez Strait. Fairfield's July mean of 72.1°F indicates more direct exposure to that air flow despite its more inland location. Mount Diablo State Park's entrance station has a July mean of 74.3°F because of its location above the inversion that limits marine air to low elevations. Most Estuary stations have July means in the sixties, but a difference of just a few degrees within that range can profoundly effect summer climate. Berkeley (61.5°F), Richmond (62.0°F), and Oakland (62.4°F) have the lowest summer temperatures in the Estuary next to San Francisco because of their location directly east of the Golden Gate. Burlingame (62.3°F) and the San Francisco Airport (62.7°F) are also relatively low because of their location at the east end of the San Bruno coast range gap (Gilliam 1962). Kentfield (65.9°F), in contrast, is relatively warm in July because Mount Tamalpais protects it from summer fog as well as inducing its high winter rainfall. Distance from the Pacific Coast is generally a poor predictor of summer marine air flow. Redwood City (67.9°F) on the west side of the Bay, for example, is warmer than Newark (64.9°F) on the east side since the latter is more directly exposed to air flow through the Golden Gate (Felton 1965, Gilliam 1962). Coastal scrub and coastal prairie, the vegetation types most associated with summer fog, are common on the outer Pacific Coast but relatively scarce in the San Francisco Bay Estuary because the parts of it most exposed to summer fog were also those settled earliest and urbanized most completely (Hoover et al. 1966, Donley et al. 1979).

Geology – Holocene alluvium characterized by abundant clay and level topography surrounds slightly over half the Estuary and is consequently the most abundant geologic substrate beneath its adjacent non-tidal vegetation (Jennings 1977, Wahrhaftig et al. 1993). Bay Area uplands underlain by alluvium were farmed early and are now largely urbanized, but historic accounts and relict stands indicate open grassland was their overwhelmingly dominant vegetation type before settlement (Bryant 1848, McKelvey 1955). An exception was a few oak savannas where widely spaced valley oaks (*Quercus lobata*) occurred in a grassland matrix. Such savannas were most frequent around the northern part of the Estuary where rainfall was relatively high, but even there they were most frequent in areas protected from summer marine air flow.

A specialized feature of California Holocene and older alluvium with level topography is vernal pools, small closed basins that fill in winter and dry during spring. They support a characteristic specialized flora rich in annual forbs (Holland and Jain 1977). Vernal pools were long thought to result from gopher activity (Dalquest and Scheffer 1942), but are better explained

as microtopographic patterns arising from ground shaking during earthquakes (Berg 1990) or interaction of localized soil processes and wind erosion (Abbott 1984).

Non-alluvial uplands around the Estuary consist of uplifted hills underlain by a variety of pre-Holocene sedimentary and volcanic rocks. These include the Mesozoic Franciscan formation and Great Valley Beds; Cenozoic sediments consisting of Paleocene, Eocene, Miocene, Pliocene, and Pleistocene marine beds and Pliocene nonmarine deposits; and the Pliocene Sonoma volcanic deposits (Jennings 1977, Norris and Webb 1990). The influence of these rocks on vegetation is most frequently controlled by their clay content. Those with abundant clay like Paleocene, Eocene, Miocene, and Pliocene sediments weather to deep soils much like those on Holocene alluvium and predominantly support similar grassland vegetation. The Mesozoic deposits include areas where clay is abundant and others where it is scarce. As on other clay-rich substrates, deep soils and grasslands dominate the former in contrast to the thin soils and woody vegetation types predominant where clay is scarce. The Franciscan Formation, a melange of soft clay sediments and hard metamorphic rocks, has a particularly complex vegetation pattern since grass dominates the former and trees the latter. Pleistocene marine beds and the Sonoma volcanics are relatively clay poor and consequently largely support woody vegetation types like oak woodland and mixed evergreen forest (Ellen and Wentworth 1995, Critchfield 1971).

Grass is dominant on clay soils because they have a relatively high water holding capacity (Walter 1979). West of Cordelia in Solano County, for example, Dibble-Los Osos and Hambright loams occur on adjacent hills in the same climate. Dibble-Los Osos soils develop on clay-rich Eocene marine sediments and consequently have B2t horizons containing accumulated clay and a water-holding capacity of 5 to 7 inches. Hambright soils, in contrast, develop on Sonoma volcanics, lack a B2t horizon, and have a water holding capacity of only 2 to 3.5 inches (Bates 1977). Despite identical precipitation, Dibble-Los Osos soils support grassland and Hambright soils support oak woodland dominated by coast live oak (*Quercus agrifolia*) because the former's B2t retains soil water that can be used by the shallow fibrous root systems of grasses. Since Hambright soils retain much less water, the excess infiltrates to the fractured rock below where it can be utilized by deep roots of trees but not grasses. In May, evidence of the Dibble-Los Osos B2t's water retention capacity is plain in the hills above Cordelia since grass stays green there several weeks longer on Dibble-Los Osos soils than it does on the Hambright despite the frequent shade of oaks. This phenomenon illustrates that two very different vegetation types can be equally "mesic" and that oak woodland and grassland are competitive enough within this region for slight soil differences to shift dominance from one to the other.

The geologic factor that most influences vegetation around the San Francisco Bay Estuary is the physical effect of clay on soil water holding capacity, but chemical effects are also locally important. Serpentinite, associated with the Franciscan Formation and occurring at the Estuary's edge in Marin and San Francisco counties, is so chemically distinctive because of its high Mg/Ca ratio and frequent heavy metals that it supports unique vegetation types and many endemic plant species (Kruckeberg 1984). Soils beyond the limits of tides are also usually much less saline than those under tidal influence, but salts can locally accumulate to high levels in non-tidal areas where drainage is poor. Salt especially accumulates in non-tidal areas where precipitation is low, relief is subdued, and Cretaceous Great Valley beds provide a salt source (Chapman 1960; Johnson et al. 1993; Harris 1991). Geology also strongly affects microclimate wherever hills have been uplifted since their south slopes receive more sunlight, warmth, and resultant evapotranspiration than their north slopes. Vegetation on Bay Area hills is consequently relatively xeric on south slopes and relatively mesic on north slopes (Bakker 1984).

Hydrology – The influence of geology and climate on soil water is discussed above. Streams also tend to increase in frequency and flow duration as rainfall increases. Since they provide water to plants in greater quantities and different seasons than local climates, they support distinctive riparian vegetation types not found in upland areas. Not surprisingly, riparian and upland vegetation become increasingly distinct as rainfall decreases (Holstein 1984b). Streams and their associated riparian vegetation are usually narrowly linear landscape features, but they can broaden dramatically when streams reach base level and form deltas. A broad willow-composite zone now removed by urbanization that reportedly once occurred around the southern edge of San Francisco Bay (Cooper 1926) undoubtedly represented covergent deltaic riparian vegetation of several creeks that flow into the Bay.

Alluvium in streambeds tends to be coarser and thus better aerated than interfluvial alluvium, and the running water of streams is also relatively well-aerated. Streamsides consequently provide suitable environments for roots of woody riparian vegetation. In freshwater marshes, however, standing water in poorly drained interfluvial areas quickly causes anaerobic reducing conditions to develop at such shallow depths that only herbaceous vegetation with shallow, predominantly fibrous root systems can occur. The herbaceous freshwater marsh vegetation is consequently quite distinct from predominantly woody riparian vegetation (Holstein 1984a).

Freshwater marsh vegetation grades into vernal pool vegetation through a series of transitional seasonal marsh vegetation types and into moist grassland through a transitional series of lowland wet meadow and swale

types. Numerous other local hydrological features around the San Francisco Bay Estuary like springs, seeps, and shallow water tables are associated with distinctive local vegetation types. The relatively shallow water table under most valley oak savannas is a notable example.

Ecotonal Plant Communities

Plant communities surrounding the Baylands ecosystem are here classified using the system of Holland and Keil (1995). At present the most widely used and influential classifications of California vegetation are derived from Munz and Keck's (1959) mixed system, which includes taxonomic, physiognomic, and ecological information. Barbour and Major's extensive (1977) review of California vegetation, for example, was organized around a slightly modified and expanded version of Munz and Keck's system. The units of their classification were vegetationally ill-defined, however, since the plant species lists provided for each one lacked even estimates of relative dominance. Some very important plant communities like riparian forests were also missing from both Munz and Keck's system and Barbour and Major's subsequent review. It is doubtful Munz and Keck intended their brief plant community synopsis to so profoundly influence California vegetation science, however, since the primary purpose of their book was clearly floristic. Its success at remaining California's floristic standard for decades undoubtedly strongly contributed to the influence of its community classification.

Sawyer and Keeler-Wolf (1995) have recently tried to overcome the Munz and Keck system's problems by developing a comprehensive alternative that excludes ecological information from community definitions except in the case of certain specialized habitats like vernal pools. The Sawyer and Keeler-Wolf system presents its own new problems, however, since it lumps quite different stable and successional communities when they are dominated by the same species. Excluding most ecological information also causes very different coastal and alpine communities sharing only a generic relationship between their dominant species to be lumped into catch-all groupings like "Sedge series." Many local dominance types present in California's complex vegetation are also missing from their system despite its numerous series and apparent comprehensiveness.

Holland and Keil avoid these problems by greatly increasing the comprehensiveness and consistency of Munz and Keck's limited but fundamentally sound system. The result is a system outstanding for simplicity, ease of use, and realistic description and classification of California vegetation. Beginning with coastal sand dune vegetation and concluding with freshwater vegetation and anthropogenic environments, the plant community descriptions below follow the system developed by Holland and Keil.

1. Coastal Sand Dune Vegetation – Sand is a distinctive substrate for plants since water infiltrates it very rapidly leaving little moisture available for plants with shallow root systems (Walter 1979). Sand differs from other substrates like fractured rock which have similarly high infiltration rates, however, because of sand's high subsurface homogeneity and lack of resistance to root penetration. Large sand deposits are characteristic landscape features of coasts and arid areas. In Holland and Keil's (1995) system, followed here, vegetation on sand deposits of arid areas is classified as desert sand dune vegetation and consequently distinguished from vegetation on coastal sands. In California, however, some dune fields are located in areas neither coastal nor truly arid. Examples occur on the Merced River alluvial fan in Merced County and at Antioch in Contra Costa County (Wahrhaftig et al. 1993). The former was produced by outwash from glacial erosion of granite in the Yosemite Valley (Wahrhaftig and Birman 1965), but extensive Eocene to Pliocene sandstone deposits in nearby hills (Ellen and Wentworth 1995) are a likely source for the latter. Neither the Merced or Antioch dunes are discussed by Holland and Keil, but both occur in semi-arid areas and share more floristic features with their desert sand dune vegetation type than their coastal sand dune vegetation types.

Pioneer dune vegetation occurs where significant aeolian movement of sand limits development of stable soil and vegetation.

Ambrosia chamissonis is its characteristic dominant, and *Abronia latifolia*, *Achillea millefolium*, *Atriplex californica*, *Atriplex leucophylla*, *Calystegia soldanella*, *Camissonia cheiranthifolia*, *Lathyrus littoralis*, *Leymus mollis*, and *Lupinus chamissonis* are frequent associated species (Barbour and Johnson 1977).

Dune scrub occurs where stable soil and vegetation have developed on sand of dunes usually considerably older than those supporting pioneer dune vegetation. *Ericameria ericoides* is the characteristic dominant of dune scrub, and associated species include *Artemisia californica*, *Baccharis pilularis*, *Lotus scoparius*, *Lupinus arboreus* and *Lupinus chamissonis* (Barbour and Johnson 1977).

Sand is relatively rare around the San Francisco Bay estuary, but a significant deposit, the Pleistocene Merritt sand, is present at Alameda and adjacent parts of Oakland (Radbruch 1957). Since the local climate is marine, some areas with surface deposits of Merritt sand probably once supported pioneer dune and dune scrub communities similar to those now occurring along the outer Pacific Coast. The sandy area at Alameda and Oakland was one of the first places along the Bay to urbanize, however, and any dune vegetation present there was consequently eradicated before it could be described. A modern analogue with similar soils and climate is Elkhorn Slough (Monterey County), which is incised into Pleistocene deposits, the Aromas sand. Agricultural development has removed some natural vegetation around Elkhorn Slough, but remaining relict stands are still numerous. Topographic features recorded prior to development of the port of Oakland and Lake Merritt resemble those along Elkhorn Slough (Wahrhaftig and Birman 1965).

At Antioch, a sandy area is also present immediately east of Broad Slough. It is less urban than Alameda, but most of its dune vegetation was lost to sand mining prior to urbanization. A small protected remnant of such vegetation at Antioch supports several state and federally listed rare animal and plant species (Sawyer and Keeler-Wolf 1995). Antioch is significantly hotter and drier than the outer coast, and its sand probably originated from nearby sand deposits that extend southward along the inner Coast Range. The affinity of its distinctive sand dune flora and vegetation is consequently closer to Holland and Keil's (1995) desert sand dune community than to either of his coastal dune communities. Because a rain shadow occurs along the inner Coast Range, the ranges of several plant and animal species with desert affinities, including the relatively well-known San Joaquin kit fox (*Vulpes macrotis* ssp. *mutica*) (Zeiner et al. 1990), extend north along the western San Joaquin Valley to near Antioch.

2. Coastal Scrub – Coastal scrub refers to communities dominated by small shrubs in non-desert areas of California. Coastal scrub typically develops on soil and friable sediments rather than conglomerate or fractured hard rock and consists of shrubs with relatively shallow root systems.

Northern coastal scrub is a dense shrub-dominated community which most frequently occurs on steep slopes receiving strong prevailing onshore winds and at least 20 inches of precipitation, but can also occur as an ecotone between northern oak woodland and southern oak woodland on slopes with less wind. Most typically, however, it occurs where precipitation and soils are adequate for development of forests, but tree growth is prevented by strong onshore winds. Since moisture is not limiting, cover is typically complete (Heady et al. 1977).

Baccharis pilularis is the characteristic dominant, but *Mimulus aurantiacus*, *Rhamnus californica*, and *Toxicodendron diversilobum* can also occasionally be locally dominant. Characteristic understory species include *Achillea millefolium*, *Anaphalis margaritacea*, *Eriophyllum staechadifolium*, *Gaultheria shallon*, *Heracleum lanatum*, *Polystichum munitum*, *Pteridium aquilinum*, *Rubus ursinus* and *Scrophularia californica*. Northern coastal scrub is most common along the outer Pacific Coast but also occurs at suitable sites around the San Francisco Bay Estuary near the Golden Gate, in the Berkeley Hills, and in San Mateo County. *Baccharis pilularis* frequently invades disturbed grasslands and forms communities which superficially resemble northern coastal scrub but lack most of its characteristic species. Eventually such recently invasive *B. pilularis* stands may develop into stable coastal scrub or oak woodland communities (Heady et al. 1977). A protected example of northern coastal scrub occurs near the estuary at China Camp State Park.

Southern coastal scrub is a relatively open shrub-dominated community occurring most frequently on steep, dry slopes. It is commonest in areas receiving under 20 inches of precipitation but can occasionally occur in wetter areas on sunny south slopes. It typically occurs where soils otherwise suitable for grassland are excessively drained because of steepness. Because water is the primary limiting factor in southern coastal scrub, its dominant shrubs tend to be widely spaced, forming relatively incomplete cover. In spring, when water stress is briefly relieved, a diverse annual forb flora develops in interstices between the dominant shrubs (Mooney 1977).

Artemisia californica is the characteristic dominant, and common associated species include *Eriogonum nudum, Eriophyllum lanatum, Lotus scoparius, Lupinus albifrons, Mimulus aurantiacus* and *Nassella pulchra*. Small stands of southern coastal sage scrub occur in hills around the Estuary and are especially frequent east of South San Fracisco Bay and south of Suisun Bay, where precipitation is relatively low. An example occurs along the Estuary shore at Point Richmond.

Sea-bluff coastal scrub occurs where persistent salt-laden onshore winds suppress most other plant communities. Such climatic conditions resemble those in northern coastal scrub but are more extreme. In such sites the only communities are sea-bluff coastal scrub and northern coastal grassland. The former tends to occur on rocky sites with thin soils and the latter on deeper soils that tend to be heavier, but both frequently intermix in a complex mosaic (Holland and Keil 1995).

Eriophyllum stachaedifolium is the characteristic dominant, and frequently associated species include *Artemisia pycnocephala, Baccharis pilularis, Erigeron glaucus, Eriogonum latifolium* and *Lessingia filaginifolia*. Salt-laden winds strong and persistent enough to support this community enter the Estuary through the Golden Gate but rapidly lose their intensely marine character as they move inland. Havlik (1974) described small stands of this community at Yerba Buena Island, Brooks Island, Red Rock, Point Richmond, Point Fleming, and Potrero San Pablo, all places directly exposed to marine winds entering San Francisco Bay through the Golden Gate.

3. Chaparral – Chaparral refers to a widespread and characteristic California community dominated by large shrubs with evergreen sclerophyllous leaves. It is frequent in areas with precipitation between 10 and 20 inches per year and occasional in wetter areas on sunny south slopes. Chaparral occurs where rocky soils with little clay permit rapid infiltration of water and air to relatively great depths. Such conditions are most fre-

quent on steep slopes but can also occur with relatively low relief on stone alluvial fans in valleys.

Holland and Keil (1995) subdivide California chaparral into 11 subclasses, of which six occur in San Francisco Bay counties. These are not separately treated here, however, since relatively little chaparral of any kind occurs in the Estuary's immediate vicinity.

Chaparral is dominated by shrubs in the genera *Adenostoma, Arctostaphylos, Ceanothus, Cercocarpus,* and *Quercus*, which form a functional group characterized by deep root systems adapted for extracting water from deep cavities in fractured rock. The sclerophyllous leaves of chaparral shrubs are adapted for maintaining low levels of evapotranspiration and associated productivity during long growing seasons (Walter 1979, Mooney and Miller 1985). Discussions of chaparral ecology have long emphasized its adaptation to fire since its shrubs use a variety of strategies to rapidly reoccupy burns and an associated functional group of annuals has seeds that remain dormant for decades and only germinate following chaparral fires (Biswell 1974). Extensive research on *Adenostoma*-dominated chaparral suggesting a relatively short fire cycle my not be directly applicable to other chaparral types, however, since some other kinds of chaparral may have a much longer fire cycle (Keeley and Keeley 1988).

The nearest extensive chaparral to the Estuary occurs in Marin County on the slopes of Mt. Tamalpais two miles west of San Francisco Bay (Shuford 1993, Wieslander and Jensen 1945). While chaparral on alluvial fans is rapidly disappearing but still fairly common in parts of southern California (Smith 1980), it is virtually unknown in central and northern California. Cooper (1926), however, reported that chaparral that has since been extirpated formerly occurred near the southern end of San Francisco Bay on Los Gatos Creek's alluvial fan.

4. Grassland – Vegetation dominated by grasses and graminoid sedges was widespread along the shores of the San Francisco Bay Estuary prior to urban development and is still fairly common there (Bryant 1848, McKelvey 1955). It occurs in non-wetlands wherever soils with clay horizons thick enough to hold significant water near the soil surface and to exclude air from deeper horizons are directly exposed to solar radiation. Clay soils are particularly favorable for grasses and other graminoids because the near-surface water they hold is preferentially available to the dense, relatively shallow fibrous root systems of such plants. In wet climates the most mesic conditions occur on soils with high clay content because of their high water holding capacity, but in arid areas that pattern is reversed. In deserts clay holds much water from scarce precipitation near the soil surface, where solar radiation quickly evaporates it (Walter 1979). Conditions intermediate between these extremes prevail in the semiarid climate surrounding most of the Estuary. Clay soils are xeric and grass-covered on plains and south slopes, where they are directly exposed to solar radiation, but mesic and covered by forest and woodland on north slopes, where solar radiation is reduced. Grassland is most prevalent where annual precipitation is between 10 and 20 inches but becomes progressively scarcer as annual rainfall increases. Some grassland is usually present even in very wet areas, however, wherever clay is directly exposed to solar radiation. Soils with sufficient clay for grassland predominate on the recent alluvium that forms the floors of virtually all San Francisco Bay Area valleys; they are also common on hillslopes where clay-rich sediments have been uplifted (Ellen and Wentworth 1995). While direct solar radiation usually keeps grassland free of woody plants on valley floors and south-facing hillslopes, similar grassland frequently dominates understories beneath the oak woodland that occurs on north slopes because of less intense radiation (Holstein 1984a).

Native perennial grassland. Frequent relict stands and clear descriptions by early travelers leave little doubt that most native grassland near the Estuary on both valley floors and hillslopes was dominated by a rhyzomatous and largely sterile hybrid between *Leymus triticoides* and *L. condensatus* (Stebbins and Walters 1949). Hybrids between these species have been called *Leymus xmultiflorus*, but since the hybrid dominant around the Estuary is too small to match descriptions of *xmultiflorus* (Hickman 1993), it is here included in *L. triticoides*. Two frequently associated rhizomatous graminoids were *Carex barbarae* and *C. praegracilis*, the latter being especially frequent at upland-wetland ecotones. *Nassella pulchra*, a non-rhizomatous bunchgrass, has received more attention than any other species as a native grassland dominant. It frequently dominated grassland but mostly did so only near ecotones with coastal scrub and oak woodland where heavy clay grassland soils had begun to thin and dissipate or where specific substrates like serpentinite prevented development of typical grassland soils (Bryant 1848, McKelvey 1955).

Native grassland had numerous local variations ranging from topographic lows where soil water and clay accumulated to topographic highs where clay was thin and water scarce. Species indicating topographic lows (locally called swales) included *Juncus balticus, Juncus xiphioides, Ranunculus californicus,* and *Sisyrinchium bellum*, while *N. pulchra* and a variety of forbs indicated the highs. Along the Estuary shore at ecotones with tidal marsh, *Distichlis spicata*, another rhizomatous grass, was particularly prominent (Heady 1977, Holland and Keil 1995).

A scarce native grassland type especially significant for its many rare plants occurs on salt-affected soils associated with inland basins and basin rims rather than coastal tidelands (Faber 1997). These inland **alkaline grasslands** share features like the prominence of *Distichlis spicata* with the grassland-tidal marsh ecotone but often

differ from it in the presence of more bare ground and many species not occurring at the Estuary shore. Cooper (1926) reported *Hemizonia congesta* and *H. pungens* were formerly dominant on similar soils near the southern end of the Estuary that are now completely covered by urban development. The best presently extant examples of alkaline grassland in the Estuary's vicinity occur near Livermore in Alameda County and near Fairfield in Solano County. Other distinctive grassland types of unusual substrates supporting rare species are **serpentinite grassland** and **sandy soil grassland** (Skinner and Pavlik 1994).

Native annual forbland. Wester (1981) presented evidence that the southern San Joaquin Valley, an area traditionally considered former grassland, was dominated by annual forbs prior to European settlement. California vegetation classification has traditionally called all upland vegetation dominated by herbs grassland, but Wester's work suggests much of the area traditionally mapped as grassland (Kuchler 1964) was actually native annual forbland. Since native annual forbland occurs where rainfall is insufficient for most perennial grasses, it consequently was most extensive far south of the Estuary in the southern San Joaquin Valley. Numerous relict taxa suggest, however, that a narrow native annual forbland corridor extended north from there to near the Estuary shore in Contra Costa County because of a rain shadow along the inner Coast Range's eastern base. Forbland elements also probably occurred even more widely wherever local conditions like soil infertility and trampling by megafauna suppressed otherwise ubiquitous perennial grasses. Even today wildflower displays (i.e., annual forb dominance) are most spectacular locally where soil is relatively infertile (i.e., Bear Valley in Colusa County and Table Mountain in Butte County [Faber 1997]) and most spectacular generally in years, as in 1991, when winter drought suppression of competitive grasses is followed by forb-promoting heavy spring rains. Some forbland species like *Eremocarpus setigerus* have adapted well to anthropogenic land use changes but others have become rare (*Convolvulus simulans, Madia radiata*) or extinct (*Eschscholzia rhombipetala*).

Non-native annual grassland. Introduction of grazing and agriculture during the nineteenth century caused a dominance shift in almost all of California's grasslands from native perennial graminoids to Eurasian non-native annual grasses. Today dominance among such annuals changes spatially in a complex pattern reflecting soil conditions. On catenas from thick, heavy clay soils to thinner, lighter ones a typical annual grass dominance sequence *Lolium multiflorum-Bromus hordeaceus-Avena fatua-Avena barbata* replaces a simpler perennial sequence *Leymus triticoides-Nassella pulchra* still occasionally extant on the same catenas. Another common dominance sequence *Bromus hordeaceus-Bromus diandrus-Hordeum murinum* reflects shifts in soil nitrogen content from low to relatively high. The above species are the most frequently dominant non-native annual grasses, but others also occasionally participate. *Cynosurus echinatus*, for example, frequently dominates annual grassland where rainfall is relatively high. Several exotic forbs are also becoming increasingly important components in a vast exotic herbaceous vegetation type that may only temporarily be called grassland. *Vicia villosa* ssp. *varia* is increasingly planted for forage in the *Avena* zone; *Picris echioides* is important in the *Lolium* zone; and *Centaurea solstitialis*, especially, is a widespread invader of the *B. hordeaceus* zone, where *Erodium botrys* is also important when soil fertility is particularly low (Heady 1977, Holland and Keil 1995). Grazing is particularly important for maintaining replacement of native perennial grasses with exotic annual species. At numerous sites around the Estuary, for example, dominance is shifting back from exotic annual grasses to *Leymus triticoides* and *Carex barbarae* where expanding urbanization has at least temporarily caused the removal of grazing.

Coastal prairie. Where clay soils are directly exposed to marine air flow, a floristically distinct grassland occurs that Holland and Keil (1995) call northern coastal grassland but is widely known in California as coastal prairie. Coastal prairie is most frequent along the outer coast, but small amounts also likely occur near the Estuary where marine air flow is particularly direct.

Much of California's coastal prairie is now dominated by two exotic perennial grasses, *Anthoxanthum odoratum* and *Holcus lanatus*, but many distinctive native perennial grasses like *Agrostis pallens*, *Calamagrostis nutkaensis*, *Danthonia californica*, *Deschampsia cespitosa*, *Festuca idahoensis* and *Festuca rubra* can also frequently be locally dominant. Two other distinctive plant species indicative of coastal prairie are *Iris douglasiana* and *Juncus patens* (Heady et al. 1977).

5. Coastal Coniferous Forest – Forests dominated by large coniferous trees occur along the eastern Pacific Coast in a high rainfall zone extending from central California to Alaska. Holland and Keil (1995) recognize two subdivisions of coastal coniferous forest, but only one of these, redwood forest, occurs near the Estuary.

Redwood forest. Extensive forests dominated by *Sequoia sempervirens*, the well-known redwood and the world's tallest tree species, occur on the southern slopes of Mt. Tamalpais within 1.75 miles of the Estuary (Shuford 1993), but individual redwoods occur in mixed evergreen forest much less than a mile from the shore of San Pablo Bay at China Camp State Park. Redwoods are common up to about 2,000 feet in the California Coast Range wherever annual precipitation is above 40 inches and soil is relatively fertile. Despite sufficient rainfall, sensitivity to cold prevents their occurrence along the Oregon coast beyond a few miles north of the border, at high elevations in the Coast Range, or on inland mountain ranges. Contrary to an enduring myth, redwoods are negatively rather than positively associated with summer fog. Consequently, even at sites protected from onshore winds they are almost completely absent along the immediate coast wherever summer fog is frequent. Redwoods survive summer drought not because of fog drip but by storing surplus water from high winter precipitation in their massive trunks, a strategy that has produced only slightly less dramatic gigantism in other conifer species where large winter water surpluses occur with summer drought. As a consequence northern California and southern Chile, both areas with unusually wet winters and dry summers located at the outer periphery of more typical Mediterranean climate zones, are the world's two greatest centers of tree gigantism (Holstein 1984a, Zinke 1977).

Shade is so intense in the redwood forest understory that only a few plant species survive there. Two that do, *Oxalis oregana* and *Polystichum munitum*, are usually the sole understory dominants.

6. Mixed Evergreen Forest –

Central California mixed evergreen forest. Forests dominated by a mix of broadleaf and conifer evergreen trees are frequent in California where precipitation is relatively high and winter temperatures are mild. In northern California the trees most frequently dominating such mixed evergreen forests are *Arbutus menziesii*, *Lithocarpus densiflorus*, *Pseudotsuga menziesii*, and *Umbellularia californica*. In central California the term mixed evergreen forest as presently used is somewhat anomalous, however, since it often designates forests solely dominated by *Umbellularia californica*, the California laurel. Such laurel-dominated forests are frequent around the Estuary where annual rainfall is between 20 and 40 inches. At the dry end of that precipitation range laurel forests are entirely confined to very shady north slopes and canyons, but they also occur on somewhat sunnier slopes as 40 inches is approached. Above that they are almost entirely replaced by redwood forests (Sawyer et al. 1977, Wainwright and Barbour 1984).

The most commonly associated tree species in central California's laurel forests is a non-evergreen, *Acer macrophyllum*. *Arbutus menziesii* is also a frequent associate but is almost entirely confined to the rockiest slopes. Shade is so intense beneath laurel forest canopies that completely bare ground is common where drought is an added stressor, but as 40 inches is approached *Polystichum munitum* often dominates the understory. *Holodiscus discolor*, a deciduous species, is commonly dominant in shrubby openings frequent in laurel forests (Safford 1995).

7. Oak Woodland – Vegetation with an overstory dominated by oak trees is common throughout California's Mediterranean climate zone including the Estuary's vicinity. Such oak woodlands primarily vary in species and spacing of their overstory oaks. Vegetation is called savannah where oaks are widely spaced and forest where spacing is so close their canopies are closed. Woodland, as a term, describes vegetation with intermediate spacing, but tree separation is so locally variable in California's oak-tree dominated vegetation it is appropriate to use the traditional term oak woodland to refer to all of it. That generalized oak woodland can then be divided into subclasses based on its dominant species (Griffin 1977).

Since woodland oaks and grassland grasses occur in similar environmental conditions, they frequently compete directly for water and other soil resources. Specific aspects of that competition are discussed for each subclass but a few of its consequences are general. Oaks only occur where water is present in deep soil horizons, where it may arrive horizontally through shallow aquifers or vertically when precipitation is abundant enough to infiltrate past dense but relatively shallow grass root systems. Grassland grasses, in contrast, only occur where solar radiation is direct because overstory trees are either absent or so widely spaced their canopies are not contiguous (Walter 1979).

Coast live oak woodland, which is dominated by *Quercus agrifolia*, is distinctive among oak woodland subclasses because it consists almost exclusively of closed canopy forests. As a consequence it is frequently treated as a subclass of mixed evergreen forest rather than oak woodland. It is included here with oak woodland, however, because of the affinities of both its dominant tree and the majority of its fauna (Griffin 1977).

Coast live oak woodland occurs widely around the Estuary where annual precipitation is between 15 and 40 inches and continentality is at least partially moderated by marine influences. Marine air flow through Carquinez Strait even permits occurrence of coast live oak woodland with two isolated Coast Range-related mammal populations (*Sylvilagus bachmani riparius* and *Neotoma fuscipes riparia*) on the Central Valley floor near Lodi (Zeiner et al. 1990).

In hills on clay soils coast live oak woodland is frequently present as an extensive ecotone between grassland and mixed evergreen forest since it occurs on slopes shadier than the former but sunnier than the latter. On slopes where rockier substrates and lighter soils permit infiltration of more water to greater depths, however, coast live oak is less limited by solar exposure and can even occur on south slopes. North of Carquinez Strait, for example, adjacent ridges with identical microclimates differ only in their substrates. Ridges underlain by sediments of the clay-rich Eocene Markley Formation are covered by grassland and have coast live oak woodland only on north slopes and in canyons, while those underlain by hard but fractured rocks of the Pliocene Sonoma volcanics are covered by coast live oak woodland on all exposures but north slopes and canyons, where *Umbellularia*-dominated mixed evergreen forest occurs. The

great vegetational difference is a result of the way in which the two substrates respond to precipitation — rain rapidly infiltrates to deep levels on the fractured volcanics where it can be utilized by oak roots, whereas it is held at the surface on the clay-rich Markley where it is more available to grass roots. Rapid infiltration on the volcanics causes such xeric conditions in its surface soils that its few stands of annual grassland cease productivity and dry two weeks earlier than Markley grasslands dominated by the same species (Bates 1977, Ellen and Wentworth 1995).

Coast live oak woodland differs from other oak woodland subclasses in the relative rarity of annual grasses in its understory. The most frequent dominant there is *Toxicodendron diversilobum*, poison oak, but *Rubus ursinus* and *Symphoricarpus mollis* are also often important (Safford 1995).

Valley oak woodland consists of several structurally diverse communities sharing dominance by *Quercus lobata* that include savannah and woodland on clay hillslopes and savannah, woodland, and closed canopy forest on alluvial plains over shallow unconfined aquifers. Alluvial valley oak woodland often occurs on the outer edges of riparian forest corridors (see below) on relatively fine, heavy soils distinct from the coarse alluvial soils under typical riparian stream bank vegetation. Tree spacing in alluvial valley oak woodland is related to water stress since canopies closed when subsurface water is abundant become progressively more open as water stress increases, resulting first in woodland and then savannah. Much alluvial valley oak forest was removed because it coincided with highly desired agricultural soils, but a few stands are extant in the Central Valley and elsewhere. Alluvial valley oak woodland was probably always scarce near the Estuary, however, since it is better adapted to inland Califonia's hot summers than to the outer Coast Range's relatively marine climate. One of the few examples near the Estuary is located along Green Valley Creek near Cordelia in Solano County.

Valley oak woodland is most frequent near the Estuary on clay hillslopes with annual rainfall between 15 and 40 inches, where its range overlaps coast live oak woodland and foothill woodland. It is less abundant than either but more tolerant of clay soils than the former and less resistant to water stress than the latter. The understory of valley oak woodland's savannah and woodland phases typically consists of non-native annual and occasionally native perennial grassland. Vegetation beneath closed canopy valley oak alluvial forest, however, can include both grassland and features shared with riparian forest or coast live oak forest understories. Valley oak reproduction, often low because of competition with annual grass and predation of seeds and seedlings by a variety of herbivores, can be abundant in alluvial woodland when suppression of grass by flooding coincides with large acorn crops. Urban fringes are also favorable sites for valley oak reproduction because their low live-stock and wildlife populations result in lowered seed and seedling predation (Holstein 1984b, Holland and Keil 1995).

Foothill woodland is woodland and savannah vegetation wholly or partially dominated by *Quercus douglasii*, blue oak, that is widespread on hillslopes surrounding the Central Valley. Near the Estuary, foothill woodland is largely confined to the inner Coast Range. The foothill woodland environment has a relatively continental climate with cool to cold winters, very hot summers, and annual rainfall from 15 to 40 inches. Winter cold reduces understory grass growth and consequently permits infiltration of a large part of the wet season's water surplus to deep subsoil where it can be utilized by blue oaks during spring and summer. In summer high temperatures and low humidity produce very low water potentials in blue oak leaves that permit withdrawal of water tightly held by clay-rich subsoils.

Blue oak is usually the sole foothill woodland dominant on clay hillslopes, but on slopes with more rock and thinner soils it often shares dominance with *Pinus sabiniana*. Blue oaks occur on a wider range of slope exposures than many other oak species, but foothill woodland dominance often shifts to *Aesculus californicus* on shaded north slopes. In canyons and around rock outcrops *Quercus wislizenii* is also often a local dominant.

Because of foothill woodland's open canopy its understory is almost universally dominated by non-native annual grassland. Native forbs like *Holocarpha virgata*, however, are also usually frequent there. Competition is particularly intense between annual grasses and blue oak seedlings before they develop roots long enough to reach subsoil water. Seedling mortality at this stage is so intense that much foothill woodland consists almost entirely of mature blue oaks that germinated in the 1860's, a decade when severe overgrazing reduced much presumably native perennial grassland from California's rangelands. Subsequent increase of non-native annual grassland has severely restricted reproduction of foothill woodland developing at that time (Griffin 1977, Holland and Keil 1995).

8. Cliffs and Rock Outcrops -Vegetation of cliffs and rock outcrops is usually virtually ignored in surveys of California vegetation including that of Holland and Keil (1995) because its areal extent is small and it consists largely of non-vegetated surfaces. It is particularly important, however, as a habitat for rare plant species. Cliffs are unique environments where soil and competition with other plants is very limited and solar radiation is often abundant. Plants adapted to cliffs (chasmophytes) resemble epiphytes in producing small easily dispersed seeds in such great numbers that the likelihood of reaching rare suitable germination habitats is increased. Seeds reaching these light-rich habitats can afford to be small because they require little stored food.

Dudleya, the California genus with the most highly adapted chasmophytes, has a few taxa near the Estuary but is much more diverse in Southern California.

Plants of rock outcrops are less specialized than chasmophytes but may be rare since they occur in distinctive microenvironments that consequently are free from competition with surrounding vegetation. Rock outcrops and cliffs are most likely to support rare plants when they are mineralogically different from surrounding landscapes, and one mineral receiving particular attention because of its frequent association with rare plants is serpentine. Soil development is so retarded and vegetation so distinctive on serpentine that its occurrences may be viewed as extended rock outcrops even though they occasionally cover many square miles (Bakker 1984, Skinner and Pavlik 1994, Fiedler and Leidy 1987).

9. Riparian Vegetation – Riparian vegetation refers to the distinctive plant communities of streambanks and ecologically related habitats. Its most salient environmental features are relatively coarse alluvial soils typically associated with streams and root zone water supplies greater than the local climate provides. When mature, California riparian vegetation is closed canopy forest, but early successional riparian vegetation can be shrubby.

Near the Estuary riparian vegetation is overwhelmingly dominated by three species, *Acer negundo*, *Salix lasiolepis* and *Salix laevigata*, but others may dominate in specialized habitats. *Populus fremontii* and *Salix goodingii* are important where climate becomes less marine and more continental near the Central Valley; *Salix exigua* is important on sandbars and other habitats where early successional riparian vegetation is developing; *Alnus rhombifolia* and *Salix lucida* ssp. *lasiandra* are important where, as at Niles Canyon, streams with rocky beds flow perennially; and *Platanus occidentalis* and *Baccharis viminea* dominate where ones with sandy and rocky beds flow intermittently.

Typical *Acer negundo-Salix lasiolepis-Salix laevigata* riparian vegetation also is common where ecological conditions simulate streambank environments, as at lakeshores and a variety of places with shallow water tables. On the outer coast non-streambank riparian vegetation is frequent in dune slacks, but around the Estuary it at least formerly was most frequent in sausals, microdeltas occurring where stream channels and their subsurface water tables spread laterally as they entered tidal marsh. Most sausals have been lost to urbanization of the Estuary's periphery, but a small example occurs at China Camp State Park.

Common riparian understory plants near the Estuary include *Baccharis douglasii*, *Euthamia occidentalis*, *Rosa californica*, and *Rubus ursinus*. For a short distance these can also replace riparian trees as dominants at the ecotone with tidal marsh where a veneer of coarse streamside alluvium deposited on tidal mud thins as it nears the Estuary. Like sausals, however, such riparian-tidal marsh ecotones have almost entirely disappeared around the Estuary because of urbanization (Holland and Keil 1995, Holstein 1984b).

10. Freshwater Vegetation – Freshwater wetland vegetation occurs where land surfaces are saturated by freshwater or shallowly covered by it. Its two main phases near the Estuary, freshwater marshes and vernal pools, are very distinctive but also united by intermediate communities.

Freshwater marsh refers to vegetation dominated by plant species emergent from at least semi-permanent shallow freshwater. The most frequently dominant freshwater marsh species near the Estuary is *Scirpus acutus*, but *Scirpus americanus, Scirpus californicus, Typha angustifolia, Typha domingensis*, and *Typha latifolia* can also be important there as dominants. The *Typha* spp., in particular, are often dominant in early successional and nitrogen-enriched freshwater marshes.

Climate and geology have less influence on the distribution of freshwater marsh than they do on the occurrence of other plant communities. When vegetation is primarily limited by precipitation, temperature, and light, its distribution is controlled by climate, and when limited by mineral nutrition and soil texture, its distribution is controlled by geology. The primary limiting factor in freshwater marshes, however, is air, which, while superabundant at the marsh surface, falls to such low concentrations a short distance beneath it that environments too anoxic, reduced, and toxic for root growth are frequent there. All freshwater marsh dominants in California are consequently monocotyledons, which have shallow fibrous root systems readily supplied with air by aerenchyma-rich stems. Many dicotyledons including most trees and shrubs, in contrast, have solid stems and deep, non-fibrous root systems poorly adapted to anoxic conditions. California consequently lacks swamps, vegetation in semi-permanent shallow water dominated by woody plants, since it has no native trees or shrubs capable of completing life cycles in flooded environments. Buttonbush, *Cephalanthus occidentalis*, and several species of *Salix* can tolerate extended flooding, however, and frequently occur at the ecotone between freshwater marsh and riparian vegetation (Holland and Keil 1995, Holstein 1984a,b).

Both tidal and non-tidal freshwater marshes are frequent around the Estuary, but the former are most important in the Sacramento-San Joaquin Delta immediately upstream from the true estuary. The Delta consisted almost entirely of tidal freshwater marsh before it was largely converted to agricultural land, but a few remnant tidal freshwater marshes still occur there. Small non-tidal freshwater marshes often resulting from human alteration of hydrologic conditions are also widespread around the estuary (Bowcutt 1996).

Soils beneath freshwater marshes may be mineral or organic. Despite otherwise similar vegetation freshwater marshes with organic soils are technically fens. Since organic soils derived from *Scirpus acutus* rhizomes were general beneath the Delta's tidal freshwater marshes, they once constituted a single vast fen (Atwater and Belknap 1980). Mineral soils, however, generally occur beneath the many small freshwater marshes around the Estuary. Marshes develop most readily on fine, heavy mineral soils since these exclude air and create the anaerobic conditions suitable for marsh vegetation more readily than the coarse and readily aerated sediments common on streambanks beneath riparian forests. Since waterbirds quickly transport propagules permitting establishment of freshwater marsh plants at sites with suitable hydrological conditions regardless of their climatic and geological environments, freshwater marshes are among the easiest plant communities to restore (Kusler and Kentula 1990).

Continua exist between semi-perennial marshes and both moist grassland swales (see above) and vernal pools (see below). Vegetation of areas with hydrology intermediate between freshwater marshes and vernal pools pond longer than the latter but shorter than the former. These are most frequently dominated by *Eleocharis macrostachya* with normal winter wet season inundation but can also be dominated by *Cyperus eragrostis* when ponding resulting primarily from agricultural and urban runoff occurs in the warm season. Vegetation arising from both kinds of seasonal ponding is properly called seasonal marsh, but wildlife managers also frequently use the term to describe non-tidal mudflat environments extremely important for shorebird foraging. Such non-tidal mudflats have little vegetation and once commonly occurred where flooding temporarily suppressed normal grassland development on stream terraces. Streamflow control and terrace urbanization, however, have greatly reduced traditional episodically flooded shorebird habitat around the Estuary. Most non-tidal seasonal marshes presently occurring there consequently result from seasonal drawdowns of artificial ponds and floodways (SFEP 1991a,b).

Limnetic vegetation refers to floating or submerged vegetation occurring in open freshwater too deep or otherwise unsuitable for marsh vegetation. Important native components of submerged limnetic vegetation near the Estuary include *Ceratophyllum demersum, Najas guadalupensis, Potamogeton pectinatus* and *Potamogeton pusillus*, while important floating elements are *Azolla filiculoides, Lemna gibba* and *Lemna minor*. Non-native species like *Egeria densa* and *Mytiophyllum aquaticum* are now also extremely significant and often predominant elements of submerged limnetic vegetation near the Estuary, but the floating component consists almost entirely of extremely widespread and readily dispersed native species except in and near the Delta, where non-native *Eichornia crassipes* is important (Holland and Keil 1995).

Vernal pool vegetation refers to a distinctive plant community dominated by annual and short-lived perennial forbs that occurs in microtopographic basins flooded in the wet season and dry the rest of the year. Vernal pool plants are consequently adapted for beginning their life cycle like submerged limnetic species but completing it as terrestrial plants in completely dry environments. The vernal pool environment has led to adaptive radiation of numerous species primarily in the genera *Downingia, Eryngium, Lasthenia, Navarretia, Plagiobothrys,* and *Psilocarphus*, and it is these that dominate its vegetation. *Plagiobothrys bracteatus*, in particular, is the most frequent dominant of vernal pool vegetation around the Estuary. Upland vegetation around vernal pools is almost invariably non-native annual grassland (Holland 1977).

The origin of vernal pool basins is obscure but may result from seismic activity or interaction of wind erosion and soil processes (see above). To pond water and create an environment suitable for vernal pool vegetation, however, an aquaclude or barrier to water infiltration that may be a clay horizon, duripan, or bedrock must be present immediately beneath the basin. Most vernal pools and the plants adapted to them occur entirely or almost entirely in California, and few hydrologic features resembling vernal pools occur outside North America even in otherwise similar Mediterranean climates (Thorne 1984).

Vernal pools are at risk even in the Central Valley where they are most common because virtually all human activities except rangeland grazing destroy the microtopography and aquacludes that create the vernal pool environment. Around the Estuary they are even more threatened since they are extremely rare near southern San Francisco Bay and only slightly more frequent north of San Pablo and Suisun bays. Vernal pools north of Suisun Bay are particularly environmentally significant because they are often partially dominated by *Lasthenia conjugens*, a federally listed endangered species extinct throughout much of its range (Skinner and Pavlik 1994).

Artificially created basins often sufficiently resemble natural vernal pools to be colonized by a few wide-ranging and extremely tolerant pool species. More rarely a few rare species may be present in such artificial sites. The full suite of vernal pool taxa including the rarest species almost never develops in such environments, however, because soil characteristics of natural pools can rarely be replicated. As a consequence creation of artificial vernal pools has been the least successful of all wetland restoration efforts (Ferren and Gevirtz 1990, Kusler and Kentula 1990).

Vernal pools typically are freshwater environments since their primary water source is precipitation (Hanes et al. 1990). However, salt diffusion from underlying soils causes some to be slightly brackish. Seasonal pools hydrologically resembling vernal pools but lacking their characteristic biota because of elevated salinity also occur. They are called playas when their surrounding saline environment is inland (Chapman 1960, Waisel 1972) and pans when it is coastal (Adam 1990, Chapman 1960, Long and Mason 1983, Waisel 1972). Both occur in San Francisco Bay Area counties but only the latter near the Estuary shore (SFEP 1991a). Today vegetated pans near the Estuary are ubiquitously dominated by *Cotula coronopifolia*, an exotic annual that may have replaced a now extinct native annual *Plagiobothrys glaber*.

11. Anthropogenic Environments – Anthropogenic environments must be briefly considered because they collectively now dominate non-tidal uplands around the Estuary. The anthropogenic typology used here follows Mayer and Laudenslayer, Jr. (1988) rather than the more complex one of Holland and Keil (1995).

Agricultural environments historically surrounded much of the Estuary but have become increasingly scarce because of displacement by urbanization. Structurally and physiologically different elements like orchards, vineyards, and both irrigated and dry farmed cropland are included here, but all share low plant and animal diversity. Irrigated nursery crops are most important near the southern part of the Estuary; and vineyards, irrigated pastures, and dry farmed oats (*Avena sativa*) predominate near the northern part.

Urban and suburban environments now overwhelmingly dominate non-tidal uplands around the Estuary. They often structurally resemble extended and unusually diverse riparian zones since irrigated non-native trees predominantly in the genera *Acacia, Eucalyptus,* and *Pinus* are ubiquitously present above an even more diverse understory of ornamental shrubs and herbs. As a consequence, urban-suburban communities are probably the landscape unit near the Estuary with the highest plant diversity but the fewest native plants. Some native bird species have adapted to using urban areas as habitat and become common, but far fewer terrestrial species are able to do so.

Rare Plants of Ecotonal Plant Communities

Table 1.4 lists rare plant species found in the nine Bay Area counties. The table is organized using the same classification system (Holland and Keil) as was used in the previous section. It includes, for each species, the state and federal listing status, as well as the status derived from the California Native Plant Society (CNPS) inventory (Skinner and Pavlik 1994). The CNPS inventory is more complete than the state or federal listings and is organized on the following lists:

    1a. Presumed extinct

    1b. Rare, threatened, or endangered in California
       and elsewhere.

2. Rare, threatened, or endangered in California but more common elsewhere.
3. Possibly rare, but more information is needed.
4. Distribution limited: a watch list.

Plants with the greatest need for protection are on list 1b, and 1a (presumed extinct) plants are placed there if rediscovered. The CNPS inventories rare plants by county. To prepare Table 1.4, each of the CNPS-identified rare species was assigned to a modal plant community or ecotone based on information provided by state and local floras. An effort was made to place each taxon in the plant community it most frequently (but not necessarily exclusively) occurs(ed) in, however, frequently reference materials regarding a taxon were contradictory. In these cases I sought to develop a consensus view, and weighted local floras and my own field experience most heavily.

The greatest constraint in preparing this table was the frequent sparsity of ecological information regarding rare species. Preparation was easiest in areas with local floras since these are full of observations by botanists with deep knowledge of their region's plants and habitats. Tragically, however, a number of plants near the Estuary went extinct or became extremely rare in an older era when little or no ecological information was provided when plants were collected. We can only speculate regarding the niches of these taxa.

Many species are rare because they occur in rare ecological niches. Historically, these have not been the focus of plant community classification, which is most concerned with the commonest kinds of vegetation. While there was an effort to include some of the rarer niches occurring near the Estuary in Table 1.4, it is not comprehensive, and rare niches distant from the Estuary are not included. Rare plants that occur primarily in plant communities distant from the Estuary were not included in the narrative community descriptions.

It is hoped this table will generate discussion and suggestions for its improvement.

Table 1.4 Rare Plant Species* Found in the Nine Counties Adjacent to the San Francisco Bay Estuary, by Plant Community or Ecotone

1. Sand dune vegetation

A. Pioneer coastal dune vegetation

    1b. *Abronia umbellata* ssp. *breviflora* - FSC

B. Coastal dune scrub

    1b. *Agrostis blasdalei* - FSC
      Chorizanthe cuspidata var. *cuspidata* - FSC
      Chorizanthe cuspidata var. *villosa* - FSC
      Chorizanthe robusta var. *robusta* - FE
      Collinsia corymbosa
      Erysimum ammophilum - FSC
      Horkelia cuneata ssp. *sericea* - FSC
      Horkelia marinensis - FSC
      Layia carnosa - FE, SE
      Lessingia germanorum - FE, SE
      Lupinus tidestromii - FE, SE
      +*Gilia capitata* ssp. *chamissonis*
      +*Gilia millefoliata*

    4. *Monardella undulata*

C. Inland dune vegetation

    1b. *Erysimum capitatum* ssp. *angustatum* - FE, SE
      Oenothera deltoides ssp. *howellii* - FE, SE

2. Coastal scrub

A. Northern coastal scrub

    1b. *Delphinium bakeri* - FPE, SR
      Lilium maritimum - FC
      +*Lupinus latifolius* var. *dudleyi*

    3. *Lupinus eximius* - FSC

    4. *Cirsium andrewsii*
      Collinsia multicolor
      Piperia michaelii
      Sanicula hoffmannii

B. Southern coastal scrub

C. Sea-bluff coastal scrub

    1b. *Cirsium occidentale* var. *compactum* - FSC
      Grindelia hirsutula var. *maritima* - FSC
      Phacelia insularis var. *continentis* - FSC
      Silene verecunda ssp. *verecunda* - FSC
      +*Agrostis clivicola* var. *punta-reyesensis*
      +*Gilia capitata* ssp. *tomentosa*
      +*Piperia elegans* ssp. *decurtata*

    4. *Arabis blepharophylla*
      Ceanothus gloriosus var. *gloriosus*
      Erysimum franciscanum - FSC
      Hesperevax sparsiflora var. *brevifolia*
      +*Agrostis clivicola* var. *clivicola*

3. Chaparral

    1b. *Arctostaphylos auriculata*
      Arctostaphylos densiflora - FSC, SE
      Arctostaphylos imbricata - FPT, SE
      Arctostaphylos manzanita ssp. *laevigata*
      Arctostaphylos montaraensis - FSC
      Arctostaphylos pallida - FPT, SE
      Arctostaphylos stanfordiana ssp. *decumbens*
      Ceanothus confusus - FSC
      Ceanothus divergens - FSC
      Ceanothus foliosus var. *vineatus* - FSC
      Ceanothus masonii - FSC, SR
      Ceanothus sonomensis - FSC
      Malacothamnus hallii
      Plagiobothrys uncinatus - FSC

    3. *Calyptridium parryi* var. *hesseae*
      +*Arctostaphylos manzanita* ssp. *elegans*

    4. *Ceanothus purpureus*
      Dichondra occidentalis
      Lomatium repostum
      Malacothamnus arcuatus
      Malacothamnus helleri
      Orobanche valida ssp. *howellii*
      Plagiobothrys myosotoides

A. Chaparral burns

    4. *Calandrinia breweri*
      +*Malacothrix phaeocarpa*

4. Grassland

A. Native perennial grassland

    1b. *Amsinckia grandiflora* - FE, SE
      Astragalus clarianus - FE, ST
      Blepharizonia plumosa ssp. *plumosa*
      Fritillaria pluriflora - FSC
      Tracyina rostrata
      Trifolium amoenum - FE
      +*Calochortus argillosus*

    3. *Lessingia hololeuca*

    4. *Androsace elongata* ssp. *acuta*
      Fritillaria agrestis
      +*Allium peninsulare* var. *franciscanum*
      +*Microseris paludosa*

<u>Alkaline grassland</u>

    1a. *Tropidocarpum capparideum* - FSC
    1b. *Astragalus tener* var. *ferrisiae* - FSC
      Astragalus tener var. *tener*
      Atriplex cordulata - FSC
      Atriplex depressa
      Atriplex joaquiniana - FSC
      Cordylanthus mollis ssp. *hispidus* - FSC
      Cordylanthus palmatus - FE, SE
      Delphinium recurvatum - FSC
      Hemizonia parryi ssp. *congdonii* - FC
      Isocoma arguta – FSC
      +*Trifolium depauperatum* var. *hydrophilum*

    3. *Hordeum intercedens*

    4. *Atriplex coronata* var. *coronata*
      Thelypodum brachycarpum

---

* Derived from the inventory of the California Native Plant Society (CNPS) (Skinner and Pavlik 1994)

Key to CNPS list codes:

1a.	Presumed extinct
1b.	Rare, threatened, or endangered in California and elsewhere.
2.	Rare, threatened, or endangered in California but more common elsewhere.
3.	Possibly rare, but more information is needed.
4.	Distribution limited: a watch list
+	Proposed new addition to the CNPS inventory

Key to Federal and State List Codes:

FE	Federally listed as endangered	SE	State listed as endangered
FT	Federally listed as threatened	ST	State listed as threatened
FC	Federal listing candidate	SR	State listed as rare
FPE	Proposed for Federal listing as endangered		
FPT	Proposed for federal listing as threatened		
FSC	Federal species of special concern		

Sandy soil grassland

1a. *Eriogonum truncatum*

4. *Cryptantha hooveri*
   Linanthus grandiflorus

Serpentinite grassland

1b. *Acanthomintha duttonii* - FE, SE
   Calochortus tiburonensis - FT, ST
   Castilleja affinis ssp. *neglecta* - FE, ST
   Fritillaria biflora var. *ineziana*
   Lessingia arachnoidea - FSC
   Streptanthus niger - FE, SE

3. *Eriogonum luteolum* var. *caninum*

4. *Astragalus breweri*
   Linanthus ambiguus

Moist grassland

1a. *Plagiobothrys hystriculus*

1b. *Pleuropogon hooverianus* - FSC, SR
   Sidalcea oregana ssp. *hydrophila*

2. *Carex californica*

4. *Perideridia gairdneri* ssp. *gairdneri* - FSC

B. Native annual forbland

1a. *Eschscholzia rhombipetala* - FSC

1b. *Madia radiata*

4. *Convolvulus simulans*
   +*Erodium macrophyllum*

C. Non-native annual grassland

D. Coastal prairie

1b. *Blennosperma nanum* var. *robustum* - FSC, SR
   chorizanthe valida - FE, SE
   Erigeron supplex - FSC
   Fritillaria lanceolata var. *tristulis*
   Fritillaria liliacea - FSC
   Holocarpha macradenia - FC, SE
   Limnanthes douglasii ssp. *sulphurea* - FSC, SE
   Plagiobothrys diffusus - FSC, SE
   Sanicula maritima - FSC, SR
   Triphysaria floribunda - FSC

3. *Hemizonia congesta* ssp. *leucocephala*
   Plagiobothrys chorisianus var. *chorisianus*

5. Coastal coniferous forest

A. Redwood forest

4. *Elymus californicus*

B. Closed-cone coniferous forest

1b. *Ceanothus gloriosus* var. *porrectus* - FSC
   Cupressus goveniana ssp. *pigmaea* - FSC
   Pinus radiata - FSC

C. North coast coniferous forest

2. *Boschniakia hookeri*

4. *Piperia candida*
   Pityopus californicus
   +*Galium muricatum*

6. Mixed evergreen forest

A. Central California mixed evergreen forest

1b. +*Quercus parvula* var. *tamalpaisensis*

3. +*Viburnum ellipticum*

4. *Cypripedium montanum*
   Dirca occidentalis
   Ribes victoris

7. Oak woodland

A. Coast live oak woodland

1b. *Clarkia concinna* var. *automixa*

4. *Amsinckia lunaris*
   Isocoma menziesii var. *diabolica*

B. Valley oak woodland

C. Foothill oak woodland

8. Cliffs and rock outcrops

A. Cliffs

3. +*Streptanthus tortuosus* var. *suffrutescens*

4. *Arabis modesta*

B. Rock outcrops

1b. *Arctostaphylos virgata*
   Coreopsis hamiltonii - FSC
   Penstemon newberryi var. *sonomensis*
   Phacelia phacelioides - FSC
   Sanicula saxatilis - FSC, SR
   Streptanthus callistus - FSC
   Streptanthus glandulosus var. *hoffmanii* - FSC
   Streptanthus hispidus - FSC

3. *Erigeron biolettii*
   Monardella antonina ssp. *antonina*

4. *Antirrhinum virga*
   Arabis oregona
   Arctostaphylos hispidula
   Navarretia subuligera

Serpentinite outcrops

1a. *Arctostaphylos hookeri* ssp. *franciscana* - FSC

1b. *Allium sharsmithae*
   Arctostaphylos bakeri ssp. *bakeri* - SR
   Arctostaphylos bakeri ssp. *sublaevis*
   Arctostaphylos hookeri ssp. *montana* - FSC
   Arctostaphylos hookeri ssp. *ravenii* - FE, SE
   Astragalus rattanii var. *jepsonianus*
   Calochortus raichei - FSC
   Campanula sharsmithiae - FSC
   Ceanothus ferrisae - FE
   Chlorogalum pomeridianum var. *minus*
   Clarkia franciscana - FE, SE

---

* Derived from the inventory of the California Native Plant Society (CNPS) (Skinner and Pavlik 1994)

Key to CNPS list codes:

1a.	Presumed extinct
1b.	Rare, threatened, or endangered in California and elsewhere.
2.	Rare, threatened, or endangered in California but more common elsewhere.
3.	Possibly rare, but more information is needed.
4.	Distribution limited: a watch list
+	Proposed new addition to the CNPS inventory

Key to Federal and State List Codes:

FE	Federally listed as endangered	SE	State listed as endangered
FT	Federally listed as threatened	ST	State listed as threatened
FC	Federal listing candidate	SR	State listed as rare
FPE	Proposed for Federal listing as endangered		
FPT	Proposed for federal listing as threatened		
FSC	Federal species of special concern		

Table 1.4 (continued) Rare Plant Species* Found in the Nine Counties Adjacent to the San Francisco Bay Estuary, by Plant Community or Ecotone

Cordylanthus nidularius - FC, SR
Cordylanthus tenuis ssp. *capillaris* - FE, SR
Cryptantha clevelandii var. *dissita*
Dudleya setchellii - FE
Erigeron angustatus
Erigeron serpentinus
Eriogonum nervulosum - FSC
Fritillaria falcata - FSC
Hesperolinon bicarpellatum - FSC
Hesperolinon breweri - FSC
Hesperolinon congestum - FT, ST
Hesperolinon drymarioides - FSC
Hesperolinon serpentinum
Lessingia micradenia var. *glabrata* - FSC
Lessingia micradenia var. *micradenia* - FSC
Madia hallii - FSC
Navarretia rosulata
Sidalcea hickmanii ssp. *viridis* - FSC
Streptanthus albidus ssp. *albidus* - FE
Streptanthus albidus ssp. *peramoenus* - FC
Streptanthus batrachopus - FSC
Streptanthus brachiatus ssp. *brachiatus* - FC
Streptanthus brachiatus ssp. *hoffmanii* - FC
Streptanthus glandulosus ssp. *pulchellus*
Streptanthus morrisonii ssp. *elatus* - FC
Streptanthus morrisonii ssp. *hirtiflorus* - FC
Streptanthus morrisonii ssp. *kruckebergii* - FSC
Streptanthus morrisonii ssp. *morrisonii* - FSC
+*Hoita strobilina*
+*Streptanthus breweri* var. *hesperidis*

3. *Cardamine pachystigma* var. *dissectifolia*
    +*Streptanthus glandulosus* var. *sonomensis*

4. *Acanthomintha lanceolata*
    Asclepias solanoana
    Aspidotis carlotta-halliae
    Calamagrostis ophitidis
    Calyptridium quadripetalum
    Campanula exigua
    Clarkia breweri
    Collomia diversifolia
    Cordylanthus tenuis ssp. *brunneus*
    Eriogonum argillosum
    Eriogonum ternatum
    Eriogonum tripodum
    Fritillaria purdyi
    Galium andrewsii ssp. *gatense*
    Lomatium ciliolatum var. *hooveri*
    Navarretia jepsonii
    +*Ceanothus jepsonii* var. *albiflorus*
    +*Streptanthus barbiger*

Granite and sandstone outcrops

4. *Arctostaphylos regismontana*

Volcanic outcrops

1b. *Eriastrum brandegeae* - FSC

4. *Madia nutans*

9. Riparian vegetation

1b. *Juglans californica* var. *hindsii* - FSC
    +*Triteleia lugens*

4. *Astragalus rattanii* ssp. *rattanii*

10. Freshwater vegetation

A. Freshwater marsh

1a. *Castilleja uliginosa* - FSC, SE

1b. *Alopecurus aequalis* var. *sonomensis* - FE
    Arenaria paludicola - FE, SE
    Campanula californica - FSC
    Carex albida - FE, SE
    Lilium pardalinum ssp. *pitkinense* - FE, SE
    Potentilla hickmanii - FPE, SE
    Rhynchospora californica - FSC
    Sidalcea calycosa ssp. *rhizomata*
    Sidalcea oregana ssp. *valida* - FE, SE

2. *Calamagrostis crassiglumis* - FSC
    Carex comosa
    Carex leptalea
    Rhynchospora globularis var. *globularis*

3. *Equisetum palustre*

4. *Calamagrostis bolanderi*
    Rhynchospora alba
    +*Zigadenus micranthus* var. *fontanus*

B. Limnetic vegetation

2. *Potamogeton filiformis*
    Potamogeton zosteriformis

4. *Azolla mexicana*
    Ranunculus lobbii

C. Vernal pools

1b. *Blennosperma bakeri* - FE, SE
    Gratiola heterosepala - SE
    Lasthenia burkei - FE, SE
    Lasthenia conjugens - FE
    Legenere limosa - FSC
    Limnanthes vinculans - FE, SE
    Navarretia leucocephala ssp. *bakeri*
    Navarretia leucocephala ssp. *pauciflora* - FE, ST
    Navarretia leucocephala ssp. *plieantha* - FE, SE
    Neostapfia colusana - FT, SE
    Tuctoria mucronata - FE, SE

2. *Downingia pusilla*

3. *Myosurus minimus* ssp. *apus* - FSC
    Pogogyne douglasii ssp. *parviflora*

---

* Derived from the inventory of the California Native Plant Society (CNPS) (Skinner and Pavlik 1994)

Key to CNPS list codes:

1a.	Presumed extinct
1b.	Rare, threatened, or endangered in California and elsewhere.
2.	Rare, threatened, or endangered in California but more common elsewhere.
3.	Possibly rare, but more information is needed.
4.	Distribution limited: a watch list
+	Proposed new addition to the CNPS inventory

Key to Federal and State List Codes:

FE	Federally listed as endangered	SE	State listed as endangered
FT	Federally listed as threatened	ST	State listed as threatened
FC	Federal listing candidate	SR	State listed as rare
FPE	Proposed for Federal listing as endangered		
FPT	Proposed for federal listing as threatened		
FSC	Federal species of special concern		

4. *Eryngium aristulatum* var. *hooveri* - FC
   Psilocarphus brevissimus var. *multiflorus*
   Psilocarphus tenellus var. *globiferus*

D. Thermal springs

1b. *Dichanthelium lanuginosum* var. *thermale* - FSC, SE
   Plagiobothrys strictus - FE, ST
   Poa napensis - FP, SE

11. Anthropogenic environments

A. Agricultural

B. Urban-suburban

12. Coastal marsh

A. Brackish marsh

1b. *Aster lentus* - FSC
   Cirsium hydrophilum var. *hydrophilum* - FE
   Cordylanthus mollis ssp. *mollis* - FE, SR
   Lathyrus jepsonii var. *jepsonii* - FSC
   Lilaeopsis masonii - FSC, SR

2. *Limosella subulata*

B. Saltmarsh

1b. *Castilleja ambigua* ssp. *humboldtiensis* - FSC
   Cordylanthus maritimus ssp. *palustris* - FSC
   Suaeda californica - FE

3. *Polygonum marinense* - FSC

4. *Eleocharis parvula*
   Grindelia stricta var. *angustifolia*

13. Ecotones

A. Grassland-oak woodland

1b. *Helianthella castanea* - FSC
   Monardella villosa ssp. *globosa*

4. *Linanthus acicularis*

B. Grassland-rock outcrops

1b. *Balsamorhiza macrolepis* var. *macrolepis*
   Clarkia concinna ssp. *raichei* - FSC
   Layia septentrionalis
   Pentachaeta bellidiflora - FE, SE
   Stebbinsoseris decipiens - FSC

4. *Micropus amphibolus*

C. Mixed evergreen-chaparral

1b. *Arctostaphylos andersonii* - FSC
   Arctostaphylos canescens ssp. *sonomensis*
   Cupressus abramsiana - FE, SE
   Eriogonum nudum var. *decurrens*
   Lupinus sericatus
   Penstemon rattanii var. *kleei*

4. *Calystegia collina* ssp. *oxyphylla* - FSC
   Erythronium helenae

Lilium rubescens
Monardella viridis ssp. *viridis*

D. Mixed evergreen-serpentinite outcrops

4. *Calochortus umbellatus*

E. Rock outcrops-riparian

1b. *Delphinium californicum* ssp. *interius* - FSC

4. *Trichostema rubisepalum*

F. Serpentinite outcrops-riparian (including serpentine seeps)

1b. *Cirsium fontinale* var. *campylon* - FSC
   Cirsium fontinale var. *fontinale* - FE, SE
   Cirsium hydrophilum var. *vaseyi* - FSC

4. *Astragalus clevelandii*
   Cypripedium californicum
   Delphinium uliginosum
   Helianthus exilis
   Mimulus nudatus
   Senecio clevelandii var. *clevelandii*

G. Coastal coniferous forest-riparian

1b. *Pedicularis dudleyi* - FSC, SR

4. *Cypripedium fasciculatum* - FSC
   Pleuropogon refractus

H. Oak woodland-serpentinite outcrops

1b. *Eriophyllum latilobum* - FE, SE

I. Oak woodland-chaparral

1b. *Calochortus pulchellus*

4. *Eriophyllum jepsonii*

J. Alkaline grassland-pans

1a. *Plagiobothrys glaber*
   Plagiobothrys mollis var. *vestitus* - FSC

K. Coastal coniferous forest-coastal prairie

1b. *Sidalcea malachroides*

L. Freshwater marsh-riparian

1b. *Sagittaria sanfordii* - FSC

2. *Hibiscus lasiocarpus*

M. Grassland-southern coastal scrub

2. *Senecio aphanactis*

N. Coastal prairie-northern coastal scrub

1b. *Delphinium luteum* - FPE, SR

O. Grassland-chaparral

1b. *Clarkia imbricata* - FE, SE
   Horkelia tenuiloba

P. Northern coastal scrub-riparian

4. *Veratrum fimbriatum*

---

* Derived from the inventory of the California Native Plant Society (CNPS) (Skinner and Pavlik 1994)

Key to CNPS list codes:

1a. Presumed extinct
1b. Rare, threatened, or endangered in California and elsewhere.
2. Rare, threatened, or endangered in California but more common elsewhere.
3. Possibly rare, but more information is needed.
4. Distribution limited: a watch list
+ Proposed new addition to the CNPS inventory

Key to Federal and State List Codes:

FE	Federally listed as endangered	SE State listed as endangered
FT	Federally listed as threatened	ST State listed as threatened
FC	Federal listing candidate	SR State listed as rare

FPE Proposed for Federal listing as endangered
FPT Proposed for federal listing as threatened
FSC Federal species of special concern

References

Abbott, P. L. 1984. The origin of vernal pool topography, San Diego County, California. *In:* S. Jain and P. Moyle (eds). Vernal pools and intermittent streams: A symposium sponsored by the Institute of Ecology Univ. of Calif., Davis May 9 and 10, 1981, Institute of Ecology Publication # 28, Davis, Calif. UC Davis Institute of Ecology. pp. 18-29.

Adam, P. 1990. Saltmarsh ecology. Cambridge, UK: Cambridge Univ. Press.

Atwater, B. F. and D. F. Belknap. 1980. Tidal wetland deposits of the Sacramento-San Joaquin Delta, California. *In:* M. Field, A. Bouma, I. Colburn, R. Douglas and J. Ingle (eds). Quaternary depositional environments of the Pacific Coast, Pacific Coast Paleogeography Symposium 4. Los Angeles: Pacific Section Society of Economic Paleontologists and Minerologists. pp. 89-103.

Bakker, E. 1984. An island called California: an ecological introduction to its natural communities, 2nd edition. Berkeley: UC Press.

Barbour, M. G. and A. F. Johnson. 1977. Beach and dune. *In:* M. Barbour and J. Major (eds). Terrestrial vegetation of Calif. New York: Wiley. pp. 223-261.

Barbour, M. G. and J. Major (editors). 1977. Terrestrial vegetation of California. New York: Wiley.

Bates, L. A. 1977. Soil survey of Solano County, California. Washington DC: USDA Soil Conservation Service.

Berg, A. W. 1990. Formation of Mima mounds: a seismic hypothesis. Geology 18: 281-4.

Biswell, H. H. 1974. Effects of fire on chaparral. *In:* T. Kozlowski and C. Ahlgren (eds). Fire and ecosystems. New York: Academic Press. pp. 321-364.

Bowcutt, F. 1996. A floristic study of Delta Meadows River Park, Sacramento County, California. Madrono 43: 417-431.

Bryant, E. 1848. What I saw in California (1985 reproduction by Univ. of Nebraska Press, Lincoln, Nebraska).

Chapman, V. J. 1960. Salt marshes and salt deserts of the world. London: Leonard Hill.

Cooper, W. S. 1926. Vegetational development upon alluvial fans in the vicinity of Palo Alto, California. Ecology 7: 1-21.

Critchfield, W. B. 1971. Profiles of California vegetation. USDA Forest Service Research Paper PSW-76. Berkeley: US Forest Service.

Dalquest, W. W. and V. B. Scheffer. 1942. The origin of the Mima mounds of western Washington. Journal of Geology 50: 68-84.

Donley, M. W., S. Allan, P. Caro, and C. P. Patton. 1979. Atlas of California. Culver City, Calif.: Pacific Book Center.

Ellen, S. D. and C. M. Wentworth. 1995. Hillside materials and slopes of the San Francisco Bay region. US Geological Survey Professional Paper 1357. Denver: US Geological Survey.

Faber, P. M. (editor). 1997. California's wild gardens: A living legacy. Sacramento: Calif. Native Plant Society.

Felton, E. L. 1965. California's many climates. Palo Alto, Calif.: Pacific Books.

Ferren, W. R., Jr. and E. M. Gevirtz. 1990. Restoration and creation of vernal pools: cookbook recipes or complex science? *In:* D. Ikeda and R. Schlising (eds). Vernal pool plants: their habitat and biology. Chico, Calif.: Calif. State Univ., Chico. pp. 147-178.

Fiedler, P. L. and R. A. Leidy. 1987. Plant communities of Ring Mountain Preserve, Marin County, California. Madrono 34: 173-192.

Gilliam, H. 1962. Weather of the San Francisco Bay region. Berkeley: UC Press.

Griffin, J. R. 1977. Oak woodland. *In:* M. Barbour and J. Major (eds). Terrestrial vegetation of California. New York: Wiley. pp. 383-415.

Hanes, W. T.; B. Hecht; and L. P. Stromberg. 1990. Water relationships of vernal pools in the Sacramento Region, California. *In:* D. Ikeda and R. Schlising (eds). Vernal pool plants: their habitat and biology. Chico, Calif.: Calif. State Univ., Chico. pp. 49-60.

Harris, T. 1991. Death in the marsh. Covelo, Calif.: Island Press.

Havlik, N. 1974. The vegetation of the "other coast". Fremontia 2: 14-19.

Heady, H. F. 1977. Valley grassland. *In:* M. Barbour and J. Major (eds). Terrestrial vegetation of California. New York: Wiley. pp. 491-514.

Heady, H. F.; T. C. Foin; M. M. Hektner; D. W. Taylor; M. G. Barbour; and W. J. Barry. 1977. Coastal prairie and northern coastal scrub. *In:* M. Barbour and J. Major (eds). Terrestrial vegetation of California. New York: Wiley. pp. 733-760.

Hickman, J. C. (editor). 1993. The Jepson manual: higher plants of California. Berkeley: UC Press.

Holland, R. F. and S. K. Jain. 1977. Vernal pools. *In:* M. Barbour and J. Major (eds). Terrestrial vegetation of California. New York: Wiley. pp. 515-533.

Holland, V. L. and D. J. Keil. 1995. California vegetation. Dubuque, Iowa: Kendall/Hunt.

Holstein, G. 1984a. Water balance climate and vegetation form and function. PhD dissertation, Univ. of Calif., Davis, Calif.

Holstein, G. 1984b. California riparian forests: deciduous islands in an evergreen sea. *In:* R. Warner and K. Hendrix (eds). California riparian systems: ecology, conservation, and productive management. Berkeley: UC Press. pp. 2-22.

Hoover, M. B., H. E. Rensch, E. G. Rensch, and W. N. Abeloe. Historic spots in California, 3rd edition. Stanford, Calif.: Stanford Univ. Press.

Jennings, C. W. 1977. Geologic map of California. Reston, Va.: US Geological Survey.

Johnson, S; G. Haslam; and R. Dawson. 1993. The great Central Valley: California's heartland. Berkeley: UC Press.

Keeley, J. E. and S. C. Keeley. 1988. Chaparral. *In:* M. Barbour and W. Billings (eds). North American terrestrial vegetation. Cambridge, UK: Cambridge Univ. Press. pp. 165-207.

Kruckeberg, A. R. 1984. California serpentines: flora, vegetation, geology, soils, and management problems. Berkeley: UC Press.

Kuchler, A. W. 1964. Potential natural vegetation of the United States. American Geographical Society Special Publication # 36. New York: American Geographical Society.

Kusler, J. A. and M. E. Kentula (editors). 1990. Wetland creation and restoration: The status of the science. Covelo, Calif.: Island Press.

Long, S. P. and C. F. Mason. 1983. Saltmarsh ecology. Glasgow: Blackie.

Louderback, G. D. 1951. Geologic history of San Francisco Bay. *In:* O. Jenkins (ed). Geologic guidebook of the San Francisco Bay counties: Calif. Division of Mines Bulletin 154. San Francisco: Calif. Division of Mines. pp. 75-94.

Mayer, K. E. and W. F. Laudenslayer, Jr. 1988. A guide to wildlife habitats in California. Sacramento: Calif. Dept. Fish and Game.

McKelvey, S. D. 1955. Botanical exploration of the Trans-Mississippi West: 1790-1850. Jamaica Plain, Mass.: The Arnold Arboretum of Harvard Univ.

Mooney, H. A. 1977. Southern coastal scrub. *In:* M. Barbour and J. Major (eds). Terrestrial vegetation of California. New York: Wiley. pp. 471-489.

Mooney, H. A. and P. C. Miller. 1985. Chaparral. *In:* B. Chabot and H. Mooney (eds). Physiological ecology of North American plant communities. London: Chapman and Hall. pp. 213-231.

Munz, P. A. and D. D. Keck. 1959. A California flora. Berkeley: UC Press.

Norris, R. M. and R. W. Webb. 1990. Geology of California, 2nd edition. New York: Wiley.

Radbruch, D. H. 1957. Areal and engineering geology of the Oakland West Quadrangle, California. Miscellaneous gelogical investigations map 1-239. Washington DC: US Geological Survey.

Safford, H. D. 1995. Woody vegetation and succession in the Garin Woods, Hayward Hills, Alameda County, California. Madrono: 42: 470-489.

San Francisco Estuary Project (SFEP). 1991a. Status and trends report on wetlands and related habitats in the San Francisco Estuary. Oakland: San Francisco Estuary Project.

_____. 1991b. Status and trends report on wildlife of the San Francisco Estuary. Oakland: San Francisco Estuary Project.

Sawyer, J. O.; D. A. Thornburgh; and J. R. Griffin. 1977. Mixed evergreen forest. *In:* M. Barbour and J. Major (eds). Terrestrial vegetation of California. New York: Wiley. pp. 359-381.

Sawyer, J. O. and T. Keeler-Wolf. 1995. A manual of California vegetation. Sacramento: Calif. Native Pant Society.

Shuford, W. D. 1993. The Marin County breeding bird atlas: a distributional and natural history of coastal California birds. Bolinas, Calif.: Bushtit Books.

Skinner, M. W. and B. M. Pavlik. 1994. California Native Plant Society's inventory of rare and endangered vascular plants of California, Special Publication #1, 5th ed. Sacramento: Calif. Native Plant Society.

Smith, R. L. 1980. Alluvial scrub vegetation of the San Gabriel River floodplain, California. Madrono 27: 126-138.

Stebbins, G. L. and M. S. Walters. 1949. Artificial and natural hybrids in the Gramineae, tribe Hordeae. III. Hybrids involving *Elymus condensatus* and *E. triticoides*. American Journal of Botany: 36: 291-301.

Thorne, R. F. 1984. Are California's vernal pools unique? *In:* Jain, S. and P. Moyle (eds). Vernal pools and intermittent streams: A symposium sponsored by the Institute of Ecology University of Calif., Davis May 9 and 10, 1981, Institute of Ecology Publication #28. Davis, Calif.: UC Davis Institute of Ecology. pp. 1-8.

Wahrhaftig, C. and J. H. Birman. 1965. The Quaternary of the Pacific Mountain System in California. *In:* H. Wright and D. Frey (eds). The Quaternary of the United States. Princeton, NJ: Princeton Univ. Press. pp. 299-340.

Wahrhaftig, C.; S. W. Stine; and N. K. Huber. 1993. Quaternary geologic map of the San Francisco Bay 4" x 6" quadrangle, United States. Denver: US Geological Survey.

Wainwright, T. C. and M. G. Barbour. 1984. Characteristics of mixed evergreen forest in the Sonoma Mountains of California. Madrono 31: 219-230.

Waisel, Y. 1972. Biology of halophytes. New York: Academic Press.

Walter, H. 1979. Vegetation of the earth and ecological systems of the geo-biosphere, 2nd edition. New York: Springer-Verlag.

Wernstedt, F. L. 1972. World climatic data. Lemont, Pa.: Climatic Data Press.

Wester, L. 1981. Composition of native grasslands in the San Joaquin Valley, California. Madrono 28:

231-241.

Wieslander, A. E. and H. A. Jensen. 1945. Vegetation types of California. Berkeley, Calif.: US Forest Service.

Zeiner, D. C.; W. F. Laudenslayer, Jr.; K. E. Mayer; and M. White. California's wildlife: Volume III: Mammals. Sacramento: Calif. Dept. Fish and Game.

Zinke, P. J. 1977. The redwood forest and associated north coast forests. *In:* M. Barbour and J. Major (eds). Terrestrial vegetation of California. New York: Wiley. pp. 679-698.

2

Estuarine Fish and Associated Invertebrates

Opossum Shrimp

Neomysis mercedis

Bruce Herbold

General Information

The opossum shrimp is a native mysid shrimp that is an important food for many estuarine fish, especially young striped bass. Since 1994, their role of dominant planktonic shrimp has been overwhelmed by the introduced species, *Acanthomysis* (Orsi and Mecum 1996).

Reproduction

The common name of the opossum shrimp derives from the fact that females carry their eggs and young in a pouch at the base of the last two pairs of legs. Young are released at a well-developed stage. Fecundity is related both to adult size and season (Heubach 1969).

Reproduction is continuous but the rate is strongly controlled by temperature and food supply. Thus, the rate is high during spring and summer months and slows down as temperature and insolation decline. The wintertime population is composed largely of large adults, whose greater fecundity allows rapid development of high densities as temperatures and phytoplankton densities rise. The autumn decline in density has been variously attributed to seasonal changes in high temperature, low dissolved oxygen, predation, and food supply (Turner and Heubach 1966, Heubach 1969, Siegfried et al. 1979, Orsi and Knutson 1979).

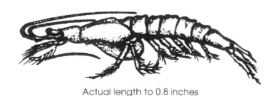

Actual length to 0.8 inches

ARO. M. Roper

Food and Feeding

The diet of *N. mercedis* varies with size. At release, young shrimp eat mostly phytoplankton and rotifers. Adult diets include phytoplankton and rotifers but the diet shifts more to copepods, particularly *Eurytemora affinis* (Herbold et al. 1992).

Distribution

N. mercedis is found in greatest abundance in Suisun Bay and the western Delta, although it occurs as far upstream as Sacramento, the lower reaches of the Mokelumne River, and in the San Joaquin River to above Stockton.

Population Status and Influencing Factors

During most of the 1980s, the opossum shrimp population varied considerably, but remained at a lower level of abundance than existed in the early 1970s. Opossum shrimp abundance fell dramatically after 1986 and remained at very low levels from 1990 to 1993 (CDFG 1994). As a general trend, opossum shrimp populations have declined substantially in Suisun Bay, yet they have occasionally rebounded to high levels (BDOC 1993).

Reasons for the system-wide declines of several zooplankton taxa in the Bay-Delta Estuary are not known. Although the declines occurred at about the same time as declines in phytoplankton and various fish species, no cause-and-effect relationships have been established (CDWR 1992). However, several factors have been identified which are believed to have some influence on the decline of zooplankton in the Estuary.

Decrease in food supply has been associated with the decline in abundance of rotifers and the copepod, *E. affinis*. The decline of rotifers in the Delta appears to be strongly associated with declining concentrations of chlorophyll *a*, which formerly characterized the areas of greatest rotifer abundance (Herbold et al. 1992). However, chlorophyll and many zooplankton species have similar spatial distributions, and correlations between the two groups can arise through movement of the entrapment zone in the Estuary. Also, while it is commonly assumed that chlorophyll is a good measure of food availability for zooplankton, *E. affinis* can subsist on detrital matter and requires larger particles than those that make up total chlorophyll. In addition, small zooplankton could provide food for many of the larger zooplankton species (Kimmerer 1992). Consistently low *E. affinis* abundance in recent years has been named as a factor that has probably contributed to the decline of opossum shrimp (Herbold et al. 1992).

Introduced species have also been named as a potential cause for the decline in zooplankton abundance. For example, the introduction of *Sinocalanus* has been identified as a possible cause of the decline in abundance of *E. affinis* (Kimmerer 1992), although the introduced copepod does not have the same habitat requirements as the native copepods (NHI 1992). However, based on the known feeding habits of a related species of *Sinocalanus*, *S. doerrii* may prey on native copepods (Herbold et al. 1992). In addition, predation by the introduced Asian clam, *Potamocorbula amurensis*, has been suggested as a factor in the decline of rotifer (Herbold et al. 1992) and *E. affinis* populations. *E. affinis* abundance in Suisun Bay decreased substantially when the clam became abundant there in 1988 (CDWR 1992). Since 1994 *Neomysis* abundance has dropped to less than that of an introduced species of mysid shrimp which has increased in abundance (Orsi 1996). Competition with both the clam and new shrimp are likely to prevent re-establishment of *Neomysis* at the levels of their former abundance.

The decline in the abundance of opossum shrimp and other zooplankton species (e.g., *E. affinis*) that are found in the entrapment zone in relatively high abundances has been correlated with Delta outflow. It is presumed that low outflow reduces opossum shrimp abundance by: (1) restricting the entrapment zone to deeper, more upstream channels which are less likely to promote high densities of opossum shrimp; and (2) producing weaker landward currents along the bottom so that the ability of opossum shrimp transported downstream to return to the entrapment zone is reduced. It has also been presumed that larger numbers of opossum shrimp may be exported through the Central Valley Project and State Water Project pumps as a result of the increased proportion of inflow diverted during drought years when the entrapment zone is upstream in the Estuary. The location of the entrapment zone within the lower river channels during dry years increases the vulnerability of opossum shrimp to such displacement (Herbold et al. 1992). However, analyses by Kimmerer (1992) suggest that exports by the water projects are not a major source of losses for opossum shrimp and *E. affinis* populations, primarily due to the small percentage of entrapment zone volume (and entrapment zone organisms) diverted. Depending on the timing, location, and quantity of withdrawals, in-Delta water diversions, whose net consumption is on the same order of export flows, may result in

a higher rate of loss to resident zooplankton populations than export pumping.

Pollutants may be another factor in the decline of zooplankton in the upper Estuary. For example, rice herbicides have been shown to be toxic to opossum shrimp (CDWR 1992). However, rice herbicides are largely confined to the Sacramento River, not the entire Estuary. No Estuary-wide decline in planktonic crustaceans have been associated with the timing of herbicide occurrence in the river (NHI 1992).

Trophic Levels

The opossum shrimp is a primary and secondary consumer.

Proximal Species

Predators: Striped bass, longfin smelt, splittail.
Prey: Various copepods, various phytoplankton.
Competitors: *Potamocorbula amurensis*, *Acanthomysis* spp.

Good Habitat

Good habitat appears to be similar to that of Delta smelt; a well-dispersed area of open water with salinities in the range of 2 to 6 ppt for most of the year and clean, non-toxic over-wintering habitat in freshwater through the winter and early spring. Dead-end sloughs both in Suisun Marsh and upstream apparently serve as important refuges from predation during the annual period of low abundance and slow growth. With the advent of newly introduced competitors in the open waters of the Estuary it is possible that such refugia will become important for the year-round maintenance of opossum shrimp.

References

Bay-Delta Oversight Council (BDOC). 1993. Draft briefing paper on biological resources of the San Fran. Bay/Sac.-San Joaquin Delta Estuary. September 1993. 42 pp. plus appendices.

California Department of Fish and Game (CDFG). 1994. Comments on key issues of the State Water Resources Control Board's June workshop for review of standards for San Francisco Bay/Sacramento-San Joaquin Delta Estuary. Presented by Perry L. Herrgesell, Chief of Bay-Delta and Special Water Projects Division, June 14, 1994. 68 pp.

California Department of Water Resources (CDWR). 1992. Bay-Delta fish resources. Ca. Dept. of Water Res. Sacramento, Ca. July 1992. 46 pp. (WRINT-DWR-30)

Herbold, B., P.B. Moyle and A. Jassby. 1992. Status and trends report on aquatic resources in the San Francisco Estuary. San Francisco Estuary Project. Public Report. March 1992. 257 pp. plus appendices.

Heubach, W. 1969. *Neomysis awatchschensis* in the Sacramento-San Joaquin Estuary. Linmol. Oceanogr. 14: 533-546.

Kimmerer, W. 1992. An evaluation of existing data in the entrapment zone of the San Francisco Bay Estuary. Interagency Ecological Studies Program for the Sac./San Joaquin Estuary. Tech. Rept. 33. September 1992. FS/BIO-IATR/92-93. 49 pp.

Natural Heritage Institute (NHI). 1992. Causes of decline in estuarine fish species. Presented to the State Wat. Res. Contr. Bd. Water Rights Phase of the Bay Delta Estuary Proceedings. St. Wat. Res. Contr. Bd. exhibit WRINT-NHI-9. 29 p plus appendices.

Orsi, J.J. and A.C Knutson. 1979. The role of mysid shrimp in the Sacramento-San Joaquin Estuary and factors affecting their abundance and distribution. *In:* T.J. Conmos (ed). San Francisco Bay: The urbanized estuary, Pac. Div., Am. Assoc. Adv. Sci., San Francisco, Ca. pp. 401-408.

Orsi, J.J. and W.L. Mecum. 1996. Food limitation as the probable cause of a long-term decline in the abundance of *Neomysis mercedis,* the opossum shrimp, in the Sacramento-San Joaquin estuary. *In*: J.T. Hollibaugh (ed). San Francisco Bay; The ecosystem. Pacific Division, Amer. Assoc. for the Advancement of Science, San Francisco, Ca. pp. 375-402,

Siegfried, C.A., M.E. Kopache and A.W. Knight. 1979. The distribution and abundance of *Neomysis mercedis* in relation to the entrapment zone in the western Sacramento-San Joaquin Delta. Trans. Am. Fish. Soc. 108: 262-270.

Turner, J.L. and W. Heubach. 1966. Distribution and concentration of *Neomysis awatchschensis* in the Sacramento-San Joaquin Delta. *In:* D.W. Kelley (ed). Ecological studies of the Sac.-San Joaquin Delta. Ca. Dept. Fish and Game, Fish Bull. No. 133: 105-112.

Dungeness Crab

Cancer magister

Robert N. Tasto

General Information

Dungeness crab has been the object of an immensely popular commercial and recreational fishery in the San Francisco region since 1848. The San Francisco fishery, which occurs exclusively outside the Golden Gate, was long a mainstay of statewide commercial landings. However, beginning in the early 1960s, it underwent a severe and longterm decline which persisted until the mid-1980s. The principal causes of the decline have been related to changes in ocean climate, increased predation, and possibly pollution (Wild and Tasto 1983). Landings in the past decade have rebounded to some extent and are generally able to accomodate local market demand, but the northern California fishery (Eureka and Crescent City) continues to be the major provider of Dungeness crabs throughout the rest of California. The value of the Dungeness crab resource extends beyond the traditional economic return to the fishermen, seafood processors, and retail markets, as it is an important element in the tourism industry of San Francisco.

California commercial and recreational fishing regulations pertaining to Dungeness crab have been designed to protect this species from over-harvesting. The standard commercial fishing gear is a baited 3.5-foot diameter metal trap, weighing 60 to 120 pounds (Warner 1992). California regulations set a 6.25-inch carapace width (cw) size limit, prohibit the take of female crabs, and, like most states, have established a specific fishing season to protect reproducing and egg-bearing crabs. A limited recreational fishery allows the take of female crabs and has a smaller size restriction (5.75 inches cw); a 10-crab bag limit is placed on the sportfishers. Recreational gear consists of a variety of traps, hoops, and nets of different sizes, shapes, and materials. It is currently

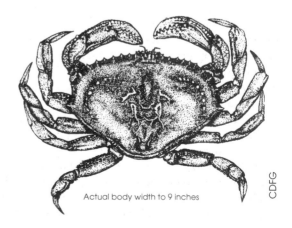

Actual body width to 9 inches

CDFG

illegal to catch Dungeness crab of any size in San Francisco Bay.

Reproduction

Mating occurs in nearshore coastal waters, from March through May, between hard-shelled males and recently molted, soft-shelled females. Fertilized eggs are extruded in the fall and lay protected beneath the female's abdominal flap in a sponge-like mass until hatching occurs from late December to mid-January (Wild and Tasto 1983). Fecundity ranges from 500,000 to 2,000,000 eggs, depending upon the size of the female (Warner 1992). *C. magister* is capable of about four broods over its reproductive life span (Hines 1991).

Growth and Development

Dungeness crab life stages include the egg, larval, juvenile, and adult. Dungeness crab eggs range in diameter from 0.016 to 0.024 inches (Warner 1992). There are a total of six larval stages (five zoeae and one megalopa) which spend about 3 to 4 months in both nearshore and offshore coastal waters; larval timing is believed to coincide with peak plankton production (Hines 1991). Late-stage megalopae, which have returned to the coast, bays, and estuaries via ocean currents and other mechanisms, settle onto relatively open sandy areas (Oresanz and Gallucci 1988) and subsequently metamorphose to the first bottom-dwelling instar stage generally between April and June. It is at this stage that the young crabs enter San Francisco Bay in large numbers, relative to year-class strength, seemingly aided by strong bottom currents (Tasto 1983). San Francisco Bay-reared crabs molt more frequently than those juveniles found in the near coastal environment and reach sexual maturity (approximately 4 inches wide) after nearly one year (Wild and Tasto 1983). This rate of growth is substantially greater than that found in open areas along the Pacific coast and may be due to increased availability of food and/or overall warmer temperatures of estuaries (Tasto 1983, Gunderson et al. 1990, Wainwright and Armstrong 1993). It is believed that the large number of molts necessary to reach sexual maturity in an estuarine environment is due, in large part, to the demands of osmoregulation (Oresanz and Gallucci 1988).

Food and Feeding

Larval Dungeness crab in the water column are planktivorous, whereas the juvenile and adult crabs are opportunistic foragers on larger bottom-dwelling organisms. In the San Francisco Estuary, juvenile crabs have been shown to feed on clams, crustaceans, and small fishes (Tasto 1983). In Grays Harbor, Washington, juvenile crab diets consisted primarily of *Crangon* shrimp, juvenile fish, and bivalves (Gunderson et al. 1990). By comparison to other cancrid crabs, the small chelae of *C. magister* are better suited for soft-bodied, mobile prey found on sandy bottoms (Oresanz and Gallucci 1988). One study has suggested that size-specific feeding on clams in the laboratory was due to an attempt to minimize handling time of the prey in a competitive situation (Palacios and Armstrong 1990).

The most common predators on juvenile crabs within the San Francisco Estuary include bottom-feeding fishes such as starry flounder, English sole, Pacific tomcod, Pacific staghorn sculpin, white croaker, pile perch, sturgeon, and several elasmobranchs (sharks, skates, and rays) (Reilly 1983a). The principal predator on young-of-the-year Dungeness crab in Gray's Harbor Estuary was found to be the Pacific staghorn sculpin (Fernandez et al. 1993a). In addition, cannibalism is reported to occur among all age groups (Warner 1992).

Distribution

Dungeness crab range from the Aleutian Islands to Santa Barbara, but are rare south of Point Conception (Warner 1992). The pelagic larval forms are found distributed widely in both nearshore and offshore waters, but return to the coast, bays, and estuaries where the juvenile and adult stages are mostly found from the intertidal zone to approximately 300 feet (Hatfield 1983, Reilly 1983b, Warner 1992). San Francisco Bay, as is the case with other coastal estuaries, is an important nursery area for the offshore stock. The vast majority of individuals in the Bay are juveniles of a single year-class, having entered in the spring of one year and exited approximately 1 year later (Tasto 1983, McCabe et al. 1988). Juveniles are often found in tidal and navigational channels early in summer, but spread out over mudflats and into protected shoreline areas as they develop over the year (**Figures 2.1** and **2.2**).

Population Status and Influencing Factors

Few population estimates have been made on individual Dungeness crab stocks along the Pacific coast because there is significant variation in year-class strength, purportedly due to environmental conditions and density-dependent factors (Botsford and Hobbs 1995). However, commercial crab landings, monitored annually by state and, in some instances, federal resource agencies, appear to be a reliable indicator of relative abundance.

The most important factors affecting overall population numbers in the San Francisco area (i.e., Half Moon Bay to Bodega Bay) include ocean temperatures (hatching success), ocean currents (larval drift), predation, commercial fishing, and, possibly, pollution of nursery habitat (Wild and Tasto 1983). Although labo-

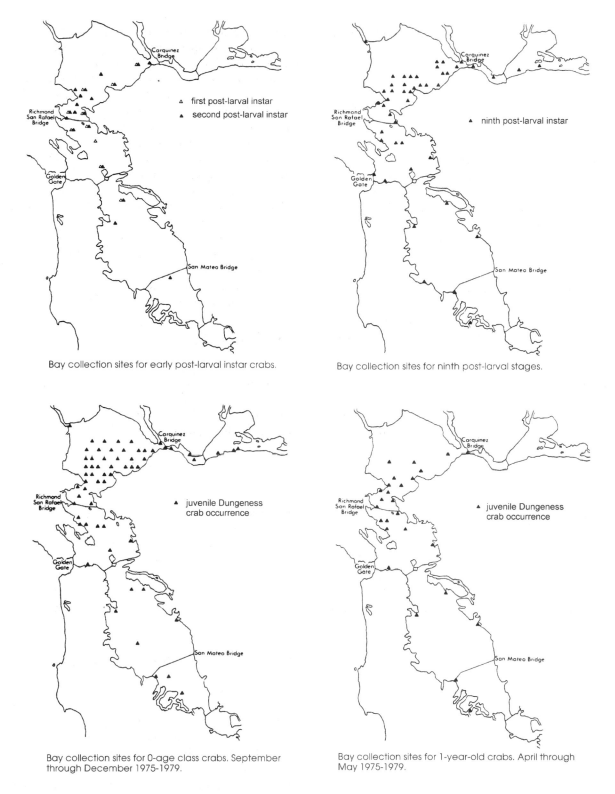

first post-larval instar
second post-larval instar

Bay collection sites for early post-larval instar crabs.

ninth post-larval instar

Bay collection sites for ninth post-larval stages.

juvenile Dungeness crab occurrence

Bay collection sites for 0-age class crabs. September through December 1975-1979.

juvenile Dungeness crab occurrence

Bay collection sites for 1-year-old crabs. April through May 1975-1979.

Figure 2.1 Seasonal Distribution of Juvenile Dungeness Crab Within San Francisco Bay (Tasto 1983)

ratory results show that cannibalism may be an important determinant in the abundance and structure of some populations (Fernandez et al. 1993b), year-class strength and recruitment to the fishery do not appear to be dependent upon success of any particular "critical" stage (McConnaughey and Armstrong 1990). Within the San Francisco Estuary, juvenile abundance varies considerably from year to year, but is often highest in San Pablo Bay and lowest in south Bay (Tasto 1983, CDFG 1987).

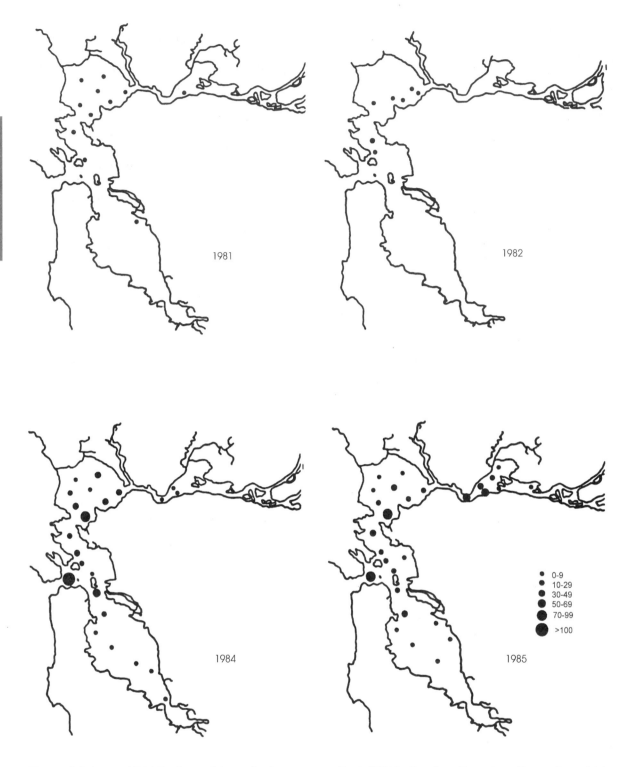

Figure 2.2 Annual Distribution of Juvenile Dungeness Crab Within the San Francisco Bay – Caught by Otter Trawl, May-December (CDFG 1987)

Trophic Levels

Larvae are planktivores making them primary consumers (phytoplankton) and secondary consumers (zooplankton). Juveniles and adults are higher order consumers.

Proximal Species

Predators: Chinook and coho salmon* (prey on late larval stages); *Carcinonemertes errans** (predator worm on egg masses); Dungeness crab (cannibalism by larger instars, principally females, on small juveniles), starry flounder, English sole, Pacific tomcod, Pacific staghorn sculpin, white croaker, brown smoothhound shark, and skate (prey on juveniles); and humans (commercial and recreational fishing for adults*).

* Generally takes place outside of San Francisco Bay.

Prey: Crustaceans, bivalves (clams), small fishes.

Good Habitat

Juvenile crabs appear to prefer sandy or sandy-mud substrate, but can be found on almost any bottom type (e.g., shell debris). Structurally complex habitats that provide protection from predation (e.g., high relief shell, eel grass, drift macroalgae, etc.) are favored over bare mud or open sand (Fernandez et al. 1993a, Iribarne et al. 1995, Eggleston and Armstrong 1995, McMillan et al. 1995).

Chemical and physical characteristics of the water column and sediment are also important habitat features. Juvenile Dungeness crab in the San Francisco Estuary seem to be somewhat intolerant of salinities lower than 10 ppt (Tasto 1983, CDFG 1987). Maximum growth appears to occur at 15°C or above (Kondzela and Shirley 1993, McMillan et al. 1995); and studies in Washington State have shown that juvenile crab have stable metabolic rates at elevated estuarine temperatures (e.g., 14 to 16°C), whereas older crabs were more stable at colder temperatures (Gutermuth and Armstrong 1989). This is consistent with the tendancy for juvenile crabs to emigrate out of estuaries into colder coastal waters as they approach sexual maturity.

Although no single pollutant, or suite of pollutants, has been shown to significantly affect Dungeness crab, various studies on different life stages have shown sensitivity to oiled sediments, dissolved oxygen levels below 5 ppm, low ammonia concentrations, pesticides, and chlorinated wastewater (Wild and Tasto 1983, Emmett et al. 1991). Juvenile crab abundance in the Bay has been shown to be negatively correlated to Delta outflow (CDFG 1987).

References

Botsford, L.W. and R.C. Hobbs. 1995. Recent advances in the understanding of cyclic behavior of Dungeness crab (*Cancer magister*) populations. ICES Mar. Sci. Symp., 199: 157-166.

California Department of Fish and Game (CDFG). 1987. Delta outflow effects on the abundance and distribution of San Francisco Bay fish and invertebrates, 1980-85. Exhibit 60. State Wat. Res. Ctrl. Bd., Wat. Qual./Wat. Rights Proc. on San Fran. Bay/Sac.- San Joaquin Delta. 337 pp.

Eggleston, D.B. and D.A. Armstrong. 1995. Pre- and post-settlement determinants of estuarine Dunge-ness crab recruitment. Ecological Monographs, 65 (2): 193-216.

Emmett, R.L., S.L. Stone, S.A. Hinton and M.E. Monaco. 1991. Distribution and abundance of fishes and invertebrates in west coast estuaries, Volume II: species life history summaries. ELMR Rep. No. 8 NOAA/NOS Strategic Envir. Ass. Div., Rockville, MD. 329 pp.

Fernandez, M.E., O. Iribarne and D.A. Armstrong. 1993a. Habitat selection by young-of-the-year Dungeness crab *Cancer magister* Dana and predation risk in intertidal habitats. Mar. Ecol. Prog. Ser., Vol. 92: 171-177.

Fernandez, M.E., D.A. Armstrong and O. Irbarne. 1993b. First cohort of young-of-the-year Dungeness crab (*Cancer magister*) reduces abundance of subsequent cohorts in intertidal shell habitats. Can. J. Fish. Aquat. Sci. 50: 2100-2105.

Gunderson, D.R., D.A. Armstrong, Y.-B. Shi and R.A. McConnaughey. 1990. Patterns of estuarine use by juvenile English sole (*Parophrys vetulus*) and Dungeness crab (*Cancer magister*). Estuaries 13(1): 59-71.

Gutermuth, F. Brandt and D.A. Armstrong. 1989. Temperature-dependent metabolic response of juvenile Dungeness crab (*Cancer magister* Dana): ecological implications for estuarine and coastal populations. J. Exp. Mar. Biol. Ecol. 126: 135-144.

Hatfield, S.E. 1983. Intermolt staging and distribution of Dungeness crab, *Cancer magister*, megalopae. *In:* Wild and Tasto (eds). Life history, environment, and mariculture studies of the Dungeness crab, *Cancer magister*, with emphasis on the central California fishery resource. Ca. Dept. Fish and Game, Fish Bull. (172): 85-96.

Hines, A.H. 1991. Fecundity and reproductive output in nine species of *Cancer* crabs (Crustacea, Brachyura, Cancridae). Can. J. Fish. Aquat. Sci. 48: 267-275.

Iribarne, O., D. Armstrong and M. Fernandez. 1995. Environmental impact of intertidal juvenile Dungeness crab enhancement: effects on bivalves and crab foraging rate. J. Exp. Mar. Biol. Ecol. 192: 173-194.

Kondzela, C.M. and T.C. Shirley. 1993. Survival, feeding, and growth of juvenile Dungeness crabs from southeastern Alaska reared at different temperatures. Jour. of Crust. Biol., 13 (1): p. 25-35.

McCabe, G.T. Jr., R.L. Emmett, T.C. Coley and R.J. McConnell. 1988. Distribution, density, and size-class structure of Dungeness crabs in the river-dominated Columbia River Estuary. Northwest Science 62(5): 254-262.

McConnaughey, R.A. and D.A. Armstrong. 1990. A juvenile critical stage in the Dungeness crab (*Cancer magister*) life history. Abstracts of the 1990 annual meeting of the National Shellfisheries Assoc. Williamsburg, VA. p. 133-134.

McMillan, R.O., D.A. Armstrong and P.A. Dinnel. 1995. Comparison of intertidal habitat use and growth rates of two northern Puget Sound cohorts of 0+ age Dungeness crab, *Cancer magister*. Estuaries 18(2): 390-398.

Oresanz, J.M. and V.F. Gallucci. 1988. Comparative study of postlarval life-history schedules in four sympatric species of *Cancer* (Decapoda: Brachyura: Cancridae). Jour. Crust. Biol. 8(2): 187-220.

Palacios, R. and D.A. Armstrong. 1990. Predation of juvenile soft-shell clam (*Mya arenaria*) by juvenile Dungeness crab. Abstracts of the 1990 annual meeting of the National Shellfisheries Assoc. Williamsburg, VA. p. 445-446.

Reilly, P.N. 1983a. Predation on Dungeness crabs, *Cancer magister*, in central Califirnia. *In:* Wild and Tasto (eds). Life history, environment, and mariculture studies of the Dungeness crab, *Cancer magister*, with emphasis on the central California fishery resource. Ca. Dept. Fish and Game, Fish Bull. (172): 155-164.

_____. 1983b. Dynamics of Dungeness crab, *Cancer magister*, larvae off central and northern California. *In:* Wild and Tasto (eds). Life history, environment, and mariculture studies of the Dungeness crab, *Cancer magister*, with emphasis on the central California fishery resource. Ca. Dept. Fish and Game, Fish Bull. (172): 57-84.

Tasto, R.N. 1983. Juvenile Dungeness crab, *Cancer magister,* studies in the San Francisco Bay area. *In:* Wild and Tasto (eds). Life history, environment, and mariculture studies of the Dungeness crab, *Cancer magister*, with emphasis on the central California fishery resource. Ca. Dept. Fish and Game, Fish Bull. (172): 135-154.

Wainwright, T.C. and D.A. Armstrong. 1993. Growth patterns in the Dungeness crab (*Cancer magister* Dana): synthesis of data and comparison of models. Jour. Crust. Biol. 13(1): 36-50.

Warner, R.W. 1992. Dungeness crab, p. 15-18. *In:* W.S. Leet, C.M. Dewees and C.W. Haugen (eds). California's living marine resources. Ca. Sea Grant Publ. UCSGEP-92-12, 257 pp.

Wild, P.N. and R.N. Tasto. 1983. Life history, environment, and mariculture studies of the Dungeness crab, *Cancer magister*, with emphasis on the central California fishery resource. Ca. Dept. Fish and Game, Fish Bull. (172): 352 pp.

Rock Crabs

Cancer antennarius and *Cancer productus*

Robert N. Tasto

General Information

The brown rock crab *(Cancer antennarius)* is found along the west coast of North America from Washington State to Baja California; the red rock crab *(Cancer productus)* has a slightly more northerly distribution, i.e., Alaska to San Diego (Carroll and Winn 1989). A small recreational fishery exists for brown and red rock crabs in central San Francisco Bay and parts of south Bay and San Pablo Bay. Most rock crabs in this fishery are caught from piers and jetties by a variety of baited hoop nets and traps. A modest commercial fishery also occurs throughout California waters, with the vast majority of the catch taking place from Morro Bay southward (Parker 1992). Ex-vessel value for the commercial fishery approached $2 million in the mid-1980s (Carroll and Winn 1989) and appears to be unchanged since then. Unlike their close relative, the Dungeness crab, which has a significant amount of muscle tissue in the body, rock crabs, generally, have been sought after for their claws only. In recent years, however, live whole crabs have become a larger part of the retail market. California Department of Fish and Game regulations prohibit the commercial take of crabs less than 4.25 inches carapace width (cw), require that sport-caught crabs must be 4.0 inches cw or greater, and impose a bag limit of 35 crabs per day.

Reproduction

Mating takes place between a soft-shelled (recently molted) female and hard-shelled male. Male brown rock crabs have been reported to outnumber females by a ratio of 1.6/1 (San Mateo County coast) during all seasons (Breen 1988), although studies by Carroll (1982) at Diablo Cove showed that females were more abundant in the fall, with no other seasonal trends for either sex. Unfertilized eggs remain within the female for approximately three months, following mating, and then are fertilized by the stored sperm as they are released (Parker 1992). The fertilized eggs are then carried until hatching (6 to 8 weeks) in a sponge-like mass beneath the female's abdominal flap (Parker 1992). Female body size is the principal determinant of reproductive output and fecundity, with red rock crab having 172,600 to 597,100 eggs per brood and brown rock crab having 156,400 to 5,372,000 eggs per brood (Hines 1991). Like the Dungeness crab, ovigerous female rock crabs have been observed buried in the sand at the base of rocks in shallow waters protecting their eggs (Reilly 1987). Also, some red rock crab females have been detected emigrating out of estuaries prior to spawning to avoid osmotic stress (Oresanz and Gallucci 1988).

Hatching takes place in spring and early summer in central California (Carroll 1982). The planktonic larvae then settle to the bottom before beginning the juvenile stage. Juvenile abundance is highest in San Francisco Bay during the summer months (CDFG 1987). Much like other cancrids, larval release in spring coincides with peak plankton production, and settlement in the summer is optimal for growth (Hines 1991). The reproductive life span for the red rock crab is approximately four years with four broods, and for the brown rock crab it is approximately seven years with up to 10 broods (Hines 1991).

Growth and Development

Brown rock crabs are known to go through 10 to 12 molts before reaching sexual maturity at about 3 inches cw, and will likely molt one to two times per year thereafter (Parker 1992). The average number of red rock crab instars is 13 over the total life span (Oresanz and Gallucci 1988). Studies in Humboldt Bay (O'Toole 1985) found ovigerous red rock crab as small as 3.7 inches cw. Brown rock crabs have reached a maximum 6.5 inches cw and red rock crabs, the larger of the two species, at 8 inches cw (Carroll and Winn 1989, Parker 1992). Maximum life span of the brown rock crab has been estimated at 5-6 years (Carroll 1982).

Food and Feeding

Rock crabs are both nocturnal predators and scavangers and have been shown to feed upon hard-shelled organisms such as clams, snails, and barnacles (Parker 1992). The large chelae of these crabs is well-suited to forage on the hard shells of more sedentary prey of their rocky habitats (Oresanz and Gallucci 1988). Red rock crab feed upon intertidal mussels and barnacles (Robles et al. 1989). Juvenile rock crabs are preyed upon by other macroinvertebrates and demersal fishes, whereas adults are prey items for marine mammals (Carroll 1982). Very little is known about the specific food habits of, or predators upon, these two species of rock crabs within San Francisco Bay; however, the sportfishery within the Bay accounts for the loss of an indeterminate number of adult crabs.

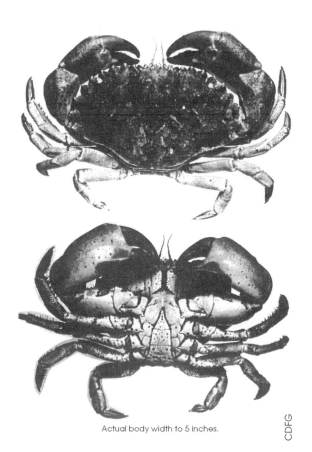

Actual body width to 5 inches.

CDFG

Brown Rock Crab, *Cancer antennarius*.
Top and bottom: Views of 5 in. male crab.

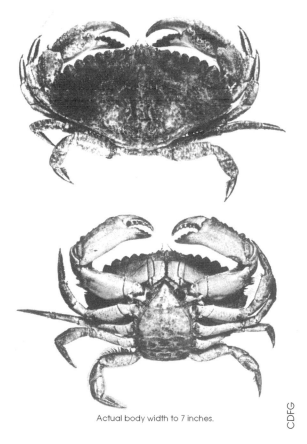

Actual body width to 7 inches.

CDFG

Red Rock Crab, *Cancer productus*.
Top: top surface of 6.5 in. male. Bottom: under surface of 5.75 in. female.

Distribution

Both rock crab species inhabit the low intertidal zone to depths of 300 feet or more (Parker 1992) and, although their microhabitat utilization patterns are similar, they appear to be different in how they utilize estuaries (Oresanz and Gallucci 1988). The brown rock crab is principally a marine species and does not osmoregulate well in brackish waters, whereas the red rock crab can successfully inhabit brackish areas. All stages of the red and brown rock crab have been collected in San Francisco Bay, including larvae and ovigerous females (**Tables 2.1** and **2.2**). Areas of peak abundance appear to be in Central Bay, the northern portion of South Bay, and the southern portion of San Pablo Bay, with the red rock crab having a somewhat greater distribution than the brown rock crab (CDFG 1987). In general, rock crab movement is local (Breen 1988, Carroll and Winn 1989). At Fitzgerald Marine Reserve along the San Mateo County coast, studies demonstrated that juvenile brown rock crab are most abundant in July, although no seasonal trend in the settlement of early instars was evident (Breen 1988). In Santa Barbara County, Reilly (1987) found all stages of rock crabs to be most abundant in the fall.

Population Status and Influencing Factors

There are no known estimates of the overall population size or knowledge of recruitment mechanisms for San Francisco Bay rock crabs. Most studies have shown that population densities of rock crabs were well below $1/m^2$

(Carroll 1982, Breen 1988). Small, local populations of rock crab can be overfished, although there is no evidence suggesting that overfishing occurs in the Bay. Data from the Interagency Ecological Study Program indicate that there is a negative relationship between abundance of both rock crab species and outflow from the Delta (CDFG 1987).

Trophic Levels

Rockcrab larvae are planktivores and, as such, are both primary consumers (phytoplankton) and secondary consumers (zooplankton). Juveniles and adults are higher order consumers.

Proximal Species

Predators: Marine mammals, humans (recreational fishery).
Prey: Bay mussels, barnacles.

Good Habitat

Not surprisingly, both species have been shown to prefer rocky shore, subtidal reef, or coarse gravel and sand substrate (Carroll and Winn 1989). Opportunity for concealment appears to be an important feature of red rock crab habitat in British Columbia studies (Robles et al. 1989). Juvenile brown rock crab, when settling from the last larval stage, appear to accept both sand and rock as suitable substrate (Carroll and Winn 1989), and red rock crab also tend to settle out onto structurally complex substrates (Oresanz and Gallucci 1988).

Table 2.1 Annual Abundance of Rock Crabs Caught by Otter Trawl (crabs/tow) in the San Francisco Estuary (CDFG 1987)

Species and Size Class	1980	1981	1982	1983	1984	1985	1986
C. antennarius (all sizes)	0.101	0.047	0.010	0.015	0.071	0.033	0.007
C. antennarius (<50mm)	0.098	0.037	0.005	0.015	0.067	0.024	0.007
C. gracilis (all sizes)	0.035	0.103	0.044	0.182	0.333	0.240	0.174
C. gracilis (<20mm)	0.003	0.005	0.034	0.080	0.079	0.064	0.095
C. productus (all sizes)	0.014	0.032	0.005	0.010	0.055	0.071	0.088
C. productus (<50mm)	0.014	0.027	0.002	0.005	0.040	0.050	0.081

Table 2.2 Annual Abundance of Rock Crabs Caught by Ring Net (crabs/tow) in the San Francisco Estuary (CDFG 1987)

Species and Size Class	1980	1981	1982*	1983	1984	1985	1986
C. antennarius (all sizes)	-	-	0.113	0.095	0.296	0.491	0.407
C. antennarius (<50mm)	-	-	0	0.009	0.028	0.009	0.176
C. gracilis (all sizes)	-	-	0.014	0.019	0.037	0.009	0.130
C. productus (all sizes)	-	-	0.155	0.067	2.509	4.315	0.806
C. productus (<50mm)	-	-	0	0	0.185	0.148	0.157

* Ring net survey started in May 1982

Rock crabs appear to be influenced by both temperature and salinity. In various laboratory studies, both brown and red rock crab were adversely affected by exposure to water temperatures above 20°C (Carroll and Winn 1989, Sulkin and McKeen 1994). The brown rock crab is considered primarily a marine species, whereas red rock crabs can osmoregulate in more brackish water; although the latter have been shown to be adversely affected by salinities below 13 ppt (Oresanz and Gallucci 1988, Carroll and Winn 1989).

References

Breen, R.T. 1988. Sizes and seasonal abundance of rock crabs in intertidal channels at James V. Fitzgerald Marine Reserve, California. Bull. Southern Ca. Acad. Sci. 87(2): 84-87.

California Department of Fish and Game (CDFG). 1987. Delta outflow effects on the abundance and distribution of San Francisco Bay fish and invertebrates, 1980-85. Exhibit 60. State Wat. Res. Ctrl. Bd., Wat. Qual./Wat. Rights Proc. on San Fran. Bay/Sac.-San Joaquin Delta. 337 pp.

Carroll, J.C. 1982. Seasonal abundance, size composition, and growth of rock crab, *Cancer antennarius* Stimpson, off central California. J. Crust. Biol. 2: 549-561.

Carroll, J.C. and R.N. Winn. 1989. Species profiles: life histories and environmental requirements of coastal fishes and invertebrates (Pacific Southwest)—brown rock crab, red rock crab, and yellow crab. U.S. Fish Wildl. Serv. Biol. Rep. 82(11.117). U.S. Army Corps of Engineers, TR EL-82-4. 16 pp.

Hines, A.H. 1991. Fecundity and reproductive output in nine species of *Cancer* crabs (Crustacea, Brachyura, Cancridae). Can. J. Fish. Aquat. Sci. 48: 267-275.

Oresanz, J.M. and V.F. Gallucci. 1988. Comparative study of postlarval life-history schedules in four sympatric species of *Cancer* (Decapoda: Brachyura: Cancridae). Jour. Crust. Biol. 8(2): 187-220.

O'Toole, C. 1985. Rock crab survey of Humboldt Bay. U.C. Coop. Ext., Sea Grant Mar. Adv. Prog., Eureka, Ca., Interim Rep. 14 pp.

Parker, D. 1992. Rock Crabs. *In:* W.S. Leet, C.M. Dewees and C.W. Haugen (eds). California's living marine resources. Ca. Sea Grant Publ. UCSGEP-92-12, 257 pp.

Reilly, P.N. 1987. Population studies of rock crab, *Cancer antennarius,* yellow crab, *Cancer anthonyi,* and Kellet's whelk, *Kelletia kelletii,* in the vicinity of little Coho Bay, Santa Barbara County, California. Ca. Dept. Fish and Game. 73: 88-98.

Robles, C., D.A. Sweetnam and D. Dittman. 1989. Diel variation of intertidal foraging by *Cancer productus* L. in British Columbia. Jour. Nat. Hist. 23: 1041-1049.

Sulkin, S.D. and G. McKeen. 1994. Influence of temperature on larval development of four co-occurring species of the brachyuran genus *Cancer.* Marine Biology. 118: 593-600.

Bat Ray

Myliobatus californica

Kurt F. Kline

General Information

The bat ray is a member of the family Myliobatidae (eagle rays). The family is found worldwide in tropical and temperate shallow seas. Bat rays are very common and are found in sandy and muddy bays and sloughs, as well as in rocky areas and kelp beds. In shallow bays they can be found feeding in the intertidal zone during high tide.

Reproduction

Mating occurs during the summer months followed by an estimated gestation period of nine to 12 months (Martin and Cailliet 1988). The young are born alive at 220 to 356 mm wing width and weigh about 0.9 kg (Baxter 1980, Martin and Cailliet 1988). Males are mature at 450 to 622 mm wing width and two to three years, while 50% of the females are mature at 881 mm wing width and five years.

Growth and Development

The growth of juvenile bat rays is not well documented, but is likely at least 100 mm per year. They can grow to

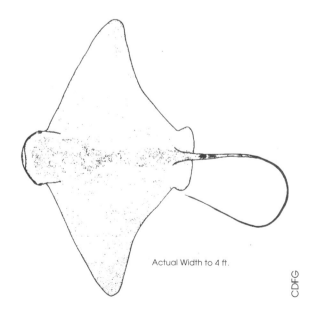

Actual Width to 4 ft.

CDFG

a wingspan of six feet (>2000 mm) though individuals this large are uncommon. The largest bat ray reported was a 95 kg female from Newport Bay (Baxter 1980).

Food and Feeding

Bat rays are opportunistic bottom feeders, feeding primarily upon benthic and epibenthic invertebrates. In Elkhorn Slough, bat rays feed primarily on clams and the echiuroid worm, *Urechis caupo*; in La Jolla kelp beds, they feed on shellfish including abalone and snails; and in Tomales Bay, they feed on polychaete worms, large clams and echiuroid worms (Karl and Obrebski 1976, Karl 1979, Talent 1982). Studies done along the southern California coast (Van Blaricom 1982) found that pits dug by feeding bat rays were an important controlling factor of infaunal community organization, opening areas for infauna recolonization and uncovering food items for other fish.

Distribution

The bat ray ranges from the Gulf of California to Oregon, and is found from shallow subtidal water to 46 m. It is common in bays and shallow sandy areas along the coast (Miller and Lea 1976).

Population Status and Influencing Factors

The current status of the bat ray in San Francisco Bay is unknown. Its distribution is likely influenced by salinity; it has occaisionally been collected in San Pablo Bay at salinities lower 20 ppt (Flemming 1999).

Trophic Levels

Bat rays are primary consumers, feeding primarily on benthic invertebrates. They are taken by fishermen using cut fish as bait, however natural feeding on fishes has not been documented.

Proximal Species

Prey: Benthic mollusks, polychaetes, crustaceans, *Urechis caupo*.

Good Habitat

Sandy to muddy shallow bottoms with abundant mollusk and polychaete populations.

References

Baxter, J.L. 1980. Inshore fishes of California. Ca. Dept. Fish and Game. 72 pp.

Flemming, R. 1999. Elasmobranchs. *In*: J. Orsi (ed). Report on the 1980-1995 fish, shrimp, and crab sampling in the San Francisco Estuary, California. IEP Technical Report 63.

Karl, S.R. 1979. Fish feeding habit studies from Tomales Bay, California. M.S. Thesis, Univ. of Pacific, Stockton, Ca., 44 pp.

Karl, S.R. and S. Obrebski. 1976. The feeding biology of the bat ray, *Myliobatis californica*, in Tomales Bay, California. *In*: C.A. Simsenstad and S.J. Lipovsk (eds). Fish food habits studies, 1st Pacific Northwest Technical Workshop, Workshop Proceedings, October 13- 15. Washington Sea Grant, Div. Mar. Res., Univ. of Washington HG :30, Seattle, pp. 181-186.

Martin, L.K. and G.M. Cailliet 1988. Age and growth determination of the bat ray, *Myliobatis californica* Gell, in Central California. Copeia 3: 763 773.

Miller, D.J. and R.N. Lea. 1972. Guide to the coastal marine fishes of California. Ca. Dept. Fish and Game Fish Bull. 157, 249 pp.

Talent, L.G. 1982. Food habits of the gray smoothhound, *Mustelus californicus*, the brown smoothhound, *Mustelus henlei*, the shovelnose guitarfish, *Rhinobatos productus*, and the bat ray, *Myliobatis californica*, in Elkhorn Slough, California. Ca. Dept. Fish and Game 68(4): 224-234.

Van Blaricom, G.R. 1982. Experimental analyses of structural regulation in a marine sand community exposed to oceanic swell. Ecological Monographs 52: 283-305.

Fish

Leopard Shark

Triakis semifasciata

Michael F. McGowan

General Information

The leopard shark (Family: Elasmobranchs) is one of the most common sharks in California bays and estuaries (Talent 1976). It is the most abundant shark in San Francisco Bay (Ebert 1986) being found especially around piers and jetties (Emmett et al. 1991). The leopard shark is an important recreational species in San Francisco Bay and a limited commercial long-line fishery has targeted it in the bay (Smith and Kato 1979). Juveniles and adults are demersal and sometimes rest on the bottom (Feder et al. 1974). Although other elasmobranchs occur in euhaline bays and estuaries of the U. S. Pacific coast, the leopard shark was the only shark or ray included among 47 fish and invertebrate species in the life history summaries of west coast estuarine species prepared by the National Oceanic and Atmospheric Administration's Estuarine Living Marine Resources (ELMR) program (Emmett et al. 1991). These species were selected on the basis of commercial value, recreational value, indicator species of environmental stress, and ecological importance. That the leopard shark was selected is an indication of its importance in estuaries in general and in San Francisco Bay where it is the most abundant shark.

Reproduction

The leopard shark is a live bearer with internal fertilization, but no yolk-sac placenta. Mating occurs in the spring, primarily during April and May soon after the females give birth to from 4-29 pups (Compagno 1984). Pupping can occur from March through August with a peak in April or May (Ackerman 1971). In San Francisco Bay leopard sharks pup almost exclusively in South Bay (CDFG Bay Trawl data). The center of abundance of pups <300 mm long is south of, and just north of the Dumbarton Bridge.

Growth and Development

Embryonic development is direct and internal and takes 10-12 months. At birth pups are 18-20 cm long. Females mature when 12-14 years old at a length of 110-129 cm.

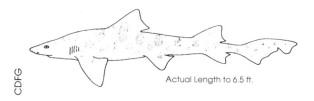

CDFG

Actual Length to 6.5 ft.

Males mature earlier and at smaller sizes than females. Growth rates are slow. In San Francisco Bay tagged leopard sharks grew 1.4 cm/yr (Smith and Abramson 1990).

Food and Feeding

Primary foods of the leopard shark are benthic and epibenthic crustaceans, clam siphons, echinuroid worms, and small fishes.

Distribution

The leopard shark is found from Mazatlan, Mexico including the Sea of Cortez to Oregon (Miller and Lea 1976). In California it is most common in estuaries and bays south of Tomales Bay (Monaco et al. 1990). Leopard sharks are apparently resident in San Francisco Bay, although some move out in fall and winter (Smith and Abramson 1990) and several size classes appear in the California Department of Fish and Game length data.

Population Status and Influencing Factors

The leopard shark probably has no predators except larger sharks and humans. Its broad dietary range should protect it from food limitation. Heavy fishing mortality poses a threat to the leopard shark, as it does to all sharks, because of its slow growth, long time to maturity, and low fecundity. The minimum size limit recommended by Smith and Abramson (1990) for sustainable fishing in San Francisco Bay was 100 cm (40 in). Areas of high freshwater input causing low salinity are largely avoided by leopard sharks.

Trophic Levels

Juveniles and adults are secondary and higher carnivores.

Proximal Species

Predators: Larger sharks, humans.
Prey: Yellow shore crab, *Urechis caupo*, ghost shrimp, rock crabs, octopus, shiner perch, arrow goby, Pacific herring, northern anchovy, topsmelt.
Cohabitors: Smoothhound sharks form mixed schools with leopard sharks.

Good Habitat

Leopard sharks are primarily a marine species which occupies bays and estuaries unless freshwater flows lower salinity excessively. Sandy and muddy bottom areas are preferred, although they may be found near rocky areas and kelp beds along the coast. Estuaries are used as pupping and rearing areas for young sharks. Shallow mud and sand flats are used for foraging during high tide (Compagno 1984).

References

Ackerman, L.T. 1971. Contributions to the biology of the leopard shark, *Triakis semifasciata* (Girard) in Elkhorn Slough, Monterey Bay, California. M.A. Thesis, Sacramento State College, Sacramento, CA, 54 pp.

Compagno, L.J. 1984. FAO species catalogue. Vol. 4. Sharks of the world. An annotated and illustrated catalogue of shark species known to date. Part 2. Carcharhiniformes. FAO Fish. Synop. 125(4): 433-434.

Ebert, D.A. 1986. Observations on the elasmobranch assemblage of San Francisco Bay. Ca. Dept. Fish and Game 72(4): 244-249.

Emmett, R.L., S.L. Stone, S.A. Hinton and M.E. Monaco. 1991. Distribution and abundance of fishes and invertebrates in west coast estuaries, Volume II: species life history summaries. ELMR Rep. N. 8. NOAA/NOS Strategic Environmental Assessments Div., Rockville, MD, 329 pp.

Feder, H.M., C.H. Turner and C. Limbaugh. 1974. Observations on fishes associated with kelp beds in southern California. Ca. Dept. Fish Game, Fish Bull. 160, 144 pp.

Miller, D.J. and R.N. Lea. 1976. Guide to the coastal marine fishes of California. Fish Bull. 157, Ca. Dept. Fish and Game , Sacramento, Ca.. Sea Grant reprint of 1972 edition with addendum added 1976.

Monaco, M.E., R.L. Emmett, S.A. Hinton and D.M. Nelson. 1990. Distribution and abundance of fishes and invertebrates in West Coast estuaries, volume I: data summaries. ELMR Report No. 4. Strategic Ass. Div., NOS/NOAA, Rockville, Maryland. 240 pp.

Smith, S.E. and N. J. Abramson. 1990. Leopard shark *Triakis semifasciata* distribution, mortality rate, yield, and stock replenishment estimates based on a tagging study in San Francisco Bay. Fish. Bull 88: 371-381.

Smith, S.E. and S. Kato. 1979. The fisheries of San Francisco Bay: past, present and future. *In:* T.J. Conmos (ed). San Francisco Bay: The urbanized estuary, Pac. Div., Am. Assoc. Adv. Sci., San Francisco, Ca. pp. 445-468.

Talent, L.G. 1976. Food habits of the leopard shark, *Triakis semifasciata*, in Elkhorn Slough, Monterey Bay, California. Ca. Fish Game 62(4): `286-298.

Pacific Herring

Clupea pallasi

Robert N. Tasto

General Information

The Pacific herring (Family: Clupeidae) resource in the San Francisco Estuary is widely recognized for its commercial, recreational, and ecological values. The commercial fishery concentrates on ripe females for their roe (eggs) which are then exported to Japan, although there is some limited effort for the fresh fish market and for live bait by recreational salmon trollers (Spratt 1981, Lassuy 1989). Fishermen traditionally catch herring in nearshore areas of the Bay with gillnets or in deeper waters with round-haul nets, and there also is a relatively new roe-on-kelp fishery operated from rafts (Spratt 1981, CDFG 1992). The economic value of the fishery based upon ex-vessel prices paid to the fishermen in 1995-96 was approximately 16.5 million dollars (CDFG, unpub. data).

Reproduction

Adult herring congregate outside of San Francisco Bay before entering and generally spend about 2 weeks in the Bay before spawning (CDFG 1987). Spawning takes place from early November through March, with peak activity in January (Spratt 1981, CDFG 1992). The timing of spawning is believed to coincide with increased levels of plankton production as a food source for larvae (Lassuy 1989), as well as the presence of freshwater flows (Emmett et al. 1991). Pacific herring spawn primarily on vegetation, rock rip-rap, pier pilings, and other hard substrates in intertidal and shallow subtidal waters (Spratt 1981, Lassuy 1989, Emmett et al. 1991). Spawning occurs in waves of 1 to 3 days, occasionally up to a week in length, and often at night in conjunction with high tides (Spratt 1981). Waves are separated by one to several weeks over the length of the season with larger fish tending to spawn first (Lassuy 1989). The number and size of the waves is related to the distribution of the dominant year classes (CDFG 1992).

Egg-deposition is thought to be facilitated by the brushing of the female's vent up against the substrate, and, while there is no pairing of the sexes, the spawning area will be white with milt from the males so that the rate of fertilization is usually high (Hart 1973). Pa-

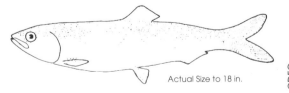

Actual Size to 18 in.

CDFG

Fish

cific herring eggs adhere to the substrate in amounts ranging from a few eggs to as many as eight layers thick (Spratt 1981). The fecundity of herring is approximately 4,000 to 134,000 eggs per female, depending upon its distribution and size (Hart 1973, Emmett et al. 1991). As with spawning, most hatching takes place at night, and will occur in 10 to 15 days under 8.5° to 10.7°C temperatures; longer if the water is colder (Emmett et al. 1991). The average in San Francisco Bay is 10.5 days at 10.0°C (CDFG 1992).

Growth and Development

Pacific herring eggs are approximately 1.0 mm in diameter, and 1.2 to 1.5 mm after fertilization (Hart 1973). A newly hatched larva, with yolk sac, is about 6 to 8 mm total length (TL) and will develop swimming powers at about 20 mm TL (CDFG 1992). Metamorphosis to the juvenile stage occurs from 25 to 35 mm TL and takes place over two to three months (Emmett et al. 1991). They are free-swimming at this stage and begin to form shoreline-oriented schools (CDFG 1992). Juveniles are 35 to 150 mm TL depending upon regional growth rates, which in turn are affected by population size and environmental conditions (Emmett et al. 1991). In the Bay Area, there are no apparent differences in the growth rates of males and females (Spratt 1981). Adults range in size from 130 to 260 mm TL, and locally it takes two to three years to reach maturity (Spratt 1981, Emmett et al. 1991). The San Francisco Bay population ranges from 110 to 250 mm TL (CDFG 1992; Ken Ota, Pers. Comm.) It is possible that some Pacific herring in more northern climates may exceed 15 years in age, but few have been noted to live longer than nine years (Emmett et al. 1991).

Food and Feeding

Pacific herring larvae, juveniles, and adults are selective pelagic planktonic feeders and move toward the water's surface to feed at dusk and dawn (Emmett et al. 1991). Generally, prey items will change with growth and geographic distribution. Larvae feed on diatoms, invertebrate and fish eggs, crustacean and mollusc larvae, bryzoans, rotifers, and copepods (Hart 1973). Juveniles consume a variety of crustaceans, as well as mollusc and fish larvae; while adults eat mostly planktonic crustaceans and fish larvae (Hart 1973, Emmett et al. 1991). In winter, there is an overall reduction in adult Pacific herring feeding as stored energy is used for ripening reproductive products and, during their spawning migration and inshore "holding" period, herring may severely limit or stop feeding entirely (Lassuy 1989).

Herring eggs are eaten by various species of fish (e.g., sturgeon), ducks (e.g., surf scoter), and gulls (CDFG 1992). Larvae are often prey for large pelagic in-

vertebrates and various fishes, while juveniles and adults are consumed by a variety of fishes (e.g., spiny dogfish shark, Chinook salmon, Pacific staghorn sculpin, and striped bass), seabirds (e.g., Brandts cormorants, brown pelicans, and western gulls), and marine mammals, such as harbor seals (Hart 1973, Lassuy 1989, Emmett et al. 1991). Predation is considered to be the greatest source of natural mortality for juvenile and adult Pacific herring (CDFG 1992).

Distribution

Major populations exist in the eastern Pacific between San Francisco Bay and central Alaska (Hart 1973). Within San Francisco Bay, the principal spawning areas are found along the Marin County coastline (i.e., Sausalito, Tiburon Penninsula, and Angel Island), at the San Francisco waterfront and Treasure Island, on the east side of the Bay from the Port of Richmond to the Naval Air Station at Alameda, and on beds of vegetation in Richardson Bay and South Bay (**Figure 2.3**) (Spratt 1981, CDFG 1992). After hatching, the larvae are clumped and controlled largely by tidal factors, and following disappearance of the yolk sac and the onset of feeding, their distribution becomes patchy (CDFG 1992). Larvae and young juveniles are found in the Bay between November and April and their greatest densities are in the shallow waters of upper South Bay, Central Bay, and San Pablo Bay. Juveniles are found in the deeper areas of the Bay (peak in Central Bay) between April and August, and, for the most part, have left the Bay by late June at sizes that approach 80 mm TL (CDFG 1987). They eventually move to offshore or nearshore areas and do not return to the Bay until they are mature and ready for spawning. There is conflicting evidence of a strong correlation between juvenile abundance, as measured by young-of-the-year surveys, and recruitment to the adult spawning population two years later (Herbold et al. 1992)

Population Status and Influencing Factors

San Francisco Bay population levels fluctuate widely and have ranged between approximately 6,000 tons and 100,000 tons spawning biomass, as measured by spawn deposition surveys and hydroacoustic monitoring of fish schools (CDFG 1992). 1995-96 season estimates were approximately 99,000 tons, second highest on record (CDFG, unpub. data). Year-class strength is often determined in the first six months of life (Hart 1973, Lassuy 1989, Emmett et al. 1991). Egg mortalities can result from tidal exposure and dessication, abrubt or severe temperature or salinity changes, low oxygen levels, wave action, suffocation by high egg densities or siltation, pollution, and predation (Lassuy 1989, Emmett et al. 1991). Factors related to natural mortality of larvae

Figure 2.3 Traditional Pacific Herring Spawning Areas in Central San Francisco Bay

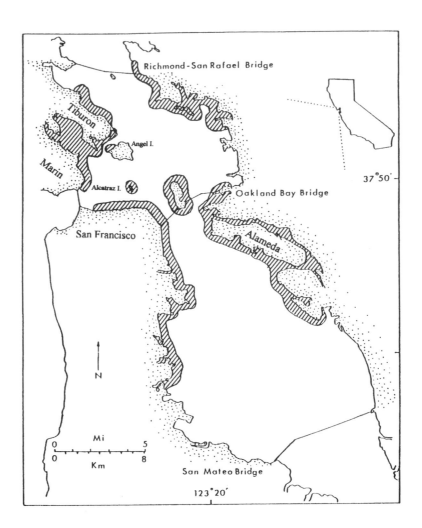

in the Bay include competition and other density dependent mechanisms, as well as starvation during their initial feeding period and changes in dispersal patterns. Juveniles and adult survival is affected by competition, predation, disease, spawning stress, and fishing (Emmett et al. 1991).

Predation appears to be the single most important factor affecting population levels (Lassuy 1989). In addition to commercial and recreational fishing, humans influence herring survival by impacting water and habitat quality. Spawning habitat quantity and Delta outflows are not thought currently to be limiting factors in determining the Bay's herring population size (CDFG 1987 and 1992).

Trophic Levels

Larvae are planktivores (primary and secondary consumers). Juveniles and adults are primary and higher order consumers.

Proximal Species

Egg Predators: Gulls, diving ducks, white sturgeon, atherinids (topsmelt and jacksmelt), surf perches, rock crabs.

Larvae predators: Young salmonids, pelagic invertabrates.
Juvenile Predators: California halibut, young salmonids, harbor seals, harbor porpoise.
Adult Predators: California halibut, California sea lion, harbor seals, harbor porpoise.
Habitat: Eel grass (spawning substrate).
Prey: Striped bass, copepods.

Good Habitat

It is frequently stated that herring prefer sea grasses (e.g., *Zostera marina*) or algae (e.g., *Gracilaria* sp.) as spawning substrate (Lassuy 1989, Emmett et al. 1991); however, a variety of seemingly less attractive surfaces have proven to be very successful in the Estuary. Rigidity, smooth texture, and the absence of sediment appear to be important components of suitable substrates (Lassuy 1989). Larvae and juveniles need quiescent and productive shallow subtidal areas as rearing habitat.

In northern waters, the optimal salinity range for spawning is reported to be 8 to 22 ppt and 13 to 19 ppt for eggs and larval survival (CDFG 1987). Also in these areas, temperatures in the range of 5.5 to 8.7° C have been shown to be best for egg development (Emmett et al. 1991); however, 10 to 12°C temperatures are about average for the spawning grounds in San Francisco Bay (Lassuy 1989). Optimal temperatures for juveniles and adults appear to be a few degrees higher than for eggs or larvae (Lassuy 1989). It has been suggested that eggs need a minimum dissolved oxygen concentration of 2.5 mg/L at the surface and, therefore, eggs elevated from the bottom on vegetation or other structures avoid siltation and receive better circulation for waste removal and oxygenation (Lassuy 1989). Water quality is an important factor as eggs are vulnerable to high levels of suspended particulate matter, particularly if the sediments are laden with contaminants (e.g., dredged material from urban ports). Additionally, larvae have been shown to be sensitive to the water-soluble fraction of hydrocarbons from spilled oil or other sources (Lassuy 1989).

References

California Department of Fish and Game (CDFG). 1987. Delta outflow effects on the abundance and distribution of San Francisco Bay fish and invertebrates, 1980-85. Exhibit 60. State Wat. Res. Ctrl. Bd., Wat. Qual./Wat. Rights Proc. on San Fran. Bay/Sac.-San Joaquin Delta. 337 pp.

_____. 1992. Pacific herring commercial fishing regulations. Draft environmental document. 183 pp.

Emmett, R.L., S.L. Stone, S.A. Hinton and M.E. Monaco. 1991. Distribution and abundance of fishes and invertebrates in West Coast estuaries, Volume II: species life history summaries. ELMR Rep. No. 8 NOAA/NOS Strategic Environmental Ass. Div., Rockville, MD, 329 pp.

Hart, J.L. 1973. Pacific herring. *In:* Pacific fishes of Canada. Fisheries Research Bd. of Canada, Bull. 180: 96-100.

Herbold, B., A.D. Jassby and P.B. Moyle. 1992. Status and trends report on aquatic resources in the San Francisco Estuary. U.S. Env. Prot. Agency, San Fran. Est. Proj. 368 pp.

Lassuy, D.R. 1989. Species profiles: life histories and environmental requirements of coastal fishes and invertebrates (Pacific Northwest)—Pacific herring. U.S. Fish and Wildl. Serv. Biol. Rep. 82 (11.126). U.S. Army Corps of Engrs., TR-EL-82-4. 18 pp.

Spratt, J.D. 1981. Status of the Pacific herring, *Clupea harengus pallasii*, resource in California, 1972 to 1980. Ca. Dept. Fish and Game, Fish Bull. (171). 107 pp.

Personal Communications

Ken Ota. Ca. Dept. of Fish and Game, Pacific Herring Research Project, 1996.

Northern Anchovy

Engraulis mordax

Michael F. McGowan

General Information

The northern anchovy (Family: Engraudidae) has the largest biomass and is the most abundant fish in San Francisco Bay (Aplin 1967). It is an important forage species for larger predators and consumes substantial amounts of phytoplankton and zooplankton (McGowan 1986). There is a bait fishery for northern anchovy at the mouth of the Bay. Most of the stock occurs outside the Bay in the California Current. Although northern anchovy can be found inside the bay throughout the year, their seasonal peak is generally April to October. The spring influx may be associated with the onset of coastal upwelling (P. Adams, pers. comm.). Their exodus in the autumn may be linked to cooling water temperatures inside the bay (McGowan 1986).

Reproduction

Northern anchovy spawn oval, pelagic eggs approximately 1.5 x 0.75 mm in size. Peak spawning is thought to occur at night at about 10 pm. Females can produce up to 130,000 eggs per year in batches of about 6,000. The eggs hatch in approximately 48 hours depending on temperature. Larvae were collected in Richardson Bay within San Francisco Bay by Eldridge (1977). Spawning was documented in San Francisco Bay in 1978 by collections of eggs and larvae from south of the Dumbarton Bridge to San Pablo Bay (McGowan 1986). Based on differential distributions of eggs and larvae, spawning occurs in the channels while larvae seek out the productive shallows. Although the biomass of northern anchovy within the bays is small relative to that in the California Current, the bay is a favorable habitat for reproduction because of ample food for adults to produce eggs, abundant zooplankton prey for larvae, and protection of eggs and larvae from offshore transport to less productive areas by coastal upwelling.

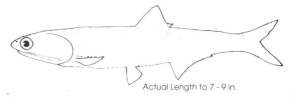

Actual Length to 7 - 9 in.

CDFG

Growth and Development

Larvae grow from 2.5 to 25 mm in about two months, at which time they are considered juveniles. Growth is rapid within the warm productive bay environment. Based on analysis of length frequencies, some juveniles that were spawned late in the summer overwinter in the bay (McGowan 1986). The others apparently depart at the same time as the adults in autumn.

Food and Feeding

Larvae eat dinoflagellates and zooplankton, while adults filter-feed in dense patches of large phytoplankton or small zooplankton, but selectively pick larger zooplankters from the water (O'Connell 1972).

Distribution

The northern anchovy occurs from Queen Charlotte Islands, Canada to Cabo San Lucas, Baha California and into the Sea of Cortez. It can be found in all estuaries within this range. There is a subpopulation which occupies the Columbia River plume, an "offshore estuary." In San Francisco Bay, they occur from Suisun Bay to South Bay, but are most abundant downstream of the Carquinez Strait (Herbold et al. 1992). There is a seasonal influx of northern anchovy into the bay in spring when water temperatures and plankton production begin to rise in the bay and when nearshore upwelling generally begins. Adults exit the bay in autumn, but some late-spawned juveniles may overwinter within the bay.

Population Status and Influencing Factors

Northern anchovy populations off California range in the hundreds of thousands of tons. Their biomass increased dramatically following the decline of the sardine stock, suggesting that competitive interactions might control population fluctuations. Historical records of fish scales in sediments suggests that large fluctuations in both anchovy and sardine populations have occurred in the past and were not strongly correlated with each other.

Variable survival of eggs and larvae due to environmental factors probably influences population size more than predation or fishing. Active research into the causes of northern anchovy population dynamics has contributed immensely to our understanding but without resolving whether starvation, predation, advection, or other cause is the key limiting factor.

Trophic Levels

First-feeding larvae may eat phytoplankters, larger larvae selectively pick copepods and other zooplankters from the water, juveniles and adults pick or filter plank-ton, fish eggs, and fish larvae, depending on food concentrations. Larvae and older stages should be considered as secondary and higher consumers.

Proximal Species

Predators: California halibut, Chinook and coho salmon; rockfishes, yellowtail, tunas, sharks, and almost all California current fish; harbor seal; northern fur seal; sea lions; common murre; brown pelican; sooty shearwater; cormorant spp.

Potential Competitors: Sardine. Jacksmelt, topsmelt, and other schooling planktivores are potential competitors and predators on young life stages.

Good Habitat

Northern anchovy occupy near surface waters where the water temperature should be between 10° and 25° C. Eggs tend to be in water with salinities from 32-35 ppt, but juveniles and adults are abundant in fresher bays and estuaries as well as marine waters. Spawning in San Francisco Bay occurs at higher temperatures and lower salinities than spawning in coastal areas. Northern anchovy are typical species of areas with high production such as coastal upwelling regions and estuaries.

References

Aplin, J.A. 1967. Biological survey of San Francisco Bay 1963-1966. Report for Ca. Dept. Fish and Game, MRO, Sacramento, Ca. Ref. 67-4. 131pp.

Eldridge, M.B. 1977. Factors influencing distribution of fish eggs and larvae over eight 24-hour samplings in Richardson Bay, California. Ca. Dept. Fish Game 63: 101-106.

Herbold, B., A.D. Jassby and P.B. Moyle. 1992. Status and trends report on aquatic resources in the San Francisco estuary. The San Francisco Estuary Project, Oakland, Calif., 257 pp. plus apps.

McGowan, M.F. 1986. Northern anchovy, *Engraulis mordax,* spawning in San Francisco Bay, California 1978-1979, relative to hydrography and zooplankton prey of adults and larvae. Fish. Bull., U.S. 84(4):879-894.

O'Connell, C.P. 1972. The interrelation of biting and filtering in the feeding activity of the northern anchovy (*Engraulis mordax*). J. Fish. Res. Board Can. 29:285-293.

Personal Communications

P. Adams, National Marine Fisheries Service, Tiburon.

Sacramento Splittail

Pogonichthys macrolepidotus

Ted R. Sommer

General Information

The Sacramento splittail (Family: Cyprinidae) is one of California's largest native minnows and is the only surviving member of its genus. In 1994 it was proposed for listing as a Threatened species by U.S. Fish and Wildlife Service based on concerns about reduced abundance and distribution (Meng and Kanim 1994, Meng and Moyle 1995). The species supports a small sport fishery in winter and spring, when it is caught for human consumption and live bait for striped bass angling.

Reproduction

Adult splittail generally reach sexual maturity at about 2 years of age (Caywood 1974). Some males mature at the end of their first year and a few females mature in their third year. An upstream spawning migration occurs November through May, with a typical peak from January-March. Spawning is thought to peak during February-June, but may extend from January-July. Although submerged vegetation is thought to be the preferred spawning substrate, egg samples have not yet been collected on any substrate. Reproductive activity appears to be related to inundation of floodplain areas, which provides shallow, submerged vegetation for spawning, rearing and foraging (Caywood 1974, Sommer et al. 1997). Splittail have high fecundity like most cyprinids. Reported fecundities range from 5,000 to 266,000 eggs per female, depending on age (Daniels and Moyle 1983). Generally, female splittail will have more than 100,000 eggs each year.

Growth and Development

The morphological characteristics of splittail eggs, larvae, and juveniles have been described and recent culturing studies (Bailey 1994) are providing preliminary information on early life history requirements and development. Very little is known about factors that influence splittail egg and larval development.

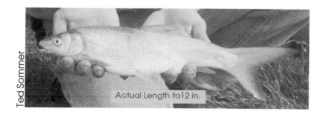

Ted Sommer

Actual Length to 12 in.

Mature splittail eggs are 1.3 to 1.6 mm in diameter with a smooth, transparent, thick chorion (Wang 1986 cited in CDWR and USBR 1994). The eggs are adhesive or become adhesive soon after contacting water (Bailey 1994). The eggs appear to be demersal and it is assumed that they are laid in clumps and attach to vegetation or other submerged substrates. Under laboratory conditions, fertilized eggs incubated in fresh water at 19°C (±0.5°C) start to hatch after approximately 96 hours. Asynchronous hatching of egg batches from single females has been observed in preliminary culturing tests.

Early hatched larvae are 6 mm long, have not developed eye pigment, and are physically underdeveloped. The last larvae to hatch have developed eye pigmentation and are morphologically better developed. Larvae are 7.0 to 8.0 mm total length (TL) when they complete yolk-sac absorption and become free swimming; postlarvae are up to 20 mm (±4.2 mm) TL. First scale formation appears at lengths of 22 mm standard length (SL) or 25 mm to 26 mm TL. It is unknown when exogenous feeding actually begins, but preliminary observations indicate that newly hatched larvae may have undeveloped mouths. Well-developed mouths are observed in postlarvae between 8.1 mm and 10.4 mm TL.

Sacramento splittail are a relatively long-lived minnow, reaching ages of 5, and possibly, up to 7 years. Studies from Suisun Marsh indicate that young-of-the-year (YOY) grow approximately 20 mm per month (mm/month) from May through September and then decrease to < 5 mm/month through February (Daniels and Moyle 1983). In their second season they grow at about 10 mm/month until the fall when somatic growth declined and gonadal development began. The adult growth rate ranges from 5 to 7 mm/month. During gonad development, which occurs primarily between September and February, the growth rate slows to less than 5 mm/month. The largest recorded splittail measured between 380 mm and 400 mm.

Food and Feeding

Feeding studies describe splittail as opportunistic benthic foragers. Splittail feeding appears highest in the morning and early afternoon. Studies from the Sacramento River found that their diets were dominated by oligochaetes, cladocerans, and dipterans (Caywood 1974). Samples from the lower San Joaquin River included copepods, dipterans, detritus and algae, clams (*Corbicula*) and amphipods (*Corophium* spp.). Copepods were the dominant food items. These findings were similar to results of feeding studies from Suisun Marsh (Daniels and Moyle 1983), where the diet consisted predominantly of detritus in both percent frequency of occurrence (74%) and percent volume (57%). A smaller portion of the stomach contents (41% by volume) consisted of animal matter, mostly crustaceans (35% by volume). Opossum shrimp (*Neomysis mercedis*) were the dominant crustacean food item (37% frequency; 59% volume less detritus) both daily and seasonally for splittail in Suisun Marsh. Other minor prey items included molluscs, insects, and fish.

Food selection studies from Suisun Marsh suggest that splittail specifically select *Neomysis* as their main prey item in the Estuary (Herbold 1987). Fullness indices data indicate that condition factors of splittail are linked to *Neomysis* abundance. Splittail did not switch to alternate and more prevalent food items, as was observed for other native resident species.

Distribution

The historical range of splittail included all low gradient portions of all major tributaries to the Sacramento and San Joaquin rivers, as well as some other freshwater tributaries to San Francisco Bay (Meng and Moyle 1995). A confounding issue is that the collection season and life stage for most of the early observations are unknown, so the relative importance of each location to different age classes of splittail cannot be established.

Splittail are presently most common in the brackish waters of Suisun Bay, Suisun Marsh, and the Sacramento-San Joaquin Delta. The data suggest that splittail inhabit much of their historical range and have been located in previously unreported sites (**Table 2.3**). Much of the loss of splittail habitat is attributable to migration barriers, but loss of floodplain and wetlands due to diking and draining activities during the past century probably represents the greatest reduction in habitat.

Within the San Francisco Estuary, splittail were collected from southern San Francisco Bay and at the mouth of Coyote Creek in Santa Clara County around the turn of the century. To our knowledge, no other splittail have been collected in this part of San Francisco Bay (Aceituno et al. 1976). However, splittail are caught in San Francisco Bay and San Pablo Bay in wet years. Adults and young are abundant in two tributaries to San Pablo Bay, the Napa and Petaluma rivers. The core of distribution of adult splittail during summer appears to be the region from Suisun Bay to the west Delta. Splittail are also present in some of the smaller tributaries and sloughs of Suisun Bay, including Peyton Slough, Hastings Slough, and Pacheco Creek.

Population Status and Influencing Factors

Abundance estimates for YOY and adult splittail were developed recently (Sommer et al. 1997) from several Interagency Ecological Program surveys. The survey equipment for the Program includes otter trawls, midwater trawls, beach seines, and townets.

Abundance of YOY declined in the Estuary during the six-year drought, which commenced in 1987 (**Figure 2.4**). There was a strong resurgence in YOY in 1995, when abundance estimates were the highest on record for State Water Project, Central Valley Project, beach seine, Outflow/Bay otter trawl, and Outflow/Bay study midwater trawl. The midwater trawl index was the second highest on record. The response

Table 2.3 Historical and Recent Collections of Splittail[a]

River	Distance (km) from Mouth of River to Collection Site			Distance (km) to first dam
	Rutter (1908)	Caywood (1974)	Sommer et al. (1997)	
Sacramento	483	387	331	387 (Red Bluff)
Feather	109	[b]	94	109 (Oroville)
American	49	37	19	37 (Nimbus)
San Joaquin	435[c]	[b]	201	295 (Sack)
Mokelumne	n/a	25	63	63 (Woodbridge)
Napa	n/a	21	10	n/a
Petaluma	n/a	25	8	16[d]

(a) For the purposes of comparing present and historical distribution, we assumed that collection of any life stage of splittail constituted evidence that a given location was part of the range of the species. The results should be considered as the minimum range only; there had not been sufficient sampling in sites farther upstream to conclusively show that they were not present. To illustrate the fact that much of the loss of channel habitat is attributable to migration barriers, the location of the first dam on each river is included.

(b) Records indicate that splittail were collected, but it is unclear where.

(c) Rutter (1908) was cited by FWS (1994) as the source of an observation of splittail at Fort Miller (km 435), near the current site of Friant Dam on the San Joaquin River. However, Rutter's distribution was based on Girard (1854), who reported two Pogonichthys species, *P. symetricus* and *P. inaquilobus* in the San Joaquin system. *P. symetricus*, collected from Fort Miller, is unlikely to have been a splittail (*P. macrolepidotus*) because Girard reported the "lobes of the caudal fin are symmetrical". Girard's description of *P. inaequilobus* had an asymmetrical tail and other features similar to that of splittail, but the collection location is listed as "San Joaquin River" without reference to a specific site.

(d) Dam was removed in 1994.

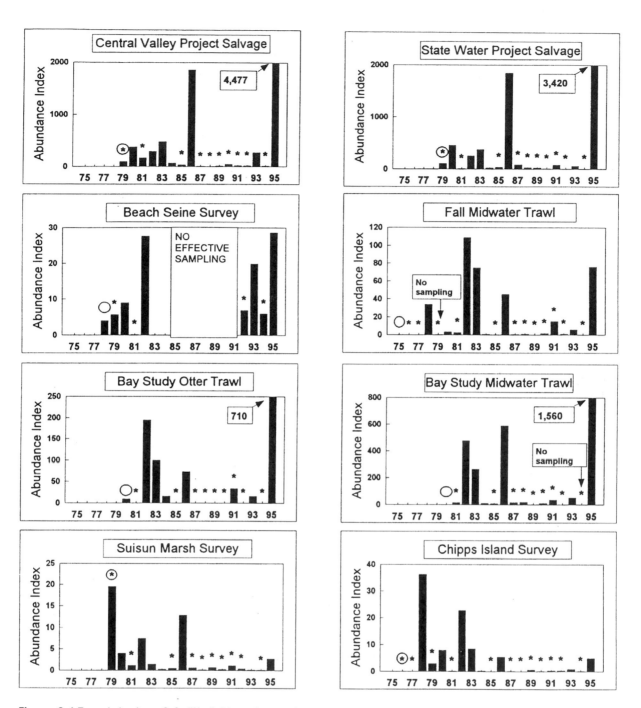

Figure 2.4 Trends in Age-0 Splittail Abundance for 1975-1995 as Indexed by Eight Independent Surveys. The first data point in each series is marked with a circle. Dry years are identified with asterisks above the data points—all other years are wet.

was not as dramatic for the Suisun Marsh, Chipps Island, or townet surveys, but there was a clear increase in abundance for each relative to the previous nine years.

There appears to be no consistent decline in adult abundance for most of the surveys (**Figure 2.5**). However, both the Suisun Marsh and Chipps Island surveys show significantly lower abundance in the early to mid-1980s (Sommer et al. 1997).

Floodplain inundation appears to be a key factor responsible for strong year classes, based on both statistical and limited observational data (Sommer et al. 1997). Higher flows increase inundation of floodplain areas, such as the Yolo Bypass, which provides spawning, rearing, and foraging habitat. The species has little or no stock recruitment relationship. This is best illustrated from data collected in 1995, when exceptionally large numbers of young splittail were produced by a stock

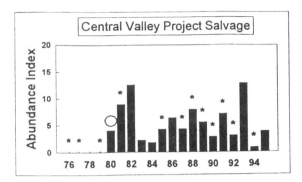

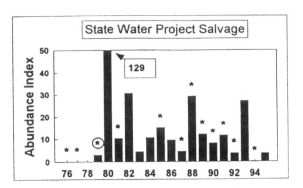

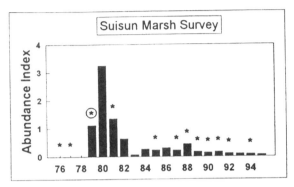

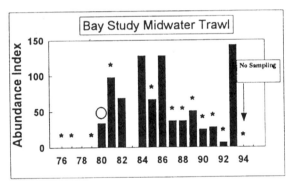

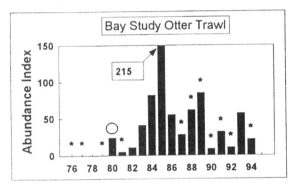

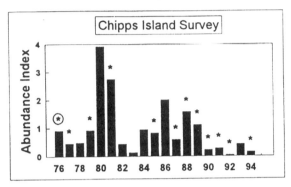

Figure 2.5 Trends in Adult Splittail Abundance for 1976-1995 as Indexed by Six Independent Surveys. The first data point in each series is marked with a circle. Dry years are identified with asterisks above the data points—all other years are wet.

that should have been depleted by drought conditions in seven of the previous eight years.

Attributes that help splittail respond rapidly to improved environmental conditions include a relatively long life span, high reproductive capacity, and broad environmental tolerances (Sommer et al. 1997). Additional factors that may affect population levels include habitat loss, recreational fishing, entrainment, and toxic compounds.

Trophic Levels

Splittail are secondary consumers.

Proximal Species

Predators: Striped bass, centrarchids.

Prey: Oligochaetes, zooplankton (cladocerans and copepods), terrestrial insects, opossum shrimp (*Neomysis mercedis*), mollusks.

Good Habitat

Sacramento splittail are one of the few freshwater cyprinids that are highly tolerant of brackish water. Although they have been collected at salinities as high as 18 ppt, abundance is highest in the 0-10 ppt salinity range (Sommer et al. 1997). Physiological studies show that splittail have critical salinity maxima of 20-29 ppt (Young and Cech 1996). Splittail also tolerate a wide range (7-33° C) of water temperatures in the laboratory, which fits well with thermal fluctuations associated with its habitat. Depending upon the acclimation temperature (range 12-20° C), critical thermal maxima ranged from 22-33° C. As further evidence of the general hardiness of the species, splittail appear to be tolerant of low dissolved oxygen levels and strong water currents.

Splittail are numerous within small dead-end sloughs, those fed by freshwater streams, and in the larger sloughs such as Montezuma and Suisun (Daniels and Moyle 1983). Juveniles and adults utilize shallow edgewater areas lined by emergent aquatic vegetation. Submerged vegetation provides abundant food sources and cover to escape from predators. Shallow, seasonally flooded vegetation is also apparently the preferred spawning habitat of adult splittail (Caywood 1974).

References

Aceituno, M.E., M.L. Caywood, S.J. Nicola and W.I. Follett. 1976. Occurrence of native fishes in Alameda and Coyote Creeks, California. Ca. Dept. Fish and Game 62(3):195-206.

Bailey, H. 1994. Culturing studies on splittail. IEP Newsletter, Summer 1994. p. 3.

Caywood, M.L. 1974. Contributions to the life history of the splittail *Pogonichthys macrolepidotus* (Ayres). Master's thesis. Ca. State Univ., Sacramento.

Daniels, R.A. and P.B. Moyle. 1983. Life history of the splittail (Cyprinidae: *Pogonichthys macrolepidotus* (Ayres)) in Sacramento-San Joaquin estuary. U.S. Natl. Marine Fish. Bull. 81: 647-654.

California Department of Water Resources and U.S. Bureau of Reclamation (CDWR and USBR). 1994. Effects of the Central Valley Project and State Water Project on Delta smelt and Sacramento splittail. Prepared for U.S. Fish and Wildl. Serv., Ecol. Services, Sacramento, CA.

Herbold, B. 1987. Patterns of co-occurrence and resource use in a non-coevolved assemblage of fishes. Ph.D. dissertation. Univ. of Ca., Davis.

Meng, L. and N. Kanim. 1994. Endangered and threatened wildlife and plants; proposed determination of threatened status for the Sacramento splittail. Fed. Reg. 59:004: 862-868.

Meng, L. and P.B. Moyle. 1995. Status of splittail in the Sacramento-San-Joaquin estuary. Transactions of the Amer. Fisheries Society 124: 538- 549.

Sommer, T.R., R. Baxter and B. Herbold. 1997. The resilience of splittail in the Sacramento-San Joaquin Estuary. Transactions of the Amer. Fisheries Society 126: 961-976.

Young, P.S. and J.J. Cech. 1996. Environmental tolerances and requirements of splittail. Transactions of the Amer. Fisheries Society 125: 664-678.

Chinook Salmon

Oncorhynchus tshawytscha

Lt. Dante B. Maragni

General Information

The Chinook salmon (Family: Salmonidae) is morphologically distinguished from other *Oncorhynchus* species of the northern Pacific Ocean by its large size, small black spots on both caudal fin lobes, black pigment along the base of the teeth (McPhail and Lindsey 1970 as cited in Healey 1991), and varying shades of flesh color from white through shades of pink and red (Healey 1991). The Chinook salmon life history (**Figure 2.6**) is characterized by adult migration from the ocean to natal freshwater streams to spawn, and juvenile migration seaward as smolts in their first year of life. During the smoltification process, juvenile Chinook salmon undergo physiological, morphological, and behavioral changes that stimulate emigration and prepare them for life in the marine environment (Healey 1991).

The Sacramento-San Joaquin Chinook salmon of California exists as four races—winter, spring, fall, and late-fall—as defined by the timing of adult spawning migration (Mason 1965, Frey 1971, Moyle 1976, Healey 1991). In 1989, the Sacramento River winter-run Chinook salmon was listed as threatened under the federal Endangered Species Act by the National Marine Fisheries Service (NMFS) (54 FR 32085). NMFS reclassified the winter-run as endangered in 1994 (59 FR 440) based on: 1) the continued decline and increased variability of run sizes since its listing as a threatened species in 1989, 2) the expectation of weak returns in certain years as a result of two small year classes (1991 and 1993), and 3) continuing threats to the population. The State of California listed the winter-run as endangered under the California Endangered Species Act in 1989. In 1995, the Oregon Natural Resources Council and R. Nawa petitioned NMFS to list Chinook salmon along the entire West Coast, including the States of California, Idaho, Oregon, and Washington, under the federal Endangered Species Act (54 FR 32085). The State of California presently includes on its list of species of special concern the late-fall (Class 2–special concern) and the spring-run (Class 1–qualified as threatened or endangered) Chinook salmon. Spring-run Chinook salmon

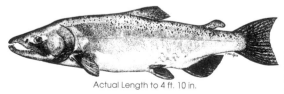

Actual Length to 4 ft. 10 in.

Moyle 1976

Figure 2.6 Life History of Chinook Salmon (USFWS 1995)

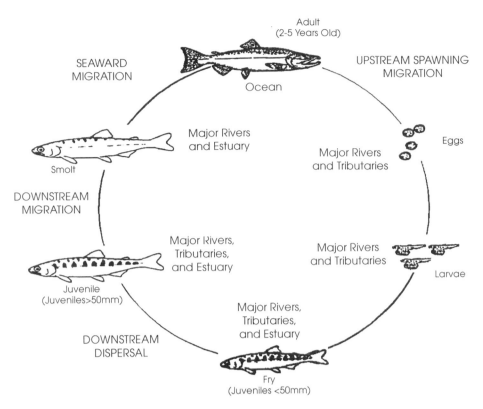

have also been given a special category by the state and are considered a "monitored" species.

Chinook salmon support commercial, recreational, and tribal subsistence fisheries. However, due to the state of Pacific Coast Chinook salmon populations, the U. S. Department of Commerce declared the U.S. Pacific Coast salmon commercial fishery, excluding Alaska, a disaster and has provided emergency relief funding for displaced fisherman in 1995 and 1996 (59 FR 51419, 60 FR 5908). Also, the federal Central Valley Project Improvement Act requires restoration actions to double the Chinook salmon population in the Sacramento-San Joaquin River system in California by the year 2002 estimated from average population levels from 1967 to 1991 (CDFG 1993).

Reproduction

The Chinook salmon is anadromous; that is, it spends most of its adult life in the ocean and returns to freshwater streams to spawn. Chinook salmon typically spend 3-6 years maturing in the ocean before returning as adults to their natal streams to spawn (Moyle 1976, Eschmeyer et al. 1983). Historically, most Sacramento-San Joaquin Chinook salmon returning to spawn have been four years of age (Clark 1929). The Chinook salmon is also semelparous in its reproductive strategy in that it dies after it spawns. Thus, the life span of the Chinook salmon is 3-6 years. All adults die after spawning except some "jacks" (i.e., precocious males

that mature early in freshwater) (Miller and Brannon 1982).

Chinook salmon can be grouped into two types based on variations in their life histories: stream-type and ocean-type. Stream-type Chinook salmon populations are most commonly found north of 56°N latitude along the North American coast and characterized by long freshwater residence as juveniles (1+ years). Ocean-type Chinook salmon populations are most commonly found south of 56°N latitude and characterized by short freshwater residence as juveniles (2-3 months). Chinook salmon of the Sacramento-San Joaquin River system are predominantly ocean-type (Healey 1991). Adult upstream migration and juvenile downstream migration of the Sacramento-San Joaquin Chinook salmon differ among the four races. Sacramento-San Joaquin Chinook salmon populations' migration characteristics are listed in **Table 2.4** (Bryant, pers. comm.).

The Chinook salmon normally spawns in large rivers and tributaries, and typically in deeper water and larger gravel than other Pacific salmon (Scott and Crossman 1973). In preparation for spawning, a female Chinook salmon digs a shallow depression in the gravel of the stream bottom in an area of relatively swift water by performing vigorous swimming movements on her side near the bottom (Emmett et al. 1991, Healey 1991). This depression is referred to as a "redd," and can be 1.2-10.7 m (3.9-35.1 ft) in diameter (Chapman 1943). The female then deposits a group or "pocket" of eggs in the redd (Emmett et al. 1991, Healey 1991). From 2,000 to 14,000 eggs are laid per female, with 5,000 eggs per female being average (Rounsefell 1957, Moyle 1976, Bell 1984). The eggs are in turn fertilized by one or more males. During spawning, a female will be attended by one dominant male and occasionally other subdominant males. The female then buries the eggs by displacing gravels upstream of the redd (Emmett et al. 1991, Healey 1991).

Growth and Development

Chinook salmon eggs are spherical, non-adhesive, and the largest of all the salmonids (6.0-8.5 mm (0.24-0.33 in) in diameter) (Rounsefell 1957, Scott and Crossman 1973, Wang 1986). The incubation range is from 4-6 weeks, depending on levels of dissolved oxygen, biochemical oxygen demand, water temperature, substrate, channel gradient and configuration, water depth, water velocity and discharge (Reiser and Bjornn 1979, Alaska Department of Fish and Game 1985).

Larval sizes range from 20-35 mm (0.79-1.38 in) in length (Wang 1986). Yolk sac fry, termed "alevins," remain in the gravel from 2-3 weeks until the yolk sac is absorbed (Scott and Crossman 1973, Wydoski and Whitney 1979), whence they emerge from the gravel as fry. Fry develop into parr beginning the smoltification process as they encounter increasing salinities during their migration from freshwater to the ocean. Parr acquire a silver color as they transform into smolts during the smoltification process (Healey 1991). Fry and smolts can stay in freshwater from 1-18 months (Beauchamp et al. 1983), with residency periods differing with race (**Table 2.4**). Outmigration periods vary with outflow conditions. High outflows will carry fry downstream, while seasons with low outflow cause fry to rear longer in upstream areas where they grow much larger. Juvenile Chinook salmon in these two differing scenarios

have substantially different habitat requirements (Kjelson et al. 1982). The fry to smolt life stages' size range is 2-152 cm (0.6-42.9 in), but is usually less than 91 cm (25.7 in), in length (Wydoski and Whitney 1979).

Juvenile Chinook salmon migration into estuaries has been reported to occur at night (Seiler et al. 1981) and during daylight (Dawley et al. 1986). Juveniles may move quickly through estuaries (Dawley et al. 1986) or reside there for up to 189 days (Simenstad et al. 1982). Juvenile Chinook salmon gain significant growth in estuarine habitats as they smolt and prepare for the marine phase of their life (MacDonald et al. 1987). The juveniles of most stocks of Chinook salmon appear to migrate north upon entering the ocean (Wright 1968, Healey 1991). Chinook salmon produced in streams from the Rogue River (Oregon) and south appear to rear in the ocean off northern California-southern Oregon (Cramer 1987). The stream-type Chinook salmon move offshore early in their ocean life, whereas ocean-type Chinook salmon remain in sheltered coastal waters. Stream-type Chinook salmon maintain a more offshore distribution throughout their ocean life than do ocean-type (Healey 1991). Chinook salmon reach maturity in 3-6 years (Moyle 1976).

Food and Feeding

Chinook salmon larvae and alevins feed on their yolk. Chinook salmon juveniles and adults are carnivorous, "opportunistic" feeders, feeding on a variety of terrestrial and aquatic insects, crustaceans, and fish (Emmett et al. 1991).

Juveniles in freshwater consume primarily terrestrial and aquatic insects, amphipods and other crustaceans, and sometimes fish (Becker 1973, Higley and Bond 1973, Scott and Crossman 1973, Craddock et al. 1976, Muir and Emmett 1988, Sagar and Glovea 1988).

Table 2.4 Migration Characteristics of Sacramento-San Joaquin Chinook Salmon Runs (Bryant 1997)

Characteristic	Winter	Spring	Fall	Late-fall
ADULT				
Immigration Period	December - July	March - July	June - December	October - April
Peak Immigration	March	May -June	September - October	December
Spawning Period	late April - early August	late August - late October	late September - December	January - late April
Peak Spawning	early June	mid September	late October	early February
JUVENILE				
Emergence Period	July - October	November - March	December - March	April - June
Freshwater Residency Period	5 - 10 months July - April	3 - 15 months November - January (year 2)	4 - 7 months December - June	7 - 13 months April - April (year 2)
Estuarine Emigration Period	November - May	March - June & November - March	March - July	October - May

In estuaries, juveniles feed in intertidal and subtidal habitats of tidal marshes. In these habitats, juveniles prey upon insects, gammarid amphipods, harpacticoid copepods, musids, chironomids, decapod larvae, and small (larval and juvenile) fish (Levy and Levings 1978, Levy et al. 1979, Northcote et al. 1979, Healey 1980a, Levy and Northcote 1981, Healey 1982, Kjelson et al. 1982, Simenstad et al. 1982, Simenstad 1983, McCabe et al. 1986). In low flow years when juveniles are larger, their food source will include crab megalops, squid, and small fish (e.g., northern anchovy, Pacific herring, rockfish) (Beauchamp et al. 1983).

Smaller juvenile Chinook salmon having recently migrated into the marine environment feed on amphipods, euphausiids, and other invertebrates, and small (larval and juvenile) fish (Healey 1980b, Peterson et al.1983, Emmett et al. 1986). Larger juvenile and adult Chinook salmon in the ocean feed primarily on fish (e.g., northern anchovy, Pacific herring, and Pacific sandlance), as well as squid, euphausiids, decapod larvae, and other invertebrates (Silliman 1941, Merkel 1957, Prakash 1962, Ito 1964, Hart 1973, Fresh et al. 1981). Immigrating adult Chinook salmon do not actively feed in freshwater (Emmett et al. 1991).

Distribution

Chinook salmon eggs and alevins are benthic and infaunal. Fry and parr are benthopelagic. Parr become pelagic as they enter smoltification. Smolts, ocean-dwelling and maturing juveniles, and adults are pelagic (Alaska Department of Fish and Game 1985). Adults are bottom-oriented in freshwater (Emmett et al. 1991).

Chinook salmon eggs, alevins, fry, and parr occur in riverine areas from just above the intertidal zone to altitudes of 2,268 m (7,441 ft) above sea level (Allen et al. 1991). Smolts are riverine and estuarine. Ocean-dwelling juveniles are neritic and epipelagic, and found within 128 m (420 ft) of the surface (Fredin et al. 1977). Adults may be neritic and estuarine, but are riverine during their spawning migration and may travel upstream more than 4,700 km (2,920 mi) from the ocean (Emmett et al. 1991) as flows and passage allow. Most tributaries are now dammed for water supply, which limits the extent of upstream migration (USFWS 1995).

The Chinook salmon is the least abundant of the major Pacific salmon species (Emmett et al. 1991, Healey 1991). However, it is the most abundant salmon in California (McGinnis 1984). The Chinook salmon is recorded as far north as the Coppermine River in Arctic Canada, and south to northeastern Hokkaido, Japan, and southern California (Ventura River) (Hart 1973, Scott and Crossman 1973). It is, however, rarely found in freshwater south of the Sacramento-San Joaquin River system of California (Eschmeyer et al. 1983).

While Chinook salmon are found in all estuaries north of San Francisco Bay in California, except Tomales Bay (Monaco et al. 1990), California's largest populations of Chinook salmon originate in the Sacramento-San Joaquin River system (Fry 1973). Spring-run Chinook salmon are extinct in the San Joaquin River and only remnant runs remain in a few Sacramento River tributaries. Historically, spring-run Chinook salmon spawned in small tributaries that have essentially all been blocked to migration by large dams. Fall and late-fall Chinook salmon are main stem spawners. Winter-run Chinook salmon are unique to the Sacramento River and spawned in coldwater tributaries above Shasta Dam prior to its construction (Sacramento River Winter-Run Chinook Salmon Recovery Team 1996). While distribution of outmigrating juvenile Chinook salmon is not well known in the San Francisco Bay, they have been found throughout, including the South Bay on high outflow years.

Population Status and Influencing Factors

Chinook salmon populations have declined substantially, with winter-run at the point of near extinction and spring-run at severely depressed population levels (**Table 2.5**). Whereas spring-run historically outnumbered all other runs, fall-run comprises the bulk of the present Chinook salmon population. The remnant "endangered" population of winter-run now depend on cold water releases from Shasta Reservoir, and the protection of the federal Endangered Species Act.

No single impact can be attributed to the decline of Chinook salmon populations and the important Chinook salmon fishery. High mortality for Chinook salmon occurs during the early freshwater life stages (eggs, fry, parr) (Emmett et al. 1991). This mortality is caused by redd destruction, siltation and destruction of spawning grounds, extremely high or low water temperatures, low dissolved oxygen, loss of cover, disease, food availability and competition, and predation (Reiser and Bjornn 1979). Besides the above factors, human impacts such as river flow reductions, the construction of dams and the consequent creation of reservoirs, water diversions, logging practices, and pollution have affected population abundances (Raymond 1979, Netboy 1980, Stevens and Miller 1983). Factors influencing survival of adult Chinook salmon are equally numerous. In the ocean, Chinook salmon are impacted by oceanographic conditions, disease, food availability and competition, predation, and overfishing (Fraidenburg and Lincoln 1985, Emmett et al. 1991). In freshwater, adults are subject to natural factors such as drought and flood, and human impacts including fishing, dams, road construction and other development, flood protection, dredging, gravel mining, timber harvest, grazing, and pollution (USFWS 1995).

Trophic Levels

Chinook salmon are primary and secondary consumers as juveniles and secondary consumers as adults.

Proximal Species

Juvenile Predators: Sacramento squawfish (*Ptychocheilus grandis*), riffle sculpin (*Cottus gulosus*), channel catfish (*Ictalurus punctatus*), steelhead trout (*Oncorhynchus mykiss*), striped bass (*Morone saxatilis*), centrarchids, rockfish (*Sebastes* spp.), kingfishers, egrets, herons, terns, grebes, pelicans.

Adult Predators: Pacific lamprey (*Lampetra tridentata*), harbor seal (*Phoca vitulina*), California sea lion (*Callorhinus ursinus*), killer whale (*Orcinus orca*), North American river otter (*Lutra canadensis*), American black bear (*Ursus americanus*), bald eagle (*Haliaeetus leucocephalus*).

Juvenile Prey: Terrestrial insects, aquatic insects, chironomids, copepods, amphipods, mysids, euphausiids, decapod larvae, bay shrimp.

Adult Prey: Euphausiids, decapods, squid, Pacific herring (*Clupea pallasi*, northern anchovy (*Engraulis mordax*), osmerids, rockfish (*Sebastes* spp.), Pacific sandlance (*Ammodytes hexapterus*).

Good Habitat

Chinook salmon eggs develop only in freshwater, but larvae can tolerate salinities of up to 15 ppt at hatching. Three months after hatching juvenile Chinook salmon can tolerate full seawater, with faster growing individuals better able to handle salinity changes (Wagner et al. 1969). Juveniles and adults occur in freshwater to euhaline waters. Successful egg incubation occurs from just above freezing to 20.0°C (68.4°F) (Olsen and Fos-

Table 2.5 Estimated Number of Sacramento-San Joaquin Chinook Salmon Returning to Spawn: 1967-1991 (Mills and Fisher 1994) (Continued on next page.)

Year	Sacramento Fall-run Chinook[1]			San Joaquin Fall-run Chinook[2]			Sacramento Late-fall-run Chinook[3]		
	grilse	adult	total	grilse	adult	total	grilse	adult	total
1967	38,410	104,790	143,200	1,176	21,359	22,535	5,730	31,478	37,208
1968	18,181	155,859	174,040	11,211	6,577	17,788	1,910	32,823	34,733
1969	48,528	208,289	256,817	1,935	49,662	51,597	1,747	35,431	37,178
1970	30,121	147,279	177,400	8,539	28,550	37,089	1,823	17,367	19,190
1971	35,775	140,691	176,466	2,986	38,580	41,566	2,277	12,046	14,323
1972	43,795	80,622	124,417	2,454	12,321	14,775	2,398	29,155	31,553
1973	40,640	197,193	237,833	674	6,438	7,112	711	21,493	22,204
1974	25,364	185,953	211,317	762	3,625	4,387	329	6,116	6,445
1975	29,691	141,884	171,575	968	6,258	7,226	816	15,847	16,663
1976	21,926	155,767	177,693	505	3,894	4,399	581	14,699	15,280
1977	22,831	139,971	162,802	60	990	1,050	873	8,217	9,090
1978	23,635	115,363	138,998	254	2,473	2,727	959	7,921	8,880
1979	46,397	152,982	199,379	456	3,897	4,353	44	8,696	8,740
1980	25,472	110,833	136,305	702	5,600	6,302	566	7,181	7,747
1981	42,575	145,503	188,078	8,022	20,295	28,317	168	1,429	1,597
1982	43,396	129,388	172,784	2,681	14,214	16,895	186	955	1,141
1983	41,714	88,676	130,390	32,312	10,970	43,282	1,221	12,053	13,274
1984	41,030	115,509	156,539	18,335	37,641	55,976	2,357	3,550	5,907
1985	41,563	211,695	253,258	4,311	71,873	76,184	1,670	5,990	7,660
1986	27,356	212,739	240,095	3,117	18,588	21,705	490	6,220	6,710
1987	66,364	150,965	217,329	18,269	6,689	24,958	780	13,663	14,443
1988	26,517	197,841	224,358	1,138	20,798	21,936	2,094	8,589	10,683
1989	24,060	116,726	140,786	282	3,489	3,771	286	9,589	9,875
1990	9,443	83,499	92,942	312	663	975	1,536	5,385	6,921
1991	11,546	87,070	98,616	207	647	854	888	5,643	6,531
AVERAGE	33,053	143,083	176,137	4,867	15,844	20,710	1,298	12,861	14,159

[1] Escapement data for the Sacramento River and its tributaries north of and including the American River.
[2] Escapement data for the Mokelumne, Cosumnes, Calaveras, Stanislaus, Tuolumne and Merced rivers.
[3] Escapement data for the main stem Sacramento River above Red Bluff Diversion Dam.

ter 1955), however, best incubation temperatures are 5.0-14.4°C (41.0-57.9°F) (Bell 1984). The upper lethal temperature for Chinook salmon is 25.1°C (77.2°F) (Brett 1952), but may be lower depending on other water quality factors (Ebel et al. 1971). Eggs and alevins are found in areas with flow of 20-150 cm/sec (0.7-5 ft/sec) and juveniles where flows are 0.5-60.0 cm/sec (0.02-2 ft/sec) (at pool edges). Adults can migrate upstream in flows up to 2.44 m/sec (8 ft/sec) (Thompson 1972). Successful egg development requires redds to have adequate dissolved oxygen ($\geq$5.0 mg/L), water temperatures (4-14°C [39-57°F]), substrate permeability, sediment composition ($\leq$25% fines, $\leq$6.4 mm [0.25 in] in diameter), surface flows and velocities, and low biochemical oxygen demand (Reiser and Bjornn 1979).

Juveniles in freshwater avoid waters with $\leq$4.5 mg/L dissolved oxygen at 20°C (68°F) (Whitmore et al. 1960). Migrating adults will pass through water with dissolved oxygen levels as low as 5 mg/L (Hallock et al. 1970). Excessive silt loads ($\geq$4,000 mg/L) may halt Chinook salmon movements or migrations. Silt can also hinder fry emergence, and limit benthic invertebrate (food) production (Reiser and Bjornn 1979). Freshwater inflow into estuaries is critical for providing adequate water temperatures, food production, and overall beneficial environmental conditions for juvenile outmigration. High freshwater flows allow for cooler water temperatures, while also stimulating and sustaining production of food. High river flows improve juvenile survival and enable active migration into estuaries and on to the ocean.

In addition to specific hydrologic components, physical habitat requirements of interrelated instream gravel, riparian, and tidal marsh habitats comprise the healthy ecosystem in which Chinook salmon spawn and rear. Chinook salmon eggs and alevins require clean, loose gravel and occur in spawning gravel or cobble that

Table 2.5 (continued) Estimated Number of Sacramento-San Joaquin Chinook Salmon Returning to Spawn: 1967-1991 (Mills and Fisher 1994)

YEAR	Sacramento Springl-run Chinook[4]			Sacramento Winter-run Chinook[5]			Central Valley Total Chinook Salmon		
	grilse	adult	total	grilse	adult	total	grilse	adult	total
1967	11,397	12,297	23,694	24,985	32,321	57,306	81,698	202,245	283,943
1968	3,317	11,827	15,144	10,299	74,115	84,414	44,917	281,202	326,119
1969	2,843	24,492	27,335	8,953	108,855	117,808	64,006	426,729	490,735
1970	1,420	6,017	7,437	8,324	32,085	40,409	50,228	231,297	281,525
1971	2,464	6,336	8,800	20,864	32,225	53,089	64,366	229,878	294,244
1972	1,343	7,053	8,396	8,541	28,592	37,133	58,531	157,743	216,274
1973	2,082	9,680	11,762	4,623	19,456	24,079	48,729	254,261	302,990
1974	2,538	5,545	8,083	3,788	18,109	21,897	32,782	219,347	252,129
1975	7,683	15,670	23,353	7,498	15,932	23,430	46,656	195,591	242,247
1976	4,067	22,006	26,073	8,634	26,462	35,096	35,712	222,829	258,541
1977	5,421	8,409	13,830	2,186	15,028	17,214	31,372	172,614	203,986
1978	1,093	7,063	8,156	1,193	23,669	24,862	27,134	156,489	183,623
1979	707	2,203	2,910	113	2,251	2,364	47,717	170,029	217,746
1980	3,734	8,081	11,815	1,072	84	1,156	31,545	131,780	163,325
1981	8,249	13,066	21,315	1,744	18,297	20,041	60,757	198,591	259,348
1982	4,528	21,644	26,172	270	972	1,242	51,061	167,947	219,008
1983	672	3,809	4,481	392	1,439	1,831	76,311	116,947	193,258
1984	4,373	3,988	8,361	1,869	794	2,663	67,965	161,481	229,446
1985	3,792	7,631	11,423	329	3,633	3,962	51,665	300,822	352,487
1986	1,606	17,290	18,896	451	2,013	2,464	33,020	256,850	289,870
1987	4,177	7,330	11,507	236	1,761	1,997	89,826	180,408	270,234
1988	2,132	9,521	11,653	708	1,386	2,094	32,589	238,136	270,725
1989	884	6,304	7,188	53	480	533	25,566	136,587	162,153
1990	948	4,376	5,324	16	425	441	12,256	94,347	106,603
1991	433	1,208	1,641	38	153	191	13,112	94,721	107,833
AVERAGE	3,276	9,714	12,990	4,687	18,421	23,109	47,181	199,955	247,136

[4] Escapement data for the main stem Sacramento River above Red Bluff Diversion Dam.
[5] Escapement data for the main stem Sacramento River above Red Bluff Diversion Dam.

is 1.3-10.2 cm (0.5-10.2 in) in diameter (Reiser and Bjornn 1979). Juveniles in freshwater are found within areas of shallow riffles and deep pools over various substrates, ranging from silt bottoms to large boulders (Chapman and Bjornn 1968). Juveniles in estuaries occur in intertidal and tidal habitats over mud, sand, gravel, and eelgrass (*Zostera* spp.) (Healey 1980a). Adults in marine waters show no sediment preference, but may be associated with gravel-cobble bottoms in rivers and streams during upstream migration (Alaska Department of Fish and Game 1985).

In riverine areas, both submerged cover, such as boulders, woody debris, and aquatic vegetation, and overhead cover, such as continuous riparian vegetation canopies, undercut banks, and turbulent water, provide shade, food, and protection against predation to juvenile Chinook salmon. Estuaries appear to play a vital role in Chinook salmon life history as well, and specifically, tidal marsh habitat is of great importance to juvenile salmonids (Dorcey et al. 1978, Levy et al. 1979, Meyer 1979, Levy and Northcote 1981, Healey 1982, MacDonald et al. 1987, 1988). Juvenile Chinook salmon forage in the intertidal and shallow subtidal areas of tidal marsh mudflat, slough, and channel habitats, and open bay habitats of eelgrass and shallow sand shoal areas. These productive habitats provide both a rich food supply and protective cover within shallow turbid waters (McDonald 1960; Dunford 1975, cited from Cannon 1991). The distribution of juvenile Chinook salmon changes tidally, with fry moving from tidal channels during flood tides to feed in nearshore marshes.

Tidal marshes are most heavily used by fry, whereas smolts tend to utilize deeper waters. Fry disperse along the edges of marshes at the highest points reached by the tide, then retreat into the tidal channels with the receding tide. Smolts congregate in surface waters of main and secondary sloughs and move into shallow subtidal areas to feed (Levy and Northcote 1981, Levings 1982, Allen and Hassler 1986, Healey 1991).

In addition to good water quality, adequate flows, and productive spawning and rearing habitat, state-of-the-art positive barrier screens on water diversions, protection from excessive harvest, and free access to upstream migration or well-designed ladders for adult passage offers promising overall habitat for healthy Chinook salmon populations.

References

Alaska Department of Fish and Game. 1985. Alaska habitat management guide, southcentral region, volume I: life histories and habitat requirements of fish and wildlife. Dept. of Fish and Game, Juneau, Al. 429 pp.

Allen, M.A. and T.J. Hassler. 1986. Species profiles: Life histories and environmental requirements of coastal fishes and invertebrates (Pacific Southwest), Chinook salmon. U.S. Fish and Wildl. Serv. Biol. Rept. 82 (11.49). U.S. Army Corps of Engrs., TR EL-82-4. 26 pp.

Allen, M.J., R.J. Wolotira, Jr., T.M. Sample, S.F. Noel and C.R. Iten. 1991. Salmonids: life history descriptions and brief harvest summaries for salmonid species of the northeast Pacific Ocean and eastern Bering Sea. Technical memorandum, NOAA, NMFS, Northwest and Alaska Fisheries Center, Seattle, Wash.

Beauchamp, D.A., M.F. Shepard and G.B. Pauley. 1983. Species profiles: life histories and environmental requirements of coastal fishes and invertebrates (Pacific Northwest), Chinook salmon. U.S. Fish and Wildl. Serv. Biol. Rept. 82(11.6). U.S. Army Corps of Engrs., TR EL-82-4. 15 pp.

Becker, C.D. 1973. Food and growth parameters of juvenile Chinook salmon, *Oncorhynchus tshawytscha*, in central Columbia River. Fish. Bull., U.S. 71:387-400.

Bell, M.C. 1984. Fisheries handbook of engineering requirements and biological criteria. Fish Passage Development and Evaluation Program, U.S. Army Corps of Engrs., North Pac. Div., Portland, OR. 290 pp.

Brett, J.R. 1952. Temperature tolerance in young Pacific salmon, genus *Onchorhynchus*. Journal Fish. Res. Bd. of Canada 9(6):265-323.

California Department of Fish and Game (CDFG). 1993. Restoring Central Valley streams: A plan for action. Sacramento, California.

Cannon, T.C. 1991. Status of the Sacramento-San Joaquin Chinook salmon and factors related to their decline. Report prepared for the National Marine Fisheries Service, Southwest Region, by Envirosphere Company, Newport Beach, Ca.. 11pp.

Chapman, W.M. 1943. The spawning of Chinook salmon in the main Columbia River. Copeia 1943:168-170.

Chapman, W.M. and T.C. Bjornn. 1968. Distribution of salmonids in streams with special reference to food and feeding. *In*: T.G. Northcote (ed). Salmon and trout in streams, pp. 153-176. H.R. MacMillan Lectures in Fisheries, Univ. of British Columbia, Vancouver, British Columbia, Canada.

Clark, G.H. 1929. Sacramento-San Joaquin salmon (*Oncorhynchus tshawytscha*) fishery of California. Fish Bull. No. 17, Ca. Dept. Fish and Game, Sacramento, Ca.

Craddock, D.R., T.H. Blahm and W.D. Parente. 1976. Occurrence and utilization of zooplankton by juvenile Chinook salmon in the lower Columbia River. Transactions of the Amer. Fish. Soc. 105:72-76.

Cramer, S.P. 1987. Oregon studies to increase regional salmon production. Annual progress report, Marine Resources Region, Oregon Dept. Fish and Wildl., Portland, Oregon. 15 pp.

Dawley, E.M., R.D. Ledgerwood, T.H. Blahm, C.W. Sims, J.T Durkin, R.A. Kirn, A.E. Rankis, G.E. Monan and F.J. Ossiander. 1986. Migrational characteristics, biological observations, and relative survival of juvenile salmonids entering the Columbia River Estuary, 1966-1983. Final report to Bonneville Power Administration, Contract DE-A179-84BP39652, 256 pp. Available Northwest and Alaska Fisheries Center, 2725 Montlake Blvd. East, Seattle, Washington, 98112.

Dorcey, A.H.J., T.G. Northcote and D.V. Ward. 1978. Are the Fraser marshes essential to salmon? Lecture Series No. 1, Westwater Research Centre, Univ. of British Columbia, Vancouver, British Columbia, Canada. 29 pp.

Dunford, W.E. 1975. Space and food utilization by salmonids in marsh habitat of the Frazer River Estuary. M.S. thesis, Dept. of Zoology, Univ. of British Columbia, Vancouver, British Columbia, Canada.

Ebel, W.J., E.M. Dawley and B.H. Monk. 1971. Thermal tolerance of juvenile Pacific salmon and steelhead trout in relation to supersaturation of nitrogen gas. Fish. Bull., U.S. 69(4):833-843.

Emmett, R.L., D.R. Miller and T.H. Blahm. 1986. Food of juvenile Chinook, *Oncorhynchus tshawytscha*, and coho, *O. kisutch*, salmon off the Northern Oregon and Southern Washington Coasts, May-September 1980. Ca. Dept. Fish and Game 72(1):38-46.

Emmett, R.L., S.A. Hinton, M.E. Monaco and S.L. Stone. 1991. Distribution and abundance of fishes and invertebrates in West Coast estuaries, volume II: species life history summaries. ELMR Report No. 4. Strategic Assessment Branch, NOS/NOAA, Rockville, Maryland. 329 pp.

Eschmeyer, W.N., W.S. Herald and H. Hammann. 1983. A field guide to Pacific Coast fishes of North America. Houghton Mifflin Co., Boston, Massachusetts. 336 pp.

Fraidenburg, M.E. and R.H. Lincoln. 1985. Wild Chinook salmon management: an international conservation challenge. No. Amer. J. Fish. Mgmt. 5(3A):311-329.

Fredin, R.A., R.L. Major, R.G. Bakkala and G.K. Tanonaka. 1977. Pacific salmon and high seas salmon fisheries of Japan. Proceedings report, NOAA, NMFS, Northwest and Alaska Fisheries Center, Seattle, Washington. 324 pp.

Fresh, K.L., R.D. Cardwell and R.R. Koons. 1981. Food habits of Pacific salmon, baitfish, and their potential competitors and predators in the marine waters of Washington, August 1978 to September 1979. Progress report no. 145, Washington Dept. of Fisheries, Olympia, Washington. 58 pp.

Frey, H.W. 1971. California's living marine resources and their utilization. Ca. Dept. Fish and Game, Sacramento, Ca. 148 pp.

Fry, D.H. 1973. Anadromous fishes of California. Ca. Dept. Fish and Game, Sacramento, Ca. 111 pp.

Hallock, R.J., R.F. Elwell and D.H. Fry, Jr. 1970. Migrations of adult king salmon (*Oncorhynchus tshawytscha*) in the San Joaquin Delta. Ca. Dept. Fish and Game Bull. 151:1-92.

Hart, J.L. 1973. Pacific fishes of Canada. Bulletin of the Fisheries Research Board of Canada, bulletin no. 180. 740 pp.

Healey, M.C. 1980a. Utilization of the Nanaimo River Estuary by juvenile Chinook salmon, *Oncorhynchus tshawytscha*. Fish. Bull., U.S. 77(3):653-668.

_____. 1980b. The Ecology of Juvenile Salmon in Georgia Strait, British Columbia. *In:* W.J. McNeil and D.C. Himsworth (eds). Salmonid Ecosystems of the North Pacific, pp. 203-229. Oregon State Univ. Press, Corvallis, Oregon.

_____. 1982. Juvenile Pacific salmon in estuaries: the life support system. *In:* V.S. Kennedy (ed). Estuarine comparison. Academic Press, New York, NY, pp. 315-341.

_____. 1991. Life history of Chinook Salmon (*O. Tshawytscha*). *In:* C. Groot and L. Margolis (ed). Pacific salmon life histories, pp. 331-391. UBC Press, Univ. of British Columbia, Vancouver, British Columbia, Canada.

Higley, D.L. and C.E. Bond. 1973. Ecology and production of juvenile spring Chinook salmon, *Oncorhynchus tshawytscha*, in an entropic reservoir. Fish. Bull., U.S. 71(3):877-891.

Ito, J. 1964. Food and feeding habits of Pacific salmon (genus *Oncorhynchus*) in their ocean life. Bull. of the Hokkaido Reg. Fish. Res. Lab. 29:85-97. (Fisheries Research Board of Canada Translation Service 1309).

Kjelson, M.A., P.F. Raquel and R.W. Fisher. 1982. Life history of fall-run Chinook salmon, *Oncorhynchus tshawytscha* in the Sacramento-San Joaquin Estuary, California. *In:* V.S. Kennedy (ed). Estuarine comparisons. Academic Press, New York, NY, pp. 393-411.

Levings, C.D. 1982. Short term use of a low-tide refugia in a sandflat by juvenile Chinook, (*Oncorhynchus tshawytscha*), Fraser River Estuary. Can. Tech. Rpt. Fish and Aq. Sci. 1111. 7 pp.

Levy, D.A. and C.D. Levings. 1978. A description of the fish community of the Squamish River Estuary, British Columbia: relative abundance, seasonal changes, and feeding habits of salmonids. Fish. Env. Canada, Fish. Mar. Serv. Manuscript Rept. No. 1475. 63 pp.

Levy, D.A. and T.G. Northcote. 1981. The distribution and abundance of juvenile salmon in marsh habitats of the Fraser River Estuary. Technical report no. 25, Westwater Research Centre, Univ. of British Columbia, Vancouver, British Columbia, Canada. 117 pp.

Levy, D.A., T.G. Northcote and G.J. Birch. 1979. Juvenile salmon utilization of tidal channels in the Fraser River Estuary, British Columbia. Technical report no. 23, Westwater Research Centre, Univ. of British Columbia, Vancouver, British Columbia, Canada. 70 pp.

MacDonald, J.S., I.K. Birtwell and G.M. Kruzynski. 1987. Food and habitat utilization by juvenile salmonids in the Campbell River Estuary. Can. J. Fish. and Aquatic Sci. 44:1233-1246.

MacDonald, J.S., C.D. Levings, C.D. McAllister, U.H.M. Fagerlund and J.R. McBride. 1988. A field experiment to test the importance of estuaries for Chinook salmon (*Oncorhynchus tshawytscha*) survival: short-term results. Can. J. Fish. and Aquatic Sci. 45(8):1366-1377.

Mason, J.E. 1965. Salmon of the North Pacific Ocean—part IX. Coho, Chinook, and masu salmon in offshore waters. International North Pacific Fisheries Commission, Bulletin No. 6. 135 pp.

McCabe, G.T., Jr., R.L. Emmett, W.D. Muir and T.H. Blahm. 1986. Utilization of the Columbia River Estuary by subyearling Chinook salmon. Northwest Science 60(2):113-124.

McDonald, J. 1960. The behavior of Pacific salmon fry during their downstream migration to freshwater and saltwater nursery areas. J. Fish. Res. Bd. Canada 17(5):655-676.

McGinnis, S.M. 1984. Freshwater fishes of California. Univ. of California Press, Berkeley, Ca. 316 pp.

McPhail, J.D. and C.C. Lindsay. 1970. Freshwater fishes of northwestern Canada and Alaska. Bull. Fish. Res. Bd. Canada, No. 173. 381 pp.

Merkel, T.J. 1957. Food habits of king salmon, *Oncorhynchus tshawytscha* (Walbaum), in the vicinity of San Francisco, California. Ca. Dept. Fish and Game 43(4): 249-270.

Meyer, J.H. 1979. A Review of the literature on the value of estuarine and shoreline areas to juvenile salmonids in Puget Sound, Washington. U.S. Fish and Wildl. Serv., Fisheries Assistance Office, Olympia, Washington. 24 pp.

Miller, R.J. and E.L. Brannon. 1982. The origin and development of life history patterns in Pacific salmonids. *In*: E. L. Brannon and E. O. Salo (eds). Salmon and trout migratory behavior symposium, pp. 296-309. School of Fisheries, Univ. of Washington, Seattle, Washington.

Mills, T.J. and F. Fisher. 1994. Central Valley anadromous sport fish annual run-size, harvest, and population estimates, 1967 through 1991. Second draft. Inland Fisheries Tech. Rept., Ca. Dept. Fish and Game, Sacramento, Ca. 62 pp.

Monaco, M.E., R.L. Emmett, S.A. Hinton and D.M. Nelson. 1990. Distribution and abundance of fishes and invertebrates in West Coast estuaries, volume I: data summaries. ELMR Report No. 4. Strategic Assessment Branch, NOS/NOAA, Rockville, Maryland. 240 pp.

Moyle, P.B. 1976. Inland Fishes of California. Univ. of California Press, Berkeley, Ca. 405 pp.

Muir, W.D. and R.L. Emmett. 1988. Food habits of migrating salmonid smolts passing Bonneville Dam in the Columbia River, 1984. Regulated river reservoir management 2:1-10.

National Marine Fisheries Service (NMFS). 1989. Endangered and threatened species, critical habitat; winter-run Chinook salmon. Federal Register 32085. Vol. 54(149).

_____. 1994. Endangered and threatened species; status of Sacramento River winter-run Chinook salmon. Federal Register 440. Volume 59(2).

_____. 1994. West Coast salmon fisheries; northwest emergency assistance plan. Federal Register 51419. Volume 59(195).

_____. 1995. West Coast salmon fisheries; northwest emergency assistance program; revisions. Federal Register 5908. Volume 60(20).

Netboy, A. 1980. The Columbia River salmon and steelhead trout, their fight for survival. Univ. of Washington Press, Seattle, Washington. 180 pp.

Northcote, T.G., N.T. Johnston and K. Tsumura. 1979. Feeding relationships and food web structure of Lower Fraser River fishes. Tech. Rept. no. 16, Westwater Research Centre, Univ. of British Columbia, Vancouver, British Columbia, Canada.

Olsen, P.A. and R.F. Foster. 1955. Temperature tolerance of eggs and young of Columbia River Chinook salmon. Transactions of the Amer. Fish. Soc. 85:203-207.

Peterson, W.T., R.D. Brodeur and W.A. Pearcy. 1983. Feeding habits of juvenile salmonids in the Oregon coastal zone in June 1979. Fish. Bull., U.S. 80(4):841-851.

Prakash, A. 1962. Seasonal changes in feeding of coho and Chinook (spring) salmon in southern British Columbia waters. J. Fish. and Aquatic Sci. 19(5):851-866.

Raymond, H.L. 1979. Effects of dams and impoundments on migrations of juvenile Chinook salmon and steelhead from the Snake River, 1966-1975. Transactions of the Amer. Fish. Soc. 108(6):505-529.

Reiser, D.W. and T.J. Bjornn. 1979. Habitat requirements of anadromous salmonids. *In*: W.R. Meehan (ed). Influence of forest and rangeland management on anadromous fish habitat in the Western United States and Canada, pp. 1-54. U.S. Forest Service general technical report PNW-96, Northwest Forest Range Experimental Station, Portland, Oregon.

Rounsefell, G.A. 1957. Fecundity of North American salmonidae. Fish. Bull., U.S. 122:451-468.

Sacramento River Winter-Run Chinook Salmon Recovery Team. 1996. Recommendations for the recovery of the Sacramento River winter-run Chinook salmon. March 8, 1996. Prepared under the direction of the National Marine Fisheries Service.

Sagar, P.M. and G.J. Govea. 1988. Diet, feeding, periodicity, daily ration, and prey selection of a riverine population of juvenile Chinook salmon, *Oncorhynchus tshawytscha* (Walbaum). J. Fish Biol. 33:643-653.

Seiler, D., S. Neuhauser and M. Ackley. 1981. Upstream/downstream salmonid trapping project, 1977-1980. Progress Report No. 144, Washington Dept. of Fisheries, Olympia, Washington. 197 pp.

Scott, W.B. and E.J. Crossman. 1973. Freshwater fishes of Canada. Bull. of Fish. Res. Bd. of Canada, Bull. No. 184. 966 pp.

Silliman, R.P. 1941. Fluctuations in the diet of Chinook and silver salmon (*Oncorhynchus tshawytscha* and *O. kisutch*) of Washington as related to the troll catch of salmon. Copeia, 2:80-97.

Simenstad, C.A. 1983. The ecology of estuarine channels of the Pacific Northwest Coast: a community profile. U.S. Fish and Wildl. Serv. Biol. Serv., Biol. Rept. 83(5). 181 pp.

Simenstad, C.A., K.L. Fresh and E.O. Salo. 1982. The role of Puget Sound and Washington coastal estuaries in the life history of Pacific salmon: an unappreciated function. *In*: V.S. Kennedy (ed). Estuarine comparisons, pp. 343-364. Academic Press, New York, NY.

Stevens, D.E. and L.W. Miller. 1983. Effects of river flow on abundance of young Chinook salmon, American shad, longfin smelt, and Delta smelt in the Sacramento-San Joaquin river system. No. Amer. J. Fish. Mgmt. 3:425-437.

Thompson, K. 1972. Determining stream flows for fish life. *In*: Proceeding, Instream Flow Requirements Workshop, pp. 31-50. Pacific Northwest River Basin Commission, Vancouver, Washington.

United States Fish and Wildlife Service (USFWS). 1995. Working paper: habitat restoration actions to double natural production of anadromous fish in the Central Valley of California. Volume 2. May 9, 1995. Prepared under the direction of the Anadromous Fish Restoration Program Core Group. Stockton, California.

Wagner, H.H., F.P. Conte and J.L. Fessler. 1969. Development of osmotic and ionic regulation in two races of Chinook salmon (*Oncorhynchus tshawytscha*). Comparative Biochemical Physiology 29:325-341.

Wang, J.C.S. 1986. Fishes of the Sacramento-San Joaquin Estuary and adjacent waters, California: A guide to the early life histories. Tech. Rept. No. 9. Interagency Ecological Study Program for the Sacramento-San Joaquin Estuary. Ca. Dept. of Water Res., Ca. Dept. Fish and Game, U.S. Bureau of Reclamation, and U.S. Fish and Wildl. Serv.

Whitmore, C.M., C.E. Warren and P. Doudoroff. 1960. Avoidance reactions of salmonid and centrarchid fishes to low oxygen concentrations. Transactions of the Amer. Fish. Soc. 89(1):17-26.

Wright, S.G. 1968. The origin and migration of Washington's Chinook and coho salmon. Information Booklet No. 1, Washington Dept. of Fisheries, Olympia, Washington. 25 pp.

Wydoski, R.S. and R.R. Whitney. 1979. Inland fishes of Washington. Univ. of Washington Press, Seattle, Washington. 220 pp.

Personal Communications

Greg Bryant, Fisheries Biologist, National Marine Fisheries Service, Southwest Region, Protected Species Division, Eureka, California.

Fish

Steelhead

Oncorhynchus mykiss irideus

Robert A. Leidy

General Information

Steelhead (Family: Salmonidae) are the anadromous (sea-run) form of resident rainbow trout. Behnke (1992) proposed classification of steelhead on the west coast of the United States into a coastal subspecies, *O. m. irideus*, and an inland subspecies, *O. m. gairdneri*. California is considered to have only coastal steelhead (Behnke 1992). In California steelhead may be classified into two races, summer and winter steelhead, based upon the timing of upstream migration into freshwater. The San Francisco Estuary and its tributary streams support winter steelhead. Steelhead are a polymorphic species and as such populations within a stream may be anadromous, resident, or mixtures of the two forms that presumably interbreed (Titus et al., *in press*). Steelhead do not support a commercial fishery within the San Francisco Estuary and its tributaries. It is illegal for commercial salmon trollers to possess steelhead (McEwan and Jackson 1996). There is a inland recreational sportfishery for steelhead that is dependent largely on hatchery operations to sustain populations. The estimated net annual economic benefit of doubling steelhead stocks within the Sacramento/San Joaquin river systems is estimated at 8.0 million dollars (Meyer Resources Inc. 1988).

Reproduction

Polymorphic salmonids exhibit a high degree of life history variation (Titus et al., *in press*). Steelhead within the San Francisco Estuary may be classified as "ocean-maturing" or "winter" steelhead that typically begin their spawning migration in the fall and winter, and spawn within a few weeks to a few months from when they enter freshwater (McEwan and Jackson 1996). Ocean maturing steelhead enter freshwater with well-developed gonads and spawn shortly after entering a river or stream. Steelhead begin upstream migration after one to four growing seasons at sea (Burgner et al. 1992). A small number of immature fish (i.e., grilse) may also move upstream after spending only a few months in the ocean.

Releases of cold water from several large Central Valley reservoirs on the Sacramento River system may induce steelhead to begin to move into upstream tributaries as early as August and September. This means that upstream migrating steelhead may be observed within San Francisco Bay and Suisun Marsh/Bay between August and March. Ocean-maturing steelhead typically spawn between December and April, with most spawning occurring between January through March.

Steelhead are iteroparous and do not die after spawning as do other Pacific salmon; therefore, they may return to the ocean and spawn again the following year. The frequency of return spawning for a given population is generally unknown. Steelhead spawn in redds constructed by the female over a gravel/cobble substrate. Eggs are deposited in the redd and then fertilized by the male. The number of eggs produced is largely a function of the size of the female, and may range from 200 to 12,000 eggs over the geographic range of steelhead (Scott and Crossman 1973, Moyle 1976). Steelhead within the Sacramento River drainage average between 1,000 to 4,500 eggs (Mills and Fisher 1994).

Growth and Development

Steelhead eggs are spherical to slightly irregular in shape, non-adhesive, demersal, and range in diameter from 3-6 mm (Wang 1986). Incubation of eggs is dependent upon water temperature in the redd. Wales (1941) observed hatching at approximately 19 days at an average water temperature of 15.5° C and 80 days at about 4.5° C. For Waddell Creek in coastal San Mateo County, steelhead hatching time was estimated at 25 to 35 days, with emergence beginning at 2-3 weeks following hatching (Shapovalov and Taft 1954). Steelhead length at hatching ranges between 14 to 15.5 mm total length (TL), with alevins ranging between 23-26 mm TL (Wang 1986). Alevins emerge from the gravel following yolk sac absorption as fry or juveniles ready to actively feed.

Steelhead remain in freshwater for one to four years (usually two years) before downstream migration as "smolts", at an average size ranging between 13 cm and 25 cm TL (Moyle 1976). Age at emigration is highly variable, but may occur earlier in warmer, more productive streams where juveniles can reach smolt size at a younger age (Moyle et al. 1995). Most Sacramento River juvenile steelhead emigrate as 1-year-old fish during spring and early summer (Barnhart 1986, Reynolds et al. 1993), although Shapovalov and Taft (1954) found that steelhead moved downstream in Waddell Creek during all months of the year. While steelhead may spend up to four years in the ocean, most only survive to age two. In the ocean steelhead may grow at a rate of 1.2 inches per month and reach a length of 23 inches in two years.

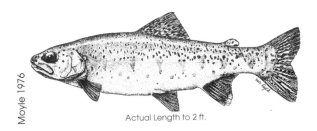

Moyle 1976

Actual Length to 2 ft.

Food and Feeding

Rearing juvenile steelhead are primarily drift feeders utilizing a variety of terrestrial and aquatic insects, including emergent aquatic insects, aquatic insect larvae, snails, amphipods, opossum shrimp, and various species of small fish (Moyle 1976). Larger steelhead will feed on newly emergent steelhead fry. Emigrating adult and juvenile steelhead may forage in the open water of estuarine subtidal and riverine tidal wetland habitats within the Estuary, although the importance of these areas as rearing habitat for juveniles is not well documented. Apparently upstream migrating steelhead rarely eat and therefore exhibit reduced growth (Pauley and Bortz 1986).

Distribution

Steelhead populations are native to Pacific Ocean coastal drainages of the Kamchatka Peninsula and scattered mainland locations of Asia and in the western Pacific from the Kuskokwim River in Alaska to Malibu Creek in southern California (Titus et al., *in press*, McEwan and Jackson 1996, Moyle 1976). Although the life-history characteristics of steelhead are generally well known, the polymorphic nature of the subspecies has resulted in much confusion over the status and distribution of steelhead in San Francisco Estuary and its tributaries. Historically, the Sacramento-San Joaquin River systems supported large runs of steelhead (McEwan and Jackson 1996). Presumably, most streams with suitable habitat within the San Francisco Estuary also supported steelhead, however accurate population estimates for individual streams are not available (Skinner 1962, Leidy 1984).

Currently, small steelhead runs of unknown size are known to exist in South San Francisco Bay in San Francisquito Creek, San Mateo County; Guadalupe River and Coyote and Upper Penitencia creeks, Santa Clara County; Alameda Creek, Alameda County; and possibly San Leandro Creek, Alameda County (R. Leidy, unpub. data). Within Central San Francisco Bay steelhead runs are believed to occur in Corte Madera Creek and its tributaries, Miller Creek, Novato Creek, and possibly Arroyo Corte Madera del Presideo Creek, Marin County (R. Leidy, unpub. data). Within San Pablo Bay, steelhead make spawning runs in the Napa River and several of its tributary streams and Huichica Creek, Napa County; and the Petaluma River and Sonoma Creek and several of their tributary streams, Sonoma County (R. Leidy, unpub. data). Tributaries to Suisun Bay and adjacent drainages that support steelhead runs of unknown size include the Sacramento and San Joaquin rivers; Green Valley and Suisun creeks, Solano County; and Walnut Creek and possibly Alhambra, Pinole, Wildcat, and San Pablo creeks, Contra Costa County (R. Leidy,

unpub. data). Steelhead may also be present in other tributary streams below migration barriers within the Estuary, but currently there is little or no data on their status in many streams. Steelhead adults and smolts may be found foraging in and migrating through estuarine subtidal and riverine tidal habitats within all areas of the San Francisco Estuary.

Population Status and Influencing Factors

Nehlsen et al. (1991) identified at least 43 steelhead stocks at moderate to high risk of extinction, with more than 23 stocks believed to have been extirpated, on the west coast of the United States. Steelhead in California are estimated to number roughly 250,000 adults, which is one half the adult population of 30 years ago (McEwan and Jackson 1996). As a result of this precipitous decline, the National Marine Fisheries is currently reviewing the status of steelhead to determine if they warrant listing under the Endangered Species Act. Estimates of the average annual steelhead run size for the Sacramento-San Joaquin River system, including San Francisco Bay tributaries, range between 10,000 and 40,000 adults (Hallock et al. 1961, McEwan and Jackson 1996). The *California Fish and Wildlife Plan* (CDFG 1965) estimated an annual run size for the Sacramento above the mouth of the Feather River of approximately 30,000 fish, and a total for the reminder of the entire Central Valley of 40,000 steelhead, including tributaries to San Francisco Bay. This likely places the size of steelhead runs in San Francisco Bay tributaries at well below 10,000 fish, however, the fact remains that reliable estimates for individual streams tributary to San Francisco Estuary do not exist.

General factors influencing steelhead population numbers during upstream migration, spawning, and incubation include barriers to passage, diversions, flow fluctuations, water temperature, and other water quality parameters, such as sedimentation of spawning habitats. Factors affecting juvenile rearing habitat and emigration within the San Francisco Estuary and its tributary streams include low summer flows combined with high water temperatures. Within Suisun Bay/Marsh the downstream migrating steelhead are adversely affected by altered flows, entrainment, and mortality associated with trapping, loading, and trucking fish at state and federal pumping facilities. In addition, dredging and dredged material disposal within the San Francisco Estuary may contribute to degradation of steelhead habitat and interference with migration, foraging, and food resources (LTMS 1996).

Trophic Levels

Larvae are primary consumers. Juveniles and adults are primary and higher order consumers.

Proximal Species

Egg Predators: Freshwater sculpins.
Juvenile and Smolt Predators: Other large freshwater, estuarine, and marine piscivorous fish.
Juvenile and Adult Predators: Harbor seals and other pennipeds.
Habitat/Cover: Riparian, emergent, and palustrine wetland vegetation.
Major Prey Items: Aquatic and terrestrial insects, amphipods, snails, mysid shrimp, small fish.

Good Habitat

The preferred water depth for steelhead spawning ranges from six to 24 inches, while fry and parr prefer water depths of between two to 14 inches and 10 to 20 inches, respectively (Bovee 1978). Steelhead prefer to spawn in areas with water velocities of approximately two ft/sec (range = 1-3.6 ft/sec), although optimal spawning velocity is partially a function of the size of fish; larger fish can successfully spawn in higher water velocities (Barnhart 1986). Optimal spawning substrate is reported to range from 0.2 to 4.0 inches in diameter, but steelhead will utilize various mixtures of sand-gravel and gravel-cobble (Bovee 1978, Reiser and Bjornn 1979). Optimal temperature requirements for steelhead vary as follows: adult migration, 46° to 52° F; spawning, 39° to 52° F; incubation and emergence, 48° to 52° F; fry and juvenile rearing, 45° to 60° F, and smoltification, < 57° F (Bovee 1978, Reiser and Bjornn 1979, Bell 1986). While egg mortality begins to occur at 56° F and fish are known to have difficulty extracting oxygen from the water at temperatures exceeding 70° F (Hooper 1973), steelhead populations are often adapted to local environmental conditions where preferred temperature conditions are regularly exceeded for prolonged time periods (McEwan and Jackson 1996).

Some other important factors that are critical to maintaining optimal steelhead habitat include water quality and quantity, habitat heterogeneity, migration barriers, and introduced salmonids. Steelhead require relatively "good" water quality (e.g., low suspended sediment and contaminant loads and other forms of pollution), as well as sufficient flows for spawning, rearing, and migration. Diverse stream habitats consisting of shallow riffles for spawning and relatively deep pools, with well-developed cover, for rearing are important factors. The importance of estuarine or riverine tidal wetlands within the San Francisco Estuary for rearing/foraging or migrating steelhead are not well understood.

References

Barnhart, R.A. 1986. Species profiles: life histories and environmental requirements of coastal fishes and invertebrates (Pacific Southwest)—steelhead. U.S. Fish. Wildl. Serv. Biol. Rep. 82(11.60). U.S. Army Corps of Engrs., TR EL-82-4. 21 pp.

Behnke, R.J. 1992. Native trout of western North America. Amer. Fish. Soc. Monograph no. 6. 275 pp.

Bell, M.C. 1986. Fisheries handbook of engineering requirements and biological criteria. Fish Passage Development and Evaluation Program, U.S. Army Corps of Engrs., No. Pacific Div., Portland, OR. 290 pp.

Bovee, K.D. 1978. Probability-of-use-criteria for the family Salmonidae. Instream Flow Information Paper 4, U.S. Fish Wildl. Serv., FWS/OBS-78/07. 79 pp.

Burgner, R.L., J.Y. Light, L. Margolis, T. Okazaki, A Tautz and S. Ito. 1992. Distribution and origins of steelhead trout (*Oncorhynchus mykiss*) in offshore waters of the north Pacific Ocean. International North Pacific Fisheries Commission. Bull No. 51.

California Department of Fish and Game (CDFG). 1965. California fish and wildlife plan. Sacramento, CA.

Hallock, R.J., W.F. Van Woert and L. Shapovalov. 1961. An evaluation of stocking hatchery-reared steelhead rainbow trout (*Salmo gairdneri gairdneri*) in the Sacramento River system. Ca. Dept. Fish and Game Fish Bull. No, 114. 74 pp.

Hooper, D.R. 1973. Evaluation of the effects of flows on trout stream ecology. Dept. of Eng. Res., Pacific Gas and Electric Co., Emeryville, CA. 97 pp.

Leidy, R.A. 1984. Distribution and ecology of stream fishes in the San Francisco bay drainage. Hilgardia 52(8): 1-175.

Long-term Management Strategy (LTMS). 1996. Draft long term management strategy for the placement of dredged material in the San Francisco Bay Region. Prepared by the LTMS Multi-Agency Writing Team for the LTMS Management Committee. Vol II, Appendices.

Meyer Resources Inc. 1988. Benefits from present and future salmon and steelhead production in California. Report to the California Advisory Committee on Salmon and Steelhead. 78 pp.

McEwan, D. and T.A. Jackson. 1996. Steelhead restoration and management plan for California. Ca. Dept. Fish and Game, Inland Fisheries Division, Sacramento, CA. 234 pp.

Mills, T.J. and F. Fisher. 1994. Central Valley anadromous sport fish annual run-size, harvest, and population estimates, 1967 through 1991. Ca. Dept. Fish and Game. Inland Fisheries Division Tech. Rept.. Draft. 70 pp.

Moyle, P.B. 1976. Inland Fishes of California. Univ. of California Press. 405 pp.

Moyle, P.B., R.M. Yoshiyama, J.E. Williams and E.D. Wikramanayake. 1995. Fish species of special concern in California. Ca. Dept. Fish and Game. Inland Fisheries Division, Rancho Cordova, CA. 272 pp.

Nehlsen, W., J.E. Williams and J.A. Lichatowich. 1991. Pacific salmon at the crossroads: stocks at risk from California, Oregon, Idaho, and Washington. Fisheries 16 (2): 4-21.

Pauley, G.B. and B.M. Bortz. 1986. Species profiles: life histories and environmental requirements of coastal fishes and invertebrates (Pacific northwest): steelhead trout. U.S. Fish and Wildl. Serv. Biol. Rept. 82(11.62). 24 pp.

Reiser, D.W. and T.C. Bjornn. 1979. Habitat requirements of anadromous salmonids. USDA, Forest Service, Pacific Northwest Forest and Range Experiment Station, Portland, OR, General Tech. Rept. PNW-96. 54 pp.

Reynolds, F.L., T.J. Mills, R. Benthin and A. Low. 1993. Restoring Central Valley streams: a plan for action. Ca. Dept. Fish and Game. Inland Fisheries Division, Rancho Cordova, CA.

Scott, W.B. and E.J. Crossman. 1973. Freshwater fishes of Canada. Bull. Fish. Res. Brd. Can. 184. 966 pp.

Shapovalov, L. and A.C. Taft. 1954. The life histories of the steelhead rainbow trout (*Salmo gairdneri gairdneri*) and silver salmon (*Oncorhynchus kisutch*) with special reference to Waddell Creek, California, and recommendations regarding their management. Ca. Dept. Fish and Game, Fish Bull. 98. 375 pp.

Skinner, J.E. 1962. An historical review of the fish and wildlife resources of the San Francisco Bay Area. Ca. Dept. Fish and Game Water Projects Br. Rpt. No. 1.

Titus, R.G., D.C. Erman and W.M. Snider. *In press.* History and status of steelhead in California coastal drainages south of San Francisco Bay. Ca. Dept. Fish and Game, Fish Bull.

Wales, J.H. 1941. Development of steelhead trout eggs. Ca. Dept. Fish and Game 27: 250-260.

Wang, J.C.S. 1986. Fishes of the Sacramento-San Joaquin estuary and adjacent waters, California: A guide to the early life histories. Interagency Ecolog. Study Prog. for the Sacramento-San Joaquin Estuary. Interagency Ecological Workshop, Asilomar, CA.

Delta Smelt

Hypomesus transpacificus

Ted R. Sommer
Bruce Herbold

General Information

The Delta smelt (Family Osmeridae) is a small, short-lived native fish which is found only in the Bay-Delta Estuary. The species was listed as threatened in 1993 under the Federal Endangered Species Act. Habitat loss is thought to be one of the most important elements in causing its decline. New water quality standards adopted by the state in 1995 are aimed in part at improving habitat conditions (SWRCB 1995).

Reproduction

The Delta smelt has low fecundity and is primarily an annual species, although a few individuals may survive a second year (Herbold et al. 1992). The location and season of Delta smelt spawning varies from year to year. Spawning, which occurs in shallow freshwater (CDFG 1992b, USFWS 1994), has been known to occur at various sites within the Delta, including the lower Sacramento and San Joaquin rivers and Georgiana Slough, and in sloughs of the Suisun Marsh (USFWS 1994). In 1996, newly emerged Delta smelt larvae were found in the Napa River, Cordelia Slough, Montezuma Slough, and in the San Joaquin River up to Stockton (CDFG unpub. data). Based on egg and larval trawls in recent low flow years, it appears that a significant portion of Delta smelt spawning now takes place in the northern and western Delta (CDWR 1992).

Spawning may occur from late winter (December) to early summer (July). In 1989 and 1990, two spawning peaks occurred, one in late-April and another early-May (USFWS 1994). Spawning has been reported to occur at about 45° to 59° F (7-15° C) in tidally influenced rivers and sloughs, including dead-end sloughs and shallow edge waters of the upper Delta. Most spawning occurs in fresh water, but some may occur in brackish water in or near the entrapment zone (Wang 1991). The demersal, adhesive eggs sink and attach to hard substrates, such as submerged tree branches and roots, gravel

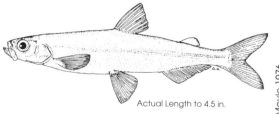

Actual Length to 4.5 in.

Moyle 1976

or rocks, and submerged vegetation. Survival of adhesive eggs and larvae is probably significantly influenced by hydrology at the time of spawning (CDWR and USBR 1994). Moyle et al. (1992) found no correlation between female length and fecundity. Females of 59-70 mm standard length (SL) ranged in fecundity from 1,247 to 2,590 eggs per fish, with an average of 1,907.

Spawning stock does not appear to have a major influence on Delta smelt year class success. However, the low fecundity of this species, combined with planktonic larvae which likely have high rates of mortality, requires a large spawning stock if the population is to perpetuate itself. This may not have been an important factor in the decline of Delta smelt, but it may be important for its recovery (CDFG 1992b).

Growth and Development

Newly hatched larvae are planktonic and drift downstream near the surface to the freshwater/saltwater interface in nearshore and channel areas. Maeger (1993) found that larvae hatched in 10 to 14 days under laboratory conditions and started feeding on phytoplankton at day four and on zooplankton at day six. Growth is rapid through summer, and juveniles reach 40 to 50 mm fork length (FL; the measure to the bottom of the fork of the tail fin) by early August. Growth slows in fall and winter, presumably to allow for gonadal development. Adults range from 55 to 120 mm FL, but most do not grow larger than 80 mm FL. Delta smelt become sexually mature in the fall at approximately seven to nine months of age. The majority of adults die after spawning.

Food and Feeding

Newly hatched larvae feed on rotifers and other microzooplankton. Older fish feed almost exclusively on copepods. Prior to 1988, Delta smelt ate almost solely the native *Eurytemora affinis* (Herbold 1987). During the 1980s *Eurytemora affinis* was displaced by the introduced copepod *Pseudodiaptomus forbsii* throughout Suisun Bay, and Delta smelt shifted to a diet of *Pseudodiaptomus forbsii* (P. Moyle, pers. comm.).

Distribution

Delta smelt are endemic to the Sacramento-San Joaquin Estuary. They have been found as far north as the confluence of the American and Sacramento rivers and as far south as Mossdale on the San Joaquin River. Their upstream range is greatest during periods of spawning. Larvae subsequently move downstream for rearing. Juvenile and adult Delta smelt commonly occur in the surface and shoal waters of the lower reaches of the Sacramento River below Isleton, the San Joaquin River below Mossdale, through the Delta, and into Suisun Bay

(Moyle 1976, Moyle et al. 1992). Downstream distribution is generally limited to western Suisun Bay. During periods of high Delta outflow, Delta smelt populations do occur in San Pablo Bay, although they do not appear to establish permanent populations there (Herbold et al. 1992). Recent surveys, however, show that Delta smelt may persist for longer periods in Napa River, a tributary to San Pablo Bay (IEP, unpub. data).

Rearing and pre-spawning Delta smelt generally inhabit a salinity range of less than 2 ppt (parts per thousand), although they have been collected at salinities as high as 10 to 14 ppt (CDFG 1992b). Abundance of pre-spawning adults typically peaks upstream of the entrapment zone (CDWR and USBR 1994).

Population Status and Influencing Factors

Seven surveys, although not specifically designed to gather data on Delta smelt populations in the Estuary, have charted the abundance of Delta smelt. The summer townet survey, which began in 1959 and was primarily designed to measure striped bass abundance, is considered one of the best measures of Delta smelt abundance because it covers much of the species' habitat and represents the longest historical record. Although the abundance indices vary considerably, they generally remained low between 1983 and 1993. In recent years moderately wet conditions have produced relatively high abundances in the summer townet survey. The reduced population levels during the 1980s appear to have been consistent throughout the Delta and Suisun Bay, but declines may have occurred as early as the mid-1970s in the eastern and southern portions of the Delta (CDWR and USBR 1993).

The midwater trawl survey provides one of the best indexes of smelt abundance because it covers most of the range of Delta smelt (CDWR and USBR 1994). From 1967 through 1975, fall catches were generally greater than 10 smelt per trawl per month (in 6 of 8 years); from 1976 through 1989, catches were generally less than 10 smelt per trawl per month (in 13 of 14 years). Since 1986, catches have averaged considerably less than one smelt per trawl per month. The frequency of occurrence of Delta smelt in the trawls has also declined. Prior to 1983, Delta smelt were found in 30% or more of the fall trawl catches. In 1983-1985, they occurred in less than 30% of the catches, and since 1986, they have been caught in less than 10% of the trawls (Herbold et al. 1992). In 1993, the midwater trawl index was the sixth highest of the 25 years of record. In 1994, the index dropped to a 28-year low, but it rebounded again in 1995. Unlike the summer townet survey indices, the mean catches of Delta smelt have not declined in the midwater trawl survey. The smelt population is more dispersed in the summer than in the fall. The summer populations have decreased in average densities while the fall populations have decreased in numbers of schools (CDFG 1992b). Data from the Bay Study and the Suisun Marsh study show sharp declines in Delta smelt at about the same time. The exact timing of the decline is different in most of the sampling programs, but falls between 1982 and 1985 (Herbold et al. 1992).

As a result of the sharp decline in abundance in the 1980s, the Delta smelt was listed as a federal "threatened" species by the U.S. Fish and Wildlife Service in March 1993 and as a State "threatened" species by the California Department of Fish and Game in December 1993.

No single factor appears to be the sole cause of the Delta smelt decline; however declines have been attributed primarily to restricted habitat and increased losses through entrainment by Delta diversions (CDWR 1992, Herbold et al. 1992, USFWS 1994). Reduced water flow may intensify entrainment at pumping facilities as well as reduce the quantity and quality of nursery habitat. Outflow also controls the location of the entrapment zone, an important part of the habitat of Delta smelt. A weak, positive correlation exists between fall abundance of Delta smelt and the number of days during spring that the entrapment zone remained in Suisun Bay (Herbold 1994). The number of days when the entrapment zone has been in Suisun Bay during the February through June period is one of only two parameters found so far that predicts Delta smelt abundance (Herbold 1994). Reduced suitable habitat and increased entrainment occurs when the entrapment zone moves out of the shallows of Suisun Bay and into the channels of the lower Sacramento and San Joaquin rivers as a result of low Delta outflow. The movement of the entrapment zone to the river channels not only decreases the amount of area that can be occupied by smelt, but also decreases food supply (Herbold et al. 1992).

Delta smelt in the western delta are vulnerable to entrainment by the pumps of the State Water Project and the Central Valley Project, as well as local agricultural diversions (CDWR 1992, NHI 1992, Herbold et al. 1992). Diversions in the northern and central Delta, where smelt are most abundant, are likely the greatest source of entrainment (USFWS 1994). Larvae and juveniles appear to be particularly vulnerable to pumping because screens are not effective for these life stages (CDWR and USBR 1994). Whether entrainment, as estimated by salvage, affects abundance remains to be demonstrated statistically. However, the relative effects of entrainment are higher in dry years, when the abundance of Delta smelt is typically lowest and the distribution of the species shifts closer to the pumps in the interior Delta. Water diversions such as Contra Costa Canal, PG&E's power plants, and in-Delta agricultural diversions, potentially entrain Delta smelt in numbers comparable to or greater than at the Central Valley Project and State Water Project pumps. However, initial results

from Interagency Ecological Program studies have found few Delta smelt in agricultural diversions.

Although the effects of the recent high diversions of fresh water, especially when coupled with drought conditions from 1987-1992, are the most likely causes of the decline in the Delta smelt population, other contributing factors may include: the presence of toxic compounds in the water, competition and predation, food supply, disease, very high outflows, and low spawning stock.

Toxic contaminants have been identified as a factor that could affect Delta smelt survival (USFWS 1991). Possible pollutants include heavy metals, pesticides, herbicides, and polycyclic aromatic hydrocarbons. An inverse relationship has been found between copper applications to ricefields and Delta smelt abundance (Herbold, unpub. data), but no toxicity studies have been conducted to verify the degree to which pollutants in water and sediments affect Delta smelt.

Research conducted by Bennett (1995) suggests that competition with inland silversides, a non-native fish that arrived in the Bay around 1975, working synergistically with low flows, has contributed to Delta smelt decline. Inland silversides were found to be voracious predators of larval fish in both field and laboratory experiments. In addition, smelt and silversides may compete for copepods and cladocerans. Hatching and larval smelt may be extremely vulnerable to schools of foraging silversides, especially in low-outflow years when Delta smelt are forced into narrower, upstream channels, where silverside competition and predation may be increased. Evidence suggests that other non-native species, such as chameleon goby and striped bass, are either direct predators or compete with Delta smelt for food or habitat (CDWR and USBR 1994). However, it is questionable if striped bass is an important factor when both striped bass and Delta smelt were abundant in the 1960s, and the smelt was not a significant prey of the bass (CDFG 1992b).

Exact food requirements of Delta smelt are not known, but prey densities in the Estuary appear low relative to other systems in the United States, creating the potential for food limitation (Miller 1991). Moreover, there have been several changes in the species composition of zooplankton, with unknown effects on Delta smelt. The 1988 decline of *Eurytemora affinis*, a copepod which has been the primary food supply of Delta smelt, has been identified as a possible factor in the decline of smelt in the Estuary (CDFG 1992b). However, it may be that declines in *E. affinis* abundance, due to the introduction of other copepod species, is not an important factor because the smelt has shifted its diet and now consumes *Pseudodiaptomus forbesi*, which was introduced into the Estuary in 1986. The clam, *Potamocorbula amurensis*, may have an indirect effect on smelt populations by reducing its food supply (Herbold et al. 1992).

In some years disease is thought to cause widespread mortality of some fish species in the Estuary, but mortality of Delta smelt has not been specifically observed (Stevens et al. 1990). *Mycobacterium*, a genus of bacteria known to cause chronic infections in fish and other species, has been the major cause of mortality of Delta smelt held in the laboratory, and it may cause deaths among wild fish as well (Hedrick 1995).

The period of the Delta smelt decline includes unusually wet years with exceptionally high outflows. Very high outflows may be detrimental to the planktonic smelt larvae, which may be transported out of the Delta and into San Pablo and San Francisco bays with no way to get back upstream (CDFG 1992b).

It is possible that the size of the spawning stock influences population levels. However, there is not a statistically significant stock-recruitment relationship for Delta smelt, so this factor is not considered a primary factor regulating abundance (CDWR and USBR 1994).

Trophic Levels

Delta smelt are secondary consumers.

Proximal Species

Egg and larvae predators: Inland silversides, *Menidia beryllina.*
Juvenile and adult predators: Striped bass, *Morone saxatilis* (likely).
Prey: *Eurytemora affinis, Pseudodiaptomus forbsii,* rotifers (e.g., *Trichocerca).*

Good Habitat

Spawning habitat has been as widely dispersed as the Napa River to Stockton in 1996. The predominate feature appears to be shallow, freshwater conditions with some sort of solid substrate for the attachment of eggs. Spawning has been reported to occur at about 45-59° F (7-15° C) in tidally influenced rivers and sloughs including dead-end sloughs and shallow edge waters of the upper Delta.

Juvenile and adult Delta smelt commonly occur in the surface and shoal waters of the lower reaches of the Sacramento River below Mossdale, through the Delta, and into Suisun Bay (Moyle 1976, Moyle et al. 1992). Rearing and pre-spawning Delta smelt generally inhabit a salinity range of less than 2 ppt, although they have been collected at salinities as high as 10 to 14 ppt (CDFG 1992a). Analysis of the salinity preferences using midwater trawl data indicate that Delta smelt distribution peaks upstream of the entrapment zone (Obrebski 1993)[1]. It should be noted, however, that the distribution of Delta smelt is fairly broad, particularly in years when abundance levels are high (CDWR and USBR 1993). Evidence from the 1993 year class also demonstrates that salt field position does not necessarily regulate Delta smelt distribution in all years. In late 1993 and early 1994, Delta smelt were found in Suisun Bay region despite the fact that X2[2] was located upstream. Samples collected in this area demonstrated that high levels of the copepod *Eurytemora* were present, suggesting that food availability may also influence smelt distribution (CDWR and USBR 1994).

Although these results show that the Delta smelt is not an entrapment zone specialist, there is evidence that their abundance is correlated with X2. Herbold (1994) found a significant relationship between the number of days X2 was in Suisun Bay during February through June versus midwater trawl abundance. Furthermore, when the entrapment zone is in Suisun Bay and both deep and shallow water exists, Delta smelt are caught most frequently in shallow water (Moyle et al. 1992).

Results from the University of California, Davis provide an indication of environmental tolerances of Delta smelt (Swanson and Cech 1995). The study found that although Delta smelt tolerate a wide range of water temperatures (<8° C to >25° C), warmer temperatures apparently restrict their distribution more than colder temperatures.

References

Bennett, W.A. 1995. Potential effects of exotic inland silversides on Delta smelt. Interagency Program Newsletter. Winter 1995: 4-6.

California Department of Fish and Game (CDFG). 1992a. A re-examination of factors affecting striped bass abundance in the Sacramento-San Joaquin Estuary. Entered by the Ca. Dept. of Fish and Game for the State Wat. Res. Cont. Bd. 1992 Water Rights Phase of the Bay-Delta Estuary Proceedings. (WRINT-DFG-2) 59 pp.

_____. 1992b. Written testimony on Delta smelt. Submitted by the Ca. Dept. of Fish and Game to the

---

[1] The entrapment zone, also referred to by a variety of other discriptive terms, such as the "mixing zone," the "null zone," and and the "zone of maximum turbidity," is the area within an estuary where the freshwater from a stream meets with the salt water of the ocean. This zone is biologically highly productive, and considered to be of critical importance to the aquatic food web of the Estuary.

[2] "X2" is the geographic location, measured in kilometers above the Golden Gate, of the entrapment zone. X2 is largely a function of outflow, such that when outflow is high, X2 is closer to the Golden Gate. X2 was used by U.S. Fish and Wildlife Service in defining Delta Smelt's critical habitat under the Endangered Species Act (USFWS 1994).

State Wat. Res. Cont. Bd. June 1992. (WRINT-DFG-9) 44 pp.

California Department of Water Resources (CDWR). 1992. Bay-Delta fish resources. Sacramento, CA. July 1992. (WRINT-DWR-30) 46 pp.

California Department of Water Resources and U.S. Bureau of Reclamation (CDWR and USBR). 1993. Biological Assessment. Effects of the Central Valley Project and State Water Project on Delta smelt. Prepared by the Ca. Dept. of Water Res. and the U.S. Bureau of Reclamation for the U.S. Fish and Wildlife Service. October 1993. 134 pp.

_____. 1994. Biological Assessment. Effects of the Central Valley Project and State Water Project on Delta Smelt and Sacramento Splittail.

Hedrick, R.P. 1995. Disease Research in Delta Smelt. Report to Dept. of Wat. Res.: Contract B-59299.

Herbold, B. 1987. Patterns of co-cccurrence and resource use in a non-coevolved assemblage of fishes. Ph.D dissertation. Univ. of California, Davis. Vii+81 pp.

_____. 1994. Habitat requirements of Delta smelt. Interagency Program Newsletter. Winter 1994: 1-3.

Herbold, B., P. Moyle and A. Jassby 1992. Status and trends report on aquatic resources in the San Francisco Estuary. San Fran. Est. Proj. Public Rept. March 1992. 257 pp. plus appendices.

Miller, L. 1991. 1990 Working Papers of the Food Chain Group. Interagency Program Working Papers 1-6. FCG-1990. 71 pp.

Moyle, P. 1976. Inland Fishes of California. Univ. of California Press, Berkeley. 405 pp.

Moyle P., B. Herbold, D. Stevens and L. Miller. 1992. Life history and status of Delta smelt in the Sacramento-San Joaquin Estuary, California. Transactions of the Am. Fisheries Soc. 121:67-77.

Natural Heritage Institute (NHI). 1992. Causes of decline in estuarine fish species. Testimony presented by Dr. Peter Moyle, Univ. of Ca., Davis to the

State Wat. Res. Cont. Bd. June 1992. 35 pp. (WRINT-NHI-9)

Obrebski, S. 1993. Relationships between Delta smelt abundance and the entrapment zone position. Draft report for Dept. of Water Res.. 29 pp.

Stevens, D.E., L.W. Miller and B.C. Bolster. 1990. Report to Fish and Game Commission: A status review of Delta smelt (*Hypomesus transpacificus*) in California. Dept. of Fish and Game. Candidate Species Status Report 90-2.

Swanson, C. and J. Cech. 1995. Environmental tolerances and requirements of the Delta smelt, *Hypomesus transpacificus*. Report to Dept. of Water Resources: Contracts B-59449 and B-58959.

State Water Resources Control Board (SWRCB). 1995. Water quality control plan for the San Fran. Bay/Sac.-San Joaquin Estuary. 95-1WR, May 1995. Sacramento, Ca.. 45 pp plus appendices.

Wang, J.C.S. 1991. Early life stages and early life history of Delta smelt, *Hypomesus transpacificus*, in the Sacramento-San Joaquin Estuary, with comparison of early life stages of the longfin smelt, *Spirinchus thaleichthys*. Interagency Program Tech. Rept. 28. 52 pp.

U.S. Fish and Wildlife Service (USFWS). 1991. Federal Register: Endangered and threatened wildlife and plants: proposed threatened status for the Delta smelt. Dept. of the Interior, Fish and Wildlife Service. 50 CFR Part 17. 56(192): 50075-50083. October 3, 1991.

_____. 1994. Biological opinion on the operation of the Central Valley Project and State Water Project effects on Delta smelt. February 4, 1994. U.S. Fish and Wildlife Service, Region 1, Portland, OR. 34 pp.

Personal Communications

Peter Moyle, University of California, Davis.

Longfin Smelt

Spirinchus thaleichthys

Frank G. Wernette

General Information

The longfin smelt (Family: Osmeridae) is a three to seven-inch long silvery fish (Moyle 1976). Longfin smelt were the most abundant smelt species in the Bay-Delta Estuary prior to 1984 and have been commercially harvested (Wang 1986). In 1993, the U.S. Fish Wildlife Service (USFWS) was petitioned to list the longfin smelt under the federal Endangered Species Act. In January 1994, however, USFWS determined that the longfin smelt did not warrant listing because other longfin smelt populations exist along the Pacific Coast, the Bay-Delta Estuary population does not appear to be biologically significant to the species as a whole, and the Bay-Delta Estuary population may not be sufficiently reproductively isolated (Federal Register Vol. 59 No. 869, January 6, 1994). Still, longfin smelt are typically addressed in Biological Assessments because of the decline in their abundance after 1982 and the relatively small increase in abundance following a wet year in 1993. The species may also be considered in the future for listing under the California Endangered Species Act.

The longfin smelt is an euryhaline species with a 2-year life cycle. Spawning occurs in fresh water over sandy-gravel substrates, rocks, or aquatic plants. Spawning may take place as early as November and extend into June, although the peak spawning period is from January to April. After hatching, larvae move up into surface water and are transported downstream into brackish-water nursery areas. Delta outflow into Suisun and San Pablo bays has been positively correlated with longfin smelt recruitment because higher outflow increases larval dispersal and the area available for rearing. The longfin smelt diet consists of mysids, although copepods and other crustaceans also are eaten. Longfin smelt are preyed upon by fishes, birds, and marine mammals (Federal Register Vol. 59 No. 4, January 3, 1994).

In the Bay-Delta Estuary, the decline in longfin smelt abundance is associated with freshwater diversion from the Delta. Longfin smelt may be particularly sensitive to adverse habitat alterations because their 2-year life cycle increases their likelihood of extinction after con-

secutive periods of reproductive failure due to drought or other factors. Relatively brief periods of reproductive failure could lead to extirpations (Federal Register Vol. 59 No. 4, January 3, 1994).

Although the southernmost populations of longfin smelt are declining, little or no population trend data are available for estuaries in Oregon and Washington. Longfin populations may not be isolated since there is little genetic variation between northern and southern populations. Under prolonged drought conditions however, only the Colombia River and San Francisco Bay stocks may survive.

Reproduction

Maturation of longfin smelt begins late in the second summer of their life in August and September. As they mature, the smelt begin migrating upstream from San Francisco and San Pablo bays toward Suisun Bay and the Delta. Longfin smelt spawn in fresh water, primarily in the upper end of Suisun Bay and in the lower and middle Delta. In the Delta, they spawn mostly in the Sacramento River channel and adjacent sloughs (Wang 1991). During the recent drought, when saline water intruded into the Delta, larval longfin smelt were found near the Central Valley Project and State Water Project export facilities in the southern Delta (Wang 1991). Ripe adults, larvae, and juveniles are salvaged at the export facilities in every below normal or drier water year (Baxter, pers. comm.). The eggs are adhesive and are probably deposited on rocks or aquatic plants. Longfin smelt eggs hatch in 37-47 days at 45° F.

Growth and Development

Shortly after hatching, longfin smelt larvae develop a gas bladder that allows them to remain near the water surface (Wang 1991). The larvae do not vertically migrate, but instead remain near the surface on both the flood and ebb tides (CDFG 1992). Larvae are swept downstream into nursery areas in the western Delta and Suisun and San Pablo bays with larval dispersal farther downstream in years of high outflow than in years of low outflow (CDFG 1992; Baxter, pers. comm.). Early development of gas bladders by longfin smelt causes the larvae to remain near the surface much longer than Delta smelt larvae. That factor and earlier spawning period help explain why the longfin smelt larvae are dispersed much farther downstream in the Estuary than are Delta smelt larvae (Baxter, pers. comm.). Larval development occurs primarily in the February through May period and peaks during February-April (CDFG 1992).

Metamorphosis of longfin smelt from the larval to juvenile form begins 30-60 days after hatching, depending on temperature. Most longfin smelt growth occurs during the first summer, when length typically reaches

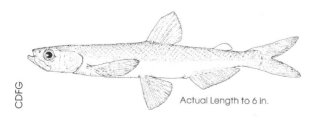

Actual Length to 6 in.

CDFG

6 to 7 cm. During their second summer, smelt reach 9 to 11 cm in length (NHI 1992). Most longfin smelt spawn and die at two years of age (CDFG 1992).

Food and Feeding

The main prey of adult longfin smelt is the opossum shrimp, *Neomysis mercedis* (NHI 1992). There is little information on food habitats of longfin smelt larvae, but fish larvae of most species, including Delta smelt, are known to feed on phytoplankton and small zooplankton, such as rotifers and copepod nauplii (Hunter 1981, USBR 1993). Juvenile longfin smelt feed on copepods, cladocerans, and mysids. The mysid *Neomysis mercedis* is the most important prey of larger juveniles.

Distribution

Longfin smelt are widely distributed in estuaries on the Pacific Coast. They have been collected from numerous river estuaries from San Francisco to Prince William Sound in Alaska (Moyle 1976).

Longfin smelt are euryhaline meaning they are adapted to a wide salinity range. They are also anadromous. Spawning adults are found seasonally as far upstream in the Delta as Hood, Medford Island, and the Central Valley Project and State Water Project fish collection facilities in the southern Delta. Historically, before construction of Shasta Dam in 1944, saline water intruded in dry months as far upstream in the Delta as Sacramento, so longfin smelt may have periodically ranged farther upstream than they do currently (Herbold et al. 1992).

Except when spawning, longfin smelt are most abundant in Suisun and San Pablo bays, where salinity generally ranges between 2 ppt and 20 ppt (NHI 1992). Pre-spawning adults and yearling juveniles are generally most abundant in San Pablo Bay and downstream areas as far as the South Bay and in the open ocean.

Population Status and Influencing Factors

Abundance estimates were developed from otter trawl and midwater trawl sampling conducted by the Outflow/Bay study as part of the Interagency Ecological Program. Fall midwater trawl surveys provide the longest index of longfin smelt abundance.

Results of the fall midwater trawl surveys indicate that, like Sacramento splittail abundance, longfin smelt abundance has been highly variable from year to year, with peaks and declines coinciding with wet and dry periods. Longfin smelt abundance has steadily declined since 1982. Abundance continued to be suppressed during the drought years beginning in 1987. Longfin abundance was very low from 1987 to 1992, with 1992 having the lowest index on record. Abundance increased

moderately in 1993 following the drought during a period of improved Delta outflow.

Year-class abundance of longfin smelt appears to depend on the environmental conditions experienced by the eggs and young fish. Generally, year-class abundance is positively related to Delta outflow (i.e., high abundance follows high outflow during winter and spring). Factors possibly contributing to the recent decline in longfin smelt abundance are reduced Delta outflow, entrainment in diversions, introductions of exotic species, loss of habitat, and the recent drought.

Delta Outflow – Higher outflows result in higher longfin smelt survival. An index of survival computed as the ratio of the index of abundance from fall midwater trawl surveys to an index of larval abundance in previous springs was strongly correlated (r=0.95) with December-August outflow. Delta outflow or factors associated with outflow affect survival of larvae and early juveniles. Delta outflow may be the single most important factor controlling longfin smelt abundance. High outflows increase dispersion downstream, available habitat, and possibly, food availability. High outflow may also reduce predation and the effects of other adverse factors (i.e., toxin concentrations). Low outflow conditions reduce downstream dispersion and increase vulnerability to entrainment in Delta diversions.

Longfin smelt abundance (according to the fall midwater trawl survey index) is positively related to Delta outflow (Stevens and Miller 1983, CDFG 1992). Regression analysis indicated that 79% of variability in the midwater trawl survey index is explained by changes in January and February Delta outflow. The significant relationship between the index of abundance from the fall midwater trawl surveys and Delta outflow may reflect the effect of outflow on survival of larvae and early juveniles. Year-class strength may be largely determined by survival of the early life stages.

High Delta outflow may increase the amount of suitable brackish water rearing habitat; reduce salinity in the Estuary, reducing competition and predation by marine organisms; reduce predation because young smelt are more dispersed and turbidity is higher; increase phytoplankton and zooplankton production; and increase transport of larvae out of the Delta and away from diversions (CDFG 1992; Stevens and Miller 1983; Baxter, pers. comm.). Any of these mechanisms may be responsible for the observed relationship between Delta outflow and longfin smelt abundance.

The position of the entrapment zone[1], location of X2[2], and volume of critical nursery habitat are determined by Delta outflow. In addition to the relationship with outflow, the fall midwater trawl survey index has a positive relationship with the location of X2 and the volume of critical nursery habitat (Jassby 1993, Herrgesell 1993).

Delta smelt abundance tends to be highest when X2 has an intermediate value (i.e., X2 is located in upper Suisun Bay). The location of X2 is also a good predictor of longfin smelt abundance. Since X2 and the volume of critical nursery habitat are largely determined by Delta outflow, the relationship between longfin smelt abundance and the location of X2 or volume of critical habitat may simply reflect effects of outflow or other correlates of outflow on longfin smelt abundance.

Lower San Joaquin River – Reverse flow in the lower San Joaquin River usually transports relatively fresh water drawn from the Sacramento River and may increase upstream migration of adults to the southern Delta. Reverse flow may also transport larvae to the southern Delta. In the southern Delta, adults, larvae, and juveniles are vulnerable to entrainment, predation, and other sources of mortality.

Entrainment – Entrainment of longfin smelt by Delta diversions affects spawning adults, larvae, and early juveniles. Older juveniles and prespawning adults generally inhabit areas downstream of the Delta. Salvage at both the Central Valley Project and State Water Project fish protection facilities has varied greatly between years. Salvage represents entrainment, but the number of fish salvaged is often much lower than total number entrained because fish, particularly those smaller than about 20-30 mm, pass through the fish screens at the salvage facilities and, therefore, are not salvaged.

With the exception of 1986, a wet year, the annual salvage of longfin smelt at the Central Valley Project and State Water Project pumps was much higher during 1984-1990 than during 1979-1983. The decline in abundance in 1984 may be attributable to increased entrainment by the Central Valley Project and State Water Project pumps and other diversions, but reduced Delta outflow, discussed previously, may be a more important factor affecting abundance.

Entrainment of adult longfin smelt has a potentially greater adverse effect on the population than entrainment of larvae and young juveniles because unless the adults have already spawned, their reproductive value is much greater than that of younger fish. Adult smelt are entrained at the State Water Project and Central Valley Project pumping facilities primarily during November-February. The number of adults entrained is low relative to the number of juveniles entrained.

Longfin smelt larvae have been captured in the southern Delta near the Central Valley Project and State Water Project export facilities (Spaar 1990, 1993; Wang 1991). Larval smelt are too small to be salvaged at the State Water Project and Central Valley Project fish pro-

tection facilities. Based on the high salvage rates of young-of-year juveniles in some years, it can be assumed that many thousands of longfin smelt larvae were also entrained, especially during February through April.

During years of high flows, most longfin smelt adults spawn in the western Delta, and their larvae are generally transported out of the Delta and therefore are unlikely to be entrained in Delta diversions in large numbers. During the 1987-1992 drought and other low flow years, however, outflows were low and exports were high. Adults, larvae, and juveniles remained in the Delta, as indicated by salvage at the Central Valley Project and State Water Project fish protection facilities. Most juveniles were entrained during April-June and averaged 30-45mm long, with length correlated with the month of entrainment. Thus, longfin smelt suffer not only loss of larval dispersal and rearing habitat in a drought, but also from higher rates of entrainment.

Adult, juvenile, and larvae longfin smelt are vulnerable to entrainment in diversions other than exports at the Central Valley Project and State Water Project pumps, including diversions to PG&E's power generating plants, industrial diversions, agricultural diversions, and others. However, entrainment of longfin smelt in these diversions has not been extensively evaluated.

Other Factors – Other factors that may affect survival of longfin smelt include food limitation and presence of toxic materials and introduced species. Abundance of *Neomysis* and other zooplankton prey (e.g., rotifers) of longfin smelt have declined in recent years (Obrebski et al. 1992). It is not known what effect the decline in prey abundance has had on longfin smelt; however, food limitation may be important because year-class strength of many fish populations, particularly species with planktonic larvae, may be strongly influenced by feeding conditions during the larval life stage (Lasker 1981).

Agricultural chemicals (including pesticides and herbicides), heavy metals, petroleum-based products, and other waste materials toxic to aquatic organisms enter the Estuary through nonpoint runoff, agricultural drainage, and municipal and industrial discharges. The effects of toxic substances have not been tested on longfin smelt, but recent bioassays indicate that water in the Sacramento River is periodically toxic to larvae of the fathead minnow, a standard EPA test organism (Stevens et al. 1990). The short life span of longfin smelt and relatively low position in the food chain probably reduce the accumulation of toxic materials in their tissues and make them less susceptible to injury than species that live longer (NHI 1992).

Many exotic species have invaded the Estuary in recent years. These species may compete with or prey on longfin smelt. No single invasion of exotic species parallels the decline the longfin smelt closely enough to suggest that competition from or predation by the species

---

[1] The entrapment zone, also referred to by a variety of other discriptive terms, such as the "mixing zone," the "null zone," and and the "zone of maximum turbidity," is the area within an estuary where the freshwater from a stream meets with the salt water of the ocean.

[2] "X2" is the geographic location, measured in kilometers above the Golden Gate, of the entrapment zone.

was a primary cause of the longfin smelt's recent decline. The effects of multiple-species invasion, which have occurred in the Estuary, are extremely difficult to assess. The effects of exotic species invasions on longfin smelt is likely not large since Delta outflow explains over 60% of the variation in abundance (Baxter, pers. comm.).

Trophic Levels

Longfin smelt are secondary consumers.

Proximal Species

Predators: Brown pelican, river otter, striped bass, centrarchids.

Prey: Zooplankton (cladocerans), opossum shrimp (*Neomysis mercedis*), crustaceans (copepods).

Good Habitat

Longfin smelt are typically pelagic and use the larger sloughs and rivers of the Delta and Bay. The optimal salinity habitat for non-spawning adults is 2 to 20 ppt. Optimal salinity habitat for spawning adults is 0 to 2 ppt. Optimum habitat for spawning includes submergent vegetation that can be used as a substrate for the adhesive eggs. High quality habitat is also defined as having low levels of exposure to entrainment into water export facilities and agricultural or managed wetland diversions. Adjacent runoff of agricultural pesticides is minimal or does not occur in good habitat areas.

Juvenile longfin use the open water, shallow shoal areas of San Pablo and Suisun bays after being transported downstream from spawning areas in the Delta. An average X2 location in upper Suisun Bay defines good habitat conditions for longfin smelt. Adjacent tidal wetlands are important to supporting the nutrient cycling and carbon input functions which in turn support the prey species upon which longfin feed.

References

California Department of Fish and Game (CDFG). 1992. Estuary dependent species. (Exhibit 6.) Entered by the Ca. Dept. of Fish and Game for the State Wat. Res. Cont. Bd. 1992 Wat. Qual./ Wat. Rights Proceedings on the San Fran. Bay/ Sac.-San Joaquin Delta. Sacramento, CA.

Herbold, B., A.D. Jassby and P.B. Moyle. 1992. Status and trends report on aquatic resources in the San Francisco Estuary. San Francisco Estuary Project, U.S. Env. Protection Agency. Oakland, CA.

Herrgesell, P.L. 1993. 1991 annual report. Interagency Ecological Studies Program for the Sacramento-San Joaquin Estuary. Ca. Dept. Fish and Game. Stockton, CA.

Hunter, J.R. 1981. Feeding ecology and predation of marine fish larvae. *In:* R. Lasker (ed). Marine fish larvae. Univ. of Washington Press. Seattle, WA.

Jassby, A.D. 1993. Isohaline position as a habitat indicator for estuarine resources: San Francisco estuary. *In:* SFEP 1993. Managing freshwater discharge to the San Francisco Bay/Sacramento-San Joaquin Delta Estuary: the scientific basis for an estuarine standard, Appendix 3.

Lasker, R. 1981. The role of a stable ocean in larval fish survival and subsequent recruitment. *In:* R. Lasker (ed). Marine fish larvae. pp. 80-87. Univ. of Washington Press. Seattle, WA.

Moyle, P.B. 1976. Inland Fishes of California. Univ. of California Press. Berkeley, CA.

Natural Heritage Institute (NHI). 1992. Petition for listing under the Endangered Species Act, longfin smelt and Sacramento splittail. San Francisco, CA.

Obrebski, S., J.J. Orsi and W.J. Kimmerer. 1992. Long-term trends in zooplankton distribution and abundance in the Sacramento-San Joaquin estuary in California. (FS/BIO-IATR/92-93, Tech. Rept. 32.) Ca. Dept. of Water Res.. Sacramento, CA. Prepared for Interagency Ecological Studies Program for the Sacramento-San Joaquin Estuary, Stockton, CA.

Spaar, S.A. 1990. Results of 1988 striped bass egg and larva study near the State Water Project and Central Valley Project facilities in the Sacramento-San Joaquin Delta. A cooperative study by Ca. Dept. of Water Res., State Wat. Res. Cont. Bd., U.S. Fish and Wildl. Serv., Ca. Dept. of Fish and Game, U.S. Bur. of Rec., and U.S. Geol. Survey. Prepared for Interagency Ecological Study Program for the Sacramento-San Joaquin Estuary, Stockton, CA.

_____. 1993. 1992 entrainment of eggs and larvae to the State Water Project and Central Valley Project intakes in the Sacramento-San Joaquin Delta. January. Ca. Dept. of Water Res. Sacramento, CA.

Stevens, D.E. and L.W. Miller. 1983. Effects of river flow on abundance of young Chinook salmon, American shad, longfin smelt, and Delta smelt in the Sacramento-San Joaquin River system. No. Amer. J. Fish. Mgmt. 3:425-437.

Stevens, D.E., L.W. Miller and B.C. Bolster. 1990. Report to the Fish and Game Commission: a status review of the Delta smelt (*Hypomesis transpacificus*) in California. (Candidate Species Status Report 90-2.) Ca. Dept. Fish and Game. Stockton, CA.

U.S. Bureau of Reclamation (USBR). 1993. Effect of the Central Valley Project and State Water Project on Delta smelt. Prepared by Ca. Dept. of Water Res. and U.S. Bureau of Reclamation, Mid-Pacific Region. Prepared for U.S. Fish and Wildl. Service, Ecological Services, Sacramento Field Office, Sacramento, CA.

Wang, J.C.S. 1986. Fishes of the Sacramento-San Joaquin Estuary and adjacent waters, California: A guide to the early life histories. (FS/10-4ATR86-9). Ca. Dept. of Water Res. Sacramento, CA. Prepared for Interagency Ecological Study Program for the Sacramento-San Joaquin Estuary, Sacramento, CA.

_____. 1991. Early life stages and early life history of the Delta smelt, *Hypomesus transpacificus,* in the Sacramento-San Joaquin Estuary, with comparison of early life stages of the longfin smelt, *Spirinchus thaleichthys.* (FS/BIO-IATR/91-28. Tech. Rept. 28). Ca. Dept. of Water Res. Sacramento, CA. Prepared for Interagency Ecological Studies Program for the Sacramento-San Joaquin Estuary, Stockton, CA.

Personal Communications

Randall Baxter, Assoc. Fisheries Biologist, California Department of Fish and Game.

Jacksmelt

Atherinopsis californiensis

Michael K. Saiki

General Information

Although jacksmelt (Family: Atherinidae) is not an important commercial fish, it nevertheless constitutes the largest portion of "smelt" captures in California (Emmett et al. 1991). This species is also commonly caught by recreational anglers fishing from piers (Frey 1971). In an ecological sense, jacksmelt occupy an important niche in trophic pathways of nearshore coastal, bay, and estuarine ecosystems (Clark 1929, Allen and DeMartini 1983, CDFG 1987).

Reproduction

Emmett et al. (1991) describes the sexual and reproductive characteristics of jacksmelt as gonochoristic (its gender is determined by developmental rather than hereditary mechanisms) and iteroparous (it has the capacity to

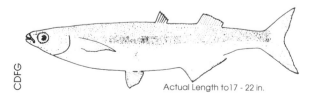

CDFG

Actual Length to17 - 22 in.

survive and spawn beyond one or multiple spawning seasons). Spawning occurs several times during a spawning season (Clark 1929). The eggs are demersal and adhesive, and can often be found on vegetation in shallow nearshore coastal habitats and in estuaries and bays (Clark 1929, Wang 1986).

Adults move inshore and into bays and estuaries to spawn during late winter and early spring (Clark 1929, Wang 1986). In San Francisco Bay, spawning occurs from October to early August (Wang 1986). Spawning in San Pablo Bay reportedly occurs from September to April (Ganssle 1966). Eggs are laid on substrates/vegetation (e.g., *Zostera* spp., *Gracilaria* spp., hydroids) in which they become entangled (Frey 1971, Wang 1986). Embryonic development is indirect and external, and if given a suitable environment, the yellowish-orange eggs hatch within seven days (Wang 1986). The fecundity of jacksmelt is not yet documented, but probably exceeds 2,000 eggs per female (Emmett et al. 1991). Unfertilized jacksmelt eggs are spherical in shape and 0.9-2.2 mm in diameter (Clark 1929); fertilized eggs are 1.9-2.5 mm in diameter (Wang 1986).

Growth and Development

After hatching, larvae remain on the bottom for a moment and then actively swim near the surface (Wang 1986). Larvae vary in size from 7.5 to 8.6 mm immediately after hatching, to about 25 mm long prior to the juvenile transformation (Clark 1929, Wang 1986). At eight days posthatch, they average 10.5-11.7 mm in length whereas at 24 days posthatch, they average 17.6-20.3 mm in length (Middaugh et al. 1990). Juveniles can attain 110 mm during their first year, and 180-190 mm after two years (Clark 1929). All individuals mature by their third year, but some may grow quickly and mature in their second year (Clark 1929). Adult jacksmelt have been reported to attain a length of 780 mm and an age of 11 years (Miller and Lea 1972, Frey 1971) but, more typically, the maximum size is 200 mm total length, and the maximum age is 9-10 years (Clark 1929).

Food and Feeding

The jacksmelt is omnivorous (Bane and Bane 1971, Ruagh 1976). Larvae live on their yolk-sac for about 48 hours after hatching when it is fully absorbed (Middaugh et al. 1990). Major food items for jacksmelt include algae (*Ulothrix* spp., *Melosira moniliformis, Enteromorpha* spp., and other filamentous algae), benthic diatoms, crustaceans (mysids, copepods, decapod larvae), and detritus (Bane and Bane 1971, Ruagh 1976). In addition, stomach analyses of juvenile jacksmelt show that amphipods are a common food item, indicating that juveniles may feed on the bottom (Wang 1986).

Distribution

Jacksmelt occur from Santa Maria Bay, Baja California, northward to Yaquina Bay, Oregon (Miller and Lea 1972, Eschmeyer et al. 1983). However, this species is uncommon north of Coos Bay, Oregon (Emmett et al. 1991).

Prior to or after the spawning season, adult jacksmelt typically occur in coastal waters near shore (Baxter 1960). Ruagh (1976) mentioned that jacksmelt are usually caught within 5 km of shore where they often school with topsmelt (*Atherinops affinis*).

Locally, jacksmelt have been reported to spawn in San Francisco Bay (Wang 1986) and San Pablo Bay (Ganssle 1966, Wang 1986). Juveniles are also present in San Francisco Bay (Baxter 1960, Aplin 1967), San Pablo Bay (Ganssle 1966), Carquinez Strait (Messersmith 1966), and occasionally in Suisun Bay (Wang 1986, Herbold et al. 1992, Jones and Stokes Assoc. 1979) and Napa marsh (Jones and Stokes Assoc. 1979). The amount of freshwater inflow seemingly affects the local distribution of jacksmelt. During years of low freshwater inflow, jacksmelt occur as far upstream as Carquinez Strait and San Pablo Bay, but during high-flow years they are seemingly restricted to Central San Francisco Bay and South San Francisco Bay (CDFG 1987).

Population Status and Influencing Factors

Presently, jacksmelt are particularly abundant in Tomales, Central San Francisco, South San Francisco, and San Pablo bays (Emmett et al. 1991). Midwater trawl samples performed in South San Francisco Bay between 1980-1988 showed that jacksmelt were the second most common species caught, behind northern anchovy (Herbold et al. 1992). Furthermore, jacksmelt were more abundant and occurred more frequently than topsmelt in the South Bay (Herbold et al. 1992). In San Pablo and Central San Francisco bays, Herbold et al. (1992) reported that jacksmelt were the third most common species caught. Midwater trawl samples performed in the Carquinez Strait between 1961-1962 found over 9% of the total catch consisted of jacksmelt (Messersmith 1966). Herbold et al. (1992) noted that during 1980-1988 jacksmelt numbers seemed to vary widely in the Central Bay and are seemingly unpredictable from year to year, whereas numbers in the South Bay show little variation from year to year.

Although specific studies relating fish abundance to environmental variables were not found during our search of the literature, jacksmelt may be vulnerable to pollution and habitat modifications because they depend on embayments and estuaries for spawning.

Trophic Levels

Omnivorous (primary and higher order consumers).

Proximal Species

Predators: Yellowtail (*Seriola lalandei*), sharks and other piscivorous fishes, piscivorous birds (e.g., brown pelicans and gulls).
Prey: Small crustaceans, algae.
Habitat: Kelp (cover for juveniles and adults); algae, hudroids, and eelgrass (spawning substrate).
Parasites: Nematodes sometimes found living in flesh.

Good Habitat

Bays and estuaries provide important spawning habitat for jacksmelt. In general, the preferred spawning areas are situated in shallow nearshore habitats containing submerged vegetation (Wang 1986). Water quality variables suitable for embryo development are as follows: temperature, 10-12° C; and salinity, polyhaline and as low as 5 ppt (Wang 1986). Schools of larvae occur near the water surface over a variety of substrates, but mostly sandy and muddy bottoms and in the kelp canopy (Frey 1971). Optimum larval and juvenile survival and growth appears to be at salinities of 10-20 ppt, indicating that larvae may prefer mesohaline environments (Middaugh and Shenker 1988, Middaugh et al. 1990). Juveniles and adults prefer sandy bottoms in murky water at depths of 1.5-15 m below the surface (Feder et al. 1974). Furthermore, they seem to use open waters in San Francisco Bay and sloughs in and near Suisun Marsh and Napa Marsh (Jones and Stokes Assoc. 1979). Jacksmelt are apparently more sensitive than topsmelt to fluctuations in salinity and temperature (Emmett et al. 1991).

References

Allen, L.G. and E.E. Demartini. 1983. Temporal and spatial patterns of near shore distribution and abundance of the pelagic fishes off San Onofre-Oceanside, California. Fish Bull., U.S. 81(3):569-586.

Aplin, J.A. 1967. Biological survey of San Francisco Bay, 1963-1966. Ca. Dept. Fish and Game, Marine Resources Operations. MRO Ref. 67-4, 131 pp.

Bane, G.W. and A.W. Bane. 1971. Bay fishes of northern California with emphasis on the Bodega Tomales Bay area. Mariscos Publ., Hampton Bays, NY, 143 pp.

Baxter, J.L. 1960. Inshore fishes of California. Ca. Dept. Fish and Game, Sacramento, CA, 80 pp.

California Department of Fish and Game (CDFG). 1987. Delta outflow effects on the abundance and distribution of San Francisco Bay fish and invertebrates, 1980-1985. Exhibit 60, entered at the State Wat. Res. Cont. Bd. 1987 Wat. Qual./Wat. Rights Proceeding on the San Fran. Bay/Sac.-San Joaquin Delta. Ca. Dept. Fish and Game, Stockton, CA, 345 pp.

Clark, F.N. 1929. The life history of the California jack smelt, *Atherinopsis californiensis*. Ca. Fish and Game, Fish Bull. 16, 22pp.

Emmett, R.L., S.L. Stone, S.A. Hinton and M.E. Monaco. 1991. Distribution and abundance of fishes and invertebrates in west coast estuaries, Vol. II: species life history summaries. ELMR Rep. No. 8. NOAA/NOS Strategic Environ. Assessments Div., Rockville, MD, pp. 190-193.

Eschmeyer, W.N., W.S. Herald and H. Hammann. 1983. A field guide to Pacific coast fishes of North America. Houghton Mifflin Co., Boston, MA, 336 pp.

Feder, H.M., C.H. Turner and C. Limbaugh. 1974. Observations on fishes associated with kelp beds in southern California. Ca. Fish and Game, Fish Bull. 160, 144 pp.

Frey, H.W. 1971. California's living marine resources and their utilization. Ca. Dept. Fish and Game, Sacramento, CA, 148 pp.

Ganssle, D. 1966. Fishes and decapods of San Pablo and Suisun Bays. *In:* D.W. Kelley (comp). Ecological studies of the Sacramento-San Joaquin Estuary. Ca. Fish and Game, Fish Bull. 133:64-94.

Herbold, B.A., A.D. Jassby and P.B. Moyle. 1992. Status and trends report on aquatic resources in the San Francisco Estuary. U.S. EPA Publ. Report, San Francisco, CA. pp. 163 & 172.

Jones and Stokes Assoc., Inc. 1979. Protection and restoration of San Francisco bay fish and wildlife habitat. Vol. 1 & 2. U.S. Fish and Wildl. Serv. and Ca. Fish and Game. Sacramento, CA.

Klingbeil, R.A., R.D. Sandell, and A.W. Wells. 1974. An annotated checklist of the elasmobrachs and teleosts of Anaheim Bay. *In:* E.D. Lane and C.W. Hill (eds). The marine resources of Anaheim Bay. Ca. Fish and Game, Fish Bull. 165:79-90.

Messersmith, J.D. 1966. Fishes collected in Carquinez Strait in 61-62, *In:* D.W. Kelley, (comp). Ecological Studies of the Sacramento-San Joaquin Estuary, Part I. pp. 57-63. Ca. Dept. Fish and Game, Fish Bull 133.

Middaugh, D.P. and J.M. Shenker. 1988. Salinity tolerance of young topsmelt, *Atherinops affinis*, cultured in the laboratory. Ca. Fish and Game 74(4):232-235.

Middaugh, D.P., M.J. Hemmer, J.M. Shenker and T. Takita. 1990. Laboratory culture of jacksmelt, *Atherinopsis californiensis*, and topsmelt, *Atherinops affinis* (Pisces: Atherinidae), with a description of larvae. Ca. Fish and Game 76(1):4-43.

Miller, D.J. and R.N. Lea. 1972. Guide to the coastal marine fishes of California. Ca. Dept. Fish and Game, Fish Bull. 157, 235 pp.

Ruagh, A.A. 1976. Feeding habits of silversides (Family Atherinidae) in Elkhorn Slough, Monterey Bay, California. M.S. Thesis, Ca. State Univ. Fresno, CA, 60 pp.

Wang, J.C.S. 1986. Fishes of the Sacramento-San Joaquin estuary and adjacent waters, California: A guide to the early life histories. Tech. Rept. No. 9. Interagency Ecological Study Program for the Sacramento-San Joaquin Estuary. Ca. Dept. Water Res., Ca. Dept. Fish and Game, U.S. Bureau Reclam., U.S. Fish Wildl. Serv., various paginations.

Topsmelt

Atherinops affinis

Michael K. Saiki

General Information

On the West Coast, topsmelt (Family: Atherinidae) are represented by five recognized subspecies of which only one, the San Francisco topsmelt *(Atherinops affinis affinis)*, inhabits San Francisco Bay (Wang 1986). Topsmelt are a small but tasty food fish taken from piers by recreational anglers (Emmett et al. 1991). However, commercial fishing for topsmelt is limited, with the species comprising only about 15-25% of the total "smelt" catch (Bane and Bane 1971, Frey 1971). Ecologically, topsmelt are an important prey item for many piscivorous birds and fishes (Feder et al. 1974).

Reproduction

According to Emmett et al. (1991), the topsmelt is gonochoristic (its gender is determined by developmental rather than hereditary mechanisms) and iteroparous (it has the capacity to survive and spawn beyond one or multiple spawning seasons). Adults move into shallow sloughs and mud flats in late spring and summer to spawn (Wang 1986). In San Francisco Bay, spawning occurs from April to October, with peaks in May and June (Wang 1986). Although eggs are deposited singly, the thick chorion bearing 2-8 filaments becomes entangled in aquatic vegetation, resulting in the formation of large clusters of eggs (Wang 1986). Topsmelt seemingly spawn in batches, laying eggs more than once during a spawning season (Fronk 1969, Wang 1986). The fecundity of topsmelt ranges from 200 eggs/fish for females measuring 110-120 mm in length to about 1,000 eggs/fish for females measuring 160 mm or more in length (Fronk 1969). Hatching time varies from 35 days at 13°C to less than 9 days at 27°C (Hubbs 1969).

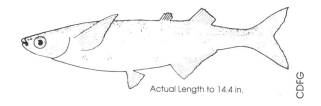

Actual Length to 14.4 in.

CDFG

Growth and Development

Topsmelt eggs are spherical in shape and approximately 1.5-1.7 mm in diameter (Wang 1986). Between nine and 35 days after fertilization, eggs hatch into planktonic larvae that measure 4.3-4.9 mm total length (TL) and 0.0011 grams wet weight (Emmett et al. 1991) or 5.1-5.4 mm standard length (SL) (Middaugh et al. 1990). Larvae measure 9.5-10.0 mm after the yolk-sac is absorbed, and begin to develop juvenile characteristics when approximately 18.5 mm long (Wang 1986). Juveniles may vary in length from 18.5 to 120.0 mm (Schultz 1933, Fronk 1969). Topsmelt mature in their second or third year, depending on subspecies, and may live six to nine years (Schultz 1933, Feder et al. 1974). Adults can attain as much as 120 mm in length for the southernmost subspecies (*A. affinis littoralis*) and as much as 370 mm in length for the northernmost subspecies (*A. affinis oregonia*) (Schultz 1933, Fronk 1969, Eschmeyer et al. 1983). In general, northern varieties grow larger than southern subspecies (Schultz 1933).

Food and Feeding

The topsmelt is characterized by an omnivorous diet (Quast 1968, Horn and Allen 1985). Topsmelt from bay and estuarine habitats consume mostly plant material (diatoms, filamentous algae, and detritus), whereas those from ocean habitats feed mainly on planktonic crustaceans (gammarid and caprellid amphipods, mysids, ostracods, copepods, and crustacean larvae) (Moyle 1976, Quast 1968, Fronk 1969). Juveniles and adults forage mostly during daylight near the surface in deep water or on the bottom in shallow water (Hobson et al. 1981).

Distribution

Topsmelt can occur from the Gulf of California northward to Vancouver Island, but are usually rare north of Tillamook Bay, Oregon (Miller and Lea 1972, Hart 1973, Eschmeyer et al. 1983). The five subspecies are *A. affinis oregonia* (occurs from Oregon to Humboldt Bay, California), *A. affinis affinis* (occurs in San Francisco Bay and surrounding waters to Monterey, California), *A. affinis littoralis* (occurs from Monterey to San Diego Bay, California), *A. affinis cedroscensis* (the kelp topsmelt), and *A. affinis insularium* (the "island topsmelt," occurs around the Santa Barbara Islands, California) (Schultz 1933, Feder et al. 1974).

In San Francisco Bay, spawning has been observed in the South Bay near the Aquatic Park in Berkeley and at the Dumbarton Bridge (Wang 1986). Small schools of larvae often occur near the surface of both shallow water and open water, and are particularly abundant in tidal basins (e.g., Aquatic Park in Berkeley; Lake Merritt in Oakland) and the sluggish waters of the South Bay

(e.g., Robert Crown Memorial Park; Hunters Point; San Mateo Bridge; Dumbarton Bridge) (Wang 1986). Juvenile topsmelt generally move into open waters of the bay or into coastal kelp beds. Some juveniles may occur in Suisun Bay during summer and early fall as the salt wedge moves to the upper reaches of the Estuary (Wang 1986). In general, topsmelt seem to be much less common outside of the South Bay.

Population Status and Influencing Factors

Field studies indicate that topsmelt are among the most abundant fish species occurring in shallow-water sloughs of South San Francisco Bay (Jones and Stokes Assoc. 1979, Woods 1981, Herbold et al. 1992). Herald and Simpson (1955) reported that topsmelt were commonly caught in a fixed fish-collecting device located at the Pacific Gas and Electric Company power plant in South San Francisco Bay. Furthermore, Wild (1969) reported that topsmelt was the most abundant species of fish sampled at the mouth of Plummer Creek (located in South San Francisco Bay). Midwater trawls fished at several locations in South San Francisco Bay during 1980-1988 also yielded numerous topsmelt (Herbold et al. 1992). South Bay topsmelt increased in abundance during two of the recent drought years, but otherwise did not show consistent year-to-year patterns (Herbold et al. 1992).

Several factors may directly influence the abundance of topsmelt: salinity, water temperature, freshwater inflows, entrainment on intake screens at power plants and water diversions, and availability of spawning substrate. In Newport Bay, California, topsmelt abundance was significantly correlated with water temperature and salinity (Allen 1982). By comparison, no relationship was found between abundance indices and river flow in San Francisco Bay (CDFG 1987). Although this species is commonly impinged on intake screens of power plants and water diversions, this source of mortality may not be significant for bay populations (San Diego Gas and Electric 1980). In the Tijuana Estuary of southern California, abundance of topsmelt eggs and larvae was positively correlated with algal mats (Nordby 1982). In other words, topsmelt eggs and larvae were seemingly more abundant in areas with dense algal growth. Because this species uses algal mats and shallow-water eelgrass beds for spawning, destruction or removal of these types of vegetation may adversely affect topsmelt abundance.

Trophic Levels

Topsmelt are omnivorous (primary and higher order consumers).

Proximal Species

Predators: Many piscivorous birds and fishes.

Prey: Diatoms (major); diatoms, chironomid midge larvae, and amphipods (minor).
Habitat: Eel grass and micro algae (spawning substrate); kelp beds (adult and juvenile cover).
Cohabitors: Schools with shiner perch and jacksmelt.

Good Habitat

In general, topsmelt can tolerate a relatively broad range of environmental conditions during the time that they inhabit San Francisco Bay. However, for successful spawning to occur, they require submerged vegetation for egg attachment, water temperatures of 10-25°C, and salinities of less than 72 ppt (Schultz 1933, Carpelan 1955, Fronk 1969). By comparison, larvae must be able to school near the surface in shallow open-water areas, particularly tidal basins (Wang 1986). Young-of-the-year topsmelt are common in middle to low salinity portions of the Estuary (Wang 1986). Although juveniles can tolerate salinities varying from 2 ppt to 80 ppt, growth and survival are reduced at salinities above 30 ppt (Middaugh and Shenker 1988). In addition, juveniles and adults are seemingly eurythermal, but temperatures of 26-27° C or higher may cause stress (Carpelan 1955, Ehrlich et al. 1979). Within San Francisco Bay, topsmelt utilize mudflats for breeding, spawning, and as nursery areas for young. Subtidal areas with sandy bottoms are relied on heavily as nursery and foraging areas. Intertidal streambeds are major foraging areas (Jones and Stokes Assoc. 1979). Recent studies indicate that embryonic and larval stages of topsmelt are sensitive to the effects of pollution (Singer et al. 1990, Anderson et al. 1991, Goodman et al. 1991, Hemmer et al. 1991). Thus, habitats used by topsmelt for spawning and rearing must not be exposed to appreciable amounts of pollution.

References

Allen, L.G. 1982. Seasonal abundance, composition, and productivity of the littoral fish assemblage in upper Newport Bay, California. Fish Bull., U.S. 80(4):769-790.

Anderson, B.S., D.P. Middaugh, J.W. Hunt and S.L. Turpen. 1991. Copper toxicity to sperm, embryos and larvae of topsmelt, *Atherinops affinis*, with notes on induced spawning. Mar. Environ. Res. 31:17-35.

Bane, G.W. and A.W. Bane. 1971. Bay fishes of northern California with emphasis on the Bodega Tomales Bay area. Mariscos Publ., Hampton Bays, NY, 143 pp.

California Department of Fish and Game (CDFG). 1987. Delta outflow effects on the abundance and distribution of San Francisco Bay fish and invertebrates, 1980-1985. Exhibit 60, entered for the State Wat. Res. Cont. Bd. 1987 Wat. Quality/Wat. Rights Proceeding on the San Fran. Bay/Sac.-San Joaquin Delta. Ca. Dept. Fish and Game, Stockton, CA, 345 p.

Carpelan, L.H. 1955. Tolerance of the San Francisco topsmelt, *Atherinopsis affinis affinis*, to conditions in salt-producing ponds bordering San Francisco Bay. Ca. Dept. Fish and Game 41(4):279-284.

Ehrlich, K.F., J.M. Hood, G. Muszynski and G.E. McGowen. 1979. Thermal behavioral responses of selected California littoral fishes. Fish bull., U.S. 76(4):837-849.

Emmett, R.L., S.L. Stone, S.A. Hinton and M.E. Monaco. 1991. Distribution and abundance of fishes and invertebrates in West Coast estuaries, Volume II: Species life history summaries. ELMR Rep. No. 8. NOAA/NOS Strategic Envir. Assess. Div., Rockville, MD, 329 pp.

Eschmeyer, W.N., W.S. Herald and H. Hammann. 1983. A field guide to Pacific Coast fishes of North America. Houghton Mifflin Co., Boston, MA, 336 pp.

Feder, H.M., C.H. Turner, and C. Limbaugh. 1974. Observations of the fishes associated with kelp beds in Southern California. Ca. Dept. Fish and Game, Fish Bull. 160, 138 pp.

Frey, H.W. 1971. California's living marine resources and their utilization. Ca. Dept. Fish and Game, Sacramento, CA, 148 pp.

Fronk, R.H. 1969. Biology of *Atherinops affinis littoralis* Hubbs in Newport Bay. M.S. Thesis, Univ. Ca., Irvine, CA, 106 pp.

Goodman, L.R., M.J. Hemmer, D.P. Middaugh, and J.C. Morre. 1991. Effects of fenvalerate on the early life stages of topsmelt (*Atherinops affinis*). Environ. Toxicol. Chem. 11:409-414.

Hart J.L. 1973. Pacific fishes of Canada. Fish. Res. Board Can., Bull. No. 180, 740 pp.

Hemmer, M.J., D.P. Middaugh, and V. Comparetta. 1991. Comparative acute sensitivity of larval topsmelt, *Atherinops affinis*, and inland silversides, *Menidia beryllina*, to 11 chemicals. Environ. Toxicol. Chem. 11:401-408.

Herald, E.S. and D.A. Simpson. 1955. Fluctuations in abundance of certain fishes in South San Francisco Bay as indicated by sampling at a trash screen. Ca. Dept. Fish and Game 41(4):271-278.

Herbold, B.A., A.D. Jassby and P.B. Moyle. 1992. Status and trends report on aquatic resources in the San Francisco Estuary, U.S. EPA publ. Rept., San Francisco, CA.

Hobson, E., W.N. McFarland and J.R. Chess. 1981. Crepuscular and nocturnal activities of Californian near shore fishes, with consideration of their scotopic visual pigments and the photic environment. Fish Bull., U.S. 79(1):1-30.

Horn, M.H. and L.G. Allen. 1985. Fish community ecology in southern California bays and estuaries. Chapter 8. *In:* A. Yanez-Arancibia (ed). Fish community ecology in estuaries and coastal lagoons: towards an ecosystem integration, p. 169-190 DR (R) UN AM Press, Mexico.

Hubbs, C. 1969. Developmental temperature tolerance and rates of four Southern California fishes, *Fundulus parvipinnis, Atherinops affinis, Leuresthes tenuis,* and *Hypsoblennius* sp. Ca. Dept. Fish and Game 51(2):113-122.

Jones and Stokes Assoc., Inc. 1979. Protection and restoration of San Francisco bay fish and wildlife habitat. Vol. 1 & 2. U.S. Fish and Wildl. Serv. and Ca. Dept. Fish and Game. Sacramento, CA.

Middaugh, D.P. 1990. Laboratory culture of jacksmelt, *Atherinopsis californiensis,* and topsmelt, *Atherinops affinis* (Pisces: Atherinidae), with a description of larvae. Ca. Dept. Fish and Game 76(1):4-43.

Middaugh, D.P., M.J. Hemmer, J.M. Shenker and T. Takita. 1990. Laboratory culture of jacksmelt, *Atherinopsis californiensis,* and topsmelt, *Atherinops affinis* (Pisces: Atherinidae), with a description of larvae. Ca. Dept. Fish and Game 76(1):4-43.

Miller, D.J. and R.N. Lea. 1972. Guide to the coastal marine fishes of California. Ca. Dept. Fish and Game, Fish Bull. 157, 235 pp.

Moyle, P.B. 1976. Inland Fishes of California. Univ. Ca. Press, Berkeley, CA. 405 pp.

Nordby, C.S. 1982. The comparative ecology of ichthyoplankton within Tijuana Estuary and its adjacent nearshore waters. M.S. Thesis, San Diego State Univ., San Diego, CA. 101 pp.

Quast, J.C. 1968. Observations on the food of the kelp-bed fishes. Ca. Dept. Fish and Game, Fish Bull. 139:109-142.

San Diego Gas and Electric. 1980. Silvergate power plant cooling water intake system demonstration (in accordance with section 316(b) Federal Water Pollution Control Act Amendment of 1972). San Diego Gas and Electric, San Diego, CA, various pagination.

Schultz, L.P. 1933. The age and growth of *Atherinops affinis oregonia.* Jordan and Snyder and other subspecies of bay smelt along the Pacific coast of the United States. Wash. State Univ. Publ. Biol. 2(3):45-102.

Singer, M.M., D.L. Smalheer, R.S. Tjeerdema, and M. Martin. 1990. Toxicity of an oil dispersant to the early life stages of four California marine species. Environ. Toxicol. Chem. 9:1387-1395.

Wang, J.C.S. 1986. Fishes of the Sacramento-San Joaquin estuary and adjacent waters, California: A guide to the early life histories. Tech. Rep. No. 9. Interagency ecological study program for the Sacramento-San Joaquin Estuary. Ca. Dept. of Water Res., Ca. Dept. Fish and Game, U.S. Bureau Reclam., U.S. Fish Wildl. Serv.

Wild, P. 1969. Marine species present in Plummer Creek, San Francisco Bay. M.S. Thesis, San Jose State Univ., Ca.

Woods, E. 1981. Fish utilization. *In:* T. Niesen and M. Josselyn (eds). The Hayward Regional Shoreline marsh restoration: Biological succession during the first year following dike removal. pp 35-46. Rep. 1. Tiburon center for environmental studies, Tiburon, Ca., 178 pp.

Threespine Stickleback

Gasterosteus aculeatus

Robert A. Leidy

General Information

The threespine stickleback (Family: Gasterosteidae) is a small laterally-compressed fish with three spines on the dorsum and from 1 to 35 bony plates on the sides (Moyle 1976). Largely as a matter of taxonomic convenience, Miller and Hubbs (1969) suggested that there are two forms: *G. a. aculeatus* for the fully-plated, anadromous form; and *G. a. microcephalus* for the partially-plated freshwater/resident form. The threespine stickleback is a polymorphic species and as such, populations within the San Francisco Estuary and its tributary streams support resident/freshwater and anadromous/saltwater forms, as well as mixtures of the two forms that presumably interbreed (Moyle, pers. comm.). The threespine stickleback has no commercial value, but has important scientific value, especially to evolutionary biologists.

Reproduction, Growth and Development

The following discussion is taken largely from Moyle (1976) unless otherwise referenced. Threespine sticklebacks typically complete their life cycle within one year although some individuals may live two to three years. Individuals from freshwater populations typically do not exceed 60 mm total length (TL), while anadromous forms may exceed 80 mm TL. Adult females are usually larger than adult males.

Anadromous forms migrate into freshwater breeding areas as water temperatures increase during April through July, although some stickleback populations may remain in estuarine environments to spawn if suitable habitat is present (Moyle 1976, Wang 1986).

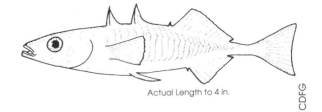

Actual Length to 4 in.

CDFG

Anadromous forms typically spawn earlier than freshwater populations. Spawning typically occurs at 15° to 18°C (Vrat 1949, Wang 1986). Males begin to display bright green and red breeding coloration as they move away from schools to set up breeding territories and construct nests.

Nests are excavated in the substrate as shallow pits. The pits are then covered with algae or other plant fragments and formed into a tunnel that is held together by a sticky renal secretion (Greenbank and Nelson 1959). Females are then courted by males into the nest where the female may lay between 50 and 300 eggs in several spawnings. Eggs are spherical and average 1.5-1.7 mm in diameter (Wang 1986). A pair can spawn up to six times within a 10-15 day period (Wang 1986). Following egg laying, the male drives away the female, fertilizes the eggs, and then begins to incubate the eggs while defending the nest from other sticklebacks and predators. The male is known to circulate water over the eggs by fanning his pectoral fins and to clean the eggs with his mouth. Immediately prior to hatching the male tears apart the nest and breaks apart the egg clusters which is thought to increase the survival of hatching young (Wang 1986). Length at hatching is between 4.2 and 5.5 mm TL (Vrat 1949, Kuntz and Radcliffe 1917).

Stickleback eggs hatch in six to eight days at temperatures of between 18° to 20° C (Breder and Rosen 1966). The fry remain in the nest for several days where they continue to be guarded by the male. Fry eventually form schools of similar-size sticklebacks or other species, usually in shallow water habitats containing dense vegetation (Wang 1986).

Juveniles are most abundant in late summer, followed by drastic declines in abundance in the fall and winter (Wang 1986). It is unknown whether populations of juveniles within the San Francisco Estuary make extensive migrations into open water/subtidal habitats within the Estuary. Moyle (1976) states that freshwater and anadromous populations range from complete ecological separation to complete interbreeding.

Food and Feeding

Threespine sticklebacks are visual feeders primarily on small benthic organisms or organisms living on submerged, rooted, or floating macrophytes such as insect larvae, chironomid midge larva, and ostracods (Hynes 1950, Beukema 1963, Hagen 1967). Anadromous forms feed mostly on free-swimming crustaceans (Barraclough and Fulton 1967, 1978; Barraclough et al. 1968). In a study of threespine stickleback diet in San Pablo Creek, a tributary to San Pablo Bay, Snyder (1984) found the diet consisted of approximately 42% insects (mainly chironomid larvae), 28% crustacea (mainly ostracods), and 10% earthworms (Lumbricidae). Fish eggs and plant material accounted for approximately 9% of the diet (Snyder 1984).

Distribution

Threespine stickleback are native to the coastal waters of Mediterranean Europe, north to Russia, and east to Japan and Korea (Moyle 1976). In North America, threespine stickleback populations occur on the East coast south to Chesapeake Bay, and on the West coast south from Alaska to Baja California. In California, populations are found below barriers such as dams and falls in coastal streams, including the San Francisco Estuary and its tributary streams, and in the Central Valley (Moyle 1976).

Within the San Francisco Estuary, threespine stickleback are widely distributed and often locally abundant in fresh-, brackish-, and saltwater intertidal upper marsh and riverine tidal marsh habitats (Leidy 1984; Leidy, unpub. data; Cathy Hieb, unpub. data). Leidy (1984) recorded threespine stickleback in 43% of 457 samples of Estuary streams between elevation 0 to 123 m.

Threespine stickleback are also abundant in large areas of formerly tidal salt and brackish marsh that have been converted to salt ponds in the South Bay and San Pablo Bay (Lonzarich 1989, Herbold et al. 1992). Carpelan (1957) recorded threespine stickleback as one of the most numerous fish in the Alviso salt ponds in the South Bay. Apparently, threespine stickleback persist in these ponds, particularly near the mouth of the Napa River, until salinities become too high (i.e., salinities between 40 to 50 ppt) (Herbold et al. 1992). There are approximately 9,059 acres of salt ponds in the Napa-Solono area of the North Bay and 27,497 acres in the South Bay that may be considered available for use by threespine stickleback on a seasonal basis (Meiorin et al. 1991).

Population Status and Influencing Factors

The current status of threespine stickleback within the San Francisco Estuary may be regarded as secure. Threespine stickleback populations currently are widespread and locally abundant in suitable habitats within the San Francisco Estuary. Because sticklebacks can readily disperse through estuarine and marine environments they are able to regularly recolonize habitats from which they may been extirpated. Important factors negatively influencing population numbers likely include excess siltation and turbidity, increased water temperatures by the removal of riparian vegetation through stream channelization, pollution, loss of nesting, feeding, and cover habitat by the removal of aquatic macrophytes, the construction of barriers such as dams or drop structures, and the introduction of exotic piscivorous fish.

Trophic Levels

Larvae are primary consumers. Juveniles and adults are primary and higher order consumers.

Proximal Species

Major Predators: Kingfisher, egrets, herons, and other wading birds.

Other Predators: Adult salmonids and other large freshwater, estuarine, and marine piscivorous fish terrestrial and aquatic snakes.

Major Prey: Aquatic insects and crustacea, earthworms, fish eggs and vegetation.

Habitat/cover: Riparian, submerged, floating, and emergent wetland and aquatic vegetation.

Good Habitat

Freshwater populations of threespine stickleback prefer clear, cool backwater and pool habitats containing submerged, floating, or emergent vegetation, with sand or small-sized gravel substrates (Moyle 1976, Leidy 1984). This species is typically uncommon in silted pools with moderate to high turbidities (Leidy 1984). Marine and estuarine populations are pelagic, although they tend to remain to close to the shore (Moyle 1976). Threespine stickleback is uncommon where water temperatures regularly exceed 24° C (Moyle 1976).

References

Barraclough, W.E. and J.D. Fulton. 1967. Data record. Number, size composition and food of larval and juvenile fish caught with a two-boat surface trawl in the Strait of Georgia. July 4-8, 1966. Fish. Res. Board Can. Rep. Ser. 940. 82 pp.

_____. 1978. Data record. Food of larval and juvenile fish caught with a surface trawl in Saanich Inlet during June and July 1966. Fish. Res. Board Can. Rep. Ser. 1003. 78 pp.

Barraclough, W.E., D.G. Robinson and J.D. Fulton. 1968. Data record. Number, size composition, weight and food of larval and juvenile fish caught with a two-boat surface trawl in Saanich Inlet, April 23 -July 21, 1968. Fish. Res. Board Can. Rep. Ser. 1004. 305 pp.

Beukema, J. 1963. Experiments on the effects of the hunger state on the risk of prey of the three-spined stickleback. Arch. Nees. Zool. 15: 358-361.

Breder, C.M. and D.E. Rosen. 1966. Modes of reproduction in fishes. Am. Mus. Nat. Hist., New York. 941 pp.

Carpelan, L.H. 1957. Hydrobiology of the Alviso salt ponds. Ecology 38(3): 375-390.

Greenbank, J. and P.R. Nelson. 1959. Life history of the threespine stickleback, *Gasterosteus aculeatus* Linnaeus in Karluk Lake and Bare Lake, Kodiak Island, Alaska. U.S. Fish Wild. Serv. Fish Bull. 59(153): 537-559.

Hagen, D.W. 1967. Isolating mechanisms in three-spine sticklebacks (*Gasterosteus*). J. Fish. Res. Bd. Canada 24(8): 1637-1692.

Herbold, B., P. Moyle and A. Jassby 1992. Status and trends report on aquatic resources in the San Francisco Estuary. San Fran. Est. Proj. Public Rept. March 1992. 257 pp. plus appendices.

Hynes, H.B.N. 1950. The food of freshwater sticklebacks (*Gasterosteus aculeatus* and *Pygosteus pungitius*), with a review of methods used in studies of the food of fishes. J. An. Ecol. 19(1): 36-58.

Kuntz, A. and R. Radcliffe. 1917. Notes on the embryology and larval development of twelve teleostean fishes. Bull. U.S. Bur Fish. 35: 87-134.

Miller, R.R. and C. L. Hubbs. 1969. Systematics of *Gasterosteus aculeatus* with particular reference to intergradation and introgression along the Pacific Coast of North America: a commentary on a recent contribution. Copeia 1: 52-69.

Leidy, R.A. 1984. Distribution and ecology of stream fishes in the San Francisco Bay drainage. Hilgardia 52(8): 1-175

Lonzarich, D. 1989. Life history and patterns of distribution in salt pond fishes: a community level study. M.S. Thesis, San Jose State University, Ca..

Meiorin, E.C., M.N. Josselyn, R. Crawford, J. Calloway, K. Miller, R. Pratt, T. Richardson, and R. Leidy. 1991. Status and trends report on wetlands and related habitats in the San Francisco Estuary. U.S. Environmental Protection Agency, San Francisco Estuary Project. 209 pp. + appendices.

Moyle, P.B. 1976. Inland Fishes of California. Univ. of California Press. 405 pp.

Snyder, R.J. 1984. Seasonal variation in the diet of the threespine stickleback, *Gasterosteus aculeatus*, in Contra Costa County, California. Ca. Fish and Game 70(3): 167-172.

Vrat, V. 1949. Reproductive behavior and development of eggs of the threespine stickleback (*Gasterosteus aculeatus*) of California. Copeia 4: 252-260.

Wang, J.C.S. 1986. Fishes of the Sacramento-San Joaquin estuary and adjacent waters, California: a guide to the early life histories. Tech. Rept. 9. Prepared for the Interagency Ecological Study program for the Sacramento-San Joaquin Estuary. Interagency Ecological Workshop, Asilomar, CA. 1990.

Personal Communications

Peter Moyle, University of California, Davis

Brown Rockfish

Sebastes auriculatus

Kurt F. Kline

General Information

The brown rockfish (*Sebastes auriculatus*) is a member of the family Scorpaenidae, one of the largest fish families in the western Pacific. The family is dominated by the rockfishes (*Sebastes spp.*), a genus which is represented by over 50 species on the northwest Pacific coast.

The brown rockfish is the most common rockfish in San Francisco Bay (Alpin 1967, Wang 1986), and the Bay appears to be an important nursery area for juveniles (Kendall and Lenarz 1986, Baxter 1999). Brown rockfish are the most common rockfish caught by sport anglers in the Bay (W. Van Buskirk, pers. comm) and the third most frequently caught rockfish in the San Francisco region (Karpov et al. 1995). Most brown rockfish are caught by anglers fishing from partyboats, skiffs, piers, and the shoreline (Miller and Gotshall 1965, Karpov et al. 1995). It is also a minor, but important, component of the nearshore commercial fishery; in the San Francisco area, the majority of brown rockfish are caught by hook and line for the live or whole fresh fish markets. Since the early 1990s, the brown rockfish has been the most common species sold in the live in San Francisco markets (C. Ryan, pers. comm.).

Reproduction

All rockfishes, including the brown rockfish, are viviparous. Fertilization is internal and the larvae develop in the egg capsule within the ovarian cavity. The larvae hatch within the ovary and are released with little yolk remaining and ready to feed. The embryos develop in 40-50 days after fertilization and the larvae hatch about 1 week before extrusion (Kendall and Lenarz 1986). Brown rockfish larvae are 4.7-6.7 mm at hatching (Delacy et al. 1964) and pelagic for several months. Although brown rockfish fecundity is not known, *Sebastes* females typically produce 100,000 to 1,000,000 eggs per brood (Kendall and Lenarz 1986). Brown rockfish may have multiple broods within one year, with parturition

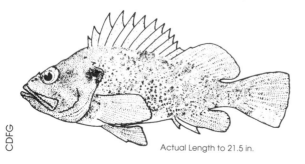

CDFG

Actual Length to 21.5 in.

from December-January and May-July in Central California (Wyllie-Echeverria 1987).

Although gravid brown rockfish have been collected in San Francisco Bay, most parturition is believed to occur in coastal waters (Kendall and Lenarz 1986, Wang 1986). In San Francisco Bay, mature females were observed in winter and spring and larvae have been collected in winter and spring (Wang 1986).

Growth and Development

Brown rockfish juveniles are pelagic until 20-30 mm, whereas older juveniles settle out of the water column and are strongly association with some type of physical structure (Turner et al. 1969, Kendall and Lenarz 1986). Pelagic juveniles have been collected in nearshore coastal waters from April through June, while benthic juveniles are common in nearshore coastal waters and the Bay (Kendall and Lenarz 1986). In San Francisco Bay, age-0 juveniles were usually first collected from April to July and were common through summer and fall (Wang 1986, Baxter 1999).

Juvenile brown rockfish apparently spend several years in a very restricted home range in the Bay and gradually move to deeper waters and nearshore. Juvenile brown rockfish tagged in the Bay have been recaptured more than 80 km away in nearshore coastal waters (Kendall and Lenarz 1986).

Both male and female brown rockfish reach maturity as early as age 3 (260 mm TL); half reach maturity at age 5 (310 mm TL); and all are mature at age 10 (380 mm TL) (Wyllie-Echeverria 1987). Both sexes grow at similar rates and reach a maximum size of about 550 mm TL (Miller and Lea 1972). In southern California, the oldest male was 18 years, the oldest female 20 years (Love and Johnson 1998).

Food and Feeding

In San Francisco Bay, smaller juvenile brown rockfish (<130 mm TL) prey primarily upon small crustaceans, including amphipods, copepods, caridean shrimp, and *Cancer* crabs. Larger fish (130-310 mm TL) prey upon larger crustaceans (caridean shrimp, *Cancer* crabs, *Upogebia*) and fish (Ryan 1986).

Distribution

The brown rockfish ranges from Hipolito Bay, Baja California, to southeast Alaska (Miller and Lea 1972). It most often solitary, but may be found in small aggregations (Love and Johnson 1998). In the ocean, it is most common in shallow rocky reefs (5-20 m), but also found over sand flats near eelgrass and in kelp beds while in bays and estuaries it is found near piers and over rubble (Feder et al. 1974, Matthews 1990, Love and Johnson 1998).

In San Francisco Bay the brown rockfish is found primarily in Central San Francisco Bay, to a lesser degree in South San Francisco and San Pablo bays, and occasionally in Carquinez Strait and western Suisun Bay (Ganssle 1966, Messersmith 1966, Wang 1986, Baxter 1999).

Suitable habitat and salinity are the primary factors influencing distribution of brown rockfish in the Bay. Benthic juveniles and adults are strongly associated with structure, including rocky reefs, piers and jetties, breakwaters, and riprap. In the Bay, most brown rockfish were collected at salinities > 20l (median 28.3l, 90th percentile 31.8l, 10th percentile 21.5l, Baxter 1999, CDFG, unpubl. data).

Population Status and Influencing Factors

There is a modest brown rockfish population in the San Francisco Bay region. San Francisco Bay is a nursery area for brown rockfish, and most juveniles immigrate to the Bay from the nearshore coastal area soon after settlement. It is not clear if resident adult brown rockfish spawn successfully in the Bay. Juveniles rear in the Bay for several years, and the population is comprised of several year classes. But there is no reliable index or measure of year class strength in the Bay, as brown rockfish are strongly associated with structure, and are undoubtedly undersampled by trawls or other towed nets typically used by research studies.

Trophic Levels

Secondary carnivore. Feeds primarily on crustaceans and fishes.

Proximal Species

Prey: Crustaceans (caridean shrimp, *Cancer* crabs, *Upogebia*, amphipods, copepods), polychaetes, fishes, herring eggs.
Predators: Larger predatory fishes, including striped bass.

Good Habitat

Structure, including piers and rocky shores, in the higher salinity regions of the Bay

Acknowledgments

Some of the material in this report was summarized from the brown rockfish chapter in IEP Technical Report 63, which is referenced below (Baxter 1999).

References

Aplin, J.A. 1967. Biological survey of San Francisco Bay, 1963-1966. Ca. Dept. Fish and Game, Marine Resources Operations. MRO Ref. 67-4, 131 pp.

Baxter, R. 1999. Brown rockfish. *In*: J. Orsi, ed. Report on the 1980-1995 fish, shrimp, and crab sampling in the San Francisco Estuary, California. Interagency Ecological Program for the Sacramento-San Joaquin Estuary Tech. Rept. No. 63.

Delacy, A.C., C.R. Hitz, and R.L. Dryfoos. 1964. Maturation, gestation, and birth of rockfish (*Sebastodes*) from Washington and adjacent waters. Washington Dept. of Fisheries, Fishery Research Paper 2(2):51-67.

Feder, H.M., C.H. Turner and C. Limbaugh. 1974. Observations of the fishes associated with kelp beds in southern California. Ca. Dept. of Fish and Game Fish Bull. 160, 144 pp.

Ganssle, D. 1966. Fishes and decapods of San Pablo and Suisun Bays. *In*: D.W. Kelly (ed). Ecological studies of the Sacramento San Joaquin Estuary, Part 1, Ca. Dept. of Fish and Game Fish Bull. 133: 64-94.

Karpov, K., P. Albin and W. Buskirk. 1995. The marine recreational fishery in northern and cetral California. Ca. Dept. Fish and Game Fish Bull. 176.

Kendall Jr., A.W. and W.H. Lenarz. 1986. Status of early life history studies of northeast Pacific rockfishes. Proceedings of the International Rockfish Symposium. October 1986. Anchorage, Alaska.

Love, M.S. and K. Johnson. 1998. Aspects of the life histories of grass rockfish, *Sebastes rastrelliger*, and brown rockfish, *S. auriculatus*, from southern California. US Fish. Bull. 87:100-109.

Matthews, K.R. 1990. An experimental study of the habitat preferences and movement patterns of copper, quillback, and brown rockfish (*Sebastes spp.*). Env. Biol. Fishes 29:161-178.

Messersmith, J. 1966. Fishes collected in the Carquinez Strait in 1961-1962. *In*: D.W. Kelly (ed). Ecological Studies of the Sacramento-San Joaquin Estuary, Part 1. Ca. Dept. of Fish and Game Fish Bull. 133:57-63.

Miller, D.J. and D. Gotshall. 1965. Ocean sportfish catch and effort from Oregon to Pt. Arguello, July 1957 to June 1961. Ca. Dept of Fish and Game Fish Bull. 130, 135 pp

Miller, D.J. and R.N. Lea. 1972. Guide to the coastal marine fishes of California. Ca. Dept. of Fish and Game Fish Bull. 157, 249 pp.

Ryan, C.J. 1986. Feeding habits of brown rockfish, *Sebastes auriculatus*, associated with a dock in San Francisco Bay, California. M. A. Thesis, San Francisco State University, 88 pp.

Turner, C.H., E.E. Ebert and R.R. Given. 1969. Manmade reef ecology. Ca. Dept. Fish and Game, Fish. Bull. 146: 221p.

Wang, J.C.S. 1986. Fishes of the Sacramento-San Joaquin Estuary and adjacent waters, California:

A guide to the early life histories. Interagency Ecological Study Program for the Sac.-San Joaquin Estuary, Tech. Rept. No. 9.

Wyllie-Echeverria, T. 1987. Thirty-four species of California rockfishes: maturity and seasonality of reproduction. US Fishery Bulletin 85(2):229-250.

Personal Communications

Wade Van Buskirk. Recreational Fisheries Information Network Database, Pacific States Marine Recreational Fisheries Monitoring

Connie Ryan. California Department of Fish and Game, Ocean Fisheries Research Unit - Menlo Park

---

Pacific Staghorn Sculpin

Leptocottus armatus armatus

Robert N. Tasto

General Information

The Pacific staghorn sculpin (Family: Cottidae) is found from Kodiak Island, Alaska to San Quintin Bay, Baja, California (Miller and Lea 1972). It is the only true euryhaline species among the California cottids (CDFG 1987), and appears to move freely between fresh and saltwater environments (Moyle 1976). It is regarded as a nuisance species by many sportfishermen, but has shown some limited value as bait for gamefish (particularly striped bass) in the Estuary. Bolin (1944) recorded its maximum depth of capture offshore coastal California at 300 feet. It is a target species of the National Status and Trends Program (Emmett et al. 1991), as it is considered an indicator of stress in the estuarine environment, and may spend its entire life in Pacific coast estuaries.

Reproduction

Pacific staghorn sculpin may reach sexual maturity in their first year, and sex ratios within a population appear to favor females slightly (Boothe 1967, Tasto 1975). In northern California, spawning begins in October (Tomales Bay) or November (San Francisco Bay), peaks in January-February, and ends in March (Jones 1962,

Boothe 1967). In southern California (Anaheim Bay), spawning does not begin until December, but also peaks in January-February and ends around mid-March (Tasto 1975). Fertilization is external. Staghorn sculpin eggs are adhesive and laid in shallow subtidal and intertidal waters. Fecundity averages 5,000 eggs per female (Jones 1962), and ranges from 2,000 to 11,000 eggs per female (Moyle 1976). Eggs range from 1.36 to 1.50 mm in diameter and hatch in 9 to 14 days at 15.5°C (Emmett et al. 1991).

Growth and Development

At hatching, Pacific staghorn sculpin larvae range from 3.9 to 4.8 mm total length (TL) (Jones 1962). Metamorphosis to the juvenile begins after about 2 months, when the larvae are 15 to 20 mm standard length (SL) (Emmett et al. 1991). The juvenile size range is approximately 20 to 120 mm TL (Jones 1962), and there appears to be considerable overlap in the length distribution of 0+ and 1+ fish, particularly in the summer and fall (CDFG 1987). The staghorn sculpin reaches maturity at about 120 mm TL its first year, and can grow to over 200 mm TL (3 years old) in California (Jones 1962). In southern California, growth was determined to be curvilinear (Tasto 1975). The largest specimen recorded was about 30 cm (Barnhart 1936).

Food and Feeding

Pacific staghorn sculpin larvae are planktivorous (Emmett et al. 1991). The juvenile and adult forms are, however, demersal predators, particularly over intertidal and shallow subtidal mudflats, and have been shown to feed on a variety of non-burrowing benthic organisms (Jones 1962, Boothe 1967, Tasto 1975). Feeding behavior of the staghorn sculpin is thought to be continuous, although there appears to be a preference for feeding at night (Tasto 1975). The principal food items for staghorn sculpin within San Francisco Bay were found to be bay shrimp (*Crangon* spp.), bay goby (*Lepidogobius lepidus*), mud crab (*Hemigrapsus oregonensis*), callianassid shrimp (i.e., *Upogebia*), and a variety of amphipods, isopods, and polychaetes (Boothe 1967). Elkhorn Slough studies showed predation on epifaunal crustaceans and infaunal and epifaunal worms (Barry et al. 1996). In Anaheim Bay, major food items were similar to Elkhorn Slough and San Francisco Bay, including callianasiid shrimp (i.e., *Callinassa sp.*), mud crab, and arrow goby (*Clevelandia ios*) (Tasto 1975). Jones (1962) found that in Tomales Bay, staghorn sculpin fed heavily upon *Upogebia* and *Crangon* shrimp. In Grays Harbor, Washington, the staghorn sculpin's diet consisted of amphipods, crangonid shrimp, small fish, *Upogebia* sp., juvenile Dungeness crab, and polychaetes (Armstrong et al. 1995). Several studies indicate that the staghorn sculpin

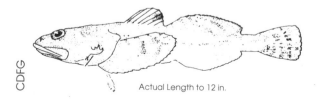

CDFG

Actual Length to 12 in.

Fish

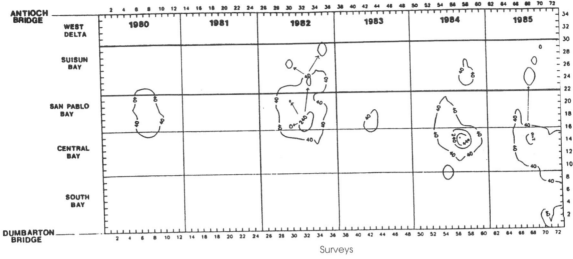

Figure 2.5 Spatial and Temporal Distribution of Young-of-the-Year Pacific Staghorn Sculpin (CDFG 1987)

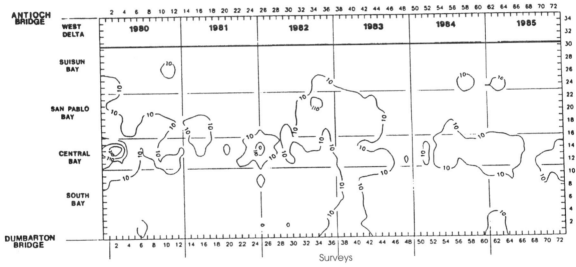

Figure 2.6 Spatial and Temporal Distribution of Adult Pacific Staghorn Sculpin (CDFG 1987)

is an important prey item for aquatic birds, particularly the great blue heron (Tasto 1975, Bayer 1985, Emmett et al. 1991).

Distribution

Pacific staghorn sculpin have been collected in all four subregions of the Bay. Larval abundance was determined to be highest from December through March, peaking in February, in various parts of the Estuary south of the Carquinez Bridge (CDFG 1987). Small juveniles are often found intertidally; catch patterns suggest that, during their first year, these early post larval forms move gradually from shallow inshore areas to deeper Bay waters (CDFG 1987, Emmett et al. 1991). In studies conducted in Yaquina Bay, Oregon, young-of-the-year first appeared in December, and were collected through April

(Bayer 1985). Juveniles and adults are most frequently captured in central Bay and San Pablo Bay, and are more abundant in the channels in winter, and on the shoals in spring and summer (**Figures 2.5** and **2.6**). Adults experience their widest distribution during high Delta outflow, and it appears that a portion of the adult population moves out of the Estuary by late spring of their second year (CDFG 1987). In Elkhorn Slough (Monterey County), staghorn sculpin were highest in abundance, and frequently the dominant species, at sampling stations furthest inland, near sources of fresh water (Yoklavich et al. 1991). A tidal marsh population studied in Anaheim Bay, a relatively small embayment in southern California with little freshwater input, was composed almost entirely of juveniles (Tasto 1975). Pacific staghorn sculpin can also be found a mile or two up coastal streams in association with exclusively freshwater species (Moyle 1976).

Population Status and Influencing Factors

Multiple gear catch statistics from 1980-85 showed that Pacific staghorn sculpin was the most abundant of all the sculpins caught in the Estuary, and approximately 4% of all fishes caught by otter trawl and beach seine (CDFG 1987). The highest abundance of larvae noted in this study occurred during years of low Delta outflows, yet juvenile and adult numbers showed no quantifiable relationship to magnitude of flows (CDFG 1987). Larval success is thought to be the determining factor in overall recruitment to local populations (Emmett et al. 1991).

Trophic Levels

Larvae are first and second order consumers (Emmett et al. 1991). Adults and juveniles are higher order consumers.

Proximal Species

Predators: Diving ducks, great blue heron, western grebe, Caspian tern, loons, cormorants, gulls, marine mammals.
Prey: *Crangon* shrimp (principal prey item), bay goby (prey of large adults), mud crab, callianassid shrimp, amphipods (juvenile prey item, dominant in fresh water).
Competitor: Starry flounder.

Good Habitat

Success of local staghorn sculpin populations depends upon the quality and quantity of suitable habitat. Newly settled juveniles use intertidal and shallow subtidal mudflats for protection and feeding (Tasto 1975), although older juveniles and adults are said to prefer more sandy substrates and somewhat deeper waters (Bayer 1981, Emmett et al. 1991). Pacific staghorn sculpin are known to bury themselves in soft substrates, and have been found buried in mudflats after the tide has retreated (Tasto 1975, Bayer 1985). Staghorn sculpin have also been found associated with eelgrass (Bayer 1981).

Water quality factors are equally important for successful populations. Demersal eggs hatch most successfully at 26 ppt and larvae survive best at 10 to 17 ppt (Jones 1962). Greatest catches of larvae were in surface salinities of 18 to 30 ppt (CDFG 1987). The juvenile stage appears to be the most euryhaline, with the maturing and adult forms most likely to be found in the higher salinity waters (CDFG 1987, Emmett et al. 1991). Laboratory experiments have shown that adult *L. armatus* can survive 67.5 ppt at 12°C, but gradually lose their tolerance of high salinities as temperatures rise to 25°C (Morris 1960). Since larval development is planktonic, it does not appear that, under normal conditions in the San Francisco Estuary, either temperature or salinity are very limiting to distribution.

References

Armstrong, J.L., D.A. Armstrong and S.B. Mathews. 1995. Food habits of estuarine staghorn sculpin, *Leptocottus armatus*, with focus on consumption of juvenile Dungeness crab, *Cancer maagister*. Fishery Bulletin. Vol. 93: 456-470.

Barnhart, P.S. 1936. The marine fishes of southern California. Univ. Ca. Press. Berkeley. 209 pp.

Barry, J.P., M.M. Yoklavich, G.M. Cailliet, D.A. Ambrose and B.S. Antrum. 1996. Trophic ecology of the dominant fishes in Elkhorn Slough, California, 1974-1980. Estuaries., Vol. 19 (1): 115-138.

Bayer, R.D. 1981. Shallow water ichthyofauna of the Yaquina Estuary, Oregon. Northwest Science, 55(3): 182-193.

_____. 1985. Shiner perch and Pacific staghorn sculpins in Yaquina Estuary, Oregon. Northwest Science, 59(3): 230-240.

Bolin, R.L. 1944. A review of the marine cottid fishes of California. Stanford Ichthyol. Bull., 3: 1-135.

Boothe, P. 1967. The food and feeding habits of four species of San Francisco Bay fish. Ca. Dept. Fish and Game, Mar. Res. Oper. Reference (67-13). 155 pp.

California Department of Fish and Game (CDFG). 1987. Delta outflow effects on the abundance and distribution of San Francisco Bay fish and invertebrates, 1980-85. Exhibit 60. Ca. Dept. Fish and Game. State Wat. Res. Ctrl. Bd., Wat. Qual./Wat. Rights Proc. on San Fran. Bay/Sac.-San Joaquin Delta. 337 pp.

Emmett, R.L., S.L. Stone, S.A. Hinton and M.E. Monaco. 1991. Distribution and abundance of fishes and invertebrates in west coast estuaries, Volume 11: species life history summaries. ELMR Rep. No. 8. NOAA/NOS Strategic Environmental Assessments Div., Rockville, MD. 329 pp.

Jones, A.C. 1962. The biology of the euryhaline fish *Leptocottus armatus armatus* Girard (Cottidae). Univ. of Ca. Publ. in Zool., 67 (4): 321-368.

Miller, D.J. and R.N. Lea. 1972. Guide to the coastal marine fishes of California. Ca. Fish Bull (157). Coop. Ext. Univ. Ca. Div. of Ag. and Nat. Res. Publ. 4065. 249 pp.

Morris, R.W. 1960. Temperature, salinity, and southern limits of three species of Pacific cottid fishes. Limnology and Oceanography, 5(2): 175-179.

Moyle, P.B. 1976. Inland Fishes of California. Univ. Ca. Press. Berkeley. 405 pp.

Tasto, R.N. 1975. Aspects of the biology of Pacific staghorn sculpin, *Leptocottus armatus* Girard, in Anaheim Bay. *In*: E. David Lane and Cliff W. Hill (eds). The marine resources of Anaheim Bay. Ca. Dept. Fish and Game, Fish Bull. (165): 123-135

Yoklavich, M.M., G.M. Cailliet, J.P. Barry, D.A. Ambrose and B.S. Antrum. 1991. Temporal and spatial patterns in abundane and diversity of fish assemblages in Elkhorn Slough, California. Estuarine Research Federation, Vol. 14, No. 4: 465-480.

Prickly Sculpin

Cottus asper

Bruce Herbold

General Information

Sculpins (Family: Cottidae) are specialized for living on the bottom, generally hiding in the nooks and crannies among rocks or rooted vegetation. Their large, flattened heads and proportionally small bodies, their fan-shaped pectoral fins, and their lack of an air bladder allow sculpins to hold their position even in wave-swept coasts or high-velocity mountain streams. The use of such habitats, combined with their secretive habits and cryptic coloration, make sculpins difficult to see by predators, prey, or inquisitive fish biologists. The large mouth relative to body size permits sculpins to consume prey almost as large as themselves. Sculpins are found in the northern Pacific Ocean and New Zealand. Most members of the family are marine but a number of species (most in the genus *Cottus*) occur in the fresh waters of North America.

Reproduction

Sculpins generally spawn in the late winter or early spring, although some upstream populations seem to delay spawning into the early summer (Wang 1986). Male sculpins prepare for spawning by moving downstream and establishing a nest site where they clean off some kind of overhanging structure such as a flat rock, tule root, or beer can (Kresja 1965, Moyle 1976). Females then enter the spawning area and, after a nocturnal courtship, attach their eggs to the prepared overhanging structure. Females produce between 280 and 11,000 eggs (Patten 1971), but one male may court many females and end up with a nest containing up to 30,000 eggs (Kresja 1965). Males stay in the nest protecting the eggs and circulating water around them until they hatch. Hatching rates appear to improve in saltier water (Millikan 1968). After hatching, the larvae become

Moyle 1976

Actual Length to 9 in.

planktonic and are carried further downstream. Young sculpins (15-30 mm SL, Broadway and Moyle 1978) settle to the bottom and begin a general upstream movement (McLarney 1968, Mason and Machidori 1976).

The amount of movement associated with spawning appears to vary tremendously among sculpin populations (Wang 1986). Earlier observers suggested that substantial downstream movements were only found in coastal populations, not in the Central Valley (Kresja 1967). However, very high densities of newly hatched prickly sculpins have been reported from the Delta and Suisun Bay (Turner 1966, Wang 1986), as well as in upstream sites (Wang 1986) which has led to the conclusion that the Central Valley contains both 'migratory' and 'non-migratory' populations. Recent studies suggest that the same may be true in coastal streams, such as the Eel River, where young prickly sculpins were found 100 km above the river mouth (Brown et al. 1995). Regardless of the degree to which they move for spawning, mainstem rivers appear to be an important habitat for most prickly sculpin populations. Young prickly sculpins are often found in saline water at the tributary mouths in spring months (Leidy pers. comm.).

Growth and Development

Fry at hatching average six mm total length. Newly emerged fry swim soon after hatching and appear to drift downstream as plankton for three to five weeks. This early developmental pattern leads to high concentrations in the slower waters of the Delta (Turner 1966). Young fish assume a bottom-feeding existence at sizes of 20 to 30 mm, at which time they appear to begin moving upstream (McLarney 1968).

Food and Feeding

Sculpins have a reputation amongst anglers as predators on salmonid eggs and fry (Munro and Clements 1937, Shapovalov and Taft 1954, Reed 1967) which is probably undeserved (Moyle 1976, 1977). Diet studies generally show that sculpins prey principally on invertebrates, with younger prickly sculpins eating planktonic crustaceans and older fish eating larger, benthic animals and small fish (Moyle 1976). In Suisun Marsh their diet is predominately benthic amphipods of the genus *Gammarus* (Herbold 1987).

Distribution

Prickly sculpins are found in fresh to brackish water from the Kenai Peninsula in Alaska to the Ventura River in southern California. In California's Central Valley, they can be found in the lower reaches of most foothill streams. Prickly sculpins often overlap in distribution with the similar riffle sculpin (*Cottus gulosus*) which is found more in upper elevations. Neither is found in the upper Pit River drainage. Their range includes tidal habitats of brackish salinity, such as Suisun Marsh. Prickly sculpins are found from headwaters to the mouths of many of the small tributaries that flow into San Francisco Bay, (including Alameda Creek, Walnut Creek, Corte Madera Creek, Coyote Creek and the Petaluma River; Leidy 1984).

Habitats

Like freshwater sculpins generally, prickly sculpins use very diverse habitats from small headwater streams to coastal estuaries, and are widely distributed from Alaska to southern California (Moyle 1976). Whatever the habitat, prickly sculpins usually are found under some sort of cover: rocks in streams, vegetation in pools and marshes, or simply at depth in lakes and reservoirs (Moyle 1976, Brown et al. 1995).

Population Status and Influencing Factors

Many of the most recent, successful invading species of the Estuary have the potential to affect prickly sculpins. In 1986, the Asiatic clam (*Potamocorbula amurensis*) began a rapid and thorough domination of the benthic community. Although the decline in abundance of other benthic species has been well-documented, there is no information on the impact of these changes on the diet, distribution, or abundance of prickly sculpin. Also in the mid-1980s, the Estuary was invaded by the shimofuri goby (*Tridentiger bifasciatus*) which lives in the same kinds of habitats and microhabitats as prickly sculpin. However, the very small mouth of the goby reduces the likelihood of interspecific competition. Since 1996, mitten crabs (*Eriochier sinensis*) have become extremely abundant and are voracious and indiscriminate predators on benthic organisms. Mitten crabs undergo an annual upstream migration to spawn that results in a large overlap with the range of prickly sculpins. In the Eel River of northern California, it appears likely that the introduction of predatory pikeminnows (*Ptychocheilus grandis*) has resulted in a substantial change in sculpin behavior when compared to the similar Smith River (Brown and Moyle 1991, Brown et al. 1995, White and Harvey in press). In the tributary creeks of the San Francisco Bay drainage, prickly sculpins are often associated with native species and are usually absent in areas where large non-native predatory fish are found (Leidy 1984). No work has been done to document interactions of prickly sculpin with the vastly changed benthic community of the Central Valley.

Habitat changes and degradations of water quality are associated with a restricted range of prickly sculpins in the San Joaquin River watershed (Brown 1998). Sculpins are part of an assemblage of native species that are characteristic of smaller San Joaquin tributaries that have suffered little change in habitat structure or water quality. Unfortunately, the close associations of land use practices, habitat alteration and water quality degradation in the rest of the watershed make it impossible to identify the effects of individual environmental variables on sculpin biology.

As in the San Joaquin River, prickly sculpins in Suisun Marsh tend to be found most often in association with other native fishes and in less disturbed habitats (Herbold 1987). However, the actual physical parameters of low dissolved solids and high gradient that characterize usual sculpin sites in the San Joaquin River, are absent in Suisun Marsh. This suggests that the impacts of land use and disturbance on the distribution and abundance of prickly sculpins are not simple and that the parameters that reflect disturbance in one area may not be causally connected to the parameter of importance to sculpins in that area.

California's immense water projects appear to have had little effect on prickly sculpins. Construction of dams has isolated populations and prevented the downstream movements exhibited elsewhere, but populations have remained large in the warmwater reservoir behind Friant Dam. Prickly sculpins are also found in stream habitats upstream of impassable dams on a number of other Central Valley streams. Water export from the Delta has resulted in the establishment of new populations of prickly sculpins within the facilities of the state and federal projects, as well as within aquatic habitats in southern California outside the historic range of prickly sculpin (Wang 1986). The impacts of these introductions on the native species in southern California streams have been little studied.

Trophic Levels

Prickly sculpins are secondary and tertiary consumers.

Proximal Species

Predators: Centrarchids and pikeminnows.
Prey: Planktonic crustacea (for young); benthic invertebrates, particularly gammarid amphipods; *neomysis*; juvenile fish.
Habitat: Emergent aquatic vegetation (root masses).

Good Habitat

In contrast to staghorn sculpins (*Leptocottus armatus*), prickly sculpins larger than 20 mm are usually found in association with some kind of complex, physical cover. In upstream sites, cover consists of interstices in cobble, root wads and woody debris and even discarded soda cans and tires. In downstream sites, cover usually consists of root wads of emergent aquatic vegetation. Although more tolerant of salinity than most other California fresh-water fish, sculpins are seldom found in salinities greater than 10 ppt.

References

Broadway, J.E. and P.B. Moyle. 1978. Aspects of the ecology of the prickly sculpin, *Cottus asper* Richardson, a persistent native species in Clear Lake, Lake County, California. Environ. Biol. Fishes 3(4):337-343.

Brown, L.R. and P.B. Moyle. 1991. Changes in habitat and microhabitat partitioning within an assemblage of stream fishes in response to predation by Sacramento squawfish (*Ptychocheilus grandis*). Can. J. Fish. Aquat. Sci. 48:849–856.

Brown, L.R., S.A. Matern and P.B. Moyle. 1995. Comparative ecology of prickly sculpin, *Cottus asper*, and coastrange sculpin, *C. aleuticus*, in the Eel River, California. Env. Biol. Fish. 42:329–343.

Herbold, B. 1987. Patterns of co-cccurrence and resource use in a non-coevolved assemblage of fishes. Ph.D dissertation. Univ. of California, Davis. Vii+81 pp.

Krejsa, R.J. 1965. The systematics of the prickly sculpin, *Cottus asper*: an investigation of genetic and non-genetic variation within a polytypic species. Ph.D. dissertation, Univ. of British Columbia.

Kresja, R. 1967. The systematics of prickly sculpin (*Cottus asper* Richardson) a polytypic species: part II. Studies on the life history, with especial reference to migration. Pac. Sci. 21:414-422.

Leidy, R.A. 1984. Distribution and ecology of stream fishes in the San Francisco Bay drainage. Hilgardia 52(8):1-173.

Mason, J.C. and S. Machidori. 1976. Populations of sympatric sculpins, *Cottus aleuticus* and *Cottus asper*, in four adjacent salmon-producing coastal streams on Vancouver Island, B. C. Fish. Bull. 74:131–141.

McLarney, W.O. 1968. Spawning habits and morphological variation in the coastrange sculpin, *Cottus aleuticus*, and the prickly sculpin, *Cottus asper*. Trans. Amer. Fish. Soc. 97:46-48.

Millikan, A.E. 1968. The life history and ecology of *Cottus asper* Richardson and *Cottus gulosus* (Girard) in Conner Creek, Washington. M.S. Thesis. Univ. Wash. 81 pp.

Moyle, P.B. 1976. Inland Fishes of California. Univ. of California Press. 405 pp.

_____. 1977. In defense of sculpins. Fisheries 2:20-23.

Munro, J.A. and W.A. Clemens. 1937. The American merganser in British Columbia and its relation to the fish population.. Biol. Bd. Canada Bull. 6(2):1-50

Patten, B.G. 1971. Spawning and fecundity of seven species of northwest Amcrican Cottus. Amer. Mid. Nat. 85(2): 493-506.

Reed, R.J. 1967. Observations of fishes associated with spawning salmon. Trans. Amer. Fish. Soc. 96(1) 62-66.

Shapovolov, L. and A.C. Taft. 1954. The life histories of the steelhead trout (*Salmo gairdneri gairdneri*) and silver salmon (*Oncorhynchus kisutch*) Ca. Dept. Fish and Game, Fish Bull. 98:1-375.

Turner, J.L. 1966. Distribution of threadfin shad, *Dorosoma petenense*, tule perch, *Hysterocarpus traskii*, and crayfish spp. in the Sacramento-San Joaquin Delta. *In:* J.L. Turner and D.W. Kelley (eds). Ecological studies of the Sacramento-San Joaquin Delta, Part II. pp 160-168. Ca. Dept. Fish and Game, Fish Bull. 136.

Wang, J.C.S. 1986. Fishes of the Sacramento-San Joaquin Estuary and Adjacent Waters: a Guide to the Early Life Histories. Interagency Ecological Study Program for the Sacramento-San Joaquin Estuary, Tech. Rep. No 9. Sacramento, Ca.

White, J.L. and B.C. Harvey. *In press*. Habitat separation of prickly sculpin, *Cottus asper,* and Coast range sculpin, *C. aleuticus*, in the mainstem Smith River, northwestern California. Copeia.

Personal Communications

Robert Leidy, U.S. Environmental Protection Agency

Striped Bass

Morone saxatilis

Ted R. Sommer

General Information

Striped bass (Family: Percichthyidae) were introduced into the Estuary in 1879, leading to a successful commercial fishery within 10 years (Herbold et al. 1992). The commercial fishery for striped bass was banned in 1935 following a substantial decline in abundance which appears to have begun at the turn of the century. The species are presently the principal sport fish caught in San Francisco Bay and is estimated to bring approximately $45 million per year into local economies in the Estuary.

Reproduction

Striped bass are present in the San Francisco Estuary throughout the year (Moyle 1976). They generally congregate in San Pablo and Suisun Bays in autumn and move into the Delta and Sacramento River system on their spawning migration during winter and early spring. The timing and location of spawning depends on temperature, flow and salinity, but typically peaks in May and early June. The annual spawning distribution appears to shift between the Sacramento and San Joaquin rivers and the Delta.

Striped bass spawn in freshwater, with optimum spawning at salinities of less than 1 ppt (Moyle 1976). The species has exceptionally high fecundity—females commonly broadcast from 0.5 to 4.5 million semi-buoyant eggs into the water column. The drifting eggs hatch in the current in about 2 days. Eggs and newly-hatched larvae are carried downstream to the Delta and Suisun Bay. Larvae show peak abundance at the upstream edge of the entrapment zone, located at a salinity of approximately 2 ppt.

Growth and Development

Striped bass grow to about 38 mm by late July or August (Moyle 1976). They typically reach 23 to 35 cm FL by their second year, 38 to 39 cm fork length (FL;

Actual Length to 4 ft.

the measure to the bottom of the fork of the tail fin) on their third year, and 48 to 50 cm in their fourth year. Growth of older adults is 1 to 3 cm annually. Most females mature at four to six years, but many are mature by the end of their third year. Males typically mature at two to three years old. Although striped bass apparently have the potential to live in excess of 30 years, most adults are three to seven years old.

Food and Feeding

Striped bass are gregarious pelagic predators (Moyle 1976). They begin feeding at a length of 5-6 mm on several invertebrates including cladocerans and copepods. Copepods generally dominate the diet of 7 to 11 mm larvae, but the opposum shrimp, *Neomysis,* become a more important food source in larger individuals. Young-of-the-year feed mostly on opossum shrimp, but amphipods, copepods, and threadfin shad are important alternative prey items. Fish gradually become a more important food source in juvenile bass (13 to 35 cm FL). Subadult and adult bass (age 2+) are primarily piscivorous, although they are highly opportunistic depending on prey availability.

Distribution

In contrast to the coastal Atlantic populations of striped bass, most of the local population spend their lives in the San Francisco Estuary. However, recent tagging studies suggest that striped bass are spending more time in Suisun Bay, the Delta, and surrounding freshwater areas (Sweetnam 1990). The current distribution of the species includes San Francisco Bay, San Pablo Bay, Suisun Bay, the Delta, tributaries of the Sacramento River and the Pacific Ocean (Herbold et al. 1992).

Population Status and Influencing Factors

Adult abundance has declined over the past 30 years, from over 1.5 million in the late 1960s to about 0.5 million in recent years (CDFG 1992). The decline was most dramatic between the beginning and the end of the 1970s, prompting the initiation of a hatchery stocking program to supplement natural production (Harris and Kohlhorst 1996). Stocking was conducted from 1981 through 1991—hatchery fish presently comprise a substantial percentage (e.g., 35% of the 1990 year class) of the adult population.

Year class abundance is assumed to depend on the environmental conditions experienced by the eggs and young fish (CDFG 1987, 1992). However, a steady decline in the survival rate of yearlings stocked into the Estuary suggests that habitat conditions for older fish also play an important role (Harris and Kohlhorst 1996). Abundance of young bass is strongly correlated with

Delta outflow and entrapment zone position, although in recent years this relationship has deteriorated. For example, in 1995 striped bass production was exceptionally poor despite wet conditions that increased the abundance of several other outflow-dependent species. Entrainment at diversions is known to be substantial, and there is statistical evidence that these losses affect abundance. Nonetheless, losses at the projects during the 1980s were at least partially mitigated using hatchery fish, yet the population decline has continued. The reduction in several invertebrate prey species has also been dramatic, particularly since the introduction of the Asian clam *Potamocorbula*. The decline in survival of stocked fish strongly suggests that competition for food has had an effect on the population. Other potentially important factors include toxic substances, exotic species and illegal fishing.

Trophic Levels

Striped bass are secondary and higher order consumers.

Proximal Species

Major Prey Items: Zooplankton (cladocerans and copepods), terrestrial insects, opossum shrimp (*Neomysis mercedis*), splittail, salmon, threadfin shad, American shad.

Good Habitat

Striped bass are able to tolerate a wide range of environmental conditions, illustrated by their ability to move regularly between salt- and fresh-water (Moyle 1976). Optimal temperatures for spawning appear to be from 15.6° to 20.0° C. Low oxygen (4 ppm) and high turbidity are also tolerated. Large rivers or tidal channels with moderate water velocities are required to keep the eggs and larvae suspended in the water column. Young-of-the-year striped bass show highest abundance in the entrapment zone, the region where fresh- and salt-water mix.

References

California Department of Fish and Game (CDFG). 1987. Factors affecting striped bass abundance in the Sacramento-San Joaquin river system. CDFG Exhibit 25, State Water Resources Control Board Bay Delta Hearings, Sacramento, CA.

_____. 1992. A re-examination of factors affecting striped bass abundance in the Sacramento-San Joaquin estuary. State Water Resources Control Board Bay Delta Hearings, Sacramento, CA.

Harris, M.D. and D.W. Kohlhorst. 1996. Survival and contribution of artificially-reared striped bass in the Sacramento-San Joaquin Estuary. IEP Newsletter, Spring 1996.

Herbold, B., A.D. Jassby and P.B. Moyle. 1992. Status and trends report of aquatic resources in the San Francisco estuary. San Francisco Estuary Project, USEPA, Oakland, CA.

Moyle, P.B. 1976. Inland Fishes of California. Univ. of California Press.405 pp.

Sweetnam, D. 1990. Recent changes in striped bass migratory patterns in the Sacramento-San Joaquin estuary. Interagency Ecological Workshop, Asolimar, CA., 1990.

White Croaker

Genyonemus lineatus

Kurt F. Kline

General Information

The white croaker (Family: Sciaenidae) is found in small schools (Skogsberg 1939) and ranges from Magdalena Bay, Baja California, to Mayne Bay, Vancouver Island, British Columbia (Baxter, 1980, Hart 1973, Miller and Lea 1972). It is abundant in San Francisco Bay, and supports both commercial and sport fisheries in nearshore coastal waters, and a sport fishery in the Bay.

Reproduction

Approximately 50% of all white croakers are mature after their first year and all are mature by their fourth year (Love et al. 1984). Along the coast, spawning appears to take place in water from eight to 36 meters deep (Love et al. 1984). In San Francisco Bay spawning occurs from September through May (Wang 1986), with most yolk-sac larvae (YSL) collected from November through March (CDFG, unpub. data). Females batch spawn 18-24 times per season, with a batch consisting of 800-37,200 eggs (Love et al. 1984).

Growth and Development

White croaker eggs are pelagic, spherical and transparent. Under laboratory conditions (~20°C), eggs hatched in 52 hours. The newly hatched YSL are poorly devel-

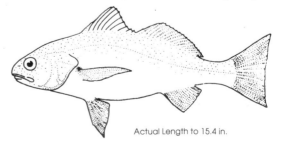

Actual Length to 15.4 in.

CDFG

Fish

oped, but by the sixth day the yolk-sac is absorbed, the swim bladder is inflated and feeding begins (Watson 1982).

Throughout their life, white croaker growth is fairly constant (Love et al. 1984). They may live to 12 years (Love et al. 1984) and reach a total length (TL) of 41.1 cm (Miller and Lea 1972).

Distribution

Along the coast, the greatest densities of larvae are found near the bottom between 15 and 20 meters. The smallest juveniles are common from 3 to 6 meters, and move to deeper water as they grow. Most adults are found in waters less than 30 meters, although white croakers have been recorded to 183 meters (Love et al. 1984).

Within San Francisco Bay, most of the pelagic eggs and YSL are found in Central Bay (Wang 1986; CDFG, unpub. data). As the larvae develop to the post yolk-sac stage, they move toward the bottom. Tidal currents probably transported white croaker larvae to South and San Pablo bays. High outflow events during the winter, which increases the gravitational currents, may increase the transport of larvae to San Pablo Bay (Fleming, pers. comm.). By September, most of the young-of-the-year (YOY) migrate to Central Bay and by winter, emigrate from the Bay (Fleming 1999)

Within the Bay, YOY white croaker are found at lower salinities and higher temperatures than the one year and older fish (1+), reflecting the broader distribution of YOY. The movements of older YOY and 1+ white croaker out of the Bay during the late fall and winter may be temperature related.

Population Status and Influencing Factors

The California Department of Fish and Game's Bay Study has generated annual abundance indices for white croaker since 1980. The abundance of YOY white croaker has fluctuated greatly over the past 19 years (**Figure 2.7**). Highest abundance indices of YOY were in 1980, 1986, 1992, 1993, and 1994. White croaker 1+ indices peaked between 1988 and 1991.

From 1981 to 1986, white croaker 1+ catches were dominated by the 1980 year class and from 1987 to 1993, they were dominated by the large 1986 year class. However, the relative size of a year class as YOY is not indicative of the future abundance of 1+ fish in the Bay. For example, the 1986 year class apparently contributed to the subsequent 1+ indices more than either the 1980 or the 1993 year classes. The drought from 1987-1992 may have caused greater use of the Bay by the 1986 year class than either 1980 or 1993 year classes.

Examination of the annual indices shows no relationship between the number of mature fish and YOY, while the length frequency data shows that single year

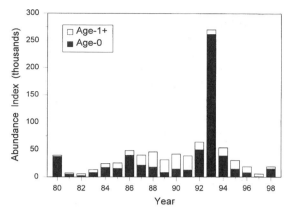

Figure 2.7 Annual Abundance Indices of White Croaker (Hieb 1999)

classes tend to dominate subsequent years' 1+ catch and the monthly catch per unit effort (CPUE) shows seasonal migration patterns within and out of the Bay. From these data, one could draw the following conclusions: 1) the white croaker "population" within the Bay is an extension of the nearshore coastal population; 2) factors that influence the nearshore population of white croaker are independent of the Bay; and 3) factors that influence the Bay "population" appear to be the salinity, temperature and, perhaps most importantly, the size and distribution of the nearshore population.

Trophic Levels

Secondary consumers.

Proximal Species

Prey: Northern anchovies, *Cancer* spp., shrimp spp., polychaetes.

Good Habitat

White croaker are associated with soft substrates (Love et al. 1984). In the Bay, white croaker are primarily found in areas with the most marine-like (salinity and temperature) conditions.

Acknowledgments

Some of the materials in this report are summarized from the white croaker chapter of IEP Technical Report 63 (Flemming 1999).

References

Baxter, R.L. 1980. White croaker. *Genyonemus lineatus*. Inshore fishes of California. Calif. Office of State Printing, Sacramento, Ca.

Fish

Fleming, K. 1999. White croaker. *In* J. Orsi (ed). Report on the 1980-1995 fish, shrimp, and crab sampling in the San Francisco Estuary, California. IEP Tech. Rept. No. 63.

Hart, J.L. (ed). 1973. Pacific fishes of Canada. Fish. Res. Board Can., Bull. No. 180. 740 pp.

Hieb, K. 1999. San Francisco Bay species abundance (1980-98). IEP Newsletter, Vol. 12(2): 30-34.

Love, M.S., G.E. McGowen, W. Westphal, R.J. Lavenberg and L. Martin. 1984. Aspects of the life history and fishery of the white croaker, *Genyonemus lineatus* (Sciaenidae), off California. Fishery Bull. 82(1): 179-198.

Miller, D.J. and R.N. Lea. 1972. Guide to the coastal marine fishes of California. Ca. Fish Game, Fish Bull. 157, 235p.

Skogsberg, T. 1939. The fishes of the family Sciaenidae (croakers) of California. Ca. Fish Game, Fish Bull. 54, 62p.

Wang, J.C.S. 1986. Fishes of the Sacramento-San Joaquin Estuary and adjacent waters, California: A guide to the early life histories. IEP Tech. Rep. No. 9. Ca. Dept. Water Res., Ca. Dept. Fish Game, U.S. Bureau Reclam. U.S. Fish Wildl. Serv.

Watson, W. 1982. Development of eggs and larvae of the white croaker, *Genyonetemus lineatus* ayres (Pices: Sciaenidae), of the southern California coast. Fish. Bull. 80:403-417.

Personal Communications

Kevin Fleming, California Department of Fish and Game, Bay-Delta and Special Water Projects Division, Stockton, CA.

Shiner Perch

Cymatogaster aggregata

Michael F. McGowan

General Information

The shiner perch (Family: Embiotocidae) is a small but abundant species common to the intertidal and subtidal zones of bays, estuaries, and the nearshore regions of California. They are commonly caught by anglers around rocks, and pilings, from shore and docks, and just about any fishing area. They are also used as live bait in the San Francisco fisheries for striped bass and California halibut.

Reproduction

The shiner perch, like other members of the family Embiotocidae, is a live-bearer. Mating is accompanied by elaborate courtship behavior and occurs primarily in the spring and summer in California (Shaw 1971). Females give birth during April and May (Odenweller 1975) in California. Fecundity ranges from 5-36 young per female, depending on size (Emmett et al. 1991).

Growth and Development

At birth, the fully developed young are 34.0-43.7 mm long (Wang 1986). Juveniles become adults at 5 cm in length. Growth is rapid the first year but slows subsequently (Odenweller 1975). Most females mature their first year. They may live 8 years and reach 20 cm long. Males mature soon after birth and rarely grow beyond 13 cm.

Food and Feeding

Embryos receive nutrition and gas exchange through ovarian placenta tissues and fluids. Juveniles and adults feed on plankton and benthos depending on availability. Prey items include copepods, isopods, amphipods, mussels, barnacle appendages, mysids, crab larvae, and other small invertebrates or protruding parts of invertebrates (Emmett et al. 1991).

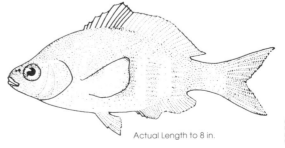

Actual Length to 8 in.

CDFG

Distribution

The shiner perch occurs near shore and in bays and estuaries from Baja California to Alaska commonly associated with aquatic vegetation. Juveniles prefer intertidal and shallow subtidal habitats in bays and estuaries (Moyle 1976). In winter they may move out of estuaries to nearshore areas and have been found as deep as 70 m (Hart 1973). In Elkhorn Slough, where they are a numerically dominant component of the fish fauna, they were classified as partial residents (Yoklavich et al. 1991).

Population Status and Influencing Factors

The availability and quality of estuarine areas for giving birth and rearing young may limit populations. Key factors are water temperature, not excessively hot (Odenweller 1975), and seagrass beds for shelter and feeding. San Francisco Bay shiner perch catches in trawl surveys declined in 1983, perhaps due to high outflow (and resulting low salinity) that year (Herbold et al. 1992). Because it uses nearshore areas, the shiner perch may have high body burdens of pesticides and other compounds (Earnest and Benville 1971), but population effects of chronic pollution have not been documented.

Trophic Levels

Shiner perch are secondary and higher level consumers. Plant matter found in some stomach analysis studies may be due to feeding on invertebrates that occur on the aquatic vegetation.

Proximal Species

Predators: Sturgeon spp., salmon spp., striped bass, California halibut, cormorant spp., great blue heron, bald eagle.
Prey: Copepods, isopods, amphipods, mussels, barnacle appendages, mysids, crab larvae, and other small invertebrates or protruding parts of invertebrates.

Good Habitat

The shiner perch appears to favor aquatic vegetation if present, but is also found over shallow sand and mud bottoms. They prefer salinities greater than 8-10 ppt and were reported in water temperatures ranging from 4 to 21°C (Emmett et al. 1991). In San Francisco Bay, they are widespread but are most abundant downstream of the Carquinez Strait. Herbold et al. (1992) considered them a euryhaline species. Eelgrass beds may be important feeding areas because shiner perch use them more at night than during the day (Bayer 1979).

References

Bayer, R.D. 1979. Intertidal shallow-water fishes and selected macroinvertebrates in the Yaquina estuary, Oregon. Unpubl. Rep., 134 pp. Oregon State Univ. Marine Sci. Cent. Library, Newport, OR. Not seen, cited in Emmett et al. 1991.

Earnest, R.D. and P.E. Benville, Jr. 1971. Correlation of DDT and lipid levels for certain San Francisco Bay fish. Pest. Monitor. Journal 5(3):235-241.

Emmett, R.L., S.L. Stone, S.A. Hinton and M.E. Monaco. 1991. Distribution and abundance of fishes and invertebrates in west coast estuaries, Vol. II: species life history summaries. ELMR Rept. No. 8. NOAA/NOS Strategic Environmental Assessments Division, Rockville, MD, 329 p.

Hart, J.L. 1973. Pacific fishes of Canada. Fish. Res. Board Can., Bull. No. 180, 740 p.

Herbold, B., A.D. Jassby and P.B. Moyle. 1992. Status and trends report on aquatic resources in the San Francisco estuary. San Francisco Estuary Project, Oakland, CA, 257 pp. + App.

Moyle, P.B. 1976. Inland Fishes of California. Univ. Ca. Press, Berkeley, CA, 405 pp.

Odenweller, D.B. 1975. The life history of the shiner surfperch, *Cymatogaster aggregata* Gibbons, in Anaheim Bay, California. *In:* E. D. Lane and C.W. Hill (eds). The marine resources of Anaheim Bay. Ca. Fish Game, Fish Bull. 165:107-115.

Shaw, E. 1971. Evidence of sexual maturation in young adult shiner perch, *Cymatogaster aggregata* Gibbons (Perciformes, Embiotocidae). Am. Mus. Nov. 2479:1-10.

Wang, J.C.S. 1986. Fishes of the Sacramento-San Joaquin estuary and adjacent waters, California: A guide to the early life histories. Tech. Rep. 9. Interagency ecological study program for the Sacramento-San Joaquin estuary. Ca. Dept. Water Res., Ca. Dept. Fish Game, U.S. Bureau Reclam. U.S. Fish Wildl. Serv., various pagination.

Yoklavich, M.M., G.M. Cailliet, J.P. Barry, D.A. Ambrose and B. S. Antrim. 1991. Temporal and spatial patterns in abundance and diversity of fish assemblages in Elkhorn Slough, California. Estuaries 14(4):465-480.

Tule Perch

Hysterocarpus traskii

Robert A. Leidy

General Information

Tule perch are the only viviparous freshwater fish native to California and the only freshwater member of the surfperch family (Embiotocidae)(Baltz and Moyle 1982). They are deep-bodied, spiny-rayed fish found in lakes, rivers, streams, and estuaries in habitats characterized by complex cover, especially well developed beds of aquatic macrophytes (Moyle 1976). There are three recognized subspecies of tule perch, *H. t. pomo* from the Russian River drainage, *H. t. lagunae* from Clear lake, and *H. t. traskii* from the Sacramento-San Joaquin drainage, which includes populations found in the San Francisco Estuary (Hopkirk 1973, Baltz and Moyle 1981 and 1982). Because of their small size, tule perch have no commercial and limited sport value.

Reproduction

Tule perch breed during July through September, but fertilization of the eggs is delayed within the female until January (Bundy 1970, Bryant 1977). Embryos develop within the females ovarian compartments and are born as juveniles in May or June, at a length of between 30-40 mm standard length (SL) (Bryant 1977). The number of fish produced per female is positively correlated with the size of the female fish and ranges between 22 and 93 (Bundy 1970, Bryant 1977).

Growth and Development

Juveniles begin schooling immediately following birth within aquatic vegetation, submerged logs, or boulders (Wang 1986). It is not known whether juveniles move into tributaries following birth, but it is interesting to note that several streams feeding into Suisun Marsh and San Pablo Bay contain large numbers of juvenile tule perch (Leidy, pers. observ.). Juveniles grow rapidly and individuals in the Sacramento-San Joaquin Delta may reach 80 to 100 mm SL following the first year of growth

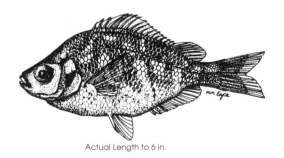

Moyle 1976

Actual Length to 6 in.

(Moyle 1976). Maximum size for tule perch is approximately 160 mm SL, although a single individual measuring 175 mm SL was collected in Napa Slough, Napa County (Leidy, unpub. data). Tule perch rarely live longer than five years (Moyle 1976).

Food and Feeding

Within the Sacramento-San Joaquin Delta and upper Estuary, tule perch feed primarily on mysid shrimp, small amphipods, midge larvae (Chironomidae), and clams (Cook 1964, Turner 1966). Hopkirk (1962) recorded that tule perch collected in brackish water habitats near the mouth of the Napa River fed mostly on small-sized brachyuran crabs, while juvenile fish feed predominantly on midge larvae and pupae. Tule perch are also known to feed on zooplankton, aquatic insects, and a variety of benthic and plant-dwelling invertebrates in lakes and rivers (Moyle 1976, Wang 1986).

Distribution

Tule perch are native to low-elevation valley waters of the Central Valley, the Sacramento-San Joaquin Delta, including Suisun Marsh and several streams tributary to the San Francisco Estuary, Clear Lake, and the Russian, Salinas, and Pajaro Rivers (Moyle 1976). Within the San Francisco Estuary tule perch have been recorded from Suisun Marsh (Herbold et al. 1992), including Montezuma Slough, Suisun Bay (Ganssle 1966), Carquinez Strait (Messersmith 1966), the Napa River and its marshes (Moyle 1976; Leidy 1984; Leidy, unpub. data), and Sonoma, Alameda, and Coyote creeks (Leidy 1984). Tule perch may be considered locally abundant in lower estuarine and riverine intertidal marsh and pelagic habitats of Suisun Marsh and several of its tributary streams, the Napa and Sonoma Creek marshes, and portions of San Pablo Bay (Leidy, unpub. data). Tule perch no longer occur in the Pajaro and Salinas rivers, and are rare in Alameda and Coyote creeks (Leidy, unpub. data).

Population Status and Influencing Factors

While the historical range of tule perch within the San Francisco Estuary has been reduced, tule perch are still locally abundant in Suisun Marsh and the Napa River and Sonoma Creek and its tidal marshes. Important factors negatively influencing population numbers likely include excess siltation and turbidity, reduced freshwater flows, pollution, removal of riparian vegetation and aquatic macrophytes through stream channelization and other flood control measures, and the resultant loss of nesting, feeding, and cover habitat, and possibly the introduction of exotic centrarchids (Moyle et al.1995). Moyle et al. (1995) identified introduced fish predators, such as smallmouth bass (*Micropterus dolomieui*), pond and dam construction, and reduced flows and poor water quality as threats to the Russian River subspecies of the tule perch. These are likely threats to the other two subspecies of tule perch as well. Interestingly, otter trawl data collected in Suisun Marsh shows a significant decline in tule perch numbers during 1983-84, a year of extremely high outflow (Herbold et al. 1992).

Trophic Levels

Juveniles and adults are primary and higher order consumers.

Proximal Species

Juvenile predators: Other large freshwater and estuarine piscivorous fish, egrets, herons and other wading birds. **Prey**: Aquatic and terrestrial insects, zooplankton, mysid shrimp, amphipods, clams, brachyuran crabs, midge larvae and pupae.

Good Habitat

Tule perch may be found in a variety of habitats from the slow-moving, turbid channels of the Delta, marshes between the mouths of Sonoma Creek and the Napa River, to relatively clear, fast-flowing rivers and streams (Moyle 1976; Leidy, unpub. data). In tidal riverine marshes, tule perch prefer slow-moving backwater and slough habitats with structurally-complex beds of floating or emergent aquatic macrophytes, overhanging banks and/or submerged woody debris. These areas serve as important feeding and breeding habitats, as well as protective rearing areas (Moyle 1976). Structurally-complex cover appears to be essential for near-term females and juveniles as refugia from predators (Moyle et al. 1995).

Although Moyle (1976) states that tule perch seldom venture into brackish water, they are present in the pelagic zone of tidal riverine and intertidal estuarine environments, such as the Napa River marshes and Suisun Marsh (Leidy, unpub. data). This suggests that some populations of tule perch may be able to tolerate brackish water conditions, or at least utilize these areas when freshwater outflows dilute surface water. In Suisun Marsh tule perch are most frequently collected in the small, heavily vegetated, dead-end sloughs where introduced centrarchids are uncommon (Moyle et al. 1985).

References

Baltz, D.M. and P.B. Moyle. 1981. Morphometric analysis of the tule perch (*Hysterocarpus traski*) populations in three isolated drainages. Copeia 1981: 305-311.

_____. 1982. Life history characteristics of tule perch (Hysterocarpus traski) populations in contrasting environments. Environ. Biol. of Fishes 7:229-242.

Bryant, G.L. 1977. Fecundity and growth of the tule perch, *Hysterocarpus traski*, in the lower Sacramento-San Joaquin Delta. Ca. Fish, Game 63(3): 140-156.

Bundy, D.S. 1970. Reproduction and growth of the tule perch, *Hysterocarpus traskii* (Gibbons), with notes on its ecology. M.S. Thesis, Univ. of Pacific, Stockton, Ca.. 52 pp.

Cook, S.F., Jr. 1964. The potential of two native California fish in the biological control of chironomid midges (Diptera: Chironomidae). Mosquito News 24(3): 332-333.

Ganssle, D. 1966. Fishes and decapods of San Pablo and Suisun Bays. *In:* J. L. Turner and D. W. Kelley (eds). Ecological studies of the Sacramento-San Joaquin Estuary, Part I. Ca. Dept. of Fish and Game Bull. 133: 57-63.

Herbold, B., A.D. Jassby and P.B. Moyle, 1992. Status and trends report on aquatic resources in the San Francisco Estuary. U.S. EPA, San Francisco Estuary Project. 257 pp.

Hopkirk, J.D. 1962. Morphological variation in the freshwater embiotocid *Hysterocarpus traskii* Gibbons. M.A. Thesis, Univ. of California, Berkeley. 159 pp.

_____. 1973. Endemism in fishes of the Clear Lake region of central California. Univ. of Ca. Publ. Zool. 96: 160 pp.

Leidy, R.A. 1984. Distribution and ecology of stream fishes in the San Francisco Bay drainage. Hilgardia 52(8): 1-175.

Messersmith, J.D. 1966. Fishes collected in Carquinez Strait in 1961-1962. *In:* J. L. Turner and D. W. Kelley, eds., Ecological studies of the Sacramento-San Joaquin Estuary, Part I. pp. 57-63. Ca. Dept. Fish and Game Bull. 133.

Moyle, P.B. 1976. Inland Fishes of California. Univ. of California Press. 405 pp.

Moyle, P.B., R.A. Daniels, B. Herbold and D.M. Baltz. 1985. Patterns indistribution and abundance of a noncoevolved assemblage of estuarine fishes in Ca.. Fish. Bull. 84: 105-117.

Moyle, P.B., R.M. Yoshiyama, J.E. Williams, and E.D. Wikramanayake. 1995. Fish species of special concern in California. Prepared for the Resources Agency, Rancho Cordova, Ca.. 272 pp.

Turner, J.L. 1966. Distribution of threadfin shad, *Dorosoma petenense*, tule perch, *Hysterocarpus traskii*, and crayfish spp. in the Sacramento-San Joaquin Delta. *In:* J. L. Turner and D. W. Kelley (eds). Ecological Studies of the Sacramento-San Joaquin Delta, Part II. Ca. Dept. Fish and Game Bull. 136:160-168.

Wang, J.C.S. 1986. Fishes of the Sacramento-San Joaquin Estuary and adjacent waters, California: A guide to the early life histories. Tech. Rept. 9. Prepared for the Interagency Ecological Study program for the Sacramento-San Joaquin Estuary.

Arrow Goby

Clevelandia ios

Kathryn A. Hieb

Fish

General Information

The arrow goby (Family: Gobiidae) is probably the most abundant native goby in San Francisco Bay. It ranges from the Gulf of California to Vancouver Island, British Columbia (Miller and Lea 1972) and is common to intertidal mudflats and shallow subtidal areas of bays, estuaries, and coastal lagoons. It is often commensal with burrowing invertebrates. The arrow goby grows to a maximum size of 45 to 50 mm total length (TL). This small fish is an important component of the intertidal food web, as it is a common prey item for a variety of birds and fishes. It has no sport or commercial value.

Reproduction

In Elkhorn Slough, ripe females were collected from December through August, but were most common from March through June (Prasad 1948). The reproductive period occurs approximately one to two months earlier in southern California—in Mission Bay, ripe females were collected from September through June, with peak abundance from November through April (Brothers 1975), while in Anaheim Bay, ripe females were collected from December through September, with peak abundance from February through June (Macdonald 1972). Ovary development is asynchronous, as ovaries are found in various stages of maturation during the spawning season (Macdonald 1972, Brothers 1975). This indicates that each female may spawn several times during the spawning season. Fecundity ranges from 800 to 1,200 eggs per female, with clutch size ranging from 150 to 350 eggs (Brothers 1975) or from 750 to 1,000 eggs (Prasad 1948).

Some disagreement exists in the literature on the deposition of the eggs and parental care. The eggs are either deposited on surfaces with no additional parental investment (Prasad 1948, Macdonald 1972) or deposited on the wall of burrows constructed by the male and guarded by the male until hatching (Brothers 1975). In Mission Bay, all males collected in January and February were brooding clutches of eggs in burrows. Typical of most gobies, the fertilized eggs are club-shaped, with an attachment thread at one pole. Hatching occurs in 10 to 12 days and the newly hatched larvae are pelagic (Prasad 1948, Brothers 1975).

Growth and Development

Newly hatched larvae range from 2.75-3.25 mm TL (Prasad 1948). Juvenile arrow gobies settle from the plankton at approximately 8 mm standard length (SL) and are found in burrows when they are 10-14 mm SL (Macdonald 1972). The arrow goby matures at one year and a length of 30 to 40 mm SL in Anaheim and Mission bays (Macdonald 1972, Brothers 1975); in Elkhorn Slough females begin to mature at 29 mm SL and all are mature at 34 mm SL (Prasad 1948). In southern California, most arrow gobies die after spawning, with a few living to two years (Macdonald 1972, Brothers 1975). In Elkhorn Slough, arrow gobies commonly live two to three years (Prasad 1948). Fish from Elkhorn Slough apparently spawn later, grow slower, mature later, and reach a larger size than fish from southern California populations (Brothers 1975).

Food and Feeding

The arrow goby preys on a variety of small invertebrates. In Mission Bay, the major prey items (percent occurrence) of juveniles and adults are harpacticoid copepods (88%), ostracods (58%), tanacians (32%), gammarid amphipods (19%), mollusc siphon tips (11%), caprellids (8%), nematodes (7%), and polychaetes (7%) (Brothers 1975). In Anaheim Bay, the most important prey items are harpacticoid copepods, nematodes, oligochaetes, ostracods, and cylcopoid copepods (Macdonald 1972). Larvae prey primarily upon the calanoid copepod *Acartia tonsa* (Macdonald 1975).

The arrow goby is preyed upon by a variety of demersal fishes, including Pacific staghorn sculpin (MacGinitie and MacGinitie 1949, Brothers 1975, Tasto 1975), California halibut (Haaker 1975, Drawbridge 1990), and diamond turbot (Lane 1975). MacGinitie and MacGinitie (1949) presumed probing shorebirds, including willets, godwits, and curlews would capture arrow gobies while exploring burrows at low tides. Arrow gobies have been found in the stomachs of greater yellowlegs and dowitchers (Reeder 1951).

Distribution

The arrow goby is common on mudflats inhabited by its invertebrate commensal hosts (Brothers 1975), with densities up to 20/m² in Anaheim Bay (Macdonald 1972). It apparently utilizes invertebrate burrows as a refuge from predators and as a temporary shelter during low tides. The arrow goby primarily inhabits burrows of the ghost shrimp (*Callianassa californiensis*), the

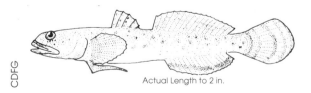

CDFG

Actual Length to 2 in.

fat innkeeper worm (*Urechis caupo*), the mud shrimp (*Upogebia spp.*), and various bivalves (Prasad 1948, Brothers 1975). Males also construct burrows for reproduction (Brothers 1975). At low tides the arrow goby is also common in remnant pools of water on the mudflats (Prasad 1948).

In San Francisco Bay, larval arrow gobies are most abundant in South and San Pablo bays, with few collected upstream of Carquinez Strait in years with low freshwater outflow (Wang 1986, CDFG 1987). Juveniles and adults are common in shallow subtidal and intertidal areas of South, Central, and San Pablo bays and have occasionally been collected in Suisun Bay (CDFG 1987). The arrow goby is also common in some tidal marsh habitats from South Bay to lower San Pablo Bay. It was the second most common species collected in otter trawl samples from Hayward Regional Shoreline Marsh channel sites (Woods 1981). The arrow goby was common in weir samples collected in Plummer Creek (South Bay near Newark), although gobies were not speciated in this study, so their relative abundance is unknown (Wild 1969). In a survey of Castro Creek, Corte Madera Creek, and Gallinas Creek marshes, the arrow goby was relatively common in otter trawl samples from creek channels and mudflats adjacent to the marshes, but rare in gill nets and not collected by minnow traps set in the marsh channels (CH$_2$M Hill 1982). A few arrow gobies were collected in Petaluma River marshes, Napa-Sonoma Marsh, but none in Suisun Marsh (CDFG, unpub. data; ANATEC Laboratories 1981; CH$_2$M Hill 1996; Matern et al. 1996).

Arrow goby larvae have been collected year-round in San Francisco Bay, with peak larval abundance from April through July (CDFG 1987). Peak abundance in beach seine samples from the Bay is from March though August; these catches include recently settled juveniles and adults (CDFG 1987). In southern California, most juveniles settle in the spring (February through May in Mission Bay, February through June in Anaheim Bay), although juveniles have been collected all but one or two months in the fall (Macdonald 1972, Brothers 1975).

Juvenile and adult arrow gobies are euryhaline and have been reported to tolerate salinities ranging from freshwater to greater than seawater (Carter 1965, as cited in Emmett et al. 1991). In San Francisco Bay, arrow goby juveniles and adults have been collected from a wide range of salinities (0.9-33.9‰), with 90% collected from 11.7 to 32.4‰ (5th and 95th percentiles, respectively, CDFG 1987 and unpub. data). The arrow goby is also reported to be eurythermal; in aquaria, gobies withstood temperatures from 4-26°C, but were "distressed" at temperatures above 22°C (Prasad 1948). In San Francisco Bay, arrow gobies were collected from 7.5 to 30.5°C, with 90% collected between 16.9 and 24.3°C (5th and 95th percentiles, respectively, CDFG 1987 and unpub. data).

Population Status and Influencing Factors

Because the arrow goby is most common in intertidal and shallow subtidal habitats, it is more effectively sampled by seines than trawls. In a beach seine survey of San Francisco Bay conducted by California Department of Fish and Game in the 1980s, the arrow goby comprised approximately 4% of the catch, ranking eigth of all fishes collected. In contrast, it comprised only 0.04% of the fishes collected by the otter trawl (Orsi 1999). As the beach seine survey has been discontinued, there is no long-term monitoring program in the Bay that effectively samples the arrow goby, and its current status is difficult to assess. From 1981 to 1986, the arrow goby beach seine annual "abundance index" varied almost 10-fold, with the highest indices in 1981 and 1986 (**Figure 2.8**).

Brothers (1975) hypothesized that arrow goby abundance and distribution could be controlled by the abundance and distribution of the commensal invertebrates, especially the ghost shrimp. Because the arrow goby is an annual species, devoting a large proportion of its resources to reproduction ("r-strategist"), it would be expected to undergo large population fluctuations.

Trophic Level

Arrow goby larvae, juveniles, and adults are secondary consumers, preying primarily on small benthic and epibenthic invertebrates.

Proximal Species

Predators: Pacific staghorn sculpin, California halibut, diamond turbot.
Prey: Harpacticoid copepods, ostracods, tanacians, gammarid amphipods, mollusk siphon tips, nematodes, oligochaetes.
Commensal Hosts: Burrowing invertebrates. Bat rays and leopard sharks impact the abundance and distribution of burrowing invertebrates.

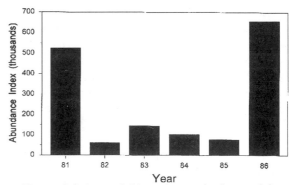

Figure 2.8 Annual Abundance Indices of Arrow Goby from San Francisco Bay, Beach Seine (CDFG, unpublished data)

Good Habitat

Good habitat for the arrow goby is shallow subtidal and intertidal mudflats inhabited by the commensal invertebrate hosts. All habitats in tidal marshes may not suitable, as the arrow goby has been collected from larger channels and adjacent mudflats, but not from smaller order channels.

References

ANATEC Laboratories, Inc. 1981. Infaunal, fish, and macroinvertebrate survey in the Hudeman Slough-Sonoma Creek watercourses. Prepared for Sonoma Valley County Sanitation District. Draft Final Report, November 1981.

Brothers, E.B. 1975. The comparative ecology and behavior of three sympatric California gobies. Ph.D. Thesis, Univ. of California, San Diego, 365 pp.

California Department of Fish and Game (CDFG). 1987. Delta outflow effects on the abundance and distribution of San Francisco Bay fish and invertebrates, 1980-1985. Exhibit 60, entered for the SWRCB 1987 Water Quality/Water Rights Proceeding on the San Francisco Bay and Sacramento-San Joaquin Delta, 345 pp.

CH₂M Hill. 1982. Equivalent protection study intensive investigation. Prepared for Chevron USA. Final Report, April 1982.

_____. 1996. Fish Sampling and Water Quality Monitoring Results. *In:* S. Miner (ed). Annual Monitoring Report, Sonoma Baylands Wetlands Demonstration Project, U.S. Army Corps of Engineers, San Francisco District and Ca. State Coastal Conservancy.

Drawbridge, M.A. 1990. Feeding relationships, feeding activity, and substrate preferences of juvenile California halibut (*Paralichthys californicus*) in coastal and bay habitats. M.S. Thesis, San Diego State University, 214 pp.

Emmett, R.L., S.A. Hinton, S.L. Stone, and M.E. Monaco. 1991. Distribution and abundance of fishes and invertebrates in west coast estuaries, Volume II: species life history summaries. ELMR Report No. 8, NOAA/NOS Strategic Environmental Assessments Division, Rockville, MD, 329 pp.

Haaker, P.L. 1975. The biology of the California halibut, *Paralichthys californicus* (Ayres), in Anaheim Bay, California. *In:* E.D. Lane and C.W. Hill (eds). The marine resources of Anaheim Bay. Ca. Dept. of Fish and Game Fish Bull. 165:137-151.

Lane, E.D. 1975. Quantitative aspects of the life history of the diamond turbot, *Hypsopsetta guttulata* (Girard), in Anaheim Bay. *In:* E.D. Lane and C.W. Hill (eds). The marine resources of Anaheim Bay. Ca. Dept. of Fish and Game Fish Bull. 165:153-173.

Macdonald, C.K. 1972. Aspects of the life history of the arrow goby, *Clevelandia ios* (Jordan and Gilbert), in Anaheim Bay, California, with comments on the cephalic-lateralis system in the fish family Gobiidae. M.A. Thesis, California State University, Long Beach, 137 pp.

_____. 1975. Notes on the family Gobiidae from Anaheim Bay. *In:* E.D. Lane and C.W. Hill (eds). The marine resources of Anaheim Bay. Ca. Dept. of Fish and Game Fish Bull. 165:117-121.

MacGinitie, G.E. and N. MacGinitie. 1949. Natural history of marine animals. McGraw-Hill, New York, N.Y. 473 pp.

Matern, S.A., L. Meng, and P.B. Moyle. 1996. Trends in fish populations of Suisun Marsh. January 1995-December 1995. Annual Report for Contract B-59998. Ca. Dept. of Water Res., Sacramento, Ca., 42 pp.

Miller, D.J. and R.N. Lea. 1976. Guide to the coastal marine fishes of California. Ca. Dept. Fish and Game Fish Bull. 157, 249 pp. SeaGrant reprint of 1972 edition with addendum added 1976.

Orsi, J. (ed). 1999 Report on the 1980-1995 fish, shrimp, and crab sampling in the San Francisco Estuary, California. IEP Tech. Rept. No. 63.

Prasad, R.R. 1948. The life history of *Clevelandia ios* (Jordan and Gilbert). Ph.D Thesis, Stanford Univ., 141 pp.

Reeder, W.G. 1951. Stomach analysis of a group of shorebirds. Condor 53:43-45.

Tasto, R.N. 1975. Aspects of the biology of the Pacific staghorn sculpin, *Leptocottus armatus*, in Anaheim Bay. *In:* E.D. Lane and C.W. Hill (eds). The marine resources of Anaheim Bay. Ca. Dept. of Fish and Game Fish Bull. 165:123-135.

Wang, J.C.S. 1986. Fishes of the Sacramento-San Joaquin estuary and adjacent waters, California: A guide to the early life histories. Interagency Ecological Studies Program for the Sacramento-San Joaquin Estuary. Tech. Rept. No. 9.

Wild, P.W. 1969. Macrofauna of Plummer Creek of San Francisco Bay collected by a specially designed trap. M.A. Thesis, San Jose State University, San Jose, Ca.. 85 pp.

Woods, E. 1981. Fish utilization. *In:* T. Niesen and M. Josselyn (eds). The Hayward Regional Shoreline marsh restorations: Biological succession during the first year following dike removal. Tiburon Center for Env. Studies, Tech. Rept. 1:35-46.

Bay Goby

Lepidogobius lepidus

Kathryn A. Hieb

General Information

The bay goby (Family: Gobiidae) ranges from Baja California to Vancouver Island, British Columbia (Miller and Lea 1976). It is common to bays and estuaries and often commensal with burrowing invertebrates on intertidal mudflats (Grossman 1979a). Because it often occupies burrows, the bay goby is not effectively sampled by trawls and seines and its relative abundance is undoubtedly greater than indicated by most surveys. It is the most abundant native goby in larval surveys of San Francisco, Humboldt, and Yaquina bays. The bay goby grows to approximately 100 mm total length (TL) and has no commercial or sport value.

Reproduction

Females with yolk filled eggs were collected from September through March, with the peak of reproductive activity from January through March in Morro Bay (Grossman 1979b). Gonadal development is asynchronous, typical of species that spawn several times a season and have a protracted spawning period. As for many other species of gobies from temperate waters, it is assumed the eggs are laid in burrows constructed by either the males or commensal invertebrate hosts and are guarded by the male until hatching (Wang 1986). Eggs are club shaped with an adhesive thread at one pole for attachment to the burrow wall or substrate.

In San Francisco Bay, larvae were collected throughout the year, with peak abundance from June to October (CDFG 1987). The period of peak abundance is similar in other Pacific Coast estuaries—peak larval abundance is from April to September in Yaquina Bay, Oregon (Pearcy and Myers 1974) and larvae were collected from April to September in Humboldt Bay (Eldridge and Bryan 1972). In San Francisco Bay, most larvae were collected in Central Bay and northern South Bay, with relatively few collected upstream of San Pablo Bay (CDFG 1987).

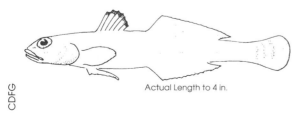

Actual Length to 4 in.

CDFG

Growth and Development

Bay goby larvae are approximately 2.5-3.0 mm TL at hatching (Wang 1986). The larvae are planktonic for three to four months (Grossman 1979b) and settle to the bottom as juveniles at approximately 25 mm TL (Wang 1986). Although the bay goby is reported to grow to about 87 mm TL (Miller and Lea 1976), specimens as large as 108 mm TL have been collected in San Francisco Bay (CDFG, unpub. data). Some bay gobies reach sexual maturity by the end of their first year and by the end of their second year all are mature (Grossman 1979b). Bay gobies reportedly live up to 7+ years (Grossman 1979b), although based upon length frequency data from San Francisco Bay (CDFG 1987, Fleming 1999), their life span may be as short as one to two years.

Food and Feeding

The bay goby is an opportunistic predator and major prey items include polychaetes, harpacticoid copepods, gammarid amphipods, and bivalves (Grossman et al. 1980). Although larger fish ($\geq$50 mm SL) and smaller fish (<50 mm SL) consume similar prey items, larger fish include more mollusks, polychaetes, and other larger prey items in their diet.

Predators of the bay goby include the California halibut (Drawbridge 1990) and the Pacific staghorn sculpin (Boothe 1967). It is assumed that other demersal piscivorous fish prey upon bay gobies.

Distribution

In San Francisco Bay, the bay goby is common from South to San Pablo bays, and is occasionally collected in Carquinez Strait and lower Suisun Bay. Densities of young-of-the-year (YOY) bay gobies are usually highest in South or San Pablo bays while densities of older fish are usually highest in Central Bay (CDFG 1987, Fleming 1999). From 1980 to 1995, the bay goby was the most common goby and the second most common fish collected by an otter trawl survey of San Francisco Bay, comprising 14.3% of all fishes collected (Orsi 1999). Although mean densities of YOY fish were higher at shoal stations than channel stations all months, older fish appear to move from the shoals to the channels in the late summer and fall (CDFG 1987 and unpub. data).

Surprisingly, the bay goby was not common in a beach seine survey conducted by CDFG in San Francisco Bay from 1980-1987; it was the fourth most common goby and comprised only 0.06% of all fishes collected by this net (Orsi 1999). These data indicate that the bay goby may not be common in the very shallow subtidal and intertidal areas of San Francisco Bay, although Grossman (1979a) concluded it to be one of the numerically dominant fish species of Morro Bay lower intertidal mudflats. The bay goby inhabits burrows of the blue mud shrimp (*Upogebia pugettensis*) and the innkeeper worm (*Urechis caupo*) and siphon holes of the geoduck clam (*Panope generosa*) in Morro Bay (Grossman 1979a). As for several other species of gobies common to San Francisco Bay, including arrow goby and longjaw mudsucker, the bay goby probably utilizes burrows as a refuge from predators and to avoid desiccation at low tides.

Few bay gobies have been collected in San Francisco Bay tidal marshes. One bay goby was reported from Gallinas Marsh and one from Corte Madera Marsh (CH$_2$M Hill 1982). Both fish were collected by gill nets, which were used to sample the larger channels. In contrast, the bay goby was the most common species collected in otter trawl samples from Corte Madera Creek channel, adjacent to Corte Madera Marsh. No bay gobies have been collected by other San Francisco Bay tidal marsh studies (Wild 1969; Woods 1981; ANATEC Laboratories1981; CH$_2$MHill 1996; CDFG, unpub. data) or by a study of fishes of Elkhorn Slough tidal marshes (Barry 1983).

Bay goby YOY are most abundant in otter trawl samples from February through June, which is a one or two months after peak abundance period for smaller juveniles from the ichthyoplankton net (CDFG 1987 and unpub. data). In several years, multiple cohorts of YOY fish have been collected; this was especially noticeable in four of the six years of the 1987-1992 drought (CDFG, unpub. data). Peak abundance of older fish is usually from May through September, which corresponds with the peak period of larval abundance in San Francisco Bay.

The bay goby has been collected primarily from polyhaline salinities in San Francisco Bay, with YOY fish collected at lower salinities than older fish (**Table 2.6**). YOY were also collected at slightly lower temperatures than older fish (**Table 2.6**). These differences in salinity and temperature by age class are reflected by the distribution of YOY somewhat further upstream than older fish and by the peak abundance of YOY in the winter and spring and older fish in summer and fall.

Population Status and Influencing Factors

Although trawls are usually considered ineffective for gobies, the bay goby is a very common fish in San Francisco Bay otter trawl surveys. As such, the abundance indices derived from trawl data may be good indicators of population trends. California Department of Fish and Game otter trawl data from 1980-1998 is the longest data set available for the Bay. The indices from 1988 to 1997 were generally higher than the pre-1988 indices (**Figure 2.9**). The relatively stable salinities year-round during the 1987-92 drought may have resulted in increased nursery habitat for this species (Hieb and Baxter 1993). The multiple cohorts of YOY collected these years, which indicate successful recruitment over a period of several months, in part support this hypothesis. Additionally, high winter outflow events may carry larvae or pelagic juveniles from the Bay.

Abundance of predators, as California halibut and Pacific staghorn sculpin, could influence the bay goby population. Additionally, factors controlling the abundance of the commensal burrowing invertebrate hosts may effect the bay goby population. This would include the abundance and distribution of intertidal and subtidal mudflat invertebrate predators, such as the bat ray and leopard shark.

Trophic Level

Secondary consumer.

Proximal Species

Predators: California halibut, Pacific staghorn sculpin.
Prey: Polychaetes, gammarid amphipods, harpacticoid copepods, bivalves.

Table 2.6 Bay Goby Salinity and Temperature Statistics: 1980-92 (CDFG unpublished data)

Age Class	Mean	5th percentile	Median	95th percentile
Salinity (ppt):				
YOY	27.3	14.9	29.2	31.7
1+ and older	28.1	17.1	29.7	32.4
Temperature (°C):				
YOY	15.4	11.3	15.2	18.8
1+ and older	16.0	12.4	16.3	18.9

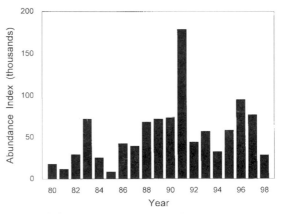

Figure 2.9 Annual Abundance Indices of All Sizes of Bay Goby, Otter Trawl (CDFG unpublished data)

Commensal Hosts: Blue mud shrimp, inn-keeper worm, geoduck clam. Bat ray and leopard shark impact the abundance of commensal hosts.

Good Habitat

Good habitat for the bay goby is shallow subtidal areas with mud or a mud/sand mixture and possibly intertidal mudflats. The presence of burrowing invertebrates, which may serve as commensal hosts, would be beneficial. There is no evidence that this species utilizes tidal marshes in San Francisco Bay or elsewhere in its range.

References

ANATEC Laboratories, Inc. 1981. Infaunal, fish, and macroinvertebrate survey in the Hudeman Slough-Sonoma Creek watercourses. Prepared for Sonoma Valley County Sanitation District. Draft Final Report, November 1981.

Barry, J.P. 1983. Utilization of shallow marsh habitats by fishes in Elkhorn Slough, California. MA Thesis, San Jose State Univ., San Jose, Ca. 91 pp.

Boothe, P. 1967. The food and feeding habits of four species of San Francisco Bay fish. Ca. Dept. Fish and Game MRO Reference No. 67-13, 155 pp.

California Department of Fish and Game (CDFG). 1987. Delta outflow effects on the abundance and distribution of San Francisco Bay fish and invertebrates, 1980-1985. Exhibit 60, entered for the SWRCB 1987 Water Quality/Water Rights Proceeding on the San Francisco Bay and Sacramento-San Joaquin Delta, 345 pp.

CH$_2$M Hill. 1982. Equivalent protection study intensive investigation. Prepared for Chevron USA. Final Report, April 1982.

_____. 1996. Fish Sampling and Water Quality Monitoring Results. *In*: Annual Monitoring Report, Sonoma Baylands Wetlands Demonstration Project, S. Miner, ed. U.S. Army Corps of Engineers, San Francisco District and Ca. State Coastal Conservancy.

Drawbridge, M.A. 1990. Feeding relationships, feeding activity and substrate preferences of juvenile California halibut (*Paralichthys californicus*) in coastal and bay habitats. M.S. Thesis, San Diego State University, San Diego, Ca. 214 pp.

Eldridge, M.B. and C.F. Bryan. 1972. Larval fish survey of Humboldt Bay, California. NOAA Tech. Rept. NMFS SSRF-665, 8 pp.

Flemming, K. 1999. Gobidae. *In*: J.Orsi (ed). Report on 1980-1995 fish, shrimp, and crab sampling in the San Francisco Estuary. IEP Tech. Rept. 63.

Grossman, G.D. 1979a. Symbiotic burrow-occupying behavior in the bay goby, *Lepidogobius lepidus*. Ca. Fish and Game 65(2):122-124.

_____. 1979b. Demographic characteristics of an intertidal bay goby (*Lepidogobius lepidus*). Environmental Biology of Fishes 4(3): 207-218.

Grossman, G.D., R. Coffin and P.B. Moyle. 1980. Feeding ecology of the bay goby (Pisces:Gobiidae). Effects of behavioral, ontogenetic, and temporal variation on diet. J. Exp. Mar. Biol. Ecol. 44:47-59.

Hieb, K. 1999. San Francisco Bay species abundance (1980-1998). IEP Mewsletter, Vol. 12(2): 30-34.

Hieb, K. and R. Baxter. 1993. Delta Outflow/San Francisco Bay Study. *In*: 1991 Annual Report, Interagency Ecological Studies Program for the Sacramento-San Joaquin Estuary, pp. 101-116

Pearcy, W.G. and S.S. Myers. 1974. Larval fishes of Yaquina Bay, Oregon: A nursery ground for marine fishes? Fishery Bulletin 72(1):201-213.

Miller, D.J. and R.N. Lea. 1976. Guide to the coastal marine fishes of California. Ca. Dept. Fish and Game Fish Bull. 157, 249 pp.

Orsi, J. (ed). 1999 Report on the 1980-1995 fish, shrimp, and crab sampling in the San Francisco Estuary, California. IEP Tech. Rept. No. 63.

Wang, J.C.S. 1986. Fishes of the Sacramento-San Joaquin estuary and adjacent waters, California: A guide to the early life histories. Interagency Ecological Studies Program for the Sacramento-San Joaquin Estuary Tech. Rept. 9.

Wild, P.W. 1969. Macrofauna of Plummer Creek of San Francisco Bay collected by a specially designed trap. M.A. Thesis, San Jose State University, San Jose, Ca.. 85 pp.

Woods, E. 1981. Fish Utilization. *In*: T. Niesen and M. Josselyn (eds). The Hayward Regional Shoreline marsh restorations: Biological succession during the first year following dike removal. Tiburon Center for Env. Studies, Tech. Rept. 1, pp 35-46.

Longjaw Mudsucker

Gillichthys mirabilis

Kathryn A. Hieb

General Information

The longjaw mudsucker (Family: Gobiidae) is the largest goby native to San Francisco Bay, reaching a size of 200 mm total length (TL). It ranges from Baja California to Tomales Bay (Miller and Lea 1972) and was successfully introduced to the Salton Sea in 1930 (Walker et al. 1961). The longjaw mudsucker is a common resident of mudflats and sloughs in estuaries and coastal streams. It is also common in salt ponds, as it can tolerate a wide range of salinities. As the tide ebbs, the longjaw mudsucker retreats to burrows or buries in the mud rather than migrate to deeper water. Due to their ability to live out of water and in freshwater for several days, mudsuckers or "mud puppies" are a sought after bait-fish; however, in recent years, the San Francisco Bay area bait fishery has targeted the yellowfin goby, a large introduced species that is very common in many shallow water habitats.

Reproduction

Male longjaw mudsuckers construct burrows for breeding, which they aggressively guard until the eggs hatch. A single female lays 4,000 to 9,000 eggs, depending on size (Weisel 1947). In southern California, spawning occurs from January through July, with peak activity apparently from February through April (Weisel 1947). In South Bay salt ponds, the spawning period is also protracted, occurring from November through June, with peak activity in February and March (Lonzarich 1989). Gonadal regression occurs from July to September, when temperatures in the salt ponds reach their maximum (de Vlaming 1972). Females were reported to spawn more than once per season in South Bay salt ponds (de Vlaming 1972) and two and possibly three times per season in the Salton Sea (Walker et al. 1961), with an interval of 40 to 50 days between spawnings (Barlow 1963). Ovarian development and spawning are asynchronous, which is typical of species that spawn more than once per season and have a protracted spawning season (de Vlaming 1972).

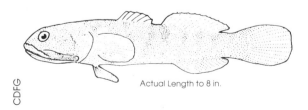

Actual Length to 8 in.

CDFG

The eggs are club shaped, 2.8-3.4 mm long, with an adhesive thread at one pole that attaches to the burrow wall. Hatching occurs in 10 to 12 days at 18°C (Weisel 1947). Larvae have been collected year-round in the Bay, with peak abundance in May and June (CDFG, unpub. data); in South Bay salt ponds, larvae were collected at salinities up to 70‰ (Lonzarich 1989).

Growth and Development

In South Bay salt ponds, longjaw mudsuckers grow to 80-100 mm standard length (SL) by the end of year one and 120-140 mm SL by the end of year two (Lonzarich 1989). Few live more than one year and none more than two years; both sexes mature at age one (Barlow 1963, Lonzarich 1989). In the Salton Sea, longjaw mudsuckers hatched in the early spring reach 60-80 mm SL by fall and 80-120 mm SL by the next spring (Walker et al. 1961).

Food and Feeding

In Elkhorn Slough, California, the longjaw mudsucker preys primarily on gammarid amphipods, especially *Orchestia traskiana*, *Eogammarus confervicolus*, *Corophium* spp., and polychaetes (Barry 1983). Dipterans, harpacticoid copepods, and grapsid crabs (primarily *Hemigrapsus oregonensis*) are also important food items. In South San Francisco Bay salt ponds, longjaw mudsucker diet varies by salinity—in the lower salinity (20-40‰) ponds, they consume primarily polychaetes and amphipods while in the higher salinity (to 84‰) ponds they consume primarily brine shrimp and waterboatmen (Lonzarich 1989). Copepods are an important prey item in the winter, when brine shrimp are unavailable.

Distribution

In San Francisco Bay, the longjaw mudsucker has been collected in South, Central, San Pablo, and Suisun bays, although it is not common upstream of Carquinez Strait. It is the least common goby collected in trawl surveys of open water habitats and larger channels, but usually the most common goby collected in smaller marsh channels. For example, it was not collected in trawls near Castro Creek, Corte Madera Creek, and Gallinas Creek marshes, but was the most abundant goby and third most abundant species collected in minnow traps set in the marsh channels (CH$_2$M Hill 1982). Similarly, in a study of a restored marsh near Hayward, it was not common in trawls of the larger channels, but the only goby and most common species collected in minnow traps set on the mudflats (Woods 1981). It was also the second most common species collected in first and second order channels of tidal marshes in lower Petaluma River (CDFG, unpub. data). This distribution has also been reported from Elkhorn Slough, where the longjaw mudsucker was not an important component of the otter trawl samples from deeper (>1.5 m) channels, but was the third most abundant species and most common goby in beach seine and channel net samples from shallower (<1.5 m) channels (Barry 1983).

The longjaw mudsucker is also common in salt ponds in San Francisco Bay. It was the most common goby and the second most common fish collected in South Bay salt ponds (Carpelan 1957, Lonzarich 1989). Lonzarich (1989) reported highest catches in the summer and fall.

Although longjaw mudsucker can tolerate a wide range of salinities, they are usually absent from fresh or slightly brackish water (Barlow 1963). They have been collected from salinities as high as 82.5‰ in the upper Gulf of California (Barlow 1963), and as high as 84‰ in South Bay salt ponds (Lonzarich 1989).

Although longjaw mudsuckers have been collected at temperatures as high as 33°C (Carpelan 1957), in laboratory thermal selection studies, they preferred temperatures from 9-23°C and strongly avoided temperatures greater than 23°C (de Vlaming 1971). In another laboratory study, Courtois (1973) concluded that the longjaw mudsucker was best adapted to temperatures between 20 and 30°C.

In intertidal areas, the longjaw mudsucker often remains in the mud or burrows at low tide and is subject to fluctuating oxygen concentrations. The jaw membranes are richly vascularized and serve as an accessory respiratory apparatus (Weisel 1947). Additionally, the longjaw mudsucker will respire aerially at low (<2.0 mg/L) oxygen concentrations; they gulp air at the water surface and hold the bubbles in their large buccopharyngeal cavity (Todd and Ebeling 1966).

Population Status and Influencing Factors

There is no survey which routinely samples the longjaw mudsucker or its preferred habitat in San Francisco Bay, so the current status of the population cannot be assessed. With the introduction and establishment of the yellowfin goby in the 1960s, the longjaw mudsucker is no longer as sought after for bait. However, the introduction of the yellowfin goby may have had a negative impact on the longjaw mudsucker, as there is substantial overlap in the habitats of the two species.

Trophic Levels

The longjaw mudsucker is a secondary consumer.

Proximal Species

Predators: Bait fishers and possibly great blue herons, egrets, and larger shorebirds.

Prey: Gammarid amphipods, polychaetes, dipterans, copepods, *Hemigrapsus oregonensis*, waterboatmen, brine shrimp.

Good Habitat

The intertidal area of tidal marsh channels is the typical habitat of the longjaw mudsucker. Because this species can tolerate a wide range of environmental conditions, "good habitat" is probably defined by the complexity of these sloughs. More complex channels, with undercut banks and pools of water at low tide, would offer more protection from predators than sloughs with little incision and ponded water. These more complex channels are typical of mature marshes vs. recently "restored" marshes.

References

Barlow, G.W. 1963. Species structure of the gobiid fish *Gillichthys mirabilis* from coastal sloughs of the eastern Pacific. Pacific Science 17:47-72.

Barry, J.P. 1983. Utilization of shallow marsh habitats by fishes in Elkhorn Slough, California. M.A. Thesis, San Jose State Univ., San Jose, Ca., 91pp.

Carpelan, L.H. 1957. Hydrobiology of the Alviso salt ponds. Ecology 38(3): 375-390.

CH$_2$M Hill. 1982. Equivalent protection study intensive investigation. Prepared for Chevron USA. Final Report, April 1982.

Courtois, L.A. 1973. The effects of temperature, availability of oxygen, and salinity upon the metabolism of the longjaw mudsucker, *Gillichthys mirabilis*. M.A. Thesis, Ca. State Univ., Hayward, Ca., 32 pp.

de Vlaming, V.L. 1971. Thermal selection behavior in the estuarine goby, *Gillichthys mirabilis* Cooper. J. Fish Biology 1971(3):277-286.

_____. 1972. Reproduction cycling in the estuarine gobiid fish, *Gillichthys mirabilis*. Copeia 1972(2): 278-291.

Lonzarich, D.G. 1989. Temporal and spatial variations in salt pond environments and implications for fish and invertebrates. M.A. Thesis, San Jose State Univ., San Jose, Ca. 81 pp.

Miller, D.J. and R.N. Lea. 1972. Guide to the coastal marine fishes of California. Ca. Dept. Fish and Game, Fish Bull. 157, 249 pp.

Todd, E.S. and W. Ebeling. 1966. Aerial respiration in the longjaw mudsucker *Gillichthys mirabilis* (Telostei:Gobiidae). Biology Laboratory, Woods Hole 130:265-288.

Walker, B.W., R.R. Whitney and G.W. Barlow. 1961. The fishes of the Salton Sea. *In:* B.W. Walker (ed). The Ecology of the Salton Sea, California, in relation to the sportfishery. Ca. Dept. Fish and Game, Fish Bull. 133:77-91.

Weisel, G.F.J. 1947. Breeding behavior and early development of the mudsucker, a gobiid fish of California. Copeia 2:77-85.

Woods, E. 1981. Fish Utilization. *In:* T. Niesen and M. Josselyn (eds). The Hayward Regional Shoreline marsh restorations: Biological succession during the first year following dike removal. Tiburon Center for Env. Studies, Tech. Rept. 1: 35-46.

California Halibut

Paralichthys californicus

Michael K. Saiki

General Information

The California halibut (Family: Bothidae) is a large marine flatfish that is sought after in the market place because of its large size and excellent taste (Frey 1971). Commercial fishing for California halibut was historically centered in the Baja California-Los Angeles area, but has recently shifted northward to the Santa Barbara region (Barsky 1990). It is harvested by gill net, trammel net, and trawl nets (Schultze 1986). California commercial fishermen landed an average of 534 tons per year from 1983 to 1987, and received $0.64-$1.59/kg in 1987 (CDFG 1988). California halibut is also highly prized by recreational anglers and is caught primarily from piers and boats using hook, line, and live bait. Over 916,000 California halibut were caught by anglers in 1985 (USDC 1986).

Reproduction

Emmett et al. (1991) described the California halibut as being gonochoristic (its gender is determined by developmental rather than hereditary mechanisms) and iteroparous (it has the capacity to survive and spawn beyond one or multiple spawning seasons). It is a broadcast spawner whose eggs are fertilized externally (Emmett et al. 1991).

The eggs of California halibut are pelagic (Allen 1988). In a laboratory tank with water depth of 2-3 m,

California halibut spawned while swimming near the water surface (Allen 1990). Adults typically move into shallow (6-20 m deep) coastal waters in early spring and usually spawn over sandy substrates (Ginsburg 1952, Frey 1971, Feder et al. 1974, Haaker 1975). Spawning occurs from February through August, peaking in May with a great number of mature fish (Frey 1971, Feder et al. 1974, Wang 1986). Spawning most often occurs when water temperatures are 15.0-16.5°C, and day lengths are greater than or equal to 10.5 hours (Caddell et al. 1990). However, abundant eggs and larvae have also been reported from nearshore coastal waters during winter-spring when surface temperatures are 13-15°C, and even during summer when surface waters occasionally reach 22°C (Lavenberg et al. 1986, Petersen et al. 1986).

During the spawning season, small (55.9-61.0 cm long) California halibut produce approximately 300,000 eggs every 7 days, whereas large (>114.3 cm long) halibut produce about 1 million eggs per day (Emmett et al. 1991).

Growth and Development

California halibut eggs are spherical in shape and 0.74-0.84 mm in diameter (Ahlstrom et al. 1984). Eggs hatch approximately two days after fertilization at 16°C (Emmett et al. 1991). Newly hatched larvae of California halibut measure about 2.0 mm total length (TL) (Ahlstrom and Moser 1975, Ahlstrom et al. 1984). The larval yolk sac is depleted about six days after hatching (Gadomski and Petersen 1988).

Metamorphosis occurs at a length of 7.5-9.4 mm (Ahlstrom et al. 1984) when the pelagic, bilaterally symmetrical larvae become benthic, asymmetrical juveniles. Along with other physical changes, the most visible part of this process is a change in pigmentation patterns and the migration of one eye across the top of the head to its final resting place close to the other eye (Moyle and Cech 1988).

Temperature has a major effect on survival of eggs and larvae of the California halibut. Successful hatching occurred at 12°, 16°, and 20°C, but death occurred prior to embryo formation at 8° and 24°C (Gadomski and Caddell 1991). At 17 days posthatch, all larvae died at 12°C, whereas survival varied from 23% to 46% at 16°, 20°, and 24°C. The survival of older larval stages of California halibut progressively increased as incubation temperatures rose from 16°C to 28°C. Temperature also affected the settlement rate of juveniles that had just completed metamorphosis.

Although juveniles are reported to vary in length from 8 mm to 430 mm (Emmett et al. 1991), males can mature at 200-300 mm standard length (SL) when 2-3 years old whereas females can mature at 380-430 mm SL when 4-5 years old (Fitch 1965, Fitch and Lavenberg

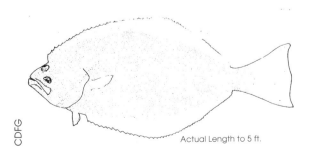

CDFG

Actual Length to 5 ft.

1971, Haaker 1975). California halibut may reach a maximum length of 1,520 mm and a maximum weight of 33 kg (Eschmeyer et al. 1983), with certain individuals living for as long as 30 years (Frey 1971).

Food and Feeding

California halibut feed initially on small invertebrates, but later switch almost exclusively to feeding on fish (Haaker 1975). Although the diet of larvae has not been examined, they probably feed on tiny planktonic organisms (Allen 1990). Small juveniles in three southern California embayments fed mostly on harpacticoid copepods and gammaridean amphipods, with some polychaetes, mysids, small fish, and crab megalopae also being taken (Haaker 1975, Allen 1988). In Anaheim Bay, California, large juveniles and small adults ate bay shrimp, topsmelt, California killifish, and gobies, whereas subadults and adults more than 23.0 cm SL consumed mostly northern anchovy, croaker, and other larger fishes (Haaker 1975). Other forage taxa in the diets included ostracods and acteonid snails. In Tomales Bay, adult California halibut (65.4-83.3 cm SL) fed on Pacific saury, Pacific herring, sanddabs, white sea perch, and California market squid (Bane and Bane 1971). The California halibut is an ambush predator (Haaker 1975). During foraging it lies partially buried on the sandy bottom and waits until its prey is close enough to seize.

Distribution

The geographic distribution of California halibut extends from the Quillayute River, Washington, southward to Magdalena Bay, Baja California (Ginsburg 1952, Miller and Lea 1972, Eschmeyer et al. 1983). However, it is common only in bays and estuaries south of Tomales Bay, California, and reaches peak abundance in estuaries south of Point Conception (Emmett et al. 1991). Recently, large numbers of mostly female California halibut were caught by recreational anglers in Humboldt Bay, with some caught as far north as Crescent City and southern Oregon (R. Baxter, pers. comm.). A survey of carcasses suggested that the females had not developed mature eggs.

Larvae of California halibut occur primarily in the upper 30 m of coastal waters, where they apparently settle or migrate from the 0-10 m stratum to the 10-20 m stratum at night (Moser and Watson 1990). Conversely, larvae over shallow water (13 m bottom depth) tend to move downward during the day (Barnett et al. 1984). Juveniles settle in shallow water on the open coast, but are more abundant in bays (Allen 1988, Moser and Watson 1990). Juveniles remain in bays for about two years until they emigrate to the coast where they settle at water depths less than 100 m, with greatest abundance at depths less than 30 m (Miller and Lea 1972, Allen

1982). Larger juveniles (greater than 20 mm in length) may move from open coastal areas to resettle in bays (Kramer 1990).

Adults move inshore during spring and summer, and offshore during winter (Ginsburg 1952, Haaker 1975). Although the inshore movements are associated with spawning, they may also be influenced by seasonal patterns in forage fish abundance. For example, during spring and summer, California grunion (*Leuresthes tenuis*) are abundant near the surf zone (Feder et al. 1974), whereas northern anchovy (*Engraulis mordax*) are abundant in bays and estuaries (Tupen 1990).

California halibut are occasionally found in Central and South San Francisco Bay (Alpin 1967, Pearson 1989) and San Pablo Bay (Ganssle 1966). Recently, eggs of a description similar to those of California halibut were collected in San Francisco Bay; however, their identity was not verified (Wang 1986). Both larval and juvenile California halibut have been captured in San Francisco and San Pablo bays (Wang 1986).

Population Status and Influencing Factors

Catch records indicate that the abundance of California halibut within its historic range was high in the late 1960s, declined in the 1970s, and increased in the 1980s. The intense El Niño in 1982-83 coincided with higher abundance and landings of halibut (Jow 1990). Overall, however, California halibut populations seem to be undergoing a long-term decline. This decline may be related to large-scale changes in the marine environment, overfishing, alterations and destruction of estuarine habitat, or a shift in location of population centers (Plummer et al. 1983). Pollution has been shown to reduce hatching success, reduce size of larvae at hatching, produce morphological and anatomical abnormalities, and reduce feeding and growth rates (MBC Applied Environmental Sciences 1987). By comparison, thermal effluents from California coastal power plants do not seemingly inhibit growth and may be advantageous to California halibut (Innis 1990).

Early records indicate that California halibut were uncommon in San Francisco Bay. Alpin (1967) sampled the Central Bay with bottom trawls during 1963-1966 and reported catching only three California halibut (two in the spring and one in June). Ganssle (1966) reported catching only two adult California halibut (May 1963, 1964) while fishing bottom trawls in San Pablo Bay. Recently, consistent high salinities probably have contributed to increased abundance of California halibut in the bay. Moreover, recent data suggest that successful year classes in 1983, 1987, and 1990 have contributed to increased abundance in the bay (CDWR 1991). These were years with warm water ocean events, and it is hypothesized that California halibut abundance in the San Francisco Bay increased because of increased local spawning, higher survival of larvae, or migration of juveniles from more southern coastal areas with warmer ocean waters (Hieb and Baxter 1994).

Abundance indices (determined from trawl samples) for California halibut in San Francisco Bay increased from 1989 to 1992 (Hieb and Baxter 1994). The 1992 index was the highest since the study began in 1980. Also, most halibut collected in San Francisco Bay are age two and older, whereas other flatfishes are caught primarily as young-of-the-year. Nevertheless, California halibut abundance indices are still very low relative to other common species of flatfish in the Bay (Hieb and Baxter 1994).

In an attempt to increase California halibut numbers, natural production has been augmented by hatchery production (Crooke and Taucher 1988). Although this effort could increase future recruitment, negative effects of the hatchery program include a possible reduction in genetic variability within natural populations and the high cost producing fish (Hobbs et al.1990).

Trophic Levels

Larvae, juveniles, and adults are carnivorous (secondary and higher order consumers).

Proximal Species

Predators: Thornback (important predator on settling juveniles), California sea lions (predator on large juveniles and adults), northern sea lions, Pacific angel shark, Pacific electric, bottlenose dolphin.
Prey:
Plankton—major prey item for larvae.
Harpacticoid copepods, gammaridean amphipods—major prey item for young juveniles.
Polychaetes, mysids, and crab—minor prey item for young juveniles.
Mysids—major prey item for juveniles.
Gobies—prey item for juveniles and adults.
Bay shrimp, ghost shrimp—prey item for older juveniles.
Topsmelt, California killifish—prey item for older juveniles and adults.
Northern anchovy—major prey item for adults.
White croakers, hornyhead turbot—prey item for large adults.
Octopus, squid, California grunion—prey item for adults.
Parasites: Trematodes, cestodes, and nematodes (endoparasites); copepods and isopods (ectoparasite).
Competitors: Speckled sanddab (potentially important).

Good Habitat

Good spawning habitat for California halibut is limited to inshore waters or bays and estuaries in moderately

shallow water where temperatures approximate 13-15°C, although successful spawning may also occur at temperatures approaching 22°C (Gadomski and Caddell 1991). Favorable characteristics for bays and estuaries that serve as nursery areas include productive habitats with abundant food supplies and shallow areas that allow juveniles to avoid predators, including adult halibut (Plummer et al. 1983). Juveniles and adults prefer sandy bottoms and water temperatures between 10-25°C, with a preference for 20.8°C (Ehrlich et al. 1979). Juveniles are relatively tolerant of reduced dissolved oxygen and increased water temperatures (Waggoner and Feldmeth 1971). Higher water temperatures induces faster growth rates and decreases the time to settlement for most young-of-the-year halibut (Gadomski et al.1990). Eggs, larvae, and adults are found in euhaline waters, but juveniles often occur in oligohaline to euhaline conditions (Haaker 1975).

References

Ahlstrom, E.H. and H.G. Moser. 1975. Distributional atlas of fish larvae in the California current region: flatfishes, 1955 through 1960. Ca. Coop. Ocean. Fish Invest., Atlas No. 23, 207 pp.

Ahlstrom, E.H., K. Amaoka, D.A. Hensley, H.G. Moser and B.Y. Sumida. 1984. Pleuronectiformes; development. *In:* H.G. Moser (chief ed). Ontogeny and systematics of fishes, p. 640-670. Allen Press, Inc., Lawrence, KS.

Allen, L.G. 1988. Recruitment, distribution, and feeding habits of young-of-the-year California halibut (*Paralichthys californicus*) in the vicinity of Alamitos Bay-Long Beach Harbor, California, 1983-1985. Bull. Southern Ca. Acad. Sci. 87:19-30.

_____. 1990. Open coast settlement and distribution of young-of-the-year California halibut, *Paralichthys californicus*, along the southern California coast between Point Conception and San Mateo Point, June-October, 1988. *In:* C.W. Haugen (ed). The California halibut, *Paralichthys californicus*, resource and fisheries. Ca. Dept. Fish and Game, Fish Bull. 174: 145-152.

Allen, M.J. 1982. Functional structure of soft-bottom fish communities of the Southern California shelf. Ph.D. Diss., Univ. Ca., San Diego, CA. 577 pp.

_____. 1990. The biological environment of the California halibut, *Paralichthys californicus*. *In:* C.W. Haugen (ed). The California halibut, *Paralichthys californicus*, resource and fisheries. Ca. Dept. Fish and Game, Fish Bull. 174.

Alpin, J.A. 1967. Biological survey of San Francisco Bay, 1963-1966. Ca. Dept. Fish and Game. MRO Ref. 67-4. 131 pp.

Bane, G.W. and A.W. Bane. 1971. Bay fishes of northern California. Mariscos Publ., Hampton Bays, NY. 143 pp.

Barnett, A.M., A.E. Jahn, P.D. Sertic and W. Watson. 1984. Distribution of ichthyoplankton off San Onofre, California, and methods for sampling very shallow coastal waters. Fish. Bull., U.S. 82:97-111.

Barsky, K.C. 1990. History of the commercial California halibut fishery. *In:* C.W. Haugen (ed). The California halibut, *Paralichthys californicus*, resource and fisheries. Ca. Dept. Fish and Game Fish Bull., No. 174: 217-227.

Caddell, S.M., D.M. Gadomski and L.R. Abbott. 1990. Induced spawning of the California halibut, *Paralichthys californicus*, (Pisces: Paralichthyidae) under artificial and natural conditions. *In:* C.W. Haugen (ed). The California halibut, *Paralichthys californicus*, resource and fisheries. Ca. Dept. Fish and Game, Fish Bull. 174.

California Department of Fish and Game (CDFG). 1988. Review of some California fisheries for 1987. Ca. Dept. Fish and Game. Ca. Coop. Ocean. Fish. Invest. Rep. 29:11-20.

California Department of Water Resources (CDWR). 1991. Interagency ecological studies program 1991 annual report for the Sacramento San Joaquin estuary (P.L. Herrgesell, comp.). Ca. Dept Fish and Game, Ca. Dept. of Water Res., U.S. Bureau Reclam., U.S. Fish & Wildl. Serv. p.104-105.

Crooke, G.A. and C. Taucher. 1988. Ocean hatcheries—wave of the future? Outdoor Ca.. 49(3):10-13.

Ehrlich, K.F., J.H. Hood, S. Muszynski and G.E. McGowen. 1979. Thermal behavior responses of selected California littoral fishes. Fish Bull., U.S. 76(4):837-849.

Emmett, R.L., S.L. Stone, S.A. Hinton, and M.E. Monaco. 1991. Distribution and abundance of fishes and invertebrates in west coast estuaries, Vol. II: species life history summaries. ELMR Rep. No. 8. NOAA/NOS Strategic Environmental Assessments Div., Rockville, MD, p. 250-255.

Eschmeyer, W.N., E.S. Herald and H. Hammann. 1983. A field guide to Pacific coast fishes of North America. Houghton Mifflin Co., Boston, MA, 336 pp.

Feder, H.M., C.H. Turner and C. Limbaugh. 1974. Observations on fishes associated with kelp beds in southern California. Ca. Fish and Game, Fish Bull. 160:1-144.

Fitch, J.E. 1965. Offshore fishes of California. 3rd revision. Ca. Dept. Fish and Game, Sacramento, CA. 80 pp.

Fitch, J.E. and R.J. Lavenberg. 1971. Marine food and game fishes of California. Univ. Ca. Press, Berkeley, CA. 179 p.

Frey, H.W. 1971. California's living marine resources and their utilization. Ca. Dept. Fish and Game, Sacramento, CA, 148 pp.

Gadomski, D.M. and S.M. Caddell. 1991. Effects of temperature on early life-history-stages of California halibut, *Paralichthys californicus*. Fishery Bull. 89:567-576.

Gadomski, D.M., S.M. Caddell, L.R. Abbott and T.C. Caro. 1990. Growth and development of larval and juvenile California halibut, *Paralichthys californicus*, reared in the laboratory. *In:* C.W. Haugen (ed). The California halibut, *Paralichthys californicus*, resource and fisheries. Ca. Dept. Fish and Game, Fish Bull. 174:85-98.

Gadomski, D.M. and J.H. Petersen. 1988. Effects of food deprivation on the larvae of two flatfishes. Mar. Ecol. Prog. Ser. 44:103-111.

Ganssle, D. 1966. Fishes and decapods of San Pablo and Suisun bays. *In:* D.W. Kelley (ed). Ecological studies of the Sacramento-San Joaquin Estuary, Part I. Ca. Dept. Fish and Game, Fish Bull. 133:64-94.

Ginsburg, I. 1952. Flounders of the genus *Paralichthys* and related genera in American waters. Fish Bull., U.S. 71:1-351.

Haaker, P.L. 1975. The biology of the California halibut, *Paralichthys californicus* (Ayres), in Anaheim Bay, California. *In:* E.D. Lane and C.W. Hill (eds). The marine resources of Anaheim Bay. Ca. Fish and Game, Fish Bull. 165:137-151.

Hieb, K. and R. Baxter. 1994. Interagency ecological studies program 1992 annual report for the Sacramento San Joaquin estuary (P.L. Herrgesell, comp.). Ca. Dept Fish and Game, Ca. Dept. of Water Res., U.S. Bureau Reclam., U.S. Fish and Wildl. Serv., p. 95-106.

Hobbs, R.C., L.W. Botsford and R.G. Kope. 1990. Bioeconomics evaluation of the culture/stocking concept for California halibut. *In:* C.W. Haugen, editor. The California halibut, *Paralichthys californicus*, resource and fisheries. Ca. Dept. Fish and Game, Fish Bull. 174.

Innis, D.B. 1990. Juvenile California halibut, *Paralichthys californicus*, growth in relation to thermal effluent. *In:* C.W. Haugen (ed). The California halibut, *Paralichthys californicus*, resource and fisheries. Ca. Dept. Fish and Game, Fish Bull. 174:153-165.

Jow, T. 1990. The California halibut trawl fishery. *In:* C.W. Haugen (ed). The California halibut, *Paralichthys californicus*, resource and fisheries. Ca. Dept. Fish and Game, Fish Bull. 174.

Kramer, S.H. 1990. Distribution and abundance of juvenile California halibut, *Paralichthys californicus*, in shallow water of San Diego county. *In:* C.W. Haugen (ed). The California halibut, *Paralichthys californicus*, resource and fisheries. Ca. Dept. Fish and Game, Fish Bull. 174.

Lavenberg, R.J., G.E. McGowen, A.E. Jahn, J.H. Petersen and T.C. Sciarrotta. 1986. Abundance of southern California nearshore ichthyoplankton: 1978-1984. Ca. Coop. Oceanic Fish. Invest. Rep. 27:53-64.

MBC Applied Environmental Sciences. 1987. Ecology of important fisheries species offshore California. Rep. to Min. Manag. Serv., U.S. Dept. Int., Washington, D.C., 251 pp. (Contract No. MMS 14-12-0001-30294).

Miller, D.J. and R.N. Lea. 1972. Guide to the coastal marine fishes of California. Ca. Fish and Game, Fish Bull. No. 157, 249 p.

Moser, H.G. and W. Watson. 1990. Distribution and abundance of early life history stages of the California halibut, *Paralichthys californicus*, and comparison with the fantail sole, *Xystreurys liolepis. In*: C.W. Haugen (ed). The California halibut, *Paralichthys californicus*, resource and fisheries. Ca. Dept. Fish and Game, Fish Bull. 174.

Moyle, P.B. and J.J. Cech, Jr. 1988. Fishes, an introduction to ichthyology, 2nd ed., p. 312. Prentice-Hall, Inc., Englewood Cliffs, NJ.

Pearson, D.E. 1989. Survey of fishes and water properties of South San Francisco Bay, California, 1973-82. NOAA Tech. Report NMFS 78. 21 pp.

Petersen, J.H., A.E. Jahn, R.J. Lavenberg, G.E. McGowen and R.S. Grove. 1986. Physical-chemical characteristics and zooplankton biomass on the continental shelf off southern California. Ca. Coop. Oceanic Fish. Invest. Rep. 27:36-52.

Plummer, K.M., E.E. DeMartini, and D.A. Roberts. 1983. The feeding habits and distribution of juvenile-small adult California halibut (*Paralichthys californicus*) in coastal waters off northern San Diego county. Calif Coop. Ocean Fish. Invest. Rep. 24:194-201.

Schultze, D.L. 1986. Digest of California commercial fish laws, January 1, 1986. Ca. Dept. Fish and Game, Sacramento, CA, 40 pp.

Tupen, J.W. 1990. Movement and growth of tagged California halibut, *Paralichthys californicus*, off the central coast of California. *In:* C.W. Haugen (ed). The California halibut, *Paralichthys californicus*, resource and fisheries. Ca. Dept. Fish and Game, Fish Bull. 174.

U.S. Dept. of Commerce (USDC). 1986. Marine recreational fishery statistics survey, Pacific coast. U.S. Dept. Comm., Nat. Ocean. Atm. Adm., Current Fish. Stat. No. 8328, 109 p.

Waggoner, J.P., III, and C.R. Feldmeth. 1971. Sequential mortality of the fish fauna impounded in construction of a marina at Dana Point, CA. Ca. Dept. Fish and Game 57(3):167-176.

Wang, J.C.S. 1986. Fishes of the Sacramento-San Joaquin Estuary and adjacent waters, California: a guide to the early life histories. Tech. Rep. No. 9, prepared for the Interagency Ecological Study Program for the Sac.-San Joaquin Estuary. Ca. Dept. Water Res., Ca. Dept. Fish and Game, U.S. Bureau Reclam. U.S. Fish Wildl. Serv.

Personal Communications

Randal Baxter, California Department of Fish and Game, Stockton.

Starry Flounder

Platichthys stellatus

Kurt F. Kline

General Information

The starry flounder is in the family Pleuronectidae, or right-eyed flounders. Pleuronectids are generally found in temperate marine environments, with only a few species found in the tropics or sub-tropics. There are 22 species found along the coast of California. The starry flounder is one of the few pleuronectids commonly found in brackish and freshwater (Orcutt 1950, Haertel and Osterberg 1967). While placed in the Pleuronectidae, the starry flounder is commonly right or left-eyed. However, it is quite distinguishable from other flatfishes due to the alternating dark gray and orange-yellow bands on the dorsal, anal, and caudal fins.

Many of the pleuronectids support commercial and sport fisheries. The starry flounder is a minor sport species in San Francisco Bay and most fish are taken from boats when fishing for California halibut, sturgeon, or striped bass. It common in the commercial fishery, but as a by-catch to targeted species such as petrale sole and California halibut. In recent years, nearshore gear restrictions have resulted in a decrease in starry flounder landings, as this species is most common within a few miles of shore (Haugen 1992).

Reproduction

Spawning occurs in winter in shallow coastal areas near the mouths of rivers and sloughs (Orcutt 1950, Wang 1986, Baxter 1999). Some researchers have suggested that spawning may occur within San Francisco Bay

Actual Length to 3 ft.

(Radtke 1966, Moyle 1976); however, neither ripe female starry flounder nor mature flounder eggs or pre-flexion larvae were collected from San Francisco Bay in the early 1980s (B. Spies, pers. comm., Wang 1986).

Growth and Development

Eggs and larvae are pelagic and found mostly in the upper water column (Orcutt 1950, Wang 1986). Starry flounder larvae are approximately 2 mm long at hatching and settle to the bottom about two months after hatching, at approximately 7 mm standard length (SL) (Policansky and Sieswerda 1979, Policansky 1982). Larvae depend upon favorable ocean currents to keep them near their estuarine nursery areas before settlement. Transforming larvae and juveniles migrate from the coast to brackish or freshwater nursery areas, where they rear for 1 or more years (Haertel and Osterberg 1967, Wang 1986, Hieb and Baxter 1993). As they grow, juvenile starry flounder move to higher salinity, but appear to remain in estuaries through at least their second year of life (Haertel and Osterberg 1967, Hieb and Baxter 1993).

Most males mature by the end of their second year of life (220-276 mm SL), while females mature at 3 or 4 (239-405 mm SL) (Orcutt 1950). During the late fall and winter, mature starry flounder probably migrate to shallow coastal waters to spawn (Orcutt 1950). After spawning, some adult starry flounder return to the Bay for feeding, and are most common in the Bay from late spring through early fall (Ganssle 1966). They reach a maximum length of 915 mm (Miller and Lea 1972)

Food and Feeding

In Monterey Bay and Elkhorn Slough, the smallest starry flounder (10-99 mm SL) fed primarily on copepods and amphipods. Larger juveniles (100-199 mm SL) fed on larger amphipods, polychaetes, and bivalves (especially siphon tips). Fish >199 SL mm fed on whole crabs and bivalves, sand dollars, brittle stars, and occasionally fish (Orcutt 1950). In San Francisco Bay, a large portion of the diet of starry flounders > 199 mm was bivalves (primarily *Mya*, *Ischadium*, *Tapes*, *Solen*, *Mytilus*, and *Gemma*), polychaetes, and crustaceans (especially *Upogebia*, *Cancer magister*, *C. gracilis*, and *Hemigraphsus oregonensis*) (CDFG, unpubl. data).

Distribution

Starry flounder range from Santa Barbara, California northward to arctic Alaska, then southwesterly to the Sea of Japan (Miller and Lea 1972). Adult starry flounder inhabit shallow coastal marine water, whereas juveniles rear in bays and estuaries (Orcutt 1950, Moyle 1976, Wang 1986). Emmett et al. (1991) state that juvenile starry flounder are found almost exclusively in estuaries.

In San Francisco Bay, there is a shift in distribution with growth. Age-0 fish are found more commonly in fresh to brackish water (Suisun Bay, Suisun Marsh, and the delta), while age-1 and older juveniles are more commonly associated with brackish to marine waters (Suisun and San Pablo bays). Throughout their time in the San Francisco Bay, juvenile starry flounder are commonly found in shallow water, including shoals, intertidal areas, and tidal marshes (Woods 1981, Moyle et al 1986, Baxter 1999, CDFG, unpubl. data).

Population Status and Influencing Factors

There is evidence of a long-term decline in the San Francisco Bay starry flounder population from the Commercial Passenger Fishing Vessel log book data. Both catch/hour (CPUE) and total catch of starry flounder declined in the mid-1970s from a peak in the late 1960s and early 1970s (CDFG 1992). This decline in CPUE and catch continued at least through the early 1990s. Additionally, juvenile starry flounder abundance indices from San Francisco Bay steadily declined from the early to the late 1980s (**Figure 2.10**). Abundance remained very low through 1994 and increased somewhat from 1995-99. Outflow related mechanisms have been proposed to control recruitment of age-0 starry flounder to the Bay (CDFG 1992, Hieb and Baxter 1993). The increase in the abundance of age-0 fish from 1995 to 1999 supports this hypothesis.

Hydrologic factors and other environmental conditions in San Pablo and Suisun bays are important in determining the distribution of juvenile starry flounder. The San Francisco Estuary is close to the southern limit of the distribution for starry flounder and long-term

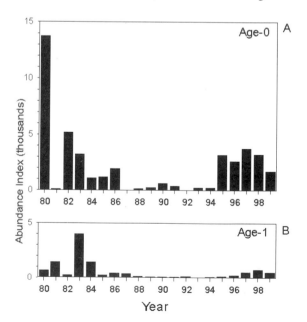

Figure 2.10 Annual Abundance Indices of Starry Flounder: A. Age-0, May-October; B. Age-1, February-October (CDFG Otter Trawl data)

changes in the oceanic environment (particularly temperature) may also affect recruitment. Ocean temperatures have been above average for the region for much of the 1980s and 1990s and it is possible that adult populations moved northward into cooler waters. Temperature can also influence spawning and early development, as increased temperatures may result in decreased hatching success and larval survival.

Trophic Levels

Primary to secondary carnivore. Feeds primarily on large benthic invertebrates and rarely on fish.

Proximal Species

Prey: Benthic invertebrates including bivalves, polychaetes, and crustaceans.

Good Habitat

Suitable habitat includes shallow to deep subtidal mud and sand flats. Juvenile rearing occurs in the shallow areas of Suisun and San Pablo bays. Open deeper waters with higher salinity are generally more acceptable for adults.

Acknowledgments

Some of the materials in this report are summarized from the Plueronectiformes chapter of IEP Technical Report 63 which is referenced below (Baxter 1999).

References

Baxter, R.. 1999. Starry flounder. *In*: J. Orsi (ed). Report on the 1980-1995 fish, shrimp, and crab sampling in the San Francisco Estuary, California. Interagency Ecological Program for the Sacramento-San Joaquin Estuary. Tech. Rept. No. 63.

California Department of Fish and Game (CDFG). 1992. Estuary dependent species, Exhibit #6. *In*: State Wat. Qual. Contr. Bd. 1992. Wat. Qual./Wat. Rights Proceedings on San Fran. Bay and the Sac./San Joaquin Delta. 97 pp.

Emmett, R.L., S.A Hinton, S.L. Stone and M.E. Monaco. 1991. Distribution and abundance of fish and invertebrate in the west coast estuaries. Vol. II: Species life history summaries. NOAA/NOS Strategic Envir. Assessment Div., Rockville, MD ELMR Rep. No. 8, 329 pp.

Ganssle, D. 1966. Fishes and decapod of San Pablo and Suisun Bays. *In:* D.W. Kelly (ed). Ecological studies of the Sacramento San Joaquin Estuary, Part 1. Ca. Dept. Fish and Game Fish Bull. 133:64-94.

Garrison, K.J. and B.S. Miller. 1982. Review of the early life history of Puget Sound fishes. Univ. of Washington. Fish. Res. Inst. Seattle, Washington. UW 8216: 729p.

Haertel, L. and C. Osterberg. 1967. Ecology of zooplankton, benthos, and fishes in the Columbia River Estuary. Ecology 48(3): 459-472.

Haugen, C.W. 1992. Starry flounder. *In:* W.S. Leet, C.W. Dewees, and C.W. Haugen (eds). California's living marine resources and their utilization. California Sea Grant.

Hieb, K. and R. Baxter. 1993. Delta Outflow/San Francisco Bay Study. *In:* P.L. Herrgesell (compiler). 1991 Annual Report, Interagency Ecological Studies Program for the Sacramento-San Joaquin Estuary, pp. 101-116

Interagency Ecological Studies Program for the Sacramento–San Joaquin Estuary (IESP) 1993. 1991 Annual Report. P.L. Herrgesell, compiler. Sacramento, Ca. 150 pp.

Miller, D.J. and R.N. Lea. 1972. Guide to the coastal marine fishes of California. Ca. Fish and Game Fish Bull. 157, 249 pp.

Moyle, P.B. 1976. Inland Fishes of California. Univ. of California Press, Berkeley, Ca., 405 pp.

Moyle, P.B., R.A. Daniels, B. Herbold, and D.M. Baltz. 1986. Patterns in distribution and abundances of a noncoevolved assemblage of estuarine fishes in California. Fishery Bulletin 84(1):105-117.

Orcutt, H.G. 1950. The life history of the starry flounder, *Platichthys stellatus* (Pallus). Ca. Fish Game Fish Bull. 78, 64 pp.

Policansky, D. 1982. Influence of age, size, and temperature on metamorphosis in starry flounder, *Platichthys stellatus*. Can. J. Aquatic Sci. 39(3):514- 517.

Policansky, D. and P. Sieswerda. 1979. Early life history of the starry flounder, *Platichthys stellatus,* reared through metamorphosis in the laboratory. Trans. Amer. Fish. Soc. 108(3):326 327.

Radtke, L.D. 1966. Distribution of smelt, juvenile sturgeon, and starry flounder in the Sacramento-San Joaquin Delta with observations on food of sturgeon. *In:* J.L. Turner and D.W. Kelley (Comp). Ecological studies of the Sacramento-San Joaquin Delta, Part II. Ca. Dept. Fish and Game, Fish Bull. 136: 115-129.

Wang, J.C.S. 1986. Fishes of the Sacramento-San Joaquin Estuary and adjacent waters, California: A guide to the early life histories. Interagency Ecological Study Program for the Sac.-San Joaquin Estuary, Tech. Rep. 9, 345 pp.

Woods, E. 1981. Fish Utilization. In: The Hayward Regional Shoreline marsh restorations: Biological succession during the first year following dike removal. T. Niesen and M. Josselyn, eds. Tiburon Center for Environmental Studies, Tech. Rept. 1:35-46.

Personal Communications

Bob Spies, Applied Marine Sciences, Livermore, California.

3

Invertebrates

Franciscan Brine Shrimp

Artemia franciscana Kellogg

Brita C. Larsson

General Information

The Franciscan brine shrimp, *Artemia franciscana* (formerly *salina*) (Bowen et al. 1985, Bowen and Sterling 1978, Barigozzi 1974), is a small crustacean found in highly saline ponds, lakes or sloughs that belong to the order Anostraca (Eng et al. 1990, Pennak 1989). They are characterized by stalked compound eyes, an elongate body, and no carapace. They have 11 pairs of swimming legs and the second antennae are uniramous, greatly enlarged and used as a clasping organ in males. The average length is 10 mm (Pennak 1989). Brine shrimp commonly swim with their ventral side upward. *A. franciscana* lives in hypersaline water (70 to 200 ppt) (Maiss and Harding-Smith 1992).

In the Bay area, the optimum temperature for *A. franciscana* is 21-31°C. In the winter, when temperatures fall below this range, brine shrimp populations decline and their growth becomes stunted (Maiss and Harding-Smith 1992). Other environmental factors such as wind, salinity, and the quantity and quality of phytoplankton may also affect Bay area populations of *A. franciscana* and

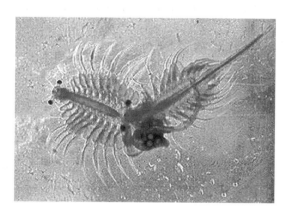

their effects on this species are currently being investigated (Maiss and Harding-Smith 1992).

Reproduction, Growth, and Development

Artemia franciscana has two types of reproduction, ovoviviparous and oviparous. In ovoviviparous reproduction, the fertilized eggs in a female can develop into free-swimming nauplii, which are set free by the mother. In oviparous reproduction, however, the eggs, when reaching the gastrula stage, become surrounded by a thick shell and are deposited as cysts, which are in diapause (Sorgeloos 1980). In the Bay area, cysts production is generally highest during the fall and winter, when conditions for *Artemia* development are less favorable. The cysts may persist for decades in a suspended state. Under natural conditions, the lifespan of *Artemia* is from 50 to 70 days. In the lab, females produced an average of 10 broods, but the average under natural conditions may be closer to 3-4 broods, although this has not been confirmed. Each brood contains from 30 to 100 offspring which mature in 10-25 days (Maiss and Harding-Smith 1992). The larva grows and differentiates through approximately 15 molts (Sorgeloos 1980).

Food and Feeding

Artemia franciscana feed on phytoplankton and blue-green algae that occur in Bay area salt ponds (Maiss and Harding-Smith 1992).

Distribution

Artemia franciscana occurs in highly saline waters throughout western North America, Mexico, and in the Caribbean (Bowen et al. 1985). In California, *A. franciscana* occurs from sea level to 1,495m and in many parts of the state, but its distribution is spotty because of this species salinity requirements (Eng et al. 1990). Historically in the Bay area they were found in salt pannes and sloughs were hypersaline conditions occurred. Currently they occur in salt ponds in the northern and southern portion of San Francisco Bay that are used for the commercial production of salt. Salt ponds cover approximately 111 km and in the North bay 36 Km off the Bay's shoreline (Lonzarich 1989). The distribution of *Artemia* in these salt ponds is limited by the salinity of the ponds. The optimum salinity range for *Artemia* is 70 ppt to 175 ppt (Carpelan 1957). They do not occur where the salinity is above 200 ppt.

Population Status and Influencing Factors

Commercial salt production in San Francisco Bay is currently an active industry, so habitat for *A. franciscana* is not limited and populations are large due to ample amounts of habitat. Donaldson et al. (1992) sampled a 496 acre salt pond in the San Francisco Bay National Wildlife Refuge and estimated the highest winter adult population at 40 billion and the lowest winter population at 4.5 billion. Brine shrimp populations are lowest in the winter and peak in the summer months when their optimal temperatures occur so these numbers are conservative for a maximum population value for the pond. Current populations of the brine shrimp probably far exceed historic populations because the salt ponds in which they occur are manmade. Salt ponds occurred naturally and there is even some evidence that the Ohlone Indians manipulated a portion of the Bay shoreline for salt production but never was there as much salt pond habitat for brine shrimp as currently occurs in the Bay area.

Trophic Level

Artemia franciscana is a primary consumer.

Proximal Species

Anderson (1970) lists sightings of 55 bird species using salt ponds in San Francisco Bay. Mallards, California gulls, whimbrels, Wilson's phalarope, eared grebes and American avocets are several species which feed on *A. franciscana*. Western and least sand pipers, willets, greater yellow legs and Bonaparte's gulls are commonly seen roosting and feeding in the salt pond environment and most likely feed on *Artemia* in these ponds (Maiss and Harding-Smith 1992).

Good Habitat

Brine shrimp occur in salt ponds adjacent to San Francisco Bay that have salinities ranging from 70 to 200 ppt but are most common when the range is between 90 and 150 ppt (Maiss and Harding-Smith 1992). Harvey et al. (1988) reported that up to 46% of the 23,465 acres of active salt ponds in South Bay are within the 70-200 ppt salinity range in the summer and contain brine shrimp.

References

Anderson, W. 1970. A preliminary study of the relationship of saltponds and wildlife-South San Francisco Bay. Calif. Fish and Game 56(4):240-252.

Barigozzi, C. 1974. *Artemia*: a survey of its significance in genetic problems. *In:* T. Tobshansky, M. K. Hecht and W.C. Steere (eds). Evolutionary Biology (7). Plenum Press, New York, NY. Pp. 221-252.

Bowen, S.T. and G. Sterling. 1978. Esterase and malate dehydrogenase isozyme polymorphism in S. *artemia* populations. Comp. Biochem. and Physio. 61B:593-595.

Bowen, S.T., E.A. Fogarino, K.N. Hitchner, G.L. Dana, V.H.S. Chow, M.R. Buoncristiani and J.R. Carl. 1985. Ecological isolation in *Artemia*: population differences in tolerance of anion concentrations. J. Crustacean Biology 5:106- 129.

Carpelan, L.H. 1957. Hydrobiology of the Alviso salt ponds. Ecology 38:375-390.

Donaldson, M.E., D.E. Conklin, and T.D. Foin. 1992. Population dynamics of *Artemia Franciscana* in the San Francisco Bay National Wildlife Refuge: Phase II. Interim Report #2.

Eng, L.L. D. Belk, and C.H. Eriksen. 1990. California Anostraca: distribution, habitat, and status. J. Crustacean Biology 10:247-277.

Harvey, T.E., P.R. Kelly, R.W. Towe, and D. Fearn. 1988. The value of saltponds for Waterbirds in San Francisco Bay and considerations for future management. Presentation at the Wetlands '88: Urban Wetlands and Riparian Habitat Conference, June 26-29, Oakland, CA.

Lonzarich, D. 1989. Life History and Patterns of Distribution in Salt pond Fishes: A Community Level Study. M.S. thesis San Jose University, Ca.

Maiss, F.G. and E.K. Harding-Smith. 1992. San Francisco Bay National Wildlife Refuge final environmental assessment of commercial brine shrimp harvest. U.S. Fish and Wildlife Service, San Francisco Bay National Wildlife Refuge, Newark, Ca. 27p.

Pennak, R.W. 1989. Freshwater invertebrates of the United States. 3rd edition. Protozoa to Mollusca. John Wiley and Sons, Inc. New York, NY. 628 p.

Sorgeloos, P. 1980. Life history of the brine shrimp *Aretmia*. *In:* G. Persoone, P. Sorgeloos, O. Roels and E. Jaspers (eds). The Brine Shrimp *Artemia*. Universa Press Wetteren, Belgium. pp.xxi-xxiii.

Invertebrates

California Vernal Pool Tadpole Shrimp

Lepidurus packardi Simon

Brita C. Larsson

General Information

The California vernal pool tadpole shrimp is a small crustacean found in ephemeral freshwater pools that belong to the order Notostraca. They are characterized by sessile compound eyes, a shield-like carapace covering the head and much of the trunk, and a telson that is a flat and paddle-shaped protuberance. They can reach a length of 50 mm and have approximately 35 pairs of legs and two long cercopods (Pennak 1989). Tadpole shrimp are primarily benthic organisms that swim with their legs down. They can also climb or scramble over objects and plow through bottom sediments (Federal Register 1994). Information about the biology of this species is limited and incomplete (Ahl 1991).

Reproduction, Growth, and Development

Much of what is known about the reproduction, growth, and development of *L. packardi* comes from studies by Ahl (1991) and Longhurst (1955). Their life history is dependent on ephemeral freshwater pools. In California, vernal pools are generally hydrated during the rainy season, which extends from winter to early spring. Populations of tadpole shrimp are reestablished from diapaused eggs when winter rains rehydrate vernal pools. Once a pool rehydrates, the eggs hatch over a three week period, some hatching within the first four days. It takes another three to four weeks for the tadpole shrimp to become sexually reproductive. Populations consist of both males and females, though late in the season, pools are often dominated by males. After copulation, fertilized eggs descend into the foot capsule of the female (Desportes and Andrieux 1944). The eggs are sticky and when they are deposited they adhere to plant matter and sediment particles (Federal Register 1994). A female can have up to six clutches of eggs, totaling about 861 eggs during her lifetime (Ahl 1991). Depending on the depth and persistence of water in a pool, some eggs hatch immediately. The remainder inter diapause and lie dormant in the sediment during the dry portion of the year (Ahl 1991).

Food and Feeding

Tadpole shrimp feed on organic detritus and living organisms such as fairy shrimp and other invertebrates (Pennak 1989, Fryer 1987).

Distribution

L. packardi is endemic to vernal pools in the Central Valley, coast ranges and a limited number of sites in the Transverse Range and Santa Rosa Plateau (Federal Register 1994). The distribution of this species is not well known for the Bay area. Recently, *L. packardi* was collected at the Warm Springs Seasonal Wetland which is a part of the Don Edwards San Francisco Bay National Wildlife Refuge (Caires et al 1993). Other populations have been found north of the eastern half of Potrero Hills in the North Bay (S. Forman, Pers. obs.). Seasonal wetlands occur sporadically in both the North and South Bay and may provide additional habitat for this species. Surveys in seasonal wetlands surrounding San Francisco Bay may contribute and increase information on the distribution of this species.

Population Status and Influencing Factors

Current status of the population of tadpole shrimp in the Bay area is not known. Loss of seasonal wetland habitat in the Bay area may be significantly affecting the population of this species especially since distribution information for the Bay area is so limited.

Trophic Level

Lepidurus packardi is most likely a secondary consumer.

Proximal Species

Waterfowl, western spadefoot toad, and tadpoles.

Good Habitat

Lepidurus packardi inhabits vernal pools. They have been found in pools ranging in size from 5 square meters to 36 hectares. The water in the pools can be clear to turbid. The pools often have low conductivity, TDS, and alkalinity (Federal Register 1994, Eng et al. 1990). The pools dry up in the late spring and are dry in the summer and fall then fill with rain water in the winter and early spring. Vernal pool formations occur in grass bot-

Dr. J.L. King

tomed swales of grasslands in old alluvial soils, underlain by hardpan or in mud bottomed pools (Federal Register 1994). Pools with cobblely hardpan bottoms also serve as habitat (Gallagher 1996). Gallagher (1996) found that the depth, volume, and duration of inundation of a pool was important for the presence of *L. packardi* in vernal pools when compared to the needs of other branchiopods. He found *L. packardi* did not reappear in ponds that dried and rehydrated during the study period, while other Branchiopod species did. *L. packardi* needs deeper and longer-lasting pools if they are to persist over a rainy season in which both wet and dry periods occur. Temperature variation in pools where *L. packardi* have been found to vary from 3 to 23°C (Gallagher 1996). Salinity, conductivity, dissolved solids, and pH of the water in vernal pools are also important in determining the distribution of tadpole shrimp (Federal Register 1994).

References

Ahl, J.S. 1991. Factors affecting contributions of the tadpole shrimp, *Lepidurus packardi*, to its over summering egg reserves. Hydrobiologia 212:137-143.

Caries, T.D. Dawn, D. DiNunzio, A. Harris, N. Kogut, M. Kutiled, S.H. Ladd, J. Stanziano, M. Stickler and A. Webber. 1993. Sur la biologie de Lepidurus apus. Bull. Soc. Zool. Fr. 69:61-68.

Desportes, C. and L.H. Andrieux. 1944. Sur la biologie de *Lepidurus apus*. Bull. Soc. Zool. Fr. 69:61-68.

Eng, L.L., D. Belk and C.H. Eriksen. 1910. California Anostraca: distribution, habitat, and status. J. crustacean Biology 10:247-277.

Federal Register. 1994. Endangered and threatened plants: determination of endangered status for the conservancy fairy shrimp. Longhorn fairy shrimp, and vernal pool tadpole shrimp; and threatened status for the vernal pool fairy shrimp. Fed. Reg. 59:48136-48153.

Fryer, G. 1987. A new classification of the branchiopod Crustacea. Zool. J. Linn. Soc. 91:357-383.

Gallagher, S.P. 1996. Seasonal occurrence and habitat characteristics of some vernal pool Branchiopods in Northern California, U.S.A. J. Crustacean Biology 16(2):323-329.

Longhurst, A.R. 1955. A review of the Notostraca. Bull. Br. Mus. Nat. Hist. Zool. 3:1-57.

Pennak, R.W. 1989. Freshwater invertebrates of the United States. 3rd edition. Protozoa to Mollusca. John Wiley and Sons, Inc. New York, NY. pp628.

Personal Communication

Steve Forman, LSA Associates, Incorporated

Reticulate Water Boatman

Trichocorixa reticulata Guerin

Wesley A. Maffei

Description and Systematic Position

Trichocorixa reticulata is a small hemipteran, approximately 3-5mm in length, that belongs to the family Corixidae. This insect, also known as the salt marsh water boatman, can be recognized by the fine network of lines on its hemelytra (outer wing covers), the 10-11 dark transverse bands on the pronotum, and the pala of front legs not exceeding two-thirds the width of an eye along the ventral margin (**Figure 3.1**).

Distribution

Sailer (1948) states that this insect is found along the Pacific Coast from northern San Francisco Bay south to Peru. Populations from Kansas, New Mexico, Texas, Florida, and the Hawaiian Islands have also been recorded. One isolated record was reported in China but this has been unconfirmed. Within the San Francisco Bay environs this water boatman can be found in mid to upper marsh tidal pools and man-made salt ponds. **Figure 3.2** shows the locations around the Bay Area where *T. reticulata* have been collected, and **Table 3.1** shows the collection dates.

Suitable Habitat

T. reticulata prefers saline environments. Cox (1969) found this insect in southern California coastal salt ponds with salinities ranging from brackish up to 160 ‰ and Jang (1977) states that this water boatman can occur in ponds with salinities up to 170 ‰. Carpelan (1957) found the Alviso population in Cargill salt ponds that ranged from 23 ‰ up to 153 ‰. In all instances it was found that the greatest numbers of individuals and the most reproduction occurred in saline environments with a salinity range of 35-80 ‰.

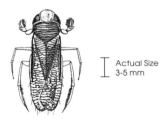

Actual Size
3-5 mm

Wes Maffei

Figure 3.1 Reticulate Water Boatman –
Trichocorixa reticulata

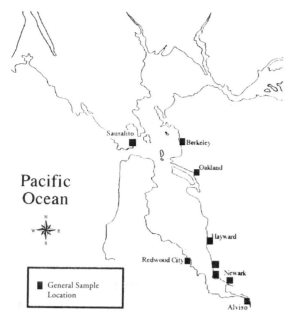

Figure 3.2 Known *Trichocorixa reticulata* Localities Within San Francisco Bay Tidal and Diked Marshes

Table 3.1 Known Collection Sites For *Trichocorixa reticulata* [1]

Location	Date Specimen(s) Collected
Sausalito	29 Oct 1921
Redwood City	15 Jun 1922, 24 Apr 1923, 8 May 1923
Berkeley	18 Apr 1962
Oakland	14 Apr 1930
Baumberg Tract, Hayward	8 Oct 1989
Coyote Hills Park	25 Oct 1988, 11 May 1989
Mowry Slough	25 Sep 1997
Alviso (Coyote Creek)	12 Aug 1980

[1] Information assembled from specimens contained within the California Academy of Sciences Insect Collection, University of California Berkeley Essig Museum, University of California Bohart Museum, San Jose State University Edwards Museum, San Mateo County Mosquito Abatement District Insect Collection, and private collections of Dr. J. Gordon Edwards and Wesley A. Maffei.

Biology

Sailer (1942) believes that all species of *Trichocorixa* over winter as adults. Scudder (1976) states that Tones (unpub.) has found that in Saskatchewan, *Trichocorixa verticalis interiores* over winters in the egg stage.

Eggs are laid singly on submerged vegetation or objects on the bottom substrate. Developmental time for eggs and immatures can very considerably with temperature.

Adult water boatman are both herbivorous and predatory feeding on algal cells and various microorganisms. Although Corixids are aquatic in all life stages, the adults are capable of leaving the water and dispersing by flight. Maffei (unpub.) has noted that south San Francisco Bay populations are attracted to dark colored objects, with adults landing in large numbers on the hoods of green or burgundy colored vehicles while adjacent white vehicles had few if any specimens.

Reproduction

Cox (1969) and Carpelan (1957) have noted that peak reproduction occurs in saline environments with salinities ranging between 35 ‰ and almost 80 ‰. Egg laying is continuous during spring, summer and fall with the greatest number of nymphs occurring during April and May. Cox (1969) has also found that crowding of adults led to increased egg production in females.

Balling and Resh (1984) have reported, that the number of generations per year for the Petaluma Marsh population was at least in part dependent on the longev-ity of the tidal ponds. They found that ponds which dried during late summer contained over wintering, non-reproducing adults while water filled ponds would produce another generation. Reproduction does occur year-round but Cox (1969) states that salinity and adult densities influence the number of eggs laid and the maturation rates of the immature stages. Balling and Resh (1984) noted that the time between generations of the Petaluma Marsh population was also affected by variable egg development times, variable instar development rates, and inter-pond differences in recruitment of adults. In general, it has been determined that environmental conditions can cause water boatmen to either accelerate or delay their development and production of subsequent generations.

Significance to Other Wetlands Taxa

This insect is considered an important prey item for shore birds. Howard (1983) studied the esophageal contents of 35 Ruddy Ducks, *Oxyura jamaicensis*, at the Alviso salt ponds and found that this water boatman comprised 12.6% of the total food volume. Howard also examined the gizzard contents of 53 Ruddy Ducks and found that 25.5% of the total food volume was water boatmen. Anderson (1970) analyzed the stomach contents of 10 Ruddy Ducks and found that water boatman, snails and Widgeon grass seeds were the primary components of their diet. He also found Least Sandpipers, Wilson's Phalarope and Northern Phalarope's utilized this insect as part of their diets.

Conservation Needs and Limiting Factors

Salinity and the length of time tidal marsh ponds contain water seem to be the primary driving forces affecting both developmental rates and reproduction.

References

Anderson, W. 1970. A preliminary study of the relationship of salt ponds and wildlife—South San Francisco Bay. Calif. Dept. Fish and Game 56(4):240-252.

Balling, S.S. and V. Resh. 1984. Life history and variability in the water boatman *Trichocorixa reticulata* (Hemiptera: Corixidae) in San Francisco Bay salt marsh ponds. Ann. Ent. Soc. Amer. 77(1):14-19.

Carpelan, L.H. 1957. Hydrobiology of the Alviso Salt Ponds. Ecology 38:375-390.

Cox, M.C. 1969. The biology of the euryhaline water boatman *Trichocorixa reticulata* (Guerin-Meneville) M.S. Thesis, San Diego State Univ. 84pp.

Howard, J.A. 1983. Feeding ecology of the ruddy duck on the San Francisco Bay National Wildlife Refuge. M.A. Thesis, San Jose State Univ. 53 pp.

Jang, E.B. 1977. Hydromineral regulation in the saline water corixid *Trichocorixa reticulata*. M.S. Thesis, Hayward State Univ. 79 pp.

Maffei, W. 1989-1996. Unpublished field notes.

Sailer, R.I. 1942. The genus Trichocorixa (Hemiptera: Corixidae). Phd Thesis, Univ. of Kansas, Lawrence, Kansas. 118pp.

Scudder, G.E. 1976. Water-boatmen of saline waters (Hemiptera: Corixidae). pp. 263-289. *In:* L. Cheng (ed). Marine Insects. North-Holland Publ., Amsterdam. 581pp.

Additional Readings

Hungerford, H.B. 1948. The Corixidae of the western hemisphere (Hemiptera). Univ. Kans. Sci. Bull. 32: 827pp.

Usinger, R.L. (ed). 1956. Aquatic insects of California. Univ. Calif. Press, Berkeley. 508pp.

Tiger Beetles

Cicindela senilis senilis, C. oregona,
and *C. haemorrhagica*

Wesley A. Maffei

Description and Systematic Position

Cicindela senilis senilis, C. oregona, and *C. haemorrhagica* are moderate sized beetles, approximately 10-15mm in length, that belong to the family Cicindelidae (Figure 3.3). These beetles, also known as tiger beetles, can be easily identified by their large, bulging eyes and long, sickle-shaped mandibles that bear small teeth. Adults of *C. senilis* and *C. oregona* are usually shining metallic blue to green on the ventral surface with the dorsum dull coppery brown and bearing small yellowish-white irregular markings. *Cicindela haemorrhagica* is similar in appearance to both *C. senilis* and *C. oregona* except that the ventral surface of the abdomen is usually bright red. The larvae are S-shaped, yellowish-white, have the head and the first thoracic segment flattened, an enlarged hump on the fifth abdominal segment with hooks, and large mandibles that are similar to the adults.

Distribution

Historically the San Francisco Estuary, including the beaches just outside of the Golden Gate Bridge, was home to four species of tiger beetles. These were: *Cicindela haemorrhagica, C. hirticollis, C. oregona oregona* and *C. senilis senilis.* Only two species, *C. haemorrhagica* and *C. senilis senilis* are present today with *C. haemorrhagica* in decline within or near the tidal areas of the San Francisco Bay Estuary. *Cicindela oregona oregona* may still be present within the estuary but the last known population was destroyed in 1996.

The dominant tiger beetle, *C. senilis senilis,* is currently found throughout the south and central portions of the estuary with one population having been identified from Grizzly Island in 1991. Museum records in-

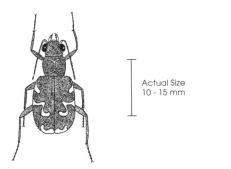

Actual Size
10 - 15 mm

Wes Maffei

Figure 3.3 Tiger Beetle – *Cicindela senilis senilis*

Invertebrates

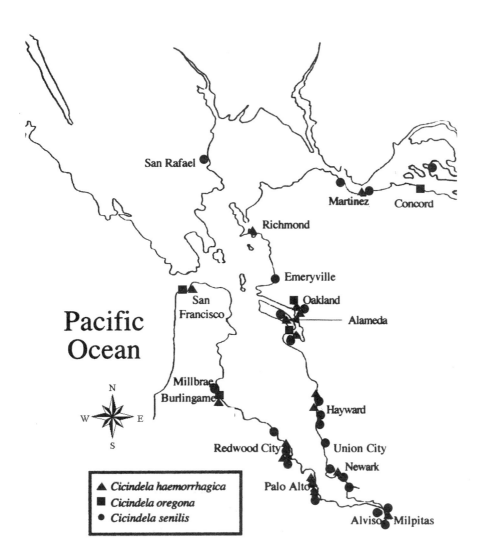

Suitable Habitat

San Francisco Bay tiger beetles are commonly found along open, muddy margins of creeks and streams and also along the muddy margins of salt pannes that are occasionally inundated by high tides. High, dry banks of channels and open areas of levees associated with salt ponds and muted tidal marshes tend to be favored sites for *C. senilis senilis*. Habitat utilized by both adults and larvae can be characterized as having extensive areas of fine silt or sandy clay-like soil, exposed to full sun, with minimal to moderate vegetation, and being located near water. *C. haemorrhagica* and *C. oregona oregona* have shown a preference for wet, sandy beach-like areas that may or may not be influenced by fresh water from creeks and canals.

Biology

The specific biology of San Francisco Bay tiger beetles is not well known. The information that follows is a general-

dicate that this beetle was also found in San Rafael, Martinez and Port Costa but these sites have not been sampled in over 40 years. *C. haemorrhagica,* has become increasingly scarce as its habitat continues to be altered for human needs. This beetle is currently found at Trojan Marsh (San Leandro), Hayward Landing (Hayward), Salt Ponds west of Newark and the Richmond Field Station (Richmond). Historically this beetle had a broader distribution with sites as far north as Martinez and south throughout most of the south San Francisco Bay. The populations at Alameda, Bayfarm Island and Oakland no longer exist and other sites identified from museum records have apparently not been sampled in at least three or more decades (Maffei, unpub.). *C. oregona* is probably no longer present within the tidal and diked marshes of the San Francisco Bay. The last known population was at Bayfarm Island and was extirpated in 1996 when the site was graded in preparation for development. **Figure 3.4** shows the locations around the Bay Area where *C. senilis senilis, C. oregona,* and *C. haemorrhagica* have been collected, and **Table 3.2** shows the collection dates.

Table 3.2 Known Collection Sites for Tiger Beetle Populations[1]

Location	Date Specimen(s) Collected	Location	Date Specimen(s) Collected
Cicindela haemorrhagica		***Cicindela senilis senilis***	
Martinez	28 Aug 1959, 21 Sep 1959	San Rafael (*)	23 May 1941, 20 May 1951
Richmond Field Station	24 Apr 1993	Milbrae	1 Sep 1912, 2 Jun 1912, 3 Oct 1914
Alameda	23 Aug 1930, 24 Aug 1930,	San Mateo	24 Oct 1952
	4 Jul 1932	Redwood City (Salt Marsh)	16 Sep 1951, 15 Jul 1951, 15 Jun 1952
San Francisco	31 Jan 1944 (***)	Redwood City (Harbor)	15 Jun 1952
Burlingame	7 Oct 1969	Redwood City	15 Apr 1952, 26 Sep 1952
Lake Merritt	Jul 1906	Bair Island	9 Mar 1997
Oakland	15 Aug 1902	East Palo Alto (Marsh)	13 Jul 1951
Redwood City (nr Yt. Harbor)	15 Jun 1952	Palo Alto (Salt Marsh)	23 May 1921
Redwood City (Saltmarsh)	31 Jul 1951	Grizzly Island (wildlife area)	10 Oct 1991
Palo Alto Yacht Harbor	29 Jun 1969	Port Costa	21 Sep 1947
East Palo Alto	31 Jul 1951	Martinez	28 Aug 1955, 28 Sep 1955
Milpitas	15 Jul 1966, 26 Jul 1966	Emeryville	20 Aug 1936
Newark (2 mi west of)	25 Jun 1975, 24 Jul 1980	Lake Merritt	4 Oct 1904, 9 Oct 1904, 12 Sep 1907, 12 Apr 1909
Bayfarm Island	21 Jun 1990	Alameda	Jun 1901, 16 Aug 1902, 9 May 1907
Russell Salt Marsh, Hayward	30 Jul 1996, 27 May 1997	Bayfarm Island	May 1939
Trojan Marsh	2 Aug 1997	Oliver Salt Ponds, Hayward	5 Aug 1989, 2 Jul 1990
		Whale's Tail Marsh (Hayward)	12 Apr 1993, 8 Apr 1993, 11 Mar 1993
Cicindela oregona		Baumberg Salt Ponds	Mar 1989, 1 Apr 1990, 13 Jun 1989, 11 Mar 1997
San Francisco Beach	14 Apr 1957	Patterson Hill Marsh, Fremont	11 Apr 1989
Burlingame	22 May 1952	Newark (2 mi west of)	25 Jun 1975, 24 Jul 1980
Bayfarm Island	11 Apr 1972, Jul 1989, 21 Jun 1990, Jul 1993, Aug 1993, 12 Apr 1993, 1 Sep 1995	Dumbarton Bridge (Newark)	9 May 1952
		Newark Salt Flats	17 Jun 1966
Oakland (*)	Jun 1906, 16 Aug 1902	W. End Mowry Slough	19 Sep 1997
Concord (*)	27 Apr 1935	Brinker Marsh	Mar 1989, 10 Mar 1997
		E. End Albrae Slough, Fremont	12 Mar 1997
Cicindela hirticollis (data from Graves 1988)		Dixon Rd, Milpitas	23 Jun 1956
Oakland	no date	Milpitas (wet sand)	1 May 1966, 12 Oct 1966
San Francisco	1907?	Alviso	21 Mar 1947, 22 Mar 1947, 27 Mar 1947, 12 Apr 1947, Apr 1954, 14 Apr 1955, 15 Apr 1955, 12 May 1959, 19 May 1959, 8 Jun 1980

* May or may not be within the confines of the Ecosystem Goals Project.

*** Probably a dubious record, suspect mislabeled specimen.

[1] Information assembled from specimens contained within the California Academy of Sciences Insect Collection, University of California Berkeley Essig Museum, University of California Bohart Museum, San Jose State University Edwards Museum, San Mateo County Mosquito Abatement District Insect Collection, and private collections of Dr. J. Gordon Edwards and Wesley A. Maffei

ized biology for these insects drawn from the studies of other species and a summary article by Pearson (1988).

Adults of these beetles are active on hot, sunny days and are exceedingly quick both in flight and on the ground. When approached these insects will run away or fly for a short distance, land, and then face their pur-

suer. Larvae and adults are predators, feeding on other insects. Prey items for San Francisco Bay tiger beetles include but are not limited to the Brine Flies *Ephydra cinerea, Ephydra millbrae, Lipochaeta slossonae,* and *Mosillus tibialis,* and various beetles belonging to the families Carabidae and Tenebrionidae. Pearson and

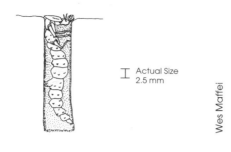

Figure 3.5 *Cicindela senilis senilis* Larva in Burrow

I Actual Size
2.5 mm

Wes Maffei

C. haemorrhagica do not emerge until mid to late June and are usually present through September.

Reproduction

Males initiate copulation by approaching a female in short sprints which is similar to the intermittent sprinting used when foraging. Once close enough to a potential mate, the male leaps onto their back, grasping the thorax with his mandibles and the elytra with his front and middle legs. The male's hind legs remain on the ground and the coupling sulci of the female receives his mandibles. Males frequently mount both males and females of any tiger beetle species present. Females try to dislodge intruding males by rolling on their backs, lurching and then running out into bright sunshine. It is believed that the fit of the male mandibles into the female sulci may be species specific and that this feature allows other males, and females of other species, to rid themselves of unwanted mates (Freitag 1974).

Oviposition usually occurs when the female touches the ground with her antennae and bites the soil with her mandibles. The ovipositor is then extended and with a thrusting motion of the abdomen a hole up to 1 cm is excavated. One egg is deposited in the hole and it is then covered over so that no evidence of disturbance exists. The choice of soil type for oviposition has been found to be extremely critical for many species (Knisley 1987, Leffler 1979, Shelford 1912, Willis 1967).

Availability of prey has been found to directly affect female mortality and the number of eggs produced. Adult beetles in prey poor habitats were only found to approach maximum fecundity during years of high rainfall and high prey populations (Pearson and Knisley 1985). Prey availability for larvae was found to affect the size of later instars, which ultimately affected the size of the adults produced and individual fecundity (Hori 1982a, Pearson and Knisley 1985).

Mury (1979) found that adults of some species of tiger beetles also fed on dead organisms. Faasch (1968) and Swiecimski (1956) found the adults located live prey visually while dead prey were found tactilely. Adult beetles tend to frequent the muddy margins of their habitat where prey items are readily encountered while the immature stages tend to be found in the drier areas.

The eggs, larvae and pupae are subterranean, with the larvae living in vertical burrows and waiting near the top to seize any prey that passes by (**Figure 3.5**). Prey items are captured with the mandibles and pulled down to the bottom of the burrow where it is ingested. Faasch (1968) found that a dark object against a light background released the prey-catching behavior. Burrows are enlarged by loosening the soil with the mandibles and using the head and pronotum to push the soil to surface. At the surface, the soil is flicked off by flipping the head and pronotum backward (Shelford 1908, Willis 1967). The depth of larval tunnels has been found to range between 15 and 200 cm depending on the age of the larva, the species of tiger beetle, the season and soil type and conditions (Criddle 1910, Willis 1967, Zikan 1929).

Larvae undergo three molts with the time for development lasting one to four years and averaging about two years (Willis 1967). Pearson and Knisley (1985) found that the availability of food effected rate of development and was therefore a limiting resource in the life cycle of tiger beetles. They found that ample prey shortened the developmental time from egg to adult with 60 days total developmental time having been observed for some laboratory reared beetles. Prior to pupation, the last instar larva plugs the tunnel entrance and excavates a chamber or pupal cell. The period for pupation is usually short, lasting no more than 30 days.

Larvae can be found throughout the year while adults are present from March through October. Peak adult activity for the south San Francisco Bay *Cicindela senilis senilis* populations is from late April through June (Maffei, unpub.). Blaisdell (1912) noted that adults of *C. senilis*, which emerged in the fall, would hibernate.

Significance to Other Wetlands Taxa

These beetles may be a potential prey item for shore birds. Cramp and Simmons (1983) cite a stomach content analysis study of the European race of Snowy Plover, *Charadrius alexandrinus alexandrinus*, in Hungary which revealed the presence of 28 tiger beetles. Swarth (1983) noted that these beetles were occasionally eaten by Snowy Plovers found at Mono Lake. Marti (1974) found tiger beetle parts in burrowing owl pellets that were studied in the northeastern part of Larimer County, Colorado.

Conservation Needs and Limiting Factors

Nagano (1982) has stated that some tiger beetles are considered to be good indicators of coastal wetlands disturbance, with the least disturbed habitats having the greatest species diversity. San Francisco Bay tidally influenced wetlands appear to have two species of tiger beetle, with those sites that have had minimal disturbance or that have not seen much human activity for long periods of time having the highest populations (Maffei, unpub.). Unfortunately, few sites exist that have not been subjected to human activity. This has resulted in a loss of species diversity, with potential tiger beetle habitat usually having only a single species present and having small disjunct populations. Historically, there were sites that had more than one species present within a given habitat (ie. Lake Merritt, Bayfarm Island and Burlingame).

San Francisco Bay populations of *Cicindela senilis senilis* and *C. haemorrhagica* prefer to be near permanent or semi-permanent bodies of water utilizing tidal pannes with sizable unvegetated flats and/or nearby minimally vegetated levees. *Cicindela haemorrhagica* has shown a preference for sandy beach-like sites but can utilize dry, fine silty sites as is evidenced by the population at Russell Salt Marsh, Hayward. Both species of beetles need to have fine silty clay-like or sandy clay soils, that are unvegetated or sparsely vegetated, within in which to breed. Bright sunshine and minimal flooding are also important factors.

The immature stages of other species of tiger beetles have been found to inhabit a smaller range of the habitat than the adults and are not capable of tolerating as much variation in physical factors such as soil moisture, soil composition and temperature (Hori 1982b, Knisley 1987, Knisley 1984, Knisley and Pearson 1981, Shelford 1912, Shelford 1908). The length and duration of flooding can also be important, although what the specifics of these parameters are for San Francisco Estuary tiger beetles is not clear.

Larochelle (1977) found that many species of adults are readily attracted to lights. What impact this might have on San Francisco Bay Tiger Beetles with respect to dispersal and survival is unknown.

References

Blaisdell, F.S. 1912. Hibernation of *Cicindela senilis* (Coleoptera). Ent. News. 23:156-159.

Cramp, S. and K. Simmons (eds). 1983. The birds of the western palearctic. Vol. III. Oxford Univ. Press, Oxford. pp. 153-165.

Criddle, N. 1910. Habits of some mannitoba tiger beetles (Cicindelidae). II. Can. Ent. 42:9-15.

Faasch, H. 1968. Beobachtungen zur biologie und zum verhalten von *Cicindela hybrida* L. und *Cicindela campestris* L. und experimentelle analyse ihres beutefangverhaltens. Zool. Jarhb. Abt. Syst. Oekol. Geogr. Tiere 95:477-522.

Freitag, R. 1974. Selection for a non-genitalic mating structure in female tiger beetles of the genus *Cicindela* (Coleoptera: Cicindelidae). Can. Ent. 106:561-568.

Hori, M. 1982a. The biology and population dynamics of the tiger beetle, *Cicindela japonica* (Thunberg). Physiol. Ecol. Jpn. 19:77-212.

_____. 1982b. The vertical distribution of two species of tiger beetles at Sugadaira (Mt. Neko-Dake), Nagano Prefecture, with special reference to their habitat preferences. Cicindela 14:19-33.

Knisley, C.B. 1987. Habitats, food resources and natural enemies of a community of larval *Cicindela* in Southeastern Arizona (Coleoptera: Cicindelidae). Can. J. Zool. 65:191-200.

_____. 1984. Ecological distribution of tiger beetles (Coleoptera: Cicindelidae) in Colfax County, New Mexico. Southwest. Nat. 29:93-104.

Knisley, C.B. and D.L. Pearson. 1981. The Function of turret building behaviour in the larval tiger beetle, *Cicindela willistoni* (Coleoptera: Cicindelidae). Ecol. Ent. 6:401-410.

Larochelle, A. 1977. Cicindelidae caught at Lights. Cicindela 9:50-60.

Leffler, S.R. 1979. Tiger beetles of the pacific northwest (Coleoptera: Cicindelidae). Unpub. PhD Thesis. Univ. Wash., Seattle. 731 pp.

Maffei, W. 1989-1996. Unpublished field notes.

Marti, C.D. 1974. Feeding ecology of four sympatric owls. The Condor. 76(1):45-61.

Nagano, C.D. 1982. The population status of seven species of insects inhabiting Tijuana Estuary National Wildlife Refuge, San Diego County, California. Report to the Office of Endangered Species.

Pearson, D.L. 1988. Biology of tiger beetles. Ann. Rev. Ent. 33:123-147.

Pearson, D.L. and C.B. Knisley. 1985. Evidence for food as a limiting resource in the life cycle of tiger beetles (Coleoptera: Cicindelidae). Oikos 45:161-168.

Pearson, D.L. and E.J. Mury. 1979. Character divergence and convergence among tiger beetles (Coleoptera: Cicindelidae). Ecology 60:557-566.

Shelford, V.E. 1908. Life histories and larval habits of the tiger beetles (Cicindelidae). Zool. J. Linn. Soc. 30:157-184.

_____. 1912. Ecological succession. Biol. Bull. Woods Hole Mass. 23:331-370.

Swarth, C.W. 1983. Foraging ecology of snowy plovers and the distribution of their arthropod prey at Mono Lake, California. Master's Thesis, Calif State Univ., Hayward.

Swiecimski, J. 1956. The role of sight and memory in food capture by predatory beetles of the species *Cicindela hybrida* L. (Coleoptera: Cicindelidae). Pol. Pismo Ent. 26:205-232.

Willis, H.L. 1967. Bionomics and zoogeography of tiger beetles of saline habitats in the Central United

Invertebrates

States (Coleoptera: Cicindelidae). Univ. Kans. Sci. Bull. 47:145-313.

Zikan, J.J. 1929. Zur Biologie der Cicindeliden brasiliens. Zool. Anz. 82:269-414.

Additional Readings

Arnett, R.H. 1968. The beetles of the United States (A manual for identification). Ann Arbor, Mich.: The American Entomological Institute, xii + 1112pp.

Dunn, G.W. 1892. Coleoptera and mollusca of the Ocean Beach at San Francisco. ZOE 2(4):310-312.

Dunn, G.W. 1891. Tiger beetles of California. ZOE 2(2):152-154.

Graves, R.C. 1988. Geographic distribution of the North American tiger beetle *Cicindela hirticollis* Say. Cicindela 20(1):1-21.

Willis. 1968. Artificial key to the species of *cicindela* of North America north of Mexico. J. Kans. Ent. Soc. 41(3):303-317.

Western Tanarthrus Beetle

Tanarthrus occidentalis Chandler

Wesley A. Maffei

Description and Systematic Position

Tanarthrus occidentalis is a small beetle, approximately 3-5mm in length, that belongs to the family Anthicidae (**Figure 3.6**). The head, pronotum, legs and abdomen are reddish-orange and the elytra are usually brown or black with the apical and basal third sometimes reddish or yellowish in color. This beetle can be separated from similar bay area Anthicid beetles by noting the distinct medial constriction of the eleventh antennal segment. It can further be separated from *Formicilla* spp., a similar appearing bay area Anthicid of marshes and grasslands, by examining the posterior margin of the mesepisternum which lacks a posterior fringe of long hairs.

Chandler (1979) has indicated that this beetle is very similar to *T. iselini*, which is found only in central New Mexico, but can readily be separated by antennal morphology.

Distribution

Tanarthrus occidentalis was first collected in 1976 and subsequently described as a new taxon by Chandler in 1979. Specimens were collected from the Cargill salt pans, now part of the San Francisco Bay National Wildlife Refuge, adjacent to Dum-barton Bridge, Alameda County, California. Additional populations have been identified from the salt pans of the Baumberg tract, Hayward, California, and from Bayfarm Island, Alameda, California. In 1996 the Bayfarm Island population was extirpated due to modification of their habitat in preparation for anticipated development. Surveys of the south and central San Francisco Bay area have revealed no other populations at this time (Maffei, unpub.). **Figure 3.7** shows the locations around the Bay Area where *T. occidentalis* specimens have been collected, and **Table 3.3** shows the collection dates.

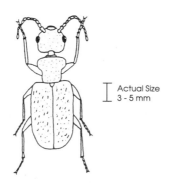

Actual Size 3 - 5 mm

Wes Maffei

Figure 3.6 Western Tanarthrus Beetle – *Tanarthrus occidentalis*

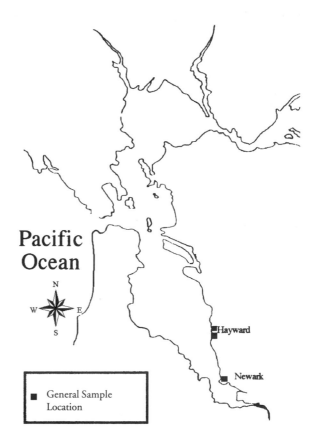

Pacific Ocean

N
W   E
S

Hayward

Newark

■ General Sample Location

Figure 3.7 Known *Tanarthrus occidentalis* Localities Within San Francisco Bay Tidal and Diked Marshes

Table 3.3 Known Collection Sites For *Tanarthrus occidentalis* [1]

Location	Date Specimen(s) Collected
2 mi W. Newark, off Dumbarton Bridge (salt Pans) 1978	27 May 1976, 15 May
Oliver South #2 Salt Pond, Hayward	5 Aug 1989
Baumberg Salt Pond #11, Hayward	2 Jun 1989, 13 Jun 1989, 5 Aug 1989, 8 Aug 1989, 10 Jul 1997

[1] Information assembled from specimens contained within the California Academy of Sciences Insect Collection, the University of California Berkeley Essig Museum, the University of California Bohart Museum, the San Jose State University Edwards Museum, the San Mateo County Mosquito Abatement District Insect Collection, and the private collections of Dr. J. Gordon Edwards and Wesley A. Maffei.

Suitable Habitat

Tanarthrus occidentalis has been found in no other locality except for abandoned crystallizer ponds and salt pannes of southern San Francisco Bay. In all instances these sites remain dry for most of the year except during late winter when temporary pools of rainwater form. Habitat can be characterized as having extensive areas of salt crystals interspersed with open areas of fine silt and very little or no vegetative cover.

Biology

The biology of this beetle is not fully understood. Maffei (unpub.) has observed the Baumberg tract population and found that the adults commonly occur out on inactive, salt encrusted crystallizer ponds. These beetles were observed feeding on the carcasses of the brine flies *Ephydra cinerea* and *Lipochaeta slossonae* (family Ephydridae) which were still in the webs of unidentified Dictynid spiders. They appeared to function as "house cleaners" being able to move freely about the web site unmolested by the resident spider. Peak adult activity is May through September.

The immature stages of this beetle have not been located at this time. Larvae of other members of the beetle family Anthicidae feed on detritus and one species has been recorded as a predator.

Reproduction

Unknown.

Significance to Other Wetlands Taxa

This beetle has been identified as part of the immature Snowy Plover Diet (Page et al. 1995, Feeney and Maffei 1991). Its relationship to other taxa, other than Dictynid spiders, that utilize abandoned salt crystallizers is unknown at this time.

Conservation Needs and Limiting Factors

The conservation needs and limiting factors associated with this beetle are not very clear. Its association only with salt encrusted areas, other than the margins of salt ponds, that remain dry for most of the year appears to be the primary limiting factor.

References

Chandler, D.S. 1979. A new species of *tanarthrus* from California (Coleoptera: Anthicidae). Pan-Pacific Ent. 55(2):147-148.

Feeney, L.R. and W.A. Maffei. 1991. Snowy plovers and their habitat at the Baumberg Area and Oliver Salt Ponds, Hayward, California. Prepared for the City of Hayward. 162pp.

Maffei, W.A. 1989-1995. Unpublished field notes.

Page, G.W., J.S. Warriner, J.C. Warriner and P.W.C. Patton. 1995. Snowy plover (*Charadrius alexandrinus*). *In:* A. Poole and F. Gill (eds). The birds of North America, # 154 The Academy of Natural Sciences, Philadelphia, PA, and The American Ornithologists' Union, Washington, D.C.

Additional Readings

Arnett, R.H. 1968. The beetles of the united states (a manual for identification). Ann Arbor, Mich.: The American Entomological Institute, xii + 1112pp.

Chandler, D.S. 1975. A revision of *Tanarthrus* LeConte with a presentation of its mid-cenozoic speciation (Coleoptera: Anthicidae). Trans. Amer. Ent. Soc. 101:319-354.

Invertebrates

Inchworm Moth

Perizoma custodiata

Wesley A. Maffei

Description and Systematic Position

Perizoma custodiata is a small moth, with a wingspan of approximately 22-29mm, that belongs to the family Geometridae. This moth, commonly known as a measuring worm or inch worm moth, has an alternating pattern of vertical light and dark bands on the fore wings with plain, pale tan hind wings (**Figure 3.8**). The variation in width and intensity of the fore wing banding has caused different entomologists to describe this moth as a new taxon on four different occasions (Guenee 1857, Hulst 1896, Packard 1876). Wright (1923) noted the difficulty in separating examples of the "different species" of the Pacific Coast recognized at that time, stating that they intergrade so much that he found it difficult to tell one from another.

Larvae are a uniform light green or tan in color and attain a maximum size of approximately 30mm.

Distribution

Coastal areas from central northern California south along the coast of Baja California and including the Gulf of California. Found throughout San Francisco Bay tidal and diked salt marshes. **Figure 3.9** shows the locations around the Bay Area where *Perizoma custodiata* have been collected, and **Table 3.4** shows the collection dates.

Suitable Habitat

Upper middle to high marsh that has berms or levees with adequate populations of Alkali Heath (*Frankenia salina*).

Biology

Adults are on the wing from March through November, with peak adult populations occurring during late spring and early summer.

Larvae have been observed feeding on *Frankenia salina* (Maffei, unpub.) and Packard (1876) has noted that the larvae of other members of the genus *Perizoma* live on low growing plants with the pupa being subterranean. Caterpillars have been observed on Alkali Heath that was inundated by high tides of 6.3 or greater at the Whale's Tail Marsh, Hayward, California. The eggs and larvae have not been found during the winter months, and it is presumed that these moths over winter as pupae.

Reproduction

The number of generations per season and the number of eggs per female is apparently unknown for San Francisco Bay populations.

Significance to Other Wetlands Taxa

Snowy plovers have been observed consuming adult moths at the Baumberg Tract in Hayward, California (Feeney and Maffei 1991). This insect may also be a part of other shore bird and passerine bird diets.

The digger wasp, *Ammophila aberti*, has been observed provisioning its nests with the larvae of this moth (Maffei, unpub.).

Adult moths are pollinators of *Frankenia salina* and are probably pollinators for many of the other flowering plants within diked and tidal marshes.

Figure 3.9 Known *Perizoma custodiata* Localities Within San Francisco Bay Tidal and Diked Marshes

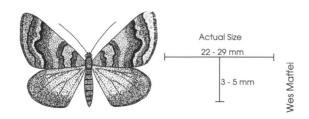

Figure 3.8 Inchworm Moth – *Perizoma custodiata*

Table 3.4 Known Collection Sites For *Perizoma custodiata*[1]

Location	Date Specimen(s) Collected	Location	Date Specimen(s) Collected
West Pittsburg	15 Feb 1957, 21 Mar 1957, 19 Sep 1957	South Marin Co. Shore	12 Apr 1950
Martinez	30 Aug 1962	San Francisco	1 Sep 1909, 25 Sep 1909, 9 Oct 1909, 15 Jun 1919, 5 Oct 1919, 21 Oct 1919, 9 Nov 1919, 30 Sep 1920, 4 Oct 1920, 22 Oct 1920, 24 Oct 1920, 11 Dec 1920, 30 Dec 1920, 4 Jan 1921, 6 Sep 1921, 17 Oct 1921, 26 Oct 1922, 14 Jul 1925, 15 Sep 1925
Richmond	18 Jun 1956, 12 Apr 1959		
Berkeley	11 Mar 1923, 3 Nov 1923		
Berkeley (Bayshore)	27 Jul 1916, 16 May 1955		
Alameda	12 May 1918, 13 May 1920		
Dumbarton Marsh	22 Jul 1968, 20 Sep 1968, 22 Nov 1968		
Shoreline Int. Ctr. (Hwyd)	2 Jul 1990	San Francisco (Dunes)	7 Apr 1961
Baumberg Tract (Hayward)	24 Feb 1990, 1 Apr 1990	Millbrae	10 Sep 1914
Napa	5 May (no year)	San Mateo	3 Oct 1920
Petaluma	13 May 1936, 15 May 1938 17 Apr 1939, 12 May 1940	Palo Alto	12 Jun 1933, 27 Jun 1933, 22 Jul 1933, 11 Aug 1933, 26 Apr 1954
Mill Valley (Slough)	17 Jun 1950	E. Palo Alto	May 1978
Mill Valley	23 Mar 1920, 5 Sep 1923, 26 Nov 1924, 3 Oct 1926	Bair Island	1 Mar 1987, 9 Mar 1997

[1] Information assembled from specimens contained within the California Academy of Sciences Insect Collection, University of California Berkeley Essig Museum, University of California Bohart Museum, San Jose State University Edwards Museum, San Mateo County Mosquito Abatement District Insect Collection, and private collections of Dr. J. Gordon Edwards and Wesley A. Maffei.

Conservation Needs and Limiting Factors

Frankenia salina has been identified as the larval host plant for this moth (Maffei, unpub.). Upper middle to high marsh areas with small dense patches of this plant support fairly high numbers of this organism. Its wide distribution along the Pacific Coast would seem to preclude this organism from any immediate danger of extirpation.

References

Feeney, L.R. and W.A. Maffei. 1991. Snowy plovers and their habitat at the Baumberg Area and Oliver Salt Ponds, Hayward, California. Prepared for the City of Hayward. 162pp.

Guenee, M.A. 1857. Histoire naturelle des insectes. species general des lepidopteres par M.M. Boisduval et Guenee. Tome 9. Uranides et Phalenites. Vol. 2, 584pp.

Hulst, G.D. 1896. Classification of the Geometrina of North America. Trans. Amer. Ent. Soc.23:245-386.

Maffei, W.A. 1989-1996. Unpublished field notes.

Packard, A.S. 1876. A Monograph of the geometrid moths or phalaenidae of the United States. Report of the U.S. Geological Survey of the Territories. 10:1-607.

Wright, W.S. 1923. Expedition of the California Academy of Sciences to the Gulf of California in 1921. Proc. Calif. Acad. Sci. 4th Series. 12(9):113-115.

Additional Readings

Hodges, R.W. (ed). 1983. Check list of the Lepidoptera of America North of Mexico. E.W. Classey Ltd, Oxfordshire, England. 284pp.

Holland, W.J. 1903. The moth book. Doubleday, Page and Co., New York. 479pp.

Pygmy Blue Butterfly

Brephidium exilis Boisduval

Wesley A. Maffei

Description and Systematic Position

Brephidium exilis, also known as the Pygmy Blue, is a small butterfly, with a wingspan measuring approximately 13-20mm (**Figure 3.10**). Adult butterflies have the dorsal surface of the wings brown with the basal third to half light blue. The ventral surface of the wings are grayish white with pale brown bands and a row of iridescent black and silver spots along the outer edge of the hind wing. The eggs are flattened, light bluish-green in color, and have a fine raised white mesh on the surface. Larvae are pale green or cream colored and have a finely punctate surface with white tipped tubercles, a yellowish white dorsal line, and a bright yellow substigmatal line (**Figure 3.11**). Some specimens may lack the lateral substigmatal line but all mature larvae have a frosted appearance which resembles the ventral surface of salt bush leaves or the flower heads of pigweed. The pupae can be quite variable in color but are usually light brownish yellow, have a dark brown dorsal line, and have the wing pads pale yellowish green in color sprinkled with brownish dots.

Three subspecies of this butterfly have been recognized with *Brephidium exilis* noted as the western subspecies (Scott 1986).

Distribution

Brephidium exilis is found from southwestern Louisiana and Arkansas westward to California and south to Venezuela (Howe 1975, Scott 1986). Strays have been noted as far north as Kansas and Idaho. This butterfly is widely distributed throughout the San Francisco Bay, being particularly abundant in salt marshes (Tilden 1965). **Figure 3.12** shows the locations around the Bay Area where *B. exilis* have been collected, and **Table 3.5** shows the collection dates.

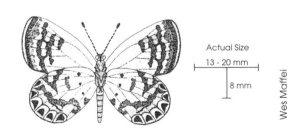

Figure 3.10 Adult Pygmy Blue Butterfly – *Brephidium exilis*.

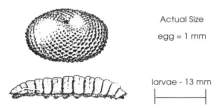

Figure 3.11 *Brephidium exilis* Egg and larva (from Comstock 1927)

Suitable Habitat

Prefers lowland areas such as alkali flats, salt marshes, vacant lots, roadsides and desert prairie with various Chenopodiaceae and Aizoaceae.

Biology

The adult flight period for San Francisco Bay populations is late February through October, with peak abundance occurring in September (Comstock 1927, Garth and Tilden 1986, Tilden 1965).

Larvae feed on most parts of the host plant. Recorded larval hosts are: *Atriplex canescens, A. coulteri, A. serena, A. leucophylla, A. patula hastata, A. semibaccata, A. rosea, A. cordulata, A. hymenelytra, A. coronata, A. lentiformis breweri, Suaeda fruticosa, S. californica, S. torreyana, Salicornia virginica, Chenopodium album, C.*

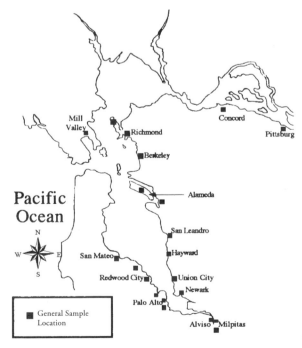

Figure 3.12 Known *Brephidium exilis* Localities Within San Francisco Bay Tidal and Diked Marshes

Table 3.5 Known Collection Sites For *Brephidium exilis*[1]

Location	Date Specimen(s) Collected	Location	Date Specimen(s) Collected
West Pittsburg	15 Apr 1957	Oakland	8 Apr 1938
Avon	27 Aug 1972	San Leandro	14 Aug 1935
Richmond Point	3 Oct 1964	Milpitas	29 Nov 1974
Richmond	10 Aug 1953	Alviso	1 Nov 1985, 11 Jun 1986
Berkeley (Shoreline)	8 Jun 1915, 22 Jun 1989, 18 Oct 1995	Palo Alto	4 Oct 1908, 8 Jun 1909, 1 Oct 1935, Aug 1937, 10 Jul 1967
West Berkeley	20 Jun 1987, 31 Oct 1987, 23 Nov 1987, 25 Jun 1988, 23 Jun 1990	East Palo Alto	14 Jun 1952
		Menlo Park	20 Sep 1958, 9 Oct 1958
Alameda 1918	12 May 1918, 17 May	Redwood City	28 Jul 1963
		San Mateo	4 Oct 1955, 10 Oct 1955
		San Carlos Airport	11 Aug 1977
Larkspur	20 Sep 1958		

[1] Information assembled from specimens contained within the California Academy of Sciences Insect Collection, University of California Berkeley Essig Museum, the University of California Bohart Museum, San Jose State University Edwards Museum, San Mateo County Mosquito Abatement District Insect Collection, and private collections of Dr. J. Gordon Edwards and Wesley A. Maffei.

leptophyllum, Salsola iberica, S. kali tenuifolia, Halogeton glomeratus, Trianthema portulacastrum, and *Sesuvium verrucosum* (Comstock 1927, Garth and Tilden 1986, Howe 1975, Scott 1986, Tilden 1965).

Nagano and coworkers (1981) found this butterfly to be an indicator of saline soils.

Reproduction

This butterfly has many generations within one season, with one generation often overlapping the next (Howe 1975). Scott (1986) states that males patrol all day over the host plants in search of females. Eggs are laid singly and can be found anywhere on the host plant, but are usually on the upper surfaces of leaves. The number of eggs produced per female is unknown.

Significance to Other Wetlands Taxa

Most likely a prey item for birds utilizing the marshes of the estuary. Larvae may also be a food item for insectivorous vertebrates. South bay populations of this butterfly are parasitized by the small black tachinid fly *Aplomya theclarum* (Maffei, unpub.).

Conservation Needs and Limiting Factors

None.

References

Comstock, J.A. 1927. Butterflies of California. Los Angeles. Privately Published. 334pp.

Garth, J.S. and J.W. Tilden. 1986. California butterflies. University of California Press, Berkeley. 246pp.

Howe, W.H. 1975. The butterflies of North America. Doubleday and Co., New York. 633pp.

Maffei, W.A. 1995. Unpublished field notes.

Nagano, C.D., C.L. Hogue, R.R. Snelling and J.P. Donahue. 1981. The insects and related terrestrial arthropods of the Ballona Creek Region. *In:* The Biota of the Ballona Region, Los Angeles County, California. Report to the Los Angeles County Dept. of Regional Planning. pp. E1-E89.

Scott, J.A. 1986. The butterflies of North America. Stanford University Press, Stanford. 583pp.

Tilden, J.W. 1965. Butterflies of the San Francisco Bay Region. University of California Press, Berkeley. 88pp.

Additional Readings

Hodges, R.W. (ed). 1983. Checklist of the Lepidoptera of America North of Mexico. E.W. Classey Ltd.Oxfordshire, England. 284 pp.

Summer Salt Marsh Mosquito

Aedes dorsalis (Meigen)

Wesley A. Maffei

Description and Systematic Position

The summer salt marsh mosquito, *Aedes dorsalis*, is a medium sized mosquito measuring approximately 5-6 mm in length. Freshly emerged adults are one of the most brightly colored marsh mosquitoes found within the San Francisco Estuary. These insects are brilliant gold in color, have a dorsal white band running the length of the abdomen and have broad white bands on the tarsal segments of the legs. Older specimens may be yellow or yellowish-brown in color and the markings on the abdomen may be incomplete if the scales have been rubbed off. The immature stages can be identified by insertion of the siphon tuft at or beyond the middle of the siphon tube, a broadly incomplete anal saddle, presence of a weak saddle hair and moderate to short anal papillae. The presence of single upper and lower head hairs has been used as an additional diagnostic feature but this can be inconsistent, especially in later instar larvae.

The similarity of this mosquito to *Aedes melanimon* Dyar has resulted in some confusion with early efforts to identify both adults and larvae. Detailed studies of different populations of both of these mosquitoes have helped to clarify and verify the systematic position of both of these insects (Bohart 1956, Chapman and Grodhaus 1963).

Distribution

This mosquito can be found throughout most of the United States, southern Canada, Europe and Asia (Carpenter and LaCasse 1955, Darsie and Ward 1981). Within California, this mosquito can be found in coastal salt marshes and the brackish waters of the Sacramento and San Joaquin Delta (Bohart 1956, Bohart and Washino 1978).

Suitable Habitat

Larvae are found in a variety of brackish and freshwater habitats throughout their world range (Carpenter and LaCasse 1955). Within San Francisco Bay *A. dorsalis* are usually encountered in temporarily flooded tidal marsh pannes, heavily vegetated ditches and brackish seasonal wetlands. Adults prefer open habitats such as grasslands, open salt marsh and the edges of woodlands.

Biology

Adults are aggressive day biting mosquitoes that have been found capable of traveling distances of more than 30 miles (Rees and Nielsen 1947). Flights of adults in Alameda County have been known to disperse distances of more than five miles from their larval source (Maffei, unpub.). Garcia and Voigt (1994) studied the flight potential of this mosquito in the lab and found that the adults exhibited strong flight characteristics which they believed helped them to adapt to the strong winds encountered in their preferred open habitats. Females are readily attracted to green, grassy fields and will rest there waiting for available hosts (Maffei, unpub.).

Host studies have shown that large mammals are preferred, especially cattle and horses (Edman and Downes 1964, Gunstream et al. 1971, Shemanchuk et al. 1963, Tempelis et al. 1967). The effects of adult feeding activity on livestock can be severe resulting in reduced feeding and in some instances injury to animals attempting to evade severe attacks. Recent adult activity within the San Francisco Estuary has impacted outdoor school activities, businesses and residents, resulting in at least two instances where medical attention was required for people reacting to multiple bites (Maffei, unpub.).

Eggs are deposited individually on the mud along the edges of tidal pools or the receding water line of brackish seasonal wetlands. Winter is passed in the egg stage and hatching occurs with the first warm weather of spring. Additional hatches occur with subsequent refloodings of the larval habitat. Eggs can remain viable for many years with only part of any given brood hatching during any single flooding event.

The larval stage can last from four to fourteen days with duration being primarily dependent on temperature. Other factors that can regulate rate of larval development include competition for space and quality and availability of nutrients. Rees and Nielsen (1947) found larvae that completed their development in saline pools of the Great Salt Lake with salt concentrations as high as 120 ‰. Washino and Jensen (1990) reared larvae, from Contra Costa County salt marshes, in solutions simulating 0, 10, 50 and 100% concentrations of seawater and found that survivorship improved as salt content approached that of seawater.

Total developmental time, from egg to adult, has been observed to occur in less than one week (Maffei, unpub.).

Reproduction

Male mating swarms have been observed occurring over low growing bushes, prominent objects and open fields (Dyar 1917, Garcia et al. 1992). Both observations noted that swarming activity began at sunset and that the swarms were not more than two to three meters above the ground. Swarming and mating usually occurs on the marsh within a few days of adult emergence and is followed by random dispersal of host seeking adults.

The number of gonotrophic cycles and eggs produced per female remains unclear for San Francisco Bay populations. Early work by Telford (1958) found that 12 broods and approximately eight generations occurred during one breeding season at Bolinas in Marin County. The number of generations per year does vary with respect to weather and tidal conditions.

Significance to Other Wetlands Taxa

This species of mosquito is commonly found in association with the tidal pool brine fly *Ephydra millbrae* and the water boatman *Trichocorixa reticulata*. Both the brine fly and the water boatman have been identified as food sources for shorebirds and waterfowl (Anderson 1970; Feeney and Maffei 1991; Howard 1983; Maffei, unpub.; Martin and Uhler 1939). The larvae of this mosquito may also be a food source for these birds and adults may be a food source for swallows.

Conservation Needs and Limiting Factors

This mosquito, like other species of mosquitoes, is extremely opportunistic. Care must be taken when altering or restoring seasonal or tidal wetlands. Sites that drain poorly will create habitat that can readily produce very large numbers of aggressive biting adults. Plans for long term maintenance of seasonal and tidal wetlands should include resources for mosquito control as the need arises. The dynamic nature of these types of habitats coupled with human activities can easily convert a non-breeding site into a major mosquito producing source.

References

Anderson, W. 1970. A preliminary study of the relationship of salt ponds and wildlife—South San Francisco Bay. Calif. Dept. Fish and Game 56(4):240-252.

Bohart, R.M. 1948. Differentiation of larvae and pupae of *Aedes dorsalis* and *Aedes squamiger*. Proc. Ent. Soc. Wash. 50:216-218.

_____. 1956. Identification and distribution of *Aedes melanimon* and *Aedes dorsalis* in California. Proc. C.M.C.A. 24:81-83.

Bohart, R.M. and R.K. Washino. 1978. Mosquitoes of California. Third Ed. Univ. Calif. Div. Agr. Sci., Berkeley, Publ. 4084. 153 pp.

Carpenter, S.J. and W.J. LaCasse. 1955. Mosquitoes of North America. Univ. Calif. Press, Berkeley. 360 pp.

Chapman, H.C. and G. Grodhaus. 1963. The separation of adult females of *Aedes dorsalis* (Meigen) and *Ae. melanimon* Dyar in California. Calif. Vector Views 10(8):53-56.

Darsie, R.F. and R.A. Ward. 1981. Identification and geographical distribution of the mosquitoes of North America, North of Mexico. Mosq. Syst. Suppl. 1:1-313.

Dyar, H.G. 1917. Notes on the *Aedes* of Montana (Diptera: Culicidae). Ins. Ins. Mens. 5:104-121.

Edman, J.D. and A.E.R. Downe. 1964. Host blood sources and multiple-feeding habits of mosquitoes in Kansas. Mosq. News 24:154-160.

Feeney, L.R. and W.A. Maffei. 1991. Snowy plovers and their habitat at the Baumberg Area and Oliver Salt Ponds, Hayward, California. Prepared for the City of Hayward. 162pp.

Garcia, R. and W.G. Voigt. 1994. Flight potential of three salt marsh mosquitoes from San Francisco Bay. Ann. Rep. Mosq. Cont. Res., Univ. Calif. pp. 46-48.

Gunstream, S.E., R.M. Chew, D.W. Hagstrum and C.H. Tempelis. 1971. Feeding patterns of six species of mosquitoes in arid Southeastern California. Mosq. News 31:99-101.

Howard, J.A. 1983. Feeding ecology of the ruddy duck on the San Francisco Bay National Wildlife Refuge. M.A. Thesis, San Jose State University. 53 pp.

Maffei, W.A. 1990-1997. Unpublished field notes.

Martin, A.C. and F.M. Uhler. 1939. Food of game ducks in the United States and Canada. USDA. Tech. Bull. #634. 156pp.

Rees, D.M. and L.T. Nielsen. 1947. On the biology and control of *Aedes dorsalis* (Meigen) in Utah. Proc. N.J. Mosq. Exterm. Assoc. 34:160-165.

Shemanchuk, J.A., A.E.R. Downe and L. Burgess. 1963. Hosts of mosquitoes (Diptera: Culicidae) from the irrigated pastures of Alberta. Mosq. News. 23(4):336-341.

Telford, A.D. 1958. The pasture *Aedes* of Central and Northern California. Seasonal History. Ann. Ent. Soc. Amer. 51:360-365.

Tempelis, C.H., D.B. Francy, R.O. Hayes and M.F. Lofy. 1967. Variations in feeding patterns of seven culicine mosquitoes on vertebrate hosts in Weld and Larimer Counties, Colorado. Amer. J. Trop. Med. Hyg. 7:561-573.

Washino, R.K. and T. Jensen. 1990. Biology, ecology and systematics of *Aedes dorsalis*, *Ae. melanimon*, and *Ae. campestris* in Western North America. Ann. Rep. Mosq. Cont. Res., Univ. Calif. pp 40-41.

Invertebrates

Winter Salt Marsh Mosquito

Aedes squamiger (Coquillett)

Wesley A. Maffei

Description and Systematic Position

Aedes squamiger is a medium-sized to large mosquito, measuring approximately 6-9mm in length, that belongs to the fly family Culicidae (**Figure 3.13**). Adults have a distinctive black and white speckled appearance and large, flat scales along the wing veins which separates this fly from other San Francisco Bay mosquitoes. Larvae can be identified by the presence of an incomplete anal saddle, a siphon tuft distal to the pecten row, an anal saddle hair as long or longer than the anal saddle, and upper and lower head hairs that are usually branched (**Figure 3.14**).

This mosquito was described as a new taxon by Coquillett in 1902 from specimens collected from the cities of Palo Alto and San Lorenzo, California. Bohart (1948) differentiated the larvae and pupae of *Aedes dorsalis* and *Aedes squamiger* thereby providing a means of separating the immature stages of these two species which are very similar in appearance. In 1954, Bohart described and provided keys to the first stage larvae of California *Aedes* and further clarified the differences between these two mosquitoes.

Distribution

This mosquito is found along the Pacific Coast region from Marin and Sonoma counties, California, south to Baja California, Mexico (Bohart and Washino 1978, Carpenter and LaCasse 1955, Darsie and Ward 1981, Freeborn and Bohart 1951). **Figure 3.15** shows the distribution of *Aedes squamiger* in 1950. The current distribution within the San Francisco Bay area is very similar, with additional sites having been identified along the shoreline of the East Bay.

Suitable Habitat

Preferred habitat consists primarily of coastal pickle weed tidal and diked marshes, especially salt marsh pools that are diluted by winter and early spring rains. Cracked ground of diked wetlands and old dredge disposal sites are also a favorite habitat for deposition of eggs and development of larvae. This mosquito prefers brackish or saline habitats and has not been found in truly fresh water marshes. Bohart, et. al. (1953) found larvae of various stages in pools with salinities ranging from 1.2 ‰ to 35 ‰. Studies by Garcia and coworkers (1992, 1991) indicated that optimal larval development occurred at salinities between 5 ‰ and 15 ‰.

Biology

Eggs hatch as early as late September and can continue to hatch with the accumulation of rainfall from each successive storm event. Maffei (unpub.) found larvae that hatched from the incidental flooding of a marsh by a duck club as early as late September. Bohart, et. al. (1953) states that three to six major hatches of eggs occur during the fall months. It is believed that only part of the eggs laid during the prior spring season hatch with a decreasing percentage of the remaining eggs hatching during successive years. Garcia, et al. (1991) found that as many as four floodings were necessary to hatch all of the eggs from field collected samples. Bohart and Washino (1978) state that the eggs are usually dormant from April through September and that this obligatory diapause is terminated by the decreasing fall temperatures that fall below 7°C. Garcia et al. (1991) found that hatching does not occur until the eggs have been exposed to temperatures that are less than 10°C. Voigt (pers comm.) believes that once the eggs have been thermally

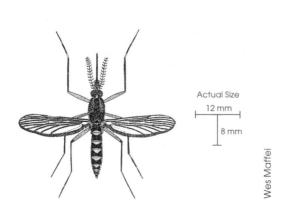

Figure 3.13 Adult Winter Salt Marsh Mosquito – *Aedes squamiger*

Actual Size

12 mm

8 mm

Wes Maffei

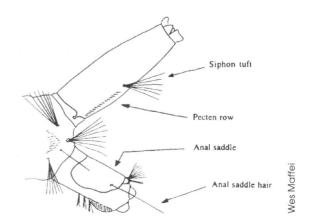

Figure 3.14 Terminal Abdominal Segment of a Fourth Instar Larva

Siphon tuft

Pecten row

Anal saddle

Anal saddle hair

Wes Maffei

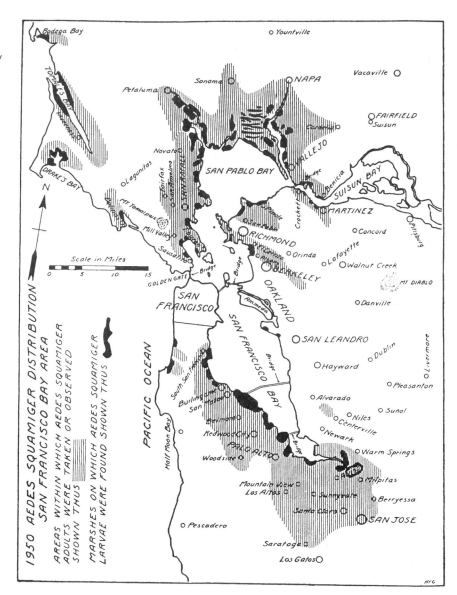

Figure 3.15 *Aedes Squamiger* Distribution in the San Francisco Bay Area, 1950

From Aarons, 1954

conditioned that hatching can then occur anytime in the future following submersion. This may possibly help to explain summer hatches following flooding of sites by inadvertant human activity (Maffei, unpub.).

Larvae are principally found in salt marsh pools that are diluted by fall and winter rainfall. Bohart and coworkers (1953) found that a minimum of 48 days were required for the development of the aquatic stages before adult emergence, with the first pupae having been found during the first week of February. Under "normal" conditions pupae are usually found from the last two weeks of February through the beginning of March. Estimates of the number of larvae per acre vary from 1.65 million to 1.45 billion depending on environmental factors (Aarons 1954, Aarons et al 1951, Lowe 1932). Larvae are capable of remaining submerged for extended periods of time where they browse on vegetation and mud. Garcia, et al (1990) calculated the minimum developmental threshold for development of larvae to the adult

stage to be 4.4°C. Additional studies by Garcia and coworkers (1991) found that first and second instar larvae had developmental thresholds that were 2-4°C lower than the later instars. From these data , they concluded that the lower developmental thresholds of the earlier instars allowed larvae from later hatching installments to emerge as adults in closer synchrony with those larvae that hatched earlier in the season. They also noted that larvae and pupae could survive in the mud at sites that underwent periodic draw-down of the water. Garcia, et al. (1990) also studied the diapause habit of the last instar larvae and concluded that this interesting trait probably contributed in some degree to the partial synchronous emergence of the adults.

Adults usually emerge during the last week of February through the end of March. Emergence of adults in April has occurred from unusually heavy late winter and early spring rains that have caused late egg hatches with rapid larval development. Adults usually fly to areas away from their breeding sites, using ravines and natural or man made waterways from the marshes to the local hills as passageways. From these passageways the adults spread laterally into the wind protected areas of the surrounding community (Freeborn 1926). It is believed that at these protected sites adults mate and and seek blood meals (Telford 1958). Gray (1936) noted that this mosquito flew the longest distance of any California mosquito from its larval source. Aarons (1954) noted that adults were found in Saratoga, some 10 miles from the nearest known larval source. Other workers have found that adults of this mosquito are capable of traversing distances of more than 15 miles from any possible larval site (Aarons, et. al. 1951, Krimgold and Herms 1934, Lowe 1932, Stover 1931, Stover 1926). Biting activity begins in April and usually ends by early June. Rabbit baited traps in the east bay have collected adults from 16 March to 28 June (Garcia et al. 1983). Adults are known to be aggressive day and early dusk biting mosquitoes. This species along with the Summer Salt Marsh Mosquito, *Aedes dorsalis*, were the first mosquitoes to become the primary focus of organized mosquito control efforts in California. The first mosquito control campaigns were undertaken at San Rafael in 1903 and also at Burlingame in 1904. The earliest written record of what is believed to be the attacks of *Aedes squamiger* and *Aedes dorsalis* on humans was in a diary entry of Father Juan Crespi in April of 1772 (Bolton 1927). In his diary he describes the vicious attacks of mosquitoes that sorely afflicted his party while traveling along the eastern side of San Francisco Bay. Aarons, et al. (1951) states that there is reason to believe that the salt marsh mosquitoes made certain times of the year almost unbearable for the early Indians.

Females oviposit in those parts of the marshes that are not under water. Eggs are laid on plants and along the muddy margins of ponds close to the water line. Most of the eggs are located in these higher areas of the marshes and will therefore not hatch without a combination of tides and rainfall. For diked marshes, at least a few inches of rainfall must occur to inundate the eggs and stimulate hatching. Maffei (unpub.) has found that the runoff of as little as one inch of rainfall from city streets into marshes used as flood control basins can flood a marsh sufficiently to hatch eggs and produce larvae. Females that oviposit in late spring will deposit eggs in the lower portions of the marshes and it is these eggs that hatch first with tidal activity only or ponding of early rain water runoff.

Reproduction

Observations on mating swarms have shown that *Aedes squamiger* tends to swarm approximately one hour before to one-half hour after sunset (Garcia et. al. 1992). Swarms can consist of a few to several thousand indi-

viduals that hover over prominent objects such as trees or large bushes and can occur at heights ranging from six to approximately 50 feet (Bohart and Washino 1978, Garcia et. al. 1992). Garcia et al. (1992, 1983) found that adults traveled back and forth to the marshes quite readily producing a new batch of eggs with each trip. He also found that the highest parous condition observed was seven, with average parity rates ranging between 3 and 5.4. Garcia, et al. (1992) found a direct correlation between wing length and the number of eggs produced with larger females producing more eggs. The maximum number of eggs produced per female was less than 250. Garcia, et al. (1990) also found that temperature played an important role in longevity, ovarian development and oviposition. Females held at 15°C were still alive 50 days after their last blood meal and average longevity was about 35 days when kept at 20°C. The minimum temperature threshold for ovarian development or oviposition was found to be about 15°C.

Significance to Other Wetlands Taxa

Aedes squamiger larvae are frequently found in association with larvae of the Summer Salt Marsh Mosquito, *Aedes dorsalis*, and the Winter Marsh Mosquito, *Culiseta inornata*. The adults of these mosquitoes may be a possible food source for swallows and the larvae may be a food source for waterfowl.

Conservation Needs and Limiting Factors

This mosquito, like other species of mosquitoes, is extremely opportunistic. Care must be taken when altering or restoring seasonal or tidal wetlands. Sites that drain poorly will create habitat that can readily produce very large numbers of aggressive biting adults. Plans for long term maintenance of seasonal and tidal wetlands should include resources for mosquito control as the need arises. The dynamic nature of these types of habitats coupled with human activities can easily convert a non-breeding site into a major mosquito producing source.

References

Aarons, T. 1954. Salt marsh mosquito survey in the San Francisco Bay Area 1950-1953. Proc. C.M.C.A. 22:75-78.

Aarons, T., J.R. Walker, H.F. Gray and E.G. Mezger. 1951. Studies of the flight range of *Aedes Squamiger*. Proc. C.M.C.A. 19:65-69.

Bohart, R.M. 1948. Differentiation of larvae and pupae of *Aedes dorsalis* and *Aedes squamiger*. Proc. Ent. Soc. Wash. 50:216-218.

_____. 1954. Identification of first stage larvae of California *Aedes* (Diptera: Culicidae). Ann. Ent. Soc. Amer. 47:356-366.

Bohart, R.M. and R.K. Washino. 1978. Mosquitoes of California. Third Edition. Univ. Calif. Div. Agr. Sci., Berkeley, Publ. 4084. 153pp.

Bohart, R.M., E.C. Mezger and A.D. Telford. 1953. Observations on the seasonal history of *Aedes squamiger*. Proc. C.M.C.A. 21:7-9.

Bolton, H.E. 1927. Journal of Father Juan Crespi. Univ. Calif. Press, Berkeley.

Carpenter, S.J. and W.J. LaCasse. 1955. Mosquitoes of North America. Univ. Calif. Press, Berkeley. 360pp.

Coquillett, D.W. 1902. New Diptera from North America. Proc. U.S.N.M. 25:83-126.

Darsie, R.F. and R.A. Ward. 1981. Identification and geographical distribution of the mosquitoes of North America, North of Mexico. Mosq. Syst. Suppl. 1:1-313.

Freeborn, S.B. 1926. The mosquitoes of California. Univ. Calif. Publ. Ent. 3:333-460.

Freeborn, S.B. and R.M. Bohart. 1951. The mosquitoes of California. Bull. Calif. Insect Survey. 1:25-78.

Garcia, R., B. Des Rochers and W. Tozer. 1983. Biology and ecology of *Aedes squamiger* in the San Francisco Bay Area. Ann. Rep. Mosq. Cont. Res., Univ. Calif. pp. 29-31.

Garcia, R., W.G. Voigt and A.K. Nomura. 1992. Ecology of *Aedes Squamiger* in the Northern San Francisco Bay Area. Ann. Rep. Mosq. Contr. Res., Univ. Calif. pp. 53-57.

Garcia, R., W.G. Voigt, A.K. Nomura and A. Hayes. 1991. Biology of *Aedes squamiger*. Ann. Rep. Mosq. Cont. Res., Univ. Calif. pp 51-52.

_____. 1992. Biology of *Aedes squamiger*. Unpub. Progress Report for Alameda County Mosquito Abatement District. 7 pp.

Gray, H.F. 1936. Control of pest mosquitoes for comfort. Civil Eng. 6(10):685-688.

Krimgold, D.B. and H.P. Herms. 1934. Report on salt marsh breeding and migration of the San Francisco Bay Area in March 1934. Unpublished Report.

Lowe, H.J. 1932. Studies of *Aedes Squamiger* in the San Francisco Bay Region. Proc. C.M.C.A., Paper No. 1.

Maffei, W.A. 1990-1996. Unpublished field notes.

Stover, S.E. 1926. Eradication of salt marsh mosquitoes. Weekly Bull., Calif. State Board of Health. Vol. V(44).

_____. 1931. Conference notes and discussion on flight habits of salt marsh mosquitoes. Proceedings of the California Mosquito Control Association. 2:11 & 14.

Telford, A.D. 1958. The pasture *Aedes* of Central and Northern California. Seasonal History. Ann. Ent. Soc. Amer. 51:360-365.

Additional Readings

Meyer, R.P. and S.L. Durso. 1993. Identification of the mosquitoes of California. Calif. Mosquito and Vector Control Assoc., Sacramento. 80pp.

Quayle, H.J. 1906. Mosquito control work in California. Univ. Calif. Agric. Exp. Sta. Bull. #178, pp 1-55.

Washino's Mosquito

Aedes washinoi Lansaro and Eldridge

Wesley A. Maffei

Description and Systematic Position

Aedes washinoi was described as a new taxon by Lanzaro and Eldridge in 1992 and was determined to be a sibling species of *Aedes clivis* and *Aedes increpitus*. Prior to 1992, all three species of mosquitoes were known as *Aedes increpitus*. Adults of this mosquito are almost impossible to separate from its sibling species, when using morphological features, and can also sometimes be confused with *Aedes squamiger*. The easiest way to distinguish *Ae. squamiger* and *Ae. washinoi* is to examine the wing scales. *Aedes squamiger* has very broad, flat, platelike scales on the wings whereas *Ae. washinoi* will have the usual thin, pointed wing scales. The wings of *Ae. washinoi* will also tend to be uniformly dark with a concentration of pale scales on the anterior wing veins. In all other respects, both *Ae. squamiger* and *Ae. washinoi* share a similar black and white speckled appearance. The larvae of this mosquito can be difficult to separate but Darsie (1995) has provided additions to Darsie and Wards 1981 keys to facilitate identification.

Distribution

This mosquito is found from Portland, Oregon south to Santa Barbara, California and eastward into the lower Sierra Nevada mountains. Populations of this mosquito have also been found along the eastern Sierra Nevada Range at Honey Lake.

Suitable Habitat

Within the San Francisco Estuary the preferred habitat is shallow ground pools and upland fresh to slightly brackish water sites that are next to salt marshes or in riparian corridors. These habitats also tend to be dominated by willow or cotton wood trees and/or black berry vines.

Biology

Larvae usually hatch during early winter after a series of successive storm events has filled ground depressions with water. Additional hatches of larvae can occur if late winter and early spring rains refill drying larval sites. Larvae of this mosquito also exhibit a late fourth instar diapause and partial synchronous adult emergence similar to that observed in *Aedes squamiger*. Adults emerge during late winter and early spring and can persist through early June, depending on weather conditions.

Females are aggressive day biting mosquitoes that tend not to travel far from their larval sources. Maffei (unpub.) found that adult mosquitoes traveled a maximum distance of one and one-half miles from their larval habitat and that local, man made canals were used as a passageway into the surrounding community.

Eggs are deposited in the muddy margins adjacent to the receding water line of the larval habitat and hatch the following winter when reflooded.

Reproduction

Adults have been observed swarming under or near the tree canopy of their larval habitat (Garcia, et al. 1992).

Significance to Other Wetlands Taxa

Unknown.

Conservation Needs and Limiting Factors

This mosquito, like other species of mosquitoes, is extremely opportunistic. Care must be taken when altering or restoring seasonal wetlands or riparian corridors. Sites that have shallow ground pools and willow or cotton wood trees or blackberry vines will create habitat that can readily produce very large numbers of aggressive biting adults. The restoration of historical willow groves should not occur if homes are within two miles of the project site.

References

Darsie, R.F. 1995. Identification of *Aedes tahoensis, Aedes clivis* and *Aedes washinoi* using the Darsie/Ward keys (Diptera: Culicidae). Mosq. Syst. 27(1):40-42.

Darsie, R.F. and R.A. Ward. 1981. Identification and geographical distribution of the mosquitoes of North America, north of Mexico. Mosq. Syst. Suppl. 1:1-313.

Garcia, R., W.G. Voigt and A.K. Nomura. 1992. Ecology of *Aedes squamiger* in the northern San Francisco Bay Area. Ann. Rep. Mosq. Contr. Res., Univ. Calif. pp. 53-57.

Lanzarro, G.C. and B.F. Eldridge. 1992. A classical and population genetic description of two new sibling species of *Aedes (Ochlerotatus) increpitus* Dyar. Mosq. Syst. 24(2):85-101.

Maffei, W.A. 1990-1995. Unpublished field notes.

Additional Readings

Bohart, R.M. and R.K. Washino. 1978. Mosquitoes of California. Third Edition. Univ. Calif. Div. Agr. Sci., Berkeley, Publ. 4084. 153 pp.

Freeborn, S.B. and R.M. Bohart. 1951. The mosquitoes of California. Bull. Calif. Insect Survey. 1:25-78.

Meyer, R.P. and S.L. Durso. 1993. Identification of the mosquitoes of California. Calif. Mosquito and Vector Control Assoc., Sacramento. 80 pp.

Western Encephalitis Mosquito

Culex tarsalis Coquillett

Wesley A. Maffei

Description and Systematic Position

The western encephalitis mosquito is a medium sized mosquito measuring approximately 5-6 mm in length. This fly was described in 1896 as a new taxon by Coquillett from specimens gathered in the Argus Mountains of Inyo County, California (Belkin et al. 1966).

Adults can be identified by using the following morphological features: legs with bands of pale scales overlapping the tarsal joints; femur and tibia of the hind legs with a pale stripe or row of pale spots on the outer surface; proboscis with a complete median pale band; ventral abdominal segments with v-shaped patches of darkened scales; and the inner surface of the basal antennal segment with patches of pale scales. The larvae can be recognized by the four to five pairs of ventrally located siphon tufts that are nearly in line with each other (**Figure 3.16**) and the 3-branched lateral abdominal hairs found on segments III to VI.

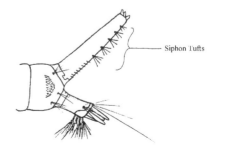

Figure 3.16 Terminal Abdominal Segment of *C. tarsalis larva*

Distribution

This mosquito has been found in central, western and southwestern United States, southwestern Canada and northwestern Mexico (Carpenter and LaCasse 1955, Darsie and Ward 1981). Within California, this fly has been found in every county from elevations below sea level to almost 10,000 feet (Bohart and Washino 1978, Meyer and Durso 1993).

Suitable Habitat

The immature stages are found in all types of fresh water habitats except treeholes. Poorly drained pastures, rice fields, seepages, marshes and duck club ponds are especially favored as breeding habitat for this mosquito. Telford (1958) found larvae in salt marsh pools with salinities up to 10 ‰. Urban sources include poorly maintained swimming pools, ornamental ponds, storm drains, flood control canals, ditches, waste water ponds and most man made containers (Beadle and Harmston 1958, Bohart and Washino 1978, Harmston et al. 1956, Meyer and Durso 1993, Sjogren 1968).

Adults rest by day in shaded or darkened areas such as mammal burrows, tree holes, hollow logs, under bridges, in caves, in eves and entry ways of residences, brush piles and in dense vegetation (Mortenson 1953, Loomis and Green 1955, Harwood and Halfill 1960, Price et al. 1960, Rykman and Arakawa 1952).

Biology

Adult females of this species usually feed at night. Precipitin tests indicate a wide variety of hosts consisting of various birds and mammals with an occasional reptile or amphibian (Anderson et al. 1967, Edman and Downe 1964, Gunstream et al. 1971, Hayes et al. 1973, Reeves and Hammon 1944, Rush and Tempelis 1967, Shemanchuk et al. 1963, Tempelis 1975, Tempelis et al. 1967, Tempelis et al. 1965, Tempelis and Washino 1967). Reeves (1971) states that host availability and season are probably the most important considerations in the adult host feeding pattern. The availability of nesting birds during spring and early summer may account for the preponderance of identified, early season, avian blood meals. With the progression of the summer season, availability and behaviour of bird hosts varies and a switch to mammal hosts occurs (Hammon et al. 1945, Hayes et al. 1973, Reeves and Hammon 1944, Reeves et al. 1963, Tempelis et al. 1967, Tempelis and Washino 1967). Adults pass the winter months in facultative diapause which is triggered by short day length and low ambient temperatures. In the warmer parts of southern California adults are active year round while in San Francisco Bay populations inactivity usually occurs from December through February. Additional periods of low temperatures or unseasonably warm winters can vary the time spent in diapause.

Flight range studies indicate that this mosquito will readily disperse from its larval source. Reeves et al. (1948) found that adults generally dispersed two miles or less, although prevailing winds helped to distribute marked females up to three miles. Bailey et al. (1965) studied the dispersal patterns of Yolo County, California populations and found that prevailing winds were important to adult dispersal with significant numbers of adults having traveled seven miles within two nights. The maximum distance traveled was recorded at 15.75 miles. From their studies they concluded that the likely dispersal distance of Sacramento Valley populations was probably about 20-25 miles. It was further concluded that most locally controlled mosquito sources are repeatedly reinfested during the summer because these mosquitoes travel so readily with the wind.

The larval stages feed on a wide variety of microorganisms, unicellular algae and microscopic particulate matter. The amount of time required to complete development from egg to adult varies depending on water temperature, availability of food and crowding. Bailey and Gieke (1968) found that water temperatures of 69°F to 86°F were optimal for larval development. Beyond 86°F, the larval stage lasted about eight days but mortality was very high. Mead and Conner (1987) found the average developmental rates from egg to adult to be 18.7 days at 67°F and 7.4 days at 88°F.

Reproduction

Male mating swarms occur shortly before to just after sunset. Harwood (1964) found that initiation of the mating swarm was related to changes in the light intensity and that light levels of approximately 7 foot candles would initiate crepuscular flight activity. He further found that lab colonized males could be induced to swarm when abrupt changes in light intensity occurred.

Lewis and Christenson (1970) studied female ovipositional behaviour and found that the initial search for oviposition sites by females occurs close to the lowest available surface. Groups of eggs, also known as egg rafts, are deposited directly onto the water with the average number of eggs per raft varying between 143 to 438 (Bock and Milby 1981, Buth et al. 1990, Reisen et al. 1984). Environmental factors such as water temperature, crowding and availability of food have been found to affect development of the immature stages, which in turn, affects the size of the female mosquito and ultimately the number of eggs and egg rafts produced. Logan and Harwood (1965) studied the effects of photoperiod on ovipositional behaviour of a Washington strain of *Culex tarsalis* and found that peak oviposition occurred within the first hour of darkness and light.

Autogeny, or the development of eggs without a blood meal, does occur with this mosquito. Moore (1963) found that autogenous *Culex tarsalis*, from Sacramento Valley, California, produced an average of 116 eggs per female with an observed maximum of 220. He also found that the level of autogeny decreased from spring to summer. Spadoni et al. (1974) also studied autogeny in *Culex tarsalis* populations from the same region finding similar results and detecting autogeny as early as April. They further found that no autogenous egg development was observed in overwintering females from November through February and that the mean number of eggs produced per autogenous female was 144.

Significance to Other Wetlands Taxa

This mosquito is the primary vector of Western Equine Encephalitis (WEE) and Saint Louis Encephalitis (SLE) viruses for most of the western United States (Brown and Work 1973, Longshore et al. 1960, Reeves and Hammon 1962, Work et al. 1974). Rosen and Reeves (1954) have also determined that this fly is an important vector of avian malaria.

Larvae of the Winter Marsh Mosquito, *Culiseta inornata*, are frequently found with the immature stages of this mosquito during fall and spring. The larvae of this insect may be a possible food source for waterfowl.

Conservation Needs and Limiting Factors

Sound water management practices should include consultations with local public health and mosquito or vector control agencies to prevent or at least minimize the production of this mosquito from managed, restored or newly created wetlands. Adequate resources need to be provided in all short and long term management plans to help protect humans and horses from the encephalitis viruses that can be vectored by this mosquito.

References

Andersen, D.M., G.C. Collett and R.N. Winget. 1967. Preliminary host preference studies of Culex tarsalis Coquillett and Culiseta inornata (Williston) in Utah. Mosq. News 27:12-15.

Bailey, S.F. and P.A. Gieke. 1968. A study of the effect of water temperatures on rice field mosquito development. Proc. Calif. Mosq. Cont. Assoc. 36:53-61.

Bailey, S.F., D.A. Eliason and B.L. Hoffman. 1965. Flight and dispersal of the mosquito *Culex tarsalis* Coquillett in the Sacramento Valley of California. Hilgardia 37(3):73-113.

Beadle, L.D. and F.C. Harmston. 1958. Mosquitoes in sewage stabilization ponds in the Dakotas. Mosq. News 18(4):293-296.

Belkin, J.N., R.X. Schick and S.J. Heinemann. 1966. Mosquito studies (Diptera: Culicidae) VI. Mosquitoes originally described from North America. 1(6):1-39.

Bock, M.E. and M.M. Milby. 1981. Seasonal variation of wing length and egg raft size in *Culex tarsalis*. Proc. C.M.V.C.A. 49:64-66.

Bohart, R.M. and R.K. Washino. 1978. Mosquitoes of California. Third Edition. Univ. Calif. Div. Agr. Sci., Berkeley, Publ. 4084. 153 pp.

Brown, D. and T.H. Work. 1973. Mosquito transmission of arboviruses at the Mexican Border in Imperial Valley, California 1972. Mosq. News 33:381-385.

Buth, J.L., R.A. Brust and R.A. Ellis. 1990. Development time, oviposition activity and onset of diapause in *Culex tarsalis*, *Culex restuans* and *Culiseta inornata* in Southern Manitoba. J. Amer. Mosq. Cont. Assoc. 6(1):55-63.

Carpenter, S.J. and W.J. LaCasse. 1955. Mosquitoes of North America. Univ. Calif. Press, Berkeley. 360pp.

Darsie, R.F. and R.A. Ward. 1981. Identification and geographical distribution of the mosquitoes of North America, North of Mexico. Mosq. Syst. Suppl. 1:1-313.

Gunstream, S.E., R.M. Chew, D.W. Hagstrum and C.H. Tempelis. 1971. Feeding patterns of six species of mosquitoes in arid Southeastern California. Mosq. News 31:99-101.

Hammon, W. McD., W.C. Reeves and P. Galindo. 1945. Epidemiologic studies of encephalitis in the San Joaquin Valley of California 1943, with the isolation of viruses from mosquitoes. Amer. J. Hyg. 42:299-306.

Harmston, F.C., G.B. Schultz, R.B. Eads and G.C. Menzies. 1956. Mosquitoes and encephalitis in the irrigated high plains of Texas. Publ. Hlth. Repts. 71(8):759-766.

Harwood, R.F. 1964. Physiological factors associated with male swarming of the mosquito *Culex tarsalis* Coq. Mosq. News 24:320-325.

Harwood, R.F. and J.E. Halfill. 1960. Mammalian burrows and vegetation as summer resting sites of the mosquitoes *Culex tarsalis* and *Anopheles freeborni*. Mosq. News 20:174-178.

Hayes, R.O., C.H. Tempelis, A.D. Hess and W.C. Reeves. 1973. Mosquito host preference studies in Hale County, Texas. Amer. J. Trop. Med. Hyg. 22:270-277.

Lewis, L.F. and D.M. Christenson. 1970. Ovipositional site selection in cages by *Culex tarsalis* as influenced by container position, water quality, and female age. Proc. Utah Mosq. Abate. Assoc. 23:27-31.

Logen, D. and R.F. Harwood. 1965. Oviposition of the mosquito *Culex tarsalis* in response to light cues. Mosq. News 25(4):462-465.

Longshore, W.A., E.H. Lennette, R.F. Peters, E.C. Loomis and E.G. Meyers. 1960. California encephalitis surveillance program. Relationship of human morbidity and virus isolation from mosquitoes. Amer. J. Hyg. 71:389-400.

Loomis, E.C. and D.H. Green. 1955. Resting habits of adult *Culex tarsalis* Coquillett in San Joaquin County, California, November, 1953 Through November, 1954. A preliminary report. Proc. Calif. Mosq. Cont. Assoc. 23:125-127.

Mead, S.S. and G.Conner. 1987. Temperature related growth and mortality rates of four mosquito species. Proc. C.M.V.C.A. 55:133-137.

Meyer, R.P. and S.L. Durso. 1993. Identification of the mosquitoes of California. Calif. Mosq. Cont. Assoc., Sacramento, Calif. 80 pp.

Moore, C.G. 1963. Seasonal variation in autogeny in *Culex tarsalis* Coq. in Northern California. Mosq. News. 23(3):238-241.

Mortenson, E.W. 1953. Observations on the overwintering habits of *Culex tarsalis* Coquillett in nature. Proc. Calif. Mosq. Cont. Assoc. 21:59-60.

Price, R.D., T.A. Olson, M.E. Rueger and L.L. Schlottman. 1960. A survey of potential overwintering sites of *Culex tarsalis* Coquillet in Minnesota. Mosq. News 20:306-311.

Reeves, W.C. 1971. Mosquito vector and vertebrate host interaction: the key to maintenance of certain arboviruses. *In:* A.M. Falls (ed). Ecology and physiology of parasites. Univ. of Toronto Press, Toronto, pp 223-230.

Reeves, W.C. and W. McD. Hammon. 1944. Feeding habits of the proven and possible mosquito vectors of western equine and Saint Louis encephalitis in the Yakima Valley, Washington. Amer. J. Trop. Med. 24:131-134.

_____. 1962. Epidemiology of the arthropod-borne viral encephalitides in Kern County. Univ. Calif. Publ. Hlth. 4:1-257.

Reeves, W.C., B. Brookman and W. McD. Hammon. 1948. Studies of the flight range of certain *Culex* mosquitoes, using a fluorescent dye marker, with notes on *culiseta* and *anopheles*. Mosq. News 8:61-69.

Reeves, W.C., C.H. Tempelis, R.E. Bellamy and M.F.Lofy. 1963. Observations on the feeding habits of *Culex tarsalis* in Kern County, California using precipitating antisera produced in birds. Amer. J. Trop. Med. Hyg. 12:929-935.

Reisen, W.K., M.M. Milby and M.E. Bock. 1984. The effects of immature stress on selected events in the life history of *Culex tarsalis*. Mosq. News 44(3):385-395.

Rosen, L. and W.C. Reeves. 1954. Studies on avian malaria in vectors and hosts of encephalitis in Kern County, California III. The comparative vector ability of some of the local culicine mosquitoes. Amer. J. Trop. Med. Hyg. 3:704-708.

Rush, W.A. and C.H. Tempelis. 1967. Biology of *Culex tarsalis* during the spring season in Oregon in relation to western encephalitis virus. Mosq. News 27:307-315.

Rykman, R.E. and K.Y. Arakawa. 1952. Additional collections of mosquitoes from wood rat's nests. Pan-Pac. Ent. 28:105-106.

Shemanchuk, J.A., A.E.R. Downe and L. Burgess. 1963. Hosts of mosquitoes (Diptera: Culicidae) from the irrigated pastures of Alberta. Mosq. News. 23(4):336-341.

Sjogren, R.D. 1968. Notes on Culex tarsalis Coquillett Breeding in Sewage. Calif. Vector Views 15(4):42-43.

Telford, A.D. 1958. The pasture *Aedes* of Central and Northern California. Seasonal history. Ann. Ent. Soc. Amer. 51:360-365.

Tempelis, C.H. 1975. Host feeding patterns of mosquitoes, with a review of advances in analysis of blood meals by serology. J. Med. Ent. 11(6):635-653.

Tempelis, C.H. and R.K. Washino. 1967. Host feeding patterns of *Culex tarsalis* in the Sacramento Valley, California, with notes on other species. J. Med. Ent. 4:315-318.

Tempelis, C.H., W.C. Reeves, R.F. Bellamy and M.F. Lofy. 1965. A three-year study of the feeding habits of *Culex tarsalis* in Kern County, California. Amer. J. Trop. Med. Hyg. 14:170-177.

Tempelis, C.H., D.B. Francy, R.O. Hayes and M.F. Lofy. 1967. Variations in feeding patterns of seven culicine mosquitoes on vertebrate hosts in Weld and Larimer counties, Colorado. Amer. J. Trop. Med. Hyg. 7:561-573.

Work, T.H., M. Jozan and C.G. Clark. 1974. Differential patterns of western equine and Saint Louis encephalitis virus isolation from *Culex tarsalis* mosquitoes collected at two sites in Imperial Valley. Proc. C.M.C.A. 42:31-35.

Additional Readings

Anderson, A.W. and R.F. Harwood. 1966. Cold tolerance in adult female *Culex tarsalis* (Coquillett). Mosq. News 26(1):1-7.

Bellamy, R.E. and W.C. Reeves. 1963. The winter biology of *Culex tarsalis* in Kern County, California. Ann. Ent. Soc. Amer. 56:314-323.

Edman, J.D. and A.E.R. Downr. 1964. Host-blood sources and multiple-feeding habits of mosquitoes in Kansas. Mosq. News 24(2):154-160.

Harwood, R.F. and J.E. Halfill. 1964. The effect of photoperiod on fatbody and ovarian development of *Culex tarsalis*. Ann. Ent. Soc. Amer. 57:596-600.

Harwood, R.F. and N. Takata. 1965. Effect of photoperiod and temperature on fatty acid composition of the mosquito *Culex tarsalis*. J. Ins. Physiol. 11:711-716.

Winter Marsh Mosquito

Culiseta inornata (Williston)

Wesley A. Maffei

Description and Systematic Position

The winter marsh mosquito was described from specimens collected in the Argus Mountains, Inyo County, California, in 1893 (Belkin, et al 1966). This insect is one of California's largest mosquitoes, measuring approximately 8-10 mm in length. Adults are generally light brown to reddish-brown in color and lack any unusual or distinctive markings. Diagnostic features of the imagines include: tip of the abdomen bluntly rounded; wings with the radial and medial cross veins nearly in line with each other; anterior wing veins with intermixed light and dark scales; and wings without distinct patches of dark scales (**Figure 3.17**). Larvae can be identified by the presence of only one tuft of hairs inserted near the base of the pecten row on the siphon and by having the lateral hairs of the anal saddle distinctly longer than the anal saddle (**Figure 3.18**).

Distribution

This mosquito can be found throughout the United States, southern Canada and northern Mexico over a wide range of elevations and habitats (Carpenter and LaCasse 1955). Populations of the winter marsh mosquito have been found throughout California except in Mariposa County (Meyer and Durso 1993).

Suitable Habitat

The immature stages can be found in a wide variety of habitats ranging from duck club ponds, ditches, seepages, rainwater pools, salt marshes and manmade containers. Telford (1958) found larvae in Marin County marshes with salinities ranging from 8 ‰ to 26 ‰.

Adults are usually found resting near their larval habitats during their breeding season while summer aestivating adults are presumed to utilize animal burrows in upper marshes and adjacent uplands (Barnard and Mulla 1977, Shemanchuk 1965).

Biology

Adults are present fall, winter and spring and enter facultative diapause in the summer as a means of surviving the hot, dry California summers. Aestivating females are thought to emerge from mammalian burrows and shelters in the fall following decreased temperatures and the first fall rains. Meyer, et al. (1982a, 1982b) found that optimal flight activity occurred between temperatures of 48°F and 64°F, with a sharp decrease below 43°F and above 64°F. Washino, et al. (1962) studied populations of this mosquito in Kern County, California and found that small numbers of adult females persisted throughout the summer period.

Adult female mosquitoes feed primarily on large domestic mammals although populations associated with brackish marshes have been significantly pestiferous to humans within the San Francisco Estuary (Bohart and Washino 1978; Maffei, unpub.). Precipitin tests have shown that the primary hosts are cattle, sheep, horses and pigs (Bohart and Washino 1978, Edman and Downe 1964, Edman et al. 1972, Gunstream et al. 1971, Reeves and Hammon 1944, Shemanchuk et al. 1963, Tempelis 1975, Tempelis et al. 1967, Tempelis and Washino 1967, and Washino et al. 1962).

Flight range studies have found that the maximum distance traveled was 14 miles (Clarke 1943). Adults of San Francisco Bay populations tend to stay close to their larval source, usually traveling less than two miles for a blood meal. Wind and proximity of available hosts are probably important factors affecting adult dispersal and may help account for the variability observed between different populations of this mosquito.

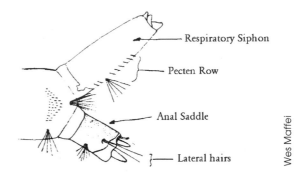

Figure 3.18 Terminal Abdominal Segment of a Fourth Instar Larva

Wes Maffei

Invertebrates

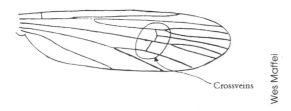

Wes Maffei

Figure 3.17 Wing of an Adult *Cs. inornata*

Adults can be attracted to lights. Bay area mosquito abatement Districts monitor adult populations of this mosquito by using New Jersey light traps. Barnard and Mulla (1977) found that the trapping efficiency of New Jersey light traps could be improved by increasing the intensity of the incandescent light bulbs used from 25W to 100W.

Studies of lab colonized females by Owen (1942) found that the average life expectancy for adults was about 97 days with a maximum of 145 days. Weather conditions, specifically temperature and humidity, and availability of nutrients will affect adult longevity.

Total developmental time from egg to adult has been studied by Shelton (1973) and Mead and Conner (1987) and both found that water temperatures above 78°F were lethal to larval development. Average developmental times ranged from 48 days at 51°F to 13 days at 74°F. Shelton (1973) also noted that as water temperature increased beyond 68°F, average body weight and adult survivorship decreased markedly.

Reproduction

Rees and Onishi (1951) found that adults usually do not swarm and that freshly emerged females are mated by waiting males. Copulation usually occurs end to end vertically, with the female above the male, and is completed in about 3.5 to 6.5 hours.

Groups of eggs, also known as egg rafts, are deposited directly on the water. Buxton and Breland (1952) studied the effects of temporary dessication and found that eggs were still viable after three to four days exposure in damp leaves at various temperatures. They also found that the eggs tolerated exposure to temperatures as low as 17.6°F and had a hatch rate as high as 98%. The survival of larvae hatched from eggs exposed at 17.6°F was low varying from 50% to 100% mortality following 24 and 48 hours exposure respectively.

Significance to Other Wetlands Taxa

Winter Marsh Mosquito larvae are frequently found in association with larvae of *Aedes squamiger* and the Encephalitis Mosquito, *Culex tarsalis*. The larvae of this mosquito may be a possible food source for waterfowl.

Conservation Needs and Limiting Factors

This mosquito, like other species of mosquitoes, is extremely opportunistic. Care must be exercised when managing, altering or restoring seasonal wetlands. Sites that pond water will produce very large numbers of adults. Care must be exercised when manipulating water levels in diked marshes. The fall flooding of these types of wetlands for waterfowl management can produce enormous numbers of adults. The proximity of human habitation or recreational facilities can be seriously affected by the biting activity of these mosquitoes.

References

Barnard, D.R. and M.S. Mulla. 1977. Postaestival adult activity in *Culiseta inornata* (Williston) in relation to larval breeding and changes in soil temperature. Proc. Calif. Mosq. Cont. Assoc. 45:183-185.

Belkin, J.N., R.X. Schick and S.J. Heinemann. 1966. Mosquito studies (Diptera: Culicidae) VI. Mosquitoes originally described from North America. 1(6):1-39.

Bohart, R.M. and R.K. Washino. 1978. Mosquitoes of California. Third Edition. Univ. Calif. Div. Agr. Sci., Berkeley, Publ. 4084. 153 pp.

Buxton, J.A. and O.P. Breland. 1952. Some species of mosquitoes reared from dry materials. Mosq. News. 12(3):209-214.

Carpenter, S.J. and W.J. LaCasse. 1955. Mosquitoes of North America. Univ. Calif. Press, Berkeley. 360pp.

Clarke, J.L. 1943. Studies of the flight range of mosquitoes. J. Econ. Ent. 36:121-122.

Edman, J.D. and A.E.R. Downe. 1964. Host blood sources and multiple-feeding habits of mosquitoes in Kansas. Mosq. News 24:154-160.

Edman, J.D., L.A. Weber and H.W. Kale II. 1972. Host-feeding patterns of florida mosquitoes II. *Culiseta*. J. Med. Ent. 9:429-434.

Gunstream, S.E., R.M. Chew, D.W. Hagstrum and C.H. Tempelis. 1971. Feeding patterns of six species of mosquitoes in arid southeastern California. Mosq. News 31:99-101.

Kliewer, J.W., T. Miura, R.C. Husbands and C.H. Hurst. 1966. Sex pheromones and mating behaviour of *Culiseta inornata* (Diptera: Culicidae). Ann. Ent. Soc. Amer. 59(3): 530-533.

Maffei, W. 1990-1995. Unpublished field notes.

Mead, S. and G. Conner. 1987. Temperature-related growth and mortality rates of four mosquito species. Proc. C.M.V.C.A. 55:133-137.

Meyer, R.P. and S.L. Durso. 1993. Identification of the mosquitoes of California. Calif. Mosq. Cont. Assoc., Sacramento, Calif. 80 pp.

Meyer, R.P., R.K. Washino and T.L. McKenzie. 1982a. Studies on the biology of *Culiseta inornata* (Diptera: Culicidae) in three regions of Central California, USA. J. Med. Ent. 19(5):558-568.

_____. 1982b. Comparisons of factors affecting preimaginal production of *Culiseta inornata* (Williston) (Diptera: Culicidae) in two different habitats of Central California. Env. Ent. 11(6):1233-1241.

Owen, W.B. 1942. The biology of *Theobaldia inornata* Williston in captive colony. J. Econ. Ent. 35:903-907.

Rees, D.M. and K. Onishi. 1951. Morphology of the terminalia and internal reproductive organs and copulation in the mosquito *Culiseta inornata* (Williston). Proc. Ent. Soc. Wash. 53:233-246.

Reeves, W.C. and W. McD. Hammon. 1944. Feeding habits of the proven and possible mosquito vectors of western equine and Saint Louis encephalitis in the Yakima Valley, Washington. Amer. J. Trop. Med. 24:131-134.

Telford, A.D. 1958. The pasture *Aedes* of Central and Northern California. Seasonal History. Ann. Ent. Soc. Amer. 56:409-418.

Tempelis, C.H. 1975. Host-feeding patterns of mosquitoes, with a review of advances in analysis of blood meals by serology. J. Med. Ent. 11(6):635-653.

Tempelis, C.H. and R.K. Washino. 1967. Host feeding patterns of *Culex tarsalis* in the Sacramento Valley, California, with notes on other species. J. Med. Ent. 4:315-318.

Tempelis, C.H., D.B. Francy, R.O. Hayes and M.F. Lofy. 1967. Variations in feeding patterns of seven culicine mosquitoes on vertebrate hosts in Weld and Larimer counties, Colorado. Amer. J. Trop. Med. Hyg. 7:561-573.

Shelton, R.M. 1973. The effect of temperature on the development of eight mosquito species. Mosq. News 33(1):1-12.

Shemanchuk, J.A. 1965. On the hibernation of *Culex tarsalis* Coquillett, *Culiseta inornata* Williston, and *Anopheles earlei* Vargas, (Diptera: Culicidae) in Alberta. Mosq. News 25(4):456-462.

Shemanchuk, J.A., A.E.R. Downe and L. Burgess. 1963. Hosts of mosquitoes (Diptera: Culicidae) from the irrigated areas of Alberta. Mosq. News. 23(4):336-341.

Washino, R.K., R.L. Nelson, W.C. Reeves, R.P. Scrivani and C.H. Tempelis. 1962. Studies on *Culiseta inornata* as a possible vector of encephalitis virus in California. Mosq. News. 22(3):268-274.

Additional Readings

Darsie, R.F. and R.A. Ward. 1981. Identification and geographical distribution of the mosquitoes of North America, north of Mexico. Mosq. Syst. Suppl. 1:1-313.

Brine Flies

Diptera: Ephydridae

Wesley A. Maffei

Description and Systematic Position

There are numerous species of brine flies (Diptera: Ephydridae) that can be found within the confines of the San Francisco Bay region. Three are exceptionally numerous within the bay's tidal and diked seasonal wetlands. These are: *Ephydra cinerea, Ephydra millbrae* (**Figure 3.19**), and *Lipochaeta slossonae* (**Figure 3.20**). Adults can readily be recognized by the following features: head—lacking oral vibrissae, having a swollen protruding face, and having small diverging postvertical setae; wings -with the costa broken near the subcosta and humeral crossvein, and lacking an anal cell.

Adult flies are small in size (*E. cinerea* 2-3 mm in length, *E. millbrae* 4-5 mm in length, and *L. slossonae* 2-3 mm in length) and have unpatterned wings. The coloration for each is as follows: *E. cinerea*—opaque bluish-grey with a greenish tinge and legs with knees and most tarsal segments yellow; *E. millbrae*- brownish grey with brown legs; and *L. slossonae*—whitish grey with a black-brown thoracic dorsum and legs having yellow tarsal segments.

The immature stages are small yellowish-white larvae bearing eight pairs of ventral prolegs with two or three rows of hooks. The last pair of prolegs are enlarged and have opposable hooks and the last abdominal segment bears elongate respiratory tubes with terminal spiracles. The puparium is similar in shape to the last larval stage and is generally dark yellow to brown in color (**Figure 3.21**).

Distribution

Ephydra millbrae is found throughout the San Francisco Bay Area in mid to upper marsh tidal pools that are infrequently affected by the tides. *E. cinerea*

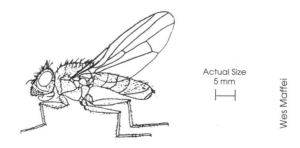

Figure 3.19 Adult *Ephydra millbrae* (Adapted from Jones (1906) and Usinger (1956))

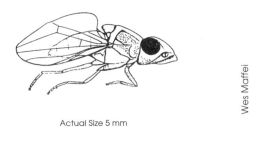

Figure 3.20 Adult *Lipochaeta slossonae*
(Adapted from Jones (1906) and Usinger (1956))

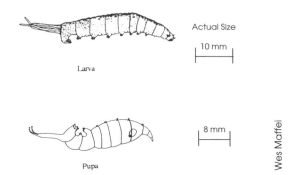

Wes Maffei

Figure 3.21 *Ephydra millbrae* Larva and Pupa
(Adapted from Jones (1906) and Usinger (1956))

is closely associated with hypersaline environments, especially salt ponds of the south and north bay. *Lipochaeta slossonae* is commonly found in or near crystallizer ponds of the south bay and possibly also in salt ponds with salt concentrations somewhat above that of sea water in other parts of the San Francisco Bay region. **Figure 3.22** shows the locations around the Bay Area where brine flies have been collected, and **Table 3.6** shows the collection dates.

Suitable Habitat

Saline and hypersaline environments.

Biology

Simpson (1976) has summarized marine Ephydrid fly biology and a modified portion of that is presented here. Eggs are deposited in the water and hatch after one to

Figure 3.22 Known Brine Fly Localities Within San Francisco Bay Tidal and Diked Marshes

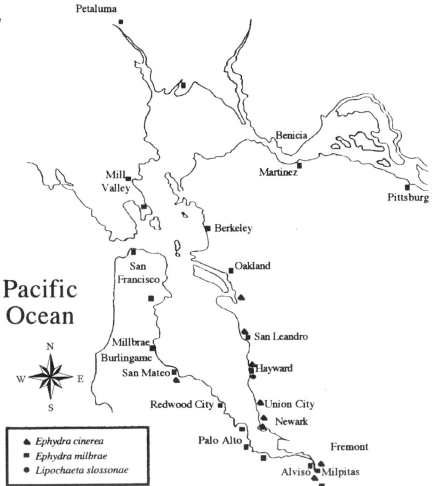

five days. The larva immediately begins feeding and will pass through three instars. First and second instar larvae shed their cuticles in order to pass on to the next larval stage. The cuticle of the last larval instar is not shed but instead forms the protective pupal covering, also known as the puparium. Adults emerge three to ten days after the onset of pupation by inflating a balloon-like ptilinum inside their heads. The ptilinum forces a circular cap off of the front of the puparium allowing the adults to emerge. Deflation of the ptilinum and attainment of normal adult coloration occurs within 0.5 to 1.5 hours. Total developmental time from deposition of eggs to emergence of adults ranges from two to five weeks.

Adults are generally reluctant to fly and when disturbed will usually fly very close to the ground for very short distances (Simpson 1976 and Wirth 1971).

Lipochaeta slossonae adults have the peculiar habit of resting with the wings and legs held very close to the body, giving the appearance of a tube or torpedo. Should the wind cause them to lose their footing, they simply roll freely across the substrate until stopped by some object such as large salt crystals of crystallizer ponds or a spiders web. Dictynid spiders frequently build webs on crystallizer ponds collecting large numbers of these flies (Maffei, unpub.).

Precise food habits have been determined for only a few species of Ephydrids with adults of *E. cinerea* known to feed on masses of blue-green algae and the alga *Enteromorpha sp.* while *L. slossonae* utilizes various diatoms and dinoflagellates. Cheng and Lewin (1974) observed that *L. slossonae* would fluidize the silt or sandy substrate by vigorously shaking their bodies, thereby freeing some of the microorganisms upon which they feed.

Table 3.6 Known Collection Sites For Brine Flies [1]

Location	Date Specimen(s) Collected	Location	Date Specimen(s) Collected
Ephydra cinerea		***Ephydra millbrae***	
Oakland (Tide Flat)	20 Jul 1937	Sears Pt. (Solano Co.)	29 Jun 1951
San Leandro	19 Nov 1947	Mill Valley (Slough)	17 Apr 1950
Baumberg Tract (Hayward)	25 May 1989, 2 Jun 1989, 8 Jun 1989	Tiburon	5 Jul 1927
		San Francisco	22 May 1915
Fremont (Mouth of Coyote Hills Slough)	15 Jul 1976	Colma (Colma Creek)	5 May 1974
Dumbarton Marsh	4 Jul 1968, 19 Jul 1968, 3 Aug 1968, 17 Aug 1968, 20 Aug 1968, 15 Sep 1968, 20 Sep 1968, 3 Oct 1968, 4 Nov 1968, 9 Nov 1968	Millbrae	20 Mar 1908, 1 Sep 1912
		San Mateo	3 Oct 1920
		Foster City	20 Mar 1973
		Redwood City	Apr 1923, 10 Apr 1923
Newark	13 Aug 1930	Menlo Park	31 Jul 1955
Alvarado	2 Aug 1931	Dumbarton Dr. (San Mateo Co.)	30 Dec 1947
Alviso (Artesian Slough)	1 Jun 1980	Palo Alto	28 Jul 1894, 6 Aug 1894, 30 Jun 1915
Alviso	2 Oct 1969, 18 Nov 1971		
Milpitas	29 Nov 1974	Palo Alto (Salt Marshes)	2 Apr 1906
San Mateo	3 Oct 1920, 4 Aug 1925, 10 May 1931	Mountain View	12 May 1915, 18 May 1915, 12 Jul 1924
		Pittsburg	25 Nov 1923
Lipochaeta slossonae		Martinez	31 Aug 1962
Oliver Salt Ponds (Hayward)	5 Aug 1989	Berkeley	29 Mar 1929, 26 Sep 1947
Baumberg Tract (Hayward)	4 Jun 1989	Oakland	20 Jun 1949
		San Leandro	19 Nov 1947
		Baumberg Tract (Hayward)	29 May 1989, 24 Feb 1990
		Alviso	29 Mar 1942, 10 Apr 1969
		Alviso Yacht Harbor	26 Feb 1971
		Milpitas	29 Nov 1974
		San Jose	21 Oct 1977

[1] Information assembled from specimens contained within the California Academy of Sciences Insect Collection, the University of California Berkeley Essig Museum, the University of California Bohart Museum, the San Jose State University Edwards Museum, the San Mateo County Mosquito Abatement District Insect Collection, and the private collections of Dr. J. Gordon Edwards and Wesley A. Maffei.

Larvae apparently feed on the same organisms as the adults (Brock, et al. 1969).

The known salinity tolerances for the different brine flies varies. Jones (1906) observed that *E. millbrae* will occur in salt water pools with salinities up to 42 ‰. *Ephydra cinerea* and *L. slossonae* seem to prefer saline environments much higher than 42 ‰ but are not entirely restricted to these hypersaline habitats (Maffei, unpub.).

Nemenz (1960) studied the ability of immature *E. cinerea* to maintain proper water balance in high saline environments and found that the larvae had a normal osmotic pressure of 20.4 atmospheres in their haemolymph. He concluded that the adaptation to highly concentrated salt solutions was partly due to a relatively impermeable cuticle and probably also to active osmotic regulation.

Reproduction

Females begin laying eggs one to two weeks after they emerge. *Ephydra cinerea* has been observed to walk down stems of aquatic vegetation or emergent objects to oviposit underwater. The other Ephydrid flies oviposit on the water surface, where the eggs quickly sink to the bottom. Jones (1906) states that the eggs of *E. millbrae* are deposited on the floating mats of its puparia. Females deposit between 10 and 60 eggs and may require up to 20 days to complete deposition of their eggs.

Significance to Other Wetlands Taxa

These insects are an important prey item of shore birds and game ducks (Martin and Uhler 1939). Feeney and Maffei (1991) observed Snowy Plovers and Maffei (unpub.) observed California Gulls, Black Necked Stilts and American Avocets charging through large assemblages of brine flies catching disturbed adults as they attempted to fly away. Murie and Bruce (1935) have observed populations of the Western Sandpiper, *Calidris mauri*, feeding on Brine Flies near the Dumbarton bridge. Anderson (1970) found Lesser Scaups, Dunlins, Avocets, Western Sandpipers and Northern Phalaropes feeding on *Ephydra cinerea* in the salt ponds of southern Alameda County.

These flies are a common prey item of spiders, especially the Dictynidae and Salticidae. The tiger beetle, *Cicindela senilis senilis*, will catch these flies, and the adults of the Anthicid beetle, *Tanarthrus occidentalis*, utilizes the carcasses of these flies as a food source.

Conservation Needs and Limiting Factors

Ephydra cinerea seems to prefer the hypersaline environs of salt ponds and has shown poor ability to adapt to the tidal pools of mid elevation tidal marshes. The larvae of this fly are also easily out competed by *E. millbrae* in salt marsh tidal pools.

The frequency of flooding and duration of flooding or drying periods limits the reproductive success of *E. millbrae*.

References

Anderson, W. 1970. A preliminary study of the relationship of saltponds and wildlife—South San Francisco Bay. Calif. Fish and Game 56(4):240-252.

Brock, M.L., R.G. Weigert and T.D. Brock. 1969. Feeding by *Paracoenia* and *Ephydra* on the microorganisms of hot springs. Ecology 50:192-200.

Cheng, L. and R.A. Lewin. 1974. Fluidization as a feeding mechanism in beach flies. Nature 250(5462):167-168.

Feeney, L.R. and W.A. Maffei. 1991. Snowy plovers and their habitat at the Baumberg Area and Oliver Salt Ponds, Hayward, California. Prepared for the City of Hayward. 162pp.

Jones, B.J. 1906. Catalogue of the *Ephydridae*, with bibliography and description of new species. Univ. Calif. Publ. Ent. 1(2):153-198.

Maffei, W. 1989-1996. Unpublished field notes.

Martin, A.C. and F.M. Uhler. 1939. Food of game ducks in the United States and Canada. U.S.D.A. Tech. Bull. #634. 156pp.

Murie, A. and H.D. Bruce. 1935. Some feeding habits of the western sandpiper. The Condor. 37:258-259.

Nemenz, H. 1960. On the osmotic regulation of the larvae of *Ephydra cinerea*. J. Insect Physiol. 4:38-44.

Simpson, K.W. 1976. Shore flies and brine flies (Diptera: Ephydridae). Pages 465-495 *In:* L. Cheng (ed). Marine insects. North-Holland Publ. Co., Amsterdam.

Usinger, R.L. (ed). 1956. Aquatic insects of California. Univ. Calif. Press, Berkeley. 508pp.

Wirth, W.W. 1971. The brine flies of the genus Ephydra in North America (Diptera: Ephydridae). Ann. Ent. Soc. Amer. 64(2):357-377.

Additional Readings

Wirth, W.W., W. Mathis and J.R. Vockeroth. 1987. Ephydridae. Pages 1027-1047 *In:* J.F. McAlpine (ed). Manual of nearctic Diptera. Research Branch Agriculture Canada, Ontario.

Invertebrates

Jamieson's Compsocryptus Wasp

Compsocryptus jamiesoni Nolfo

Wesley A. Maffei

Description and Systematic Position

Compsocryptus jamiesoni is a moderate sized wasp, approximately 15-25mm in length, that belongs to the family Ichneumonidae, tribe Mesostenini. Overall body ground color is rusty red-brown with the middle of the face, vertex and occiput of the head, apical third of the antennae, and the thoracic sutural markings black. The wings are light brownish-yellow with three dark brown transverse bands, the apical pair of bands merging near the posterior margin of the wing (**Figure 3.23**). Females have an ovipositor measuring approximately 6mm in length and the base of the third abdominal tergite black. Nolfo (1982) has indicated that this wasp is very similar to both *Compsocryptus calipterus brevicornis* and *Compsocryptus aridus,* which have been found within the confines of the San Francisco Bay Region exclusive of its salt marshes. Males of this wasp are very similar to *Compsocryptus calipterus brevicornis* but can readily be separated by the absence of any dark markings on the apex of the hind femur. Females are similar to *Compsocryptus aridus* but differ in having the body color rusty red-brown rather than brownish-yellow and the dark markings of the wings broader.

Distribution

This wasp was first collected in 1981 and subsequently described as a new taxon by Nolfo in 1982 from specimens collected at the salt marshes in Alviso, Santa Clara County, California. Additional populations have been identified from the salt marshes of the eastern San Francisco Bay as far north as San Leandro, California (Maffei, unpub.). Surveys for this wasp from other parts of the San Francisco Estuary have not been done at this time. **Figure 3.24** shows the locations around the Bay Area

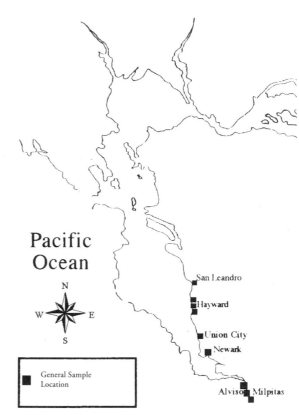

Figure 3.24 Known *Compsocryptus jamiesoni* Localities Within San Francisco Bay Tidal and Diked Marshes

where *Compsocryptus jamiesoni* have been collected, and **Table 3.7** shows the collection dates.

Suitable Habitat

Compsocryptus jamiesoni have only been found on short grass or herbage in or near tidal and muted tidal marshes.

Table 3.7 Known Collection Sites For *Compsocryptus jamiesoni* [1]

Location	Date Specimen(s) Collected
Trojan Marsh (San Leandro)	11 Sep 1997
Oliver Salt Ponds (Hayward)	23 Sep 1989
Baumberg Tract (Hayward)	4 Jun 1989
Shoreline Int. Ctr. (Hwyd)	1 Jul 1990, 2 Jul 1990
Ecology Marsh	24 Aug 1994
Hetch-Hetchy Marsh	16 Jul 1997
Alviso (Triangle Marsh)	3 Jun 1980
Santa Clara (Topotype)	2 Sep 1928
San Jose (Topotype)	16 Aug 1982

1 Information assembled from specimens contained within the California Academy of Sciences Insect Collection, University of California Berkeley Essig Museum, University of California Bohart Museum, San Jose State University Edwards Museum, San Mateo County Mosquito Abatement District Insect Collection, and private collections of Dr. J. Gordon Edwards and Wesley A. Maffei.

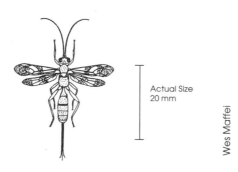

Figure 3.23 Jamieson's Compsocryptus Wasp – *Compsocryptus jamiesoni*

Biology

Little is known concerning the biology of this wasp. Other members of the tribe Mesostenini are known to be parasitic in cocoons of lepidoptera and other ichneumonids, puparia of diptera and other wasps, and the egg sacs of spiders (Townes 1962). Adults regularly utilize dew or rainwater from foliage and nectar from flowers when available and can be found from April through October. The peak flight period for *C. jamiesoni* is June through August (Maffei, unpub.).

Reproduction

Unknown.

Significance to Other Wetlands Taxa

Unknown.

Conservation Needs and Limiting Factors

Unknown.

References

Maffei, W. 1989-1996. Unpublished field notes.

Nolfo, S. 1982. *Compsocryptus jamiesoni*, new ichneumonid from California (Hymenoptera: Ichneumonidae). Ent. News. 93(2):42

Townes, H. and M. Townes. 1962. Ichneumon-flies of America north of Mexico: Part III. subfamily Gelinae, tribe Mesostenini. Bull. U.S.N.M. 216(3):1-602.

A Note on Invertebrate Populations of the San Francisco Estuary

Wesley A. Maffei

The study of San Francisco Bay invertebrate populations and their interrelationships has usually been given low priority or altogether neglected during the planning and implementation of enhancement or restoration projects. Environmental assessments of habitat quality and health have frequently forgotten about the terrestrial or semi-aquatic invertebrates that are usually very sensitive to environmental changes. Arthropods, especially insects, are sensitive indicators of environmental disturbance or change (Lenhard and Witter 1977, Hellawell 1978, Hawkes 1979).

A survey of the literature shows that few studies have been done on the biology and ecology of the terrestrial and semi-aquatic invertebrates within the San Francisco Estuary. What is known about these organisms generally comes from studies of invertebrate populations well outside of this geographic area. For many of the common species, this is probably adequate. Unfortunately, little information exists about what species are found within the different wetland habitats, and less still is known about the impacts of wetlands projects on the existing invertebrate populations. Those species that are pests (i.e., mosquitoes) are fairly well known, while taxa such as Jamieson's compsocryptus wasp or the western tanarthrus beetle, which were described as new to science within the last twenty years, have poorly known or completely unknown biologies. This lack of basic information, specifically what species exist where, coupled with an understanding of their basic biologies, warrants careful consideration and research. The fact that unknown populations of organisms, or unique, sensitive, or threatened and endangered taxa do exist within or near the tidal reaches of the Bay suggests that more care should be taken when planning enhancement or restoration projects. The relationship of some invertebrate species to the success of other organisms (i.e. plants or invertebrates) needs to be clarified.

Some invertebrates are known to play a significant role in the life cycles of other organisms. Functioning as pollinators, herbivores, scavengers, predators, and prey, terrestrial and semi-aquatic invertebrates are a significant component of any habitat or community. It became apparent through the course of the Goals Project that the experts on many of the key species of fish and wildlife were not always clear about the roles played by invertebrates with respect to the survival of their target species or communities. This prompted the construction of some graphic displays, in this case food webs, by which to illustrate what little is known about the roles performed by the largest and most easily overlooked group of organisms in our estuary, the invertebrates.

Food webs are frequently used to illustrate the complex relationships between organisms within a given area or habitat. Unfortunately, they cannot hope to tell the entire story. Factors such as the seasonality of the organisms, length of time and time of year the studies were performed, the limited number of organisms that can be included in the web, and the complexity of the habitat or ecosystem being studied tend to result in webs that over generalize what actually exists or has been observed.

The following sample invertebrate webs are undoubtedly incomplete. They have been assembled from many hours of field observation in the southern portion of the San Francisco Estuary, and from an exhaustive search of the literature. The most notable feature of all of these webs is the delicate relationships that exist between all of the organisms involved. The potential reduction or loss of one member of the web clearly illustrates how its associates could be impacted. It should be noted that not all of the organisms that have been found or studied are represented. The organisms in-

cluded in these webs are those routinely found in association with the plant or plants that are indicated by the boxes with the thickened black borders. **Figures 3.25, 3.26,** and **3.27** are examples of partial webs developed to illustrate the relationship of some of the organisms associated with the plant species alkali heath (*Frankenia salina*), common pickleweed (*Salicornia virginica*), and willow (*Salix lasiolepis*), respectively. **Figures 3.28** and **3.29** are examples of partial webs that illustrate the relationships of organisms within mid-marsh pans and crystallizer pond habitats. The web for the organisms associated with old crystallizer ponds was included to illustrate that even in this inhospitable habitat, webs of life can and do exist. When known vertebrate relationships for most of the webs have been included. **Table 3.8** is a brief summary of the descriptions and biologies of some of the invertebrates from the alkali heath web. **Table 3.9** is a listing of the scientific names associated with a major common name category. It is hoped that these tables might help the reader better visualize the nature of the relationships shown for the different organisms included in the webs.

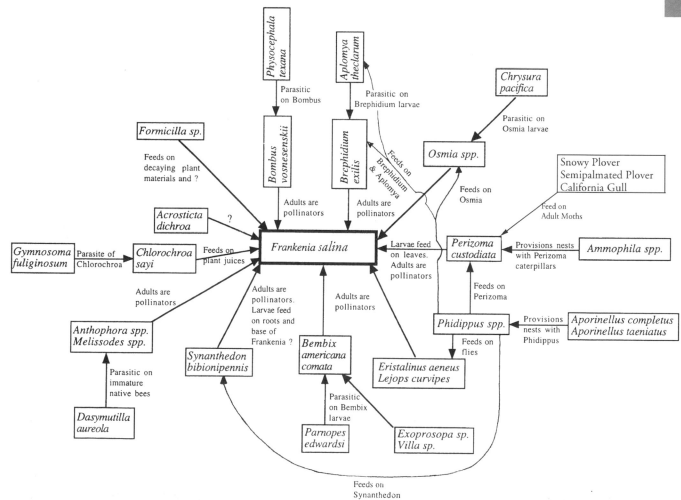

Figure 3.25 A Partial Web of the Organisms Associated With Alkali Heath (*Frankenia salina*) in San Francisco Tidal Marshes

Table 3.8 Partial Summary of Organisms Associated with Alkali Heath.

Bees and Wasps

Bombus vosnesenskii – A moderate to large sized bumblebee that is mostly black with a small amount of yellow on the thorax and posterior portion of the abdomen. Adults tend to nest in abandoned rodent burrows along levees and adjacent upland habitat.

***Anthophora* spp.** – A moderate sized native bee, belonging to the family *Anthophoridae*, that is light brown to grayish brown in appearance and has long antennae. Adults collect pollen from flowers, are solitary, and dig fairly deep burrows in the ground. Burrows are usually lined with a waxy substance. Frequently visited plants are *Brassica* spp., *Frankenia* sp. and hemlock.

***Melissodes* spp.** – A small to moderate sized native bee, belonging to the family *Anthophoridae*, which is grayish in color. Pollen collecting habits are similar to *Anthophora* spp.

***Osmia* spp.** – A bluish-black bee with smoky colored wings, that belongs to the family of bees known as leaf cutting bees, or *Megachilidae*. This genus of bees is commonly known as mason bees because of their habit of building small earthen cells on or under stones, in abandoned burrows, in holes in boards, twigs and logs, and in plant galls.

***Ammophila* spp.** – A long, slender solitary digger wasp belonging to the family *Sphecidae*. These wasps build simple, vertical burrows, that are provisioned with moth caterpillars. Nests usually occur in fine, silty or sandy soil with minimal vegetation.

Aporinellus completus and ***Aporinellus taeniatus*** – Small black spider wasps (family *Pompilidae*) that provision their nests with jumping spiders (genus *Phidippus*).

Chrysura pacifica – A small iridescent bluish-purple to bluish-green wasp, measuring up to 10mm in length. This wasp parasitizes the leaf cutting bee *Osmia*.

Parnopes edwardsi – A moderate sized brilliant light green wasp, measuring about 10–13mm, that parasitizes the sand wasp *Bembix americana*.

Bembix americana – A large sand wasp that is bluish gray in color with pale white markings on the abdomen. The eyes are usually bright yellow to yellowish-green in color. Adult wasps provision their ground nests with adult flies.

Dasymutilla aureola – A golden yellow to bright orange insect known as a velvet ant. These insects are not closely related to ants but do have the appearance of looking like an ant. Velvet ants provision their burrows with ground nesting bees and wasps.

Beetles

***Formicilla* sp.** – A very small, brown to tan colored beetle, known as an Ant-like flower beetle. These beetles are known to feed on decaying vegetation and can sometimes be very common at the bases of *Frankenia* sp.

Stink Bugs

Chlorochroa sayi – A moderately sized (one-half inch) stink bug that is pale to deep green in color. This insect is known for releasing a foul smelling odor when disturbed or threatened.

Butterflies and Moths

Perizoma custodiata – A moderate sized moth belonging to the family of moths known as measuring worms, or *Geometridae*. Adults are tan gray or brown in color and have dark geometric bands across the forewings. Larvae are about one inch long, light green in color and feed on the leaves of *Frankenia*. Adults are present throughout the year, with peak populations occurring from spring through fall.

Brephidium exilis – A very small brown and blue butterfly that is a frequent visitor of *Frankenia*.

Synanthedon bibionipennis – A small moth, belonging to the family of moths known as clear wing moths, or *Sesiidae*. Adults emerge in late May to early June and can be found through late September. These insects are frequently associated with *Frankenia* sp. It is believed that the larvae may feed on the roots and the bases of *Frankenia* sp. plants. Currently, this is the only clear wing moth known to inhabit the levees of mid to upper tidal marshes within the San Francisco Estuary.

Flies

Gymnosoma fuliginosum – A small, bright orange and black fly that is parasitic on the green stink bug, *Chlorochroa sayi*.

Physocephala texana – A bright red and black fly, about one-half an inch long, that parasitizes the bumblebee *Bombus vosnesenskii*.

Aplomya theclarum – A very tiny black fly, with a bright silver face, that parasitizes the larvae of the pygmy blue butterfly.

Acrosticta dichroa – A small, bright green and red fly with one brown spot at the tips of the wings. This fly is frequently seen walking up and down the stems of *Frankenia* holding it's wings outstretched and rotating them in opposite directions. Biology unknown.

***Exoprosopa* spp.** and ***Villa* spp.** – Small to moderate sized, fuzzy looking flies that are commonly known as bee flies. *Villa* spp. is light brown in color with clear wings and *Exoprosopa* spp. is brown and white banded with brightly patterned brown and clear wings. Both species of flies are parasites of immature sand wasps of the genus *Bembix*.

Eristalinus aeneus –A moderate sized, shiny olive green fly that is commonly known as a hover fly or flower fly. The larvae of this fly are known as rat-tailed maggots and are found in somewhat saline or brackish pools of tidal marshes. Adult flies are an important food source for *Bembix* sand wasps and spiders.

Lejops curvipes – A moderate sized flower fly, measuring about 10–15mm, that is bright reddish-orange, with a central black stripe on the abdomen and mostly black legs.

Spiders

***Phidippus* spp.** – Two species are common within our marshes. One is solid black with the top of the abdomen bright red and can reach a size up to one-third of an inch. The other is dark gray with variegated white lines and reaches a size of about a quarter of an inch.

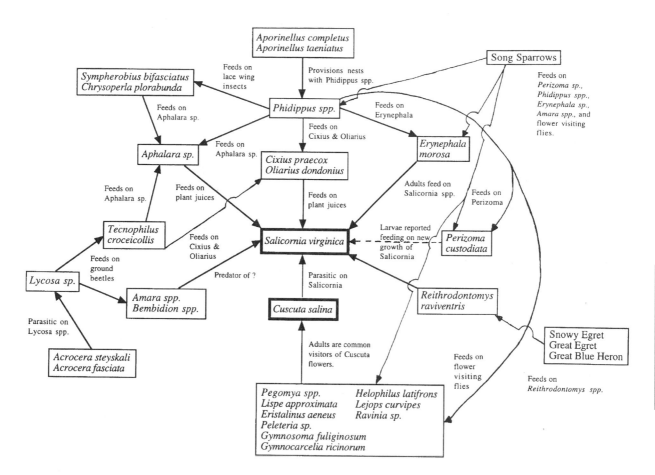

Figure 3.26 A Partial Web of the Organisms Associated With Common Pickleweed (*Salicornia virginica*) in San Francisco Bay Lower High Tidal Marshes

The need for terrestrial invertebrate surveys has become more apparent with the increase in wetland enhancement and restoration projects. The conversion of one habitat type to another "more valuable" or "more improved" habitat type can and usually does have significant impacts on the often-unnoticed invertebrate populations that exist within them. In some cases these impacts can be positive, while in other instances the opposite is true. **Table 3.10** lists by site and date(s) those known terrestrial and semi-aquatic invertebrate surveys or species studies.

It is hoped that these preliminary illustrations and discussions will shed a small amount of light on the complexity of the commonly overlooked micro fauna that exists within the tidal and diked habitats of our estuary. It is further hoped that this glimpse might stimulate others to investigate further the biology and ecology of the terrestrial micro fauna within these habitats. We must improve our understanding of the importance of invertebrates to the survival of the other bayland organisms if we are to make better-informed decisions about the future of habitats and organisms of the San Francisco Bay.

References

Anderson, W. 1970. A preliminary study of the relationship of salt ponds and wildlife - South San Francisco Bay. Calif. Dept. Fish and Game. 56:240-252.

Anderson, J., A. Bryant, L. Heinemann, V. Jennings, M. Kilkenny, R. Owens, L. Rogers, B. Summers, M. Savinsky, J. Trapani, R. Williamson and S. Zimmer. 1980. An ecological study of a South San Francisco Bay salt marsh. Unpubl. Report, San Jose State Univ. 199 pp.

Balling, S.S. 1974. The influence of mosquito control recirculation ditches on aspects of San Francisco Bay salt marsh arthropod communities. Unpubl. PhD Dissertation, Univ. Calif., Berkeley. 292 pp.

Balling, S.S. and V.H. Resh. 1982. Arthropod community response to mosquito control recirculation ditches in San Francisco Bay salt marshes. Environ. Ent. 11(4):801-808.

_____. 1983. Mosquito control and salt marsh management: factors influencing the presence of Aedes larvae. Mosq. News 43(2):212-218.

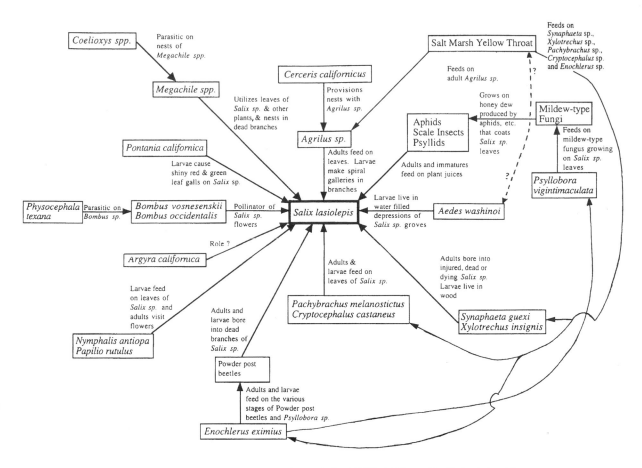

Figure 3.27 A Partial Web of the Organisms Associated With Willow (*Salix lasiolepis*)

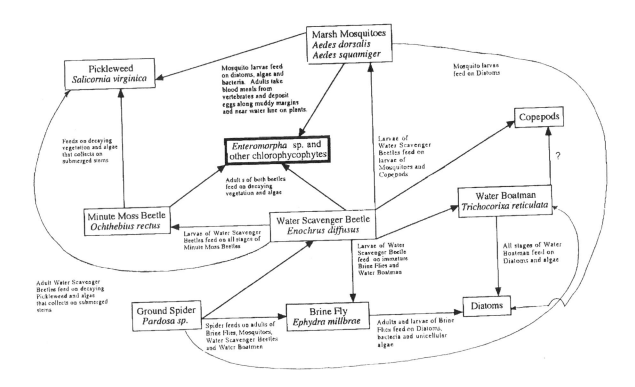

Figure 3.28 Partial Web of Organisms Associated With Mid-Tidal Marsh Pans

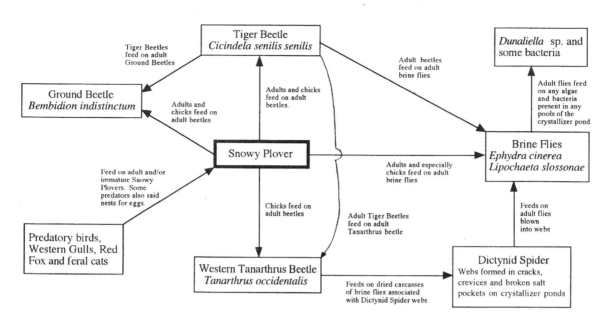

Figure 3.29 A Partial Web of the Organisms in the Baumberg and Oliver Brothers Salt Crystallizer Ponds, Hayward, California

_____. 1984. Life history and variability in the water boatman *Trichocorixa reticulata* (Hemiptera: Corixidae) in San Francisco Bay salt marsh ponds. Ann. Ent. Soc. Amer. 77(1):14-19.

_____. 1991. Seasonal patterns in a San Francisco Bay, California, Salt Marsh Arthropod Community. Pan. Pac. Ent. 67(2):138-144.

Barnby, M.A. and V.H. Resh. 1980. Distribution of arthropod populations in relation to mosquito control recirculation ditches and natural channels in the Petaluma salt marsh of San Francisco Bay. Proc. C.M.V.C.A. 48:100-102.

Barnby, M.A., J.N. Collins and V.H. Resh. 1985. Aquatic and macroinvertebrate communities of natural and ditched potholes in a San Francisco Bay salt marsh. Estuarine, Coastal and Shelf Science. 20:331-347.

Bergey, E.A., S.F. Balling, J.N. Collins, G.A. Lamberti and V.H. Resh. 1992. Bionomics of invertebrates within an extensive *Potamogeton pectinatus* bed of a California marsh. Hydrobiologia 234:15-24.

Caires, T., D. Dawn, D. DiNunzio, A. Harris, N. Kogut, M. Kutilek, S.H. Ladd, J. Stanziano, M. Stickler and A. Webber. 1993. Preliminary survey of biodiversity in the Warm Springs seasonal wetland, Alameda County, California. Report for the U.S. Fish and Wildl. Serv. 46 pp.

Cameron, G.N. 1969. Environmental determination of insect species diversity in two salt marsh communities. Unpub. PhD Dissertation, Univ. Calif., Davis. 136 pp.

_____. 1972. Analysis of insect trophic diversity in two salt marsh communities. Ecology. 53:58-73.

Carpelan, L.H. 1957. Hydrobiology of the Alviso salt ponds. Ecology 38:375-390.

Chandler, D.S. 1979. A new species of Tanarthrus from California (Coleoptera: Anthicidae) Pan Pac. Ent. 55(2):147-148.

Collins, J.N., S.S. Ballindo and V.H. Resh. 1983. The Coyote Hills Marsh model: calibration of interactions among floating vegetation, waterfowl, invertebrate predators, alternative prey, and anopheles mosquitoes. Proc. C.M.V.C.A. 51:69-73.

Coquillett, D.W. 1902. New Diptera from North America. Proc. U.S.N.M. 25:83-126.

Doane, R.W. 1912. New western tipula. Ann. Ent. Soc. Amer. 5:41-61.

Donaldson, .E., D.E. Conklin and T.D. Foin. 1992. Population dynamics of *Artemia franciscana* in the San Francisco Bay National Wildlife Refuge: Phase II. Interim Report #2.

Feeney, L.R. and W.A. Maffei. 1991. Snowy plovers and their habitat at the Baumberg Area and Oliver Salt Ponds, Hayward, California, March 1989 through May 1990. Report Prepared for the City of Hayward, Calif. 162 pp.

Feeney, L.R., J.A. Alvarez and W.A. Maffei. 1996. Oakland deep draft navigation improvements protection plan for burrowing owls. Pt III. results of the implementation of the proposed mitigation plan. Report prepared for the Port of Oakland Environmental Dept. 92 pp. Plus Indices.

Table 3.9 Food Web Taxa by Major Common Name Category

Butterflies and Moths

Brephidium exilis
Nymphalis antiopa
Papilio rutulus
Perizoma custodiata
Synanthedon bibionipennis

Hoppers and Psyllids

Aphalara sp.
Aphids
Cixius praecox
Oliarius dondonius
Psyllids
Scale Insects

Flies

Acrocera steyskali
Acrocera fasciata
Acrosticta dichroa
Aedes dorsalis
Aedes squamiger
Aedes washinoi
Aplomya theclarum
Argyra californica
Ephydra millbrae
Eristalinus aeneus
Exoprosopa spp.
Gymnocarcelia ricinorum
Gymnosoma fuliginosum
Helophilus latifrons
Lejops curvipes
Lipochaeta slossonae
Lispe approximata
Pegomya spp.
Peleteria sp.
Physocephala texana
Ravinia sp.
Villa spp.

Beetles

Agrilus sp.
Amara spp.
Bembidion spp.
Cicindela senilis senilis
Cryptocephalus castaneus
Enochlerus eximius
Enochrus diffusus
Erynephala morosa
Formicilla spp.
Ochthebius rectus
Pachybrachus melanostictus
Powder post Beetles
Psyllobora vigintimaculata
Synaphaeta guexi
Tanarthrus occidentails
Tecnophilus croceicollis
Xylotrechus insignis

Ants, Wasps and Bees

Ammophila spp.
Anthophora spp.
Aporinellus completus
Aporinellus taeniatus
Bembix americana comata
Bombus vosnesenskii
Bombus occidentalis
Cerceris californicus
Chrysura pacifica
Coelioxys spp.
Dasymutilla aureola
Megachile spp.
Melissodes spp.
Osmia spp.
Parnopes edwardsi
Pontania californica

Bugs

Chlorochroa sayi
Trichocorixa reticulata

Lacewings

Chrysoperla plorabunda
Sympherobius bifasciatus

Spiders

Dictynid Spider
Lycosa spp.
Pardosa sp.
Phidippus spp.

Birds

Great Blue Heron
Great Egret
Salt Marsh Yellow Throat
Snowy Egret
Snowy Plover
Song Sparrows
Western Gull

Mammals

Feral Cat
Red Fox
Reithrodontomys raviventris

Plants

Cuscuta salina
Dunaliella sp.
Enteromorpha sp.
Frankenia salina (= grandifolia)
Salicornia virginica
Salix lasiolepis

Fungi

Mildew type fungus

Fowler, B.H. 1977. Biology and life history of the salt marsh snail, *Assiminea californica*, (Tryon, 1865) (Mesogastropoda: Rissoacea). Unpubl. M.A. thesis, San Jose State Univ., San Jose, Calif. 143 pp.

Garcia, R., W.G. Voigt and A.K. Nomura. 1992. Ecology of *Aedes squamiger* in the northern San Francisco Bay Area. Ann. Rep. Mosq. Cont. Res., Univ. Calif. pp. 53-57.

Garcia, R., W.G. Voigt, A.K. Nomura and A. Hayes. 1992. Biology of *Aedes squamiger*. Unpub. progress report for Alameda County Mosquito Abatement District. 7 pp.

Gustafson, J.F. and R.S. Lane. 1968. An annotated bibliography of literature on salt marsh insects and related arthropods in California. Pan. Pac. Ent. 44(4):327-331.

Gustafson, J.F., R.L. Peterson and V.F. Lee. 1973. Additional references to previous lists of salt marsh arthropods. Unpublished paper, California Academy of Sciences, Entomology Dept.

Table 3.10 Known Terrestrial or Semi-aquatic Invertebrate Surveys or Studies of Selected Invertebrate Taxa[1]

Locale	Date of Study	Reference(s)
Alviso Salt Ponds, Charlston to Alviso Slough	1951-1952	L.H. Carpelan (1957)
Outer Coyote Creek Tributary	1980	J. Anderson, et. al. (1980)
Warm Springs Seasonal Wetlands, Fremont	1993	T. Caires, et. al. (1993)
	1995	W. Maffei, (unpub. field notes)
Dumbarton Point Marsh, Fremont	1968	R.S. Lane (1969)
Coyote Hills Marsh, Fremont	1983-1984	E.A. Bergey, et. al. (1992)
Ecology Marsh, Fremont	1994	C. Daehler and D. Strong (1995)
	1996-1996	W. Maffei (unpub. field notes)
Baumberg and Oliver Salt Ponds	1989-1990	L. Feeney and W. Maffei (1991)
	1997-1997	W. Maffei (unpub. field notes)
Oakland Airport, Burrowing Owl Mitigation Area	1995	L. Feeney, et al.. (1996)
Richmond Field Station	1992-1994	J.A. Powell (unpub. Paper, 1994)
Petaluma Marsh	1977-1978	S. Balling and V. Resh (1991, 1982) M. Barnby and V. Resh (1980) V. Resh and S. Balling (1983)
	1980-1980	S. Balling and V. Resh (1984)
	1979	S. Balling (1982)
	1981-1981	M. Barnby (1985)
Cullinan Ranch, USGS Survey	1995(?)	M. Paquin (unpub.)
Suisun Marsh, Between Cutoff and Suisun Sloughs	1978-1979	S. Balling (1982) S. Balling and V. Resh (1982) V. Resh and S. Balling (1983)
Suisun Marsh	1972-1973	A.M. Shapiro (1975a, b, 1974)

[1] The studies shown pertain primarily to insects and arachnids and do not include the numerous biological studies on mosquitoes.

Hellawell, J.M. 1978. Biological surveillance of rivers. National Environment Research Council and Water Research Centre, Stevenage, England. 332 p.

_____. 1986. Biological indicators of freshwater pollution and environmental management. Elsevier, London, England. 546 p.

Jones, B.J. 1906. Catalogue of the *Ephydridae*, with bibliography and description of new species. Univ. Calif. Publ. Ent. 1(2):153-198.

Josselyn, M.A. 1983. The ecology of San Francisco Bay tidal marshes: a community profile. U.S. Fish and Wildl. Serv., Biol. Services, Washington D.C. FWS/OBS-83-23. 102 pp.

Josselyn, M. and J. Buchholz. 1984. Marsh restoration in San Francisco Bay: A guide to design and planning. Paul F. Romberg Tiburon Center for Environmental Studies, Tech. Rep. #3, San Francisco State Univ. 103 pp.

Lamberti, G.A. and V.H. Resh. 1984. Seasonal patterns of invertebrate predators and prey in Coyote Hills Marsh. Proc. C.M.V.C.A. 52:126-128.

Lane, R.S. 1969. The insect fauna of a coastal salt marsh. M.A. thesis. San Francisco State Univ. San Francisco, Calif. 78pp.

Lanzarro, G.C. and B.F. Eldridge. 1992. A classical and population genetic description of two new sibling species of *Aedes* (Ochlerotatus) *increpitus* Dyar. Mosq. Syst. 24(2):85-101.

Lonzarich, D.G. 1989. Temporal and spatial variations in salt pond environments and implications for fish and invertebrates. M.A. thesis, San Jose State Univ. 81 pp.

Madrone Associates. 1977. The natural resources of Napa Marsh. Coastal Wetland Ser. #19. Calif. Dept. Fish and Game, Sacramento. 96 pp.

Maffei, W.A. 1989-1997. Unpublished field notes.

Mason, H.L. 1969. A Flora of the marshes of California. Univ. of Calif. Press, Berkeley. 878 pp.

Nichols, F.H. 1973. A review of benthic faunal surveys in San Francisco Bay. U.S. Geol. Surv. Cir. #677. 20 pp.

Nolfo, S. 1982. *Compsocryptus jamiesoni*, new Ichneumonid from California (Hymenoptera: Ichneumonidae). Ent. News. 93(2):42.

Powell, J.A. 1994. Richmond Field Station Lepidoptera. Unpublished report, Essig Museum, Univ. Calif. Berkeley. 9 pp.

Quayle, H.J. 1906. Mosquito control work in California. Univ. Calif. Agric. Exp. Sta. Bull. #178, pp 1-55.

Race, M. 1981. Field ecology and natural history of *Cerithidea californica* (Gastropoda: Prosobranchia) in San Francisco Bay. Veliger 24(1):18-27.

Resh, V.H. and S.S. Balling. 1983a. Ecological impact of mosquito control recirculation ditches on San Francisco Bay marshlands: study conclusions and management recommendations. Proc. C.M.V.C.A. 51:49-53.

_____. 1983b. Tidal circulation alteration for salt marsh mosquito control. Environ. Manag. 7(1):79-84.

Shapiro, A.M. 1974a. A salt marsh population of *Lycaena helloides* (Lepidoptera: Lycaenidae) feeding on Potentilla (Rosaceae). Ent. News. 85:40-44.

_____. 1974b. Butterflies of the Suisun Marsh, California. J. Res. on the Lepidoptera. 13(3):191-206.

_____. 1975. Supplementary records of butterflies in the Sacramento Valley and Suisun Marsh, lowland central California. J. res. on the Lepidoptera. 14(2):100-102.

Tilden, J.W. 1965. Butterflies of the San Francisco Bay Region. University of California

4

Amphibians and Reptiles

California Tiger Salamander

Ambystoma californiense

Mark R. Jennings

General Information

The California tiger salamander (Family: Ambystomatidae) is a large (75-125 mm SVL) terrestrial salamander with several white or yellow spots or bars on a jet-black field (Stebbins 1985). Although often referred to as a subspecies of the more widespread tiger salamander (*A. tigrinum*; e.g., see Frost 1985, Stebbins 1985, Zeiner et al. 1988), the California tiger salamander is currently recognized as a full species (Jones 1989, Shaffer et al. 1993, Barry and Shaffer 1994). In 1992, the California tiger salamander was petitioned for listing as an endangered species (Long 1992) based on concerns about population declines due to the extensive loss of habitat, introductions of non-native aquatic predators, and interbreeding with introduced salamanders originally brought in as live fish bait (Long 1992; see also Jennings and Hayes 1994). The U.S. Fish and Wildlife Service ruled that the petition was warranted but precluded by pending listing actions on higher priority species (Sorensen 1994).

Reproduction

Most adults probably reach sexual maturity in two years, but some individuals may take longer during periods of unfavorable conditions such as annual droughts (Shaffer et al. 1993). Adults migrate during the night from subterranean refuge sites (small mammal burrows) to breed-

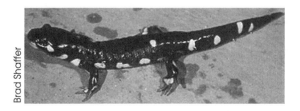

Brad Shaffer

ing ponds after the onset of relatively warm winter rains (late November-early March) where courtship and egg deposition occurs (Twitty 1941, Barry and Shaffer 1994, Loredo and Van Vuren 1996). Males may precede females to breeding ponds (Shaffer et al. 1993, Loredo and Van Vuren 1996) and distances travelled by adults from refuge sites to breeding sites may be up to 1.6 km (Austin and Shaffer 1992). Females lay single or small groups of 2-4 eggs (8.5-12 mm in diameter) on detritus, submerged vegetation, or on the benthos of relatively shallow rain pools (Storer 1925). The number of eggs laid per female is unknown. During periods of low rainfall, California tiger salamanders may not reproduce (Jennings and Hayes 1994). After reproducing, adults return to subterranean refuge sites, some to the same small mammal burrows they emerged from earlier in the year (Shaffer et al. 1993).

Growth and Development

Eggs hatch after 2-4 weeks (Storer 1925, Twitty 1941), and gilled aquatic larvae take a minimum of at least 10 weeks to successfully reach metamorphosis (Anderson 1968, Feaver 1971). Larvae lack legs upon hatching at 10.5 mm total length, but quickly grow four legs within 1-2 weeks. Larvae generally are about 75 mm in total length and weigh about 10 grams at metamorphosis into juveniles, although they may remain in water (for up to six months) and grow to much larger sizes with a better chance of survival after metamorphosis (Jennings and Hayes 1994). Overwintering of larvae, which is common with several species of *Ambystoma* (see Stebbins 1985), is unusual with *A. californiense* because of the temporary nature of its natural breeding habitat (Shaffer et al. 1993). All records of overwintering or aseasonal metamorphosis are based on salamanders in artificially-created habitats (Jennings, unpubl. data).

Upon metamorphosis (usually early May-through July), juveniles disperse in mass at night away from desiccating breeding ponds into terrestrial habitats (Zeiner et al. 1988, Loredo and Van Vuren 1996, Loredo et al. 1996). Juveniles have also been known to disperse during periods of unfavorable conditions (e.g., August) resulting in mass mortality (Holland et al. 1990). Both adults and juveniles seek refuge in small mammal burrows (especially those of California ground squirrels (*Spermophilus beecheyi*) and Botta's pocket gophers (*Thomomys bottae*) [Barry and Shaffer 1994, Loredo et al. 1996]) and spend most of the year underground until the onset of cooler and wetter surface conditions (Jennings and Hayes 1994). Juveniles probably feed on invertebrates in subterranean mammal burrows and grow throughout the year. During the winter months however, both juveniles and adults emerge from burrows and forage at night on the surface for extended periods of time, although adults appear to do all their foraging after completing their reproductive activities (Shaffer et al. 1993).

California tiger salamanders are relatively long-lived animals, reaching ages of 20 years or more in captivity (Jennings, unpubl. data). The average life span of adults in the wild is unknown.

Food and Feeding

Larval California tiger salamanders subsist on aquatic invertebrates (Oligochaetes, Cladocera, Conchostraca, Ostracoda, Anostraca, Notostraca, Chironomids, *etc.*), as well as the larvae of western spadefoots (*Scaphiopus hammondii*), California toads (*Bufo boreas halophilus*), and Pacific treefrogs (*Hyla regilla*), if the latter are present in breeding ponds (Anderson 1968; Feaver 1971; Jennings, unpubl. data). Larval salamanders are also highly cannibalistic (Jennings, unpubl. data). Good numbers of food organisms in breeding ponds appear to be important for the survival and rapid growth of salamander larvae to metamorphosis (Jennings, unpubl. data).

Juvenile and adult salamanders subsist on terrestrial invertebrates (Oligochaetes, Isopoda, Orthoptera, Coleoptera, Diptera, Araneida, Gastropoda, *etc.*; Stebbins 1972; Morey and Guinn 1992; Jennings, unpubl. data). There is no evidence of adult salamanders feeding in aquatic environments (Jennings, unpubl. data).

Distribution

The historical distribution of the California tiger salamander ranged from the vicinity of Petaluma, Sonoma County and Dunnigan, Colusa-Yolo County line (Storer 1925) with an isolated outpost north of the Sutter Buttes at Gray Lodge, Butte County (Hayes and Cliff 1982) in Central Valley, south to vernal pools in northwest Tulare County, and in the South Coast Range south to ponds and vernal pools between Bulleton and Lompoc in the Santa Ynez drainage, Santa Barbara County (Jennings and Hayes 1994). The known elevational range extends from 3 m-1054 m (Shaffer et al. 1993). The species has disappeared from about 55% of its historic range (Jennings and Hayes 1994).

In the Bay Area, California tiger salamanders have disappeared from almost all of the lower elevation areas (<50 m), save one small site on the San Francisco Wildlife Refuge near Fremont, Alameda County (Jennings, unpubl. data). There are scattered populations currently inhabiting vernal pool and stockpond habitats in hills surrounding the South Bay (Jennings, unpubl. data), to the nort of Coyote Hills in Suisun, and in northern Contra Costa. A group of relict populations is also present in the North Bay region in vernal pool habitats near Petaluma (Shaffer et al. 1993) (**Figure 4.1**).

Current Status and Factors Influencing Population Numbers

Based on the data presented in Shaffer et al. (1993) and Jennings and Hayes (1994), California tiger salamanders appear to have disappeared from approximately 58% and 55% (respectively), of their historic range in the state (Sorensen 1994). This salamander is most affected by land use patterns and other anthropogenic events which fragment habitat and create barriers between breeding and refuge sites (Jennings and Hayes 1994). Some of the more important factors negatively influencing salamander populations include: conversion and isolation of vernal pool habitats (and surrounding oak woodland and grasslands) to agriculture and urbanization (Barry and Shaffer 1994); lowering of the groundwater table by

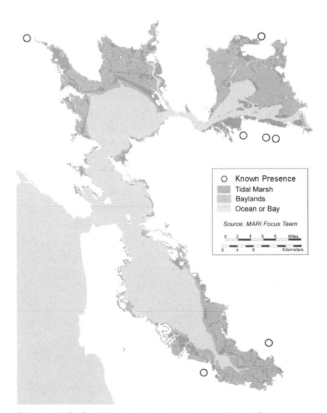

Figure 4.1 California Tiger Salamander – Some Current Locations

Amphibians & Reptiles

overdraft (Jennings and Hayes 1994); mortality of juvenile and adult salamanders by vehicles on roads (Twitty 1941); the introduction of non-native predators such as mosquitofish (*Gambusia affinis*), bullfrogs (*Rana catesbeiana*) and crayfish (specifically *Procambarus clarkii*) into breeding habitats (Shaffer et al. 1993); the widespread poisoning of California ground squirrels and other burrowing rodents (Loredo et al. 1996); and interbreeding with introduced salamanders originally brought in as live fish bait (Shaffer et al. 1993). Juvenile and adult salamanders have also been found in a number of human-created habitats such as septic tank lines, pipes, wells, wet basements, and permanent irrigation ponds (Jennings and Hayes 1994). Such habitats may not be suitable for the long-term survival or successful reproduction of local salamander populations.

Trophic Levels

Larval and post-metamorphic life stages are secondary consumers.

Proximal Species

Predators: Common [=San Francisco] garter snake, Coast garter snake, Central Coast garter snake, California red-legged frog, bullfrog, shrews, striped skunk, opossum, herons, and egrets. Ducks and predacious aquatic insects prey on larvae only.
Prey: Oligochaetes, snails, and terrestrial insects. Zooplankton and aquatic insects are prey for larvae.
Habitat: California ground squirrel and valley pocket gopher (maintain tiger salamander's terrestrial habitats)

Good Habitat

The best habitats for California tiger salamanders are vernal pool complexes with colonies of California ground squirrels or Botta's pocket gophers within the complex or nearby (Shaffer et al. 1993). Such habitats are normally associated with grasslands or oak woodlands (Barry and Shaffer 1994). Additionally, there needs to be abundant invertebrate resources and other native amphibian larvae in the vernal pools used by breeding salamanders.

References

Anderson, P.R. 1968. The reproductive and developmental history of the California tiger salamander. Unpubl. M.A. Thesis, Fresno State College, Fresno, Calif. vii+82 p.

Austin, C.C. and H.B. Shaffer. 1992. Short-, medium-, and long-term repeatability of locomotor performance in the tiger salamander *Ambystoma californiense*. Functional Ecology, 6(2):145-153.

Barry, S.J. and H.B. Shaffer. 1994. The status of the California tiger salamander (*Ambystoma californiense*) at Lagunita: A 50-year update. J. of Herpetology, 28(2):159-164.

Feaver, P.E. 1971. Breeding pool selection and larval mortality of three California amphibians: *Ambystoma tigrinum californiense* Gray, *Hyla regilla* Baird and Girard, and *Scaphiopus hammondii* Girard. Unpubl. M.A. Thesis, Fresno State College, Fresno, Calif. v+58 p.

Frost, D.R. (ed). 1985. Amphibian species of the world: A taxonomic and geographical reference. Allen Press, and the Association of Systematics Collections, Lawrence, Kansas. v+732 p.

Hayes, M.P. and F.S. Cliff. 1982. A checklist of the herpetofauna of Butte County, the Butte Sink, and Sutter Buttes, Calif. Herpetological Review, 13(3):85-87.

Holland, D.C., M.P. Hayes and E. McMillan. 1990. Late summer movement and mass mortality in the California tiger salamander (*Ambystoma californiense*). The Southwestern Naturalist, 35(2):217-220.

Jennings, M.R. and M.P. Hayes. 1994. Amphibian and reptile species of special concern in California. Final report to the Ca. Dept. Fish and Game, Inland Fisheries Div., Rancho Cordova, Ca., under Contract (8023). iii+255 p.

Jones, T.R. 1989. The evolution of macrogeographic and microgeographic variation in the tiger salamander *Ambystoma tigrinum* (Green). Unpubl. Ph.D. Dissertation, Arizona State Univ., Tempe, Az. xiii+173 p.

Long, M.M. 1992. Endangered and threatened wildlife and plants; 90-day finding and comment of status review for a petition to list the California tiger salamander. Fed. Reg., 57(224):54545-54546. [Thursday, November 19, 1992].

Loredo, I., D. Van Vuren, and M.L. Morrison. 1996. Habitat use and migration behavior of the California tiger salamander. J. of Herpetology 30(2):282-285.

Loredo, I. and D. Van Vuren. 1996. Reproductive ecology of a population of the California tiger salamander. Copeia, 1996(4):895-901.

Morey, S.R. and D.A. Guinn. 1992. Activity patterns, food habits, and changing abundance in a community of vernal pool amphibians. Pages 149-158. *In:* D. F. Williams, S. Byrne and T. A. Rado (eds). Endangered and sensitive species of the San Joaquin Valley, California: Their biology, management, and conservation. The Calif. Energy Commission, Sacramento, Calif., and the Western Section of The Wildl. Society. xv+388 p.

Shaffer, H.B., R.N. Fisher and S.E. Stanley. 1993. Status report: The California tiger salamander (*Ambystoma californiense*). Final report to the Ca. Dept. Fish and Game, Inland Fisheries Div., Rancho

Cordova, Calif., under Contracts (FG 9422 and FG 1383). 92 p.

Sorensen, P.C. 1994. Endangered and threatened wildlife and plants; 12-month petition finding for the California tiger salamander. Fed. Reg., 59(74):18353-18354. [Monday, April 18, 1994].

Stebbins, R.C. 1972. Amphibians and reptiles of California. California Natural History Guide (31). Univ. of Ca. Press, Berkeley, Los Angeles, and London. 152 p.

_____. 1985. A field guide to western amphibians and reptiles. Second edition, revised. Houghton Mifflin Company, Boston, Massachusetts. xiv+336 p.

Storer, T.I. 1925. A synopsis of the Amphibia of California. Univ. of Calif. Publications in Zoology, 27:1-342.

Twitty, V.C. 1941. Data on the life history of *Ambystoma tigrinum californiense* Gray. Copeia, 1941(1):1-4.

Zeiner, D.C., W.F. Laudenslayer, Jr. and K.E. Mayer (compiling editors). 1988. California's wildlife. Volume I. Amphibians and reptiles. California Statewide Wildlife Habitat Relationships System, Ca. Dept. of Fish and Game, Sacramento, Ca. ix+272 p.

California Toad

Bufo boreas halophilus

Mark R. Jennings

General Information

The California toad (Family: Bufonidae) is a moderate-sized (62-125 mm SUL) toad with prominent oval parotoid glands and a light middorsal stripe (Stebbins 1985). Dorsal coloration is normally dusky, gray, or greenish, with warts set in black patches (Storer 1925). Natural intergrades with boreal toads (*B. b. boreas*) in northern California and hybrids with Yosemite toads (*B. canorus*) in the Sierra Nevada have been recorded (Storer 1925, Karlstrom 1962).

Rick Fridell

Reproduction

California toads breed between January and July with higher altitude populations delaying breeding until June or July (Storer 1925). At lower elevations, toads are active all year, but at higher elevations adults emerge from hibernation sites immediately before reproducing (Stebbins 1951). Males and females congregate at night around aquatic breeding sites such as stockponds, temporary roadside pools, cement water reservoirs, and the margins of flowing streams where males call, amplexus occurs, and females lay up to 16,500 eggs in two long strings wrapped around vegetation at water depths <150 mm (Storer 1925, Livezey and Wright 1947). Eggs strings are about 5 mm in diameter and the inclusive eggs 1.7 mm in diameter (Storer 1925). After reproducing, adults generally disperse back into the surrounding terrestrial habitats such as meadows and woodlands where they use almost any sort of cover (e.g., trees, low vegetation, beds of leaves, small mammal burrows, rocks, pieces of concrete, downed logs, etc.) that provides a slight amount of moisture and protection from the drying effects of the sun and wind (Storer 1925).

Growth and Development

Eggs hatch within four days to a few weeks (depending on the prevailing water temperature; Storer 1914) and the resulting larvae normally comprise schools composed of one or more clutches (Jennings, unpubl. data). Larvae grow rapidly and usually metamorphose in 2-3 months (from April-August) at 19-52 mm (Storer 1925, Wright and Wright 1949). Recent metamorphs are 12-15 mm in total length (Wright and Wright 1949) and are often observed around the immediate margin of the breeding pond under any cover that protects them from the wind and sun (Storer 1925). The number of newly metamorphosed toads at such breeding sites can number in the thousands (Storer 1925). Young toads grow rapidly and probably reach sexual maturity in two years at lower elevations and somewhat longer at mid-higher elevations (Stebbins 1951). Both juveniles and adults are largely crepuscular, although an occasional individual will be observed during the day in wet or overcast conditions (Storer 1925).

Adults may live 10 years or more in captivity (Bowler 1977) but the longevity of toads in the wild is unknown.

Food and Feeding

Larvae are thought to be algal grazers (Stebbins 1951), but the foraging ecology of larval California toads is unknown. Juveniles and adults feed on a wide variety of terrestrial and flying invertebrates including: Oligochaetes, Isopoda, Diplopoda, Orthoptera, Plecoptera,

Dermaptera, Hemiptera, Homoptera, Coleoptera, Trichoptera, Lepidoptera, Diptera, Arachnids, and Gastropoda (Storer 1914; Eckert 1934; Stebbins 1951, 1972; Morey and Guinn 1992; Jennings, unpubl. data). Cannibalism can also occur (Stebbins 1972).

Distribution

California toads are found over most of California (except for the northernmost counties where they are replaced by boreal toads, and almost all of the Mojave and Colorado deserts where they are replaced by other toad species) from sea level to over 3,050 meters in the Sierra Nevada (Stebbins 1972). This toad is replaced at higher elevations in the central and southern Sierra Nevada by the Yosemite toad (*Bufo canorus*) [Karlstrom 1962]. California toads are widespread in the Bay Area (Stebbins 1959) (**Figure 4.2**) and are still relatively common in stockponds and other aquatic habitats in the surrounding foothills (Jennings, unpubl. data).

Current Status and Factors Influencing Population Numbers

California toads are still present throughout most of their native range in California, although they are now rare in many urban areas where they were formerly common (such as in the Los Angeles Basin; Jennings unpubl.

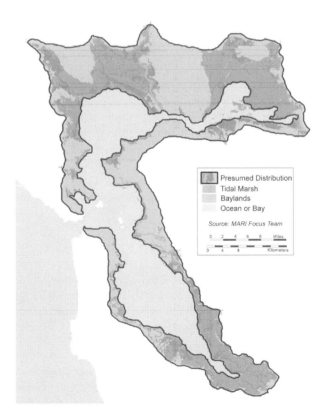

Figure 4.2 California Toad – Presumed Bay Area Distribution

data). The possible reasons for the localized declines are insecticides used in eradicating introduced Mediterranean fruit flies (*Ceratitis capitata*), changing land use patterns by agriculture and urban communities which now leave less sites containing permanent water and areas of dense vegetation (such as tule-lined canals, low ground cover, *etc.*), and habitat fragmentation by roads and dense regions of urbanization (Jennings, unpubl. data). In the Bay Area, California toads are still relatively abundant in natural and moderately-altered habitats (Stebbins 1959; Jennings, unpubl. data). The factors most associated with toad survival include local breeding ponds that last for at least two months, and sufficient cover (vegetative and small mammal burrows) that provide places for toads to feed and grow, as well as escape predators and desiccating conditions.

Trophic Levels

Larval stages are primary consumers and post-metamorphic life stages are secondary consumers.

Proximal Species

Predators: Common [=San Francisco] garter snake, coast garter snake, central coast garter snake, bullfrog, introduced predatory fishes, herons, egrets, raccoon, striped skunk, and opossum. Predacious aquatic insects prey on larvae.
Prey: Aquatic insects, Oligochaetes, Gastropoda, Isopoda, and terrestrial insects.
Habitat: Willows, cattails, tules, sedges, blackberries, riparian vegetation.

Good Habitat

California toads inhabit grasslands, woodlands, meadows, gardens, golf courses, and parks—in fact, anywhere where a permanent source of moisture is present and breeding ponds of at least two months duration are available (Storer 1925). The largest populations of toads seem to be found around stockponds or reservoirs that have an abundance of invertebrate prey, many small mammal burrows and objects (or vegetation) that are available for cover, and a lack of introduced predators (fishes and bullfrogs [*Rana catesbeiana*]) in aquatic habitats.

References

Bowler, J.K. 1977. Longevity of reptiles and amphibians in North American collections. Society for the Study of Amphibians and Reptiles, Miscellaneous Publications, Herpetological Circular (6):1-32.

Eckert, J.E. 1934. The California toad in relation to the hive bee. Copeia. 1934(2):92-93.

Karlstrom, E.L. 1962. The toad genus *Bufo* in the Sierra Nevada of California: Ecological and systematic relationships. Univ. of Calif. Publications in Zoology. 62(1):1-104.

Livezey, R.L. and A.H. Wright. 1947. A synoptic key to the salientian eggs of the United States. The American Midland Naturalist. 37(1):179-222.

Morey, S.R. and D.A. Guinn. 1992. Activity patterns, food habits, and changing abundance in a community of vernal pool amphibians. *In*: D.F. Williams, S. Byrne and T.A. Rado (eds). Endangered and sensitive species of the San Joaquin Valley, California: Their biology, management, and conservation. The Calif. Energy Commission, Sacramento, Calif., and the Western Section of The Wildl. Society. xv+388 p.

Stebbins, R.C. 1951. Amphibians of western North America. Univ. of Calif. Press, Berkeley and Los Angeles. ix+539 p.

_____. 1959. Reptiles and amphibians of the San Francisco Bay region. California Natural History Guide (3). Univ. of Calif. Press, Berkeley and Los Angeles. 72 p.

_____. 1972. Amphibians and reptiles of California. California Natural History Guide (31). Univ. of Calif. Press, Berkeley, Los Angeles, and London. 152 p.

_____. 1985. A field guide to western amphibians and reptiles. Second ed., revised. Houghton Mifflin Co., Boston, Massachusetts. xiv+336 p.

Storer, T.I. 1914. The California toad, an economic asset. U.C. J. of Agriculture, 2(3):89-91.

_____. 1925. A synopsis of the Amphibia of California. Univ. of Calif. Publications in Zoology, 27:1-342.

Wright, A.H. and A.A. Wright. 1949. Handbook of frogs and toads of the United States and Canada. Third ed. Comstock Publ. Co., Inc., Ithaca, NY. xii+640 p.

Pacific Treefrog

Hyla regilla

Mark R. Jennings

General Information

The Pacific treefrog (Family: Hylidae) is a small (19-50 mm SUL) frog with toe pads and a black eye stripe (Stebbins 1985). The dorsal coloration is highly variable—green, tan, reddish, gray, brown, or black—sometimes with dark dorsal spots (Wright and Wright 1949, Resnick and Jameson 1963, Stebbins 1972); however green or shades of brown are the usual colors observed (Nussbaum et al. 1983). For a time, these treefrogs were lumped with chorus frogs of the genus *Pseudacris* (see Hedges 1986). However, recent work has shown that Pacific treefrogs are not chorus frogs, hence the reversion to the old genus *Hyla* (Crocroft 1994).

This frog has the most notable voice of the frog world as its call has been used as a natural background sound in innumerable movies produced by Hollywood (Myers 1951).

Reproduction

Pacific treefrogs can become sexually mature in one year, but most become sexually mature in two years (Jameson 1956). At lower elevations, treefrogs are active all year, but at higher elevations adults emerge from hibernation sites immediately before reproducing (Stebbins 1951). From late November to July (beginning with the first warm rainfall), males congregate at night around any suitable shallow pond of water (or at the shallow edges of deep water ponds or reservoirs) and chorus to attract receptive females (Storer 1925, Brattstrom and Warren 1955, Schaub and Larsen 1978, Nussbaum et al. 1983), and also call to space themselves from one another (Snyder and Jameson 1965, Allan 1973). Groups of two or three males tend to call in sequence during these choruses and the sequence is consistently started by one frog known as the bout leader (Whitney and Krebs 1975).

Amphibians & Reptiles

The choruses may continue into daylight hours (Jameson 1957) and can be deafening if hundreds or thousands of calling males are involved (Stebbins 1959; Jennings, unpubl. data). Females attracted to these calls usually select the bout leader to mate with (Whitney and Krebs 1975). Upon amplexus, females lay approximately 20-25 packets containing 9-70 (usually 22-25) eggs on submerged aquatic vegetation or on the bottom of shallow pools (Smith 1940, Livezey and Wright 1947), generally at depths >100 mm (Storer 1925). Egg masses are normally laid close together, one against another, or separated by <25 mm (Stebbins 1951). The eggs are about 1.3 mm in diameter and females may lay from 500 to 1,250 total eggs (Storer 1925, Smith 1940). After egg deposition, males and females remain the vicinity of the breeding pond for up to one and three months respectively, and then return to surrounding terrestrial habitats (Jameson 1957, Nussbaum et al. 1983). Females may also breed up to three times during the year (Perrill and Daniel 1983).

Growth and Development

Eggs hatch in four days to two weeks, depending on the prevailing water temperatures and the resulting larvae (6.0-7.5 mm total length) grow rapidly (Storer 1925). Larvae are also known to aggregate into large groups of several hundred individuals (Brattstrom and Warren 1955). Metamorphosis is generally within two months at anytime between February-late August (Storer 1925; Jennings, unpubl. data), at total lengths between 45 and 55 mm (Storer 1925, Wright and Wright 1949). Post-metamorphs are about 12-15 mm and grow rapidly within the first two months often doubling their size (Jameson 1956). For the first few months, post-metamorphs remain in the immediate vicinity of the breeding pond utilizing almost any cover present (rocks, vegetation, leaves, *etc.*) for protection from the drying effects of the sun and wind (Jameson 1956). After several months, juveniles disperse out into surrounding terrestrial habitats and seek places that contain moisture and are protected by the elements. Such places include small mammal burrows, rock fissures, tree cavities, dense vegetation, piles of debris, buildings, artificial drains, *etc.*, that may be 0.8 km or more from the nearest standing water (Storer 1925, Jameson 1957).

Adults may live four years or more in captivity (Jennings, unpubl. data). Longevity in the wild is apparently somewhat over three years (Jameson 1956).

Food and Feeding

Larvae are thought to be algal grazers (Storer 1925), but the foraging ecology of larval Pacific treefrogs is unknown. Juveniles and adults feed on a wide variety of terrestrial and flying invertebrates including: Oligocha-

etes, Oniscidea, Orthoptera, Hemiptera, Homoptera, Coleoptera, Lepidoptera, Diptera, Hymenoptera, Arachnids, and Gastropoda (Needham 1924; Stebbins 1951; Brattstrom and Warren 1955; Nussbaum et al. 1983; Morey and Guinn 1992; Jennings, unpubl. data).

Distribution

Pacific treefrogs are found over most of California (except drier parts of the Mojave and Colorado deserts) from sea level to around 3,670 m in the Sierra Nevada (Stebbins 1972, 1985). In the Bay Area they are very abundant (Stebbins 1959; Jennings, unpubl. data), and found throughout the region (**Figure 4.3**).

Current Status and Factors Influencing Population Numbers

Pacific treefrogs have always been abundant throughout most of their native range (e.g., see Storer 1925, Stebbins 1951, Nussbaum et al. 1983), and they still remain so even in the Sierra Nevada (Jennings 1996, *contra* Drost and Fellers 1996). Treefrogs are especially common in the Bay Area (Stebbins 1959) because of their ability to utilize habitats created by humans—especially in urban areas. Although populations are negatively influenced by the premature drying of breeding ponds and continued loss of many individuals through predation,

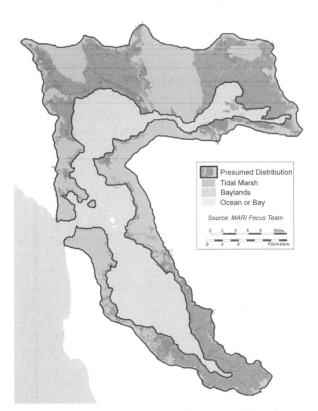

Figure 4.3 Pacific Treefrog – Presumed Bay Area Distribution

treefrogs are able to successfully reproduce in numbers to overcome these set backs (Jameson 1956, 1957).

Trophic Levels

Larval stages are primary consumers and post-metamorphic life stages are secondary consumers.

Proximal Species

Habitat: Willows, cattails, tules, and sedges.
Predators: Common [=San Francisco] garter snake, Coast garter snake, Central Coast garter snake, California red-legged frog, bullfrog, introduced predatory fishes, herons and egrets, raccoon, striped skunk, and opossum. California tiger salamander and various predacious aquatic insects prey on larvae only.
Prey: Aquatic and terrestrial insects.

Good Habitat

Pacific treefrogs can essentially inhabit almost any place that contains sufficient moisture and protection from the wind and sun, and has suitable nearby breeding sites. They can reproduce in temporary aquatic environments as small as a jar of water as long as the water remains present for two months or more (Jennings, unpubl. data) and the water temperature is below 35-38°C (Schechtman and Olson 1941). The largest populations seem to be present in complexes of shallow ponds (lacking fishes and other aquatic predators) surrounded by growths of tules (*Scirpus* sp.) and other aquatic vegetation (Jameson 1956, 1957), although Pacific treefrogs also seem to do well in golf courses, city parks, and other places that have permanent aquatic habitats and places with riparian vegetation (Jennings, unpubl. data).

References

Allan, D.M. 1973. Some relationships of vocalization to behavior in the Pacific treefrog, *Hyla regilla*. Herpetologica, 29(4):366-371.

Brattstrom, B.H. and J.W. Warren. 1955. Observations on the ecology and behavior of the Pacific treefrog, *Hyla regilla*. Copeia, 1955(3):181-191.

Crocroft, R.B. 1994. A cladistic analysis of chorus frog phylogeny (Hylidae: *Pseudacris*). Herpetologica, 50(4):420-437.

Drost, C.A. and G.M. Fellers. 1996. Collapse of a regional frog fauna in the Yosemite area of the California Sierra Nevada, USA. Conservation Biology, 10(2):414-425.

Hedges, S.B. 1986. An electrophoretic analysis of Holarctic hylid frog evolution. Systematic Zoology, 35(1):1-21.

Jameson, D.L. 1956. Growth, dispersal and survival of the Pacific tree frog. Copeia, 1956(1):25-29.

_____. 1957. Population structure and homing responses in the Pacific tree frog. Copeia, 1957(3):221-228.

Jennings, M.R. 1996. Status of amphibians. Pages 31-1—31-24. *In*: Sierra Nevada Ecosystem Project: Final Report to Congress, Volume II, Assessments and Scientific Basis for Management Options. Centers for Water and Wetland Resources, Univ. of Calif., Davis, Calif.

Livezey, R.L. and A.H. Wright. 1947. A synoptic key to the salientian eggs of the United States. The American Midland Naturalist, 37(1):179-222.

Morey, S.R. and D.A. Guinn. 1992. Activity patterns, food habits, and changing abundance in a community of vernal pool amphibians. Pages 149-158. *In*: D.F. Williams, S.Byrne, and T. A. Rado (eds). Endangered and sensitive species of the San Joaquin Valley, California: Their biology, management, and conservation. The Calif. Energy Commission, Sacramento, Calif., and the Western Section of The Wildl. Society. xv+388 p.

Myers, G.S. 1951. The most widely heard amphibian voice. Copeia, 1951(2):179.

Needham, J.G. 1924. Observations of the life of the ponds at the head of Laguna Canyon. J. of Entomology and Zoology, 16(1):1-12.

Nussbaum, R.A., E.D. Brodie, Jr. and R.M. Storm. 1983. Amphibians and reptiles of the Pacific Northwest. Univ. of Idaho Press, Moscow, Idaho. 332 p.

Perrill, S.A. and R.E. Daniel. 1983. Multiple egg clutches in *Hyla regilla*, *H. cinerea* and *H. gratiosa*. Copeia, 1983(2):513-516.

Resnick, L.E. and D.L. Jameson. 1963. Color polymorphism in Pacific tree frogs. Science, 142(3595):1081-1083.

Schaub, D.L. and J.H. Larsen. 1978. The reproductive ecology of the Pacific treefrog (*Hyla regilla*). Herpetologica, 34(4):409-416.

Schechtman, A.M. and J.B. Olson. 1941. Unusual temperature tolerance of an amphibian egg (*Hyla regilla*). Ecology, 22(4):409-410.

Smith, R.E. 1940. Mating and oviposition in the Pacific Coast tree toad. Science, 92(2391):379-380.

Snyder, W.F. and D.L. Jameson. 1965. Multivariate geographic variation of mating call in populations of the Pacific tree frog (*Hyla regilla*). Copeia, 1965(2):129-142.

Stebbins, R. C. 1951. Amphibians of western North America. Univ. of Calif. Press, Berkeley and Los Angeles. ix+539 p.

_____. 1959. Reptiles and amphibians of the San Francisco Bay region. California Natural History Guide (3). Univ. of Ca. Press, Berkeley and Los Angeles. 72 p.

_____. 1972. Amphibians and reptiles of California. California Natural History Guide (31). Univ. of Calif. Press, Berkeley, Los Angeles, and London. 152 p.

Amphibians & Reptiles

_____. 1985. A field guide to western amphibians and reptiles. Second edition, revised. Houghton Mifflin Company, Boston, Massachusetts. xiv+336 p.

Storer, T.I. 1925. A synopsis of the Amphibia of California. Univ. of Calif. Publications in Zoology, 27:1-342.

Whitney, C. L. and J.R. Krebs. 1975. Spacing and calling in Pacific tree frogs, *Hyla regilla*. Canadian J. of Zoology, 53(11):1519-1527.

Wright, A.H. and A.A. Wright. 1949. Handbook of frogs and toads of the United States and Canada. Third edition. Comstock Publishing Company, Inc., Ithaca, New York. xii+640 p.

California Red-Legged Frog

Rana aurora draytonii

Mark R. Jennings

General Information

The California red-legged frog (Family: Ranidae) is a large (85-138 mm SUL) brown to reddish brown frog with prominent dorsolateral folds and diffuse moderate-sized dark brown to black spots that sometimes have light centers (Storer 1925, Jennings and Hayes 1994a). The species is the largest native frog in the state and there are data to support elevation as a separate species from the northern red-legged frog (*R. a.aurora*) [see Hayes and Miyamoto 1984, Green 1985]; however, there is also large zone of intergradation along the Pacific slope of the North Coast Range (Hayes and Kremples 1986). In 1993, the California red-legged frog was petitioned for listing as an endangered species by the U.S. Fish and Wildlife Service (Sorensen 1993) based on a significant range reduction and continued threats to surviving populations (Miller 1994). The frog was subsequently listed as Threatened by the U.S. Fish and Wildlife Service (Miller et al. 1996).

Dan Holland

Reproduction

Adults generally reach sexual maturity in their second year for males and third year for females (Jennings and Hayes 1985), although sexual maturity may be reached earlier during years of abundant food resources (Jennings, unpubl. data). During extended periods of drought, frogs may take 3-4 years to reach maturity (Jennings and Hayes 1994a). Reproduction generally occurs at night in permanent ponds or the slack water pools of streams during the winter and early spring (late November-through April) after the onset of warm rains (Storer 1925, Hayes and Jennings 1988, Jennings and Hayes 1994a). California red-legged frogs can only successfully reproduce in aquatic environments with water temperatures $\leq 26°C$ and salinities $\leq 4.5\%$ as developing embryos cannot tolerate conditions higher than this (Jennings, unpubl. data). Larvae can tolerate somewhat higher water temperatures and salinities (Jennings, unpubl. data). Males generally appear at breeding sites from 2-4 weeks before females (Storer 1925). At breeding sites, males typically call in small, mobile groups of 3-7 individuals that attract females (Jennings and Hayes 1994a). Females amplex with males and attach egg masses containing approximately 2,000-6,000 moderate-sized (2.0-2.8 mm diameter) eggs to an emergent vegetation brace at depths usually from 75-100 mm (Storer 1925). Egg masses are normally laid at the surface of the water (Livezey and Wright 1947). California red-legged frogs are explosive breeders, usually depositing their egg masses within 3-4 week period after large rainfall events (Hayes and Miyamoto 1984). After reproduction, males usually remain at the breeding sites for several weeks before removing to foraging habitats, while females immediately remove to these foraging habitats (Jennings, unpubl. data). There is no evidence of double clutching with this species (Jennings, unpubl. data).

Growth and Development

Eggs hatch after 6-14 days (depending on the prevailing water temperature), and the resulting larvae (8.8-10.3 mm total length) require 3.5-7 months to attain metamorphosis at 65-85 mm total length (Storer 1925; Jennings, unpubl. data). Larvae, which are solitary and almost never overwinter, typically metamorphose between July and September (Storer 1925, Jennings and Hayes 1994a).

Juvenile frogs are 25-30 mm total length at metamorphosis and commonly sun themselves during the day at the edge of the riparian zone next to the breeding site. As they grow, they gradually shift from diurnal and nocturnal periods of activity, to largely nocturnal activity (Hayes and Tennant 1986). During periods of rainfall, both juveniles and a few adults may disperse away from breeding sites and may be found some distance (up to

0.8 km) away from the nearest water (Jennings, unpubl. data). Along the lower reaches of streams on the Central Coast of California which tend to almost completely dry up during the late summer, subadult and adult frogs have been found to occupy small mammal burrows under leaf litter or dense vegetation in the riparian zone (Rathbun et al. 1993). These frogs make overland trips every few days or so to isolated stream pools to rehydrate themselves although one frog remained in riparian habitat for 77 days (Rathbun *in litt.* 1994 as cited in Miller et al. 1996). Based on these observations, frogs found in coastal drainages appear to be rarely inactive, whereas those found in interior sites probably hibernate (Storer 1925).

Based on limited field data, California red-legged frogs appear to live about 8-10 years in the wild (Jennings, unpubl. data).

Food and Feeding

Larvae are thought to be algal grazers (Storer 1925), but the feeding ecology of larval California red-legged frogs is unknown. Juvenile and adult frogs have a highly variable animal food diet that includes: Amphipods, Isopods, Orthoptera, Isoptera, Hemiptera, Homoptera, Neuroptera, Coleoptera, Lepidoptera, Diptera, Hymenoptera, Arachnids, Gastropoda, small fishes, amphibians, and small mammals (Stebbins 1972, Hayes and Tennant 1985, Baldwin and Stanford 1987). Most prey that can be swallowed that are not distasteful are eaten, with larger frogs capable of taking larger prey (Jennings and Hayes 1994a). Small red-legged frogs, Pacific treefrogs (*Hyla regilla*), and California mice (*Peromyscus californicus*) may contribute significantly to the diet of subadults and adults (Arnold and Halliday 1986, Hayes and Tennant 1985).

Distribution

Historically, California red-legged frogs were found throughout the Pacific slope drainages from the vicinity of Redding, Shasta County (Storer 1925), inland and at least to Point Reyes, Marin County (Hayes and Kremples 1986), California (coastally) southward to the Santo Domingo River drainage in Baja California, Mexico (Linsdale 1932). They also historically occurred in a few desert slope drainages in southern California (Jennings and Hayes 1994b). California red-legged frogs generally occurred below 1370 m in the Sierra Nevada foothills (Jennings 1996) and 1520 m in southern California, although some of the populations toward the upper limit of the range of this frog may represent translocations (Jennings and Hayes 1994a). In the Bay Area, this frog was historically abundant enough to support an important commercial fishery just before the turn of the century (Jennings and Hayes 1985) and up to the

1950s it was still considered to be present in much of the San Francisco Bay region (Stebbins 1959). However, earlier overexploitation, subsequent habitat loss from agriculture and urbanization, and the introduction of exotic aquatic predators have presently reduced red-legged frog distribution to scattered locations in the foothills and mountains of the San Francisco Bay region (Jennings, unpubl. data) (**Figure 4.4**).

Current Status and Factors Influencing Population Numbers

Based on the data presented in Jennings and Hayes (1994a, 1994b), California red-legged frogs appear to have disappeared from approximately 70-75%, of their historic range in the state (Miller et al. 1996). This frog is most affected by land use patterns and other anthropogenic events which fragment high quality habitat and create environments unsuitable for the continued survival of the species (Jennings and Hayes 1994a, 1994b). Some of the more important factors negatively influencing frog populations include: conversion and isolation of perennial pool habitats (and surrounding riparian zones) to agriculture; reservoir construction projects; urbanization; lowering of the groundwater table by overdraft; overgrazing by domestic livestock; extended drought; mortality of juvenile and adult frogs by vehicles on roads; and the introduction of non-native predators such as mosquitofish (*Gambusia affinis*), bullfrogs (*Rana*

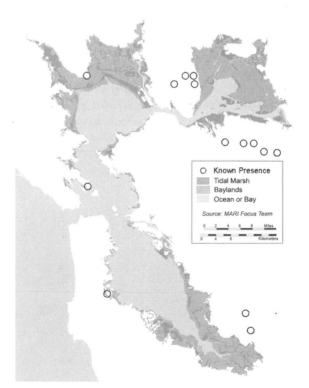

Figure 4.4 California Red-Legged Frog – Some Current Locations

catesbeiana) and crayfish (specifically *Procambarus clarkii*) into breeding habitats (Miller et al. 1996). Juvenile and adult frogs have also been found in a number of human-created habitats such as irrigation canals, golf course ponds, sewage treatment ponds, gravel pits, and intermittent irrigation ponds (Jennings and Hayes 1994a; Jennings, unpubl. data). Such habitats may not be suitable for the long-term survival or successful reproduction of local frog populations, especially near urban areas where predators such as bullfrogs and raccoons (*Procyon lotor*) are able to build up large populations as a result of human activities (Jennings, unpubl. data).

Trophic Levels

Larval stages are primary consumers and post-metamorphic life stages are secondary/tertiary consumers.

Proximal Species

Predators: Common [=San Francisco] garter snake, Coast garter snake, Central Coast garter snake, bullfrog, heron, egret, raccoon, and introduced predatory fishes. Predacious aquatic insects prey on larvae only.
Prey: California tiger salamander, Pacific treefrog, California mouse, bullfrog, and aquatic and terrestrial insects.
Habitat: Willows, cattails, tules, sedges, and blackberries.

Good Habitat

Although California red-legged frogs can occur in ephemeral or artificially-created ponds devoid of vegetation, the habitats that have been observed to have the largest frog populations are perennial, deep (>0.7 m) water pools bordered by dense, shrubby riparian vegetation (Jennings 1988, Hayes and Jennings 1986). This dense riparian vegetation is characterized by arroyo willows (*Salix lasiolepis*) intermixed with an understory of cattails (*Typha* sp.), tules (*Scirpus* sp.), or bulrushes (*Scirpus* sp.) [Jennings 1988].

References

Arnold, S.J. and T.Halliday. 1986. Life history notes: *Hyla regilla*, predation. Herpetological Review, 17(2):44.

Baldwin, K.S. and R.A. Stanford. 1987. Life history notes: *Ambystoma tigrinum californiense*, predation. Herpetological Review, 18(2):33.

Green, D.M. 1985. Differentiation in heterochromatin amount between subspecies of the red-legged frog, *Rana aurora*. Copeia, 1985(4):1071-1074.

Hayes, M.P. and M.R. Jennings. 1988. Habitat correlates of distribution of the California red-legged frog (*Rana aurora draytonii*) and the foothill yellow-legged frog (*Rana boylii*): implications for management. Pages 144-158. *In*: R.C. Szaro, K.E. Severson, and D.R. Patton (technical coordinators). Management of Amphibians, Reptiles, and Small Mammals in North America. Proceedings of the Symposium, July 19-21, 1988, Flagstaff, Arizona. U.S. Forest Serv., Rocky Mountain Forest and Range Experiment Station, Fort Collins, Colorado. General Tech. Report (RM-166):1-458.

Hayes, M.P. and D.M. Kremples. 1986. Vocal sac variation among frogs of the genus *Rana* from western North America. Copeia, 1986(4):927-936.

Hayes, M.P. and M.M. Miyamoto. 1984. Biochemical, behavioral and body size differences between the red-legged frogs, *Rana aurora aurora* and *Rana aurora draytonii*. Copeia, 1984(4):1018-1022.

Hayes, M.P. and M.R. Tennant. 1986. Diet and feeding behavior of the California red-legged frog, *Rana aurora draytonii* (Ranidae). The Southwestern Naturalist, 30(4): 601-605.

Jennings, M.R. 1988. Natural history and decline of native ranids in California. Pages 61-72. *In*: H.F. De Lisle, P.R. Brown, B.Kaufman, and B. McGurty (eds). Proceedings of the Conference On California Herpetology. Southwestern Herpetologists Society, Special Publ. (4):1-143.

Jennings, M.R. 1996. Status of amphibians. Pages 31-1—31-24. *In*: Sierra Nevada Ecosystem Project: Final Report to Congress, Volume II, Assessments and Scientific Basis for Management Options. Centers for Water and Wetland Resources, Univ. of Calif., Davis, Calif.

Jennings, M.R. and M.P. Hayes. 1985. Pre-1900 overharvest of the California red-legged frog (*Rana aurora draytonii*): The inducement for bullfrog (*R. catesbeiana*) introduction. Herpetologica, 41(1):94-103.

_____. 1994a. Amphibian and reptile species of special concern in California. Final report to the Ca. Dept. Fish and Game, Inland Fisheries Div., Rancho Cordova, Calif., under Contract (8023). iii+255 p.

_____. 1994b. The decline of native ranid frogs in the desert southwest. Pages 183-211. *In*: P.R. Brown and J.W. Wright (eds). Herpetology of the North American Deserts: Proceedings of a Symposium. Southwestern Herpetologists Society, Special Publ. (5):iv+300 p.

Linsdale, J.M. 1932. Amphibians and reptiles from Lower California. Univ. of Calif. Publications in Zoology, 38(6):345-386.

Livezey, R.L. and A.H. Wright. 1947. A synoptic key to the salientian eggs of the United States. The American Midland Naturalist, 37(1):179-222.

Miller, K.J. 1994. Endangered and threatened wildlife and plants; proposed endangered status for the California red-legged frog. Fed. Reg., 59(22):4888-4895. [Wednesday, February 2, 1994].

Miller, K.J., A. Willy, S. Larsen, and S. Morey. 1996. Endangered and threatened wildlife and plants; determination of threatened status for the California red-legged frog. Fed. Reg, 61(101):25813-25833. [Thursday, May 23, 1996].

Rathbun, G.B., M.R. Jennings, T.G. Murphey, and N.R. Siepel. 1993. Status and ecology of sensitive aquatic vertebrates in lower San Simeon and Pico Creeks, San Luis Obispo County, California. Final report prepared for the Calif. Dept. of Parks and Recreation, San Simeon Region, through Cooperative Agreement (14-16-0009-01-1909). U.S. Fish and Wildl. Serv., Natl. Ecology Research Center, Piedras Blancas Research Station, San Simeon, Calif. ix+103 p.

Sorensen, P.C. 1993. Endangered and threatened wildlife and plants; finding on petition to list the California red-legged frog. Fed. Reg. 58(136):38553. [Monday, July 19, 1993].

Stebbins, R.C. 1959. Reptiles and amphibians of the San Francisco Bay region. California Natural History Guide (3). Univ. of Calif. Press, Berkeley and Los Angeles. 72 p.

_____. 1972. Amphibians and reptiles of California. California Natural History Guide (31). Univ. of Calif. Press, Berkeley, Los Angeles, and London. 152 p.

Storer, T.I. 1925. A synopsis of the Amphibia of California. Univ. of Calif. Publications in Zoology, 27:1-342.

Western Pond Turtle

Clemmys marmorata

Mark R. Jennings

General Information

The western pond turtle (Family: Emydidae) is a moderate-sized (120-210 mm CL), drab brown or khaki-colored turtle often lacking prominent markings on its carapace (Bury and Holland, in press). Carapace coloration is usually dark brown or dull yellow-olive, with or without darker streaks or vermiculations radiating from the centers of the scutes (Ernst et al. 1994, Jennings and Hayes 1994).

There are two poorly differentiated subspecies of the western pond turtle (*C. m. marmorata* and *C. m. pallida*) with a wide zone of intergradation in central California (Bury 1970). Based on a morphological evaluation, Holland (1992) found three distinct evolutionary groups within this taxon. However, Gray (1995) found through DNA fingerprinting of *C. marmorata* samples from the extreme southern and northern edges of its range support the original designation of two distinct subspecies. Bury and Holland (in press) indicate that more comprehensive genetic studies are currently underway to determine the taxonomic status of this taxon.

In 1992, the western pond turtle was petitioned for listing as an endangered species (Sorensen and Propp 1992) based on concerns about widespread population declines due to the extensive loss of habitat, overexploitation, introductions of non-native aquatic predators (Sorensen and Propp 1992; see also Jennings and Hayes 1994). The U.S. Fish and Wildlife Service subsequently ruled that the petition was not warranted (USFWS 1993) and this turtle remains a candidate 2 species (Drewry 1994).

Reproduction

In California, sexual maturity in western pond turtles occurs at between seven and 11 years of age at approximately 110-120 mm CL with males maturing at slightly

smaller sizes and ages than females (Jennings and Hayes 1994). Sexual maturity is delayed in turtles that experience drought conditions and in more northerly populations (Jennings and Hayes 1994). Adult turtles typically mate in late April or early May, although mating can occur year-around (Holland 1985a, 1992). The nesting season is from late April to early August (Storer 1930, Buskirk 1992, Rathbun et al. 1992, Jennings and Hayes 1994, Goodman 1997a). Females emigrate from the aquatic habitats to an unshaded, upland location that may be a considerable distance (400 m or more) from riparian zones to nest (Storer 1930; Rathbun et al. 1992; Bury and Holland, in press). However, most nest locations are close to riparian zones if nesting substrates and exposures are suitable (Jennings, unpubl. data). Once a suitable site is located, females deposit from 1-13 eggs that have a thin, but hard (calcified) outer shell in a shallow (ca. 10-12 cm deep) nest (Rathbun et al. 1992, 1993)—usually in well-drained clay or silt soils (Jennings and Hayes 1994). Eggs laid in excessively moist substrates have a high probability of failing (Feldman 1982). Females can lay more than one clutch of eggs a year and may dig several "false" nests lacking eggs to deter potential predators (Rathbun et al. 1993, Goodman 1997b).

Growth and Development

Young turtles hatch at lengths of 25-29 mm CL (Ernst et al. 1994) after an incubation period of 3-4.5 months (Buskirk 1992; Bury and Holland, in press) and are thought to overwinter in the nest because there are only a few records of hatchling turtle emergence in the early fall in southern and central California (Buskirk 1992, Jennings and Hayes 1994). Most hatchling turtles are thought to emerge from the nest and move to aquatic sites in the spring (Buskirk 1992) where they typically double their length the first year and grow relatively rapidly over the next 4-5 years (Storer 1930, Holland 1985a). Young turtles spend most of their time feeding in shallow water dominated by relatively dense vegetation of submergents, short emergents, or algal mats (Buskirk 1992, Jennings and Hayes 1994). Juveniles and adults prefer slack- or slow-water aquatic habitats with basking sites such as rocks and logs (Bury 1972, Reese 1996). Water temperatures >15°C markedly increase turtle activity so many western pond turtles are probably active year around in coastal locations (Reese and Welsh 1998) and only active from March or April-October or November in interior locations (Bury and Holland, in press). Juveniles and adults seem to remain in pond environments except when ponds dry up or at higher elevations when turtles may disperse into terrestrial environments to hibernate (Jennings and Hayes 1994; Goodman 1997a, Bury and Holland, in press). In stream environments, juveniles and adults show considerable variation with regards to movements and the timing of movements into terrestrial environments (Rathbun et al. 1993, Reese and Welsh 1998). Some turtles will leave the stream during the summer when water conditions are low and water temperatures are elevated (>35°C), while others will not. However, almost turtles seem to leave streams during the winter months when large flood events are common (Rathbun et al. 1993). Additionally, some turtles will move considerable distances (e.g., 350 m) to overwinter in terrestrial habitats such as leaf litter or under the root masses of trees (Rathbun et al. 1992, 1993). Some individual turtles have displayed site fidelity for hibernation sites from year to year (Bury and Holland, in press).

Western pond turtles often move about from pool to pool in stream situations, sometimes on a daily basis during seasons of activity (Bury 1972, Reese and Welsh 1998). Distances moved along streams can be up to 5 km (Bury and Holland, in press). These turtles also have the ability to move several kilometers if their aquatic habitat dries up (Reese 1996) and they can tolerate at least seven days without water (Jennings and Hayes 1994; Bury and Holland, in press).

Western pond turtles are known to live over 42 years in the wild (Jennings and Hayes 1994) although most individuals have a much shorter life span of around 20-25 years (Bury 1972).

Food and Feeding

Juvenile and adult western pond turtles feed largely on the same items although juveniles feed more on smaller aquatic invertebrates (Bury 1986). Food items found in turtle stomachs include: algae, aquatic plants, Nematomorpha, Cladocera, Decapoda, Isopoda, Ephemeroptera (nymphs only), Odonata (nymphs only), Orthoptera, Hemiptera (nymphs and adults), Neuroptera (larvae only), Coleoptera (larvae and adults), Trichoptera (larvae only), Diptera (larvae and adults), Araneae, Gastropoda, fishes, and amphibians (Carr 1952, Holland 1985b, Bury 1986, Ernst et al. 1994, Goodman 1997a). These turtles are dietary generalists and highly opportunistic (Ernst et al. 1994). They will consume almost anything that they are able to catch and overpower. The relatively slow pursuit of these turtles results in their diet being dominated by relatively slow-moving aquatic invertebrates and carrion, although aquatic vegetation may also be eaten (Evenden 1948, Bury 1986, Baldwin and Stanford 1987), especially by females having recently laid eggs (Jennings and Hayes 1994).

Distribution

The western pond turtle historically occurred in most Pacific slope drainages from Klickitat County, Washington along the Columbia River (Slater 1962) south to Arroyo Santa Domingo, northern Baja California,

Mexico (Jennings and Hayes 1994). Isolated populations are also known from Carson, Humboldt, and Truckee drainages in western Nevada (LaRivers 1962, Banta 1963). In California the species is known from most Pacific slope drainages between the Oregon and Mexican borders below 1430 m (Jennings and Hayes 1994). Turtle observations from above this elevation are thought to be introductions (Jennings and Hayes 1994). Western pond turtles are present throughout the Bay Area (Stebbins 1959) (**Figure 4.5**), although at much lower numbers and at fewer localities than previously—especially in urban areas (Jennings, unpubl. data).

Current Status and Factors Influencing Population Numbers

The western pond turtle is declining in population size and numbers throughout its range, particularly in southern California and the San Joaquin Valley (Bury and Holland, in press). Many turtle populations in these areas of decline are now composed almost entirely of old adults without any successful recruitment (Jennings and Hayes 1994). The reasons for these declines are largely due to urbanization, agricultural development, flood control projects, exotic diseases, exploitation for the food and pet trade, extended drought, and the introduction of exotic predatory species such as largemouth bass (*Micropterus salmoides*) and bullfrogs (*Rana catesbeiana*) which also compete for the availability of prey items—especially with young turtles (Brattstrom 1988; Buskirk 1992; Jennings and Hayes 1994; Reese 1996; Goodman 1997a; Bury and Holland, in press). Turtle nests and gravid females moving overland are especially vulnerable to predation by raccoons (*Procyon lotor*), whose populations have greatly increased in many rural areas due to the increase in human populations in these areas (Bury and Holland, in press; Jennings, unpubl. data). Additionally, some of the largest turtle populations in the Central Valley and southern California are found in sewage treatment ponds. Unfortunately, such habitats are probably unsuitable for the long term survival of the species because of the lack of suitable habitat for nest sites and increased vulnerability of adult turtles to predation by humans, raccoons, and other animals (Jennings, unpubl. data).

Trophic Levels

Young turtles are essentially secondary consumers; adults are primary and secondary consumers.

Proximal Species

Predators: Raccoon, bullfrog, black bear, humans, and introduced predatory fishes. Striped skunk and opossum prey on eggs and hatchlings, and herons and egrets prey on young turtles.

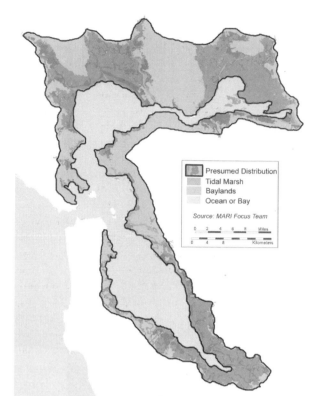

Figure 4.5 Western Pond Turtle – Presumed Bay Area Distribution

Prey: Aquatic Insects, aquatic vegetation, and California tiger salamander larvae.

Habitat: Aquatic vegetation.

Good Habitat

The largest western pond turtle populations have been observed in warm water (15-35°C), slack- or slow-water habitats, which have abundant basking sites and underwater refugia. The presence of dense stands of submergent or emergent vegetation, and abundant aquatic invertebrate resources, as well suitable nearby nesting sites and the lack of native and exotic predators, are also important components (Bury 1972; Jennings and Hayes 1994; Bury and Holland, in press).

References

Baldwin, K.S. and R.A. Stanford. 1987. Life history notes: *Ambystoma tigrinum californiense*, predation. Herpetological Review, 18(2):33.

Banta, B.H. 1963. On the occurrence of *Clemmys marmorata* (Reptilia, Testudinata) in western Nevada. The Wasmann J. of Biology, 21(1):75-77.

Brattstrom, B.H. 1988. Habitat destruction in California with special reference to *Clemmys marmorata*: A perpesctive [sic]. Pages 13-24. *In*: H.F. De Lisle, P.R. Brown, B.Kaufman, and B. McGurty (eds). Proceedings of the Conference On California Herpetology. Southwestern Herpetologists Society, Special Publ. (4):1-143.

Bury, R.B. 1970. *Clemmys marmorata*. Catalogue of American Amphibians and Reptiles:100.1-100.3.

_____. 1972. Habits and home range of the Pacific pond turtle, *Clemmys marmorata*. Unpubl. Ph.D. Dissertation, Univ. of Ca., Berkeley, Calif. 205 p.

_____. 1986. Feeding ecology of the turtle, *Clemmys marmorata*. J. of Herpetology, 20(4):515-521.

Bury, R.B. and D.C. Holland (in press). *Clemmys marmorata* (Baird and Girard 1852). Conservation Biology of Freshwater Turtles, 2.

Buskirk, J.R. 1992. An overview of the western pond turtle, *Clemmys marmorata*. Pages 16-23. *In*: K. R. Beaman, F. Caporaso, S. McKeown, and M. Graff (eds). Proceedings of the First International Symposium on Turtles and Tortoises: Conservation and Captive Husbandry. California Turtle and Tortoise Club, Van Nuys, Calif. 172 p.

Carr, A.F. 1952. Handbook of turtles: The turtles of the United States, Canada, and Baja California. Cornell Univ. Press, Ithaca, New York. xv+542 p.

Drewry, G. (ed). 1994. Endangered and threatened wildlife and plants; animal candidate review for listing as endangered or threatened species. Dept. of the Interior, Fish and Wildl. Serv. Fed. Reg. 59(219):58982-59028. [Tuesday, November 15, 1994].

Ernst, C.H., J.E. Lovich, and R.W. Barbour. 1994. Turtles of the United States and Canada. Smithsonian Institution Press, Washington and London. xxxviii+578 p.

Evenden, F.G. 1948. Distribution of the turtles of western Oregon. Herpetologica, 4(6): 201-204.

Feldman, M.1982. Notes on reproduction in *Clemmys marmorata*. Herpetological Review, 13(1):10-11.

Goodman, R.H., Jr. 1997a. The biology of the southwestern pond turtle (*Clemmys marmorata pallida*) in the Chino Hills State Park and the West Ford of the San Gabriel River, M.S. Thesis, Calif. State Polytechnic Univ., Pomona, Calif. viii+81 p.

_____. 1997b. Occurrence of devoie clutching in the southwestern pond turtle, *Clemmys marmorata pallida*, in the Los Angeles Basin. Chelonian Conservation and Biology, 2(3):419-421.

Gray, E.M. 1995. DNA fingerprinting reveals a lack of genetic variation in northern populations of the western pond turtle (*Clemmys marmorata*). Conservation Biology, 9(5):1244-1255.

Holland, D.C. 1985a. An ecological and quantitative study of the western pond turtle (*Clemmys marmorata*) in San Luis Obispo County, California. Unpubl. M.A. Thesis, Fresno State Univ., Fresno, Calif. viii+181 p.

_____. 1985b. Life history notes: *Clemmys marmorata*, feeding. Herpetological Review, 16(4):112-113.

_____. 1992. Level and pattern in morphological variation: A phylogeographic study of the western pond turtle (*Clemmys marmorata*). Unpubl. Ph.D. Dissertation, The Univ. of Southwestern Louisiana, Lafayette, Louisiana. vii+124 p.

Jennings, M.R. and M.P. Hayes. 1994. Amphibian and reptile species of special concern in California. Final report to the Ca. Dept. Fish and Game, Inland Fisheries Div., Rancho Cordova, Calif., under Contract (8023). iii+255 p.

LaRivers, I. 1962. Fishes and fisheries of Nevada. Nevada State Fish and Game Commission, Carson City, Nevada. 782 p.

Rathbun, G.B., N. Siepel, and D.C. Holland. 1992. Nesting behavior and movements of western pond turtles (*Clemmys marmorata*). The Southwestern Naturalist, 37(3): 319-324.

Rathbun, G.B., M.R. Jennings, T.G. Murphey, and N.R. Siepel. 1993. Status and ecology of sensitive aquatic vertebrates in lower San Simeon and Pico Creeks, San Luis Obispo County, California. Final report prepared for the Calif. Dept. of Parks and Recreation, San Simeon Region, through Cooperative Agreement (14-16-0009-01-1909). U.S. Fish and Wildl. Serv., Natl. Ecology Research Center, Piedras Blancas Research Station, San Simeon, Calif. ix+103 p.

Reese, D.A. 1996. Comparative demography and habitat use of western pond turtles in northern California: The effects of damming and related alterations. Unpubl. Ph.D. Dissertation, Univ. of Ca., Berkeley. xvi+253 p.

Reese, D.A. and H.H. Welsh, Jr. 1998. Habitat use by western pond turtles in the Trinity River, Calif. J. of Wildl. Management, 62(3):242-253.

Slater, J.R. 1962. Variations and new range of *Clemmys marmorata*. Occasional Papers of the Dept. of Biology, Univ. of Puget Sound (20):204-205.

Sorensen, P. and L.J. Propp. 1992. Endangered and threatened wildlife and plants; 90-day finding and commencement of status reviews for a petition to list the western pond turtle and California redlegged frog. Fed. Reg., 57(193):4561-45762. [Monday, October 5, 1992].

Stebbins, R.C. 1959. Reptiles and amphibians of the San Francisco Bay region. California Natural History Guide (3). Univ. of Ca. Press, Berkeley and Los Angeles. 72 p.

Storer, T.I. 1930. Notes on the range and life-history of the Pacific fresh-water turtle, *Clemmys marmorata*. Univ. of Ca. Publications in Zoology, 35(5):429-441.

U.S. Fish and Wildlife Service (USFWS). 1993. Endangered and threatened wildlife and plants; notice of 1-year petition finding on the western pond turtle. Fed. Reg., 58(153):42717-42718. [Wednesday, August 11, 1993].

California Alligator Lizard

Elgaria multicarinata multicarinata

Kevin MacKay
Mark R. Jennings

General Information

The California alligator lizard (Family: Anguidae) is a large (100-125 mm SVL) alligator lizard with a broad head, keeled scales, and a reddish-blotched dorsum marked with nine or more dusky crossbands between the head and hindlimbs (Stebbins 1959, 1985). The top of the head is often mottled (Fitch 1938). There is a longitudinal stripe or row of dashes down the middle of each scale row on the belly (Stebbins 1985).

All alligator lizards in the western United States were formerly placed in the genus *Gerrhonotus* (e.g., Smith 1946; Stebbins 1958, 1959, 1972, 1985; Lais 1976). However, recently revised alligator lizard systematics places these species in the genus *Elgaria* (Waddick and Smith 1974; Gauthier 1982; Good 1987a, 1987b, 1988).

Reproduction

California alligator lizards are egg layers (Smith 1946) that probably reach sexual maturity in two years at about 73 mm SVL for males and about 92 mm SVL for females (Goldberg 1972). Mating apparently occurs over a relatively long period (up to 26 hours or more), but most copulation events are considerably shorter than this (Fitch 1935). Based on data from closely related *E. m. webbii* in southern California, adults emerge from hibernation and mate from late February-late May to August-mid September, and eggs are probably laid in small mammal burrows (Stebbins 1954) or under rocks from June-mid July (Goldberg 1972) or later into August (Stebbins 1954) or early September (Burrage 1965). Clutch sizes are 5-41 (average 13) and females can lay more than one clutch a year (Burrage 1965).

Jens V. Vindum, Academy of Sciences

Growth and Development

Based on data from closely related *E. m. webbii* in southern California, incubation of the eggs probably takes 42-57 days (Atsatt 1952, Burrage 1965) and hatchlings appear from mid August-early October at 30-36 mm SVL and 0.5-0.6 g (Burrage 1965, Goldberg 1972). Juveniles grow rapidly the next season, reaching sexual maturity after about 18 months (Goldberg 1972). The longevity of California alligator lizards in the wild is unknown, but marked lizards have been recaptured after four years (Jennings, unpubl. data).

Both juveniles and adults are active in the daytime, at dusk, and at night, and have a relatively low preferred temperature range (Brattstrom 1965, Cunningham 1956, Kingsbury 1994). Because of this, they do not bask. Instead, they prefer very dense cover and often position themselves under warmed objects such as rocks or pieces of wood during certain times of the day (Kingsbury 1994). Alligator lizards frequent riparian zones where their prehensile tails are used in climbing trees and other vegetation in pursuit of prey (Cunningham 1955; Stebbins 1959, 1972). They are also found under debris such as woodpiles, brush heaps, old logs, *etc.* (Stebbins 1954).

Food and Feeding

California alligator lizards probably consume the same food items taken by *E. m. webbii*. Food items recorded in the latter include: Isopoda, Orthoptera, Isoptera, Hemiptera, Homoptera, Coleoptera (larvae and adults), Lepidoptera (larvae and adults), Diptera (larvae and adults), Scorpionida, Araneida [including the egg cases and adults of the black widow spider (*Latradectus mactans*)], Gastropoda, lizards (*Sceloporus occidentalis, S. graciosus,* and *E. multicarinata*), small mammals, and the eggs and young of small birds (Fitch 1935, Cowles 1937, Stebbins 1954, Cunningham 1956).

Distribution

California alligator lizards are found in the Sacramento Valley and surrounding foothills, from Shasta County south through the North Coast Range (Mendocino-Marin counties), the San Francisco Bay region and the South Coast Range to Ventura County (Fitch 1938). The elevational range is from sea level to around 1830 m in the Sierra Nevada (Basey and Sinclear 1980). This lizard is apparently absent from most of the San Joaquin Valley proper, but it is found on the northern Channel Islands (Fitch 1938). It intergrades with the *E. m. scincicauda* in Mendocino and Trinity counties in the north and *E. m. webbii* in Ventura County in the south and El Dorado County in the east (Stebbins 1985). They are found throughout the Bay Area (Stebbins 1959) (**Figure 4.6**).

Amphibians & Reptiles

Current Status and Factors Influencing Population Numbers

California alligator lizards are still present in good numbers over almost all of their historic range because of their ability to survive (and even thrive) in urban environments. The most important predator of these lizards in such modified habitats is the domestic cat (*Felis cattus*). In more natural habitats, alligator lizards are eaten by a number of reptile, avian, and mammal predators (Fitch 1935). They are still very abundant in the foothills of the Bay Area (Jennings, unpubl. data).

Trophic Levels

California alligator lizards are secondary/tertiary consumers.

Proximal Species

Habitat: Pickleweed, riparian vegetation, blackberries, willows.
Predators: Domestic cat, striped skunk, opossum, raccoon, heron, egret, hawks, coyote, red fox, bullfrog, common garter snake, and Coast garter snake.
Prey: Terrestrial insects, oligochaetes, and arachnids.

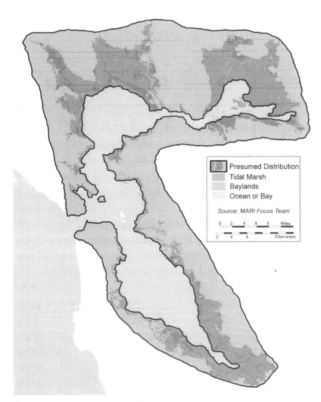

Figure 4.6 California Alligator Lizard – Presumed Bay Area Distribution

Good Habitat

California alligator lizards occupy many habitats from pickleweed flats to open grasslands, to oak woodlands, to mixed coniferous forest, to urban environments (Fitch 1935; Lais 1976; Stebbins 1954, 1985). However, the largest observed populations are in the riparian zones of oak woodlands and in coastal sage scrub near beaches (Jennings, unpubl. data).

References

Atsatt, S.R. 1952. Observations on the life history of the lizards *Sceloporus graciosus vandenburghianus* and *Gerrhonotus multicarinatus webbi*. Copeia, 1952(4):276.

Basey, H.E. and D.A. Sinclear. 1980. Amphibians and reptiles. Pages 13-74. *In*: J. Verner and A.S. Boss (technical coordinators). California Wildlife and Their Habitats: Western Sierra Nevada. U.S. Forest Serv., Pacific Southwest Forest and Range Experiment Station, Berkeley, Calif. General Tech. Report (PSW-37):iii+439 p.

Brattstrom, B.H. 1965. Body temperatures of reptiles. The American Midland Naturalist, 73(2):376-422.

Burrage, B.R. 1965. Notes on the eggs and young of the lizards *Gerrhonotus multicarinatus webbi* and *G. m. nanus*. Copeia, 1965(4):512.

Cowles, R.B. 1937. The San Diegan alligator lizard and the black widow spider. Science, 85(2195):99-100.

Cunningham, J.D. 1955. Arboreal habits of certain reptiles and amphibians in southern California. Herpetologica, 11(3):217-220.

_____. 1956. Food habits of the San Diego alligator lizard. Herpetologica, 12(3):225-230.

Fitch, H.S. 1935. Natural history of the alligator lizards. Transactions of the Academy of Science of Saint Louis, 29(1):3-38.

_____. 1938. A systematic account of the alligator lizards (*Gerrhonotus*) in the western United States and Lower Calif. The American Midland Naturalist, 20(2): 381-424.

Gauthier, J. A. 1982. Fossil xenosaurid and anguid lizards from the early Eocene Wasatch Formation, southeast Wyoming, and a revision of the Anguioidea. Contributions to Geology, Univ. of Wyoming, 21(1):7-54.

Goldberg, S.R. 1972. Reproduction in the southern alligator lizard *Gerrhonotus multicarinatus*. Herpetologica, 28(3):267-273.

Good, D.A. 1987a. An allozyme analysis of anguid subfamilial relationships (Lacertilia: Anguidae). Copeia, 1987(3):696-701.

_____. 1987b. A phylogenetic analysis of cranial osteology in the Gerrhonotine lizards. J. of Herpetology, 21(4):285-297.

_____. 1988. Allozyme variation and phylogenetic relationships among the species of *Elgaria* (Squamata: Anguidae). Herpetologica, 44(2):154-162.

Kingsbury, B.A. 1994. Thermal constraints and eurythermy in the lizard *Elgaria multicarinata*. Herpetologica, 50(3):266-273.

Lais, P.M. 1976. *Gerrhonotus multicarinatus*. Catalogue of American Amphibians and Reptiles:187.1-187.4.

Smith, H.M. 1946. Handbook of lizards; lizards of the United States and of Canada. Comstock Publishing Co., Inc., Ithaca, New York. xxi+557 p.

Stebbins, R.C. 1954. Amphibians and reptiles of western North America. McGraw-Hill Book Company, Inc., New York, Toronto, and London. xxii+536 p.

_____. 1958. A new alligator lizard from the Panamint Mountains, Inyo County, California. American Museum Novitates (1883):1-27.

_____. 1959. Reptiles and amphibians of the San Francisco Bay region. California Natural History Guide (3). Univ. of Ca. Press, Berkeley and Los Angeles. 72 p.

_____. 1972. Amphibians and reptiles of California. California Natural History Guide (31). Univ. of Ca. Press, Berkeley, Los Angeles, and London. 152 p.

_____. 1985. A field guide to western amphibians and reptiles. Second edition, revised. Houghton Mifflin Company, Boston, Massachusetts. xiv+336 p.

Waddick, J.W. and H.M. Smith. 1974. The significance of scale characters in evaluation of the lizard genera *Gerrhonotus*, *Elgaria*, and *Barisia*. The Great Basin Naturalist, 34(4):257-266.

Central Coast Garter Snake

Thamnophis atratus atratus

Mark R. Jennings

General Information

The central coast garter snake (Family: Colubridae) is a medium-sized (60-102 cm TL) garter snake with eight upper labial scales and a highly variable dorsal color throughout its range (Bellemin and Stewart 1977). Snakes usually have a dark olive to black dorsum and single yellow to orange dorsal stripe and sometimes lateral stripes of pale yellow (Stebbins 1985). The throat is a bright yellow. Both *T. a. atratus* and *T. e. terrestris* have similar dorsal and ventral colorations in habitats occupied along the central coast of California (Bellemin and Stewart 1977, Stebbins 1985). Boundy (1990) considers what is currently *T. a. atratus*, to be be actually composed of two different subspecies. However, his proposed subspecies from the mountains of the East Bay region and the South Coast Range (south of Santa Cruz County) has not been formally published.

Garter snake taxonomy has undergone a considerable number of revisions during this century, especially during the past 40 years. The snake *T. a. atratus* is often referred to as *T. elegans atratus*, or *T. couchii atratus* in the literature (e.g., see Fitch 1940, 1984; Fox 1948a, 1948b, 1951; Stebbins 1954, 1972; Fox and Dessauer 1965; Lawson and Dessauer 1979). Rossman and Stewart (1987) were the first to convincingly elevate *T. atratus* as a separate species and this arrangement has been followed by others (e.g., see Lawson 1987).

Reproduction

Central coast garter snakes are live-bearers. Females give birth from 4-14 (or more) young (ave. 8.6) in the fall (August-September) [Fox 1948a, 1948b]. Adults probably mate annually during the spring (March-April) [Fox 1948b, 1952a], but females have the ability to store sperm for up to 53 months (Stewart 1972).

Denise Loving

Growth and Development

Unknown. If similar to other garter snakes on the central coast of California, neonates are present from late August through November (Rathbun et al. 1993) and juveniles grow rapidly during the first year of their lives (Fox 1948a). Sexual maturity is reached in about 2-3 years (Fox 1948a). Longevity in the wild is unknown, but adults probably live for at least 4-5 years (Jennings, unpubl. data).

Food and Feeding

Juvenile and adult snakes feed almost entirely on fishes (e.g., *Gasterosteus aculeatus*, *Hesperoleucus symmetricus*, and *Cottus* spp.), newts (larvae and adults of *Taricha torosa*), toads (*Bufo boreas halophilus*), and frogs (e.g., larvae, juveniles, and adults of *Hyla regilla*, *Rana aurora draytonii*, *R. boylii*, and *R. catesbeiana*) [Fitch 1941; Fox 1951, 1952b; Bellemin and Stewart 1977; Boundy 1990; Barry 1994; Jennings, unpubl. data].

Distribution

Central coast garter snakes inhabit small streams, ponds, and other aquatic habitats in the San Francisco Peninsula and the East Bay Hills, Contra Costa County (south of the Sacramento River), southward through the South Coast Range to Point Conception, Santa Barbara County, and east to the western edge of the San Joaquin Valley (Fox 1951, Bellemin and Stewart 1977). Snakes north of San Francisco Bay are *T. a. aquaticus* (Fox 1951, Stebbins 1985). Their elevational distribution is from near sea level to 1290 m on Mount Hamilton (Fox 1951). They are relatively common East Bay and South Bay regions of the San Francisco Estuary (Stebbins 1959; Jennings, unpubl. data) (**Figure 4.7**).

Current Status and Factors Influencing Population Numbers

Central coast garter snakes are negatively affected by habitat alteration, especially by agriculture and urbanization which often results in intermittent aquatic habitats unsuitable for this species. These snakes are also probably negatively affected by the introduction of exotic predators such as bullfrogs (*Rana catesbeiana*) and largemouth bass (*Micropterus salmoides*), which are known to eat garter snakes (Schwalbe and Rosen 1988). However, these central coast garter snakes are still relatively abundant in aquatic habitats located in the foothills surrounding the Bay Area where urban development is less intrusive (Jennings, unpubl. data).

Trophic Levels

Central coast garter snakes are tertiary consumers.

Proximal Species

Predators: Racoon, herons, egrets, hawks, and bullfrogs.
Prey: threespine stickleback, sculpins, Pacific treefrog, California toad, foothill yellow-legged frog, California red-legged frog, bullfrog, coast range newt.

Good Habitat

Coast garter snakes are most abundant in riparian habitats with shallow ponds containing abundant numbers of native fishes and amphibians, and dense thickets of vegetation nearby (Jennings, unpubl. data). Such habitats are most common in natural sag ponds and artificial stock ponds (Barry 1994).

References

Barry, S.J. 1994. The distribution, habitat, and evolution of the San Francisco garter snake, *Thamnophis sirtalis tetrataenia*. Unpubl. M.A. Thesis, Univ. of Ca., Davis, Calif. iii+140 p.

Bellemin, J.M. and G. R.Stewart. 1977. Diagnostic characters and color convergence of the garter snakes *Thamnophis elegans terrestris* and *Thamnophis couchii atratus* along the central California coast. Bull. of the Southern Calif. Academy of Sciences, 76(2):73-84.

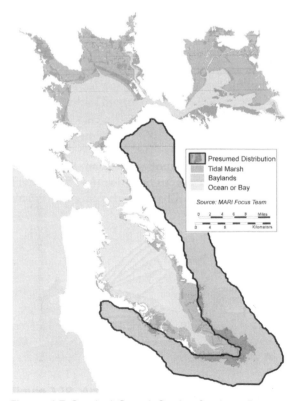

Figure 4.7 Central Coast Garter Snake – Presumed Bay Area Distribution

Boundy, J. 1990. Biogeography and variation in southern populations of the garter snake *Thamnophis atratus*, with a synopsis of the *T. couchii* complex. Unpubl. M.A. Thesis, San Jose State Univ., San Jose, Calif. 105 p.

Fitch, H.S. 1940. A biogeographical study of the *ordinoides* artenkries of garter snakes (genus *Thamnophis*). Univ. of Ca. Publications in Zoology, 44(1):1-150.

_____. 1941. The feeding habits of California garter snakes. Ca. Dept. Fish and Game, 27(2):1-32.

_____. 1984. *Thamnophis couchii*. Catalogue of American Amphibians and Reptiles:351.1-351.3.

Fox, W. 1948a. The relationships of the garter snake *Thamnophis ordinoides*. Copeia, 1948(2):113-120.

_____. 1948b. Effect of temperature on development of scutellation in the garter snake, *Thamnophis elegans atratus*. Copeia, 1948(4):252-262.

_____. 1951. Relationships among the garter snakes of the *Thamnophis elegans* rassenkreis. Univ. of Ca. Publications in Zoology, 50(5):485-530.

_____. 1952a. Seasonal variation in the male reproductive system of Pacific Coast garter snakes. J. of Morphology, 90(3):481-554.

_____. 1952b. Notes on feeding habits of Pacific Coast garter snakes. Herpetologica, 8(1):4-8.

Fox, W. and H.C. Dessauer. 1965. Collection of garter snakes for blood studies. American Philosophical Society Yearbook for 1964:263-266.

Lawson, R. 1987. Molecular studies of thamnophine snakes: 1. The phylogeny of the genus *Nerodia*. J. of Herpetology, 21(2):140-157.

Lawson, R. and H.C. Dessauer. 1979. Biochemical genetics and systematics of garter snakes of the *Thamnophis elegans-couchii-ordinoides* complex. Occasional Papers of the Museum of Zoology, Louisiana State Univ. (56):1-24.

Rathbun, G.B., M.R. Jennings, T.G. Murphey, and N.R. Siepel. 1993. Status and ecology of sensitive aquatic vertebrates in lower San Simeon and Pico Creeks, San Luis Obispo County, California. Final report prepared for the Calif. Dept. of Parks and Recreation, San Simeon Region. U.S. Fish and Wildl. Serv., Natl. Ecology Research Center, San Simeon, Calif. ix+103 p.

Rossman, D.A. and G.R. Stewart. 1987. Taxonomic reevaluation of *Thamnophis couchii* (Serpentes, Colubridae). Occasional Papers of the Museum of Zoology, Louisiana State Univ. (63):1-25.

Schwalbe, C.R. and P.C. Rosen. 1988. Preliminary report on effect of bullfrogs on wetland herpetofaunas in southeastern Arizona. Pages 166-173. *In*: R.C. Szaro, K.E. Severson, and D.R. Patton (technical coordinators). Management of Amphibians, Reptiles, and Small Mammals in North America. Proceedings of the Symposium, July 19-21, 1988, Flagstaff, Arizona. U.S. Forest Serv., Fort Collins, Colorado. General Tech. Report (RM-166):1-458.

Stebbins, R.C. 1954. Amphibians and reptiles of western North America. McGraw-Hill Book Company, Inc., New York, Toronto, and London. xxii+536 p.

_____. 1959. Reptiles and amphibians of the San Francisco Bay region. California Natural History Guide (3). Univ. of Ca. Press, Berkeley and Los Angeles. 72 p.

_____. 1972. Amphibians and reptiles of California. California Natural History Guide (31). Univ. of Ca. Press, Berkeley, Los Angeles, and London. 152 p.

_____. 1985. A field guide to western amphibians and reptiles. Second edition, revised. Houghton Mifflin Company, Boston, Massachusetts. xiv+336 p.

Stewart, G.R. 1972. An unusual record of sperm storage in a female garter snake (genus *Thamnophis*). Herpetology, 28(4):346-347.

Coast Garter Snake

Thamnophis elegans terrestris

Kevin MacKay

Mark R. Jennings

General Information

The coast garter snake (Family: Colubridae) is a medium-sized (45-107 cm TL) garter snake with eight upper labial scales and a highly variable dorsal color throughout its range (Bellemin and Stewart 1977, Stebbins 1985). Snakes usually have a reddish to solid black dorsum (sometimes with a checkerboard of dark spots or bars), and single pale to bright yellow dorsal stripe, and two lateral stripes of yellow to salmon (Fitch 1983, Stebbins 1985). The throat and belly are usually tinged with orange flecks (Fox 1951). Both *T. a. atratus* and *T. e. terrestris* have similar dorsal and ven-

Dr. Alan Francis

tral colorations in habitats occupied along the central coast of California (Bellemin and Stewart 1977, Stebbins 1985).

Reproduction

Coast garter snakes are live-bearers. Females give birth to from 4-14 young (average 8.6) in the fall (August-September) [Fox 1948, Stebbins 1954]. Adults probably mate annually during the spring (March-July) [Fox 1948, 1952a, 1956], but females have the ability to store sperm for up to 53 months (Stewart 1972).

Growth and Development

Unknown. If similar to other garter snakes on the central coast of California, neonates are present from late August through November (Rathbun et al. 1993) and juveniles grow rapidly during the first year of their lives (Fox 1948). Sexual maturity is reached in about 2-3 years (Fox 1948). Longevity in the wild is unknown, but adults probably live for at least 4-5 years (Jennings, unpubl. data).

Food and Feeding

Coast garter snakes subsist largely on slugs (Arion sp., *Ariolimax columbianus*, and others), California slender salamanders (*Batrachoseps attenuatus*), ensatinas (*Ensatina eschscholtzii*), arboreal salamanders (*Aneides lugubris*), Pacific treefrogs (*Hyla regilla*), western fence lizards (*Sceloporus occidentalis*), California voles (*Microtus californicus*), deer mice (*Peromyscus maniculatus*), young brush rabbits (*Sylvilagus bachmani*), harvest mice (*Rheithrodontomys* spp.), nestling white-crowned sparrows (*Zonotrichia leucophrys nuttalli*), and nestling song sparrows (*Melospiza melodia*) [Fitch 1941; Fox 1951, 1952b; James et al. 1983; Barry 1994]. Fox (1951) also records at least one instance of cannibalism in the wild. There is a heavy preference for slugs, rodents, and nestling birds in some areas inhabited by this snake (Fox 1951, 1952b; James et al. 1983). Coast garter snakes will also eat a wide variety of fishes and amphibians if the occasion arises (see Fox 1952b).

Distribution

Coast garter snakes inhabit the North and South Coast Ranges from just north of the Oregon border, south to Point Conception, Santa Barbara County (Fox 1951, Bellemin and Stewart 1977, Stebbins 1985). They intergrade with *T. e. elegans* at mid-elevations of the North Coast Range (Stebbins 1985). The elevational range is from near sea level to around 350 m (Fox 1951). Coast garter snakes are widely distributed in the Bay Area (Stebbins 1959) (**Figure 4.8**).

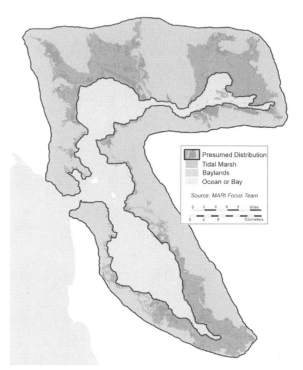

Figure 4.8 Coast Garter Snake – Presumed Bay Area Distribution

Current Status and Factors Influencing Population Numbers

Coast garter snakes are negatively affected by habitat alteration, especially by agriculture and urbanization which often results in disturbed or open habitats unsuitable for this species. Because these snakes do not require permanent aquatic habitats for long term survival like other garter snake taxa in the Bay Area, they are less affected overall by human activities. Coast garter snakes are still relatively abundant in terrestrial habitats located in the foothills surrounding the Bay Area (Jennings, unpubl. data).

Trophic Levels

Coast garter snakes are tertiary consumers.

Proximal Species

Predators: Raccoon, herons, egrets, hawks, California kingsnake, and bullfrog.
Prey: Pacific treefrog, California red-legged frog, bullfrog, Coast Range newt, oligochaetes, California mouse, California vole, white-crowned sparrow, brush rabbit (young only), shrews, slugs.

Good Habitat

Coast garter snakes inhabit meadows (such as grasslands) and clearings with second growth in the fog belt and also chaparral (Stebbins 1972). They are often abundant in canyons with coast live oaks (*Quercus agrifolia*), California bay (*Umbellularia californica*) and numerous shrubs, as well as riparian zones or other areas of dense vegetation (such as blackberries (*Rubus discolor* and *R. ursinus*), thimbleberries (*R. parviforus*) and Baccharis (*Baccharis* spp.)) next to more open areas (Fox 1951).

References

Barry, S.J. 1994. The distribution, habitat, and evolution of the San Francisco garter snake, *Thamnophis sirtalis tetrataenia*. Unpubl. M.A. Thesis, Univ. of Ca., Davis, Calif. iii+140 p.

Bellemin, J.M. and G.R. Stewart. 1977. Diagnostic characters and color convergence of the garter snakes *Thamnophis elegans terrestris* and *Thamnophis couchii atratus* along the central California coast. Bull. of the Southern Calif. Academy of Sciences, 76(2):73-84.

Fitch, H.S. 1941. The feeding habits of California garter snakes. Calif. Fish and Game, 27(2):1-32.

_____. 1983. *Thamnophis elegans*. Catalogue of American Amphibians and Reptiles:320.1-320.4.

Fox, W. 1948. The relationships of the garter snake *Thamnophis ordinoides*. Copeia, 1948(2):113-120.

_____. 1951. Relationships among the garter snakes of the *Thamnophis elegans* rassenkreis. Univ. of Ca. Publications in Zoology, 50(5):485-530.

_____. 1952a. Seasonal variation in the male reproductive system of Pacific Coast garter snakes. J. of Morphology, 90(3):481-554.

_____. 1952b. Notes on feeding habits of Pacific Coast garter snakes. Herpetologica, 8(1):4-8.

_____. 1956. Seminal receptacles of snakes. The Anatomical Record, 124(3):519-540.

James, D.K., L. Petrinovich, T.L. Patterson and A.H. James. 1983. Predation on white-crowned sparrow nestlings by the western terrestrial garter snake in San Francisco, California. Copeia, 1983(2):511-513.

Rathbun, G.B., M. R. Jennings, T.G. Murphey, and N.R. Siepel. 1993. Status and ecology of sensitive aquatic vertebrates in lower San Simeon and Pico Creeks, San Luis Obispo County, California. Final report prepared for the Calif. Dept. of Parks and Recreation, San Simeon Region, through Cooperative Agreement (14-16-0009-01-1909). U.S. Fish and Wildl. Serv., Natl. Ecology Research Center, Piedras Blancas Research Station, San Simeon, Calif. ix+103 p.

Stebbins, R.C. 1954. Amphibians and reptiles of western North America. McGraw-Hill Book Company, Inc., New York, Toronto, and London. xxii+536 p.

_____. 1959. Reptiles and amphibians of the San Francisco Bay region. California Natural History Guide (3). Univ. of Ca. Press, Berkeley and Los Angeles. 72 p.

_____. 1972. Amphibians and reptiles of California. California Natural History Guide (31). Univ. of Ca. Press, Berkeley, Los Angeles, and London. 152 p.

_____. 1985. A field guide to western amphibians and reptiles. Second edition, revised. Houghton Mifflin Company, Boston, Massachusetts. xiv+336 p.

Stewart, G.R. 1972. An unusual record of sperm storage in a female garter snake (genus *Thamnophis*). Herpetology, 28(4):346-347.

San Francisco Garter Snake

Thamnophis sirtalis tetrataenia

Mark R. Jennings

General Information

The San Francisco garter snake (*Thamnophis sirtalis tetrataenia*; Family Colubridae) is a medium sized (46-122 cm TL), snake with seven upper labial scales and a wide dorsal stripe of greenish yellow edged with black, bordered on each side by a broad red stripe followed by a black one (Barry 1978, Stebbins 1985). The belly is a bright greenish blue (often turquoise) and the top of the head is red (Stebbins 1985, Barry 1993). This snake was one of the first reptiles to be listed as Endangered by the U.S. Fish and Wildlife Service in 1967 (U.S. Fish and Wildlife Service 1985).

Although the name of this snake has been stable since Fox (1951) solved the mystery regarding the original collection of *T. s. tetrataenia* in 1855, Boundy and Rossman (1995) recently proposed that the nomenclature of *T. s. tetrataenia* be revised because the holotype of *T. s. infernalis* was found to actually be a specimen of *T. s. tetrataenia*. This proposal of substituting *T. s. infernalis* for *T. s. tetrataenia* and *T. s. concinnus* for *T. s. infernalis* (*sensu lato* Fox 1951), has been followed by Rossman et al. (1996). However, a petition has been

Ted Brown, Academy of Sciences

Amphibians & Reptiles

received and published by the International Commission on Zoological Nomenclature to conserve the usage of *T. s. infernalis* and *T. s. tetrataenia* and designate a neotype for *T. s. infernalis* (Barry and Jennings 1998). Thus, the existing usage of the Fox (1951) nomenclature should be followed until a ruling is made on the case.

Reproduction

San Francisco garter snakes are live bearers which mate during the spring (March-April) and also during the fall (September-November), the latter often in breeding aggregations of several males and one female (Fox 1952a, 1954, 1955). Neonates (18-20 cm total length) are normally born in litters of 1-35 (average 16) during late July to early August (Fox et al. 1961; Cover and Boyer 1988; Barry 1993, 1994), although a few litters are born as late as early September (Larsen 1994). Females have the ability to store sperm for up to 53 months (Stewart 1972).

Growth and Development

Snakes are most active from March to September although they can be observed during any month of the year (Wharton 1989, Barry 1994, Larsen 1994). Juveniles grow rapidly during their first year, spending much of their time feeding in riparian zones or aquatic habitats (Barry 1994). Males and females probably reach sexual maturity in two years (at about 46 cm and 55 cm total length respectively), although some slower growing snakes reach sexual maturity in three years (Barry 1994). During the summer months, subadult and adult snakes may disperse away riparian areas into adjacent habitats to feed on amphibians in rodent burrows (Barry 1993). During the winter months, juvenile and adult snakes hibernate in small mammal burrows in adjacent upland habitats (Larsen 1994). Some snakes can move large distances (>2 km) over short periods of time (Wharton 1989), but limited radio tracking data indicate that most movements are considerably shorter than this distance (Larsen 1994).

Food and Feeding

Subadult and adult San Francisco garter snakes feed largely on the larvae and post-metamorphic life stages of Pacific treefrogs (*Hyla regilla*) and California red-legged frogs (*Rana aurora draytonii*). California toads (*Bufo boreas halophilus*), introduced bullfrogs (*R. catesbeiana*), introduced mosquitofish (*Gambusia affinis*), and three-spine sticklebacks (*Gasterosteus aculeatus*) are also taken (Fox 1951, Wharton 1989, McGinnis 1984, Barry 1994). Juvenile snakes feed largely on newts (*Taricha* spp.), earthworms, and Pacific treefrogs (Barry 1993) and will refuse other most non-amphibian items offered to them (Fox 1952b, Larsen et al. 1991). Adult snakes rarely

eat California voles (*Microtus californicus*), even when they are abundantly available (Barry 1993).

Distribution

San Francisco garter snakes are a Bay Area endemic that are essentially restricted to San Mateo County, California (Stebbins 1959, Barry 1978) (**Figure 4.9**). Historically, they occurred in aquatic habitats and adjacent uplands along the San Andreas Rift Zone from near Pacifica, southeast to the Pulgas Water Temple, and along an arc from the San Gregorio-Pescadero highlands, west to the coast, and south to Point Año Nuevo (Barry 1978, 1994; McGinnis 1984). At least two recent records just south of Point Año Nuevo—from the mouth of Waddell Creek, Santa Cruz County—are questionable (Barry 1993, 1994). Intergrades with *T. s. infernalis* have been recorded in eastern San Mateo County (southeast of the Pulgas Water Temple) and extreme western Santa Clara County (Fox 1951, Barry 1994).

Current Status and Factors Influencing Population Numbers

San Francisco garter snakes have disappeared from significant portions of their native range due to habitat loss from agriculture and urbanization—especially from housing developments and freeway construction (Medders

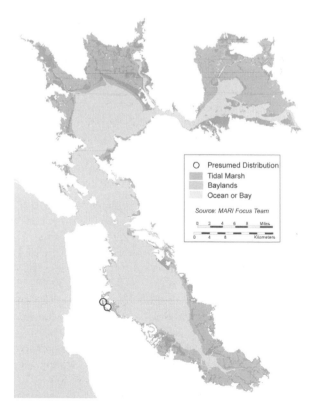

Figure 4.9 San Francisco Garter Snake – Current Known Location Restricted to San Mateo County

1976; USFWS 1985; Barry 1978, 1993). Historically, the largest known population of snakes was at a series of sag ponds (locally referred to as the "Skyline Ponds") along Hwy 35 in the vicinity of Pacifica, Daly City, San Bruno, and South San Francisco (Barry 1978, 1993, 1994; USFWS 1985). Today, this complex of ponds has been completely covered by urbanization. The large Bay Area population of snakes studied by Wharton (1989) has extensively declined due to the loss of several prey species from saltwater intrusion into the marsh (see Larsen 1994) and this population may now be close to extinction (Jennings, unpublished data). Besides the above, declines also resulted from large numbers of snakes being collected for the pet trade (especially overseas) and *T. s. tetrataenia* continues to be illegally collected for pets despite stiff penalties for doing so (e.g., see Bender 1981). Today, about 70% of the current remaining San Francisco garter snake habitat is composed of artificially constructed aquatic sites such as farm ponds, channelized sloughs, and reservoir impoundments (Barry 1993). Such habitats are often managed in ways that are detrimental to the snake and its preferred prey, the California red-legged frog (Barry 1993, 1994; Larsen 1994).

Current estimates put the number of San Francisco garter snakes at about 65 "permanent" reproductive populations of around 1500 total snakes >1 year of age (Barry 1993). About half the known populations are protected to some extent by refuges such as water preserves or state parks (Barry 1993). The key to preserving the species is to set aside adequate amounts of habitat and manage these areas for *T. s. tetrataenia* and its prey, especially California red-legged frogs (Barry 1993, Larsen 1994).

Trophic Levels

San Francisco garter snakes are tertiary consumers.

Proximal Species

Prey: Coast Range newt, California red-legged frog, threespine stickleback, Pacific treefrog, bullfrog.
Predators: Hawks, herons, egrets, bullfrog, striped skunk, opossum, and raccoon.

Good Habitat

San Francisco garter snakes are most abundant in natural sag ponds or artificial waterways that have been allowed to develop a dense cover of vegetative (Barry 1993). This is due to the presence of large amphibian populations (=prey base) and many basking sites for juvenile and adult snakes which are relatively secure from potential predators (Barry 1994). The presence of adjacent upland areas with abundant numbers of small mammal burrows are also important as hibernation sites for snakes during the winter (Larsen 1994).

References

Barry, S.J. 1978. Status of the San Francisco garter snake. Ca. Dept. Fish and Game, Inland Fisheries Endangered Species Program, Special Publ. (78-2):1-21.

_____. 1993. The San Francisco garter snake: protection is the key to recovery. Tideline, 13(4):1-3; 15.

_____. 1994. The distribution, habitat, and evolution of the San Francisco garter snake, *Thamnophis sirtalis tetrataenia*. Unpubl. M.A. Thesis, Univ. of Ca., Davis, Calif. iii+140 p.

Barry, S.J. and M.R. Jennings 1998. *Coluber infernalis* Blainville, 1835 and *Eutaenia sirtalis tetrataenia* Cope *in* Yarrow, 1875 (currently *Thamnophis s. tetrataenia* and *T. s. infernalis*; Reptilia, Serpentes): proposed conservation of the subspecific names by the designation of a neotype for *T. s. infernalis*. The Bull. of Zoological Nomenclature, 55(4):in press.

Bender, M. 1981. "Sting" operation reveals massive illegal trade. Endangered Species Tech. Bull., 6(8):1; 4.

Boundy, J. and D.A. Rossman. 1995. Allocation and status of the garter snake names *Coluber infernalis* Blainville, *Eutaenia sirtalis tetrataenia* Cope and *Eutaenia imperialis* Coues and Yarrow. Copeia, 1995(1):236-240.

Cover, J.F., Jr. and D.M. Boyer. 1988. Captive reproduction of the San Francisco garter snake *Thamnophis sirtalis tetrataenia*. Herpetological Review, 19(2):29-33.

Fox, W. 1951. The status of the gartersnake, *Thamnophis sirtalis tetrataenia*. Copeia, 1951(4):257-267.

_____. 1952a. Seasonal variation in the male reproductive system of Pacific Coast garter snakes. J. of Morphology, 90(3):481-554.

_____. 1952b. Notes on feeding habits of Pacific Coast garter snakes. Herpetologica, 8(1):4-8.

_____. 1954. Genetic and environmental variation in the timing of the reproductive cycles of male garter snakes. J. of Morphology, 95(3):415-450.

_____. 1955. Mating aggregations of garter snakes. Herpetologica, 11(3):176.

Fox, W., C. Gordon, and M.H. Fox. 1961. Morphological effects of low temperatures during the embryonic development of the garter snake, *Thamnophis elegans*. Zoologica, 46(2):57-71.

Larsen, S.S. 1994. Life history aspects of the San Francisco garter snake at the Millbrae habitat site. Unpubl. M.S. Thesis, Calif. State Univ., Hayward, Calif. ix+105 p.

Larsen, S.S., K.E. Swaim, and S.M. McGinnis. 1991. Innate response of the San Francisco garter snake and the Alameda whipsnake to specific prey items.

Transactions of the Western Section of the Wildl. Society, 27:37-41.

McGinnis, S.M. 1984. The current distribution and habitat requirements of the San Francisco garter snake, *Thamnophis sirtalis tetrataenia*, in coastal San Mateo County. Final report of work conducted under Interagency Agreement C-673 and prepared for the Ca. Dept. Fish and Game, Inland Fisheries Div., Rancho Cordova, Calif. 38 p.

Medders, S. 1976. Serpent or supermarket? Natl. Parks and Conservation Magazine, 50(4):18-19.

Rossman, D.A., N.B. Ford, and R.A. Seigel. 1996. The garter snakes; evolution and ecology. Univ. of Oklahoma Press, Norman, Oklahoma. xx+332 p.

Stebbins, R.C. 1959. Reptiles and amphibians of the San Francisco Bay region. California Natural History Guide (3). Univ. of Ca. Press, Berkeley and Los Angeles. 72 p.

_____. 1985. A field guide to western amphibians and reptiles. Second edition, revised. Houghton Mifflin Company, Boston, Massachusetts. xiv+336 p.

Stewart, G.R. 1972. An unusual record of sperm storage in a female garter snake (genus *Thamnophis*). Herpetology, 28(4):346-347.

Wharton, J.C. 1989. Ecological and life history aspects of the San Francisco garter snake (*Thamnophis sirtalis tetrataenia*). Unpubl. MA Thesis, San Francisco State Univ., San Francisco, Calif. x+91 p.

U.S. Fish and Wildlife Service (USFWS). 1985. Recovery plan for the San Francisco garter snake (*Thamnophis sirtalis tetrataenia*). U.S. Fish and Wildl. Serv., Portland, Oregon. 77 p.

Amphibians & Reptiles

5

Mammals

Salt Marsh Harvest Mouse

Reithrodontomys raviventris

Howard S. Shellhammer

Life History

Salt marsh harvest mice (SMHM) are small, native rodents which are endemic to the salt marshes and adjacent diked wetlands of San Francisco Bay and are listed as an endangered species by the U.S. Fish and Wildlife Service and the State of California (Shellhammer 1982). They range in total length from 118 to 175 millimeters and in weight from 8 to 14 grams. They are vegetarians that can drink water ranging from moderately saline to sea water. They swim calmly and well. They do not burrow, but will build ball-like nests of dry grasses and other vegetation on the ground or up in the pickleweed (Fisler 1965). Their behavior is placid, so much so that their behavior is used as a secondary criterion in identifying them to the species level.

Historical and Modern Distribution

SMHM are composed of two subspecies. The northern subspecies, *R. r. haliocoetes*, is found on the upper portions of the Marin Peninsula; in the Petaluma, Napa and Suisun marshes; as well as a disjunct series of populations on the northern Contra Costa County coast. The southern subspecies, *R. r. raviventris*, is found in the

more highly developed portions of the Bay from the Richmond area, down around the South San Francisco Bay (primarily south of a line between Redwood City and Hayward), and a disjunct series of small populations on the Marin Peninsula. Some modern distributions are indicated in **Figure 5.1** and a listing of available trapping data are included in **Appendix 5.1**.

Their chromosome number and morphology have been studied by Shellhammer, and the two subspecies show some differences in chromosome shape indicating that genetic isolating mechanisms are beginning to form between them. No recent and modern genetic studies have been completed at the present time, hence nothing is known about the genetic variability of this species and whether or not it faces problems of inbreeding and random genetic drift as its average population size decreases.

The major threats to their habitat include filling, diking, subsidence, and changes in water salinity (Shellhammer 1982, 1989). Various estimates have been made that at least 75% of all the tidal marshes around the Bay have been filled in or otherwise destroyed over the last 150 years. Most of the remaining marshes have been back-filled or diked-off, and hence most of the remaining tidal marshes are narrow strips along the bay side of the levees. Those strip marshes and most of the remaining larger marshes have lost their upper and part of their middle zones, such that there is little escape cover from high tides available. In the southern end of the South San Francisco Bay, the combination of subsidence caused by water drawdown and the freshening of that part of the Bay by massive amounts of non-saline, treated sewage effluent has changed the saline vegetation of that area to brackish and freshwater species such as bulrushes (*Scirpus sp.*), cattails (*Typha sp.*), and peppergrass (*Lepidium latifolium*), species not used by SMHM (Duke et al. 1990; Shellhammer 1982, 1989).

Because of these influences, SMHM has disappeared from many marshes and is present in very low numbers in most others. The highest consistent populations are found in relatively large marshes along the eastern edge of San Pablo Bay and in old dredge spoil

USFWS

Figure 5.1 Salt Marsh
Harvest Mouse – Some
Current Locations and
Suitable Habitat

Note: Mice are likely
present in areas identified
as "suitable" habitat based
on current information
regarding habitat types.
Mice may also be present
in other areas.

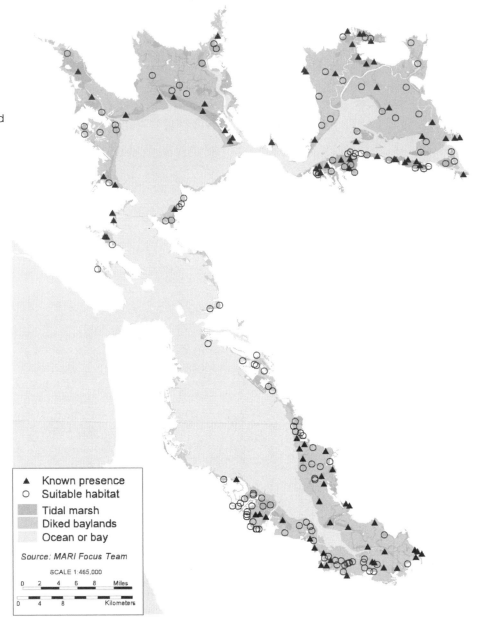

▲ Known presence
○ Suitable habitat
▨ Tidal marsh
▧ Diked baylands
☐ Ocean or bay

Source: MARI Focus Team

SCALE 1:465,000

0   2   4   6   8   Miles

0   4   8   Kilometers

disposal ponds on former Mare Island Shipyard property; most of these marshes are in or will be included in the San Pablo Bay unit of the San Francisco Bay National Wildlife Refuge (Bias and Morrison 1993, Duke et al. 1995). Other areas supporting large populations include some parts of the Contra Costa County coastline (Duke et al. 1990, 1991), some parts of the Petaluma Marshes, and the Calaveras Point Marsh in the South San Francisco Bay (Duke et al. 1990), although the latter area is deteriorating because of the declining salinity and correlated changes in vegetation.

Diked wetlands adjacent to the Bay have grown in importance as the tidal marshes bayward of their outboard dikes have decreased in size and quality (Shellhammer 1989). Most of such diked marshes in the South San Francisco Bay are being threatened by urban and industrial development along their borders. In addition, most of these diked marshes are not managed to provide adequate vegetative cover of halophytic species or to maintain their salinity over time (Duke et al. 1990, Shellhammer 1989).

Suitable Habitat

SMHM are dependent on the thick, perennial cover of salt marshes and move in the adjacent grasslands only in the spring and summer when the grasslands provide maximum cover (Fisler 1965). Their preferred habitats are the middle and upper portions of those marshes, i.e., the pickleweed (*Salicornia virginica*) and peripheral halophyte zones, and similar vegetation in diked wetlands adjacent to the Bay (Shellhammer et al. 1982, 1988). Some areas of known suitable habitat are shown in **Figure 5.1**.

Conservation and Management

There are many questions that need to be addressed in order to properly manage the SMHM. They include the following: (1) Little is known about the degree of genetic heterozygosity and polymorphism of this species. Is it variable, and hence is the SMHM resistant to increasing isolation, genetic drift, and potential increased inbreeding, or is it a species that has survived a series of genetic bottlenecks and become monomorphic and lacks resilience? Without information on its population genetics, the only prudent course of action is to argue for the largest possible population sizes of SMHM. Much more needs to be known about the population genetics of this species if it is to be properly managed over the long run. (2) It is not known how much upland edge constitutes enough of a buffer to protect SMHM from alien predators (especially cats) and human disturbance. The U.S. Fish and Wildlife Service Endangered Species biologists recommend 100 feet, but 100 feet of grassland, for example, may not be enough of a barrier to keep out dogs, cats, red foxes, or humans. (3) The impact of introduced red foxes is not known, but they have had a great impact on the California clapper rail, which is found in the same marshes with SMHM.

Control of red foxes is being carried out in those marshes in which there are rails and mice, but not in all marshes potentially containing SMHM alone. Actually, very little is known about the effects of predators on the SMHM, including the effects of the rail. (4) Little is known of the interactions between various species of rodents in diked marshes. Geissel et al. (1988) demonstrated seasonal displacement of SMHM from optimal habitat by California voles. Elaine Harding of U.C. Santa Cruz is studying (as of 1997-98) rodent interactions and has concerns that certain management practices in diked wetlands might work against SMHM. (5) Little is known about the impact of peppergrass on SMHM numbers. SMHM remain in mixed pickleweed-peppergrass communities (Duke et al. 1990, 1991), but no studies have been carried out in areas of 100% peppergrass, a condition that is becoming increasingly common in the southern end of the South San Francisco Bay. (6) Lastly, there is the strong possibility that youthful pickleweed marshes are more productive of SMHM than older ones. That is certainly the case reported by Bias (1994) and Bias and Morrison (1993) at Mare Island Naval Shipyards and in the marshes bordering the adjacent San Pablo Bay, a marsh that has been growing actively by accretion for decades. The effect of the relative youth of marshes (or possible the lack of their senescence), needs to be looked at along with the potential effects of toxics, the depth of buffer zones when marshes are bordered by either urban and industrial development, and other concerns spelled out previously in this document.

References

Bias, M.A. 1994. Ecology of the salt marsh harvest mouse in San Pablo Bay. Ph.D. dissert., Univ. of Ca., Berkeley, Calif. 243 pp.

Bias, M. A. and M. L. Morrison. 1993. Final report: salt marsh harvest mouse on Mare Island Naval Shipyard, 1989-1992. Unpubl. rpt. to Natural Resources Mgmt. Branch, Western Div., Naval Facilities Engineering Command, San Bruno, CA., 223 pp.

Duke, R.R., H.S. Shellhammer, R.A. Hopkins and E. Steinberg. 1990. San Jose Permit Assistance Program salt marsh harvest mouse trapping surveys, Spring and Summer, 1990. Prepared for CH2M Hill, Emeryville, CA by H.T. Harvey and Assoc.. Alviso, CA. Project No. 477-11.

Duke, R. R., S. B. Terrill, R. A. Hopkins, E. Steinberg and E. K. Harding. 1991. Concord Weapons Station small mammal characterization. Prepared for PRC Environmental Mgmt. Co. by H.T. Harvey and Assoc., Alviso, CA. Project 505-03.

Fisler, G.F. 1965. Adaptations and speciation in harvest mice of the marshes of San Francisco Bay. Univ. Ca. Publ. Zool. 77: 1-108.

Geissel, W.H., H.S. Shellhammer and H.T. Harvey. 1988. The ecology of the salt marsh harvest mouse (*Reithrodontomys raviventris*) in a diked salt marsh. J. Mammalogy. 69: 696-703.

Shellhammer, H.S. 1982. *Reithrodontomys raviventris*. Mammalian Species, No. 169: 1-3. The American Society of Mammalogists.

_____. 1989. Salt marsh harvest mice, urban development, and rising sea levels. Conservation Biology 3: 59-65.

Shellhammer, H.S., R. Jackson, W. Davilla, A.M. Gilroy, H.T. Harvey and L. Simons. 1982. Habitat preferences of salt marsh harvest mice (*Reithrodontomys raviventris*). Wasmann J. Bio. 40: 102-114.

Shellhammer, H.S., R.R. Duke, H.T. Harvey, V. Jennings, V. Johnson and M. Newcomer. 1988. Salt marsh harvest mice in the diked salt marshes of Southern San Francisco Bay. Wasmann J. Bio. 46: 89-103.

Additional Readings

Duke, R.R., H.S. Shellhammer, R.A. Hopkins, E. Steinberg, G. Rankin. 1995. Mare Island Naval Shipyard salt marsh harvest mouse 1994 trapping surveys. Prepared for Dames and Moore. Tucson. AZ by H.T. Harvey and Assoc., Alviso, CA. Project 921-01.

U.S. Fish and Wildlife Service (USFWS). 1984. Salt marsh harvest mouse and California clapper rail recovery plan. Portland, Oregon. 141 pp.

Mammals

Appendix 5.1 Important Data Sets for Salt Marsh Harvest Mouse (1971 - 1991). Compiled by Elaine Harding from a USFWS database.

Location	Subarea	Trap Nites	Mice	Mice Per Trap Nite	Year	Author
Alameda County						
Albrae Slough		100	2	0.02	1974, 1975	Cummings, E.
Albrae Slough		2600	15	0.006	1983	Shellhammer, H.
Albrae Slough		200	4	0.02	1984	Shellhammer, H.
Audubon Marsh		2700	4	0.001	1984	Shellhammer, H.
Audubon Marsh		300	7	0.023	1985	
Baumberg Tract			9		1985	
Cabot Boulevard		1046	6	0.006	1989	
Calaveras Point	Coyote Cr	100	0	0	1974, 1975	Cummings, E.
Calaveras Point	north of	100	0	0	1974, 1975	Cummings, E.
Calaveras Point		400	22	0.055	1990	Duke, R.
Calaveras Point		1000	104	0.104	1990	Duke, R.
Coyote Creek	Newby Isl	300	0	0	1985	
Coyote Creek	east	892	2	0.002	1990	Duke, R.
Coyote Creek		500	0	0	1990	Duke, R.
Coyote Hills		710	17	0.024	1975	Zetterquist
Coyote Hills		100	4	0.04	1980	Gilroy, A.
Coyote Hills Slough		100	0	0	1974, 1975	Cummings, E.
Coyote Hills Slough		400	0	0	1983	Shellhammer, H.
Coyote Hills Slough	area A	200	2	0.01	1983	Shellhammer, H.
Coyote Hills Slough	area D	200	0	0	1983	Shellhammer, H.
Coyote Hills Slough	area CH	200	0	0	1964	Shellhammer, H.
Coyote Hills Slough	area A	200	6	0.03	1984	Shellhammer, H.
Coyote Hills Slough	area PA	200	0	0	1984	Shellhammer, H.
Coyote Hills Slough	area CH	200	1	0.005	1984	Shellhammer, H.
Coyote Hills Slough		400	7	0.018	1984	Shellhammer, H.
Coyote Hills Slough		400	6	0.015	1985	Shellhammer, H.
Coyote Hills Slough	area 4	200	3	0.015	1985	Shellhammer, H.
Drawbridge		100	0	0	1974, 1975	Cummings, E.
Drawbridge		0	4		1978	
Dumbarton		25	3	0.12	1971	Schuat, D.B.
Dumbarton	railroad	100	0	0	1974, 1975	Cummings, E.
Dumbarton		400	13	0.033	1978	Leitner
Dumbarton		200	0	0	1980	Gilroy, A.
Dumbarton		500	6	0.012	1990, 1991	
Durham Road Marsh		200	0	0	1980	Gilroy, A.
EBRPD SMHM Preserve		540	4	0.007	1983	Kobetich
EBRPD SMHM Preserve		600	10	0.017	1984	Kobetich
EBRPD SMHM Preserve		725	7	0.01	1985	Kobetich
Emeryville Crescent		540	6	0.011	1982	Olsen, D.
Emeryville Crescent		1500	0	0	1986	
Fremont Redevelopment		900	13	0.014	1985	Kobetich
Hayward	Caltrans	300	1	0.003	1985	Jennings, V.R.
Hayward Marsh		900	21	0.023	1982	Shellhammer, H.
Hayward Marsh		1075	40	0.037	1990	
Ideal Marsh		100	1	0.01	1974, 1975	Cummings, E.
Ideal Marsh		200	0	0	1980	Gilroy, A.
Irvington STP		200	1	0.005	1985	Kobetich
Johnson Landing		900	21	0.023	1982	Kobetich
Johnson Landing		1950	15	0.008	1983	Kobetich
Leslie-Lincoln		200	0	0	1985	Jennings, V.R.
Leslie Quarry Site		300	2	0.007	1985	Shellhammer, H.

Mammals

Appendix 5.1 (continued) Important Data Sets for Salt Marsh Harvest Mouse (1971 - 1991). Compiled by Elaine Harding from a USFWS database.

Location	Subarea	Trap Nites	Mice	Mice Per Trap Nite	Year	Author
Alameda County (continued)						
Mayhew's Landing		1200	41	0.034	1985	
Mayhew's Landing		7410	23	0.003	1988	Shellhammer, H.
Mayhew's Landing		3120	36	0.012	1988-89	Johnson, V.
Meadow Gun Club		200	2	0.01	1985-	Shellhammer, H.
Mowry Slough	north of	75	2	0.027	1971	Schaub, D.B.
Mowry Slough	north of	100	0	0	1974, 1975	Cummings, E.
Mowry Slough	northeast	200	1	0.005	1980	Gilroy, A.
Mowry Slough	northwest	400	0	0	1980	Gilroy, A.
Mowry Slough	north	300	2	0.007	1985	
Mt. Eden Creek		400	5	0.013	1985	Shellhammer, H.
Mt. Eden Creek		871	9	0.01	1985	
Mud Slough	e. of Dra	200	4	0.02	1985	Jennings, V.R.
Mud Slough	w. of Dra	300	0	0	1986	Anderson, J.
Munster Site		1350	34	0.025	1985	Shellhammer, H.
Newark Slough		600	9	0.015	1978	
Newark Slough	central	200	0	0	1980	Gilroy, A.
Newark Slough	east	100	0	0	1980	Gilroy, A.
Newark Slough	headquart	365	1	0.003	1980	Gilroy, A.
Newark Slough		950	36	0.038	1982	Newcomer, M.
Newark Slough	SFC	300	4	0.013	1983	Shellhammer, H.
Newark Slough		5850	20	0.003	1983	Shellhammer, H.
Newark Slough		600	0	0	1984	Shellhammer, H.
Newark Slough		800	6	0.008	1985	Shellhammer, H.
Oakland Airport		1350	0	0	1985	Kobetich
Oakland Airport		1350	0	0	1985	Shellhammer, H.
Oakland Airport		500	0	0	1990	Xucera, T.E.
Old Alameda Creek		100	0	0	1974, 1975	Cummings, E.
Old Alameda Creek		200	0	0	1980	Gilroy, A.
Old Alameda Creek	Whale's T	400	3	0.008	1980	Gilroy, A.
Old Alameda Creek		300	2	0.007	1985	
Old Fremont Airport		900	5	0.006	1985	Kobetich
Old Fremont Airport		2400	27	0.011	1986	
?? Gun Club		200	2	0.01	1985	Shellhammer, H.
Roberts Landing		817	2	0.002	1983	Shellhammer, H.
Roberts Landing		817	2	0.002	1983	Kobetich
Roberts Landing		4350	126	0.029	1987	Shellhammer, H.
Roberts Landing		1240	28	0.023	1990	
Sulphur Creek		300	0	0	1985	
Sulphur Creek		200	1	0.005	1985	Shellhammer, H.
Thornton Ave.	Caltrans	200	1	0.005	1985	Jennings, V.R.
Turk Island		100	0	0	1974, 1975	Cummings, E.
Union City 511 Areas		1020	17	0.017	1986	
Union City Marsh	area B	600	2	0.003	1983	Shellhammer, H.
Union City Marsh		600	2	0.003	1984	Shellhammer, H.
Union City Marsh		1000	5	0.005	1985	Shellhammer, H.
University Ave	E. Palo A	160	0	0	1985	Jennings, V.R.
Warm Springs Mouse Pas	King and Ly	900	1	0.001	1985	Shellhammer, H.
Warm Springs Mouse Pas	King and Ly	450	7	0.016	1989	Foerster, K.
Warm Springs Seasonal		900	13	0.014	1985	Shellhammer, H.
Warm Springs Seasonal		1350	0	0	1988	Klinger, R.C.
Whistling Wings Duck Club		200	2	0.01	1985	Shellhammer, H.

Mammals

Appendix 5.1 (continued) Important Data Sets for Salt Marsh Harvest Mouse (1971 - 1991). Compiled by Elaine Harding from a USFWS database.

Location	Subarea	Trap Nites	Mice	Mice Per Trap Nite	Year	Author
Contra Costa County						
Antioch Point			21		1985	
Castro Creek Marsh		672	51	0.076	1981	Mishaga, R.
Concord Naval Weapons		150	12	0.08	1971	Schaub, D.B.
Concord Naval Weapons		123	4	0.033	1979	
Concord Naval Weapons		447	19	0.043	1979	Shellhammer, H.
Concord Naval Weapons		1800	22	0.012	1985	Shellhammer, H.
Concord Naval Weapons		2890	200	0.069	1991	Shellhammer, H.
Hastings Slough		1200	37	0.031	1988	Shellhammer, H.
Hoffman Marsh		80	0	0	1976	
Martinez East		200	0	0	1980	Simons, L.
Payten Shough		900	22	0.024	1988	Shellhammer, H.
Pittsburg		2800	64	0.023	1978	
Pittsburg East		100	0	0	1980	Simons, L.
Pittsburg West		100	0	0	1980	Simons, L.
Point Edith			25		1987	Botti, F.
Point Edith		800	5	0.006	1988	Shellhammer, H.
Point Edith		800	5	0.006	1988	Shellhammer, H.
Richmond Dump		200	1	0.005	1980	Simons, L.
San Pablo Creek		125	13	0.104	1971	Schaub, D.B.
San Pablo Creek		100	0	0	1974, 1975	Cummings, E.
San Pablo Creek		2480	81	0.033	1986	
Shell marsh		2270	6	0.003	1988	Shellhammer, H.
Shell marsh		800	1	0.001	1990	
Stockton Ship Channel	CWWS #22	400	0	0	1980	Shellhammer, H.
Stockton Ship Channel	CWWS #20	200	0	0	1980	Shellhammer, H.
Stockton Ship Channel	CWWS #21	200	6	0.03	1980	Shellhammer, H.
Stockton Ship Channel	CWWS #24	400	0	0	1980	Shellhammer, H.
Marin County						
Bahia	south	930	31	0.033	1984	Shellhammer, H.
Bahia	south, no	3000	68	0.023	1987	Shellhammer, H.
Bahia	north	300	3	0.01	1989	Duke, R.
Black John Slough	Mahoney S		16		1987	Bott, F.
China Camp State Park		200	2	0.01	1980	Simons, L.
Corte Madera		100	3	0.03	1971	Schaub, D.B.
Corte Madera		100	6	0.06	1974, 1975	Cummings, E.
Corte Madera		100	0	0	1976	
Corte Madera		200	2	0.01	1980	Simons, L.
Corte Madera		672	19	0.028	1981	Mishaga, R.
Corte Madera		1412	0	0	1983	Shellhammer, H.
Corte Madera		750	0	0	1990	Freas, K.E.
Gallinas Creek	north ban	100	1	0.01	1974, 1975	Cummings, E.
Gallinas Creek	south ban	100	1	0.01	1974, 1975	Cummings, E.
Gallinas Creek		672	34	0.051	1981	Mishaga, R.
Hamilton Air Force Base		300	1	0.003	1982	Newcomer, M.
John F. McInnis Park		1050	4	0.004	1986	
Larkspur ferry Marsh		480	0	0	1988	Shellhammer, H.
Muzzi Marsh	south	430	0	0	1986	
Novato Creek		100	1	0.01	1974, 1975	Cummings, E.
Petaluma Creek		200	0	0	1980	Simons, L.
Petaluma Sewage Treatm		100	0	0	1974, 1975	Cummings, E.
Pickleweed Park: San Rafael		1094	37	0.034	1990	Bias, M.A.

Mammals

Location	Subarea	Trap Nites	Mice	Mice Per Trap Nite	Year	Author
Marin County (continued)						
Spinnaker Lagoon		1200	11	0.009	1990	
Spinnaker Lagoon		1200	0	0	1991	
Marin/Sonoma County						
Petaluma River Mouth		100	0	0	1974, 1975	Cummings, E.
Napa County						
Coon Island	south end	200	2	0.01	1980	Simons, L.
Fagan Marsh	northeast	100	14	0.14	1980	Simons, L.
Deman Slough		100	0	0	1980	Simons, L.
Napa Slough	w of brid	100	1	0.01	1980	Simons, L.
San Mateo County						
Bair Island		500	3	0.006	1971	Schaub, D.B.
Bair Island	east	100	1	0.01	1974, 1975	Cummings, E.
Bair Island	Corkscrew	100	0	0	1974, 1975	Cummings, E.
Bair Island	southwest	100	1	0.01	1974, 1975	Cummings, E.
Bair Island	east	300	7	0.023	1985	
Bair Island	Corkscrew	300	3	0.01	1985	
Bair Island	southwest	220	19	0.086	1988	Botti, F.
Bay Slough		200	0	0	1980	Gilroy, A.
Belmont Slough		100	0	0	1974, 1975	Cummings, E.
Bird Island		100	1	0.01	1974, 1975	Cummings, E.
East Third Street		150	3	0.02	1989	McGinnis, S.M.
Foster City	marina si	116	0	0	1978	Johnston, D.S.
Foster City		900	0	0	1985	Shellhammer, H.
Foster City Marina Sit		900	0	0	1985	Duke, R.
Greco Island		100	2	0.02	1971	Schaub, D.B.
Greco Island		100	0	0	1974, 1975	Cummings, E.
Greco Island	south	150	0	0	1980	Gilroy, A.
Greco Island	north	150	3	0.02	1980	Gilroy, A.
Ideal Cement Marsh		250	5	0.02	1976	
Ideal Cement Marsh		900	0	0	1984	Shellhammer, H.
Ideal Cement Marsh		800	1	0.001	1985	Shellhammer, H.
Ideal Cement Marsh		978	42	0.043	1989-90	
Laumeister Marsh		100	0	0	1974, 1975	Cummings, E.
Laumeister Marsh		500	8	0.016	1990, 1991	
Palo Alto Yacht Harbor		200	1	0.005	1980	Gilroy, A.
Phelps Slough		100	0	0	1974, 1975	Cummings, E.
Ravenswood Slough		100	0	0	1974, 1975	Cummings, E.
Redwood Shores		100	0	0	1974, 1975	Cummings, E.
San Rafael Canal		1344	37	0.028	1990	Flannery, A.W.
Santa Clara County						
Alviso	south of	100	0	0	1975	Malenson, M.A.
Alviso Dump		200	0	0	1975	
Alviso Marina		100	0	0	1974, 1975	Cummings, E
Alviso Slough	west	100	0	0	1974, 1975	Cummings, E
Alviso Slough	east	100	4	0.04	1974, 1975	Cummings, E
Artesian Slough		200	0	0	1986	Anderson, J.
Calabazas Creek	south of	100	0	0	1975	Malenson, M.A.
Coyote Creek		900	11	0.012	1985	Shellhammer, H.
Coyote Creek		200	6	0.03	1990	Duke, R.
Crittenden Marsh		300	0	0	1985	
Emily Renzel Marsh	ITT marsh	4200	54	0.013	1988	Johnson, V.

Location	Subarea	Trap Nites	Mice	Mice Per Trap Nite	Year	Author
Santa Clara County (continued)						
New Chicago Marsh		100	2	0.02	1974, 1975	Cummings, E
New Chicago Marsh		1152	14	0.012	1975	Zetterquist,
New Chicago Marsh		300	0	0	1978	
New Chicago Marsh		400	0	0	1980	Gilroy, A., a
New Chicago Marsh		392	11	0.028	1985	Shellhammer, H.
New Chicago Marsh		2820	65	0.023	1986	Shellhammer, H.
New Chicago Marsh	Sammis si	1400	4	0.003	1987	Duke, R.
New Chicago Marsh		705	8	0.011	1988	Shellhammer, H.
Owens Corning Landfill		800	6	0.008	1990	Duke, R.
Palo Alto Baylands		40	1	0.025	1971	Schaub, D.B.
Palo Alto Baylands		2058	196	0.095	1972	Wondolleck, E
Palo Alto Baylands		100	0	0	1974, 1975	Cummings, E
Palo Alto Baylands		300	1	0.003	1985	
Palo Alto Baylands		1500	32	0.021	1990	
Palo Alto Flood Basin		100	0	0	1974, 1975	Cummings, E
Palo Alto Flood Basin		220	1	0.005	1975	Zetterquist,
Palo Alto Flood Basin		100	0	0	1975	Malenson, M.A.
Ravensweed Area		800	1	0.001	1990	Duke, R.
Sunnyvale		1200	3	0.003	1990	Duke, R.
Sunnyvale Baylands Park		540	0	0	1987	
Triangle Marsh	Grey Goos	20	0	0	1971	Schaub, D.B.
Triangle Marsh		4376	71	0.016	1974	Rice, V.C.
Triangle Marsh		100	23	0.23	1974, 1975	Cummings, E
Triangle Marsh		200	0	0	1976	
Triangle Marsh		922	12	0.013	1977-1978	Shellhammer, H.
Triangle Marsh		300	2	0.007	1983	Shellhammer, H.
Triangle Marsh		182	0	0	1984	Shellhammer, H.
Triangle Marsh		384	2	0.005	1985	Shellhammer, H.
Triangle Marsh		300	2	0.007	1986	Anderson, J.
Triangle Marsh		600	5	0.008	1986	Anderson, J.
Triangle Marsh		500	10	0.02	1990	Duke, R.
Triangle Marsh		1500	35	0.023	1990	Duke, R.
Solano County						
ACME Landfill Site		1200	9	0.008	1989	Foster, J.
Benicia	Marine Te	160	2	0.013	1979	Michaels, J.L.
Benicia State Park		200	0	0	1980	Simons, L., a
Chabot Creek Outfall M		483	4	0.008	1989	Ford, K.
Collinsville		1296	32	0.025	1978	Envirodyne En
Collinsville		1296	32	0.025	1978	Envirodyne En
Collinsville		1536	8	0.005	1979	
Collinsville		2350	2	0.001	1980	
Collinsville, Rail Cor		640	0	0	1979	
Cordelia Dike		150	0	0	1980	Shellhammer, H
Cullinan Ranch	S. Dutchm	2385	5	0.002	1983	Shellhammer, H
Denverton Highway		150	0	0	1980	Shellhammer, H
Ehaann Duck Club		800	3	0.004	1988	Shellhammer, H
Figueras Tract		100	2	0.02	1974, 1975	Cummings, E.
Figueras Tract		100	2	0.02	1974	Lindeman, E.
Gentry/Pierce Property		1800	10	0.006	1986	Duke, R.
Gold Hills Road Overcr		500	3	0.006	1990	
Grizzly Bay 1		300	5	0.017	1980	Shellhammer, H

Location	Subarea	Trap Nites	Mice	Mice Per Trap Nite	Year	Author
Solano County (continued)						
Grizzly Bay 2		300	2	0.007	1980	Shellhammer, H.
Grizzly Island		74	19	0.257	1971	Schuab, D.B.
Hill Slough	Windmill	150	0	0	1980	Shellhammer, H.
Hill Slough	Dump	150	0	0	1980	Shellhammer, H.
Hill Slough	wildlife	200	11	0.055	1981	
Hill Slough		300	1	0.003	1985	
Island #1		98	20	0.204	1971	Schuab, D.B.
Jackspine Wetland		150	0	0	1980	Shellhammer, H.
Joice Island		50	9	0.18	1971	Schuab, D.B.
Joice Island	powerline	300	1	0.003	1980	Shellhammer, H.
Joice Island	footbridge	300	0	0	1980	Shellhammer, H.
Joice Island		300	2	0.007	1985	
Leslie Intake	west bank	100	12	0.12	1974, 1975	Cummings, E.
Leslie Intake		150	20	0.133	1976	
Opes Road Marsh		420	0	0	1990	
Uco Slough		300	3	0.01	1986	
Mare Island Naval Ship		100	2	0.02	1974, 1975	Cummings, E.
Mare Island Naval Ship		1384	296	0.214	1985	Kovach, S.D.
Mare Island Naval Ship		2114	140	0.066	1986	Kovach, S.D.
Mare Island Naval Ship		1764	240	0.136	1987	Kovach, S.D.
Mare Island Naval Ship		14672	1005	0.068	1989	Bias et al.
Mare Island Naval Ship		9383	336	0.036	1990	Bias et al.
Mare Island Naval Ship		20502	1427	0.07	1991	Bias et al.
Meins Landing		300	2	0.007	1980	Shellhammer, H.
Meins Landing Mound		300	2	0.007	1980	Shellhammer, H.
Montezuma Site		1296	32	0.025	1978	
Montezuma Site		1800	17	0.009	1978	
Montezuma Site		1200	21	0.018	1991	Duke, R.
Morrow Island		300	0	0	1980	Shellhammer, H.
Napa River			3		1972	Rollins, G.
Nurse Slough		150	0	0	1980	Shellhammer, H.
Nurse Slough		400	7	0.018	1986	
Park Place		880	0	0	1987	
Park Place Shopping Ce		980	0	0	1987	
Rayer Island		30	1	0.033	1985	Kovach, S.D.
Roe Island		800	6	0.008	1988	Shellhammer, H.
Roe Island (east)		90	8	0.089	1985	Kovach, S.D.
Roe Island (west)		90	3	0.033	1985	Kovach, S.D.
Sears Point 1		800	21	0.026	1982	Newcomer, M.
Simmons Island		50	7	0.14	1971	Schuab, D.B.
Simmons Island	3 areas	600	4	0.007	1980	Shellhammer, H.
Simmons Island		1200	1	0.001	1985	Shellhammer, H.
Southern Solano Annexa		1109	30	0.027	1987	
Southhampton Bay (outb		375	2	0.005	1986	
Southhampton Marsh		700	18	0.026	1990	
Stockton Ship Channel	Brown's Is	400	0	0	1980	Shellhammer, H.
Stockton Ship Channel	Ryer Is	400	0	0	1980	Shellhammer, H.
Suisun Marsh Club No. 2	Bryan Par	195	6	0.031	1980	
Suisun Slough		300	4	0.013	1985	
Sulphur Springs Creek		600	0	0	1990	
Teal Boathouse		300	0	0	1980	Shellhammer, H.

Mammals

Appendix 5.1 (continued) Important Data Sets for Salt Marsh Harvest Mouse (1971 - 1991). Compiled by Elaine Harding from a USFWS database.

Location	Subarea	Trap Nites	Mice	Mice Per Trap Nite	Year	Author
Solano County (continued)						
Teal Slough		300	2	0.007	1980	Shellhammer, H.
Vennink	Building	150	0	0	1980	Shellhammer, H.
Vennink	Stockgate	300	3	0.01	1980	Shellhammer, H.
Vennink	Decoy	300	0	0	1980	Shellhammer, H.
Vennink	Bayside	150	0	0	1980	Shellhammer, H.
West Grizzly Island		300	0	0	1985	
Wildwings Duck Club (M		800	7	0.009	1988	Shellhammer, H.
Sonoma County						
Lower Tubbs Island		100	9	0.09	1971	Schaub, D.B.
Lower Tubbs Island		100	4	0.04	1974, 1975	Cummings, E.
Lower Tubbs Island		256	5	0.02	1979	Moss, J.G.
Lower Tubbs Island		100	0	0	1980	Simons, L.
Mare Island Naval Ship		672	80	0.119	1988	Stroud, M.C.
Petaluma Creek		100	7	0.07	1971	Schaub, D.B.
Petaluma River	1 m. upst	100	0	0	1974, 1975	Cummings, E.
Petaluma River Mouth		100	1	0.01	1980	Simons, L.
Sonoma Creek	east	100	2	0.02	1974, 1975	Cummings, E.
Sonoma Creek	mouth	100	2	0.02	1980	Simons, L.
Sonoma Creek		200	12	0.06	1982	Newcomer, M.
Tolay Creek Mouth		100	4	0.04	1980	Simons, L.
Tubbs Island 1		750	33	0.044	1982	Newcomer, M.
Tubbs island Accessory		205	8	0.039	1980	Simons, L.

Mammals

California Vole

Microtus californicus

William Z. Lidicker, Jr.

Life History

California voles are common inhabitants of the San Francisco Bay wetlands. They are vegetarians, feeding extensively on *Salicornia* and other marsh vegetation. They make runways through the vegetation, burrow extensively in non-flooded areas, and often utilize driftwood for cover. They are critically important prey species for a wide variety of mammalian and avian predators.

The population dynamics of voles has been studied intensively in adjacent upland grasslands (Cockburn and Lidicker 1983; Krebs 1966; Lidicker 1973; Pearson 1966, 1971; Salvioni and Lidicker 1995), but little is known about marsh populations. It is not known, for example, if most marsh populations are merely extensions of upland ones or independent demographic units. An exception is the San Pablo Creek vole; see below. Grassland populations around the Bay exhibit annual or multi-annual cycles in numbers, but the demographic behavior of salt marsh populations is unknown. Similarly, we know that grassland voles breed mainly in the wet season, and especially intensely from February through May. Voles in marshes may well be different, perhaps breeding mostly in the summer and very little during the flood-prone winters.

California voles are keystone species in grassland communities by virtue of their importance as a major prey species (Pearson 1985) and their potentially great effect on vegetation (Lidicker 1989). Thus, if similar roles are played in San Francisco Bay wetlands, these rodents may be vital to the health of the wetland communities. Because they are known to exhibit strong fluctuations in numbers (four orders of magnitude), suitable habitat patches must be large enough for the species to survive low-density bottlenecks. These voles are also known to exhibit strong non-trophic interactions with other species of mammals. The introduced house mouse

(*Mus musculus*) is strongly affected negatively by the presence of voles (DeLong 1966, Lidicker 1966). Interactions with Western harvest mice (*Reithrodontomys megalotis*) are more complex (Heske et al. 1984). At moderate *Microtus* densities harvest mice are positively influenced, presumably because the harvest mice make effective use of vole runways. However, at high vole densities, the *Reithrodontomys* are strongly negatively impacted. It is possible that salt marsh harvest mice (*Reithrodontomys raviventris*) may interact in a similarly complex way with voles. Geissel et al. (1988) demonstrated seasonal displacement of salt marsh harvest mice by voles. More subtle indirect effects may also be important. For example, if voles sustain populations of red fox (*Vulpes vulpes*), an indirect negative effect on clapper rails (*Rallus longirostris obsoletus*) may be manifest.

Historical and Modern Distributions

The taxonomic status of San Francisco Bay voles is complex. Marsh inhabiting voles from Point Isabel (Contra Costa County) south on the east side of the Bay and around to the west side as far north as Redwood City have been described as the subspecies *paludicola*. Thaeler (1961) examined these populations in detail and concluded that at least the East Bay populations could not be distinguished from the upland subspecies *californicus*. Voles from the Marin County side of the Bay are placed in *M.c. eximius*, and those from Grizzly Island (Solano County) and eastward into the Delta represent the large, dark subspecies *aestuarinus*. Of special interest and concern, Thaeler (1961) described the vole population inhabiting the marshes around the mouth of San Pablo Creek (Contra Costa County) as *M.c. sanpabloensis*. This subspecies is viewed as a species of special concern by the State of California (Williams 1986). It is darker and yellower than the adjacent populations of *M.c. californicus*. Further, its palatines are deeply excavated along their posterior borders, the rostrum is narrow, and the auditory bullae relatively inflated.

Suitable Habitat

Habitat use extends from adjacent upland grasslands into both salt and freshwater marshes, at least into those where flooding does not occur regularly. Voles are good swimmers, however, and can survive occasional inundation. Some known current locations and potential suitable habitats are shown in **Figure 5.2**.

Conservation and Management

Efforts to conserve wetlands should be aware of the endemic form *M.c. sanpabloensis* and attempt to achieve

J.K. Clark; Courtesy UC IPM Project

Figure 5.2 California Vole – Some Current Locations and Suitable Habitat

Note: Voles are likely present in areas identified as "suitable" habitat based on current information regarding habitat types. Voles may also be present in other areas.

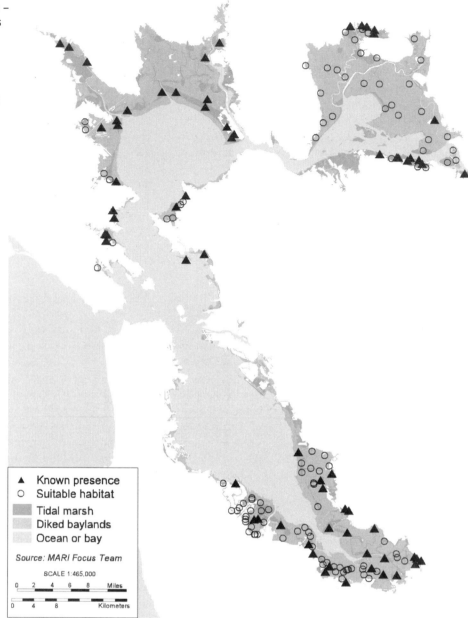

▲ Known presence
○ Suitable habitat
Tidal marsh
Diked baylands
Ocean or bay

Source: MARI Focus Team

SCALE 1:465,000

0 2 4 6 8 Miles

0   4   8   Kilometers

Mammals

representation of the other three currently recognized subspecies in the Bay Area as well. Because of their role as a major prey species, California voles are likely keystone species in the health of Bay Area wetland communities.

References

Cockburn, A. and W.Z. Lidicker, Jr. 1983. Microhabitat heterogeneity and population ecology of an herbivorous rodent, *Microtus californicus*. Oecologia 59: 167-177.

DeLong, K.T. 1966. Population ecology of feral house mice: interference by *Microtus*. Ecology 47: 481-484.

Geissel, W.H., H. Shellhammer and H.T. Harvey. 1988. The ecology of the salt marsh harvest mouse (*Reithrodontomys raviventris*) in a diked salt marsh. J. Mammology 69: 696-703.

Heske, E.J., R.S. Ostfeld and W.Z. Lidicker, Jr. 1984. Competitive interactions between *Microtus californicus* and *Reithrodontomys megalotis* during two peaks of *Microtus* abundance. J. Mammology 65: 271-280.

Krebs, C.J. 1966. Demographic changes in fluctuating populations of *Microtus californicus*. Ecol. Monogr. 36: 239-273.

Lidicker, W.Z., Jr. 1966. Ecological observations on a feral house mouse population declining to extinction. Ecol. Monogr. 36: 27-50.

_____. 1973. Regulation of numbers in an island population of the California vole, a problem in community dynamics. Ecol. Monogr. 43: 271-302.

_____. 1989. Impacts of non-domesticated vertebrates on California grasslands. *In:* L.F. Huenneke and H. Mooney (eds). Grassland structure and function: California annual grassland. Kluwer Acad. Pub., Dordrecht, The Netherlands; pp. 135-150

Pearson, O.P. 1966. The prey of carnivores during one cycle of mouse abundance. Jour. Anim. Ecol. 35: 217-233.

_____. 1971. Additional measurements of the impact of carnivores on California voles (*Microtus californicus*). J. Mammology. 52: 41-49.

_____. 1985. Predation. Pp. 536-566. *In*: R. H. Tamarin (ed). Biology of new world *Microtus*. Amer. Soc. Mammalogists Spec. Pub. No. 8; 893 pp.

Salvioni, M. and W.Z. Lidicker, Jr. 1995. Social organization and space use in California voles: seasonal, sexual, and age-specific strategies. Oecologia 101: 426-438.

Thaeler, C.S., Jr. 1961. Variation in some salt-marsh populations of *Microtus californicus*. Univ. Calif. Pub. Zool. 60: 67-94.

Williams, D. F. 1986. Mammalian species of special concern in California. Wildlife Mgt. Div. Admin. Report 86-1, Calif. Dept. of Fish and Game, Sacramento, CA. 112 pp.

Salt Marsh Wandering Shrew

Sorex vagrans haliocoetes

Howard S. Shellhammer

Life History

The salt marsh wandering shrew (SMWS) appears to have some of the most restrictive food and habitat requirements of any mammal inhabiting the marshes of the greater San Francisco Bay Region—far more, for example, than the endangered salt marsh harvest mouse (*Reithrodontomys raviventris*). While little is known of the SMWS subspecies, shrews in general are insectivores which are born in the spring and become sexually mature the following winter. SMWSs have gestation periods of about 21 days (Owen and Hoffman 1983). Many shrew species have only one litter, and adults die after the young are weaned (Jameson and Peeters 1988).

Historical and Modern Distribution

The historical range of the SMWS extended from the northern end of the San Francisco Peninsula, down through the marshes of the South San Francisco Bay, and up through the marshes of western Contra Costa County to about the Benicia Straits.

Johnston and Rudd (1957) suggested that between 1951 and 1955 shrews represented about 10% of the small mammals of the marshes. They were far less numerous in the 1970s and 80s, at least in the southern part of its range (Shellhammer, pers. obs.). Known or suspected populations as of 1986 included marshes south of Foster City and Hayward and in the San Pablo marshes of the San Pablo Bay (WESCO 1986). This subspecies of vagrant shrew is currently confined to the salt marshes of the South San Francisco Bay (**Figure 5.3**). It exists in a narrow band of tidal salt marsh and does not seem to be present in diked marshes.

Dr. Richard B. Forbes

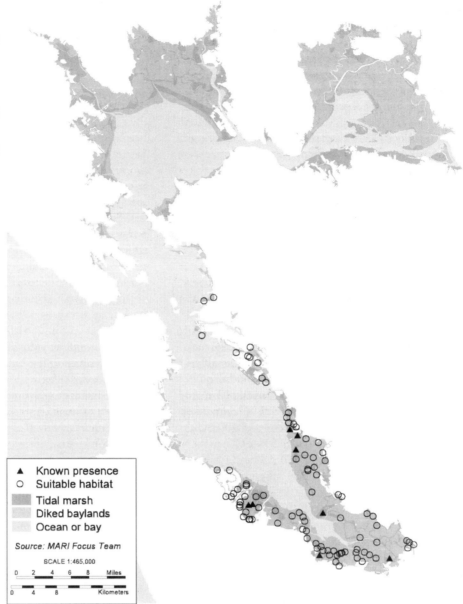

Figure 5.3 Salt Marsh Wandering Shrew – Some Current Locations and Suitable Habitat

Note: Shrews are likely present in areas identified as "suitable" habitat based on current information regarding habitat types. Shrews may also be present in other areas.

▲ Known presence
○ Suitable habitat
   Tidal marsh
   Diked baylands
   Ocean or bay

Source: MARI Focus Team

SCALE 1:465,000

0　2　4　6　8　Miles

0　　4　　8　　Kilometers

Suitable Habitat

The SMWS's habitat is wet, medium high salt marshes. It is best described by D. Williams (1983) in a draft report for the California Department of Fish and Game using material primarily from Johnston and Rudd (1957): "[Salt marsh wandering shrews] frequent areas in the tidal marshes providing dense cover, abundant food (invertebrates), suitable nesting sites, and fairly continuous ground moisture. Their center of activity is in the 'medium high marsh,' about 6 to 8 feet above sea level, and in lower marsh areas not regularly inundated. Suitable sites are characterized by abundant driftwood and other debris scattered among pickleweed (*Salicornia*). The pickleweed is usually one to two feet in height. The detritus preserves moisture and offers refuge in dry period to amphipods, isopods and other invertebrates, and resting sites for shrews. Nesting material consists of plant material, primarily *Salicornia* duff. The higher marsh, 8 to 9 feet in elevation, is too dry and offers only minimal cover—few to no shrews occupy this zone. The lower cordgrass (*Spartina*) zone is subjected to daily tidal floods and has cover too sparse for shrews."

Some potential suitable habitat locations are shown in **Figure 5.3**.

Conservation and Management

Johnston and Rudd's 1957 paper represents the last scientific work on the subspecies, per se. The rest of the reports (Williams 1983; WESCO 1986; this present effort) are all based on that study and that of Rudd 1955.

Mammals

Many changes have taken place since the early 1950s and little to nothing is known as to how such changes have affected the prey or habitat requirements of this shrew. The southern part of the San Francisco Bay has been greatly freshened by hundreds of millions of gallons of treated sewage outflows per day, and this freshening has brought about changes in plant species composition. Until point source reductions were placed on industrial sewage in the 1980s, large amounts of heavy metals, as well as polychlorinated biphenyls and petroleum hydrocarbons were poured into the Bay. In addition, the storm runoff and inflows of creeks and small rivers carried unknown amounts of pesticides, petroleum compounds, and other toxic substances. It is not known how decreased salinity and increased toxicity in the South Bay may have impacted the shrews, either directly, or indirectly, through changes in the amount and diversity of their prey. In addition to salinity, vegetation changes, and toxics, many of the marshes of the South Bay have subsided, and the *Salicornia* bands have become more degraded and more heavily inundated. Again little is known as to the effects on this shrew of such changes.

The SMWS is currently listed as "Mammalian Species of Special Concern" by the California Deptartment of Fish and Game and as a candidate species for listing in Category 2 by the U.S. Fish and Wildlife Service. Neither classification offers legal protection to its habitat. Little recent biological information is available to support its classification as a protected species, a status it merits.

References

Jameson, E.W., Jr. and H.J. Peeters. 1988. California Mammals. Univ. of Ca. Press, Berkeley, CA.

Johnston, R.F. and R.L. Rudd. 1957. Breeding of the salt marsh shrew. J. Mammalogy 38: 157-163.

Owen, J.G. and R.S. Hoffmann. 1983. *Sorex ornatus.* Mammalian Species No. 212: 1-5. The American Society of Mammalogists.

Rudd, R. L. 1955. Age, sex, and weight comparisons in three species of shrews. J. Mammalogy 36: 323-339.

Western Ecological Services Company (WESCO). 1986. A review of the population status of the salt marsh wandering shrew, *Sorex vagrans haliocoetes*, Final Report.

Williams, D.F. 1983. Mammalian species of special concern in California. Ca. Dept. Fish and Game, Nongame Wildl. Investigation, E-W-4, IV-14.1, Draft Final Report. 184 pp.

Suisun Shrew

Sorex ornatus sinuosis

Kevin MacKay

Life History

The Suisun shrew is a small (95-105 mm in total length), dark, insectivorous mammal with a long, pointed nose, and a well-developed scaly tail (37-41 mm). Suisun shrews are carnivores and predators feeding primarily upon amphipods, isopods, and other invertebrate species (WESCO 1986, Hays 1990). The shrews may also occasionally serve as prey for several large predators such as the short-eared owl (*Asio flammeus*), northern harrier (*Circus cyaneus*), and black-shouldered kite (*Elanus caeruleus*) (WESCO 1986).

The reproductive period of the Suisun shrew extends from late February through September, with the majority of breeding occurring from early spring through May. A second breeding period occurs in late summer when the young born the previous spring are mature and able to mate for the first time.

Shrews typically construct domed, cup-like nests composed of small paper scraps and dead material from plants such as pacific cordgrass (*Spartina foliosa*), pickleweed (*Salicornia virginica*), and salt grass (*Distichlis spicata*). The nests are usually placed directly on the soil surface under driftwood, planks, or wood blocks, and are situated above the high tide line to escape flooding (WESCO 1986). Runways enter from the sides and from beneath, and are not opened until two to three weeks after the birth of the young (Johnston and Rudd 1957). After the young have dispersed, the nests may be used by other small mammals such as the endangered salt marsh harvest mouse (*Reithrodontomys raviventris*) (WESCO 1986).

There are no published data on the gestation period of the Suisun shrew, but the salt marsh wandering shrew and other small shrews have a gestation period of about 21 days (Owen and Hoffmann 1983, WESCO 1986). Litter size ranges from four to six individuals, with a survival rate of 55 to 60 percent from near birth to just after weaning (Johnston and Rudd 1957). Causes of mortality include drowning from high tides, death of the mother, starvation, exposure, and predation (WESCO 1986). The young remain in the nest for up to five weeks and then move into adjacent areas (Rudd 1955).

Suisun shrews seldom reach their maximum life expectancy of 16 months, and populations turn over on an annual basis. Populations in the early spring typically consist of adults born the previous year. These individuals gradually die off during the summer months, and by fall have been almost completely replaced by young born the previous spring (Owen and Hoffmann 1983).

Mammals

Activity patterns vary according to season and reproductive condition in the Suisun shrew, but the subspecies is predominately nocturnal, especially during the breeding season. Sexually mature shrews are very active in the spring, concurrent with the breeding season, but are less active during the early summer. Young-of-the-year born in early spring become sexually mature by late summer, and their activity patterns peak during this second breeding season. Others, born later in the season are still sexually immature by late summer and remain comparatively inactive during this period (Owen and Hoffmann 1983).

Hays (1990) found that during the non-breeding season, shrews lived in loose social groups of 10 to 15 individuals. These groups contained only one adult male, and one such group occupied 0.07 ha. In the spring other adult males invade these groups, disrupting the stable structure by competing among themselves.

Territorial behavior in shrews has not been well documented in the field. However, Rust (1978) noted territorial patrolling in observations of breeding captive Suisun shrews.

Historical and Modern Distribution

One of the nine subspecies of ornate shrew that occur in California, the Suisun shrew is a relatively rare inhabitant of the salt marsh ecosystem of San Pablo and Suisun Bays (WESCO 1986). Johnston and Rudd (1957) estimated that the shrews represent approximately 10 percent of the mammalian fauna present in marsh habitats, and were less abundant than mice (*Mus sp.*), rats (*Rattus sp.*), voles (*Microtus sp.*), and harvest mice (*Reithrodontomys sp.*).

The historical extent of the Suisun shrew distribution is unknown (WESCO 1986) **(Figure 5.4)**. According to Rudd (1955) the subspecies historically inhabited the tidal saline and brackish salt marsh communities of northern San Pablo and Suisun bays, ranging from the mouth of the Petaluma River, Sonoma County on the west, eastward through Southampton and Grizzly Island to approximately Collingsville, Solano County (WESCO 1986, Rudd 1955, Williams 1983). The western extent of the range was redefined by Brown and Rudd (1981) as they identified the shrews inhabiting the marshes west of Sonoma Creek and Tubbs Island as *S. o. californicus* (WESCO 1986, Williams 1983).

However, surveys completed by Grinnell (1913) discovered Suisun shrews only at Grizzly Island. Researchers (WESCO 1986) have speculated that, at that time, the shrew was restricted to the greater Grizzly Island area because of the lack of suitable habitat throughout the rest of the historic range. The 1914 soil survey of the San Francisco Bay Area identifies most of the Napa Marsh as low tidal mud flats, a habitat that would be consistently inundated by tidal waters and thus uninhab-

itable by Suisun shrews or other small mammals. Once these areas were diked, and suitable habitat created, the shrew may have expanded its historic range into these adjacent areas (WESCO 1986).

There are no data available which directly measures the current densities of Suisun shrew populations. The number of individuals within a population appears to vary with season and habitat type. Newman (1970) estimated that the most favorable habitat supported shrew densities of as many as 111 individuals per hectare. A related species, the dusky shrew (*Sorex obscurus*), has overlapping home ranges averaging 0.037 ha in size, with a density of 37 to 42 individuals per hectare. These latter figures are probably a more accurate depiction of Suisun shrew populations as the amount of favorable habitat is limited throughout most of its range (WESCO 1986).

The Suisun shrew is currently limited in its distribution to the scattered, isolated remnants of natural tidal salt and brackish marshes surrounding the northern borders of Suisun and San Pablo bays (WESCO 1986).

Rudd (1955) identified four distinct populations of Suisun shrews: the Grizzly Island population, found throughout the marshlands east of Suisun Slough; a peripheral population found west of Suisun Slough and on Morrow Island; the Southampton population, restricted to the Benicia State Recreation Area; and the Sears Point Road population located in the Napa marshes.

No Suisun shrews were captured in either of the two most recent population studies (Williams 1983, WESCO 1986) that attempted to assess the current distribution of the shrew. This lack of trapping success can possibly be attributed to the extremely high rainfall in 1982 and 1986. Most of the low-lying marshes were flooded for extended periods of time, adversely affecting the small mammal populations. Additional trapping efforts for salt marsh harvest mice occasionally yielded *Sorex* captures; however, only one capture, at Cullinan Ranch on South Slough, was identified as *S. o. sinuosis* (WESCO 1986).

WESCO (1986) plotted all known *S. o. sinuosis* captures to delineate extant populations. Only two individual areas were identified that support populations of Suisun shrews: Grizzly Island and Solano Island Number 1. Nine additional marsh areas were also identified as having a high probability of supporting Suisun shrew populations: Skaggs Island, Appleby Bay/Coon Island, Steamboat Slough, Vallejo, Morrow Island, Cordelia Slough South, Hammond Island, Simmons/Wheeler Islands, and Collingsville (WESCO 1986).

Suitable Habitat

Suisun shrews typically inhabit saline and brackish tidal marshes characterized by pacific cordgrass (*Spartina foliosa*), pickleweed (*Salicornia virginica*), gumplant

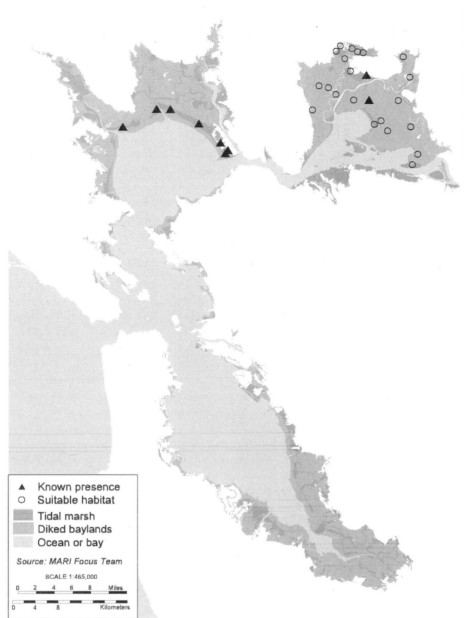

Figure 5.4 Suisun Shrew – Some Current Locations and Suitable Habitat

Note: Shrews are likely present in areas identified as "suitable" habitat based on current information regarding habitat types. Shrews may also be present in other areas.

▲ Known presence
○ Suitable habitat
▦ Tidal marsh
▦ Diked baylands
▦ Ocean or bay

Source: MARI Focus Team

SCALE 1:465,000

0 2 4 6 8 Miles

0 4 8 Kilometers

(*Grindelia humulis*), California bulrush (*Scirpus californicus*), and common cattail (*Typha latifolia*). However, shrew occurrence appears to be more strongly associated with vegetation structure rather than species composition. Suisun shrews prefer dense, low-lying vegetation which provides protective cover and suitable nesting sites, as well as abundant invertebrate prey species (Owen and Hoffmann 1983). Driftwood, planks, and other debris found above the high-tide line also affords the shrew with valuable foraging and nesting sites. In addition, adjacent upland habitats provide essential refuge areas for Suisun shrews and other terrestrial animals during periods of prolonged flooding (Williams 1986). Some areas of potentially suitable habitat for the Suisun Shrew are shown in **Figure 5.4**.

Conservation and Management

Williams (1986) identified the lack of an adequate elevational gradient of marsh vegetation and adjacent upland habitats as the principal obstacles to the recovery of Suisun shew populations in San Pablo and Suisun bays. However, as the Suisun shrew does not seem to make use of upland grasslands (Hays 1990), and because of evidence of interbreeding with *S. o. californicus*, future marsh management practices should include the provision of elevated sites that flood only occasionally, but not include upland grassland, which would encourage contact with *californicus*.

References

Brown, R.J. and R.L. Rudd. 1981. Chromosomal comparisons within the *Sorex ornatus-S. vagrens* complex. Wassman J. Bio. 39:30-35.

Grinnell, J. 1913. The species of the mammalian genus *Sorex* of west-central California. Univ. Ca. Publ. Zool. 10:179-195.

Hays, W.S. 1990. Population ecology of ornate shrews, *Sorex ornatus*. Unpub. MA dissert. in zoology, Univ. of Ca., Berkeley.

Johnson, R.F. and R.L. Rudd. 1957. Breeding of the salt marsh shrew. J. Mammology., 38:157-163.

Newman, J.R. 1970. Energy flow of a secondary consumer (*Sorex sinuosus*) in a salt marsh community. Dissert. Abst., 32B:883.

Owen, J.G. and R.S. Hoffmann. 1983. *Sorex ornatus*. Mammalian Species No. 212:1-5. American Society of Mammalogists.

Rudd, R.L. 1955. Age, sex and weight comparisons in three species of shrews. J. Mammology, 36:323-338.

Rust, A.K. 1978. Activity rhythms in the shrews, *Sorex sinuosus* Grinnell and *Sorex trowbridgii* Baird. Amer. Midland Nat., 99:369-382.

Western Ecological Services (WESCO) 1986. A review of the population status of the Suisun shrew *(Sorex ornatus sinuosus)*. Final Rept. for U.S. Fish and Wildl. Serv., Sacramento, Calif. 59 pp.

Williams, D.F. 1983. Populations surveys of the Santa Catalina, San Bernadino, and Suisun Shrews. U.S. Dept. of Int., U.S. Fish and Wildl. Servi., Endangered Species Office, Sacramento, Calif. 69 pp.

_____. 1986. Mammalian species of special concern in California. State of Calif., The Resources Agency, Ca. Dept. Fish and Game. pp. 14-15.

Ornate Shrew

Sorex ornatus californicus

Elaine K. Harding

Life History

Ornate shrews are small insectivores weighing on average five grams and with a tail short relative to the length of the head and body (Owen and Hoffmann 1983). There are nine subspecies of ornate shrew found throughout California and Mexico, and three of these are currently candidates for federal listing (USFWS 1989). *Sorex ornatus californicus* is not considered a sensitive species, although very little information is known about this subspecies, as is the case with most shrews. This subspecies may coexist with the Suisun shrew (*Sorex ornatus sinuosis*) in the marshes of San Pablo and Suisun bays. The pelage of the ornate shrew is grayish brown dorsally to a pale gray ventrally, which differentiates it from the Suisun shrew's darker pelage (Rudd 1955).

Shrews reproduce from late February through September, with peaks in late spring and summer. There is little information on this species' litter size or survival, but embryo counts ranged from four to six (Owen and Hoffmann 1983). A few young-of-the-year born in spring may mature by summer and reproduce. These shrews live no longer than 12 to 16 months. Their extremely high metabolism requires that they eat high energy foods often throughout the course of a day. *S. o. californicus* is a predator of invertebrates and may find food and cover in low, dense, moist vegetation. In wetland areas, amphipods are known to be important sources of food for shrews, but the diet of this shrew has not been thoroughly investigated.

Historical and Modern Distribution

S. ornatus californicus' range is from the Sacramento Valley southwest to the Central Coast, including the San Francisco Bay except for the southwestern portion of San Pablo Bay. A thorough account of its current range within the San Francisco Bay is not available due to a lack of identification to the species level when found incidentally during other studies. Some known and potential habitats, however, are indentified in **Figure 5.5**.

The ornate shrew may hybridize with the Suisun shrew in particular parapatric zones in North San Pablo Bay marshes. Rudd (1955) described populations at Grizzly Island and Sears Points which exhibited intermediate morphological characters between *S. o. californicus* and *S. o. sinuosus*. More recently Brown and Rudd (1981) concluded that populations at other locations once considered hybrids of the Suisun shrew (*S. o. sinuosus*) and the salt marsh wandering shrew (*S. vagrans*) are only

Mammals

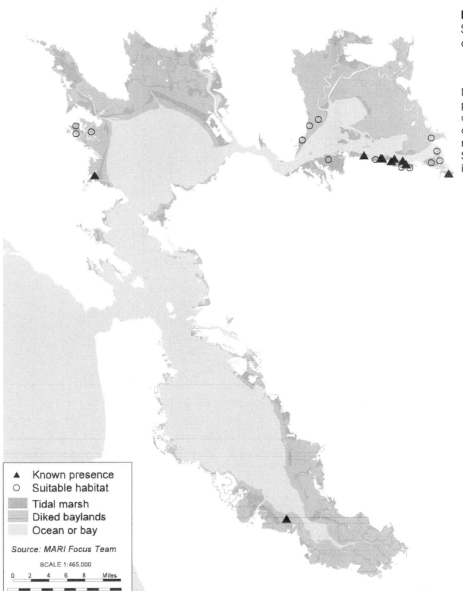

Figure 5.5 Ornate Shrew – Some Current Locations and Suitable Habitat

Note: Shrews are likely present in areas identified as "suitable" habitat based on current information regarding habitat types. Shrews may also be present in other areas.

▲ Known presence
○ Suitable habitat
■ Tidal marsh
■ Diked baylands
■ Ocean or bay

Source: MARI Focus Team

SCALE 1:465,000

0 2 4 6 8 Miles

0 4 8 Kilometers

slightly differentiated populations of *S. o. californicus*. However, further discrimination of the taxonomic status between *S. o. californicus* and *S. o. sinuosus* is needed as the two subspecies have identical karyotypes (Brown 1971).

Suitable Habitat

The ornate shrew prefers semi-arid, grassland and riparian habitats. Despite this preference, it is also found in brackish and saltwater marshes in San Pablo Bay and perhaps in other marshes throughout the Bay Area (**Figure 5.5**) based on records of identification only to the genus *Sorex*.

Conservation and Management

The ornate shrew is an uncommon inhabitant of the upland transition zones and marshes in the San Fran-

cisco Bay. Although it is not currently endangered, its local population status may be a general indicator of the health of an ecosystem, particularly as shrews are very good barometers of contaminant loads. Because they prey on a variety of invertebrates, they often bioaccumulate more rapidly than other species of similar size. It is important to monitor the status of this species and to research their potential as an indicator of wetland health.

References

Brown, R.J. 1971. A comparative study of the chromosomes of some Pacific coast shrews (Genus *Sorex*). Unpubl. Ph.D. dissertation. Univ. of Ca., Davis.

Brown, R.J. and R.L. Rudd. 1981. Chromosomal comparisons within the *Sorex ornatus–Sorex vagrans* complex. Wasmann J. Bio. 39: 30-35.

Mammals

Owen, J.G. and R.S. Hoffmann. 1983. Ornate shrew. Mammalian Species, No. 212. The American Society of Mammalogists.

Rudd, R.L. 1955. Population variation and hybridization in some California shrews. Syst. Zool. 4:21-34.

U.S. Fish and Wildlife Service (USFWS). 1989. Internal memo on the twelve month finding on a petition to list four California shrews as endangered. Sacramento Field Office.

North American River Otter

Lutra canadensis

Michael L. Johnson

Life History

Adult river otters can range in size from 900 mm to almost 1,300 mm, and can weigh from 5 to 14 kg. Clinal variation in size is present, with otters becoming smaller from north to south, especially along the Pacific Coast. Sexual dimorphism is present, with females being smaller than males. Litter sizes vary with location from 1-5, with the average litter being 2-3. Females may become pregnant every year or may become pregnant only in alternate years, depending on local conditions. Pups grow rapidly and typically emerge from the den at two months, and are weaned at about three months. Dispersal of offspring typically occurs at about one year (Melquist and Hornocker 1983), and there are reports of yearlings dispersing up to 200 km (125 mi), although typical dispersal distances are about 32 km (20 mi) (Hornocker et al. 1983). Both sexes typically mature at two years of age, and can live up to 12-15 years in the wild. Captive otters have lived as long as 25 years.

River otters are the top carnivore in riverine systems and eat a wide variety of prey. Otters are most often cited as feeding primarily on fish and secondarily on crustaceans, mammals, reptiles, birds, amphibians, and insects (Table 36.2 in Toweill and Tabor 1982, Table

5 in Melquist and Dronkert 1987). A study of food habits of river otters in the Suisun Marsh performed by scat analysis (Grenfell 1974) indicated that crayfish were the most frequent prey item, and birds and fish were alternately the second most frequent prey item, depending on season. Although individual species identification of the fish was not attempted, scales and teeth indicated that the most probable prey items were the carp (*Cyprinus carpio*), Sacramento squawfish (*Ptychocheilus grandis*), the tule perch (*Hysterocarpus traskii*), and the striped bass (*Morone saxatilis*). Mammals, plants, and reptiles appeared to be taken opportunistically, as their frequency of occurrence in scats was never higher than 10 percent.

Historical and Modern Distribution

The North American river otter is a member of the Family Mustelidae Subfamily Lutrinae Tribe Lutrini. Formerly abundant throughout much of Northern California, they are placed into the subspecies *L. c. pacifica* Rhoads (Stephens 1906, Ingles 1965, Deems and Pursley 1978). Alternate subspecies designations placed otters from California's Sacramento and San Joaquin drainages into a separate subspecies, *L. c. brevipilosus* Grinnell (Anthony 1928, Grinnell 1933) with the type locality being Grizzly Island, Suisun Bay, Solano County, California (Grinnell 1933). Although there were 18 subspecies at one time, currently there are six. It was recently proposed that these be placed into a single species with the South American river otter, and placed into a New World genus *Lontra* (Van Zyll De Jong 1987).

Northern river otters were once found in all major drainages throughout North America, possessing one of the largest geographic ranges of all mammals. The present distribution over North America extends from 25° north latitude in Florida to over 70° north latitude in Alaska, and from eastern Newfoundland to the Aleutian Islands (Toweill and Tabor 1982). In California, the distribution of river otters early in the 20th century included the Sacramento, San Joaquin and North Coast river drainages, eastward from the coast to the Sierra crest and to the Warner Mountains of Modoc County, and from the San Joaquin River east to the Sierra crest (Belfiore 1996). Grinnell placed the center of species abundance in the Sacramento-San Joaquin Delta (Grinnell 1933). Intensive trapping for pelts occurred during the latter half of the century (Ingles 1965, Duplaix 1978, Mason 1989, Halbrook et al. 1994). Recent declines are also blamed on habitat destruction or alteration as well as the deterioration in water quality (Deems and Pursley 1978, Mason 1989). The California Fish and Game Commission imposed a ban on trapping in 1969. Despite meager evidence, furbearer status reports indicated that the populations were increasing throughout California (Schrempf and White 1977), and in the early

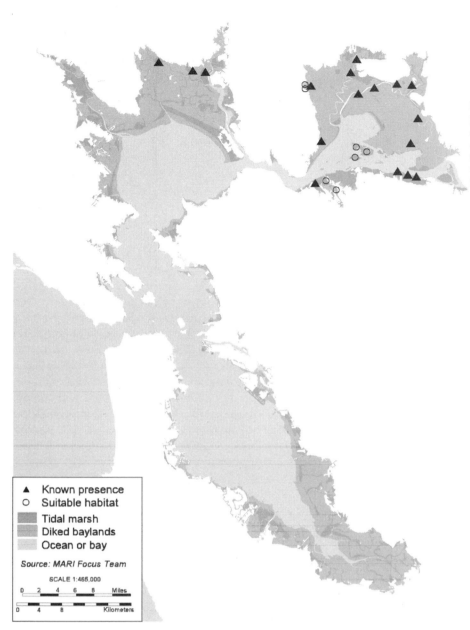

Figure 5.6 North American River Otter – Some Current Locations and Suitable Habitat

Note: Otters are likely present in areas identified as "suitable" habitat based on current information regarding habitat types. Otters may also be present in other areas.

▲ Known presence
○ Suitable habitat
▨ Tidal marsh
▨ Diked baylands
▨ Ocean or bay

Source: MARI Focus Team

SCALE 1:465,000

0 2 4 6 8   Miles

0   4   8   Kilometers

1980s the California Department of Fish and Game proposed an open river otter trapping season. However, the lack of evidence for population recovery led to maintenance of the ban in 1984 (Belfiore 1996). River otters are currently classified by U.S. Fish and Wildlife as a Class II species according to the Endangered Species Act.

The highest densities of river otters are currently found in the Klamath-Trinity River drainage, and in the Sacramento River drainage (Schrempf and White 1977). Although historical distributions do not place otters east of the Sierra crest, there are recent reports of otters in Mono and Inyo counties (Schrempf and White 1977). In the San Francisco Bay region, most river otter sitings have been in the Suisun region (**Figure 5.6**).

Suitable Habitat

Otters are found in freshwater habitats throughout northern California, as well as in brackish, salt marsh and other marine locations (Grinnell 1933, Schrempf and White 1977). Distributions are primarily associated with good river bank cover, but are not specific to any particular vegetation type (**Figure 5.6**). Otters are found at elevations as high as 9,000 feet, but prefer lower altitudes due to food preferences (Schrempf and White 1977).

Conservation and Management

Habitat loss and degradation continues to be a major problem in maintaining viable populations of river ot-

ters. Additionally, river otters are almost entirely aquatic, and therefore are at risk from contaminants that they directly contact and that may bioconcentrate through the food chain. A recent review of the association between the status of mink and otter populations and exposure to organochlorine chemicals in the Great Lakes indicates that there may be an association between higher levels of chemicals and lower harvest rates (Wren 1991), although the association needs further documentation.

Loads of chemical contaminants in the Bay-Delta system are sufficient to be toxic to invertebrates (Bailey 1993, Bennett et al. 1995). The river otter would be expected to bioaccumulate persistent, water-borne contaminants from their prey items (Ropek and Neely 1993). In fact, the San Francisco Estuary Project recommended monitoring of the river otter in the Bay-Delta system as a sentinel species for providing information about the extent of exposure incurred by wildlife in general (Bailey et al. 1995, Belfiore 1996).

References

Anthony, H.E. 1928. Field book of North American mammals. G.P. Putnams Sons, N.Y.

Bailey, H.C. 1993. Acute and chronic toxicity of the rice herbicides thiobencarb and molinate to opossum shrimp (*Neomysis mercedis*). Marine Env. Research 36: 197-215.

Bailey, H.C., S. Clark, J. Davis and L. Wiborg. 1995. The effects of toxic contaminants in waters of the San Francisco Bay and Delta. Final Report, Bay/Delta Oversight Council.

Belfiore, N. 1996. North American river otter in Northern California: population viability analysis. Unpubl. document.

Bennett, W.A., D.J. Ostrach and D.E. Hinton. 1995. Larval striped bass condition in a drought-stricken estuary: evaluating pelagic food-web limitation. Ecological Applications 5: 680-692.

Deems, Jr., E.F. and D. Pursley. 1978. North American furbearers, their management, research and har-vest status in 1976. Internat'l Assoc. of Fish and Wildl. Agencies. Univ. of Maryland, College Park, MD. 171 pp.

Duplaix, N. 1978. Otters. Proceedings of the first working meeting of the otter specialist group. IUCN. Switzerland.

Grenfell, Jr., W.E. 1974. Food habits of the river otter in Suisun Marsh, Central California. MS Thesis, Ca. State Univ., Sacramento. 43 pp.

Grinnell, J. 1933. A review of the recent mammalian fauna of California. Univ. of Ca. Press, Berkeley, CA.

Halbrook, R.S., J.H. Jenkins, P.B. Bush and N.D. Seabolt. 1994. Sublethal concentrations of mercury in river otters: monitoring environmental contamination. Archives of Environmental Contamination and Tox. 27: 306-310.

Hinton, D.E. 1995. Ecotoxicologic studies investigating the decline of the striped bass (*Morone saxatilis*) in the Sacramento and San Joaquin rivers and Delta-Bay estuary. Marine Env. Research 39: 356.

Hornocker, M.G., J.P. Messick and W.E. Melquist. 1983. Spatial strategies in three species of Mustelidae. Acta Zoologica Fennici 174: 185-188.

Ingles, L. 1965. Mammals of the Pacific states: California, Oregon and Washington. Stanford Univ. Press, Palo Alto, CA.

Mason, C.F. 1989. Water pollution and otter distribution: a review. Lutra 32(2): 97-131.

Melquist, W.E. and A.E. Dronkert. 1987. River Otter. Pp. 626-641, *In:* M. Novak, M.E. Obbard and B. Malloch (eds). Wild Furbearer Management and Conservation in North America. Ministry of Natural Resources, Ontario, Canada.

Melquist, W.E. and M.G. Hornocker. 1983. Ecology of river otters in west central Idaho. Wildl. Monographs 83: 1-60.

Ropek, R.M. and R.K. Neely. 1993. Mercury levels in Michigan river otters, *Lutra canadensis*. Journal of Freshwater Ecology 8(2): 141-147.

Schrempf, P.F. and M. White. 1977. Status of six furbearer populations in the mountains of Northern California. USDA Forest Service, California Region.

Stephens, F. 1906. California Mammals. The West Coast Printing Company, San Diego, CA.

Toweill, D.E. and J.E. Tabor. 1982. River otter. *In:* Chapman, J.A. and G.A. Feldhammer (eds). Wild Mammals of North America. John Hopkins Univ. Press, Baltimore, MD. Pp. 688-703,

Van Zyll De Jong, G.C. 1987. A phylogenetic study of the Lutrinae (Carnivora: Mustelidae) using morphologic data. Canadian Journal of Zoology 65: 2536-2544.

Wren, C.D. 1991. Cause-effect linkages between chemicals and populations of mink (*Mustela vison*) and otter (*Lutra canadensis*) in the Great Lakes Basin. J Tox. and Env. Health 33: 549-585.

Southern Sea Otter

Enhydra lutris nereis

David G. Ainley

Robert E. Jones

Life History

Individual adult sea otters show very little movement, being resident the year round where they occur. Males and females occupy home ranges of about 35 and 80 hectares, respectively. Subadult bachelor males disperse much more widely and comprise the vanguard as the population slowly expands to recolonize its former range. Pupping can occur year round, but mainly occurs December through March.

Sea otters feed mainly on benthic invertebrates, such as bivalves, abalone, urchins, cephalopods, and crustaceans, but they also eat fish. Lacking a layer of blubber, they must eat voraciously to maintain body heat, and consume 15-35% of their body weight daily (Leet et al. 1992). Their dense fur is their only insulation against the cold waters that they frequent.

Historical and Modern Distribution

The historic range of the sea otter in the eastern North Pacific extended along the coast from central Baja California, Mexico, north through the Aleutian Islands. Presently, however, owing to intensive hunting for fur in the 18th and 19th centuries, the range is much restricted and is centered around two populations, one in the Aleutian Islands and Southeast Alaska (south to Vancouver) and one in California. Each population is considered to be subspecifically distinct; the southern (or California) sea otter is listed as threatened under the Endangered Species Act (state and federal). The southern population, currently numbering a little over 2,200 animals, has grown from a few dozen animals that resided in a refugium near Pt. Sur early in this century.

In San Francisco Bay, sea otters once occurred abundantly in the central part at least as far inland as the mouth of Sonoma Creek, Sonoma/Marin County. The population in the Bay was likely in the low thousands but, for their pelts, all were hunted to extinction by the early-1800s (Skinner 1962). Sea otter teeth are very abundant in the middens of early Americans that are scattered around the Bay shores (e.g., Emeryville; Broughton 1999).

It has taken several decades for the population to spread from the focus near Pt. Sur north to San Mateo County (and south to Pismo Beach, Ventura County). In the San Francisco Bay Area, otters are regularly seen north to Pt. Reyes, Marin County; the northern most extent of the breeding population is at Pacifica, San Mateo County. Until recently, no documented sightings of sea otters in the Bay had been made, although sightings existed for the outer portion of the Golden Gate. During the 1990s, however, several sightings were confirmed in the Bay, including ones near Strawberry Point, north of Sausalito, and in Richardson Bay (McHugh 1998) (**Figure 5.7**).

Suitable Habitat

Sea otters occur in shallow, usually protected, nearshore waters to about 15 m deep. Throughout the range, which is more or less linear and continuous in California, sea otters prefer, but are not restricted to, rocky substrates near points of land (Kenyon 1969, Leet et al. 1992). The promontories provide protection from ocean swells and lush growths of kelp usually occur in these areas. The otters normally do not come to land but use the kelp for resting, support, and protection from predators (sharks). The kelp in turn is maintained by the otters through their predation of kelp grazers such as sea urchins (Dayton 1975). Thus, the invasion of rocky habitat by sea otters is followed by a recovery of the kelp forest, if not present already.

Conservation and Management

In addition to the suitable habitat described in the preceding section, the return of otters to the Bay is contingent upon the continued growth and expansion of the coastal population outside the Bay, the lack of oil pollution (oil destroys the insulating properties of sea otter pelage), and the availability of food. Other than the passage of time, as the population continues to expand, oil pollution, even low-level chronic pollution, is problematic for recolonization of the Bay by this species.

References

Broughton, J.M. 1999. Resource depression and intensification during the late holocene, San Francisco Bay: Evidence from the Emeryville shellmound

Jimmy Hu

Figure 5.7 Southern Sea Otter – Some Current Locations

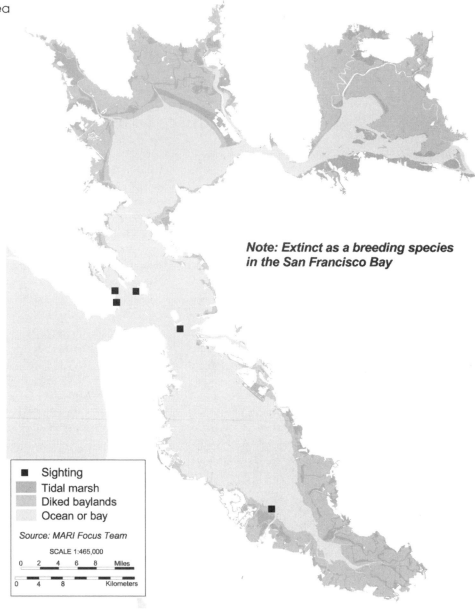

Note: Extinct as a breeding species in the San Francisco Bay

■ Sighting
▨ Tidal marsh
▨ Diked baylands
▢ Ocean or bay

Source: MARI Focus Team

SCALE 1:465,000

0 2 4 6 8 Miles

0   4   8   Kilometers

vertebrate fauna. Univ. of Ca. Press, Berkeley and Los Angeles, CA.

Dayton, P.K. 1975. Experimental studies of algal canopy interactions in a sea otter-dominated kelp community at Amchitka Island. Fish. Bull. 73:230-237.

Kenyon, K.W. 1969. The sea otter in the eastern Pacific Ocean. North Amer. Fauna No. 68, U.S. Dept. Interior, Washington, DC.

Leet, W.S., C.M. Dewees and C.W. Haugen. 1992. California's living marine resources and their utilization. Calif. Sea Grant, Sea Grant Extension Publ. UCSGEP-92-12. Davis.

McHugh, P. 1998. Rare otters surface in the S.F. Bay. *San Francisco Chronicle*, p. 1, January 17, 1998.

Skinner, J.E. 1962. An historical review of the fish and wildlife resources of the San Francisco Bay area. Calif. Dept Fish and Game, Water Projects Branch Report No. 1, Sacramento.

Important Data Sets

California Department of Fish and Game. Annual census of California sea otter population. Jack A. Ames, Monterey.

National Park Service, Golden Gate National Recreation Area and Pt. Reyes National Seashore. Archives of natural history records and sightings. Stephanie Hatch and Sarah Allen, San Francisco and Pt. Reyes Station.

Mammals

Harbor Seal

Phoca vitulina richardsi

William Z. Lidicker, Jr.
David G. Ainley

Life History

Harbor seals are the only marine mammals that are permanent residents in San Francisco Bay. During the recent past, California sea otters (*Enhydra lutris nereis*), known from numerous Indian middens, and harbor porpoises (*Phocoena phocoena*) were widespread in the Bay (Skinner 1962). Seasonally resident California sea lions (*Zalophus californianus*) use the Central Bay in the vicinity of the Golden Gate. See Ainley and Jones' accounts of the sea otter and sea lion.

Eight stomachs with food examined from individuals taken outside the Bay, but close to it, contained a variety of fish and a few octopus (Jones 1981). The most commonly taken fish were from the families Embiotocidae (surf perch) and Zoarcidae (eelpouts). Harvey and Torok (1995) identified 14 species of fish and one cephalopod from 215 fecal samples collected from seals at seven haul-out sites around the Bay in 1991-92. Five species of fish made up more than 93% of the dietary weight, and one introduced species yellowfin goby (*Acanthogobius flavimanus)*, constituted more than 54% of the total number of prey items found. Diet changed seasonally, with the goby and staghorn sculpin (*Leptocottus armatus*) predominating in the fall and winter, and plainfin midshipman (*Porichthys notatus*) and white croaker (*Genyonemus lineatus*), with jacksmelt (*Atherinopsis californiensis*) and the goby, predominating during spring and summer. Diet also differed regionally. In the extreme South Bay, the goby, sculpin, and croaker predominated; in the Central Bay, the mid-shipman predominated, comprising 91% of the diet. Curiously, no herring otoliths were found in the fecal samples.

An analysis of data from 59 radio-collared individuals revealed that frequency of diving (feeding) was greater at night (Harvey and Torok 1995). Pups are born in the spring, and a complete molt follows in early summer.

Courtesy of CCCR

About 30% of San Francisco Bay seals have reddish fur (Allen et al. 1993). This is a higher proportion than found anywhere else in the species' range (Kopec and Harvey 1995). The reddish discoloration is apparently caused by an accumulation of iron deposits (rust) on the fur, and develops rapidly following the early summer molt. The condition appears to cause the fur to become brittle, and it has been associated with shorter vibrissae and patchy fur loss (Kopec and Harvey 1995). Allen (pers. comm.), however, reports that only a few seals have shorter vibrissae and most of the fur loss occurs around orifices such as the mouth and eyes. It has been suggested that heavy metal contamination, most likely selenium, predisposes hairs to the rust accumulation (Kopec and Harvey 1995), but direct evidence for this is lacking. The speculation that the red condition is contaminant based is opposed by the fact that some seals develop red coloration while living on the outer coast (Allen, pers. comm.).

Historical and Modern Distribution

Harbor seals have been observed as far upstream as Sacramento, but little regular use is evident north of the Suisun Bay. Northerly sites are at Tubbs Island (Sonoma County) and Sister's Island (Marin). The haul-out sites associated with the Central Bay feeding area include (see Allen 1991, Harvey and Torok 1995): Sister's Island in Muzzi Marsh (a levee breached in two places to form an island), Castro Rocks, Brooks Island, Strawberry Spit (no longer used), a floating abandoned dock near Sausalito, Angel Island, Yerba Buena Island, and a breakwater at the Oakland entrance into Alameda Harbor. Included in this complex may be sites in the Golden Gate itself: Point Bonita and Land's End. Haul-out sites associated with the South Bay feeding area include: Coyote Point, Seal Slough, Belmont Slough, Bair Island, Corkscrew Slough, Greco Island, Ravenswood Point, Hayward Slough, Dumbarton Point, Newark Slough, Mowry Slough, Calaveras Point, Drawbridge, and Guadalupe Slough. **Figure 5.8** shows the locations of known current haul-out sites plus a few potential sites.

Seals may pup at any haul-out site but, generally, pupping sites are more traditional and are the least disturbed of all sites used. During the early 1990s, there were eight known pupping sites around the Bay, although more than four pups were born at only three sites: Castro Rocks, Newark Slough, and Mowry Slough (Kopec and Harvey 1995). In 1992, there were a third again as many pups born at Mowry Slough (67) than at all other sites combined (48; see also Riseborough et al. 1980). However, the previous year, there were only 39 at Mowry Slough but double (26) the 1992 number at Castro Rocks. Current counts from 1999 include 243 seals (78 pups) at Mowry Slough, 107 seals (21 pups) at Castro Rocks, and 72 seals (3 pups) at Yerba Buena Is-

Figure 5.8 Harbor Seal – Some Current Haul-out Locations and Suitable Habitat

Note: Seals are very possibly present in areas identified as "suitable" habitat based on current information regarding habitat types. Seals may also be present in other areas.

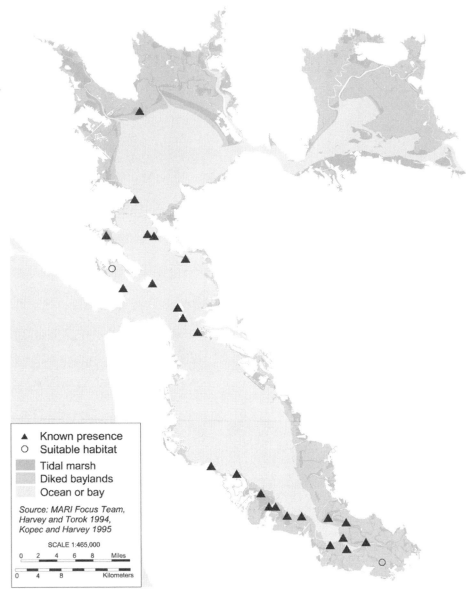

▲ Known presence
○ Suitable habitat
Tidal marsh
Diked baylands
Ocean or bay

Source: MARI Focus Team, Harvey and Torok 1994, Kopec and Harvey 1995

SCALE 1:465,000

0 2 4 6 8   Miles

0   4   8   Kilometers

Mammals

land (Green et al. 1999, Green pers. com.). Historically, there was a large rookery near Alviso (Skinner 1962); this site most likely was Mowry Slough, given a description by Fancher (1979) (Allen, pers. comm.). If Skinner's Alviso site is not Mowry Slough, then the question becomes: did the seals move the few kilometers from "near Alviso" to Mowry Slough?

Censusing harbor seals is difficult, in the Bay or anywhere, because of the changes in numbers as a function of year, season, tide, time of day and human disturbance, and frequent movements of individuals throughout the Bay and even onto the adjacent outer coast. Nevertheless, numbers in the Bay apparently did not change significantly between 1982 and 1999 (Kopec and Harvey 1995, Green et al. 1999). A census taken in 1987 tallied 524 individuals in the Bay system (Hanan et al. 1988), and censuses in 1999 tallied 641 in the Bay

(D. Green, pers. com). This population stability is in marked contrast to a steady increase during recent decades in the numbers of seals at sites along the coast, especially of Marin County (cf. Allen et al. 1989). Radio-tagged seals from San Francisco Bay have moved north to Point Reyes and south to Pescadero (Kopec and Harvey 1995). Allen (1991) believes that disturbance may be discouraging more seals from using the Bay and, thus, may be responsible for the lack of growth in the Bay. Pollutants may also be affecting the reproductive success of seals within the Bay (Kopec and Harvey 1995).

Suitable Habitat

Harbor seals feed in the deeper waters of the Bay. Kopec and Harvey (1995) identified two principal feeding areas. The first includes the area from the Golden Gate east to Treasure Island, northwest to the Tiburon Peninsula, and with a spur southward from Yerba Buena Island. Richardson's Bay, which is adjacent to this area, has been used extensively for feeding in the past, although not as much at present; feeding in Richardson's Bay may be contingent upon the presence of Pacific herring (*Clupea pallasi*; Allen 1991). This Central Bay feeding area is surrounded by nine haul-out and/or breeding sites (see above). The second major feeding area includes open Bay waters from the San Mateo Bridge southward. On the basis of the study by Kopec and Harvey (1995), this area is partitioned into five sub-areas, the largest being just west of Hayward. This South Bay feeding area is surrounded by 14 haul-out and/or breeding sites (see above).

Haul-outs must have gently sloping terrain, have deep water immediately nearby, and be free of disturbance, either by boats or by land (Allen 1991). An average of two haul-out sites are occupied by an individual seal each day, more so in the fall and winter and more so in the South Bay (Harvey and Torok 1995). Between-site movement is less frequent during the spring and summer, and is less frequent among seals in the deeper Central Bay. Haul-out sites used for pupping tend to be ones that are the most protected from disturbance. The use of such sites are persistent (traditional), and seals are slow to discover and utilize potential new pupping sites (Allen 1991).

Certain sites may be used as haul-outs at either low or high tide, e.g., seals appear to use Muzzi (Corte Madera) Marsh at high tide, but switch to Castro Rocks, 8 km away, at low tide (Allen 1991). In this case, Muzzi Marsh is separated from deep water by mud flats 2 km wide at low tide, but Castro Rocks are always surrounded by deep water.

Conservation and Management

The long association of harbor seals with humans (native Americans) in the Bay, including being actively hunted until about 1890, has made them extremely wary. They will flush from haul-out sites at 300 meters (Paulbitsky 1975, Allen et al. 1984). This makes them susceptible to harassment by persons on shore and boaters and kayakers from the Bay. Allen (1991) monitored

the gradual abandonment of Strawberry Spit by seals during the 1970s and 1980s as a result of encroachment by humans and in spite of attempts for mitigation. An engineered haul-out site nearby has yet to be accepted by seals. Haul-out sites and especially pupping sites are needed that are protected from frequent human disturbances.

Allen (1991) also noted that harbor seals of the Central Bay reduced their use of winter haul-outs in and around Richardson's Bay and used the ones farther south more frequently (i.e., Treasure and Yerba Buena islands) when the herring ceased spawning in Richardson's Bay (and spawned more along the San Francisco waterfront). Therefore, the viability of certain prey populations may be important to the well-being of harbor seals in the Bay.

References

Allen, S.G. 1991. Harbor seal habitat restoration at Strawberry Spit, San Francisco Bay. Marine Mammal Comm., Contract MM2910890-9. Natl. Tech. Infor. Serv., Alexandria, VA.

Allen, S.G., D.G. Ainley, G.W. Page and C.A. Ribic. 1984. The effect of disturbance on harbor seal haul out pattern at Bolinas Lagoon, California. U.S. Fish. Bull. 82:493-500.

Allen, S.G., H.R. Huber, C.A. Ribic and D.G. Ainley. 1989. Population dynamics of harbor seals in the Gulf of the Farallones, California. Ca. Dept. Fish and Game 75(4):224-232.

Allen, S.G., R.W. Risebrough, L. Fancher, M. Stephenson and D. Smith. 1993. Red harbor seals of San Francisco Bay. J. Mammalogy 74:588-593.

Fancher, L. 1979. The distribution, population dynamics, and behavior of the harbor seal, *Phoca vitulina richardi* [sic], in south San Francisco Bay, California. Ca. State Univ., Hayward, CA. 109pp.

Green, D., E. Grigg, H.M. Petersen, M. Galloway, A.S. Bohorquez, A.M. Sanders, S. Allen and H. Markowitz. 1999. Trends in harbor seal (*Phoca vitulina richardsi*) haul out patterns at Castro Rocks and Yerba Buena Island, San Francisco Bay, California. Marine Mammal Society Conference, Maui, Hawaii. (abstract).

Hanan, D.A., S. P. Scholl and S. L. Diamond. 1988. Harbor seal, *Phoca vitulina richardi* [sic], censuses in California, May-June, 1987. Admin. Report SWR 88-2, Southwest Region, Nat. Marine Fish. Serv., Terminal Island, CA. 49 pp.

Harvey, J.T. and M.L. Torok. 1995. Movements, dive behaviors and food habits of harbor seals (*Phoca vitulina richardsi* [sic]) in San Francisco Bay, California. Appendix (dated March 1994; 92 pp.) to A.D. Kopec and J.T. Harvey. 1995. Toxic pollutants, health indices and population dynamics of harbor seals in San Francisco Bay, 1989-1992. Moss

Landing Marine Laboratories Technical Pub. 96-4, Moss Landing, CA.

Jones, R.E. 1981. Food habits of smaller marine mammals from northern California. Proc Calif. Acad. Sci. 42: 409-433.

Kopec, A.D. and J.T. Harvey. 1995, Toxic pollutants, health indices and population dynamics of harbor seals in San Francisco Bay, 1989-1992. Moss Landing Marine Laboratories Technical Pub. 96-4, Moss Landing, CA. 138 pp.

Paulbitsky, P. A. 1975. The seals of Strawberry Spit. Pacific Discovery 28: 12-15.

Riseborough, R.W., D. Alcorn, S.G. Allen, V.C. Andertini, L. Booren, R. L. DeLong, L.E. Francher, R.E. Jones, S.M. McGinnis and T.T. Schmidt. 1980. Population biology of harbor seals in San Francisco Bay, California. Marine Mammal Comm., Washington D.C. 67 pp.

Skinner, J. E. 1962. An historical review of the fish and wildlife resources of the San Francisco Bay area. Water Projects Branch Rep. No.1, Ca. Dept. Fish and Game. 226 pp.

Personal Communications

D. Green, Project Manager, San Francisco Bay Seals Study, San Francisco State University, San Francisco, California. http://userwww.sfsu.edu/~halmark/seals.htm.

Sarah Allen, Science Advisor, National Park Service, Point Reyes National Seashore, Point Reyes, California, 94956. sarah_allen@nps.gov.

California Sea Lion

Zalophus californianus

David G. Ainley

Robert E. Jones

Life History

California sea lion is the pinniped ("seal") most often seen in zoos and circuses. In coastal waters of Central California, California sea lions prey mostly on schooling species, such as anchovies, Pacific whiting, midshipman and squid, as well as other fishes (Jones 1981). In the Bay, they feed mainly on anchovies, herring, surfperch, leopard sharks and spiny dogfish, and shrimp and crabs (Hanni and Long 1995). During the breeding season, bulls haul out at traditional breeding sites where they establish territories; females haul out to form groups, called harems, which each male tries to force onto his territory. In early summer (June), one pup is born to each adult female. Soon thereafter, the female mates with the harem master, but implantation is delayed for months while the mother nurses the pup. Pups form groups while their respective mothers forage at sea; some pups remain with their mother through the following winter (Jameson and Peeters 1988).

Historical and Modern Distribution

California sea lions occur along the West Coast of North America, from Vancouver to the Gulf of California; an isolated population exists on the Galapagos Islands and, formerly, another existed in Japan. The total population size of this species for the North American West Coast, as of 1990, was about 220,000; the population has been growing at about 10.2% per year since the early 1980s (Lowry et al. 1992). Population growth, following passage of the Marine Mammal Protection Act in 1972, is a recovery from former persecution.

Along the West Coast, the species breeds from Pt. Piedras Blancas, San Luis Obispo County, California,

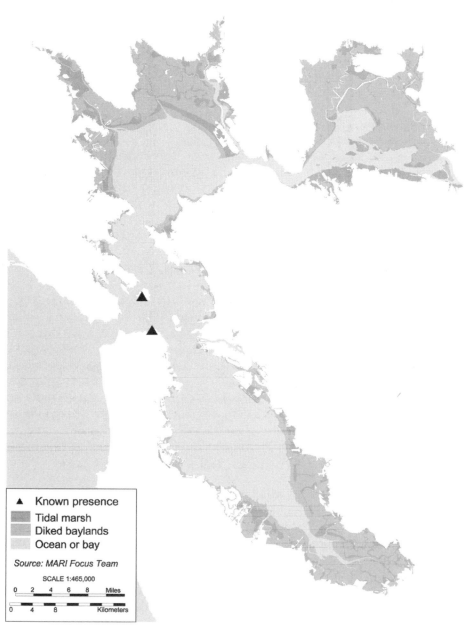

Figure 5.9 California
Sea Lion – Current
Locations and Suitable
Habitat

Note: Sea lions are likely
present in areas identified
as "suitable" habitat based
on current information
regarding habitat types.
Sea lions may also be
present in other areas.

▲ Known presence
Tidal marsh
Diked baylands
Ocean or bay

Source: MARI Focus Team

SCALE 1:465,000

0   2   4   6   8   Miles

0   4   8   Kilometers

Mammals

south to the Gulf of California, Baja California, Mexico,
although on rare occasions pups have been born at the
Farallon Islands, San Francisco County; Ano Nuevo Island, San Mateo County; and the Monterey Breakwater, Monterey County. However, virtually all the animals
that occur north of Pt. Piedras Blancas are adult and
subadult males, and subadult females.

During the May-June pupping season, few adult
California sea lions occur in Central and Northern California. Otherwise the species is present there year round.
In Central California, the largest numbers occur during
the spring (April), when males that wintered in the north
migrate south to breeding colonies; another smaller peak
occurs in early autumn during the more leisurely migration north (Huber et al. 1981). During years of warm

ocean temperatures (El Niño) much larger numbers of
California sea lions visit Central and Northern California, including many more juveniles than usual (Huber
et al. 1981).

In San Francisco Bay, California sea lions occur
year round, but with a dynamic difference from that of
the adjacent outer coast. Greatest numbers are present
during the winter herring run (Dec-Feb; Hanni, pers.
comm.). Following the winter peak, numbers decline to
just a few animals by June and July. Numbers then increase gradually before a sudden increase in December.
Known haul-out spots in San Francisco Bay are rare, and
include only Pier 39, occasionally at Angel Island, and
at Seal Rock just outside the Golden Gate (**Figure 5.9**).
The largest number haul out at Pier 39, but the phe-

nomenon is only a recent one (unlike Seal Rock, which has been used by sea lions for at least the last 100 years; Sutro 1901). At first, in winter 1989-90, only a few individuals hauled out at Pier 39, but the next year they reached an average 500 (± 100 SD) per day (February 1991); since then peak numbers during winter declined and now average about 200-300 animals per day (Marine Mammal Center, unpubl. data). The use of wharves at Pier 39 likely is the result of the following factors: 1) the increased size of the species' total population (greater now than chronicled history; Lowry et al. 1992) and concomitant expansion of habitat use, 2) the construction of the wharves in the late 1980s, 3) the increasing temperatures of the California Current (which make Northern California more suitable for this species), and 4) the chance finding of this site by several individuals seeking food during the low food year of 1989-1990 (El Niño). These pioneers thus established a tradition among a group of sea lions.

Suitable Habitat

This animal uses those deep, principally marine waters that occur in the outer Bay, off Marin and San Francisco counties (e.g., Raccoon Straits to San Francisco and out through the Golden Gate). On occasion, isolated individuals, and mostly carcasses, have been found in Milpitas, Alameda, Napa, and as far upstream in the Delta as Sacramento. When salmon were netted en masse in the Delta 100 years ago, California sea lions were attracted in large numbers as far as Sacramento to take advantage of the netting operation (Sutro 1901), much as they do today in the case of herring in the Bay (and their infamous pillaging of steelhead held at the locks in Puget Sound, Washington). If free from disturbance, it is possible that sea lions would haul out on rocky peninsulas at places such as Angel Island and Alcatraz Island.

Conservation and Management

The presence of this species in San Francisco Bay is contingent upon the availability of safe haul-out sites and easily available food. Thus, its occurrence likely is tied to the

fate of such fish as herring. The population in the Bay is sensitive to disturbance, to capture in gill nets (used illegally), and to certain diseases, such as leptospirosis, that result from the cattle that are grazing in coastal areas (and streams).

References

Hanni, K.D. and D.J. Long. 1995. Food habits of California sea lions at a newly established haulout in San Francisco Bay. 11th Biennial Conf. Mar. Mamm., Orlando. (abstract).

Huber, R.H., D.G. Ainley, R.J. Boekelheide, R.P. Henderson and B. Bainbridge. 1981. Studies of marine mammals at the Farallon Islands, 1979-80. Natl. Tech. Info. Serv., PB81-167082. Alexandria.

Jameson, E.W., Jr. and H.J. Peeters. 1988. California Mammals. Univ. of Ca. Press, Berkeley, CA.

Jones, R.E. 1981. Food habits of smaller marine mammals from northern California. Calif. Acad. Sci., Proc. 42(16): 409-433.

Lowry, M.S., P. Boveng, R.J. DeLong, C.W. Oliver, B.S. Stewart, H. DeAnda and J. Barlow. 1992. Status of the California sea lion (*Zalophus californianus californianus*) population in 1992. Natl. Mar. Fish. Serv., Southwest Fish. Sci. Center, Admin. Rpt. LJ-92-32.

Sutro, A. 1901. Letter to the Calif. State Legislature. Sacramento.

Personal Communications

Krista Hanni, The Marine Mammal Center, San Francisco

Important Data Sets

Marine Mammal Center. Annual census of sea lions at Pier 39, San Francisco. Krista Hanni.

NOAA, Southwest Fisheries Science Center, La Jolla. Annual census of pinnipeds along the California coast. Jay Barlow.

Nancy Black

Non-Native Predators:
Norway Rat and Roof Rat

Rattus norvegicus and *Rattus rattus*

Andrée M. Breaux

Life History

Norway (or brown) rats and roof (or black) rats are similar in appearance, though the roof rat has a longer tail and can vary in color between brown and black. Norway rats have coarse fur, large naked ears, and scaly tails that are shorter than their body length (less than half of total length), pigmented venters, and tuberculate molars. Norway rats are largely nocturnal and are excellent swimmers and climbers. Roof rats have tails that are longer than their body length and pale venters, and they share the tuberculate molars that distinguish both Norway and roof rats from wood rats (Kurta 1995, Jameson and Peeters 1988).

Both the Norway and roof rats are prolific breeders, and the Norway rat tends to have slightly larger litters. Large males dominate female harems and the females actively defend resources and nest sites (Kurta 1995). Sexual maturity for both the Norway and roof rats is reached at about three to four months and breeding can occur continuously throughout the year. Litter sizes for Norway rats are between four and ten young, though litters as large as 22 young have been reported (Kurta 1995). Roof rat litters are generally between five and eight young (Jameson and Peeters 1988).

The Norway rat has been described as "the most unpleasant mammal in the world" (Jameson and Peeters 1988) as a result of its tendency to eat crops in the field as well as in storage, its tendency to eat both live and dead prey, and its ability to spread deadly diseases. It is capable of catching fish and small rodents (Kurta 1995). The Norway rat is an omnivore while the roof rat is a vegetarian.

Norway Rat (*Rattus norvegicus*)

USFWS

Historical and Modern Distribution

Norway rats probably originated from the Old World tropics, but are now found globally. They are believed to have reached North America around 1775 (Kurta 1995) and are generally associated with buildings, sewers, harbors, garbage dumps, and agriculture. They reach elevations of 1,000 meters. Roof rats probably originated from the tropical Orient and can now be found in globally temperate climates. Roof rats are associated with trees, including agricultural groves, as well as with dense thickets and roofs and attics (Jameson and Peeters 1988).

The Norway and roof rats tend to occur in different habitats with the larger and presumably more powerful Norway rat occupying more urban areas, and the smaller roof rat living in more natural areas. Rats which are found in San Francisco Bay marshes are more likely to be roof than Norway rats (Jurek, pers. comm.). Where urbanization abuts natural marshes as it does in many areas of the South Bay, and garbage provides a food supply, Norway rats are likely to find the marsh habitats quite hospitable. In 1927, DeGroot noted that reclaimed land behind dikes along the San Francisco Bay shoreline was responsible for an increase in rats and a decrease in native California clapper rails (*Rallus longirostris obsoletus*): "No sooner is a dyke constructed than Norway rats appear in great numbers. Large gray fellows they are, on a dark night appearing to be as large as small cotton-tail rabbits....The Clapper Rail has no more deadly enemy than this sinister fellow" (DeGroot 1927).

In the Central Bay marshes, rats have been sighted at the Elsie Roemer Bird Sanctuary in Alameda, Crown Beach, the Martin Luther King Regional Shoreline and Arrowhead marsh sites, and on Brooks Island off the Richmond Harbor (DiDonato, pers. comm.).

Rats are not regarded as a serious problem in the North Bay marshes, except in the Corte Madera marsh where there is inadequate buffering of the marsh from urbanization. Elsewhere, the extensive agricultural lands are probably preferred as habitat by the rats over the wetter marshlands (Botti, pers. comm.).

Suitable Habitat

Not addressed for non-native predators.

Control and Management

A 1992 report on the status of wildlife in the San Francisco Bay stated that there existed a "critical need" for research on the population dynamics and distributions of introduced mammalian predators such as the red fox, the Norway rat, and the roof rat (USFWS 1992). The report stated that techniques such as the reintroduction of the coyote to control the red fox in the South Bay, should be investigated. Control of rats has not been

Roof Rat (*Rattus rattus*)

implemented and continues to be a problem in the South Bay for endangered species, such as clapper rails and, quite possibly, salt marsh harvest mice (*Reithrodontomys raviventris*). Additional threats to other target species selected by this project as representative of wetland species in the San Francisco Bay region (e.g., California voles (*Microtus californicus*), ornate shrews (*Sorex ornatus californicus*), salt marsh wandering shrews (*Sorex vagrans haliocoetes*), and amphibians, reptiles, terrestrial invertebrates in general, and some ground nesting birds) probably occur.

Studies of South Bay marshes have documented predation of not only clapper rail eggs, but also of live chicks. While the primary predators may be raccoons (*Procyon lotor*), red foxes (*Vulpes vulpes regalis*), feral dogs, or feral cats, rats have been seen in the South Bay in relatively large numbers (Foerster et al. 1990; Albertson, pers. comm.; Harding, pers. comm.). Harvey (1988), in a study of clapper rails in three south San Francisco Bay marshes, attributed 24 percent of nest failures to Norway rats. A 1992 U.S. Fish and Wildlife study of hatching success and predation for 54 active clapper rail nests in south San Francisco Bay found rodents to be responsible for 90% of the eggs destroyed and 79% of the predation at monitored nests. Rodents were thought to be the predators because of the characteristic debris left behind after feeding, in this case egg shells, egg contents, and chick body parts. Other characteristics peculiar to rodent predators is the manner of leaving half of the egg shell intact with visible tooth marks, or a U-shaped notch eaten into the side of the shell (USFWS 1992 and 1997).

Negative impacts on native mammalian populations from rats in marshes include direct predation by the omnivorous Norway rat, competition for habitat, and illness or mortality resulting from diseases. While the devastation to humans from rats carrying plague, typhus, hepatitis, and trichina worms has been known for centuries in some cases (Jameson and Peeters 1988), the devastation to native wildlife is not as well-documented.

Clearly there is a need to implement the research suggested in 1992 on the distributions and population dynamics of Norway and roof rats in San Francisco Bay wetlands. While feral cats may help control the young rat populations, cats do not tend to eat the large adult rats (Jurek, pers. comm.), and the feral cats and dogs themselves are likely to prey on the small native mammals, amphibians, reptiles, and terrestrial invertebrates that are indigenous to the wetlands. Control measures are difficult, since there is no poison specific to rats that is safe for endangered mammals, such as the salt marsh harvest mouse. Given the difficulties in any control programs (e.g., public outcry against removing feral cats and the difficulty of trapping or shooting these large rodents) the most effective control measure at this time is to protect marshes with large buffers, and to keep shelter and garbage far from the wetland edge.

References

DeGroot, D.S. 1927. The California clapper rail: its nesting habits, enemies, and habitat. Condor 29:259-270.

Foerster, K.S., J.E.Takekawa and J.D. Albertson. 1990. Breeding density, nesting habitat and predators of the California clapper rail. San Francisco Bay National Wildlife Refuge, Newark, CA.

Harvey, T.E. 1988. Breeding biology of the California Clapper rail in south San Francisco Bay. Transactions of the Western Section of the Wildlife Society 24:98-104.

Jameson, Jr., E.W. and H.J. Peeters. 1988. California mammals. California natural history guides: 52. Univ. of Ca. Press, Berkeley, CA.

Kurta, A. 1995. Mammals of the Great Lakes Region. Univ. of Michigan, Ann Arbor Press, MI.

U.S. Fish and Wildlife Service (USFWS). 1992. Status and trends report on wildlife of the San Francisco Estuary. Sacramento Fish and Wildlife Enhancement Field Office, Sacramento, CA. Prepared under EPA Cooperative Agreement, CE-009519 by the U.S. Fish and Wildlife Service.

_____. 1997. San Francisco Bay National Wildlife Refuge Complex. Unpublished data [Joy Albertson].

Personal Communications

Joy Albertson, U.S. Fish and Wildlife Service, Don Edwards San Francisco Bay National Wildlife Refuge, Newark.

Fred Botti, California Department of Fish and Game, Yountville.

Joe DiDonato, East Bay Regional Park District, Oakland.

Elaine Harding, University of California, Santa Cruz.

Ron Jurek, California Department of Fish and Game, Endangered Species Division, Sacramento.

Mammals

Non-Native Predator: Red Fox

Vulpes vulpes regalis

Elaine K. Harding

Life History

The red fox is one of the most widely distributed mammals in the world, occupying a range of habitats and elevations. There are actually two red fox subspecies in California, the introduced red fox, *Vulpes vulpes regalis*, and the native, state threatened, red fox, *Vulpes vulpes necator*, which is found only in the Sierra Nevada from 5,000 to 8,400 ft (Jurek 1992). Red fox have a head and body length of about 45.5-90.0 cm and a tail length of 30.0-55.5 cm, with a weight averaging 3-14 kg (Nowak 1991). The pelage coloration is generally pale yellowish red to deep red on the upper parts and white or ashy underneath. It can be distinguished from the gray fox by its black lower legs and white tip on the tail.

Red fox family groups usually consist of a male, a female and offspring, with the territories ranging in size from 2.6 to 20.8 square kilometers (Sargeant 1972). However, urban populations may achieve even greater densities, with home ranges as small as 0.45 sq. km in Great Britain (Trewhella et al. 1988). Den sites in urban areas are often within flood control levees, freeway embankments (Sallee et al. 1992) or salt marsh levees.

Breeding occurs from December through April, with a peak in March, with the number of offspring produced (and surviving to juvenile age) averaging 3.5 (Storm 1976). Multiple dens may be used during this time, with the females often moving the litters to different locations throughout the season. The survival of juveniles to recruitment is estimated at 0.19 in midwestern populations (Storm et al. 1976) to 0.65 in southern California populations (Sallee et al. 1992). Foxes have been reported to breed at 10 months, with yearlings often breeding their first spring. Additionally, the survival of adults in urban California populations is 0.58, higher

than the midwest at 0.23 (Storm et al. 1976). Adults may survive up to five years in the wild.

Red fox have extremely broad diets, including birds, small mammals, reptiles, amphibians, insects, vegetation and refuse (Foerster and Takekawa 1991). They are also known to be surplus killers, where food that is taken may be cached (buried in the ground) and never recovered. Because they are such capable predators, they are highly detrimental to native fauna which are not adapted to avoid or escape them. Foxes are known to decimate ground nesting bird populations, through predation of eggs, young and adults.

Historical and Modern Distribution

The red fox subspecies, *V.v. regalis*, is originally from the Great Plains, and was probably brought to the Central Valley for commercial fur farming in the late 1800s (Jurek 1992). The current distribution of fox throughout the state is based upon a study by Sallee, et al. (1992) which found occurrences of red fox in 36 counties. The greatest concentration of sightings were in the urban areas of Los Angeles and San Francisco Bay, with fox also found throughout the Central Valley and Monterey Bay areas. It is difficult to estimate the number of fox in California, but according to records kept by Animal Control in Orange County, there were 102 individuals in the county during the summer of 1991 (Sallee et al. 1992).

The red fox was first seen in South San Francisco Bay in 1986 (Foerster and Takekawa 1991), with subsequent sightings reported from all seven Bay Area counties (Sallee et al. 1992). Populations of red fox have established in or adjacent to tidal marshes, diked baylands, salt ponds, landfills, agricultural lands, golf courses, grasslands and urban areas. In particular, the fragmented wetlands of San Francisco Bay have become a likely source for expanding populations, as many avian and mammalian prey can be found within these habitats.

Suitable Habitat

Not addressed for non-native predators.

Control and Management

In the San Francisco Bay Area, red fox have been implicated in the population declines of the endangered California clapper rail, threatened western snowy plover, endangered California least tern, Caspian tern, and colonial nesting species, such as great blue herons and great egrets (Foerster and Takekawa 1991; Albertson 1995; USFWS, unpubl. data). In response to growing evidence of the impact of red fox on the clapper rail, the U.S. Fish and Wildlife Service began a Predator Management Program in 1991 (Foerster and Takekawa 1991). The subsequent removal of red fox and other targeted predators has re-

Joe DiDonato, bioQuest

Mammals

sulted in a significant increase in the local populations of California clapper rail (Harding-Smith 1994, Harding et al. 1998). Comparable success has occurred in Southern California where removal of red fox along coastal marshes was correlated with remarkable increases in the populations of light-footed clapper rails (USFWS and U.S. Navy 1990). Additionally, predator management is becoming a common method of endangered species protection, within both government (Parker and Takekawa 1993) and private sectors.

It is imperative that all future restoration and management activities within the wetland ecosystems of San Francisco Bay consider the present and future impacts of red fox on the native wildlife. Clearly, a healthy marsh can no longer be defined by simply the quantity and composition of native vegetation and wildlife, but must include the external impacts of human urbanization which alter an ecosystem's internal functioning through the introduction of contaminants, human disturbance and non-native species. The long-term viability of many avian and small mammal species will be impacted by expanding red fox populations in the bay area, so that no site will soon remain uninhabited nor unaffected by this wily species. Therefore, the quality and quantity of connections between sites, as well as the characteristics and extent of the surrounding matrix, will be of the utmost importance in understanding fox population dynamics and prey abundance within and between sites. Biologists and land managers must continue to study the dispersal patterns, demographics and predation impacts of red fox so that more effective methods of control can be developed.

References

Albertson, J.D. 1995. Ecology of the California clapper rail in south San Francisco Bay. M.A. thesis, San Francisco State Univ. S.F., CA.

Foerster, K.S. and J.E. Takekawa. 1991. San Francisco Bay National Wildlife Refuge predator management plan and final environmental assessment. U.S. Fish and Wildl. Serv., Newark, CA.

Harding, E.K., D.F. Doak, J. Albertson and J.E. Takekawa. 1998. Predator management in San Francisco Bay wetlands: past trends and future strategies, final report. Prepared for U.S. Fish and Wildl. Serv., Div. of Ecol. Services, Sacramento, CA.

Harding-Smith, E. 1994 (unpublished). Summary of California clapper rail winter populations in the San Francisco Bay, 1989 to 1993. Unpubl. report, U.S. Fish and Wildl. Serv., Newark, CA.

Jurek, R.M. 1992. Nonnative red foxes in California. Ca. Dept. Fish and Game, Nongame Bird and Mammal Section Rept. 92-04.

Nowak, R.M. 1991. Walker's mammals of the world, 5th ed. The Johns Hopkins Univ. Press.

Parker, M.W. and J.E. Takekawa. 1993. Salinas River National Wildlife Refuge predator management plan and draft environmental assessment. U.S. Fish and Wildl. Serv., Newark, CA.

Sallee, K.L., J.C. Levis and R.T. Golightly Jr. 1992. Introduced red fox in California, final report. U.S. Fish and Wildl. Serv., Sacramento, CA.

Sargeant, A.B. 1972. Red fox spatial characteristics in relation to waterfowl predation. J. of Wildl. Mgmt. 36: 225-236.

Storm, G.L., R.D. Andrews, R.F. Phillips, R.A. Bishop, D.B. Siniff and J.R. Tester. 1976. Morphology, reproduction, dispersal, and mortality of midwestern red fox populations. Wildl. Monograph 49:5-82.

Trewhella, W.J., S. Harris and F.E. McAllister. 1988. Dispersal, distance, home-range size and population density in the red fox (*Vulpes vulpes*): a quantitative analysis. J. of Applied Ecology 25:423-434.

U.S. Fish And Wildlife Service And U.S. Navy (USFWS and U.S.Navy). 1990. Draft environmental impact statement, endangered species management and protection plan. Naval Weapons Station, Seal Beach and Seal Beach National Wildlife Refuge. USFWS, Portland, OR.

Mammals

6

Waterfowl and Shorebirds

Tule Greater White-Fronted Goose

Anser albifrons gambelli

Dennis R. Becker

Introduction

The tule greater white-fronted goose or tule goose was selected to represent the geese and swans group which also includes Pacific greater white-fronted goose (*Anser albifrons frontalis*), Canada goose (*Branta canadensis*), Aleutian Canada goose (*B.c. leucopareia*), lesser snow goose (*Chen caerulescens*), and tundra swan (*Cygnus columbianus*).

Tule geese are primarily associated with managed wetlands and agriculture lands. The Suisun subregion is one of only a few important wintering areas in California. The geese/swan group is of economic and recreational importance as four of the six members of this group are hunted.

Although populations are relatively low in the San Francisco Bay Area for all species in this group, at least one representative is found in all subregions designated for the Goals process. Tule geese are primarily found in Suisun Marsh and North Bay (Napa Marsh); Pacific white-fronted geese, Suisun and North Bay; Canada geese, all subregions; Aleutian geese, Suisun and Central Bay; snow geese, all subregions; and tundra swans, Suisun and North Bay.

Courtesy USGS/NBS

Description

The tule goose is one of two subspecies of greater white-fronted geese that breed in Alaska and winter primarily in California (Swarth and Bryant 1917); the Pacific greater white-fronted goose is the other subspecies. Populations of the Pacific goose are far greater than the tule goose. The overall size of the tule goose is generally larger than the Pacific goose, although there may be overlap between the subspecies. The tule goose has a length to 34 inches (86 cm) and wing span to 65½ inches (167 cm) (Cogswell 1977). They are a medium-sized dark goose with the brown colors of the head and neck the same as the body and wings. Tule geese are a much darker brown than Pacifics. Adults have a white forehead and black blotched belly. In most tules, the forehead may show some orange coloration. Their feet are yellow and their bills are pink to orangish in color. Immatures do not have black blotched bellies.

Breeding Biology – Historically, nesting was known to occur at Redoubt Bay, in Cook Inlet, and suspected at Susitna Flats, Tuxedni Bay, Chinitna Bay, and Innoko National Wildlife Refuge (NWR), all in Alaska (Timm et al. 1982). Telemetry studies in 1995 showed breeding taking place on the Kahiltna and Yentna River Valleys northwest of Anchorage. Both areas were previously unreported as areas for tule geese. No radioed birds were found in the Redoubt or Trading Bay areas. The Redoubt Volcano eruption of 1989 may have made the area unfit for tule goose breeding. Few white-fronted geese have been counted in the area in the last five years. Nest initiation generally begins in early to mid-May or later depending on thaw on the breeding grounds. Incubation is 24-26 days. Clutch size averages 5-6 eggs (Timm et al. 1982, Zeiner et al. 1990). The subspecies is a monogamous, solitary nester, with both parents tending the young. Breeding may occur at two years of age, but three years is more common (Bellrose 1980).

Migration Ecology – Tule geese begin to leave Alaska by mid-August. By September 1 of 1980 and 1981 only a few hundred remained in Redoubt Bay or Susitna Flats (Timm et al. 1982). Generally, tule geese fly over the open ocean from Alaska to key staging areas in southeastern Oregon, i.e., Summer Lake Wildlife Management Area and Malheur NWR. Up to 50% of the population may be present at these Oregon sites by early September and approximately 1,000-2,000 birds may remain until late October (Mensik 1991). Birds are also present in the Klamath Basin of Oregon and California during these times (Wege 1984). The remaining 50% of the population over-fly the fall staging areas arriving at Sacramento NWR in early September (Timm et al. 1982, Mensik 1991). Field observations at Grizzly Island Wildlife Area in the Suisun Marsh during the mid-1980s showed the first tule geese arriving during the September 9 to September 16 period (CDFG, unpubl. data). Historically, the primary spring migration staging area was the Klamath Basin where numbers peaked in late March. Results of radio telemetry studies in 1994-95 showed that few tule geese used Lower Klamath NWR while Summer Lake, Chewaucan Marsh, and the Warner Valley, all in Oregon, provided the principal spring staging areas (USDI 1995). Tule geese begin leaving central California in February (Mensik 1991). By mid-February of 1989 more than 1,400 tule geese remained at the Grizzly Island Wildlife Area (CDFG, unpubl. data).

Wintering Ecology – Primary wintering areas in California are the Sacramento Valley and Suisun Marsh. A small number of birds use the Napa Marsh. Use is mostly at Sacramento and Delevan NWRs and adjacent rice fields. Colusa NWR also receives some use. By October and November, an estimated 90% of the tule goose population occurs in these areas (Mensik 1991). Generally, there is a winter-long interchange of geese between the three most important areas, Sacramento NWR, Delevan NWR, and Grizzly Island Wildlife Area, although for the 1995 mark-recapture survey no tule geese were observed at Grizzly Island Wildlife Area during the September ground counts (Trost and Harb 1995). Other areas where tule geese have been observed in the past include the Butte Sink, Sutter NWR, San Joaquin Valley, and Sinaloa, Mexico (Wege 1984; Ely and Takekawa 1990; Kramer, pers. comm.; Timm et al. 1982; PFSC 1991).

Distribution and Abundance

North America – In North America, tule geese have been documented in the Central Flyway, although their status there is uncertain and there are no population estimates. A specimen of this subspecies of greater white-fronted geese was collected in Texas in 1852 by Hartlaub and subsequently described as one of the greater white-fronted geese (Swarth and Bryant 1917). The bird is primarily found in the Pacific Flyway where most of the studies to locate nesting, migration, and wintering areas have been done.

Pacific Coast – Nesting is known to occur at Redoubt Bay and Susitna Flats in the Cook Inlet, Alaska.

Nesting also takes place northwest of Anchorage, Alaska in the Kahiltna and Yentna River Valleys. Ongoing telemetry studies are attempting to document additional breeding areas. Malheur NWR and Summer Lake Wildlife Management Area, along with Klamath Basin NWRs in Oregon and California, are the most important fall and spring migration stopover sites. Sacramento and Delevan NWRs and Grizzly Island Wildlife Area in the Suisun Marsh are the major wintering areas. Other areas important to winter birds are the Butte Sink, Colusa NWR, and the Napa Marsh near where the Napa River enters San Pablo Bay.

San Francisco Bay – Locally, the tule goose is only found in the Suisun and North Bay subregions. Suisun Marsh is the third most important wintering area in California. In the North Bay Region (Napa Marsh), a small population uses the marshes, sloughs, and adjacent agricultural lands (**Figure 6.1**).

Suisun – Suisun Marsh is the third most important wintering area in California. The peak population index of 1,500 was in December 1980 at Grizzly Island Wildlife Area in the Suisun Marsh. Other high indices were in December 1978 (1,000), December 1981 (1,200), February 1989 (1,229), and February 1990 (1,190) (Mensik 1991). The mid-winter waterfowl survey of January 1991 showed 1,527 tule geese. Waterfowl surveys during the period October 1992 through January 1997 showed the tule geese numbers to be generally less than 500 birds (CDFG, unpubl. data).

North Bay – The Napa Marshes of the North Bay region support a small wintering population of tule geese. Reports from duck hunters and hunting club owners are that the peak wintering population is less than 50 birds.

Central Bay – Not present.

South Bay – Not present.

Historical information

Since the late 1960s, the following information has been gathered for tule goose on an irregular basis: population size and distribution, including fall and winter counts of national wildlife refuges and state-managed wildlife areas, and periodic leg banding and color marking; production assessment, including age composition and family size counts on staging and wintering areas; and mortality assessment and harvest management, including monitoring harvest on selected public hunting areas and disease mortality on national wildlife refuges and state-managed wildlife areas.

Population Trends

Information has been gathered sporadically on tule geese in conjunction with other projects since the late 1960s. There has been more intensive study of the tule goose during the last 20 years. **Table 6.1** shows population

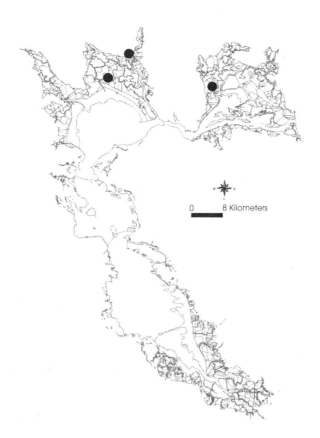

Figure 6.1 Distribution of Tule Greater White-Fronted Goose in San Francisco Bay

Open water data from the USGS Study of Waterfowl in Open Bays and Salt Ponds, 1988-1990 (USGS, unpubl.), John Takekawa (unpubl. data),

0   8 Kilometers

trend data for selected years between 1978-79 to 1989-90. The peak index of 8,615 was in September 1989. Observations of radioed and neck-collared tule geese in the fall and winter of 1995 (September 5 - December 31, 1995) documented approximately 6,000 birds in California and southern Oregon (Trost and Harb 1995).

Habitat Use and Behavior

Foraging – Foraging on the breeding grounds occurs on grasses, sedges, and aquatic plants in the intertidal mudflats, freshwater marshes, or poorly drained areas characteristic of the region. They are primarily grazers, but they will grub for roots and shoots (Zeiner et al. 1990). In the fall at Klamath Basin, they feed in ponds with alkali bulrush (*Scirpus robustus*) or harvested grain fields. Roosting occurs in open water ponds (Wege 1980). During early fall in the Sacramento Valley, they feed in harvested rice fields then shift to winter flooded uplands. Marsh units on Sacramento and Delevan NWRs with an abundance of alkali bulrush and with some open water are also used for feeding, which continues until departure in February (Wege 1980, Timm et al. 1982).

Roosting – Roosting and loafing generally occurs in open water ponds with emergents such as bulrush (*Scirpus* spp.) and cattails (*Typha* spp.). In the Suisun Marsh tule geese feed in ponds with alkali bulrush or in the barley/grass uplands of the sanctuary on Grizzly Island Wildlife Area. Roosting areas have shallowly flooded uplands with a grass-pickleweed (*Salicornia* spp.) mixture. These areas are in the closed zone to hunting. Tule

geese observed feeding in the Napa Marsh were found in tidal areas fringed by emergent cattails, tules, alkali bulrush, and cordgrass (*Spartina* spp.) with pickleweed and *Grindelia* spp. in the high areas. Two tule geese taken during hunting season in December 1954 were analyzed for food habits. Results showed alkali bulrush tuber and rhizome fragments in both with forb leafage and insect fragments (Longhurst 1955).

The managed wetlands of the Suisun Marsh are the most important habitat for tule geese in the San Francisco Bay ecosystem. These wetlands, managed for alkali bulrush and other wetland wildlife food plants are critical as feeding and roosting areas as they will feed primarily on tubers and rhizomes of alkali bulrush.

Movement – Generally, studies of daily movement of tule geese in the winter have shown that several subflocks exist (groups with specific roost sites and movement patterns). Subflocks were readily identified utilizing Sacramento NWR during studies in 1979-80 (Wege 1980). This is also probably true in other wintering areas. Birds move between Sacramento and Delevan NWRs, Grizzly Island Wildlife Area, and in the Delta. These same studies indicated that two daily feeding flights were common. At Grizzly Island Wildlife Area, short flights were made from roosting ponds to barley fields (Wege 1980).

During waterfowl hunting seasons (late October to late January), tule geese may develop different movement patterns due to the disturbance. In the Sacramento Valley, after opening of hunting season, tule geese shift to off-refuge harvested rice fields and to closed portions of

Table 6.1 Peak Monthly Population Indices* for Tule Greater White-fronted Goose on Migration, Stopover, and Wintering areas in Oregon and California for 1978-79 through 1981-82, 1988-89, and 1989-90[a]

	Sacramento Complex[b]	Grizzly Island WA	Lower Klamath NWR	Summer Lake WMA	Malheur NWR	Total
1978-79						
Nov.	1300					1300
Dec.	900	1000				1900
1979-80						
Sept.	300		500			800
Oct.	1300	500	25			1825
Nov.	1000					1100
Dec.	1000	800				1800
Jan.	700	500				1200
Feb.	400		300			700
Mar.			500			500
Apr.			500			500
1980-81						
Sept.	1000			1500		2500
Oct.	3000	500	2000			5500
Nov.	3500					3500
Dec.	3000	1500				4500
Jan.						
Feb.						
Mar.						
Apr.			1000			1000
1981-82						
Sept.	500			2100		2600
Oct.	2000	1000	1200			4200
Nov.	3500					3500
Dec.	3500	1200				4700
Jan.						
Feb.						
Mar.						
Apr.			3000			3000
1988-89						
Sept.	5100	85	100-200	644	1830	7809
Oct.	5645	300	100-200	800		6895
Nov.	5450	300		23		5773
Dec.	5300	970				6270
Jan.		1050				1050
Feb.		1229	200			1429
Mar.			500			500
1989-90						
Sept.	3400	100		1875	3240	8615
Oct.	5070	97		850	200	6217
Nov.	6258	557		56		6871
Dec.	6000	890		3		6893
Jan.		913				913
Feb.		1190				1190

* Indices reflect trends and not absolute numbers.
[a] Summarized data represent contributions from cooperators of the Pacific Flyway Study Subcommittee on the Pacific Flyway Population of Tule Greater White-Fronted Geese (principal author G. Menzik). Peak monthly counts include geese recorded in immediate vicinity of indicated survey areas.
[b] Includes Sacramento NWR, Delevan NWR, and Colusa NWR.

refuges (Timm et al. 1982). When not disturbed they generally feed early mornings and late afternoons. During hunting seasons there may be some night feeding (Cogswell 1977).

Conservation and Management

Since the late 1960s, information on tule geese has been gathered on population size and distribution, production, mortality, and harvest. In addition, habitat management and protection practices have been implemented that have included classifying areas as refuge or critical habitat, zoning laws to protect lands important to tule geese, enhancement of state, federal and private lands by controlled burning, grain farming, or marsh management, and using federal easements to provide incentives to private landowners to retain wetlands.

Contaminant Risks – No information.

Disturbance – Most Pacific Flyway tule greater white-fronted goose harvest occurs in California. Despite limited harvest information from band returns or hunter check stations, it appears harvest locations for tule white-fronted geese are similar to those for Pacific white-fronted geese. The 1979-1982 and 1987-1989 sport harvest of tule white-fronted geese on the Sacramento NWR Complex indicate that: (1) tule geese comprise a disproportionately high percentage of the harvest (30-60%) when compared to population composition (5-25%); (2) the majority of the harvest comes from Delevan NWR and adjacent areas; (3) harvest age ratios for tule geese (30%-40% young) more closely reflect those of the population than do those of Pacific white-fronted geese (70%-80% young).

Sport harvest also occurs at Grizzly Island Wildlife Area and Klamath Basin NWR. In addition, kill records indicate 20-30 tule geese are taken by private duck clubs in the Suisun Marsh and 15-20 by clubs in the Napa Marsh (Smith, pers. comm.). Limited harvest has occurred on Summer Lake Wildlife Management Area and Malheur NWR in Oregon. In addition, two tule geese marked in Alaska were shot in southeastern Texas the first year after banding (Timm et al. 1982). Estimated hunting mortality appears to represent less than 5 percent of the known total population. This is supported by the comparatively high survival estimates (>80%) the first year after banding (Timm et al. 1982).

Recommendations

The Pacific Flyway Management Plan for tule geese contains harvest guidelines by region based on population indices. Strategies are based on the objective to maintain stable populations. These basic strategies recommend liberal harvest allowances with the population above 10,000, and with more restrictive regulations until the population index reaches 3,200 when the season would be closed. These strategies are primarily for Sacramento and Delevan NWRs and Grizzly Island Wildlife Area.

Habitat management recommendations include protecting current and future breeding areas as "critical habitat". Acquisition or easement of habitat areas in California and Oregon not currently under state or federal management is recommended. Management practices on state, federal, and private lands beneficial to tule geese should be maintained.

Within the San Francisco Bay Area, the areas of greatest importance to the tule goose are Suisun and the North Bay. Important habitat elements are open water, perennial and seasonal pond, high tidal ecotone (in Napa Marsh), and emergent vegetation. Fringe marsh along sloughs is also important. Regionwide, goals to support this species should include maintaining current acreages of managed marsh, managed upland habitat, and farmed upland areas that are farmed for oat hay.

Suisun – Suisun is the most important subregion for all goose species. To maintain current population levels, we need to maintain their habitat – managed wetlands and associated upland habitat.

North Bay – Tule geese do not nest in this Estuary, but an associated species, the Canada goose, nests in the Napa Marsh of the North Bay. Currently, the North Bay has a relatively small wintering population of tule geese and Pacific greater white-front geese, but they seem to be adjusting to the habitat gains recently made in the area (Petaluma, etc.). There is potential to increase goose populations with a further increase in managed marsh habitat. Areas of importance in the North Bay include the Napa Marsh from Sears Point to Napa River, Salt Ponds 1A and 1AN, all managed marsh areas, seasonal ponds in agricultural areas, farmed uplands, and the high tidal ecotone. Current acreages of farmed and managed upland habitat should be maintained.

Central Bay – Tule geese do not currently use this subregion in great numbers, but an increase in habitat (managed marsh and managed upland habitat) could increase the subregional population. The San Pablo Reservoir is important for Aluetian Canada geese.

South Bay – Tule geese do not currently use this subregion in great numbers, but an increase in habitat (managed marsh and managed upland habitat) could increase the subregional population.

Research Needs

Comprehensive research occurred during the late 1970s and early 1980s. Work was conducted on wintering, migration stopover, and the newly discovered breeding areas. Activities included leg banding, neck collaring, and outfitting individuals with radio transmitters. Daily and seasonal movements were monitored, sport harvest documented, and social behavior observed (Timm et al. 1982, Wege 1984).

Future research should address several aspects of the tule greater white-fronted goose ecology. Winter habitat requirements would help land managers develop strategies to protect and enhance wetlands for tule geese. Additional data is needed to develop techniques for sub-specific identification. There is relatively good information on sport hunting mortality, however there is a distinct lack of data on non-sport hunting mortality due to disease, predation, subsistence hunting, and pollution. Continued improvement of fall/winter surveys will aid in obtaining concurrent peak population counts and age ratio samples on all known use areas.

Additional needs center around data gaps that are intensified by the small population size of tule geese and their physical similarity to Pacific greater white-fronted geese. Regularly scheduled surveys are needed to help answer the population status question. A better understanding of the taxonomic differences between Pacific greater white-fronted geese and tule greater white-fronted geese is needed. Estimates of production, survival, and mortality parameters are incomplete. Past research needs to be completed with analyzed and published results. Effects of some agricultural land use practices are not known. Habitat requirements are not fully delineated. There is sport harvest occurring outside of California but the magnitude and location of harvest, and thus complete wintering population size, is also unknown. (Mensik 1991).

Acknowledgments

John Takekawa of the U.S. Geological Survey, Vallejo and Greg Mensik, U.S. Fish and Wildlife Service, Sacramento National Wildlife Refuge, are the California experts on the Tule goose and their input on this report is appreciated.

References

Bellrose, F.C. 1980. Ducks, geese and swans of North America. Stackpole Books, Harrisburg, PA. 540 pp.

Cogswell, H.L. 1977. White-fronted goose (*Anser albifrons*) pp 116-118. *In:* Water birds of California. Univ. of Ca. Press, Berkeley.

Ely, C.R. and J.Y. Takekawa. 1990. Distribution of sub-populations of greater white-fronted geese in Pacific Flyway. USFWS unpubl. progress rept. 23pp.

Hartlaub, G. 1852. Descriptions de quelques nouvelles especes d'oiseauz. Revue et Magasin de Zoologie Pure et Appliquee 4 (2nd series):3-9.

Longhurst, W.M. 1955. Additional records of tule geese from Solano County, California. Condor 57: 307-308.

Mensik, J.G. 1991. Fall/winter tule white-fronted goose population surveys, 1988-1989. U.S. Fish and Wildl. Serv. unpubl. repts.

Swarth, H.S. and H.C. Bryant. 1917. A study of the races of the white-fronted goose (*Anser albifrons*) occurring in California. Univ. of Ca. Publ. Zool. 17:209-22.

Timm, D.E., M.L. Wege and D.S. Gilmer. 1982. Current status and management challenges for tule white-fronted geese. Trans. N. Am. Wildl. and Nat. Resource Conf. 47:453-63.

Trost, R.E. and L. Harb. 1995. Tule greater white-fronted goose mark-recapture survey. Presented to Pacific Flyway Council Tech. Committee, Sept. 1995. 3pp.

U.S. Department of the Interior (USDI). 1995. Determining spring migration routes and breeding areas of tule greater white-fronted geese. Progress Rept., Natl. Biol. Serv., May 31, 1995.

Wege, M. 1980. Winter ecology of tule white-fronted geese in California. USFWS, Northern Prairie Wildlife Research Center, Dixon. Progress Report 1979-1980. Project 909.10.

_____. 1984. Distribution and abundance of tule geese in California and southern Oregon. Wildfowl 35:14-20.

Zeiner, D.C., W.F. Laudenslayer, Jr., K.E. Mayer and M. White (eds). 1990. Greater white-fronted goose. *In:* California's wildlife, vol. II: Birds. Calif. Dept. Fish and Game. pp. 50-51.

Other Important References

Accurso, L.M. 1992. Distribution and abundance of wintering waterfowl on San Francisco Bay, 1988-1990. Unpubl. Master's thesis. Humboldt State Univ. Arcata, CA. 252pp.

Bauer, R.D. 1979. Historical and status report of the tule white-fronted goose. *In:* R. L. Jarvis and J. C. Bartonek (eds). Management and Biology of Pacific Flyway Geese. Oregon State Univ., Corvallis. pp 44-55.

Bent, A.C. 1925. White-fronted goose and tule goose. *In:* Life histories of North American wild fowl, Part II. Dover Publ., New York. pp 188-198.

Ely, C.R. 1979. Breeding biology of the white-fronted goose (*Anser albifrons frontalis*) on the Yukon-Kuskokwim Delta, Alaska. Thesis Univ. of Calif., Davis. 110 pp.

Subcommittee on the Pacific Flyway Population of White-Fronted Geese of the Pacific Flyway Study Committee. 1992. Pacific Flyway management plan for the tule greater white-fronted goose. Pacific Flyway Study Committee. U.S. Fish and Wildl. Serv. Rept., Portland, OR. 18pp.

Personal Communications

Gary Kramer, U.S. Fish and Wildlife Service, 1997. Manager Sacramento Complex.

Greg Mensik, U.S. Fish and Wildlife Service, 1988-89. Biologist, Sacramento Complex.

Robert Smith, Calif. Department of Fish and Game, 1997. Area manager Shasta Valley Wildlife Area, former Assistant Manager Grizzly Island, 1987-1992.

Waterfowl & Shorebirds

Mallard

Anas platyrhynchos

Steven C. Chappell
David C. Van Baren

Introduction

The mallard was selected as a representative of other dabbling ducks such as Cinnamon teal (*Anas cyanoptera*) and Gadwall (*Anas strepera*) which are found in the Suisun Marsh and the San Francisco Bay Area. All three of these species represent resident breeding populations in the San Francisco Bay Estuary, as well as migrational wintering populations from the northern breeding grounds.

The largest population of mallards occur in the Suisun subregion. Mallards were also recorded as the number one dabbling duck of the San Pablo Bay and South San Francisco Bay subregions, most often using seasonal wetlands habitats and low salinity salt ponds. The lowest numbers of mallards were recorded in the Central Bay subregion, with few mallards being recorded in the open bay habitats of all four subregions.

Description

The mallard is one of the most easily recognizable of all waterfowl species. The drake is characterized by a bright yellow bill, brilliant green head, and brown chest with a white neck ring separating the two. The drakes also have a gray body with central black tail feathers curling upward. Both sexes have white outer tail coverts, with a blue speculum bordered in white, and bright orange feet. The female is the typical mottled brown of other *Anas* species, and has an orange bill with a dark spot on top. Mallards are among the most vocal of all duck species. The hen mallard has a call which begins with a loud quack followed by a series of slowly diminishing quacks. The drake mallard, by comparison, has a very soft almost buzzing call. Adult male mallards typically average 24.7 inches in length and weigh 2.75 pounds, while the fe-

Courtesy USGS/NBS

male tends to be a little smaller at an average of 23.1 inches and weigh 2.44 pounds (Bellrose 1980).

Breeding Biology – Mallards have one of the most widespread breeding ranges of all waterfowl species, encompassing both Canada and the United States. Loose pair bonds begin to form as early as August (Barclay 1970) with nesting beginning by early April. The pair bond generally begins to weaken with the onset of incubation, rarely lasting until pipping (pre-emergence). Nesting typically occurs on the ground, in upland fields generally in stands of dense vegetation. The nest is a shallow depression in the vegetation that is lined with down and feathers plucked from the females breast. The typical clutch size is from 7-10 eggs, but can be as high as 15. Females incubate the eggs for approximately 28 days, and are the primary care provider for the ducklings which are precocial at hatching, and move about the nest in a few hours (Batt et al. 1992).

Migration Ecology – Migration occurs along four different flyways, with the heaviest used corridors being the Mississippi Flyway in the East, and the Pacific Flyway in the West (Bellrose 1980). Birds migrating to northern breeding grounds depart the wintering areas by early February, returning as food availability becomes scarce, and arriving back in the wintering grounds by early October. The most important migration corridor in the West appears to be from Alberta to the Columbia River basin with several different routes going into the Central Valley of California (Bellrose 1980).

Wintering Ecology – Mallards primarily winter throughout the United States and along the west coast of Canada, with the Atlantic flyway attracting relatively few numbers of birds (Bellrose 1980). Suisun, San Francisco Bay, the Sacramento-San Joaquin Delta, and the Central Valley are important wintering areas for the mallards in the Pacific flyway. These areas also provide important stop-over locations for mallards migrating to and from the wintering and breeding grounds.

Distribution and Abundance

North America – Mallards are the most widely distributed species of waterfowl in North America, and are found virtually everywhere in high numbers except for the Atlantic Flyway. During the 1996-1997 waterfowl season, mallard numbers in the Suisun Marsh fluctuated from a high of 29,580 on October 16, 1996, to a low of 6,105 on January 8, 1997 (CDFG 1997). Some of the primary factors influencing mallard distribution in the San Francisco Bay Estuary is the availability of areas with low salinity water, and the necessary food resources. Accurso (1992) found that the mallards were using the salt ponds in the North and South bays at 2-3 times the expected rate based on availability. These ponds had a salinity level of around 20-33 ppt.

Pacific Coast – No information.

Figure 6.2 Maximum Counts of Mallard

Open water data from the USGS Study of Waterfowl in Open Bays and Salt Ponds, 1988-1990 (USGS, unpubl.), John Takekawa (unpubl. data), and Accurso 1992.

Bayland data from the Diked Baylands Wildlife Study (DBWS), 1982-1989 (USFWS, *in prep.*).

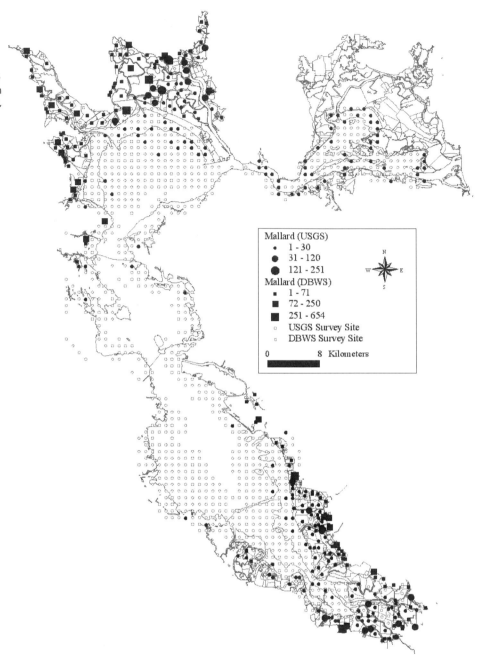

Mallard (USGS)
- • 1 - 30
- ● 31 - 120
- ⬤ 121 - 251

Mallard (DBWS)
- ▪ 1 - 71
- ■ 72 - 250
- ⬛ 251 - 654

○ USGS Survey Site
□ DBWS Survey Site

0   8 Kilometers

San Francisco Bay – In the Diked Baylands Wildlife Study (USFWS, *in prep.*), mallards were identified as the dabbling duck using seasonal wetland habitats most often in the greatest numbers for both the North and South bays. **Figure 6.2** shows the distribution of mallards around the Bay.

Historical Information

No information.

Population Trends

Since 1960 the continental population of mallards has fluctuated widely from an overall high in 1970 of 9,986,000 birds to a low of 4,960,000 birds in 1985.

During the ten year period since 1985, however, the trend in mallard numbers has been an increase to a high of 8,269,000 birds in 1995 (CDFG 1953-1997 and 1997). In 1996 and 1997, there has been a decrease in mallard numbers down to 7,643,000 (CDFG 1997). The overall Suisun Marsh mallard population has fluctuated widely since 1960 with a high of 88,885 mallards to a low of 10,876 mallards. Several years have large peaks in the total number of mallards using the marsh, which could indicate the arrival of migrants from the northern breeding grounds.

Habitat Use and Behavior

Foraging – Mallards are very opportunistic in their foraging behavior. They will feed on both natural food plants, as well as agricultural waste grains while on the wintering grounds. The primary natural foods eaten by waterfowl in the Suisun Marsh are alkali bulrush, fathen, brass buttons, watergrass, and smart weed (Rollins 1981). Aquatic invertebrates play an important role in mallard diets prior to and during the breeding season, due to the high energy demands of the hen for egg laying.

Breeding – Nest site selection begins once the flock reaches the breeding grounds, with the pairs breaking off from the flock and setting up independent home ranges. The home range will typically include one or more loafing sites consisting of bare shore surrounded by tall standing vegetation near water (Bellrose 1980). Mallards use a wide variety of vegetation types in the construction of their nests. In the Suisun Marsh the primary vegetation used is annual rye grass, lana vetch, brome, and tall wheat grass, as well as natural wetland plants within the managed wetlands. The main nesting requirement appears to be that the vegetation is dense and approximately 24 inches tall.

McLandress et al. (1996) found that the mallard nest densities in the Suisun Marsh, Central Valley, and the intermountain region of Northeastern California were higher than in the prairie breeding grounds in Canada. Canadian nest densities were found to average 10.6 mallard nests/km². In California mean nest densities ranged from 41 nests/km² in the San Joaquin Valley to 190 nests/km² in the Suisun Marsh.

Yarris et al. (1994) determined, using radiotelemetry, that some hens nesting at Grizzly Island Wildlife Area will leave the area after fledging their young, and prior to their wing molt. Yarris detected radio-tagged hens in the Delta east of Grizzly Island Wildlife Area and as far north as the southern Oregon border, locating the molting areas of 20 hens. All hens radio-tagged were detected moving in a northerly direction shortly after leaving the Suisun Marsh. Mallard ducklings are very sensitive to increasing salinity levels. Mitchum and Wobster (1988) found that water with a specific conductivity of 20 mS/cm is lethal to mallard ducklings, and ducklings exposed to 4 mS/cm will experience impaired growth.

Roosting – Mallards commonly roost in ponded areas of managed wetlands with tall emergent vegetation, but may be regularly seen loafing in open Bay habitats as well as salt ponds.

Movement – No information.

Conservation and Management

Contaminants – Disease and contaminants are directly responsible for a large amount of the waterfowl mortality each year, although the total number is unknown. Diseases such as botulism, cholera and duck viral enteritis historically have not been a major concern for duck populations in the Suisun Marsh. The only major event has occurred in this region during the winter of 1948-49 when approximately 40,000 ducks, geese, and coots died in an avian cholera outbreak in the San Francisco Bay Area (Bellrose 1980). As with all places that have historically used lead shot, there is still a possibility of incidental mortality due to lead poisoning. The danger of this disease is not that there is a large noticeable die-off every year, it is that no one knows how many individual birds ingest lead and die without ever being noticed. Bellrose (1959) concluded that 2 to 3 percent of the fall and winter waterfowl populations may fall victim to lead poisoning each year. With the current use of non-toxic shot loads in waterfowl hunting, this number should gradually become smaller as the old exposed lead shot is covered by sediment and becomes unreachable.

The maintenance of good wintering and breeding habitat in the Suisun Marsh and Napa Marsh is important to the continued use of the San Francisco Bay Estuary. This can be accomplished by the protection of seasonal wetlands and the intensive management of diked managed wetland areas.

Disturbance – Disturbance from human activities can cause temporary changes in behavior and locally affect temporal and spatial distribution of migratory and wintering waterfowl (Madsen 1994) Disturbance by humans caused both longer duration of alert and flight behavior by pintail when compared to disturbance by raptors or other animals (Wolder 1993). Considering these disturbance impacts could be similar to mallards, activities such as wildlife viewing, urbanization, and vehicle traffic may have negative effects.

Recommendations

Managed wetlands are critical habitat for both resident breeding birds and for migrants, as they provide food resources and wintering habitat. Within the region, the most important areas for mallards are the managed wetlands of Suisun Marsh, some less saline areas of San Pablo Bay, and seasonal wetlands habitat around the San Francisco Bay. To support mallards, regional goals should strive to increase the acreage of managed marsh habitat; maintain or enhance current areas of lagoon (loafing and feeding habitat) and farmed baylands (critical wintering habitat); and maintain diked marsh (especially in brackish areas), ruderal baylands (breeding and nesting habitat), low salinity salt ponds, and treatment ponds. Adjacent to the baylands, grazed and managed uplands should be maintained and increased as critical breeding habitat, and riparian habitat should be improved and increased.

Important habitat elements for mallards include seasonal ponds (most critical for food production for wintering birds); perennial pond (wintering and breeding habitat, foraging); water column/open water (loafing); clay-silt substrate (foraging); mudflats (limited use); vegetated levees and islets (nesting); eelgrass (very minor on the open bay); pan (if brackish, important for wintering, foraging, breeding); emergent vegetation; riparian zone community; vernal pools (fresh water); and artifactual vernal pools.

Suisun – The managed marshes of Suisun are the most important habitat for mallards in the San Francisco Bay. Riparian habitat is also important. Specific habitat goals for the Suisun subregion include increasing the acreage of managed marsh, diked marsh, ruderal baylands, and managed uplands; maintaining and enhancing farmed and grazed baylands; and maintaining grazed upland and riparian areas. In this subregion salinity levels preclude increasing riparian zones.

North Bay – Areas of particular importance in this subregion are the managed wetlands of the Napa River area and low salinity salt ponds. Subregional habitat goals include increasing the acreage of managed marsh, lagoon, and low salinity salt ponds; maintaining and enhancing farmed and grazed baylands; and maintaining diked marsh and ruderal baylands. Adjacent to the baylands, managed uplands and riparian zones should be increased and enhanced.

Central Bay – The Central Bay does not currently have a large population of mallards; to increase this population, critical mallard habitats (managed marsh and upland) should be increased. Areas of particular importance within this subregion are lagoons and the wetlands near Marin. Habitat goals for the Central Bay include increasing the acreage of managed marsh and lagoon, and maintaining areas of diked marsh and ruderal baylands. Adjacent to the baylands, managed uplands and riparian zones should be increased and enhanced.

South Bay – Areas of particular importance within the South Bay are managed wetlands, low salinity salt ponds, and diked wetlands. Riparian zones also show some usage by mallards. Habitat goals for the South Bay subregion include increasing the acreage of managed and diked marshes; maintaining and enhancing farmed baylands; and maintaining ruderal baylands and low salinity salt ponds. Adjacent to the baylands, managed uplands and riparian zones should be increased and enhanced.

References

Accurso, L.M. 1992. Distribution and abundance of wintering waterfowl on San Francisco Bay, 1988-1990. Unpubl. Master's thesis. Humboldt State Univ. Arcata, CA. 252pp.

Barclay, J.S. 1970. Ecological aspects of defensive behavior in breeding mallards and black ducks. Ph.D. Thesis, The Ohio State Univ., Columbus. 176 pp.

Batt, B.D.J., A.D. Afton, M.G. Anderson, C.D. Ankney, D.H. Johnson, J. A. Kadlec and G. L. Krapu. 1992. Ecology and management of breeding waterfowl. Univ. of Minnesota Press. Minneapolis, MN. 635 pp.

Bellrose, F.C. 1959. Lead poisoning as a mortality factor in waterfowl populations. Ill. Nat. Hist. Surv. Bull. 27:235-288.

Bellrose, F.C. 1980. Ducks, geese, and swans of North America. Stackpole Books. Harrisburg, PA. 540 pp.

California Department of Fish and Game (CDFG). 1953-1997. Unpublished mid-winter survey results.

_____. 1997. 1996-1997 Waterfowl season Suisun Marsh aerial waterfowl survey.

Madsen, J. 1994. Impacts of disturbance on migratory waterfowl. Ibis 137: 67-74.

McLandress, R.M., G.S. Yarris, A.E.H. Perkins, D.P. Connelly and D.G. Raveling. 1996. Nesting biology of mallards in California. J. Wildl. Mgmt. 60(1): 94-107.

Mitchum, S.A. and G. Wobster. 1988. Toxic effects of natural saline waters on mallard ducklings. J. Wildl. Disease. 24: 45-50.

Rollins, G.L. 1981. A guide to waterfowl habitat management in the Suisun Marsh. Calif. Dept. of Fish and Game. 109 pp.

U.S. Fish and Wildlife Service (USFWS). *In preparation*. Diked baylands wildlife sudy. A study of wildlife use of diked, seasonal wetlands around San Francisco Bay, 1982-1989.

Wolder, M.A. 1993. Disturbance of wintering northern pintails at Sacramento National Refuge, California. M.S. thesis. Humboldt State Univ. Arcata, CA.

Yarris G.S., M.R. McLandress and A.E.H. Perkins. 1994. Molt migration of postbreeding female mallards from Suisun Marsh, California. Condor 96: 36-45.

Waterfowl & Shorebirds

Northern Pintail

Anas acuta

Michael L. Casazza
Michael R. Miller

Introduction

The northern pintail has been historically the most common puddle duck wintering in the San Francisco Bay region. Continental population declines have been severe and the declines have been even greater within the San Francisco Bay region. This disproportionate decline in pintails using the San Francisco Bay region is alarming and needs further investigation. In particular, the Suisun Marsh has seen peak numbers decline as much as 90% over the past several decades (**Figure 6.3**). Pintails use a wide variety of habitat types throughout the region, including managed marsh, seasonal wetlands, open bay, and salt ponds. They utilize many of the habitats used by other waterfowl species. Species which are commonly found in similar habitats as pintail are green-wing teal (*A. crecca*), northern shoveler (*A. clypeata*), and American wigeon (*A. americana*). We have grouped these three species together with pintails, but the pintail will be the focus as the key species because it is relatively abundant in the San Francisco Bay region, and it uses many different habitat types, including managed wetlands, as critical wintering areas.

Description

The northern pintail is a long slender duck with narrow, angular wings. Pintails float high on the water, offering a very elegant appearance to the casual observer. They have sexually dimorphic plumage. Drakes in nuptial plumage have a chocolate brown head with a white breast and foreneck extending upward as a stripe on each side of the head. Their backs are greyish in appearance and they have two, long black tail feathers for which they are named. Drakes have a distinctive iridescent black-green

Courtesy USGS/NBS

to green speculum. The male pintail has a distinct short whistle which is heard most during winter and spring. Hen pintails are mottled brown and have a noniridescent brown to brown-green speculum. The bills of both sexes are blue-gray in color with black along the central ridge in males and black blotches in females. Both sexes have gray legs and feet. The male pintail has a total length of between 57-76 cm, and females between 51-63 cm (Austin and Miller 1995).

Breeding Biology – Under favorable wetland conditions pintails will breed in their first year. They have been known to lay as few as three and as many as 14 eggs, but their average clutch size is about eight eggs (Bellrose 1980). Pintails have been found nesting across a vast area encompassing much of the Northern Hemisphere. Their main breeding areas in North America include the prairie pothole region of Alberta, Saskatchewan, Montana, and the Dakotas, along with the arctic regions of Canada and Alaska. In California, pintails nest on the northeastern plateau, the San Joaquin Valley, and on the coastal marshes, including Suisun Marsh and San Francisco Bay. Their nests tend to be in relatively open cover and can be as far as 3 km from water (Duncan 1987). Pintails are early nesters, some initiating their nests as early as late March, depending on weather conditions and location.

Migration Ecology – The major North American migration routes range from breeding areas in northern Alaska and the prairie pothole region south to California, Mexico, Texas, and Louisiana. Pintails begin arriving on wintering areas in early August. They are also one of the first ducks to leave wintering areas, as early as mid-February, to begin migration to breeding grounds.

Wintering Ecology – California is the most important wintering area in North America, and more pintails winter here than anywhere else in the Northern Hemisphere (Bellrose 1980). Other important wintering areas include the West Coast of Mexico and the Gulf Coast regions of Texas and Louisiana.

Distribution and Abundance

North America – The 1997 breeding duck survey conducted by the U.S. Fish and Wildlife Service found 3.6 million pintails in North America, which was a significant (30%) increase over 1996, but still 19% below the long-term average (Dubovsky et al. 1997).

Pacific Coast – Pintails are known to winter throughout the Pacific Coast region, and nest here in limited numbers. Important wintering areas include the coastal marshes of British Columbia, Puget Sound, the Lower Columbia River basin, the Willamette Valley, and the northern coast of California. The inland valleys of California are the most important wintering area for pintails.

San Francisco Bay – Mid-winter surveys conducted in January each year have indicated a great de-

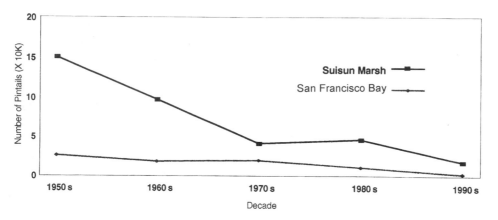

Figure 6.3 Mean Mid-Winter Survey Counts of Pintails by Decade in Suisun Marsh and San Francisco Bay (CDFG unpublished survey data)

cline in pintail numbers within the San Francisco Bay region, with the greatest proportion of that decline occurring in the Suisun Marsh (**Figure 6.3**). In the 1950s, there were close to 200,000 pintails wintering in the San Francisco Bay region, whereas the 1990s have averaged under 20,000, a decline of 90 percent.

Suisun – Northern Pintails winter in significant numbers in Suisun Marsh. Some pintails may roost on the open bays in this region (**Figure 6.4**), but most are found on managed seasonal wetlands (CDFG 1953-97). A radio telemetry study conducted from 1991-93 found pintails widely distributed throughout the managed wetlands of Suisun, with some distinct high use areas (**Figure 6.5**). The Suisun Marsh consists of approximately 23,000 hectares of marshlands and 9,300 hectares of bays and waterways and is the largest contiguous estuarine marsh in the United States (Miller et al. 1975). The majority of the pintails wintering in the San Francisco Bay region can be found in this area.

North Bay – Waterfowl surveys conducted between 1988-90 in the San Francisco Bay area indicated that North Bay salt ponds held 13-19% of the pintails (not including the managed wetlands of Suisun Marsh) (**Figure 6.4**). Open waters of the North Bay accounted for 12% of the region's pintail population in 1988-90 (Accurso 1992). Diked baylands of the North Bay had significant numbers of pintails during the winter period (**Figure 6.4**).

Central Bay – Very few pintails were observed on the Central Bay between 1988-90 (**Figure 6.4**).

South Bay – South bay salt ponds held 60-67% of the pintails wintering in the San Francisco Bay region from 1988-90 (not including the managed wetlands of Suisun Marsh), while open waters of the South Bay received very little use by pintails (**Figure 6.4**).

Historical Information

Comprehensive waterfowl surveys have been conducted since the mid-1950s which include much of the pintails

primary range. Population trends and estimates are available since that time.

Population Trends

Nationally, current pintail population estimates have increased somewhat from the all-time low of 1.8 million in 1991, and are well below goals established by the North American Waterfowl Management plan (5.1 million) (Caithamer and Dubovsky 1997). The number of pintails wintering in California has decreased dramatically from long-term averages. Locally, pintail use of the San Francisco Bay Area has declined in even greater proportion than the overall population decline.

Habitat Use and Behavior

Pintails are known to use a variety of habitats within the San Francisco Bay region, including diked fresh and estuarine wetlands, salt ponds, open bays, and mudflats (Cogswell 1977, Accurso 1992, Casazza 1995). Within the managed seasonal wetlands of the Suisun Marsh, pintails prefer to feed in habitats dominated by brass buttons (*Cotula coronopifolia*), a perennial salt tolerant herb introduced to the Bay in the late 1800s (Casazza 1995).

Foraging – Several studies have been conducted on the feeding ecology and diet of northern pintails, but none have included San Francisco Bay, and studies conducted in Suisun Marsh are outdated. Pintails are adept at separating small seeds from bottom sediments in aquatic habitats, and regularly feed on small seeds (Krapu 1974). Pintails use their long necks and tipping style to feed on or near the bottom of ponds and to utilize the benthos and seeds present at shallow depths (Krapu 1974). Pintails can exploit food sources to depths of 40 cm (Thomas 1976).

The winter diet of northern pintails consists primarily of seeds and vegetative material, with important seeds including rice (*Oryza*), swamp timothy (*Heleochloa*

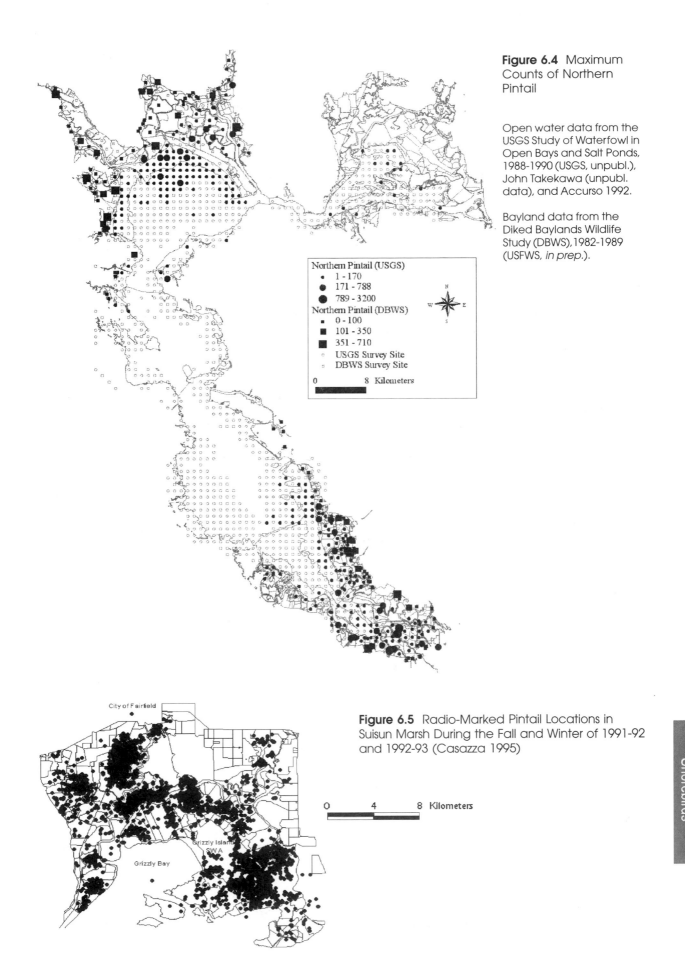

Figure 6.4 Maximum Counts of Northern Pintail

Open water data from the USGS Study of Waterfowl in Open Bays and Salt Ponds, 1988-1990 (USGS, unpubl.), John Takekawa (unpubl. data), and Accurso 1992.

Bayland data from the Diked Baylands Wildlife Study (DBWS), 1982-1989 (USFWS, *in prep.*).

Northern Pintail (USGS)
- 1 - 170
- 171 - 788
- 789 - 3200

Northern Pintail (DBWS)
- 0 - 100
- 101 - 350
- 351 - 710
- USGS Survey Site
- DBWS Survey Site

0   8 Kilometers

City of Fairfield

Grizzly Island SWA

Grizzly Bay

Figure 6.5 Radio-Marked Pintail Locations in Suisun Marsh During the Fall and Winter of 1991-92 and 1992-93 (Casazza 1995)

0   4   8 Kilometers

Waterfowl & Shorebirds

schenoides), barnyard grass (*Echinochloa crusgalli*), flat-sedges (*Carex* spp.), southern naiad (*Najas guadalupensis*), and smartweeds (*Polygonum* spp.) (Austin and Miller 1995). Miller (1987) found that plant foods accounted for nearly 100% of the diet of pintails in the Sacramento Valley in early fall, and by late winter their diet had shifted to about 40% animal matter, primarily midge larvae. In the Suisun Marsh, pintail gizzards were found to contain three main marsh seeds; brass buttons (*Cotula coronopifolia*), alkali bulrush (*Scirpus maritimus*) and fat hen (*Atriplex triangularis*) (George et al. 1965).

Roosting – Pintails roost on open water habitats, including lakes and bays, which lack extensive emergent vegetation. Pintails commonly roost on open water areas of all four regions of San Francisco Bay (**Figure 6.4**).

Movement – Pintails commonly make local and regional movements. Local movements primarily consist of evening and morning flights between roost and feeding areas, usually less than 5 km. Soon after sunset in the Suisun Marsh, radio-marked hen pintails would commonly leave open water sanctuary areas such as Joice Island, to make 1-3 km flights to feeding areas on nearby private duck clubs (**Figure 6.6**). Regional movements occur when pintails leave an area and establish new feeding and roosting sites, usually encompassing distances greater than 10 km. Radio-marked pintails commonly left the Suisun Marsh and established new feeding and roosting sites in the Delta, and the Sacramento and San Joaquin valleys (Casazza 1995). Only one radio-marked pintail moved to San Francisco Bay from Suisun Marsh during two years of study (Casazza 1995).

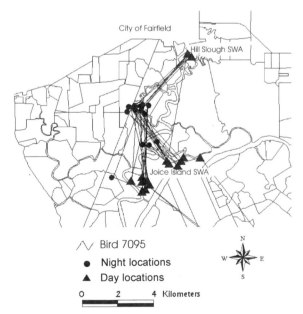

Figure 6.6 Common Day and Night Movement Patterns for Pintails Wintering in Suisun Marsh (Casazza 1995)

Conservation and Management

Contaminant Risks – Little information is known about exposure of pintails to contaminant risk in the San Francisco Bay region. Health warnings are published for greater and lesser scaup (*Aythya marila* and *A. affinis*) and surf scoters (*Melanitta perspicillata*) harvested in the San Francisco Bay region, and further investigation of contaminants in pintails is warranted. Ohlendorf and Miller (1984) found that pintails seemed to accumulate chemicals such as DDE while wintering in California, and similar accumulations of contaminants may take place in birds wintering in the San Francisco Bay region.

Disturbance – Disturbance of northern pintails was studied by Wolder (1993) on Sacramento National Wildlife Refuge in the Sacramento Valley of California. He found that human disturbance was a major factor in pintail distribution. Disturbances by humans resulted in longer time spent alert or flying than disturbances caused by raptors or other animals (Wolder 1993). Common types of disturbance include vehicle traffic, wildlife observation, and hunting.

Recommendations

Suisun currently provides critical support for pintails. North Bay and South Bay also are used by these birds. Managed marsh is the most critical habitat type for pintails in the Estuary, and for Suisun in particular, for most of winter. Uplands puddled from rain and seasonal ponding provide critical late winter/spring habitat for pintails in this region. Many of the other habitat types, such as diked marsh and muted tidal marsh, would provide even better habitat if managed for dabbling ducks. Intertidal mudflats are important feeding habitat when covered by 10-40 cm of water. Unvegetated levees and islets are important roosting habitats.

Regional goals to support pintails include increasing the acreages of managed marsh and low salinity salt ponds; maintaining and enhancing mid-tidal, muted tidal (if managed for water fowl), and diked marsh; and maintaining the acreage of intertidal flat and shallow bays. Seasonal ponds in farmed and grazed baylands should be maintained or enhanced, and mid-salinity salt ponds should be maintained but converted to low salinity. Adjacent to the baylands, irrigation ponds in farmed uplands should be maintained, and managed upland habitat should be maintained for nesting.

Suisun – All managed marsh habitat within the Suisun subregion is important to support pintails. Goals within this subregion should include maintaining the current acreages of muted tidal and managed marsh, intertidal flat, shallow bays or straights, and managed uplands. To best meet the needs of pintails, muted tidal marsh, diked marsh, and managed marsh should be managed for water levels, vegetation, and timing of flooding most beneficial to dabbling ducks. Specifically, open water 10-40 cm deep with brass button-type vegetation is best.

North Bay – North Bay salt ponds were an important habitat for pintails. Survey data indicates that at least 1000 hectares (ha) of salt ponds should be maintained to ensure at least 80% of the current use by pintails in this region. In particular, ponds 1AN, 2, 2N, and 6N had a significant amount of use by pintails. Other important areas include Slaughterhouse Point; American Canyon Marsh; the mudflats near Sonoma Creek; open, shallow water near mudflats; Point Richmond Bay; and Tubbs Island lagoon. Goals to support pintails within the North Bay include maintaining current muted tidal marshes and diked marshes and enhancing them by managing them for ducks; maintaining mid-tidal marsh, low salinity salt ponds, ruderal baylands (used for nesting), intertidal flat, and shallow bays or straights. Ponding should be enhanced in farmed or grazed baylands and adjacent uplands. Mid-salinity salt ponds should be converted to low salinity ponds, and managed upland habitat should be maintained to provide nesting habitat. Increasing managed marsh habitat would support an increase in pintail population.

Central Bay – Important areas include Point Richmond Bay mudflats, Albany mudflats, and the Emeryville Crescent. To support increased populations of pintails in the Central Bay, the current acreage of managed marsh should be increased.

South Bay – South Bay salt ponds held 60-67% of wintering pintails of the San Francisco Bay (not including Suisun) from 1988-90. Survey data indicates that at least 2,100 hectares (ha) of salt ponds should be maintained to ensure at least 85% of the current use by pintails in this region. Areas of critical importance to pintails include the Sunnyvale sewage pond, and Ponds A9 and A10. Other important areas include Ponds A3W, B3C, M1, A, and NA1; Mowry Slough; Charleston Slough; Faber Tract; the shallows near the east end of the Dumbarton Bridge; Coyote Slough; the Hayward ponds; and the Hayward treatment ponds. Goals to support pintails would include maintaing the current acreage of low salinity salt ponds and increasing it by coverting mid-salinity ponds; maintaining the current acreage of mid-tidal marsh, intertidal flat, and shallow bays and straights; and maintaining and enhancing the current acreage of muted tidal marsh and diked marsh by managing for ducks. The current acreage of managed marsh should be maintained, or else increased to increase pintail populations.

Research Needs

The disturbing decline of pintail abundance in the San Francisco Bay region needs immediate attention. Studies need to be implemented which will identify management practices that can be used to attract pintails to the region and provide a solid habitat base for these waterfowl throughout the winter. Other factors that should be investigated include effects of disturbance and contaminants on pintail abundance in this region.

Acknowledgments

We thank J. Y. Takekawa and J. Alexander for providing distribution maps from the Accurso (1988-90) and Pratt (1982-89) data sets. K. Miles, S. Chappell, and R. Pratt provided a helpful review.

References

Accurso, L.M. 1992. Distribution and abundance of wintering waterfowl on San Francisco Bay, 1988-1990. M.S. thesis. Calif. State Univ., Humboldt.

Austin, J.J.E. and M.R. Miller. 1995. Northern pintail (*Anas acuta*). *In:* A. Poole and F. Gill (eds). The birds of North America, No. 163. The Academy of Natural Sciences, Philadelphia, and The American Ornithologists' Union, Washington, D.C.

Bellrose, F.C. 1980. Ducks, geese and swans of North America. Stackpole Books. Harrisburg. PA.

Caithamer, D.F. and J.A. Dubovsky. 1997. Waterfowl population status, 1997. U.S.Fish and Wildl. Serv. Rept.

California Department of Fish and Game (CDFG). 1953-1997. Unpubl. mid-winter survey results.

Casazza, M.L. 1995. Habitat use and movements of northern pintails wintering in the Suisun Marsh, California. M.S. thesis. Ca. State Univ., Sacramento.

Cogswell, H.L. 1977. Waterbirds of California. Univ. of Calif. Press, Berkeley, Calif. Nat. Hist. Guides. No. 40. 399pp.

Dubovsky, J.A., C.T. Moore, J.P. Bladen, G.W. Smith and P. D. Keywood. 1997. Trends in duck breeding populations, 1955-97. Administrative Report, U.S. Fish and Wildl. Serv., Office of Migratory Bird Mgmt.

Duncan, D.C. 1987. Nest-site distribution and overland brood movements of northern pintails in Alberta. J. Wildl. Mgmt. 51:716-723.

George, H.A., W. Anderson and H. McKinnie. 1965. An evaluation of the Suisun Marsh as a waterfowl area. Calif Dept. Fish and Game, Admin. Rept.

Krapu, G.L. 1974. Feeding ecology of pintail hens during reproduction. Auk 91:278-290.

Miller, A.W., R.S. Miller, H.C. Cohen and R.F. Schultze. 1975. Suisun Marsh study, Solano County, California. U.S. Dept. of Agriculture, Soil Cons. Serv., Portland, OR.

Miller, M.R. 1987. Fall and winter foods of Northern pintails in the Sacramento Valley, California. J. Wildl. Mgmt. 51:405-414.

Ohlendorf, H.M. and M.R. Miller. 1984. Organochlorine contaminants in California waterfowl. J. Wildl. Mgmt. 48(3):867-877.

Waterfowl & Shorebirds

Thomas, G. 1976. Habitat use of wintering ducks at the Ouse Washes, England. Wildfowl 27:148-152.

U. S. Fish and Wildlife Service (USFWS). *In preparation*. Diked baylands wildlife sudy. A study of wildlife use of diked, seasonal wetlands around San Francisco Bay, 1982-1989.

Wolder, M.A. 1993. Disturbance of wintering northern pintails at Sacramento National Wildlife Refuge, California. M.S. thesis. Ca. State Univ., Humboldt.

Canvasback

Aythya valisineria

John Y. Takekawa
Carolyn M. Marn

Introduction

The canvasback is a diving duck that forages on aquatic plants or benthic invertebrates in mouths of rivers or channels, large wetlands, and brackish marshes. The continental population of canvasbacks has not increased greatly in the last 20 years, and based on mid-winter surveys (USFWS, unpubl. data), the population in the Estuary has continued to decline. Consequently, the canvasback is a species of special concern for the U. S. Fish and Wildlife Service, and protection of this species was one of the reasons for establishment of the San Pablo Bay National Wildlife Refuge. Associated species that use similar habitats in the Estuary include: common goldeneye (*Bucephala clangula*), greater and lesser scaup (*Aythya marila* and *A. affinis*), which also have declining continental populations, and very small populations of redhead (*A. americana*) and ring-necked ducks.

Description

The canvasback is one of our most distinctive waterfowl species and a member of the Tribe Aythyini. They have a steeply sloping bill with a body size similar to the mallard (0.9-1.6 kg; Cogswell 1977). Males are distinguished

Courtesy USGS/NBS

by their white back, underparts, and wings, black tail and breast, and red head with blood-red eyes. Females have a brown head and eyes, and a brown or dusky gray body. Redheads are similar in appearance, but have a shorter bill, and redhead males are darker. Canvasbacks are the fastest flying large duck in North America (Bellrose 1980). Their call is a weak "ik-ik-coo" (Cogswell 1977).

Breeding Biology – Canvasbacks pair during migration in March and April (Erickson 1948, Bellrose 1980). Females will breed as yearlings, but generally less successfully than in later years (Hochbaum 1944, Olson 1964, Trauger 1974). Canvasbacks are well known for their strong fidelity to natal breeding areas (Trauger 1974). Females spend one week searching for a nest site, two to three days to build the nest, and one day laying each egg. Nests occur commonly in shallow ponds of less than one acre covered by cattail and bulrush (Trauger and Stoudt 1974); however, their overlapping home ranges may reach 1,300 acres. Canvasbacks nest in deep water (greater than 6-24 inches) in ponds, marshes, sloughs, and potholes (Trauger and Stoudt 1974). They nest in late April and early May (peak, mid-May) and incubate for 24-29 days. Nest success averages 46.2%, but it is highly variable at different sites, depending on predation by raccoons, mink, skunks, coyotes, fox, weasels, crows, and magpies and desertion following flooding or parasitic laying. As much as 57% of the nests may be parasitized, primarily by redhead ducks (Trauger and Stoudt 1974). Average clutch size is 7.9 eggs, but more eggs (9.5) are found in unparasitized nests. Nest success may be as low as 17% in dry years (Serie et al. 1992), but varies from 17-62% in southwestern Manitoba (Serie et al. 1992). Renesting may occur as much as 50% of the time. Broods are reared in open, large, deep-water areas, but survival averages 25% over the first two months. The 55% of successful hens rear an average of 5.3 fledged young. Non-breeding birds form flocks in late June and July. All birds have a 3-4 week flightless wing-molt during late July and August.

Migration Ecology – Canvasbacks begin their autumn migration in September and arrive in wintering areas in early November. Their spring migration begins in February until their return to breeding areas in April. Major migration routes occur along the Upper Mississippi River and Great Lakes to the Atlantic and Gulf Coast regions, and along the Pacific Coast and Intermountain west to the west coast and Mexico. Significant migration areas in the west include Puget Sound, Great Salt Lake, Malheur and Klamath Basin National Wildlife Refuges and Carson Sink in the Great Basin. During the past two decades, use of staging areas has increased at Pyramid Lake, Klamath Basin National Wildlife Refuges while use of the Great Salt Lake, Malheur and Stillwater National Wildlife Refuge has decreased.

Wintering Ecology – Birds arrive on wintering areas in late October and increase in numbers through

December. Nearly 90% of canvasbacks produced in Alaska winter in California (Lensink 1964). The largest wintering population of canvasbacks is on the Atlantic Coast (290,000), with the greatest number on the Chesapeake Bay. A large number of birds winter along the Gulf Coast in the Mississippi River Delta and Catahoula Lake. Western wintering areas include Lake Earl in Humboldt County, the Columbia and Snake river basins, Carson Sink, the Central and Imperial valleys, and San Francisco Bay. San Francisco Bay is the major wintering area for the western population with 60,000 birds counted in 1960-1971, but only about 25,000 birds counted in 1990. Canvasbacks exhibit high winter site fidelity to the Estuary (Rienecker 1985) and generally winter in more saline areas than redhead ducks.

Distribution and Abundance

North America – Canvasbacks breed in the Arctic and Subarctic, and in the prairie and parkland areas of North America. Approximately 190,000 canvasbacks are found in the parkland areas, with a peak of 10 pairs per square mile with up to 10% of the continental population near Minnedosa, Manitoba. Other breeding areas include Alaska, Yukon, Northwest Territories, and the pothole region of southern Canada and the northern United States.

Pacific Coast – Canvasbacks migrate along the Pacific Coast to and from their northern breeding areas. They are found in most of the major estuaries along the lower west coast during winter, including Puget Sound, Willapa Bay, and Humboldt Bay with the largest populations found in the San Francisco Bay.

San Francisco Bay – Within the San Francisco Bay Estuary, canvasbacks comprise 7% of the waterfowl, and 46.5% (1989) to 54% (1990) of the mid-winter population in the Pacific Flyway (USFWS unpubl. data summarized in Accurso 1992). Many birds also stage on the Estuary during migration (Cogswell 1977).

Suisun – About 13-16% of canvasbacks in the Estuary occur in Suisun with peak numbers of greater than 6,000 canvasbacks (Accurso 1992). Eighty percent of the waterfowl in open water habitats were found in Suisun Bay proper rather than Honker Bay or Carquinez Straight (Suisun managed marshes were not included in this survey; **Figure 6.7**).

North Bay – Between 38-59% of canvasbacks wintering in the Estuary in 1988-1990 were found in the northern salt evaporation ponds (Accurso 1992). The greatest number of canvasbacks in the Estuary are found in these ponds. An additional 9.5-25.5% of canvasbacks are found in the open bay area (**Figure 6.7**).

Central Bay – Only 1% of canvasbacks are found in the Central Bay; however, hundreds have been reported in Lake Merritt adjacent to the Bay (Cogswell 1977; **Figure 6.7**).

South Bay – Up to 17% of wintering canvasbacks are found in South Bay salt evaporation ponds with an additional 1.7-1.9% in the open bay. Up to 4-5% of waterfowl in the salt evaporation ponds (peak 6,400) are canvasbacks. Canvasbacks are the third most abundant duck found in this region (**Figure 6.7**).

Historical Information

Historically, canvasbacks were likely very abundant in parts of the Estuary. Areas mapped by Jose Canizares in 1776 in the northern reach of the Estuary were labeled "Forests of the red duck" (Josselyn 1983). Canvasbacks also were described as "abundant" in San Francisco bays and marshes in the winter in the early 1900s (Grinnell and Wythe 1927), arriving in early October and departing in early April, while peaking from late November to early March. They historically used open, deeper water for roosting, foraging in inner bays and marshes closer to shore (Grinnell and Wythe 1927). Christmas Bird Counts (National Audubon Society, unpubl. data) from Palo Alto and San Jose show a population decline of 0.27% and 1.13%, respectively, from 1969 to 1996 on the basis of the small areas surveyed. The regional population of canvasbacks actually decreased by 50% from the 1970s to the mid-1980s according to annual mid-winter surveys (USFWS, unpubl. data).

Population Trends

National – The continental canvasback population averages 534,000 birds but declined between 1955 and 1993 (Hohman et al. 1995). The population is highly skewed with only 20-30% females (Trauger 1974) or 1.94 males per each female in spring (Bellrose et al. 1961) and suggests an older age structure. Females have 27% higher mortality (Geis 1959). With about 30% females, the breeding population is estimated as 140,000 pairs. There are an estimated 1.03 young per adult during the fall flight (Bellrose 1980). Adult mortality is 52%, while juvenile mortality is about 77% (Geis 1959).

Regional – In the 1950s, 79% of the wintering canvasbacks were found in the Atlantic or Pacific flyways. However, by the 1990s, 44% of the birds were found in the Central and Mississippi flyways. A large increase was also noted in Mexico. Annual survival was found to be higher in the Pacific versus the Atlantic Flyway populations (female 56-69%, male 70-82%) (Nichols and Haramis 1980). Although the overall population estimate is 2.0-2.5 males per female, the sex ratio varies from 2.9-3.2 in the Atlantic Flyway, to 1.6-1.8 in the Mississippi (Woolington 1993), to 2.2 in the Pacific (Hohman et al. 1995).

Local – San Francisco Bay remains one of the top ten major wintering areas for canvasbacks in North America. The San Pablo Bay National Wildlife Refuge

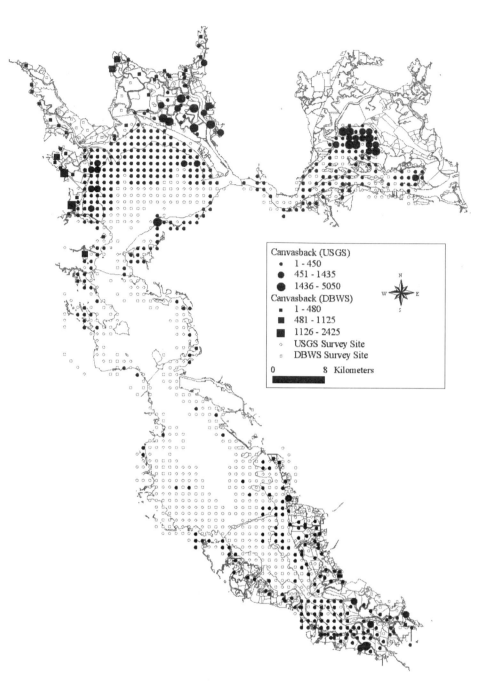

Figure 6.7 Maximum Counts of Canvasback

Open water data from the USGS Study of Waterfowl in Open Bays and Salt Ponds, 1988-1990 (USGS, unpubl.), John Takekawa (unpubl. data), and Accurso 1992.

Bayland data from the Diked Baylands Wildlife Study (DBWS), 1982-1989 (USFWS, *in prep.*).

Canvasback (USGS)
- 1 - 450
- 451 - 1435
- 1436 - 5050

Canvasback (DBWS)
- 1 - 480
- 481 - 1125
- 1126 - 2425

○ USGS Survey Site
□ DBWS Survey Site

0　　　　　　8　Kilometers

was established for protection of this species. Canvasbacks are the fifth most numerous diving duck in winter in the Estuary (Accurso 1992) and account for 6-7% of all waterfowl. Their peak numbers are observed in early to mid-January. Population numbers have decreased from 60,000 canvasbacks in the 1960s to about 25,000 birds in the early 1990s.

Habitat Use and Behavior

Unlike most ducks, canvasbacks are dependent on aquatic habitat throughout their life cycle including the breeding period (Hohman et al. 1995). They are found in estuarine and lacustrine habitats throughout California (Zeiner et al. 1990). They are benthivores that feed in shallow waters over and near intertidal mudflats (Cogswell 1977). They prefer shallow depths with 80% of canvasbacks recorded in areas of less than 3 meters depth and 60% in areas less than 2 m depth (Accurso 1992). Their use of shallow areas of <0.99 m was twice the proportion of the availability of those areas. Canvasbacks use salt evaporation ponds of low (20-33 ppt) or medium (34-63 ppt) salinity in medium-sized ponds (2-2.25 km^2). They generally roost in open water areas.

Foraging – Canvasbacks are strongly associated with foraging on aquatic plants, including wild celery (*Vallisneria americana*) with which it shares a similar scientific name. Early diet studies suggested canvasbacks foraged mostly on plants (80%) with some animal (20%) prey (Cottam 1939, Palmer 1975); food items included

Waterfowl & Shorebirds

wild celery, sago, bulrush seeds, and mollusks. In Chesapeake Bay, when wild celery, widgeon grass, eelgrass, and sago (Stewart 1962) decreased due to turbidity, nutrient enrichment, sedimentation, and salinity changes, canvasbacks switched diets to mollusks primarily (Perry and Uhler 1988). Birds on Humboldt Bay were found to consume sago pondweed, widgeon grass, and clams (Yocom and Keller 1961). Invertebrates are now their principal foods in winter (Zeiner et al. 1990). Canvasbacks in San Francisco Bay fed predominantly on 88% (South Bay) and 98% (North Bay) mollusks by volume (CDFG, unpubl. rept.). Canvasbacks may have to forage longer and consume greater quantities of clams to obtain the nutritive values obtained from aquatic plants such as wild celery (D. Jorde and M. Haramis, pers. comm.). They have a crepuscular feeding pattern (Zeiner et al. 1990).

Roosting – Canvasbacks generally roost on open water areas. They are found in larger salt evaporation ponds.

Movement – No information.

Conservation And Management

Canvasbacks are the least abundant, widely distributed game duck. They have had special hunting protection during several periods including 1936-37, 1955-74 and the present time (Anderson 1989). The goal for the continental population established by the North American Waterfowl Management Plan is 540,000 (USFWS and CWS 1994).

Contaminant Risks – Studies conducted on contaminants in canvasbacks (Miles and Ohlendorf 1995, Ohlendorf et al. 1986) indicate elevated tissue concentrations in the Estuary. Recent invasions of the Asian clam (*Potamocorbula amurensis*) indicate an exponential increase in this exotic species which may triple the concentration of selenium (Luoma and Linville 1995) in prey likely to be consumed by canvasbacks.

Disturbance – Canvasbacks may be disturbed by boats, aircraft, people, and pets. They may avoid preferred foraging areas during the day but may use these areas at night. They will use undisturbed open water roosting areas near feeding sites when available.

Recommendations

San Francisco Bay is one of the three largest wintering areas for canvasbacks in North America. The San Pablo Bay National Wildlife Refuge was established to protect canvasbacks. Canvasback numbers in the Estuary have decreased substantially over the past 20 years to about 20,000 birds. This trend may be reversed by supporting more shallow, open water habitats (<2 m in depth) with dense mollusk populations and undisturbed roosts, particularly in the North Bay and Suisun,

where they have historically been most abundant. This habitat type is also crucial to scaup, which are declining continentally.

Regionally, the most important areas for canvasback are North Bay and Suisun, although the other regions provide significant support as well. Important habitat elements to consider for canvasbacks include tidal channels; bottom; open water; mudflat; eelgrass; perennial pond; and mouths of rivers, creeks, and sloughs. Ideal pond size appears to be 1.75 - 2.25 km². Undisturbed roost sites should be at or within 2 km of foraging areas. Marshes managed for canvasback should have shallow (<2 m) open water. Salt ponds (used for feeding and roosting) managed for canvasback should have low salinity, between 34 ppt and 64 ppt.

Habitat goals for the region include increasing the current acreage of lagoons (with >2.25 km² undisturbed resting area), managed marsh, treatment ponds (with depths managed for birds), low-salinity salt ponds, and tidal reach (valuable foraging area). The current acreage of intertidal flat and shallow bay or strait is unlikely to increase, but should be maintained as feeding areas.

Suisun – The shallows of northern Suisun Bay are critical for support of canvasbacks. Other areas of importance within the Suisun subregion include the middle of Honker Bay, the shallows north of the shipping channel, and Benicia State Park. The shallows in northern Suisun Bay show high use, with counts of a few thousand birds. The middle of Honker Bay is moderately used by thousands of birds. The shallow water north of the shipping channel and the area around Benicia State Park are both moderately used by hundreds of birds. To achieve the recommended increase of the subregional population, there must be an increase in the area of large brackish shallow water. Habitat goals for the Suisun subregion include maintaining the current acreage of managed marsh, shallow bay and strait, and intertidal flat, and increasing the current acreages of lagoon, treatment pond, and tidal reach.

North Bay – Canvasbacks are most abundant in the North Bay subregion. Ponds 1AN and 1N are used by thousands of birds, and Ponds 3N, 4N, 5N are used by many thousands of birds. White Slough is also heavily used (many thousands of birds), and the marsh near Slaughterhouse Point is moderately used by thousands of birds. Birds also use the Point Pinole area by the many thousands. The mudflats near China Camp and Hamilton Air Field are moderately used by thousands of birds. We recommend restoring this subregional population by increasing large brackish shallow water areas. If Ponds 3-5 of the salt ponds are altered, suitable alternative habitats must be provided or the population may decrease substantially.

Habitat goals for the North Bay subregion include maintaining the current acreage of intertidal flat and shallow bays or straits, and increasing areas of lagoons, managed marsh, low salinity salt pond, treatment pond, and tidal reach.

Central Bay – The Berkeley Marina and Emeryville Crescent are both lightly used by a few hundred birds. Point Isabel and the Albany mudflats are used by a few hundred birds. Richardson Bay, Candlestick Point, and the shallows around the Oakland Airport also are used by hundreds of birds. To increase the limited population, increase large brackish shallow water areas. Habitat goals for the Central Bay subregion include maintaining the current acreage of intertidal flat and shallow bays or straits, and increasing areas of lagoon, managed marsh, low salinity salt pond, treatment pond, and tidal reach.

South Bay – Most bayside salt ponds are used by thousands of birds. Some ponds are used very heavily by many thousands of birds. Deep open water habitat is not used. The areas of Mowry Slough and Coyote Creek also receive moderate use by thousands of birds. We recommend maintaining the subregional population. An increase of large, shallow (<6 ft.), low salinity (less than 33 ppt) water areas would be beneficial. If salt ponds are altered, suitable alternative habitat must be provided.

Habitat goals for the South Bay subregion include maintaining the current acreage of intertidal flat and shallow bays or straits, and increasing areas of lagoon, managed marsh, low salinity salt pond, treatment pond, and tidal reach.

Research Needs

Information is needed on region-specific population relationships, diet effects, and cross-seasonal studies of diet and contaminants in their life cycle.

References

Accurso, L.M. 1992. Distribution and abundance of wintering waterfowl on San Francisco Bay, 1988-1990. Unpubl. Master's thesis. Humboldt State Univ. Arcata, CA. 252pp.

Anderson, M.G. 1989. Species closures – a case study of the canvasback. Proc. Int. Waterfowl Symp. 6: 41-50.

Bellrose, F.C. 1980. Ducks, geese and swans of North America. Stackpole Books, Harrisburg, PA. 540 pp.

Bellrose, F.C., T.G. Scott, A.S. Hawkins and J.B. Low. 1961. Sex ratios and age ratios in North American ducks. Illinois Natur. Hist. Surv. Bull. 27:391-474.

Cogswell, H.L. 1977. Water birds of California. Univ. of Ca. Press. Berkeley. 399pp.

Cottam, C. 1939. Food habits of North American diving ducks. USDA Tech. Bull. No. 643. 140pp.

Erickson, R.C. 1948. Life history and ecology of the canvas-back, *Nyroca valisineria* (Wilson) in southeastern Oregon. Ph.D. thesis, Iowa State Coll., Ames, IA. 324pp.

Geis, A.D. 1959. Annual and shooting mortality estimates for the canvasback. J. Wildl. Mgmt. 23:253-261.

Grinnell, J. and M.W. Wythe. 1927. Directory to the bird-life of the San Francisco Bay region. Pacific Coast Avifauna No. 18, Cooper Ornith. Club.

Hochbaum, H.A. 1944. The canvasback on a prairie marsh. Am. Wildl. Inst., Washington, DC. 201pp.

Hohman, W.L., G.M. Haramis, D.G. Jorde, C.E. Korschgen and J.Y. Takekawa. 1995. Canvasback Ducks. *In:* E.T. LaRoe, G.S. Farris, C.F. Puckett, P.D. Doren and M.J. Mac (eds). Our living resources. U. S. Dept. Int., Nat. Biol. Serv., Washington, D. C. pp. 40.43

Josselyn, M. 1983. The ecology of San Francisco Bay tidal marshes: a community profile. U.S. Fish and Wildl. Serv. FWS/OBS-83/23. 102pp.

Lensink, C.J. 1964. Distribution of recoveries from bandings of ducklings. U.S. Fish Wildl. Serv., Spec. Sci. Rep. Wildl. 89. 146pp.

Luoma, S.N. and R. Linville. 1995. A comparison of selenium and mercury concentrations in transplanted and resident bivalves from north San Francisco Bay. *In:* San Francisco Estuary Institute (eds). Regional monitoring program for trace substances 1995 annual report. pp. 160-170.

Miles, A.K. and H.M. Ohlendorf. 1995. Environmental contaminants in canvasbacks wintering on San Francisco Bay, California. Ca. Dept. Fish and Game 79:28-38.

Nichols, J.D. and G.M. Haramis. 1980. Sex-specific differences in winter distribution patterns of canvasbacks. Condor 82:406-416.

Ohlendorf, H.M., R.W. Lowe, P.R. Kelly, T.E. Harvey and C.J. Stafford. 1986. Selenium and heavy metals in San Francisco Bay diving ducks. J. Wildl. Mgmt. 50:64-70.

Olson, D.P. 1964. A study of canvasback and redhead breeding populations, nesting habitats, and productivity. Ph.D. diss., Univ. Minnesota, St. Paul. 100pp.

Palmer, R.S. 1975. Handbook of North American birds. Vol. III. Yale Univ. Press, New York. 560pp.

Perry, M. and F.M. Uhler. 1988. Food habits and distribution of wintering canvasbacks, *Aythya valisineria*, on Chesapeake Bay. Estuaries 11: 57-67.

Rienecker, W.C. 1985. An analysis of canvasbacks banded in California. Ca. Dept. Fish and Game 71:141-149.

Serie, J.R., D.L. Trauger and J.E. Austin. 1992. Influence of age and selected environmental factors on reproductive performance of canvasbacks. J. Wildl. Mgmt. 56:546-555.

Stewart, R.E. 1962. Waterfowl populations in the upper Chesapeake region. U. S. Fish Wildl. Serv. Spec. Sci. Rep. Wildl. 65. Washington, DC. 208pp.

Trauger, D.L. 1974. Looking out for the canvasback, Part I. Ducks Unlimited 38:12-15, 30, 36.

Trauger, D.L. and J.H. Stoudt. 1974. Looking out for the canvasback, Part II. Ducks Unlimited 38:30-31, 42, 44, 45, 48, 60.

U.S. Fish and Wildlife Service (USFWS). *In preparation*. Diked baylands wildlife study. A study of Wildlife use of diked, seasonal wetlands around San Francisco Bay, 1982-1989.

U.S. Fish and Wildlife Service and Canadian Wildlife Service (USFWS and CWS). 1994. North American waterfowl management plan, 1994 update: expanding the commitment. U. S. Fish and Wildl. Serv. Washington, D.C. 40pp.

Woolington, D.W. 1993. Sex ratios of wintering canvasbacks in Louisiana. J. Wildl. Mgmt. 57:751-757.

Yocum, C.F. and M. Keller. 1961. Correlation of food habits and abundance of waterfowl in eastern Washington. J. Wildl. Mgmt. 24:237-250.

Zeiner, D. C., W. F. Laudenslayer Jr., K. E. Mayer and M. White (eds). 1990. California's wildlife. Volume II: Birds. Calif. Resourc. Agency, Dept. Fish and Game. Sacramento.

Personal Communications
G. Michael Haramis, National Biological Service
Dennis G. Jorde, National Biological Service

Surf Scoter

Melanitta perspicillata

A. Keith Miles

Introduction

Surf scoters are the least studied of the North American waterfowl (Johnsgard 1975, Palmer 1976). San Francisco Bay appears to be the most important inshore habitat in the eastern Pacific, south of the Straits of Georgia and Puget Sound (Martell and Palmisano 1994, Small 1994). This species is representative of sea ducks that primarily use deeper, open water habitat. Associated species are white-winged scoters (*M. fusca*), black scoters (*M. nigra*), and red-breasted mergansers (*Mergus serrator*).

Description

Scoters are Anatid sea ducks of the Tribe Mergini. The surf scoter is the most common of the three North American scoters that winter at San Francisco Bay (Bellrose 1980). Adult surf scoters measure about 43 - 53 cm in length with a wing span of 76 - 86 cm, and weigh 0.7 - 1.1 kg. Adults are nearly identical in size to black scoters and slightly smaller than white-winged scoters. Male surf scoters have a distinctive hump on the bill. The coloration of all three scoters is also similar; the distinct difference is that adult male surf scoters have a white patch on the crown and nape. However, first-year males are all black and very similar in appearance to black scoters. Female and immature surf scoters have a dusky brown coloration, similar to white-winged scoters (except the latter have distinct patches of white on the wings). Surf scoters rarely vocalize, but do emit a low, guttural sound. The distinct whistling sound during flight is generated by air passing over their wings.

Breeding Biology – Scoters prefer fresh water, shallow, rocky, Arctic lakes for breeding. The breeding chronology begins with egg-laying in early June, and hatching the second or third week of July (Savard and Lamothe 1991). Nests are built away from water on the ground, and consist of a shallow excavation lined with

Courtesy USGS/NBS

Waterfowl & Shorebirds

grasses and feathers. Egg clutch and brood size are unclear because of the few observations made. Those observations have indicated clutches of about five eggs, and broods of about five young, but brood amalgamation appeared common.

Migration Ecology – Surf scoters migrate directly to the oceanic coasts from the breeding areas. Three times more birds migrate to the Pacific Coast than to the Atlantic Coast. Their subsequent southward migratory destination appears conditioned to the preferred stopover and wintering destination of individual flocks.

Wintering Ecology – Surf scoters use both offshore and inshore marine and estuarine habitats during winter. Marine habitat encompasses the entire Pacific Coast from the Aleutian Islands, Alaska to central Baja California, Mexico (Root 1988). The Canadian inside passage appears crucial as habitat. Surf scoters are common along the California coast from October to May, and San Francisco Bay appears to be the most important inshore habitat in the eastern Pacific, south of the Straits of Georgia and Puget Sound (Martell and Palmisano 1994, Small 1994).

Distribution and Abundance

North America – The breeding range of surf scoters extends from patchy sites in western Alaska, extensive occupation across the Northwest Territories to Hudson Bay, and east of the Bay into Labrador (Bellrose 1980). The wintering range extends from the Aleutian Islands to Baja California on the west coast, and from the Bay of Fundy to Florida on the east coast. They also occur on the Great Lakes and on inland bodies of water along the coastal states, but are most common either on nearshore marine waters or calm estuaries. Bellrose (1980) estimated wintering populations of surf scoters in North America at about 130,000 birds.

Pacific Coast – The wintering range extends from the Aleutian Islands to Baja California on the Pacific Coast.

San Francisco Bay – Most counts of scoters lump the three species together. Surf scoters comprise the majority of scoters observed on San Francisco Bay. Accurso (1992) identified scoters as the second most abundant waterfowl on San Francisco Bay in two wintering seasons between 1988 and 1990, accounting for about 20% of the waterfowl counted. Scoters are common throughout the open waters of San Francisco Bay. Scoters can be observed close to land near China Camp and Hamilton Airfield; near shore at the Presidio cliffs, and off Point Molate in the Central Bay; and near shore on open waters off Coyote Hills, the Edwards National Wildlife Refuge fishing pier, the bayshore levee at Foster City, and the San Mateo County NWR Fishing Pier (pers. obs.; Sequoia Audubon Society 1985).

Suisun – Flocks numbering in the high hundreds were found on the open waters of Suisun Bay in early December. Scoter numbers increased to the upper hundreds and low thousands (<10,000) later in the winter, with their distribution shifting from north to south Suisun Bay, and east to Chipps Island and Honker Bay (**Figure 6.8**). Also, scoter numbers ranged from the low hundreds to low thousands (<10,000) in the Carquinez Straits region east of Suisun as the winter season progressed.

North Bay – Beginning in mid-October, scoters were common throughout north San Francisco Bay, with the larger flocks (numbering in the mid- to upper hundreds) common near the Hamilton Airfield (Accurso 1992). By mid- to late winter, scoters were widespread in the North Bay with some flocks numbering in the thousands (**Figure 6.8**).

Central Bay – Scoters have been identified as the most abundant waterfowl in this region (Accurso 1992). Peak numbers of about 24,000 to 30,000 have been counted on the open waters of the Central Bay in the early wintering season (**Figure 6.8**).

South Bay – As the second most abundant waterfowl in this region, numbers of scoters were highest in December (about 9,500 - 11,000) in the two winters between 1989 and 1990 on the open waters in this region (Accurso 1992; **Figure 6.8**).

Historical Information

No information.

Population Trends

Mid-winter surveys (conducted in January) of scoters indicated a high of about 72,000 scoters on San Francisco Bay in 1991, and a low of 1,200 birds in 1996 (Trost 1997). Their numbers rebounded to about 28,000 in 1997. Mid-winter surveys of the western states and Mexico indicated about 69,500 scoters, which was about 20% lower than the ten year average (1987 - 1996).

Habitat Use and Behavior

Foraging – Surf scoters are strong divers, and have been observed foraging in the 2-10 m depth range (pers obs., Sequoia Audubon Society 1985, Root 1988). Scoters feed in the open waters of the Bay, and also along the cliffs at the entrance to San Francisco Bay. Their habit is to dive in the areas on the trailing side of waves breaking at the cliffs (Sequoia Audubon Society 1985). They have also been observed feeding on rock-bound intertidal or shallow subtidal mussels or scallops at high tide. Their preferred diet consists of clams inhabiting silty or sandy substrate, or mussels attached to hard substrata such as pilings or rocks (Vermeer and Bourne 1982), but are likely to opportunistically consume other molluscs and also crustaceans.

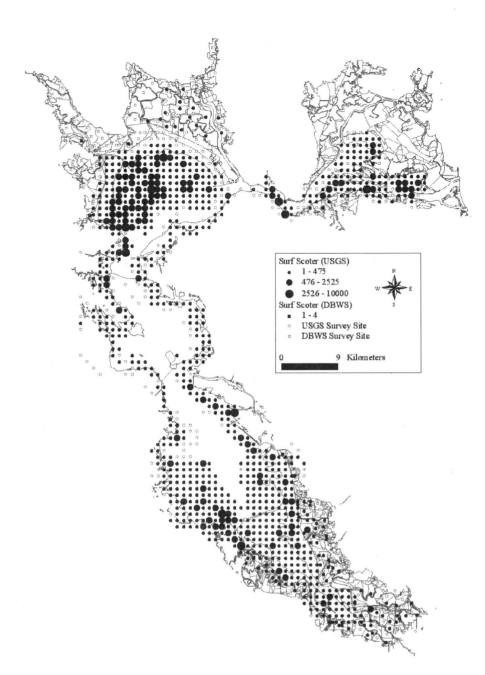

Figure 6.8 Maximum Counts of Surf Scoter

Open water data from the USGS Study of Waterfowl in Open Bays and Salt Ponds, 1988-1990 (USGS, unpubl.), John Takekawa (unpubl. data), and Accurso 1992.

Bayland data from the Diked Baylands Wildlife Study (DBWS), 1982-1989 (USFWS, *in prep.*).

Surf Scoter (USGS)
- · 1 - 475
- ● 476 - 2525
- ● 2526 - 10000

Surf Scoter (DBWS)
- ■ 1 - 4
- ○ USGS Survey Site
- ▫ DBWS Survey Site

0   9 Kilometers

Roosting – Surf scoters roost almost exclusively on open, coastal bay, or lake waters.

Movement – Movement seems related to foraging, roosting, or disturbance. Like most diving waterfowl, surf scoters probably conduct short-distance moves from area to area as prey are depleted. Flocks have been observed at the Bay riding the high tide to shore to feed on blue mussels along the rocky shore or ribbed mussels in the cordgrass habitat.

Conservation and Management

Contaminant Risks – Several studies have indicated elevated concentrations of elemental contaminants in scoters inhabiting San Francisco Bay (e.g., Ohlendorf and Fleming 1988; CDFG, unpubl.). The consequences of elevated selenium or mercury to survival or productivity of these scoters have not been determined.

Disturbance – Surf scoters appear very intolerant of human disturbance, particularly motorboats. Their foraging movement into the intertidal zones at high tide occurs at areas secluded from human disturbance or at night. Overflights by birds of prey also were observed to elicit panic response by flocks roosting on open water. Incidental mortality of scoters was recorded from commercial fishing with gill nets (Heneman 1983). However, regulations curtailing coastal gill net fishing have probably reduced the number of birds killed to those caught in nets accidentally set adrift.

Recommendations

The important habitats used by scoters are the open waters throughout San Francisco Bay, and the underlying sediments for foraging. Scoters will forage in low tidal wetlands during high tide. Scoters are susceptible to bioaccumulation of contaminants. Restoration of the Bay's shorelines to tidal wetlands should include studies of the potential for mobilization of contaminants that may be sequestered in existing soils or sediments.

Scoters primarily use the open coast. San Francisco Bay appears to be important to populations of scoters that may either be historically affiliated with the Bay or that seek refuge in the Bay during inclement weather on the coast. The Bay (all subregions) provides very crucial wintering habitat for these birds. Besides open water, other important habitat elements include clay-silt substrate, sand substrate, and rock substrate. The primary recommendation to support scoters is to maintain the current acreages of shallow bay, intertidal flat, and low tidal marsh.

Suisun – Maintain current acreages of shallow bay, intertidal flat, and low tidal marsh.

North Bay – All open waters of the North Bay are used by scoters, and particularly important are the open waters of of China Camp and Hamilton Airfield (for foraging and wind protection), and the deeper water off of Wilson Point. Maintain current acreages of shallow bay, intertidal flat, and low tidal marsh.

Central Bay – All open waters near the shoreline in the Central Bay are used by scoters. The feeding habitat near the shore at the mouth of the Bay is particularly important, and eelgrass beds sporadically distributed in Central Bay may be important. Maintain current acreages of shallow bay, intertidal flat, and low tidal marsh.

South Bay – Open waters throughout the South Bay are important for scoters. Of particular importanne are the open waters off of the Coyote Hills area and south of Coyote Hills, and the open waters near Foster City. Maintain current acreages of shallow bay, intertidal flat, and low tidal marsh.

Research Needs

Surf scoters are the least studied of the North American waterfowl (Johnsgard 1975, Palmer 1976), but recent die-offs in Alaska has raised concern about these ducks (Bartonek 1993). Elevated concentrations of contaminants have been detected in scoters, particularly in the Suisun region. Inhabitants of this region should be radio-tagged in order to determine their wintering movements and survival, and also their survival and productivity on the breeding grounds as compared to other sub-populations of scoters.

Acknowledgments

Special thanks to Janice Alexander (Biological Resources Division) for compiling and synthesizing data and maps on waterfowl distribution at San Francisco Bay, and thanks also to Bob Trost, U.S. Fish and Wildlife Service, and Mike Casazza and Mike Miller, Biological Resources Division, U.S. Geological Survey.

References

Accurso, L.M. 1992. Distribution and abundance of wintering waterfowl on San Francisco Bay, 1988-1990. Unpubl. Master's thesis. Humboldt State Univ. Arcata, CA. 252pp.

Bartonek, J.C. 1993. Sea duck and merganser hunting status, and harvests in Alaska and Pacific coastal states. U.S. Fish and Wildl. Serv., Portland, OR. 23pp.

Bellrose, F.C. 1980. Ducks, geese and swans of North America. 3rd ed. Stackpole Books, Harrisburg, PA. 540pp.

California Department of Fish and Game (CDFG). unpublished. Selenium verification studies.

Cogswell, H.L. 1977. Water birds of California. Univ. of Ca., Berkeley, CA. 399pp.

Heneman, B. 1983. Gillnets and seabirds 1983. Pt. Reyes Bird Observ. Newsletter. 63:1-3.

Johnsgard, P.A. 1975. Waterfowl of North America. Indiana Univ. Press, Bloomington, IN. 575pp.

Martell, A.M. and A.W. Palmisano. 1994. The status of sea ducks in the north Pacific Rim: toward their conservation and management. Trans. 59th No. Am. Wild. & Natur. Resour. Conf. Spec. Session 1. Conserving Internatl Resources of the North Pacific Rim. 59:27-49.

Ohlendorf, H.M. and W.J. Fleming. 1988. Birds and environmental contaminants in San Francisco and Chesapeake Bays. Mar. Pollut. Bull. 19:487-495.

Palmer, R.S. 1976. Handbook of North American birds. Volume 3, Part 2, Waterfowl. Yale Univ. Press, New Haven, CT. 560pp.

Root, T. 1988. Atlas of wintering North American birds. An atlas of Christmas bird count data. Univ. of Chicago Press. Chicago, IL. 312pp

Savard, J-P. L. and P. Lamothe 1991. Distribution, abundance, and aspects of breeding ecology of black scoters, *Melanitta nigra* and surf scoters, *M. perspicillata*, in Northern Quebec. Canad. Field-Natural. 105:488-496.

Sequoia Audubon Society. 1985. San Francisco peninsula birdwatching. Sequoia Audubon Society, Belmont, CA. 137pp.

Small, A. 1994. California birds. Their status and distribution. Ibis Publ. Co. Vista, CA. 342pp.

Trost, R.E. 1997. Pacific Flyway 1996-97 fall and winter waterfowl survey report. U.S. Fish and Wildl. Serv., Migratory Bird Mgmt. Office, Portland, OR.

Waterfowl & Shorebirds

U.S. Fish and Wildlife Service (USFWS). *In preparation*. Diked baylands wildlife study. A study of wildlife use of diked, seasonal wetlands around San Francisco Bay, 1982-1989.

Vermeer, K. and N. Bourne. 1982. The white-winged scoter diet in British Columbia waters: resource partitioning with other scoters. *In:* D.N. Nettleship, G.A. Sanger and P.F. Springer (eds). Marine birds: their feeding ecology and commercial fisheries relationships. Proceedings of the Pacific Seabird Group Symposium, Seattle, WA. pp 30-38.

Ruddy Duck

Oxyura jamaicensis

A. Keith Miles

Introduction

This diving duck is widespread and has one of the largest wintering concentrations in the San Francisco Bay Estuary. It uses a variety of open wetlands, including managed marsh areas, but prefers salt ponds found around the perimeter of San Francisco Bay. It is grouped with the bufflehead (*Bucephala albeola*), which uses similar habitat.

Description

These ducks, also known as "stifftails," are Anatid ducks of the Tribe Oxyurini. Adult ruddy ducks are small but full-bodied, measuring about 37 - 41 cm in length, with a wing span of 53 - 61 cm, and weigh 0.3 - 0.7 kg (Bellrose 1980). The ruddy duck's stiff, erect tail is its most pronounced attribute. During breeding season, adult males display a reddish-brown coloration, white throat patch, and exceptionally bright blue bills; both sexes have white cheek patches. Otherwise, males and females are the same dull brown color, except that males maintain a bright white cheek patch.

Courtesy USGS/NBS

Breeding Biology – Suitable breeding habitat consists of stable, fresh or alkaline water that supports emergent vegetation (Johnsgard and Carbonell 1996). Nests are characteristically placed deep into reedbeds with channels or easy access to open water; ruddy ducks will use nest boxes placed in the reeds. Breeding birds apparently require about 0.5 to 1.5 sq. km each, but in some places the density of nests averages one every 0.6 hectares. Males do not defend territories, but will guard an area of about 3 m around a female. Unique male courtship displays consist of "rushing" (swimming or half-swimming, half-flying in hunched position) the female, and "bubbling" (beating the bill rapidly against the breast). Courtship occurs from January into July. Pair bonding is considered loose, lasting only from just before to just after egg-laying. Egg-laying occurs from early April to late August. Ruddy ducks are known to parasitize other nests. Clutch size averages about seven eggs; incubation and rearing both average about 25 days each (Gray 1980).

Migration Ecology – Long-distance migratory behavior of ruddy ducks is not well-defined. Substantial variations have been recorded for size of migrant flocks, and it is suspected that migration at night is common (Bellrose 1980). Ruddy ducks sometimes migrate in flocks with other species of waterfowl. The best known migration route to eastern wintering areas is from the northern prairie wetlands to the Chesapeake Bay region. Migration corridors for western populations were suggested to extend from western Canada to Utah to California, and from Utah or California to the west coast of Mexico. Fall migration occurs from about mid-September into December; spring migration occurs from about February through April.

Wintering Ecology – More than half of the ruddy ducks in North America winter at or near the Pacific Coast from southern Canada to Mexico. The majority (85%) of these winter in California, primarily at San Francisco Bay. Coastal wintering areas consist of shallow-depth lagoons or estuaries. Protected or managed wetland areas around San Francisco Bay (particularly salt ponds in the South and North bays) and elsewhere in California are crucial to inland wintering populations (Root 1988).

Distribution and Abundance

North America – The breeding range of ruddy ducks extends from central British Columbia east to southern Manitoba and Minnesota, south from the western portion of the central states throughout the western states. Second to the Pacific Coast, the wintering range along the Atlantic Coast is mainly Chesapeake Bay (estimated 40,000 birds), with smaller groups further south; ruddy ducks that winter along the Gulf Coast States of the U.S. are estimated at 20,000 (Johnsgard and Carbonell 1996). Current

Figure 6.9 Maximum Counts of Ruddy Duck

Open water data from the USGS Study of Waterfowl in Open Bays and Salt Ponds, 1988-1990 (USGS, unpubl. data), John Takekawa (unpubl. data), and Accurso 1992.

Bayland data from the Diked Baylands Wildlife Study (DBWS),1982-1989 (USFWS, *in prep.*).

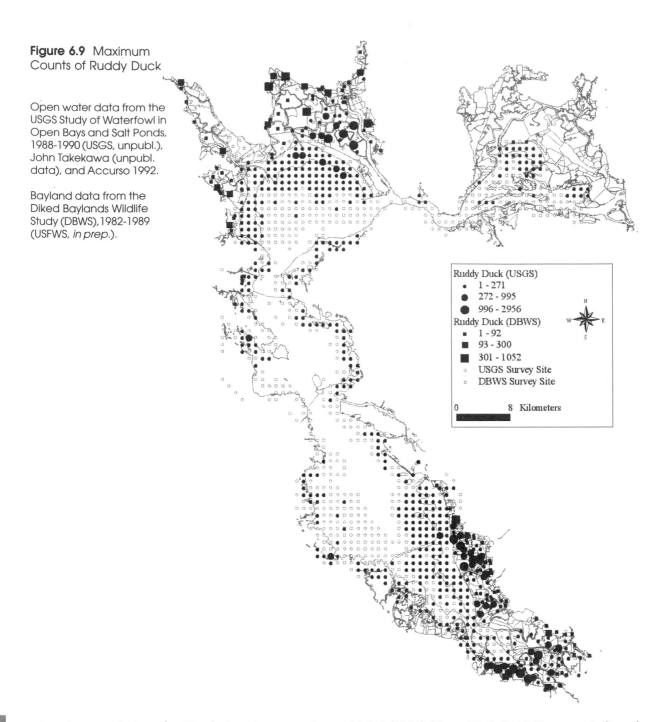

Ruddy Duck (USGS)
· 1 - 271
● 272 - 995
● 996 - 2956

Ruddy Duck (DBWS)
▪ 1 - 92
■ 93 - 300
■ 301 - 1052
○ USGS Survey Site
▫ DBWS Survey Site

0   8 Kilometers

wintering populations for North America are estimated at about 180,000.

Pacific Coast – About 85% of the estimated 122,000 (Trost 1997) ruddy ducks that migrated to the west coast of North America stayed in California in winter 1997. According to Bellrose (1980) the primary wintering areas are San Francisco Bay, Imperial and San Joaquin valleys, and southern California coastal bays. The remaining ruddy ducks migrate to the west coast of Mexico.

San Francisco Bay – The greater number of ruddy ducks that migrate to California overwinter at San Francisco Bay. Since 1986, based on mid-winter surveys, numbers have ranged from about 1,900 (1996) to

28,300 (1991) (Trost 1997). In 1997, surveys indicated about 6,200 ruddy ducks on the Bay.

Suisun – Ruddy ducks infrequently inhabit Suisun, and primarily have been observed as individuals on managed marshes or stop-over migrants on open waters (**Figure 6.9**).

North Bay – Salt ponds in the northern Bay support the second highest numbers of ruddy ducks in the San Francisco Bay region, with counts from about 1,500 to 10,000 ducks in the two winter seasons between 1988 and 1990 (Accurso 1992). Smaller flocks numbering in the hundreds were observed in the near shore, northern-most, and northwestern waters of the Bay (**Figure 6.9**).

Central Bay – Observations of ruddy ducks were usually limited to individuals in the near shore waters, or small flocks numbering fewer than 100; however, larger flocks numbering several hundred birds were observed in Richardson Bay on the west side of the Central Bay in mid-November to early December, indicating this area is probably an important stop-over for migrating ducks (Accurso 1992; **Figure 6.9**).

South Bay – Salt ponds located on the eastern and southern shores of the South Bay have supported the greatest numbers of ruddy ducks in the Bay region. These ducks numbered from about 1,300 to 19,000 ducks during the two winters between 1988 and 1990 (Accurso 1992). Smaller flocks numbering in the hundreds were observed in the near shore waters of the South Bay adjacent to the salt ponds (**Figure 6.9**).

Historical Information

No information.

Population Trends

Ruddy duck populations increased about 12 percent in North America between 1965 and 1992 (Trost 1997). The 1997 mid-winter survey that indicated about 122,000 ruddy ducks wintering in the western states and Mexico was 42 % above the 10 year average of surveys from 1987 to 1996 (Trost 1997).

Habitat Use and Behavior

Foraging – Ruddy ducks dive about 1-3 m for their food. They apparently prefer submerged aquatic vegetation, e.g., wigeon-grass or pondweed, but consume more benthic invertebrates during the summer or when vegetation is less available (Tome 1991). Their vegetative preference may be overestimated because soft-bodied insects, mollusks, or crustaceans are indiscernible in gizzards commonly used to determine food habits (Johnsgard and Carbonell 1996). Esophageal contents in ruddy ducks collected at Chesapeake Bay were mostly amphipods and other benthic invertebrates (Tome and Miles, unpubl. data). Ruddy ducks are known to feed both diurnally and nocturnally (Tome 1991). Ruddy ducks observed foraging at the salt ponds and northern and southern San Francisco Bay probably are feeding mostly on invertebrates.

Roosting – Ruddy ducks roost almost exclusively on open waters of protected estuaries, lakes, or ponds. They are most often observed roosting on salt ponds at the northern and southern regions of San Francisco Bay.

Movement – Personal observations of ruddy ducks at Chesapeake Bay indicate local flock movements between roosting and feeding areas, and we suspected that movements occurred more commonly at night. Similar habits

may occur at San Francisco Bay with these ducks moving primarily between salt ponds and nearby Bay waters.

Conservation and Management

Contaminant Risks – On the east coast, ruddy ducks have characteristically been observed wintering in heavily urbanized embayments (e.g., Baltimore Harbor), with no apparent detriment to population numbers (Tome and Miles, unpubl. data). However, when other waterfowl are considered as surrogates, then inorganic elements, such as lead, mercury, or selenium, can be toxic at low concentrations.

Disturbance – Ruddy ducks are intolerant of human presence. However, they seem tolerant of urbanization, i.e., presence of nearby roadways or highways, and moderate levels of pollution. The presence of avian predators elicit flock dispersal and flight.

Recommendations

Any efforts to restore altered wetlands to historically tidal wetlands in the San Francisco Bay region should consider the importance of human-created water impoundments, e.g., salt ponds, to wintering waterfowl populations. San Francisco Bay is the most important wintering estuary for aquatic birds on North America's Pacific Coast. The efforts of the U.S. and Canadian governments in concert with private foundations, such as Ducks Unlimited and the Nature Conservancy, have contributed to the increase in numbers of ruddy ducks and other waterfowl through the acquisition and preservation of breeding habitat. Ruddy duck populations have become dependent on San Francisco Bay's altered habitats for winter-season survival. Intensive studies must be conducted to determine the effects of tidal wetland restorations on avian populations dependent on altered habitats.

The salt ponds of the North Bay are currently the most important area for ruddy ducks, and low salinity salt ponds provide crucial wintering habitat. Other habitat types and areas are used more as migratory stop-over points, while salt ponds are the preferred, crucial habitat. Important habitat elements are clay-silt substrate and sand substrate. Regional goals to support this species would include increasing the current acreage of low salinity salt ponds, and maintaining the current acreages of tidal reach and lagoon.

Suisun – Suisun is currently little used by ruddy ducks, but an increase in the amount of low salinity salt pond may increase bird numbers in this subregion. Population is sparse and widespread in the managed marsh. Important areas include open waters (migratory stop-over) and managed marsh. Goals to support ruddy duck include maintaining the current acreages of managed marsh, tidal reach, and lagoon.

North Bay – The low salinity salt ponds are the single most important habitat for wintering ruddy ducks in the North Bay. These salt ponds supported 25 to 30% of the populations of ruddy ducks that overwintered at San Francisco Bay between 1988 and 1990 (Accurso 1992). Particularly important are Ponds 3N, 6N, 1N, 2N, 4N, 5N, 2AN, 7N, and 1AN. The first six of these ponds were crucial habitat for about 90% of the maximum counts of ruddy ducks monitored in the North Bay in 1988-1990 (Accurso 1992). The nine ponds represent 90% of the habitat (by hectares) used by ruddy ducks, and should be maintained along with the remaining ponds in the North Bay because of currently increasing numbers of these ducks. Goals to support ruddy ducks include maintaining the current acreages of tidal reach and lagoon, and increasing the amount of low salinity salt pond.

Central Bay – Ruddy ducks generally use only open water habitat in the Central Bay. Increasing the amount of low salinity salt ponds in this very urbanized subregion does not seem feasible, though this may increase the subregional population. Richardson Bay appears crucial for stop-over migrants. Goals to support ruddy duck include maintaining the current acreage of tidal reach and lagoon.

South Bay – Low salinity salt ponds are crucial wintering habitat for ruddy ducks in the South Bay region. Populations of ruddy ducks inhabiting the Bay probably are increasing (Trost 1997), and the maintenance of these salt ponds is crucial. Of particular importance are Ponds A1, A2E, A2W, A3N, A3W, A4, A9, A10, A12, A14, A18, AB1, AB2, B1, B2, B3C, B4, B5, B6, B6A, B6C, B7, B8, B8A, B9, B10, B11, B12, B13, B14, M1, M3, M4, N1, N2, N3, N3A, N4, R2, and R3. Of these, 20 ponds supported 90% of the ruddy ducks wintering in south San Francisco Bay between 1988 and 1990 (Accurso 1992). Overall, South Bay salt ponds supported from 55 to 67% of the ruddy ducks wintering at San Francisco Bay during this time period. Groups of ruddy ducks numbering from 6 to 174 ducks were observed on 39 other ponds, which are probably important for localized movements of ducks inhabiting the South Bay. Goals to support ruddy ducks in the South Bay include maintaining the current acreages of low salinity salt ponds, tidal reaches, and lagoons.

Research Needs

Any plans for habitat alteration, including the restoration of salt ponds to tidal wetlands, have to consider the potential impact on the distribution and habitat use by ruddy ducks. Studies are recommended to determine importance of salt ponds for abundance of waterfowl prey in comparison to natural ponds, and the effects of salt pond alterations on ruddy duck distribution, abundance, survival, and behavioral modification. The potential for overcrowding by waterfowl and subsequent increase in avian disease outbreaks that might result from any reduction in salt pond habitat also needs study.

Acknowledgments

Special thanks to Janice Alexander (Biological Resources Division) for compiling and synthesizing data and maps on waterfowl distribution at San Francisco Bay, and thanks also to Bob Trost, U.S. Fish & Wildlife Service, and Mike Casazza and Mike Miller, Biological Resources Division, U.S. Geological Survey.

References

Accurso, L.M. 1992. Distribution and abundance of wintering waterfowl on San Francisco Bay, 1988-1990. Unpubl. Master's thesis. Humboldt State Univ. Arcata, CA. 252pp.

Bellrose, F.C. 1980. Ducks, geese and swans of North America. 3rd ed. Stackpole Books, Harrisburg, PA. 540pp.

Gray, B.J. 1980. Reproduction, energetics, and social structure of the ruddy duck. Ph.D. dissertation thesis, Univ. of Ca., Davis, CA. 158pp.

Johnsgard, P.A and M. Carbonell. 1996. Ruddy ducks and other stifftails. Univ. of Oklahoma Press, Norman, OK. 291pp.

Root, T. 1988. Atlas of wintering North American birds. An atlas of Christmas bird count data. Univ. of Chicago Press. Chicago, IL. 312pp.

Tome, M.W. 1991. A time energy budget for female ruddy ducks breeding in Manitoba. Wilson Bulletin. 103:183-189.

Trost, R.E. 1997. Pacific Flyway 1996-97 Fall and Winter Waterfowl Survey Report. U.S. Fish and Wildl. Serv., Migratory Bird Mgmt. Office, Portland, OR.

U. S. Fish and Wildlife Service (USFWS). *In preparation*. Diked baylands wildlife study. A study of wildlife use of diked, seasonal wetlands around San Francisco Bay, 1982-1989.

Personal Communications

M.W. Tome, U.S. Geological Survey, Biological Resources Division.

Western Snowy Plover

Charadrius alexandrinus

Gary W. Page
Catherine M. Hickey
Lynne E. Stenzel

Introduction

The population of snowy plovers that breeds along the Pacific Coast of the United States and Baja California, Mexico was designated as Threatened by the U.S. Fish and Wildlife Service in March 1993. The Pacific Coast population has declined most likely due to habitat loss and degradation, but also suffers from poor nesting success primarily due to predation. Critical habitat for the plover has been identified and a recovery team was formed. Along the Pacific Coast, San Francisco Bay is the northernmost area supporting over 100 breeding snowy plovers (Page et al. 1991). Salt ponds, their levees, and pond edges, which may mimic historic salt pan habitat in some essential way for the plover, provide almost all known snowy plover nesting habitat in San Francisco Bay today. The potential importance of San Francisco Bay salt pond habitat to the persistence and recovery of the Pacific Coast population of snowy plovers should be considered in any comprehensive management plan for San Francisco Bay wetlands.

Description

The snowy plover is a small (15-17 cm long) shorebird, with a light brown back and cap; white underparts; brown to black forehead bar; brown to black lateral breast patches and cheek patches; short black bill; and black legs.

Breeding Biology – In coastal regions, snowy plovers nest on the ground on barren to sparsely-vegetated beaches and dunes, on salt evaporation pond levees and edges, and along lagoon margins. In inland areas, they nest on the shores of alkaline and saline lakes and on river bars. Their nest is a simple scrape in the ground lined with small pebbles, shell fragments, plant debris, mud chips, or other debris. Females incubate the three-egg clutch during most daylight hours and males incubate at night (Warriner et al. 1986). The incubation period averages 27 days with an additional 4-5 days for egg laying on the California coast. Females typically desert the male and brood at hatching. Males raise broods until the young fledge, about 30 days after hatching. If a nest fails, the female typically renests with the same mate, up to five times per season, until a clutch hatches. The most successful females may have up to three broods per season and the most successful males may have up to two.

Migration Ecology – Along the California Coast, including San Francisco Bay, part of the snowy plover population is resident year round and part is migratory. Birds, which nest along the coast, may migrate north or south for the winter or remain at their nesting site. Most birds which breed at inland locations migrate to the coast for the winter. In winter, birds which breed on the coast and birds which breed inland occur in the same flocks. Migrants begin returning to coastal breeding locations as early as late January or early February, but most migration is from early March to late April. Coastal breeders begin departing for wintering areas in early July and the exodus continues through October.

Wintering Ecology – In winter, snowy plovers are usually found roosting in flocks ranging in size from a few individuals to up to 300 birds. They often sit in footprints or other depressions in the sand. Foraging occurs on sandy beaches, salt evaporation ponds, or tidal flats. Although some individuals defend territories on beaches, most plovers usually forage in flocks.

Distribution and Abundance

North America – The snowy plover breeds along the coast of the Gulf of Mexico, and along the Pacific Coast of the United States and Baja California. Inland, it also breeds in the southern Great Plains, the Great Basin, San Joaquin Valley, and southern desert areas of California. Inland populations (except from San Joaquin Valley and Salton Sea) migrate to the coast for the winter. Current information suggests a breeding population of about 21,000 snowy plovers in the United States (Page et al. 1995).

Pacific Coast – Breeding and wintering occurs from southern Washington to Magdalena Bay, Baja California. Birds breeding in San Francisco Bay are considered part of the coastal breeding population. Currently, an estimated 1,900 snowy plovers breed along the west coast of the United States and at least another 1,900 along the western coast of Baja California (Page et al. 1995).

Courtesy USGS/NBS

Suisun – At most, snowy plovers probably occur in Suisun only rarely.

North Bay – Small numbers of snowy plover have been found nesting on North Bay salt ponds, and have been seen in diked, seasonal wetlands (Feeney, pers. comm.).

Central Bay – Plovers nest at Alameda Naval Air Station, and also wintered at Alameda South Shore into the 1980s (Page et al. 1986).

South Bay – Although a few pairs have been found nesting on levees in salt ponds of San Pablo Bay (i.e. two pairs in 1989), the majority of snowy plovers in San Francisco Bay nest in the South Bay in salt evaporation ponds south of the San Mateo Bridge. Surveys of South Bay salt evaporation ponds and adjacent habitats tallied the following numbers of adult snowy plover during the peak of the breeding season: 1978 (351); 1984 (270); 1989 (216); and 1991 (176). The 1991 survey excluded a portion of the Baumberg Tract where 29 adult plovers had been recorded on the 1989 survey. On all surveys, at least 87% of the adult plovers were found on the eastern side of the Bay using Guadalupe Slough as the division line.

Historical Information

There are no records of snowy plover breeding in San Francisco Bay prior to the construction of salt ponds. This species may have bred on natural playas on the inner fringes of salt marsh which existed prior to conversion of South Bay marshes to salt ponds. Snowy plovers have been documented in San Francisco Bay during winter as early as the late 1800s (Page et al. 1986).

Population Trends

The breeding population along the western coast of the United States has declined and the breeding range has become increasingly fragmented during the past century. On surveys in the late 1970s, the species was absent from 33 of 53 California coastal locations with breeding records prior to 1970 and was missing from parts of San Diego, Ventura and Santa Barbara counties, most of Orange County, and all of Los Angeles County (Page and Stenzel 1981). Along the coast of Washington, Oregon and California combined, there was an approximate 20% decline in the size of the breeding population on surveys between the late 1970s and late 1980s (Page et al. 1991). Within San Francisco Bay, the population also appears to have declined as evidenced by the drop from 351 adults on the 1978 survey to 226 (216 in South Bay) on a 1989 survey (Page et al. 1991).

Habitat Use and Behavior

Foraging – Snowy plovers feed in typical plover fashion, usually pausing, looking, then running to seize invertebrate prey from the surface of a beach, tidal flat,

or salt pan. Plovers also probe shallowly into the sand or mud for prey, or lower their heads and charge open-mouthed at aggregations of flies, snapping the bill at those that are flushed. Only anecdotal information on diet is available. In salt ponds and on beaches, flies (Diptera) are undoubtedly an important prey. On Pacific Coast beaches and tidal flats, the following prey have been recorded in the diet: mole crabs (*Emerita analoga*), small crabs (*Pachygrapsus crassipes*), polychaetes (Neridae, *Lumbrineris zonata*, *Polydora socialis*, *Scoloplos acmaceps*), amphipods (*Corophium* spp., *Ampithoe* spp., *Allorchestes* spp.), sand hoppers (*Orchestoidea* spp.), tanadaceans (*Leptochelia dubia*), flies (Ephydridae, Dolicopodidae), beetles (Carabidae, Buprestidae, Tenebrionidae), clams (*Transennella* spp.), and ostracods (Page et al. 1995). In San Francisco Bay salt evaporation ponds the following prey have been recorded: flies (*Ephydra cinerea*), beetles (*Tanarthrus occidentalis*, Bembidion), moths (*Perizoma custodiata*) and lepidopteran caterpillars (Feeney and Maffei 1991).

Breeding – Feeney and Maffei (1991) monitored snowy plover nests in the Oliver Brothers/Baumberg region salt ponds during the 1989 breeding season. They located 66 nests, and 14 broods from nests which they did not find. Assuming the broods were from nests in locations they were studying, they located a seasonal nest total ranging from one nest per 1.1 hectare (ha) to one nest per 5.8 ha in four subregions of their salt pond study area. From all day watches of parent(s) with broods, they found the daily area covered by a brood ranged from 0.1-5.5 ha and averaged 1.6 ha. They noted that vegetation was used by chicks for hiding and for foraging. Northern harriers were observed hunting in areas where young snowy plovers were the only likely prey; an American kestrel was observed taking a snowy plover chick; and a peregrine falcon was seen taking an adult snowy plover. Ravens, ground squirrels, and California gulls also prey upon snowy plover eggs.

Roosting – In San Francisco Bay, roosts of snowy plovers occur on the salt pans of dry or partly dry salt evaporators, on barren to sparsely-vegetated interior salt pond levees, and on sandy tidal flats. Up to 300 snowy plovers have been found roosting in one salt evaporator in the Baumberg Tract during winter (Feeney and Cogswell, pers. comm.).

Movement – Snowy plovers are known to move between salt pond breeding, foraging, and roosting sites, and mudflat foraging sites during all seasons. A more detailed understanding of snowy plover movements in the San Francisco Bay would require tracking color-banded individuals.

Conservation and Management

Contaminants Risks – Little information is available. In 1996 several snowy plovers at Ocean Beach became oiled after a spill in San Francisco Bay.

Disturbance – Snowy plovers are disturbed by hikers, joggers, dogs off leashes which sometimes deliberately chase them, and by avian predators. It is not uncommon for plovers to fly back and forth over a roosting area in a tight flock for up to 20 minutes after having been attacked by a merlin or a peregrine falcon.

Protective measures – Several measures are used to reduce disturbance to nesting snowy plovers. Some coastal beaches have been closed or roped off. In other areas, a combination of informative signs and fencing of individual nests are used to protect snowy plover nests from predators and people. The U.S. Fish and Wildlife Service removes non-native predators at Monterey and San Francisco bays to improve snowy plover nesting success, as well as adult and chick survival rates.

Recommendations

This is a federally listed threatened species that cannot afford to lose habitat. Plans for tidal marsh restoration should attempt to encourage natural formation of salt pan habitat at bay's edge for potential plover use. A salt evaporation system should be preserved in the South Bay that produces medium to high salinity ponds, and that is large enough to support at least 300 breeding snowy plovers. Several salt pond sites should be provided, rather than one large contiguous salt pond area. South San Francisco Bay has recently had one of the largest breeding concentrations of snowy plovers on the western coast of the United States. The recovery plan for the Pacific Coast population will at minimum require that numbers of plovers in known high concentration sites not be reduced below recent levels.

Habitat elements important to snowy plover include mudflats and sandflats (used for feeding); salt pan (used for nesting and feeding); and unvegetated levees, islets, and beaches (used for nesting, feeding, and roosting). Important geographic regions are South Bay, Central Bay, and North Bay. Regional recommendations to support snowy plover are shown in **Table 6.2**.

Suisun – There is no documentation of snowy plover use of Suisun.

North Bay – Species nests in small numbers on North Bay salt ponds. Some habitat in this region of the Bay should be maintained; however, emphasis should be placed on enhancing habitat in the more heavily-used South and Central bay areas. An area of particular importance in the North Bay is Little Island.

Central Bay – Areas of importance include the Alameda Naval Air Station and the Oakland Airport. Outboard tidal flats from Roberts Landing to San Mateo Bridge should be maintained as foraging habitat.

The Hayward Area Recreation District (HARD) wants to manage the Oliver Brothers' property for snowy plovers. California Deptartment of Fish and Game and the U.S. Fish and Wildlife Service have agreed to this objective for this site. The goal of the management is approximately 50 breeding birds.

South Bay – The goal for the South Bay subregion should be to sustain at least 300 breeding snowy plovers. Areas of importance include East Bay salt ponds between the San Mateo and Dumbarton bridges; salt pond systems south of the Dumbarton Bridge; and Oliver Brothers' property. Detailed recommendations for South Bay are provided in **Table 6.3**.

Research Needs

An up-to-date survey of the size of the breeding snowy plover population in San Francisco Bay is needed to determine if the population is continuing to decline. An effort to band snowy plovers in the San Francisco Bay area, as well as regular breeding and wintering season surveys for color-banded birds are needed to understand juvenile and adult snowy plover dispersal patterns between San Francisco Bay and coastal beaches. An analy-

Table 6.2 Regional Recommendations to Support Western Snowy Plover

Habitat Type	Recommendation
Salt Pond	Maintain sufficient mid- and high salinity salt pond systems to support at least 300 breeding snowy plovers.
Intertidal Flat	Maintain tidal flats outboard of marshes as foraging habitat.
Pan	Manage a salt pond system to provide sufficient salt pan and levees to support at least 300 breeding snowy plovers annually.

Table 6.3 Recommendations to Support Western Snowy Plover in the South Bay

Habitat Type	Recommendation
Salt Pond	Manage a salt pond system which, when combined with the Oliver Bros. property in the Central Bay, annually supports at least 300 nesting snowy plovers.
High Salinity Salt Ponds	Manage Oliver Bros. salt ponds for nesting snowy plovers from mid-March to mid-September.
Intertidal Flat	Maintain outboard tidal flats as foraging habitat.
Pan	Manage salt pond habitat to include sufficient salt pan and levees to support 300 breeding snowy plovers.

sis of breeding habitat characteristics (e.g. soil salinity, vegetative cover) and presence of breeding birds or measures of nesting success would be useful to better understand plover habitat use and to guide future management efforts.

References

Feeney, L.R. and W.A. Maffei. 1991. Snowy plovers and their habitat at the Baumberg area and Oliver salt ponds, Hayward , Calif., March 1989 through May 1990. City of Hayward, Hayward, CA.

Page, G.W. and L.E. Stenzel (eds). 1981. The breeding status of the snowy plover in California. West. Birds 12:1-40.

Page, G.W., F.C. Bidstrup, R.J. Ramer and L.E. Stenzel. 1986. Distribution of wintering snowy plovers in California and adjacent states. West. Birds 17: 145-170.

Page, G.W., L.E. Stenzel, W.D. Shuford and C.R. Bruce. 1991. Distribution and abundance of the snowy plover on its western North American breeding grounds. J. Field Ornithol. 62:245-255.

Page, G.W., J.S. Warriner, J.C. Warriner and P.W.C. Paton. 1995. Snowy plover *(Charadrius alexandrinus)*. *In:* A. Poole and F. Gill (eds).The birds of North America, No. 154. The Academy of Natural Sciences, Philadelphia, PA, and The American Ornithologists' Union, Washington, D.C.

Warriner, J.S., J.C. Warriner, G.W. Page, and L.E. Stenzel. 1986. Mating system and reproductive success of a small population of polygamous snowy plovers. Wilson Bull. 98: 15-37.

Personal Communications

Howard Cogswell, Professor Emeritus, California State University, Hayward, Calif.

Leora Feeney, Principal, Biological Field Services, 1330 8th St. Alameda, Calif. 94501.

Marbled Godwit

Limosa fedoa

Gary W. Page
Catherine M. Hickey
Lynne E. Stenzel

Introduction

San Francisco Bay holds the second largest known wintering concentration of (15,000-20,000) marbled godwits in the world. It is partly for this reason that the godwit was chosen as a focus species by the Wetland Ecosystem Goals Project's Shorebird and Waterfowl Focus Team. Additionally, although marbled godwits are more restricted to estuarine habitats than the willet (*Catoptrophorus semipalmatus*) and the American avocet (*Recurvirostra americana*), their habitat requirements may well represent those of all large shorebird species as a group (e.g. willet, long-billed curlew (*Numenius americanus*), whimbrel (*Numenius phaeopus*), black-bellied plover (*Pluvialis squatarola*), and American avocet). A comprehensive management plan for San Francisco Bay Area wetlands will need to recognize the importance of expansive tidal flats as foraging habitat during ebbing tides for large shorebird species and will need to identify important roosting and alternative foraging habitat during high tides.

Description

The marbled godwit is a large (about 45 cm), mottled, cinnamon-buff and black shorebird, with long dark gray legs and a distinctive long, bicolored, pink and black slightly upturned bill (Palmer 1967, Hayman et al. 1986). The long-billed curlew is of similar coloration and size, but has a long distinctive decurved bill. The willet is also similar in size, but is grayer and has a much shorter straight bill.

Courtesy USGS/NBS

Waterfowl & Shorebirds

Breeding Biology – Although small numbers of marbled godwits breed in tundra areas of Alaska and James Bay (Ontario), most nest on the prairies of the United States and Canada. On the prairies, nesting probably begins in May and extends into August when the last young fledge. Clutch size is four with both sexes incubating for the suspected 21-23 day incubation period. Both sexes attend the precocial young which leave the nest permanently a few hours after hatching (Palmer 1967, Johnsgard 1981).

Migration Ecology – Autumn migration begins in early July and extends into October (and possibly November) with the earliest adults likely beginning to move about a month before the young of the year, as in other shorebirds (Shuford et al. 1989). Although the winter destination of some godwits is the Atlantic coast of Florida and the Gulf of Mexico, most travel to the Pacific coast of the United States and Mexico for winter (Palmer 1967, Hayman et al. 1986). Spring migration may begin in March but is most noticeable in April and May (Palmer 1967, Shuford et al. 1989). Except for the Great Salt Lake, where tens of thousands of marbled godwits stage during spring and fall, migrating godwits are rare during migration in interior wetlands of western North America (including the Central Valley of California; PRBO, unpubl. data). There is some migration of godwits along the Pacific Coast in spring and fall.

Wintering Ecology – This species is very restricted to coastal habitats in winter where it associates most commonly with willets, long-billed curlews, American avocets, and black-bellied plovers. The regions with the largest concentrations of wintering godwits are the coast of California, the western coast of Baja California, and the eastern coast of the Gulf of California (PRBO, unpubl. data; B. Harrington, unpubl data; Morrison et al. 1992, Page et al. 1997).

Distribution and Abundance

North America – The North American (and world) population size of the marbled godwit is likely in the low hundreds of thousands of birds (Page and Gill 1994). During the past 150 years the breeding range of the marbled godwit has shrunk significantly suggesting the population is now smaller than before the colonization of North America by caucasians (Page and Gill 1994).

Marbled godwits breed from the central Prairie Provinces of Canada southward through Montana, the Dakotas and western Minnesota. Small isolated breeding populations also exist in Alaska and at James Bay, Ontario. They winter from California, Texas, and Florida, south to Central America, but rarely to South America (Johnsgard 1981).

Pacific Coast – Along the Pacific Coast, the largest concentrations of wintering godwits are likely on the coast of California, the western coast of Baja California, and the eastern coast of the Gulf of California (PRBO, unpubl. data; B. Harrington, unpubl data; Morrison et al. 1992). Very small numbers of godwits also winter at Willapa Bay on the Washington Coast (PRBO, unpubl. data).

San Francisco Bay – Marbled godwits occur in all regions of San Francisco Bay. The winter population size of as many as 20,000 individuals is the second largest known concentration of wintering marbled godwits in the world (Page et al. 1997). During migration, as many as 32,000 marbled godwits have been recorded in San Francisco Bay (PRBO, unpubl. data).

Suisun – Small numbers (low hundreds) of marbled godwits are found on the tidal flats of Suisun Bay.

North Bay. – Typically about 30% of the Bay population of marbled godwits are found in San Pablo Bay (**Figure 6.10**).

Central Bay – Central San Francisco Bay typically holds only 10-20% of the Bay total of godwits.

South Bay – During all seasons, the largest numbers of marbled godwits occur in south San Francisco Bay, usually 50-60% of the Bay total (**Figure 6.11**).

Historical Information

Godwit populations in California were believed to have decreased markedly in number by 1910 due to market hunting and destruction of breeding habitat (Grinnell et al. 1918). Grinnell and Miller (1944) report that population recovery began about 1910 and was nearly complete by 1944.

Population Trends

There is no information available on how population numbers may have changed in San Francisco Bay historically. Continentally, the breeding range of marbled godwits has shrunk during the past 150 years, and the population has also likely declined (Page and Gill 1994).

Habitat Use and Behavior

Foraging – This species characteristically probes deep into sandy to muddy substrates for invertebrate prey. Tidal flats and sandy beaches are the principal feeding habitat with wet to shallowly-flooded pastures and lawns sometimes used on high tides. Some foraging also occurs in salt marshes and occasionally on rocky reefs. In San Francisco Bay, marbled godwits forage primarily on tidal flats and to a much lesser degree in salt marshes, seasonal wetlands, and possibly salt ponds. Prey of marbled godwits in San Francisco Bay include the marine polychaete (*Neanthes succinea*), the gastropod (*Ilyanassa obsoleta*), and the pelecypods (*Gemma gemma, Mya arenaria, Macoma inconspicua*; Recher 1966). At

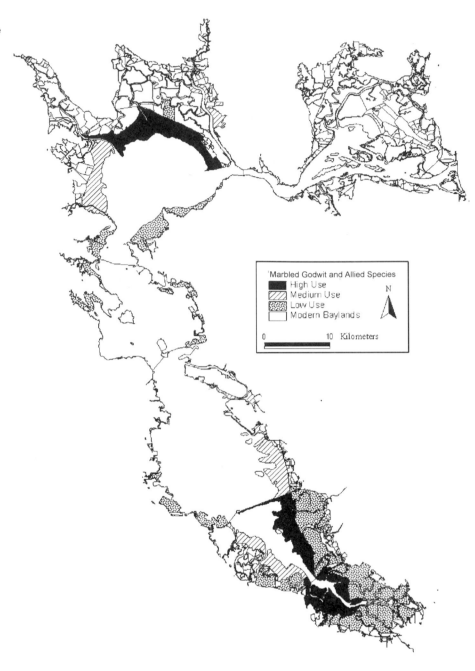

Figure 6.10 Relative Use of Different Baylands Areas by Marbled Godwit, Willet, Whimbrel, and Long-billed Curlew Combined

Data from PRBO Pacific Flyway Project, 1988-1992. Unpublished data (data from Suisun not presented).

Marbled Godwit and Allied Species
- High Use
- Medium Use
- Low Use
- Modern Baylands

N

0   10 Kilometers

Bolinas Lagoon, polychaetes are the godwit's chief prey although amphipods, decapods, small bivalves, fish, adult insects, tanaidaceans, ostracods, and gastropods are also taken (Stenzel et al. 1983). Elsewhere on the California coast, polychaetes, adult flies and gastropods have also been reported in the godwit's diet (Reeder 1951, Holmberg 1975). On sandy beaches, mole crabs (*Emerita analoga*) are also important prey (G. Page, pers. obs.).

Roosting – In San Francisco Bay, godwits congregate into flocks as large as 1,000 or more birds to roost on tidal flats when they are not covered by tides and during high tides in shallowly-flooded salt evaporation ponds, open areas in salt marsh, or other barren to moderately vegetated habitats such as salt pond levees or islands (PRBO, unpubl. data; Kelly and Cogswell 1979).

Movement – Marbled godwits forage in deeper water below the tide line compared to most other shorebirds and usually concentrate near the tide line as it advances and retreats over the flats. Roosting behavior is usually associated with high tides and feeding with low to moderately-high tides. In South San Francisco Bay, Kelly and Cogswell (1979) report the usual distance traveled between roosting and feeding areas to be about 1,000 m. They found color banded individuals consistently used the same feeding and roosting areas and some of these individuals took up residence for eight to nine months during the nonbreeding season.

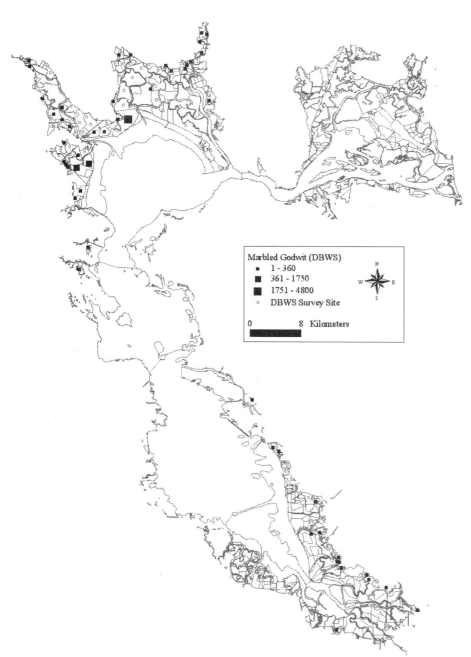

Figure 6.11 Maximum Counts of Marbled Godwit

Bayland data from the Diked Baylands Wildlife Study (DBWS), 1982-1989 (USFWS, *in prep.*).

Marbled Godwit (DBWS)
- ▪ 1 - 360
- ◾ 361 - 1750
- ◼ 1751 - 4800
- ▫ DBWS Survey Site

0   8   Kilometers

Conservation and Management

Contaminant Risks – Little to no information is available.

Disturbance – Roosting or foraging birds may be flushed by people approaching too closely, by avian predators (particularly *Falco peregrinus*), or by unleashed dogs which chase them, as well as other shorebirds. Roosting birds have been flushed by jet skiers and wind surfers (N. Warnock, pers. comm.)

Recommendations

San Francisco Bay holds the largest wintering concentration of marbled godwits in the United States, and numerous large shorebirds use salt pond systems as high tide roosting and foraging habitat. Therefore, we need to preserve enough acreage of salt pond habitat to hold large numbers of all large shorebird species. Since alternative sites should be available, rather than one large contiguous salt pond area, multiple roosts should be located in all regions of the Bay.

Important habitat elements for marbled godwits include mudflats and sandflats (used for foraging and low-tide roosting); pan, beach, and unvegetated levees and islets (used for roosting); and seasonal wetlands (when wet, used for foraging and roosting). Birds also use manmade structures for roosting.

The geographic subregions of most importance to marble godwits are South Bay, North Bay, and Central

Bay. Regional recommendations to support marbled godwits are shown in **Table 6.4**.

Suisun – Small number of marbled godwits forage on the tidal flats of Suisun Bay and roost in the managed wetlands. Areas of importance include the tidal flat of Honker Bay and the managed wetlands. All intertidal flat habitat should be maintained to provide foraging. Some shallow, sparsely vegetated managed marsh should be maintained for roosting.

North Bay – Areas of importance within the North Bay include all areas of tidal flats, seasonal wetlands, and salt ponds. Pilings extending into the Bay and the jetty in Carquinez Straights are important willet roosts. To maintain shorebird populations in the North Bay high tide roosting sites must be available. **Table 6.5** provides detailed recommendations for the North Bay.

Central Bay – It is important to preserve all existing roosts and investigate the potential to establish more roosting sites in the Central Bay. All existing tidal flat outboard of marshes should be maintained, as should Marta's Marsh and Shorebird Marsh in Marin County.

South Bay – All tidal flat is important for foraging and roosting at low tide. Maintain outboard flats and increase tidal flat along channels and in salt marsh. Mid- and high salinity ponds are important for roosting and foraging, and provide American avocet nesting habitat. Maintain some mid- to high salinity ponds as roosting and foraging habitat, and manage the former Oliver Brothers salt ponds for roosting shorebirds from September to March.

If the amount of salt pond habitat is reduced, maintain sufficient and multiple roosting sites for the current population of at least 100,000 large shorebirds. If we want to retain nesting sites for the American avocet, we need to retain some salt ponds or create alternate nesting habitat (salt pan).

References

Grinnell, J. and A.H. Miller. 1944. The distribution of the birds of California. Pac. Coast Avifauna 27.

Grinnell, J., H.C. Bryant and T.I. Storer. 1918. The game birds of California. Univ. of Ca. Press, Berkeley, CA.

Hayman, P., J. Marchant and T. Prater. 1986. Shorebirds: an identification guide. Houghton Mifflin Co., Boston.

Holmberg, N.D. 1975. The ecology of seven species of shorebirds (*Charadrii*) in north Humboldt Bay, California, 1970-1971. Unpubl. master's thesis, Humboldt State Univ, Arcata, CA.

Johnsgard, P.A. 1981. The Plovers, Sandpipers, and Snipes of the World. Univ. of Nebr. Press, Lincoln.

Kelly, P.R. and H.L. Cogswell. 1979. Movements and habitat use by wintering populations of willets and marbled godwits. *In:* F.A. Pitelka (ed). Shorebirds in marine environments. Stud. Avian Biol. No. 2: 69-82.

Morrison, R.I.G., R.K. Ross and S. Torres. 1992. Aerial surveys of nearctic shorebirds wintering in Mexico: Some preliminary results. Canadian Wildl. Service, Progress Notes, No. 201.

Page, G.W. and R.E. Gill. 1994. Shorebirds in western North America: late 1800s to late 1900s. *In:* J.R. Jehl and N.K. Johnson (eds). A century of avifaunal change in western North America. Stud. Avian Biol. No. 15: 147-160 .

Page, G.W., E. Palacios, L. Alfaro, S. Gonzalez, L.E. Stenzel and M. Jungers. 1997. Numbers of wintering shorebirds in coastal wetlands of Baja California, Mexico. J. of Field Ornithology 68: 562-574.

Palmer, R.S. 1967. Species accounts. *In*: G.D. Stout (ed). The shorebirds of North America. Viking Press, New York.

Table 6.4 Regional Recommendations to Support Marbled Godwit

Habitat Type	Recommendation
Intertidal Flat	Maintain tidal flat outboard of marshes; Increase tidal flat in salt marshes by creating wide channels with exposed flat at low tide.
Salt Ponds	Maintain some shallowly-flooded salt ponds for high tide roosting.
Treatment Pond	(Possibly potential roosting areas.)
High Tidal Marsh	Create barren to sparsely vegetated areas above high tide for roosts.
Farmed/Grazed Bayland	(When wet, could provide high tide foraging habitat in winter.)

Table 6.5 Recommendations to Support Marbled Godwit in the North Bay

Habitat Types	Recommendation
Intertidal Flat	Maintain all outboard flats; Increase channel tidal flat in salt marshes.
Salt Pond	Manage former Cargill intake pond for roosting and foraging shorebirds.
Unvegetated Shore	Maintain present acreage
Muted Tidal Marsh	Manage muted tidal diked marsh west of intake ponds and south of Napa Slough for roosting and foraging shorebirds.
Farmed/Grazed Bayland	Enhance seasonal wetlands as high tide foraging and roosting areas.

Waterfowl & Shorebirds

Recher, H.F. 1966. Some aspects of the ecology of migrant shorebirds. Ecology 47: 393-407.

Reeder, W.G. 1951. Stomach Analysis of a group of shorebirds. Condor 53: 43-45.

Shuford, W.D., G.W. Page, J.G. Evens and L.E. Stenzel. 1989. Seasonal abundance of waterbirds at Point Reyes: a coastal perspective. Western Birds 20: 137-265.

Stenzel, L.E., G.W. Page and J. Young. 1983. The trophic relationships between shorebirds and their prey. Unpubl. report of Point Reyes Bird Observatory, Stinson Beach, Calif..

U. S. Fish and Wildlife Service (USFWS). *In preparation*. Diked baylands wildlife study. A study of wildlife use of diked, seasonal wetlands around San Francisco Bay, 1982-1989.

Personal Communications

Brian A. Harrington, National Biological Service.

Nils Warnock, Point Reyes Bird Observatory, Stinson Beach, California.

Black Turnstone

Arenaria melanocephala

Stephen L. Granholm

Introduction

In the San Francisco Estuary, black turnstone is the most numerous of a group of uncommon shorebirds that typically use rocky unvegetated shores. Other species in this group include ruddy turnstone (*Arenaria interpres*), surfbird (*Aphriza virgata*), spotted sandpiper (*Actitis macularia*), black oystercatcher (*Haematopus bachmani*), and wandering tattler (*Heteroscelus incanus*). These species occur in the Estuary as migrants and winter residents. They do not breed here, except for a few pairs of oystercatchers and an occasional pair of spotted sandpipers.

Description

The black turnstone is a short-legged, short-billed shorebird, about 23 cm long, with a blackish back, chest, and legs, and a white belly. In feeding plumage it has some white speckling and a white dot in front of the eye. It displays a striking black and white harlequin pattern in flight.

Distribution and Abundance

North America/Pacific Coast – Black turnstones are found exclusively along the Pacific coast of North America. They breed in western and southern Alaska and winter from southeastern Alaska south to southern Baja California and central Sonora, Mexico (Johnsgard 1981). A few occur inland during migration.

Black turnstones are present along the California Coast from about mid-July to mid-May (Cogswell 1977, McCaskie et al. 1979), and small numbers of nonbreeders remain through the summer (Zeiner et al. 1990).

San Francisco Bay – Total counts of black turnstone for the Estuary have ranged from 40-137 birds in fall, 69-144 in winter, to 212 birds in spring (PRBO, unpubl. data).

Courtesy USGS/NBS

Waterfowl & Shorebirds

Figure 6.12 Relative Use
of Various Tidal Flat and
Adjacent Shoreline
Areas by Rocky Sub-
strate Species (Black
Turnstone, Ruddy
Turnstone, Surfbird,
Spotted Sandpiper,
Black Oystercatcher,
and Wandering Tattler)

Data from PRBO Pacific
Flyway Project, 1988-1992.
Unpublished data.

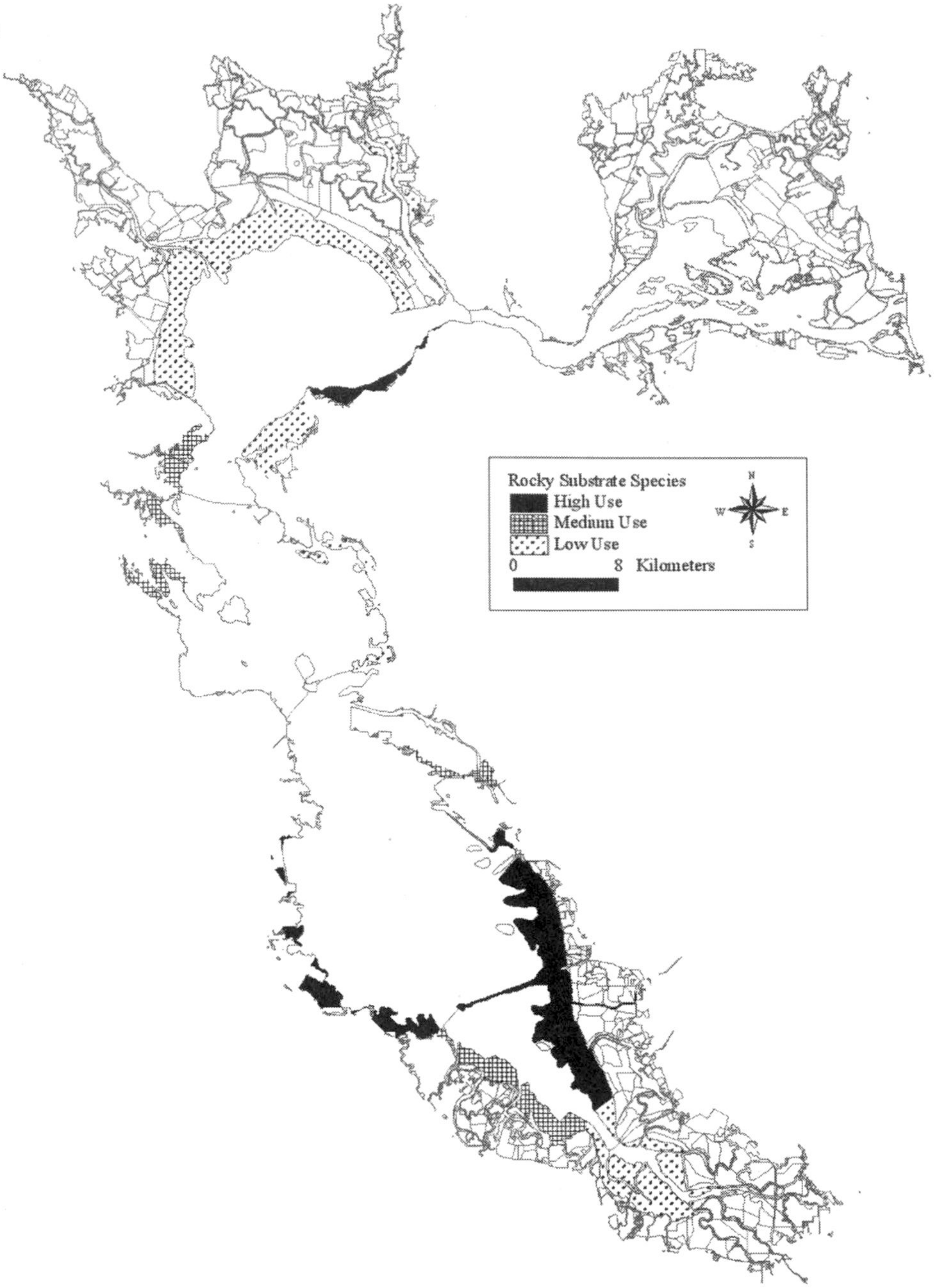

Rocky Substrate Species
■ High Use
▦ Medium Use
⬚ Low Use
0   8 Kilometers

Probably these counts underestimated black turnstone numbers, however, because the counts focused on intertidal mudflats and sandflats, rather than rocky unvegetated shores. Black turnstones do not breed in the Bay Area.

Suisun – Apparently, this species does not occur regularly east of the Carquinez Bridge.

North Bay – Black turnstones are found along the eastern shore of San Pablo Bay, primarily south of Hercules. Few are found on the western and northern shores of San Pablo Bay (north of Point San Pedro; **Figure 6.12**).

Central Bay – This species occurs widely throughout the Central Bay, in suitable habitat (**Figure 6.12**).

South Bay – In South Bay, black turnstones are found primarily north of the San Mateo Bridge, but smaller numbers are found farther south (**Figure 6.12**).

Historical Information

No information.

Population Trends

No information.

Habitat Use and Behavior

Foraging – On their wintering grounds, black turnstones feed primarily on rocky unvegetated shores, including rocky breakwaters and riprap, as well as natural rocky shorelines. They also feed on intertidal mudflats, sandflats, and sandy beaches.

Black turnstones pick food from the surface or turn over seaweed, rocks, or shells to search for prey. They feed mostly on barnacles, limpets, and other small mollusks and crustaceans (Johnsgard 1981, Paulson 1993). Black turnstones usually forage and roost in small flocks of a few birds to a few dozen (Paulson 1993).

Roosting – They roost primarily on rocky unvegetated shores above the tide level, on relatively undisturbed sites such as breakwaters, islets, and inaccessible shorelines.

Movement – Black turnstones move from their foraging grounds to nearby roosting sites at high tides.

Conservation and Management

Contaminant Risks – No specific information.

Disturbance – Frequent disturbance by people and dogs could reduce this species' ability to accumulate sufficient energy reserves for migration.

Recommendations

The black turnstone population in the San Francisco Estuary is probably limited by the availability of rocky intertidal habitat with an adequate food supply. Natural rocky shorelines are very limited in extent, and riprapped shorelines probably have less abundant invertebrate prey than natural shorelines. Like other shorebirds, this species also requires undisturbed roost sites.

Regionwide goals should include maintaining or increasing population levels within the species' current range in the San Francisco Estuary. This will require preservation of natural and semi-natural rocky shorelines and other important feeding and roosting areas, especially areas with an abundant invertebrate population. Riprap habitat is also used by these birds, but a loss of this habitat is acceptable if unavoidable as part of tidal marsh restoration. Preservation of roosting areas must include protection from disturbance by people and dogs.

Areas of importance to black turnstones are primarily found in Central Bay, North Bay (eastern portion), and South Bay (northern portion). Important habitat elements are rocky shore and unvegetated levees and islets (used for roosting). Some of the shorebirds associated with rocky substrates, in particular, ruddy turnstones, also forage on mudflat and sandflat. Regionwide goals thus should include maintaining current acreages of unvegetated shore and intertidal flats.

Suisun – Maintain current acreage of unvegetated shore and intertidal flat.

North Bay – An area of importance to black turnstones is along the eastern shore of the North Bay, south of Hercules. There is currently very little use by this species north of Hercules. Subregional goals should include maintaining current acreage of unvegetated shore and intertidal flat.

Central Bay – Maintain current acreage of unvegetated shore and intertidal flat.

South Bay – Maintain current acreage of unvegetated shore and intertidal flat.

Research Needs

Future surveys should map rocky intertidal habitats in the Estuary and identify significant feeding and roosting areas for black turnstones and other rocky intertidal shorebirds. Foraging studies should be conducted to determine the relative importance of natural and seminatural rocky shorelines, compared to riprap and other habitats.

Acknowledgments

I thank Janice Alexander for her assistance with this account.

References

Cogswell, H.L. 1977. Water birds of California. Univ. of Ca. Press, Berkeley.

Johnsgard, P.A. 1981. The plovers, sandpipers and snipes of the world. Univ. of Nebraska Press, Lincoln.

McCaskie, G., P. De Benedictis, R. Erickson and J. Morlan. 1979. Birds of northern California: an annotated field list. Golden Gate Audubon Society, Berkeley, CA.

Paulson, D. 1993. Shorebirds of the Pacific Northwest. Univ. of Washington Press and Seattle Audubon Society, Seattle.

Zeiner, D.C., W.F. Laudenslayer, Jr., K.E. Mayer and M. White (eds). 1990. Greater white-fronted goose. *In:* California's wildlife, vol. II: Birds. Calif. Dept. Fish and Game. pp 50-51.

Important Data Sets

Page, G.W., J.E. Kjelmyr and L.E. Stenzel. 1989. Results of the 21-24 April 1989 shorebird census of San Francisco Bay and coastal wetlands of the Point Reyes/Bodega Bay area. Pt. Reyes Bird Observatory, Stinson Beach, CA.

Stenzel, L.E. and G.W. Page. 1988. Results of the 16-18 April 1988 shorebird census of San Francisco and San Pablo Bays. Pt. Reyes Bird Observatory, Stinson Beach, CA.

Stenzel, L.E., J.E. Kjelmyr, G.W. Page and W.D. Shuford. 1989. Results of the first comprehensive shorebird census of northern and coastal California coastal wetlands, 8-12 September 1988. Pt. Reyes Bird Observatory, Stinson Beach, CA.

Waterfowl & Shorebirds

Red Knot

Calidris canutus

Catherine M. Hickey
Gary W. Page
Lynne E. Stenzel

Introduction

The red knot is a high-arctic breeder and a long distance migrant. Knots are most abundant on the Pacific coast of North America during spring migration and less abundant during fall (Page et al. 1979, Paulson 1993). In winter, significant numbers (hundreds to thousands) of knots appear to be localized in distribution into three areas on the Pacific coast of North America: San Francisco Bay, San Diego Bay, and Laguna Ojo de Liebre, Baja California, Mexico (PRBO, unpubl. data). In San Francisco Bay Area wetlands, knots are also very localized in distribution. The importance of San Francisco Bay, and of specific sites in the region, to the red knot should warrant special concern for this species in any comprehensive management plan for San Francisco Bay Area wetlands. Such a plan should include a combination of extensive intertidal flats as foraging habitat for the knot, and adequate, undisturbed high tide roost sites. Because red knots frequently associate with dowitchers (*Limnodromus* spp.), dunlins (*Calidris alpina*) and black-bellied plovers (*Pluvialis squatarola*), management plans to preserve, enhance, or restore habitat for red knots may also benefit these other species.

Description

The red knot is the second-largest calidrid, about the same size of dowitchers. Knots look heavy and rounded in shape (Hayman et al. 1986). The bill is blackish and faintly downcurved, the iris is dark brown, and the legs are rather short. In nonbreeding or juvenile plumage, knots have mostly white underparts, rather plain gray upperparts, gray streaking on the breast and upper belly,

Courtesy USGS/NBS

and greenish legs. Breeding-plumaged adults have dark gray legs, chestnut-red face and underparts, gray and black speckled backs, and white undertail coverts (Paulson 1993). Knot flight feathers are blackish, with distinct but narrow white wing bars, the rump is pale gray, and the tail shows broad brown bars and narrower white ones (Hayman et al. 1986).

Breeding Biology – Red knots breed inland on moist tundra and upland glacial gravel (Hayman et al. 1986). Nesting begins in late May and extends into August when the last young fledge (Harrington 1996). Knots lay four eggs at approximate one day intervals. Incubation lasts 21-23 days. Both sexes incubate, but the males primarily tend the brood. The fledgling period is approximately 18 days (Johnsgard 1981).

Migration Ecology – Red knots migrate long distances and concentrate in fewer areas than most other arctic breeding shorebirds. They are primarily coastal migrants, occurring only rarely inland in spring and fall. They are strictly coastal in winter (Hayman et al. 1986).

Wintering Ecology – Like the majority of shorebirds in San Francisco Bay, red knots feed primarily on tidal flats. At high tide they roost in flocks, particularly in salt ponds in South San Francisco Bay.

Distribution and Abundance

North America – There are three recognized subspecies of red knots that occur in North America. *C. c. islandica* breeds in the high arctic of Canada and Greenland and winters in Great Britain, France, and the Wadden Sea. *C. c. rufa* breeds in the central Canadian arctic and winters in southeastern North America, the Caribbean, parts of the northern coast of South America, and in the southern parts of South America. Harrington et al. (1988) estimate a total population of 100,000-170,000 for this subspecies. Little is known about the third subspecies, *C. c. roselaari*, which is believed to breed in northern Siberia on Wrangel Island and in Alaska and to migrate and winter along the Pacific coast of North America (Tomkovich 1992). Currently, there are no population estimates for this subspecies. A fourth subspecies, *C. c. rogersi*, breeds in northeastern Siberia and perhaps in Alaska, and winters primarily in Australia and New Zealand but possibly also on the Pacific coast of South America.

Pacific Coast – Red knots are significantly more abundant along the Pacific coast of North America during spring migration than during fall migration. Grays Harbor and Willapa Bay in Washington appear to be important staging areas for the knot in spring migration. The fall migration route of the large numbers of knots that migrate along the coast during the spring is not well-known (Paulson 1993). In winter, significant numbers of knots appear to have a localized distribution into three main areas: San Francisco Bay, San Diego Bay and La-

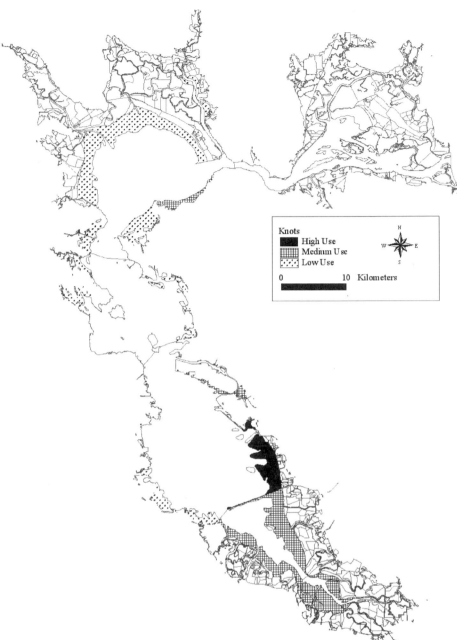

Figure 6.13 Relative Use of Different Mudflat Areas by Red Knots

Data from PRBO Pacific Flyway Project, 1988-1992. Unpublished data (data from Suisun not presented).

Knots
■ High Use
▦ Medium Use
⦂ Low Use

N

0   10   Kilometers

guna Ojo de Liebre, Baja California, Mexico. Knots do not winter regularly in the Pacific Northwest.

San Francisco Bay – Small numbers of red knots occur scattered in various wetland habitats around San Francisco Bay. Larger numbers of knots (hundreds to over one thousand) have a more localized distribution in the Bay. Within San Francisco Bay, 18 to 2,100 red knots were found on Point Reyes Bird Observatory (PRBO) counts.

Suisun – Probably uncommon to rare in Suisun.

North Bay – Large numbers of knots were recorded on intertidal flats just north of Pinole Point, Contra Costa County, but were rarely found elsewhere in San Pablo Bay on PRBO counts (**Figures 6.13** and **6.14**; PRBO counts).

Central Bay – Knots were reported on intertidal flats just north and south of the San Mateo Bridge, Alameda County. Up to 100% of the San Francisco Bay population was found in the Central Bay on PRBO counts. (**Figure 6.13**; PRBO counts).

South Bay – Knots have been reported in two salt pond complexes in Alameda County (PRBO, unpubl. data). Up to 100% of the San Francisco Bay total was found in the South Bay (**Figures 6.13** and **6.14**; PRBO counts).

Historical Information

There is no historical population estimate for red knots in San Francisco Bay. Red knot populations in North

Figure 6.14 Maximum Counts of Red Knot

Bayland data from the Diked Baylands Wildlife Study (DBWS), 1982-1989 (USFWS, *in prep.*).

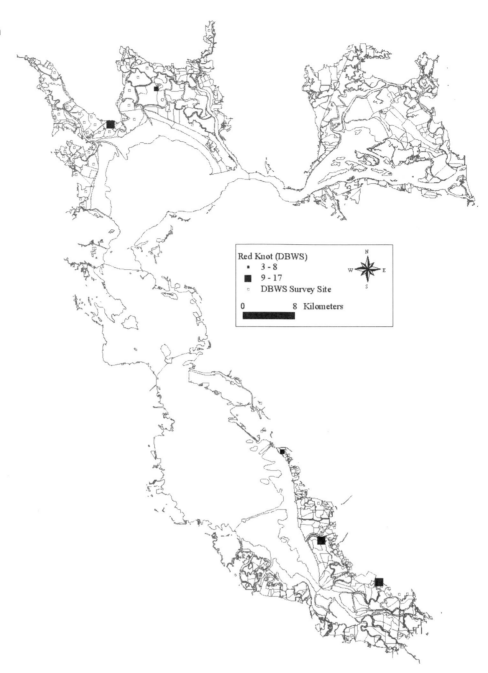

Red Knot (DBWS)
- 3 - 8
- 9 - 17
□ DBWS Survey Site

0   8 Kilometers

America suffered from intense hunting. Since legal protection was afforded, their status has improved.

Population Trends

No information.

Habitat Use and Behavior

Foraging – Knots are specialized feeders, requiring concentrated, rich food resources (Harrington 1996). Knots typically forage in cohesive flocks, feeding mainly by probing, but also by pecking at surface foods (Hayman et al. 1986). In Bolinas Lagoon, Marin County, California, Stenzel et al. (1983) found that several bivalve species (*Transennella* spp., *Protothaca* spp., *Gemma* spp., *Macoma* spp., *Mytilus* spp., and *Clinocardium* spp.) were the knot's primary prey. Other prey items included errant polychaetes (*Lumbrinerius* spp. and *Glycinde* spp.), gastropods, alga-dwelling and tube-dwelling amphipods, and trace amounts of small crustaceans, Foraminifera, tanaidaceans, and sedentary polychaetes. Other shorebird diet analyses have also determined molluscs to be the primary prey item of red knots on the western coast of North America (Sperry 1940, Recher 1966). On the Atlantic Coast, eggs of horseshoe crabs (*Limulus polyphemus*) are a staple. Adult and larval insects, as well as plant material are the primary prey items on the breeding grounds.

Roosting – Red knots are known to form dense, sometimes mixed, roosting flocks. In San Francisco Bay, salt evaporator ponds in the Hayward area appear to be important roosting habitat for knots.

Movement – Little is known about red knot movement between habitat types in the San Francisco Bay Area.

Conservation and Management

Contaminant Risks – Little or no information is available, but because red knots are localized in distribution, they are particularly vulnerable to contaminants and potential oil spills.

Disturbance – Red knots, like most other shorebirds, may be flushed by people approaching too closely, by avian and terrestrial predators, or by unleashed dogs that chase them. Knots should warrant special concern in development and management plans in the San Francisco Bay region.

Recommendations

San Francisco Bay is one of three main red knot wintering areas along the western coast of the United States. Since this species is relatively rare compared to other species occurring in the Bay, special consideration should be given to its habitat requirements and to specific areas of known use. Its habitat requirements should not be expected to be an umbrella for the associated species. Salt ponds currently used by red knots for roosting may also be used as alternate foraging habitat.

Within the Bay, areas of importance to red knot are found in North Bay, Central Bay, and South Bay. Mudflat and sandflat are important for roosting and foraging, and unvegetated levees, islets, beaches, and pans are used for roosting. Goals for this species should include maintaining tidal flat outboard of marshes for foraging habitat, and some salt ponds on the eastern side of the South Bay for roosting sites.

Suisun – There is no documentation of red knots using Suisun.

North Bay – The tidal flats between Point Pinole and Carquinez Straight are important and should be maintained. Investigation is needed to identify the important roosting areas in the North Bay subregion.

Central Bay – Central Bay tidal flats along the Hayward shoreline appear to be the most important site for red knots in the entire Bay. Roosting areas for red knots in the Alameda area need to be identified. All tidal flats on the eastern side of the Bay should be maintained and improved. The Oliver Brothers salt ponds should be maintained as roosting habitat.

South Bay – Baumberg/Hayward area salt ponds are known to hold roosting red knots. Though salt ponds are primarily for roosting, they also may be used as alternate foraging areas when intertidal flats are covered at high tide.

All tidal flat should be maintained for foraging, and the amount of flat along channels in tidal marsh should be increased. Some salt ponds should be preserved for roosting sites, especially in the Baumberg area. The Oliver Brothers salt ponds should be maintained as roosting habitat.

Research Needs

Substrate and invertebrate sampling from various intertidal flats around San Francisco Bay and San Pablo Bay would help determine whether known areas of consistent red knot concentration have a unique combination of substrate and/or food resources.

References

Harrington, B. 1996. The flight of the red knot. W.W. Norton & Co., New York.

Harrington, B.A., J.M. Haagan and L.E. Eddy. 1988. Site fidelity and survival differences between two groups of new world red knots, *Calidris canutus*. Auk 105: 439-445.

Hayman, P., J. Marchant and T. Prater. 1986. Shorebirds: an identification guide. Houghton Mifflin Co., Boston.

Johnsgard, P.A. 1981. The plovers, sandpipers and snipes of the world. Univ. of Nebraska Press, Lincoln, pp. 231-233.

Page, G.W., L.E. Stenzel and C.M. Wolf. 1979. Aspects of the occurrence of shorebirds on a central California estuary. *In:* F.A. Pitelka (ed). Shorebirds in marine environments. Stud. Avian Biol. 2: 15-32.

Paulson, D. 1993. Shorebirds of the Pacific Northwest. Univ. of Washington Press, Seattle.

Recher, H.F. 1966. Some aspects of the ecology of migrant shorebirds. Ecology 47: 393-407.

Sperry, C.C. 1940. Food habits of a group of shorebirds: woodcock, snipe, knot and dowitcher. U.S. Dept. Interior. Wildl. Research Bull. 1:1-37.

Stenzel, L.E., G.W. Page and J. Young. 1983. The trophic relationships between shorebirds and their prey. Unpubl. report of Point Reyes Bird Observatory, Stinson Beach, Calif.

Tomkovich, P.S. 1992. An analysis of the geographic variability in knots *Calidris canutus* based on museum skins. Wader Study Group Bull. 64, Suppl.: 17-23.

U. S. Fish and Wildlife Service (USFWS). *In preparation.* Diked baylands wildlife study. A study of wildlife use of diked, seasonal wetlands around San Francisco Bay, 1982-1989.

Waterfowl & Shorebirds

Western Sandpiper

Calidris mauri

Nils Warnock
Sarah E. Warnock

Introduction

The western sandpiper is the most abundant shorebird of California during fall and spring migration and the second most abundant during the winter. Largest concentrations of western sandpipers occur at coastal estuaries, but during the spring and to a lesser extent the fall, interior sites such as the western Great Basin, the Central Valley, and the Imperial Valley may host tens to hundreds of thousands of migrants. In winter, this species is more restricted to marine habitats than associated species, including least sandpiper, dunlin, and semipalmated plover. All the above species use tidal flats, salt ponds, managed wetlands, and seasonal wetland habitats in the Bay.

Description

Western sandpipers are marginally the largest of the stints. The species is sexually dimorphic with males typically smaller in size than females (Page and Fearis 1971). In basic plumage, they are pale grey with brown streaking on the crown, with white underparts. Fine, blackish streaks often join across the breast, usually heavier streaking than in semipalmated sandpipers with whom they share the special feature of partial webbing between the toes. Their typically longer, heavier, and decurved bill is also a helpful distinguishing factor. During breeding season, they have a distinctive dark streaking on their breasts with "V's" or arrowheads on flanks, and usually much more rufous in upper scapulars and head than other species likely to be encountered.

Breeding Biology – Western sandpipers are monogamous, bi-parental sub-Arctic and Arctic breeders.

Courtesy USGS/NBS

At least some begin breeding after their first year (Holmes 1971). Generally, they only lay one clutch per season, but will lay a replacement clutch if the first is lost early in the breeding season. Mean clutch completion in western Alaska occurs between 25 May and 5 June (Holmes 1972). Western sandpipers generally lay four eggs. Favored nesting habitat is moist to wet graminoid tundra, but they will also occasionally breed on lower mountain slopes (Wilson 1994). They nest in depressions in the ground typically lined with grass and under a dwarf birch (Wilson 1994). Mean incubation period is 21 days (Holmes 1973). Hatch success is 84% at the Yukon-Kuskokwim Delta, Alaska (Holmes 1972) and 55% at Nome, Alaska (Wilson 1994). Major nest predators include jaegers and foxes.

Migration Ecology – The global distribution of western sandpipers is skewed by sex. Female birds are more likely to winter at more southerly sites than males (Page et al. 1972, Harrington and Haase 1995). In California and San Francisco Bay, winter populations of western sandpipers are skewed towards males (Page et al. 1972).

At San Francisco Bay, during fall migration, adults arrive about a month earlier then juveniles (late June, July); followed by juveniles (August through October). During spring migration, peak numbers occur from 20 April though 5 May; males are followed by females (N. Warnock, unpubl. data). The length of stay at San Francisco Bay of northward migrating western sandpipers radio marked there was 9.1 ± 4.6 days ($n = 58$ birds), although these stays may have been prolonged due to temporary effects of capturing the birds (Bishop and Warnock 1998, Warnock and Bishop 1998). Birds radio marked at San Francisco Bay have been detected at all major coastal estuaries between the Bay and the Yukon-Kuskokwim Delta (with the exception of sites in Oregon, a state not monitored). Breeding destination of many of the birds migrating through the Bay appears to be the Yukon-Kuskokwim Delta (Bishop and Warnock 1998). Breeding birds from the Seward Peninsula also have been detected at San Francisco Bay, as well as wintering birds from Panama and Mexico (Butler et al. 1996).

Spectacular concentrations of western sandpipers are found during the northward spring migration with hundreds of thousands of birds concentrating at such sites as San Francisco Bay, CA, Grays Harbor, WA, Fraser River Delta, BC, Stikine River Delta, Alaska and the Copper River Delta, Alaska (Iverson et al. 1996). During spring, exchange of western sandpipers between Bolinas Lagoon (an estuary approximately 14 km northwest of San Francisco Bay) and North San Francisco Bay was found (Warnock, unpubl. data).

Wintering Ecology – First-year birds (26.6 ± 3.6 km^2) have larger winter home ranges than adults (17.2 ± 2.5 km^2), but no significant differences in size of home

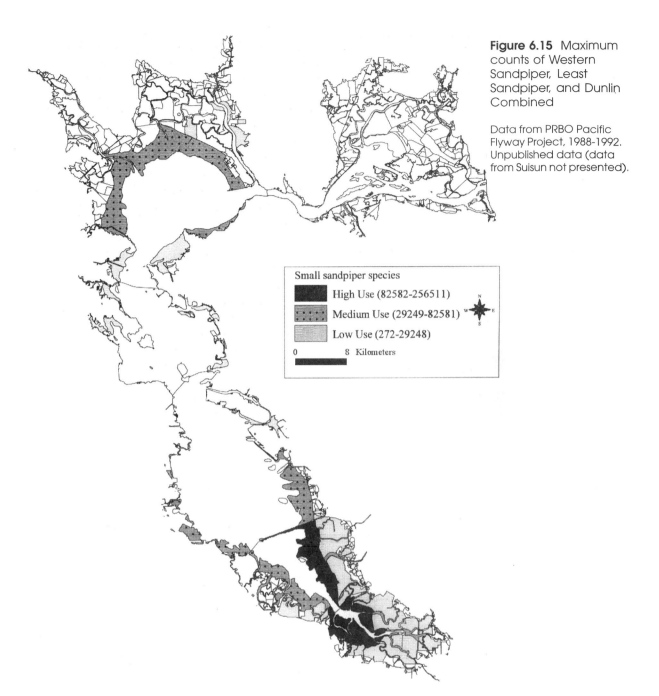

Figure 6.15 Maximum counts of Western Sandpiper, Least Sandpiper, and Dunlin Combined

Data from PRBO Pacific Flyway Project, 1988-1992. Unpublished data (data from Suisun not presented).

Small sandpiper species

High Use (82582-256511)
Medium Use (29249-82581)
Low Use (272-29248)

0   8 Kilometers

range were found between sexes (Warnock and Take-kawa 1996). Individual birds are strongly site-specific within San Francisco Bay.

Distribution and Abundance

North America – Western sandpipers breed in western Alaska from the Alaska Peninsula up to the North Slope of northern Alaska. Small numbers also breed in northeastern Russia. They commonly winter from Washington through the southeastern United States, and south through Mexico and Central America to northern Peru.

Pacific Coast – The largest winter concentrations are found from San Francisco Bay south to Panama.

Areas of largest concentrations include San Francisco Bay, Lagunas Ojo de Liebre and Guerro Negro in Baja California, Mexico (Page et al. 1997), western coast of Mexico in the Gulf of California, and coast of Panama.

San Francisco Bay – Western sandpipers are found in all parts of the San Francisco Bay Estuary. A comprehensive April count of shorebirds counted over 555,000 western sandpipers (Stenzel and Page 1988). As many as 707,000 were found during five additional spring counts. Largest numbers were found in areas of the South Bay with large expanses of mudflats at low tide backed by salt pond complexes **(Figures 6.15 and 6.16)**.

Suisun – Point Reyes Bird Observatory (PRBO) surveys indicate as many as 5,000 western sandpipers in

Waterfowl & Shorebirds

Figure 6.16 Maximum Counts of Western Sandpiper

Bayland data from the Diked Baylands Wildlife Study (DBWS), 1982-1989 (USFWS, *in prep.*).

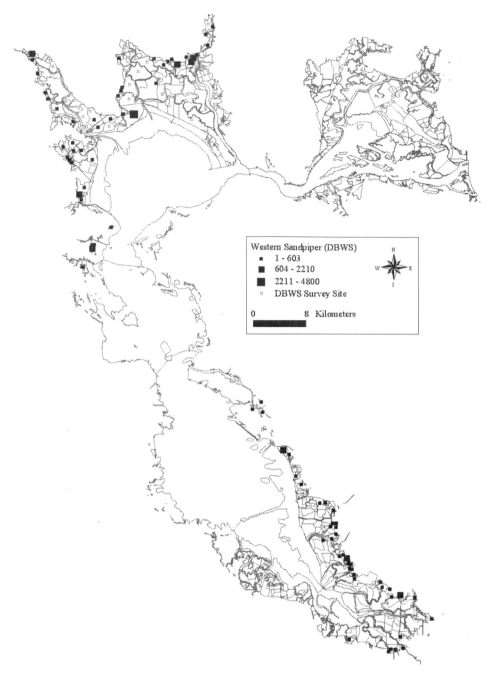

Western Sandpiper (DBWS)
- 1 - 603
- 604 - 2210
- 2211 - 4800
- DBWS Survey Site

0   8   Kilometers

the in fall, 3,400 in the winter, and possibly up to 17,000 in the spring.

　　North Bay – Sixteen percent of the San Francisco Bay total were found in San Pablo Bay (north of the Richmond Bridge). The North Bay accounted for up to 30% of the Bay total on PRBO counts.

　　Central Bay – Up to 30% of the Bay total for western sandpipers were found between the Richmond and San Mateo bridges on PRBO counts.

　　South Bay – Up to 79% of the Bay total were found south of the San Mateo Bridge on PRBO counts.

Historical Information

No information.

Population Trends

Rigorously estimated global population counts for western sandpiper are not available, but the West Coast population is estimated to be a few million birds (Page and Gill 1994). Population trends are currently unknown.

Habitat Use and Behavior

Based on a sample of 106 radio marked western sandpipers in South San Francisco Bay, birds showed seasonal differences in habitat preference both on local and regional scales (Warnock and Takekawa 1995). During winter at low tide, salt pond levees followed by mudflats were most preferred, and salt marsh plains were used the least (Warnock and Takekawa 1995). At high tide, salt-pond levees were ranked as the most preferred habitat, followed by drained salt ponds, tidal salt ponds and seasonal wetlands, and salt marsh plains were the least preferred habitat. In spring at low tide, use of habitats was significantly different from the winter. Western sandpipers preferred tidal sloughs over tidal salt ponds, drained salt ponds, and mudflats. At high tide, they preferred drained salt ponds and seasonal wetlands. At both tides, salt marsh plains were the least preferred habitat. At low tide, in all seasons, the majority of western sandpipers occur on tidal flats.

Foraging – Western sandpipers feed mainly on invertebrates but occasionally will also feed on small fish and plant matter. They are tactile feeders that typically probe in the mud for prey. On the breeding grounds at the Yukon-Kuskokwim Delta, Alaska, common food items include Diptera larvae, adult Coleoptera, and arachnids depending on the time in the breeding season (Holmes 1972). On the winter grounds, common food items include amphipods, small bivalves, annelids, and insects (Stenzel et al. 1983, Wilson 1994). At San Francisco Bay, they have been found to feed on a diverse diet of amphipods, bivalves, polychaetes, ostracods, and gastropods (Recher 1966). In salt ponds, they also feed on brine flies, insects, and seeds (Murie and Bruce 1935, Carpelan 1957, Anderson 1970). In the winter, birds have been found out on low tide mudflats during day and night (Warnock and Takekawa 1996).

Roosting – Roosting flocks sometimes number tens to thousands of individuals. Roosting sites tend to be barren to sparsely vegetated and include salt pond levees, dry to very shallow salt ponds, islands, beaches, diked baylands, etc.

Movement – Radio-tracking studies show species to be very limited in its movements within the Bay, but birds are known to move back and forth between Bolinas Lagoon and North San Francisco Bay during spring. Birds radio marked in South San Francisco Bay were not found outside the South Bay despite extensive search efforts in surrounding areas; birds typically move between Bay mudflats at low tide to salt pond roost areas at high tide regardless of time of day (Warnock and Takekawa 1996).

Conservation and Management

Contaminant Risks – Due to their small home ranges within the Bay, there is an increased potential for repeated exposure to environmental contaminants from industrial and municipal discharge (Warnock and Takekawa 1996).

Disturbance – Feeding and roosting flocks take flight in response to hunting raptors, sudden loud noises, and close approach by humans, pets, jet skies, and boats.

Introduced Species – Introduced invertebrates such as *Potamocorbula amurensis* (Nichols et al. 1990) could significantly influence the distribution and abundance of western sandpipers within the Bay.

Recommendations

The dynamics of the active salt industry provide a varied habitat for these small shorebirds. They need plenty of intertidal foraging habitat at low tide, and supertidal roosting and foraging areas at high tide. Seasonal wetlands, diked wetlands, muted tidal wetlands and salt ponds provide these supertidal functions. Salt ponds, especially when drained, provide habitat for huge numbers of birds. Any kind of habitat with muted tidal flow and less than 50% vegetative cover is important foraging habitat. Allowing these sites to become revegetated will likely negatively affect western sandpipers. Farmed and grazed baylands are crucial in extreme events such as severe winter storms or unusually high bird numbers, but an increase in this kind of habitat should not be at the expense of marsh habitat. Any expansion of tidal or supertidal habitats should not be done at the expense of intertidal mudflat habitat, which remains the most important feeding area for these birds.

To support the western sandpiper, the current acreage of tidal marsh should be increased. Mid-tidal and low tidal marsh should have no more than 60-70% vegetative cover. The current acreages of agricultural baylands, intertidal flat, treatment pond, and mid- and high salinity salt ponds should be maintained. Lagoons are important during low tide, and the acreage should be increased. Current acreages of low salinity salt pond and tidal reaches in streams should be increased. These general recommendations apply throughout the subregions.

Suisun – General recommendations given above.

North Bay – Areas of importance in the North Bay include all areas of intertidal flat, the exposed banks of Sonoma Creek and Napa and Petaluma rivers, tidal marsh channels, drained and shallow salt ponds, salt crystallizers, and Ponds 1A, 2A, and 4A. The general recommendations given above also apply to this subregion.

Central Bay – Areas of importance in the Central Bay include all areas of intertidal flat, roosting islands, and the Hayward marshes. The general recommendations given above also apply to this subregion.

South Bay – Areas of importance in the South Bay include all of the salt ponds (especially when drained), intertidal areas, seasonal wetlands, levee roost sites, diked marsh, and duck clubs. Particular locations include the Knapp property; Mowry, Newark, and Coyote sloughs; the upland marsh of tract 102 marshes, the Alviso Ponds, and Ponds RSF 1 and RSF 2. The general recommendations given above also apply to this subregion.

Research Needs

Currently, we have a poor understanding of where migrants that pass through San Francisco Bay in the spring are coming from, as well as where southward moving birds are going. The use of salt ponds by western sandpipers ought to be examined in more detail, as well as how invasive invertebrate species impact the distribution of western sandpipers within the Bay. The impact of revegetation of reclaimed salt ponds on western sandpipers using the ponds should be studied.

References

Anderson, W. 1970. A preliminary study of the relationship of saltponds and wildlife – South San Francisco Bay. Calif. Dept. Fish and Game 56: 240-252.

Bishop, M.A. and N. Warnock. 1998. Migration of western sandpipers: links between their stopover areas and breeding grounds. Wilson Bull. 110:457-462.

Butler, R.W., F.S. Delgado, H. de la Cueva, V. Pulido and B. K. Sandercock. 1996. Migration routes of the western sandpiper. Wilson Bull. 108: 662-672.

Carpelan, L.H. 1957. Hydrobiology of the Alviso salt ponds. Ecology 38: 375-390.

Harrington, B.A. and B. Haase. 1995. Latitudinal differences in sex ratios among nonbreeding western sandpipers in Puerto Rico and Ecuador. Southwest Nature 39: 188-189.

Holmes, R.T. 1971. Density, habitat, and mating system of the western sandpipers (*Calidris mauri*). Oecologia 7: 191-208.

_____. 1972. Ecological factors influencing the breeding season schedule of western sandpipers (*Calidris mauri*) in subarctic Alaska. Am. Midl. Nat. 87: 472-491.

_____. 1973. Social behaviour of breeding western sandpipers *Calidris mauri*. Ibis 115: 107-123.

Iverson, G.C., S.E. Warnock, R.W. Butler, M.A. Bishop and N. Warnock. 1996. Spring migration of western sandpipers (*Calidris mauri*) along the Pacific coast of North America: a telemetry study. Condor 98: 10-21.

Murie, A. and H.D. Bruce. 1935. Some feeding habits of the Western Sandpiper. Condor 37: 258-259.

Nichols, F.H., J.K. Thompson and L.E. Schemel. 1990. Remarkable invasion of San Francisco Bay (California, USA) by the Asian clam *Potamocorbula amurensis* II: Displacement of a former community. Mar. Ecol. Prog. Ser. 66: 95-101.

Page, G.W. and B. Fearis. 1971. Sexing western sandpipers by bill length. Bird-Band. 42: 297-298.

Page, G.W. and R.E. Gill, Jr. 1994. Shorebirds in western North America: late 1800s to late 1900s. Stud. Avian Biol. 15: 147-160.

Page, G., B. Fearis and R.M. Jurek. 1972. Age and sex composition of western sandpipers on Bolinas Lagoon, Calif. Birds 3: 79-86.

Page, G.W., E. Palacios, L. Alfaro, S. Gonzales, L.E. Stenzel and M. Jungers. 1997. Numbers of wintering shorebirds in coastal wetlands of Baja California, Mexico. J. Field Ornithology 68: 562-574.

Recher, H.R. 1966. Some aspects of the ecology of migratory shorebirds. Ecology 47: 393-407.

Stenzel, L.E. and G.W. Page. 1988. Results of the first comprehensive shorebird census of San Francisco and San Pablo Bays. Wader Study Group Bull: 54: 43-48.

Stenzel, L.E., G.W. Page, and J. Young. 1983. The trophic relationships between shorebirds and their prey. Unpubl. report. Point Reyes Bird Observatory, Stinson Beach, CA.

U. S. Fish and Wildlife Service (USFWS). *In preparation.* Diked baylands wildlife study. A study of wildlife use of diked, seasonal wetlands around San Francisco Bay, 1982-1989.

Warnock, N. and M. A. Bishop. 1998. Spring stopover ecology of migrant western sandpipers. Condor 100:456-467.

Warnock, S.E. and J.Y. Takekawa. 1995. Habitat preferences of wintering shorebirds in a temporally changing environment: Western sandpipers in the San Francisco Estuary. Auk 112: 920-930.

Wilson, W.H. 1994. Western Sandpiper (*Calidris mauri*). In: A. Poole and F. Gill (eds). The birds of North America, No. 90. Academy of Natural Sciences Philadelphia and American Ornithol. Union.

Additional Readings

Bishop, M.A. and N. Warnock. 1996. Conservation of western sandpipers along the Pacific Flyway, Summary report: 1995-1996. Unpubl. report of the Copper River Delta Institute, US Forest Service, Cordova, AK.

Rice, S.M. 1995. Residency rates, annual return rates and population estimates of semipalmated and western sandpipers at the Cabo Rojo Salt Flats, Puerto Rico. Master's thesis, Univ. of Puerto Rico, Mayaguez.

Warnock, N. and M. A. Bishop. 1996. Spring migration of western sandpipers at San Francisco Bay, California. Unpubl. report submitted to Don Edwards San Francisco Bay National Wildlife Refuge, U.S. Fish and Wildl. Serv., Newark, CA

Warnock, S.E. and J.Y. Takekawa. 1996. Wintering site fidelity and movement patterns of western sandpipers *Calidris mauri* in the San Francisco Bay Estuary. Ibis 138: 160-167.

Long-Billed Dowitcher

Limnodromus scolopaceus

John Y. Takekawa

Sarah E. Warnock

Introduction

The San Francisco Estuary supports large wintering populations of the long-billed dowitcher numbering in the low tens of thousands. More than most other abundant shorebirds, this species concentrates in fresh and brackish water wetlands. The key habitat for this bird is managed wetlands. It associates with dunlin (*Calidris alpina*), greater and lesser yellowlegs (*Tringa melanoleuca* and *T. flavipes*), black-necked stilt (*Himantopus mexicanus*), and American avocet (*Recurvirostra americana*), which also use these habitats.

Description

The long-billed dowitcher is a medium-sized shorebird (28-32 cm) with short legs and a long snipe-like bill (5.7-7.6 cm). In breeding plumage, long-billed dowitchers have cinnamon underparts with bars of black on the sides of the breast and flanks; a white wedge on the rump; black, buff, and white feathers above; and dull olive legs (Hayman et al. 1986). Although difficult to distinguish from the similar-looking short-billed dowitcher (*L. griseus*), it was identified as a separate species on the basis of morphological (Pitelka 1950) and genetic data indicating their relatively large congeneric divergence (Avise and Zink 1988). About 15% of the long-billed dowitchers are separable from short-billed dowitchers by a bill more than two times longer than the head (Richards 1988), but more consistent characteristics distinguishing the species include the "keek" vs. the "tu-tu-tu" call (Miller et al. 1984), white tail bars narrower than or equal in width to the dark tail bars, darker unspeckled throat and breast sharply distinct from underparts, foreneck densely spotted, center of breast barred, and belly lightly spotted (Wilds and Newlon 1983). Juveniles

Courtesy USGS/NBS

are distinguished by the buff appearance of their underparts and a grayer head and neck with narrow rusty fringes on their coverts.

Breeding Biology – Long-billed dowitchers do not breed in the San Francisco Bay Area. They are arctic breeders that nest in grassy or sedgy marshes, or near small lakes (Hayman et al. 1986). They arrive during late April and May, and their breeding displays include low-level hovering flights and a distinctive "pee-ter-wee-too" call. They defend comparatively small territories, and nest in small clumps of low sedges, in mounds of moss and sedge, or on the ground. They lay four eggs (olive with many elongated spots), and both sexes incubate the nest for the 20-21 day incubation.

Migration Ecology – Females form postbreeding flocks as early as late June, while males depart their breeding areas in late July or early August. Juveniles migrate 1-2 months later (Campbell et al. 1990). They peak in autumn migration in British Columbia during September and October (Campbell et al. 1990). The long-billed dowitchers are generally 5-6 weeks behind the short-billed dowitchers during migration. Long-billed dowitchers generally migrate in smaller flocks than short-billed dowitchers. Flocks of 10-100 birds are commonly observed (Campbell et al. 1990). They migrate southeast to the Atlantic Coast and along the Pacific Coast or through the midcontinent. Groups of more than 30,000 have been counted at Malheur National Wildlife Refuge in interior Oregon (Gilligan et al. 1994). Their peak spring migration lasts from late March to mid-May, and they are rare east of the Mississippi River. They are seen in Oregon during late February and early March (Gilligan et al. 1994). They are rare migrants to Japan and Europe and are vagrant to Nova Scotia, Bali, Brunei, and Thailand.

Wintering Ecology – Adult long-billed dowitchers begin arriving at Point Reyes, Marin County, California in July (Shuford et al. 1989), while juveniles arrive in mid-September. They winter in the southern United States and in Central America, as far south as Panama (Hayman et al. 1986). Those observed on inland areas in California are usually long-billed dowitchers (Cogswell 1977), but both species are found in coastal areas. They disappear during rainy periods on the coast, perhaps to the Central Valley (Shuford et al. 1989, Shuford et al. 1998).

Distribution and Abundance

North America – Long-billed dowitchers breed in coastal northeast Siberia, western and northern Alaska, the northwest MacKenzie River Delta (Cogswell 1977), and the Northern Yukon (Richards 1988). They winter in northwest and north central California, western Nevada, southern Arizona, and east to South Carolina and Florida, as far south as Guatemala and Panama, and as

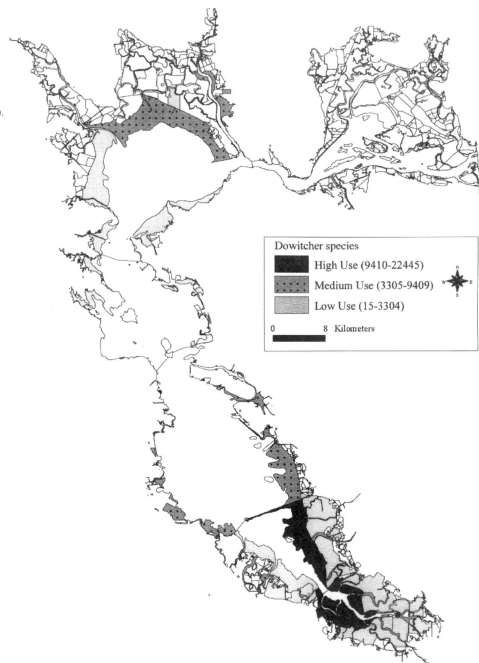

Figure 6.17 Maximum Counts of Dowitcher Species

Data from PRBO Pacific Flyway Project, 1988-1992. Unpublished data (data from Suisun not presented).

Dowitcher species
■ High Use (9410-22445)
▦ Medium Use (3305-9409)
▨ Low Use (15-3304)

0   8   Kilometers

far north as Washington State. They generally winter farther north than the short-billed dowitcher.

Pacific Coast – Long-billed dowitchers are found in both coastal and interior regions, including the Central Valley and in California lakes. Few birds are known to migrate along the western Pacific, but the San Francisco Bay Estuary is used during both migration and the winter. Estuaries in Sinaloa, Mexico also include large populations of this species (Engilis et al. 1998).

Suisun – Point Reyes Bird Observatory (PRBO) recorded up to 11,200 dowitchers in August, 6,000 in November, and 7,900 in April. This includes both *Limnodromous* species, but collections in San Francisco Bay (Takekawa and Warnock, unpubl. data) suggest most are long-billed dowitchers (**Figures 6.17** and **6.18**)

North Bay – Present, common.
Central Bay – Present, low abundance.
South Bay – Present, common.

Historical Information

There was a decline in numbers of dowitchers in eastern North America and California in the late 1880s and early 1900s because of hunting (Page and Gill 1994), until the passage of the Migratory Bird Treaty Act of 1918. The size of the populations have likely followed the abundance of mudflat habitats with benthic invertebrate prey, and this species may have benefitted by the development of salt evaporation ponds which provided high tide roost sites.

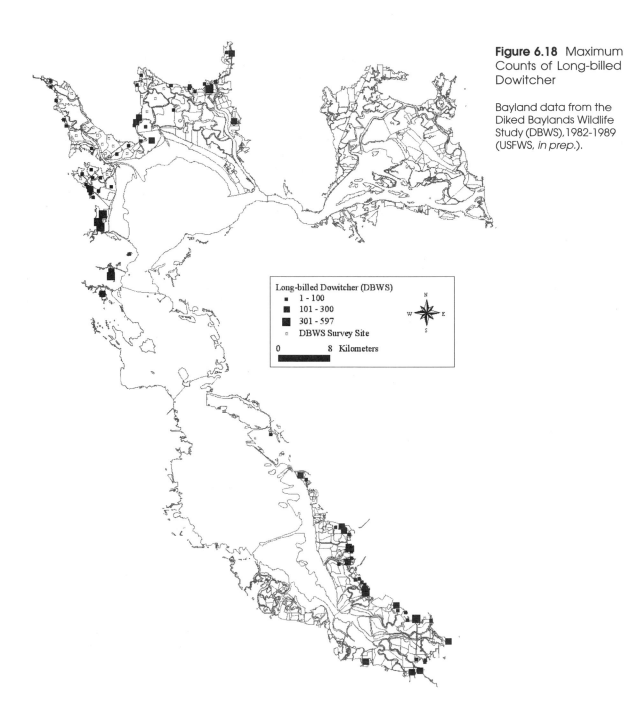

Figure 6.18 Maximum Counts of Long-billed Dowitcher

Bayland data from the Diked Baylands Wildlife Study (DBWS), 1982-1989 (USFWS, *in prep.*).

Long-billed Dowitcher (DBWS)
- ▪ 1 - 100
- ◾ 101 - 300
- ⬛ 301 - 597
- ▫ DBWS Survey Site

0   8 Kilometers

Population Trends

In Florida, there has been an upward trend in recent years (Stevenson and Anderson 1994), but it is not known whether this reflects shifting populations or true population increases. No information is reported about the long-term population trends of the West Coast.

Habitat Use and Behavior

Long-billed dowitchers prefer freshwater habitats over brackish and intertidal areas (Campbell et al. 1990, Cogwell 1977, Pitelka 1950, Takekawa and Warnock *in press*). They use seasonal wetlands, flooded fields, reservoir edges, sewage lagoons, small ponds, lake and pond muddy shores, river banks, and sewage ponds (Campbell et al. 1990). They use intertidal flats for foraging and roosting, and roost on offshore rocks and islands (Campbell et al. 1990). At Nelson Lagoon, Alaska, long-billed dowitchers were found in muddier areas than short-billed dowitchers, which were found in sandier areas (Gill and Jorgenson 1979), but in Bolinas Lagoon, California, they were found in areas of moderately to well-sorted fine sand (Page et al. 1979). Flight surveys in the Central Valley of California found 66% of dowitchers in managed wetlands, 28% in agricultural lands, 3% in sewage and evaporation ponds, and 3% in other habitats (Shuford et al. 1993).

On the East Coast, they primarily use freshwater habitats, especially impoundments, salt pans (Veit and

Petersen 1993), or shallow impounded waters with scant vegetation (Tomkins 1961). They are most commonly found on "barrow-pit habitats" of soft dredge material in the Midwest, usually disturbed sites, often successional areas with short life spans (Tomkins 1961).

Foraging – Long-billed dowitchers are probing feeders on muddy substrates. Sand may reduce the success in prey capture or detection in comparison to muddy sites (Quammen 1982). They feed with exploratory jabs (depth 1/3 bill length) and acquire prey with prolonged and vigorous probing (depth to bill length) (Burton 1972) with 99% of their foraging in the sediment (Young 1989). The appearance of their foraging has been described as "sewing-machine" activity (Richards 1988). They commonly forage in salt water during migration (Cogswell 1977), but they are most commonly reported as associated with freshwater wetlands. They often forage in water up to their belly, and were found in depths of 2-8 cm in the Central Valley, California (Elphick and Oring 1998), 4-5 cm on South Island, South Carolina (Weber and Haig 1996), and 0-16 cm at Playa Lakes of Texas (Davis and Smith, 1998). On Seward Peninsula, Alaska, dowitchers are often found in salt grass meadow (Kessel 1989). In pastures along coastal California, dowitcher abundance is negatively correlated with vegetation height (Colwell and Dodd 1995). Their time-activity budget includes 79.6% feeding, 17.4% resting or preening, and 1.9% alert (Young 1989). Their breeding area diet includes meltwater pool insects, seeds, moss, and cranefly larvae, while migration and wintering diets include midge and fly larvae, worms, and burrowing crustaceans.

Roosting – Long-billed dowitchers probably roost in shallow water or on barren to sparsely vegetated islands and levees. They have also been seen roosting in salt marsh (G. Page, pers. comm.). Roosting flocks sometimes exceed 1,000 birds. They commonly use intertidal flats for foraging and roosting, and roost on offshore rocks and islands (Campbell et al. 1990).

Movement – Long-billed dowitchers generally follow a pattern of feeding on intertidal flats during low tide and roosting in adjacent wetlands or uplands during high tides.

Conservation and Management

Contaminant Risks – Pesticide and other contaminant levels are available for dowitchers, but interpretation of results are difficult since no experimental work on the effects of these toxins on either breeding or migrating and wintering birds is available. Compared with birds in Texas, dowitchers collected at San Francisco Bay had higher selenium levels and elevated aluminum levels (C. Hui, J.Y. Takekawa, and S.E. Warnock, unpubl. data).

Disturbance – Long-billed dowitchers feed in intertidal flats and roost on nearby uplands or shallow wetlands. They are likely to be disturbed regularly by raptors, loud noises, and close approach by humans and their pets. Page and Whitacre (1975) determined that sixteen percent of dowitchers wintering at Bolinas Lagoon, California were killed by raptors.

Recommendations

Information suggests that these birds prefer fresher water habitats over brackish and intertidal habitats. Seasonal wetlands and freshwater ponds are therefore more important to this species. These species are commonly found on soft, dredged-material habitats or disturbed sites.

Unvegetated levees and islets, pans, and seasonal and perennial ponds are important roosting habitat. Mudflats, pans, and seasonal and perennial ponds are important for feeding. General regional goals to support dowitchers include increasing mid- and high tidal marsh for roosting, maintaining the current acreage of intertidal flat and salt pond, maintaining the current acreage of agricultural baylands (or increasing the areal extent of seasonal wetlands on a smaller area), and increasing the acreage of diked and managed marsh.

Suisun – Within Suisun, these birds are found primarily in managed marshes, but the timing and numbers are not well known. The goals for Suisun should include maintaining current acreages of muted tidal marsh and intertidal flat, and increasing mid-tidal marsh, diked marsh, and managed marsh to increase shallow water habitat.

North Bay – Seasonal wetlands and freshwater ponds are more important to this species in the North Bay. There is limited information available on the use of North Bay salt ponds, and also farmed and grazed bayland. Ponds 1A and 1AN, and all of the former Cargill salt ponds are critical habitat. Other important areas include the marshes of the Lower Napa River, mudflats of San Pablo Bay, and the area east of Cabana Isle. Current acreages of muted tidal marsh and intertidal flat should be maintained, and shallow managed marsh, mid-tidal marsh, and diked marsh should be increased.

Central Bay – Within the Central Bay there are limited areas of use, and unknown roost areas. The general regional goals above apply wherever applicable.

South Bay – The South Bay is the most important area in the Estuary for the long-billed dowitcher. Particular areas of importance include Ponds R1, R2, SF1, and SF2; all low salinity salt ponds; salt ponds and mudflats south of the San Mateo Bridge, and the Knapp property. The current acreages of low and mid-salinity salt ponds, muted tidal marsh, and intertidal mudflat should be maintained; and acreages of mid-tidal marsh, shallow managed marsh; and diked marsh should be increased.

References

Avise, J.C. and R.M. Zink. 1988. Molecular genetic divergence between avian sibling species: king and clapper rails, long-billed and short-billed dowitchers, boat-tailed and great-tailed grackles, and tufted and black-crested titmice. Auk 105:516-528.

Burton, P.J.K. 1972. The feeding techniques of stilt sandpipers and dowitchers. San Diego Soc. Nat. Hist. Trans. 17:63-68.

Campbell, R.W., N.K. Dawe, I. McTaggart-Cowan, J.M. Cooper, G.W. Kaiser and M.C.E. McNall. 1990. The birds of British Columbia, Vol. 2, Nonpasserines. Canadian Wildl. Service and Royal British Columbia Museum.

Cogswell, H.L. 1977. Water birds of California. Univ. of Calif. Press. Berkeley. 399pp.

Colwell, M.A. and S.L. Dodd. 1995. Waterbird communities and habitat relationships in coastal pastures of northern California. Cons. Biol. 9:827-834.

Davis, C.A. and L.M. Smith. 1998. Ecology and management of migrant shorebirds in the Playa Lakes region. Wildl. Monogr. 140:1-45.

Elphick, C.S. and L.E. Oring. 1998. Winter management of California rice fields for waterbirds. J. Appl. Ecol. 35:95-108.

Engilis, Jr., A.L.W. Oring, E. Carrera, J.W. Nelson and A. Martinez Lopez. 1998. Shorebird surveys in Ensenada Pabellones and Bahia Santa Maria, Sinaloa, Mexico: Critical habitats for Pacific Flyway shorebirds. Wilson Bull. 110(3):332-341.

Gill, R.E., Jr., and P.D. Jorgensen. 1979. Preliminary assessment of the timing and migration of shorebirds along the north central Alaska Peninsula. Stud. Avian Biol. 2: 110-120.

Gilligan, J., M. Smith, D. Rogers and A. Contreras. 1994. Birds of Oregon. Cinclus Publications, McMinnville, Oregon.

Hayman, P., J. Marchant and T. Prater. 1986. Shorebirds: an identification guide. Houghton Mifflin Co., Boston. 412pp.

Kessel, B. 1989. Birds of the Seward Peninsula, Alaska. Univ. of Alaska Press, Fairbanks.

Miller, E.H., W.W.H. Gunn, J.P. Myers and B.N. Veprintsev. 1984. Species-distinctiveness of long-billed dowitcher song (Aves: Scolopacidae). Proc. Biol. Soc. Wash. 97:804-811.

Page, G.W. and R.E. Gill, Jr. 1994. Shorebirds in western North America: late 1800's to late 1900's. Stud. Avian Biol. 15: 147-160.

Page, G. and D.F. Whitacre. 1975. Raptor predation on wintering shorebirds. Condor 77: 73-83.

Page, G.W., L.E. Stenzel, and C.M. Wolfe. 1979. Aspects of the occurrence of shorebirds on a central California estuary. Stud. Avian Biol. 2: 15-32.

Pitelka, F.A. 1950. Geographic variation and the species problem in the shore-bird genus *Limnodromus*. Univ. Calif. Publ. Zool. 50:1-108.

Quammen, M.L. 1982. Influence of subtle substrate differences on feeding by shorebirds on intertidal mudflats. Mar. Biol. 71(3).:339-343.

Quammen, M.L. 1984. Predation by shorebirds, fish, and crabs on invertebrates in intertidal mudflats: an experimental test. Ecology 65: 529-537.

Richards, A. 1988. Shorebirds: a complete guide to their behavior and migration. W. H. Smith Publ. New York. 224pp.

Shuford, W.D., G.W. Page and J.E. Kjelmyr. 1993. Distribution, abundance and habitat use of shorebirds in California's Central Valley in winter 1992-1993. Unpubl. report by Point Reyes Bird Obs., Stinson Beach, CA.

Shuford, W.D., G.W. Page, J.G. Evens and L.E. Stenzel. 1989. Seasonal abundance of waterbirds at Point Reyes: a coastal perspective. Western Birds 20: 137-265.

Shuford, W.D., G.W. Page and J.E. Kjelmyr. 1998. Patterns and dynamics of shorebird use of California's Central Valley. Condor 100:227-244.

Stevenson, H.M. and B.H. Anderson. 1994. The birdlife of Florida. Univ. of Florida Press, Gainesville, FL.

Takekawa, J.Y. and N. Warnock. *In press*. Long-billed dowitcher (*Limnodromous scolopaceus*). *In*: A. Poole and F. Gill (eds). The birds of North America. The Acadamy of Natural Sciences, Philadelphia, and the American Ornithologists' Union, Washington, D.C.

Tomkins, I.R. 1961. Migration and habitat of the long-billed dowitcher on the c0ast of Georgia and South Carolina. Wilson Bull. 76: 1880189.

U. S. Fish and Wildlife Service (USFWS). *In preparation*. Diked baylands wildlife study. A study of wildlife use of diked, seasonal wetlands around San Francisco Bay, 1982-1989.

Veit, R.R. and W.R. Petersen. 1993. Birds of Massachusetts. Massachusetts Audubon Society. Natural History of New England Series. Boston.

Weber, L.M. and S.M. Haig. 1996. Shorebird use of South Carolina managed and natural coastal wetlands. J. Wildl. Mgmt. 609(1): 73-82.

Wilds, C. and M. Newlon. 1983. The identification of dowitchers. Birding 15:151-166.

Young, A.D. 1989. Spacing behavior of visual- and tactile-feeding shorebirds in mixed-species groups. Can. J. Zool. 67: 2026-2028.

Waterfowl & Shorebirds

Wilson's Phalarope

Phalaropus tricolor

Janet T. Hanson

Introduction

Wilson's phalarope is representative of the group of shorebird species concentrated in salt ponds, including red-necked phalarope, American avocet, and black-necked stilt. Phalaropes forage by swimming in tight circles, or "spinning" on the ponds' surface to stir up prey items, a difference that sets them apart from other shorebirds. Wilson's and red-necked phalaropes are present on the Bay during fall and spring migration.

No precise information exists on local numbers of these species in the early part of this century, but current surveys suggest that they increased significantly with the development of the salt pond system, which they utilize as both foraging and roosting habitat. In addition, stilts and avocets are present year-round and make use of the levees and islands in the pond system for breeding habitat. Wilson's phalarope has suffered loss of breeding habitat in the inland wetlands it favors. On a global scale, this species appears to be declining in numbers.

Description

Wilson's phalarope is a medium-sized (22-24 cm) shorebird with mostly white plumage, short legs and a mid-length straight bill. This species is characterized by its reverse sexual dimorphism: the female is larger and more colorful in breeding plumage. In non-breeding plumage, both sexes have gray upperparts, pure white underparts, and yellow legs. There is a white superciliary line with a strong gray post-ocular line above. In breeding plumage, the females' crown and nape are pale gray. A strong black stripe runs from the bill, through the eye and down the neck. The breast is cinnamon or rusty color with a white belly and the legs are black. The breeding plumage of the male is a duller version of female (Colwell and Jehl 1994).

Courtesy USGS/NBS

Breeding Biology

Breeding Biology – Wilson's phalarope breeds on seasonal wetlands and freshwater marshes in the North American grasslands and prairies. This species is one of 13 species of shorebirds reported to practice polyandry. Females arrive first on the breeding grounds in late April-early May, followed by mixed flocks (Bent 1927). Several females often court a single male. Eggs are laid by mid-May to early June; a single nest typically contains four camouflaged eggs, buff colored with brown blotching. The male incubates while the female defends the territory. Incubation lasts approximately 23 days. The male broods and cares for the precocial young until they fledge.

Migration Ecology – Females depart as early as mid-June, followed by males and then juveniles in July (Colwell and Jehl 1994). Adults and juveniles congregate mostly on large interior alkali lakes, including Lake Abert, Oregon, Great Salt Lake, Utah, and Mono Lake, California to molt into basic plumage and accumulate fat for southbound migration (Reed et al. 1994). Smaller numbers stop on the West Coast, with San Francisco Bay's salt pond system being the major coastal staging area (Colwell and Jehl 1994). Individuals are rarely seen away from these staging areas. By mid-September, the birds have headed south to feeding grounds in South America, apparently flying non-stop from the central Pacific Coast and Great Basin staging areas to wintering grounds in South America.

Wintering Ecology – Wilson's phalaropes winter on saline lakes and freshwater marshes in southern South America, mainly in the Andean highlands of Bolivia, Peru, Chile, and Argentina (Jehl 1988).

Distribution and Abundance

North America – During breeding season, this species is found in the shallow ephemeral wetlands of interior western North America. Fall populations are estimated at 1.5 million birds on major staging areas (Jehl 1988).

Pacific Coast – The only major coastal site is San Francisco's salt pond system in the summer months.

San Francisco Bay – Wilson's phalaropes are seen almost entirely on the South Bay's salt ponds and their islands, primarily from June to August (Jurek 1973; Swarth et al. 1982, Harvey et al. 1988). Peak numbers occur in July.

Standard spring and fall shorebird surveys have fallen either too early or too late to capture peak numbers of Wilson's phalaropes. Point Reyes Bird Observatory's (PRBO) baywide counts detected maximums of 1,642 in the fall, zero in the winter, and 213 in the spring.

Suisun – PRBO fall count: 225; not seen on winter or spring counts.

North Bay – Not seen on PRBO's spring 1988 count, but see **Figure 6.19**.

Central Bay – Not seen on PRBO's spring 1988 count, but see **Figure 6.19**.

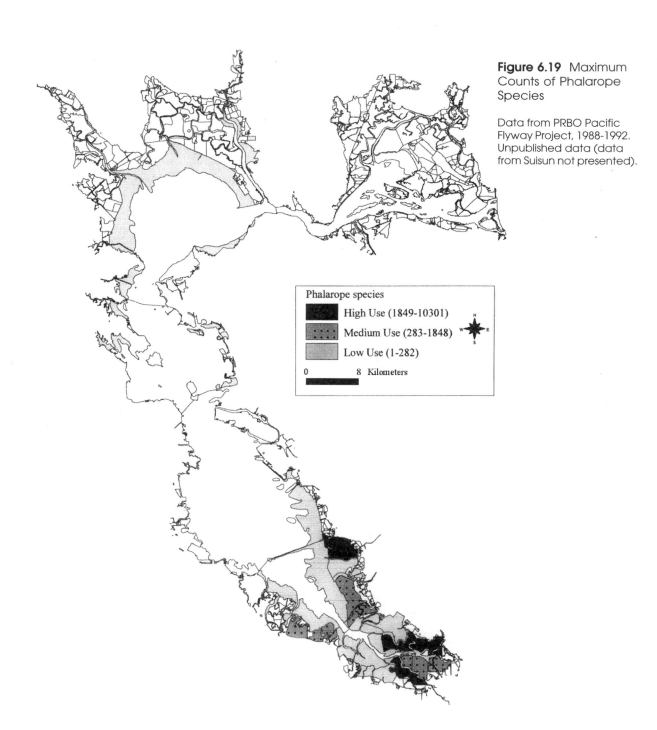

Figure 6.19 Maximum Counts of Phalarope Species

Data from PRBO Pacific Flyway Project, 1988-1992. Unpublished data (data from Suisun not presented).

South Bay – PRBO spring count: 213. Reportedly can reach a fall peak of 40,000 birds (Jehl 1988; see **Figures 6.19** and **6.20**).

Historical Information

No information.

Population Trends

It has been suggested that the global population of Wilson's phalaropes has declined due to loss of prairie wetland habitat in their breeding range (Dahl and Johnson 1991; Page and Gill 1994).

Habitat Use and Behavior

During spring high tide censuses in south San Francisco Bay, Wilson's phalaropes were most commonly found on the salt ponds and on islands in the salt ponds; they have also been observed in freshwater treatment ponds (Hanson and Kopec 1994). Harvey, et al. (1988) documented a preference for high salinity (75-200 ppt) ponds, probably due to the invertebrates that are present in more abundance at these higher salinities.

Foraging – Wilson's phalaropes forage most commonly on open water habitats, either by "spinning," or by standing in shallow water and lunging, or by scything like an avocet. Unlike other phalarope species present

Figure 6.20 Relative Use of Salt Ponds by American Avocet, Snowy Plover, Black-necked Stilt, and Phalaropes

Data from PRBO Pacific Flyway Project, 1988-1992. Unpublished data.

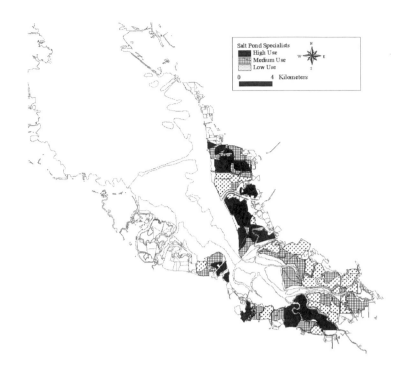

on the Bay, they also probe mudflats; foraging strategy is probably dictated by prey availability. Prey items found in five birds collected on South San Francisco Bay salt ponds included water-boatmen, pupae of brine flies, brine shrimp, seed of round stem bulrush, and larvae of brine flies and other insects (Anderson 1970).

Roosting – Wilson's phalaropes roost at night on open water. In the San Francisco Bay, they roost nocturnally on the salt ponds. On inland lakes, they also form diurnal roosting flocks on shore or on boulders (Jehl 1988). They may possibly use islands or levees in the Bay's salt pond system for this purpose but this has not been documented.

Movement – There is no recorded observation of local movements of Wilson's phalaropes. Because this species has been observed foraging on mudflats in other locations, they may be moving from the ponds to exposed mud during low tides.

Conservation and Management

Wilson's phalarope is threatened by loss of its breeding habitat, the seasonal wetlands of the interior. Many of its post-breeding locations (the salt pond system, Mono Lake, the Salton Sea, and Great Salt Lake) are undergoing change, some created by human management and some outside of that control. Threats to wintering habitat in South America are poorly understood.

Recommendations

The South Bay is the area of greatest importance to this species, and salt ponds and treatment ponds, both of which are used for foraging and roosting, are the most important habitat elements.

Wilson's phalaropes use the San Francisco Bay most heavily for two weeks in late July during their post-breeding migration, the time when they are most dependent on the Bay. Most bird surveys do not capture the true numbers of Wilson's phalaropes in the Bay because of the short duration of their visit, but the importance of the Bay to the population should not be underestimated. Wetlands could possibly be managed for this species if more was known about its requirements. Maintain medium to high salinity ponds, especially in June-August and particularly in the South Bay, where mild climatic conditions may be favored by shorebirds in general.

Suisun – Wilson's phalaropes have only been reported in small numbers from the Suisun subregion, but this may be due to the timing and nature of bird surveys in that area. Maintain or increase the current acreage of managed wetlands to support this species.

North Bay – Though pond habitat exists in the North Bay subregion, Wilson's phalaropes have not been seen. This may be due to the timing of the bird surveys, however. Maintain some of the existing salt ponds to support this species.

Central Bay – Wilson's phalaropes have not been seen in the Central Bay subregion. Promote inclusion of ponds and managed wetlands in any bayland restoration projects that may be undertaken in this highly developed area.

South Bay – Maintain the current acreages of low, mid, and high salinity salt ponds, and of treatment ponds. Particularly important within this region are the

Hayward area sewage treatment ponds; Turk Island area ponds (particularly 1C-6C); Coyote Hills Ponds 2A-4A; Coyote Creek waterbird pond; Sunnyvale sewage treatment ponds; Mountain View Pond A3N; and Ravenswood Ponds 2 and 4A.

Many more ponds in the South Bay subregion have the potential for use by Wilson's phalarope (Dumbarton; Mowry ponds; Alviso ponds; Ponds A3E and A3W in Mountain View), but birds have not been seen on these ponds yet. This may be due to the timing of the surveys.

Research Needs

Future research should investigate optimum salinities for the invertebrate prey base this species is dependent on.

References

Anderson, W. 1970. A preliminary study of the relationship of saltponds and wildlife-south San Francisco Bay. Calif. Dept. Fish and Game 56: 240-252.

Bent, A.C. 1927. Life histories of North American shorebirds. Part 1. U. S. Natl. Mus. Bull. No. 142.

Colwell, M.A. and J.R. Jehl. 1994. Wilson's phalarope (*Phalaropus tricolor*). *In:* A. Poole and F. Gill (eds). Birds of North America, No. 83. Philadelphia: The Academy of Natural Sciences, Washington, D.C. and The American Ornithologists' Union.

Dahl, T.E. and C.E. Johnson. 1991. Status and trends of wetlands in the conterminous United States, mid-1970s to mid-1980s. U. S. Fish and Wildl. Serv., Washington, D.C.

Hanson, J.T. and D. Kopec. 1994. Habitat location and utilization by wintering and migrating shorebirds during high tides in south San Francisco Bay. A draft report of the San Francisco Bay Bird Observatory.

Harvey, T.E., P.R. Kelly, R.W. Lowe and D. Fearn. 1988. The value of saltponds in San Francisco Bay and considerations for future management. Presented at: Wetlands '88: Urban Wetlands and Riparian Habitat, June 26-29, 1988, Oakland, CA.

Jehl, J.R., Jr. 1988. Biology of eared grebe and Wilson's phalarope in the nonbreeding season: A study of adaptations to saline lakes. Stud. Avian Biol. 12: 1-74.

Jurek, R.M. 1973. California Shorebird Study, Project Final Report.

Page, G. and R. Gill. 1994. Shorebirds in western North America: late 1800s to late 1900s. Stud. Avian Biol. 15: 147-160.

Reed, J.M., N. Warnock and L.W. Oring. 1994. Censusing shorebirds in the western Great Basin of North America. Int. Wader Studies 9: 1-81.

Stenzel, L.E. and G.W. Page. 1988. Results of the 16-18 April shorebird census of San Francisco and San Pablo bays. A draft report of Point Reyes Bird Observatory. PRBO Contrib. No. 401.

Swarth, C., C. Akagi and P. Metropulos. 1982. The distribution patterns and ecology of waterbirds using the Coyote Hills salt ponds. U. S. Dept. of Interior, Fish and Wildlife Service, San Francisco Bay National Wildlife Refuge. 69pp.

Waterfowl and Shorebirds of the San Francisco Bay Estuary

John Y. Takekawa
Gary W. Page
Janice M. Alexander
Dennis R. Becker

Introduction

Waterfowl and shorebirds are characterized by their mobility and strong dependence on aquatic and wetland habitats. The San Francisco Bay Estuary is renown as a major North American refuge for many species of waterfowl and shorebirds during their migration and wintering (August through April) periods, and it provides breeding habitat during the summer for a few species (e.g., mallard *Anas platyrhynchos*, black-necked stilt *Himantopus mexicanus*, snowy plover *Charadrius alexandrinus nivosus*). The Estuary is recognized as a Western Hemisphere Shorebird Reserve Network site of international importance for more than a million shorebirds in migration (Kjelmyr et al. 1991; PRBO, unpubl. rept.) and as the winter home for more than 50% of the diving ducks in the Pacific Flyway (Accurso 1992) with one of the largest wintering populations of canvasbacks (*Aythya valisineria*) in North America.

Current populations of shorebird and waterfowl species in the Estuary are a reflection of human alterations (see Nichols et al. 1986) that have resulted in increased numbers of some species while others have decreased. We do not know how many distinct populations depend on the habitats of this ecosystem and contribute to diversity and stability of continental populations. For example, northern pintails (*Anas acuta*) in the South Bay have little interchange with birds in the Central Valley, and they may represent a distinct subpopulation (M. Miller, pers. comm.). Western sandpipers (*Calidris mauri*) show strong site fidelity to small areas in the South Bay and do not leave that subregion during the winter (Warnock and Takekawa 1996).

Loss of more than 90% of the wetlands in the past 150 years has greatly altered the ecosystem, resulting in

Waterfowl & Shorebirds

the proposed listing or protection of more than one hundred species, many associated with tidal salt marsh habitats. Many projects to rehabilitate or restore wetlands, especially tidal salt marshes, have been proposed to benefit listed species in the Estuary. For example, the San Francisco International Airport recently proposed restoration of salt ponds in the South Bay, used heavily by both waterfowl and shorebirds, to tidal marsh as mitigation for runway expansion. However, results of such wetland restoration efforts are highly variable (Race 1985), and the efforts to complete successful salt marsh restorations for certain species may come at the expense of shorebird and waterfowl populations that use the existing habitats, including salt evaporation ponds. Critical habitats for waterfowl and shorebirds include tidal flats; sparsely vegetated wetland elements (levees, islets, beaches); managed wetlands; large, persistent seasonal ponds with lots of open water; and active and inactive salt evaporation ponds.

Unfortunately, we lack specific information relating abundance of current populations to the amount of their habitats. We are unable to predict how reduction of present wetland habitat used by these species may affect their populations. Thus, we recommend care in implementing large-scale changes and encourage further study of critical habitats and better delineation of the regional populations present in the ecosystem. We also offer several principles to guide management efforts while considering the habitat needs of waterfowl and shorebirds (Goals Project 1999: Appendix C), and emphasize that these species are unlikely to benefit from tidal marsh conversions when the conversion is from another wetland type. Finally, we support an ultimate goal of accepting no net loss of shorebird and waterfowl resources and populations in the ecosystem while conducting restoration or enhancement projects.

Waterfowl

The San Francisco Bay region is identified as one of the 34 waterfowl habitat areas of major concern in the North American Waterfowl Management Plan (USFWS 1989). More than 30 species of waterfowl are found in the San Francisco Bay ecosystem. These species are commonly divided into dabbling ducks, which feed at the surface or in shallow water to the depth of their body length, diving ducks, which forage underwater, and swans and geese, which feed on plants by grubbing in sediments of wetlands or fields. Mid-winter waterfowl surveys (USFWS, unpubl. data) of the San Francisco Bay and Delta include more than 700,000 waterfowl, and surveys of the open bays and salt ponds (Accurso 1992) include more than 300,000 individuals, a 25% decrease from the earliest surveys in the 1950s. In 1988-1990, dabbling ducks comprised up to 57,000 of the waterfowl in the open bays and ponds of the Estuary, while diving ducks com-

prised up to 220,000 of the total. For this review, we selected six species as representative taxa of the waterfowl and the habitats they use in the ecosystem.

Dabbling ducks represent 8-30% of total waterfowl numbers. Northern pintail (*Anas acuta*) use a wide variety of habitats, including managed marsh, seasonal wetlands, open bay, and salt ponds (see *Northern Pintail profile*). They were historically the most common dabbling ducks in the ecosystem, but recent population declines of this species have been severe (90% decrease in Suisun Marsh). Pintails in the South Bay subregion have little interchange with birds in the Central Valley (M. Miller, pers. comm.) and may comprise a distinct population with a unique breeding area. Mallards (*Anas platyrhynchos*) have large economic and recreational importance as a hunted species, and are the most abundant dabbling duck in diked baylands, and especially seasonal wetlands, low salinity salt ponds, and managed marshes of the San Pablo and South Bay subregions.

However, the Estuary is most recognized for the large populations of diving ducks, both bay ducks and sea ducks. Canvasbacks (*Aythya valisneria*) are bay ducks that were identified as a species of special concern because of declining numbers, but the Estuary still supports the largest population of canvasbacks in the Pacific Flyway and represents one of the largest wintering areas in North America (see *Canvasback profile*). Protecting their open bay habitats was part of the reason that the San Pablo Bay National Wildlife Refuge was established in the 1970s. They traditionally foraged on aquatic plants in mouths of rivers or channels, but now primarily consume nonindigenous mollusks in open bays or salt ponds. The Estuary also is a major wintering area for up to 140,000 greater and lesser scaup (*A. marila* and *A. affinis*), a species we associate with canvasbacks that comprises more than 40% of the waterfowl in the open bays and salt ponds. However, scaup have suffered an unexplained continental decline in the past decade. Smaller diving ducks of the Estuary include the ruddy duck (*Oxyura jaimaicensis*) and bufflehead (*Bucephala albeola*), which use a variety of managed marsh areas and

Mallards have significant economic and recreational importance as a hunted species. Hunting proponents lead many efforts to preserve and restore waterfowl habitat.

Calif. Dept. Fish and Game

salt ponds in the baylands. The wintering population of ruddy ducks is one of the largest in North America (see *Ruddy Duck profile*), and as many as 7,000 bufflehead also are found in the Estuary.

Many sea ducks have declining populations which resulted in organization of a Sea Duck Joint Venture under the North American Waterfowl Management Plan. Sea ducks use open-water marine habitats, and surf scoters (*Melanitta perspicillata*) are one of the least studied of the North American waterfowl (see *Surf Scoter profile*). San Francisco Bay appears to be the most important inshore habitat for this species in the eastern Pacific, south of the Straits of Georgia and Puget Sound. Surf scoters are the second most numerous species in the ecosystem, with estimates as high as 73,000 birds in 1991 (Trost 1997).

Geese and swans are of economic and recreational importance, as four of the six members of this group are hunted, and overpopulation of geese may cause large urban and agricultural damage. These species are associated primarily with managed wetlands and agricultural lands in the region. Tule geese (*Anser albifrons gambeli*) were chosen to represent geese and swans, because they are recognized as one of the smallest goose populations in the world (> 7,000), and Suisun Marsh is one of the few wintering areas where it is found. Formerly, geese were present in larger numbers in the San Francisco Bay Estuary, but they are now down to a remnant few, primarily in Suisun Marsh. A population of what was perhaps a few hundred greater white-fronted geese (and possibly the tule subspecies) in the North Bay now number less than 20 individuals (L. Allen, pers. comm.), and thousands of lesser snow geese (*Anser caerulescens caerulescens*), which were once reported in the South Bay, no longer occur in the region.

Waterfowl Habitat Considerations

Salt Evaporation Ponds – In one of the only studies to examine wetland conversion effects on ducks, the body condition of mallards decreased significantly following loss of salt pans and fish ponds in Spain (Rodrigues and Fabiao 1997). Alternate roosting areas were 13 km farther from feeding areas, which may have resulted in higher energy costs for travel. Salt evaporation ponds supported 30-41% of the waterfowl in the San Francisco Bay Estuary, 9-14% in the former North Bay ponds, and 21-27% in the South Bay ponds (Accurso 1992). Many of the birds found in the Estuary during migration (September-October, March-April) were found in these areas. Up to 42,000 diving ducks have been counted in the North Bay ponds, including 30% of the ruddy ducks in the Estuary, 59% of the canvasbacks, and 38% of the bufflehead. As many as 15% of the dabbling ducks were also found in these ponds, including 19% of the northern pintail and 47% of the

mallards. Eighty-three percent of waterfowl were found in 54% of the salt pond area with salinities of 20-93 ppt, with most birds preferring 20-33 ppt areas. Pond size explained much of the variation in counts, with less than 2% of the use on small ponds < 150 ha, and most diving duck use on ponds 200 to 550 ha.

South Bay salt ponds supported up to 76,000 or 27% of the Estuary's total waterfowl. This area provided the largest haven for ruddy ducks (up to 67% of the population), and supported 17% of the canvasbacks, 50% of the bufflehead, and up to 86% (47,000) of dabbling ducks, including the majority (90%) of northern shovelers. Waterfowl were concentrated in lower salinity (20-63 ppt) ponds, with few birds present in ponds above 154 ppt. Most waterfowl used ponds of moderate size, from 50 to 175 ha.

Open Bay Areas – Up to 50% or 140,000 of the diving ducks surveyed in the Estuary during the winter were counted in the North Bay subregion. Densities were as high as 653 birds/100 ha. The populations include up to 35% of the scoter, 26% of the canvasbacks, and 12% of the scaup. Most of the use was in water depths < 4 m, although much of the open bay area was less than 6 m. The Central Bay supported 17% of the waterfowl, or up to 53,000 birds including 20% of the diving ducks. This area was important for scoter (up to 50%), scaup (16%), and bufflehead (13%), but only 1% of the dabbling ducks. The South Bay supported 9-11% or 36,000 of the waterfowl in the Estuary, and was important for scaup (18%) and scoter (16%). The open waters of Suisun Bay supported only 12% of waterfowl in the Estuary, including up to 15% of the diving ducks (17% of scaup, 16% of scoter, and 16% of canvasbacks).

Shorebirds

Shorebirds are aquatic birds with cylindrical bills varying considerably in length and curvature, reflecting different foraging strategies. Among the 31 species encountered regularly on San Francisco Bay, a wide range of sizes is evident from the sparrow-sized least sandpiper (*Calidris minutilla*) to the duck-sized long-billed curlew (*Numenius americanus*). They feed primarily on invertebrates obtained on tidal flats, salt ponds, managed wetlands and other habitats. Most tidal flat specialists are found concentrated in the North and South bays (**Figure 6.21**; G. Page, unpubl. data). Recent survey information indicates that San Francisco Bay supports very high numbers of shorebirds of most species during migration and winter compared with other wetlands along the Pacific Coast of the United States (Page et al. 1999). San Francisco Bay has been recognized as a site of hemispheric importance to shorebirds by the Western Hemisphere Shorebird Reserve Network.

The Waterfowl and Shorebirds Focus Team selected seven "key" shorebird species as a basis for defining regional wetland habitat goals for shorebirds. The key shorebird species were selected based on their taxonomic grouping, population status, and habitat use (Goals Project 1999). The Pacific Coast population of western snowy plover was selected because it is federally listed as a threatened species, and about 10% of the listed population (over 100 pairs) has been recorded breeding in the Estuary, primarily in South Bay salt evaporation ponds (see *Snowy Plover profile*). The red knot (*Calidris canutus*) was selected because the Estuary is one of only three wetlands on the Pacific Coast supporting as many as several hundred wintering individuals, and they are found foraging in tidal flats of the Central and South bays and roosting in salt ponds.

The western sandpiper is the most abundant shorebird in the Estuary (see *Western Sandpiper profile*), and represents small sandpipers and plovers, while the marbled godwit (*Limosa fedoa*) was selected to represent large sandpipers and plovers. Tidal flats are the most important foraging habitat of all these species, and they roost at high tides in salt ponds, managed wetlands, seasonal wetlands, and other habitats above the high tide line. The long-billed dowitcher (*Limnodromous scolopaceus*) and its associates are singled out as potentially deriving more benefit from managed brackish water wetlands and seasonal wetlands than other shorebirds (see Takekawa and Warnock, in press). The black turnstone (*Arenaria melanocephala*) represents shorebirds that use gravel to rocky intertidal habitat (see *Black Turnstone profile*), although none of these rocky intertidal species are abundant in the Bay, numbering at most in the low hundreds.

The Wilson's phalarope (*Phalaropus tricolor*) was chosen to represent those shorebirds that, in addition to the snowy plover, are most dependent on the salt ponds for foraging habitat. These salt pond specialists are found patchily distributed (Figure 6.22; G Page, unpubl. data), especially in the South Bay salt ponds, depending on water level and salinity. Some members of this group, including the Wilson's and red-necked phalarope (*Phalaropus lobatus*), occur only during spring and fall migration, while the others, including black-necked stilt and American avocet (*Recurvirostra americana*), are resident and nest primarily in South Bay salt ponds.

Shorebird Habitat Considerations

Except for anecdotal information suggesting an increase by shorebird species using salt ponds as their primary foraging or breeding habitat, there are no consistent historic data on changes in abundance of shorebirds in the Estuary during the past 150 years when most human-induced habitat alterations have occurred. The most recent mapping of historic and current habitats by the San Francisco Estuary Institute (SFEI) indicates that tidal flats outboard of the salt marshes have increased in the North Bay and South Bay subregions, but that the total amount of tidal flat has decreased in all subregions, primarily due to loss of tidal flats along slough channels in salt marshes. Since the majority of the shorebirds in the Bay use tidal flats as their primary foraging habitat, the amount of foraging areas, and possibly the abundance of these species, may have decreased in the past 150 years, unless artificial salt ponds and managed wetlands have compensated for the tidal flat losses.

For the majority of shorebirds that forage primarily on tidal flats, conversion of salt ponds might be mitigated (by an unpredictable degree) by creating wide, gently-sloped tidal flats along large channels in restored tidal marsh. Tidal salt marsh and slough channels do not, however, provide high tide roosting habitat for most shorebird species, which require barren to sparsely vegetated sites above the high tide line. Thus, in projects where tidal marshes replace existing habitats, suitable roosting areas in reasonable proximity to tidal flats will need to be constructed to replace roosting areas that are lost.

For the salt pond specialists, substantial areas of salt pond habitat should be maintained in both the North Bay and South Bay subregions. If portions of the existing salt pond systems are converted to tidal marsh and managed salt ponds, it will not be feasible to set aside ponds with important shorebird habitat in a piecemeal fashion. Instead, smaller salt pond systems should be retained and activity managed to produce salinities and water depths most favorable to shorebirds and the other aquatic species targeted for protection. Low, wide, barren to sparsely-vegetated internal levees with fine scale topographic relief should be incorporated into the pond design as nesting and roosting substrate. In addition, salt marsh restoration efforts should attempt to recreate playas that occurred in historic salt marshes.

Since the success of marsh restoration efforts are likely to be highly unpredictable and the value of slough mudflats and salt marsh playa for shorebirds is not well understood, incorporation of these habitats into restored marshes should not be counted as replacement habitat for shorebirds. Further research must be undertaken to

Shorebirds on the mudflats at Charlston Slough, South San Francisco Bay

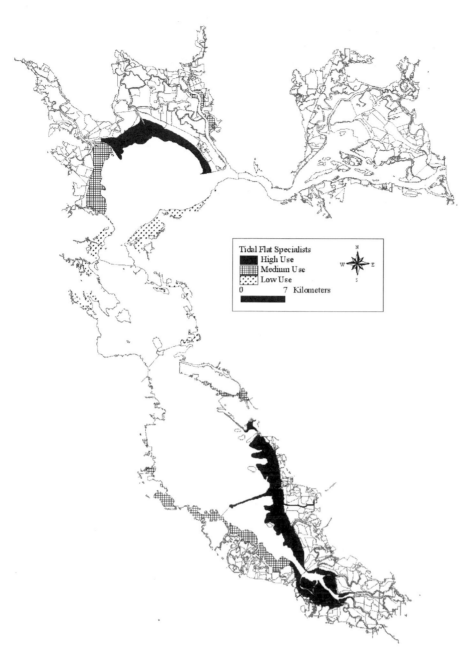

Figure 6.21 Relative Use (High, Medium, Low) of Different Mudflat Areas by Tidal Flat Specialists, as Indicated from the Proportion of Shorebirds Counted in Different Survey Areas

Data from PRBO Pacific Flyway Project, 1988-1992. Unpublished data.

Tidal Flat Specialists
High Use
Medium Use
Low Use

0   7   Kilometers

N
W   E
S

estimate the amount of salt pond habitat that should be intensively managed for shorebirds and other target species. The maintenance of at least the current numbers of shorebirds relying extensively on salt pond habitat will require an adequate acreage of suitable ponds for 25,000 wintering American avocets, 5,000-7,000 wintering black-necked stilts, tens of thousands of migrating Wilson's and red-necked phalaropes in the fall, and 300 breeding snowy plovers.

General Recommendations for Waterfowl and Shorebirds

It is important to maintain existing populations of waterfowl and shorebirds in the Bay while increasing habitat for other species that are dependent on salt marsh. Increasing the acreage of salt marsh will come at the expense of other habitats, especially salt ponds and managed wetlands that are also important for waterfowl and shorebirds. Maintaining current shorebird and waterfowl populations will thus require increasing the carrying capacity of remaining salt ponds and managed wetlands or recreating their function in new locations.

Suisun – Although these wetlands are managed primarily for waterfowl habitat by private land owners, populations of one of the major target species, northern pintail, have decreased by as much as 90%. Thus, despite the best management efforts, populations of waterfowl in the Suisun Marsh have decreased. Any conversion of managed wetland habitats will result in a loss of waterfowl. Conversion of this area should proceed gradually to provide time to evaluate population changes and the effects of the loss of habitat. Conversion or loss of this habitat type must be offset by enhanced manage-

Waterfowl & Shorebirds

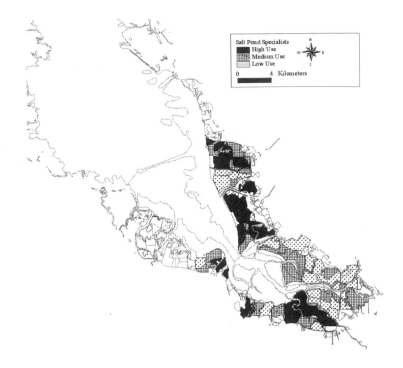

Figure 6.22 Relative Use (High, Medium, Low) of Different South Bay Salt Pond Areas by Salt Pond Specialists as Indicated from the Proportion of Shorebirds Counted in Different Survey Areas

Data from PRBO Pacific Flyway Project, 1988-1992. Unpublished data.

ment of existing areas or mitigation with alternative areas. Shorebirds are present in the tens of thousands. Management should be promoted to improve areas for their populations.

North Bay – The former salt evaporation ponds in this region are a critical area for waterfowl and shorebirds. Ongoing conversion should be linked to enhanced management of existing areas or mitigation. In this subregion, conversion of 50% of the former salt ponds may result in loss of 24% of the 42,000 waterfowl that are counted in these ponds (**Figure 6.23**; J. Takekawa, unpubl. data). Change in salt pond areas may already be resulting in reduction of waterfowl numbers (USFWS mid-winter surveys, unpubl. data). Thus, there is an immediate need to develop alternative managed marsh areas in this subregion. Although mudflat habitats seem abundant in the North Bay, shorebird roosting habitats may be limiting and should be increased.

Central Bay – This subregion is highly urbanized and is used least by both waterfowl and shorebirds. Any additional roosting habitat that can be protected from disturbance would be beneficial in maintaining or improving existing populations. Restoration of any large, shallow ponds would likely benefit waterfowl and shorebirds. Wetland rehabilitation in urban areas should be encouraged.

South Bay – The majority of the waterfowl and shorebirds in the South Bay use the salt evaporation ponds for roosting or feeding habitat during the winter. Conversion or loss of this habitat type must be offset by enhanced management of existing areas or mitigation with alternative areas, including created salt ponds, managed wetlands, and seasonal wetlands. For example,

analysis of waterfowl survey data from 1988-1990 suggests that if 50% of the salt ponds are converted, 15% of the 76,000 waterfowl may be lost (**Figure 6.24**; J. Takekawa, unpubl. data). An increasing number of waterfowl would be displaced if more area was converted.

Although mudflat foraging habitat seems adequate, with salt pond conversion, suitable roosting habitat for shorebirds may become limiting. Little is known about how salt ponds and seasonal wetlands provide food for shorebirds and protected microclimate areas during adverse weather. Thus, we recommend not more than 50% or 15,000 acres of salt ponds in the South Bay be converted to other habitats without careful planning for habitat mitigation for shorebird and waterfowl populations. We also recommend an increase in seasonal wetlands as migration habitat and roosting areas.

Enhancing Tidal Marsh Restoration Projects for Waterfowl and Shorebirds

Waterfowl and shorebirds may use several elements in tidal salt marshes. As restoration or rehabilitation is undertaken, these elements should be provided when possible.

1. Larger channels with large mudflats are often used by shorebird and waterfowl species and should be encouraged in tidal marsh design.
2. Muted tidal areas provide temporal diversity which may provide good habitat, especially for diving ducks.
3. Unvegetated levees and islets with gradual slopes that are durable, and bare areas that remain unvegetated with limited management should be constructed as roosting sites.

Waterfowl & Shorebirds

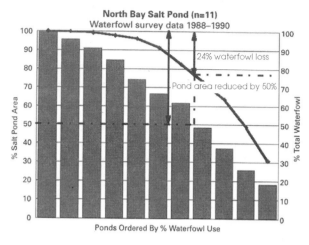

Figure 6.23 Waterfowl Use of Salt Ponds in the North Bay Ordered from Most to Least Waterfowl Use

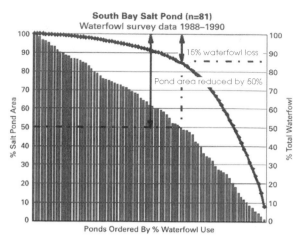

Figure 6.24 Waterfowl Use of Salt Ponds in the South Bay Ordered from Most to Least Waterfowl Use

4. A diverse mix of pans and ponds should be retained in marsh plains for high tide roosting and foraging areas.

5. Designs should be made to minimize disturbance by people, pets, and predators.

6. Surveys of waterfowl and shorebirds should be conducted prior to restoring areas to tidal salt marsh so losses may be evaluated and suitably mitigated.

Research Needs

Relationships among habitat change and change in populations of waterbirds have been studied in other estuaries (see Goss-Custard et al. 1997). We should learn from these efforts and develop a research program in the San Francisco Bay Estuary to examine questions raised during the Habitat Goals Project, including the following topics:

1. Determine the feasibility of designing ponds or systems from the existing salt evaporation ponds which can support the current populations of waterfowl and shorebirds.

2. Evaluate what constitutes a good roosting area for different species of shorebirds, including distance from feeding areas. Areas used within tidal salt marshes should be included.

3. Estimate the size and composition of shorebird populations in Suisun subregion.

4. Determine the importance of non-mudflat habitats such as salt ponds and seasonal wetlands as foraging areas, especially during inclement weather.

5. Examine seasonal wetland use and extent (not currently shown in the EcoAtlas), including diked farmland, grazed baylands, diked marsh, managed marsh, and ruderal baylands through wet and dry years.

6. Test differences in shorebird and waterfowl response to different actions in managed wetlands by measuring use-days and numbers.

7. Relate diving ducks use of wetlands by area size and water depth.

8. Quantify shorebird foraging and roosting in wetlands other than intertidal flats, including intertidal pans, low and medium salinity ponds, managed marsh, diked marsh, muted tidal, and seasonal ponds. Include factors such as tidal cycle, salinity, vegetation, and distance to intertidal flats.

9. Describe use of wetlands by salinity and prey differences for waterfowl and shorebirds.

10. Provide more information about the effects of disturbance on waterfowl and shorebirds to develop suitable habitat buffer zones.

11. Determine the effects of channelization, levee alteration, and use of dredged-spoil on mobilization of contaminants sequestered in soils or sediments and bioaccumulation in waterfowl and shorebirds.

12. Characterize hydrology, biology, and chemistry of salt ponds heavily- and lightly-used by waterfowl and shorebirds to examine the differences.

13. Determine habitat values and use by waterfowl and shorebirds of managed wetlands versus tidal wetlands.

14. Investigate the effect non-native invertebrates and plants (e.g. *Potamocorbula amurensis, Spartina alterniflora*) on waterfowl and shorebirds.

15. Evaluate methods to reduce effects of non-native predators on waterfowl and shorebirds.

16. Examine the effects of contaminants on breeding birds.

17. Pilot Projects – encourage monitored experiments in wetland restoration or mitigation. Pilot Projects should:

Waterfowl & Shorebirds

a. Include repeatable waterbird surveys before and after project actions.

b. Examine maintenance or creation of salt pond systems, including low to mid-salinity ponds in the absence of commercial production. Habitat values and use should be maximized while minimizing maintenance costs.

c. Test methods of constructing habitat elements with low maintenance requirements such as bare roosting islands, intertidal pans, and non-tidal seasonal ponds.

d. Examine differences in use of different wetland unit sizes.

e. Test methods of increasing shorebird and waterfowl use of managed marshes.

f. Increase monitoring efforts on existing projects with habitat elements valuable for waterfowl and shorebirds.

g. Employ adaptive management by applying earlier findings to change design elements through time.

h. Conduct preliminary sampling for contaminants of areas designated for salt marsh restoration.

i. Conduct preliminary sampling of salt ponds for invertebrate community, salinity, and other water quality characteristics.

References

Accurso, L.M. 1992. Distribution and abundance of wintering waterfowl on San Francisco Bay 1988-1990. Unpubl. Master's Thesis. Humboldt State Univ. Arcata, CA. 252pp.

Goals Project. 1999. Baylands ecosystem habitat goals. A report of habitat recommendations prepared by the San Francisco Bay Area Wetlands Ecosystem Goals Project. U.S. Environmental Protection Agency, San Francisco, CA/S.F. Bay Regional Water Quality Control Board, Oakland, CA.

Goss-Custard, J.D., R. Rufino and A. Luis (eds). 1997. Effect of habitat loss and change on waterbirds. ITE Symposium No. 30 and Wetlands International Publ. No. 42. The Stationary Office, London.

Nichols, F.H., J.E. Cloern, S.N. Luoma and D. H. Peterson. 1986. The modification of an estuary. Science 231:567-573.

Page, G.W., L.E. Stenzel and J.E. Kyelmyr. 1999. Overview of shorebird abundance and distribution of the Pacific Coast of the contiguous United States. Condor 101:461-471.

Race, M.S. 1985. Critique of present wetlands mitigation policies in the United States based on an analysis of past restoration projects in San Francisco Bay. Environ. Mgmt. 9:71-82.

Rodrigues, D. and A. Fabiao. 1997. Loss and change of habitat and possible effects on mallard populations of Mondego and Vouga river basins. *In*: J.D. Goss-Custard, R. Rufino and A. Luis (eds). Effect of habitat loss and change on waterbirds. ITE Symposium No. 30, Wetlands International Publ. No. 42. Centre for Ecology and Hydrology, Natural Environment Research Council, London. pp 127-130.

Takekawa, J.Y. and N. Warnock. *In press*. Long-billed dowitcher (*Limnodromous scolopaceus*). *In*: A. Poole and F. Gill (eds). The birds of North America. The Academy of Natural Sciences, Philadelphia, and The American Ornithologists' Union, Washington, D.C.

Trost, R.E. 1997. Pacific Flyway 1996-97 Fall and winter waterfowl survey report. U.S. Fish and Wildlife Service, Migratory Bird Mgmt. Office, Portland, OR. unpubl. data.

Warnock, S.E., and J.Y. Takekawa. 1996. Wintering site fidelity and movement patterns of western sandpipers *Calidris mauri* in the San Francisco Bay Estuary. Ibis 138:160-167.

United States Fish and Wildlife Service (USFWS). 1989. Concept plan for waterfowl habitat protection. North American waterfowl management plan, category 27. U. S. Dep. Int., Fish Wildl. Serv. Rep., Portland, OR.

Personal Communications

Janet Kjelmyr, Staff Biologist, Point Reyes Bird Observatory, Stinson Beach, California.

Michael Miller, U.S. Geological Survey, Biological Resources Division, Dixon Field Station, California.

L. Allen, Canvasback Duck Club, Napa, California.

7

Other Birds of the Baylands Ecosystem

Eared Grebe

Podiceps nigricollis

Howard L. Cogswell

Introduction

The eared grebe is a small, stocky-bodied bird that may be found in a variety of habitats within the San Francisco Estuary, and particularly in the salt ponds of the South Bay. The eared grebe acquires its name from the golden tufts of feathers that fan out behind the eyes of the adult in breeding plumage.

Description

Breeding Biology – Eared grebes nest primarily on medium-sized to large lakes with marshy borders. They build a floating nest attached to underwater or emergent vegetation, as is typical of grebes. Where successful, they typically nest in colonies from a few pairs to many hundreds. In California, most breeding occurs at lakes east of the Sierra Nevada-Cascade mountain ranges. However, at least in wet years, nesting colonies have been found in the Sacramento and San Joaquin valleys, inland valleys of coast-slope southern California, and at such mountain lakes as Lake Tahoe and the Big Bear-Baldwin lakes in San Bernardino County (Grinnell and Miller 1944; miscell. records).

S. H. Hinshaw

In the Bay Area, a colony of 70 or more eared grebes nested in 1983 in northwest Pleasanton on out-of-use sewage ponds with marsh at one corner. There were at least 65 young produced at this site that were still flightless when the pond was drained in July, and the adults all left. Most of the young that survived in the remaining border ditch were captured, banded, and released at Coyote Hills or Lake Chabot (personal field notes and Amer. Birds 37:1022). An apparently larger colony (101 nests in use or being built on July 15) the same year was successful in Crittenden Marsh near Moffett Field, 39 juveniles being seen there on August 19 (Bousman, pers. comm.). At least 12 adults and 15 "immatures" were noted in the same marsh in August 1986, and 10 nests (seven with eggs) were also there in June 1992, but these disappeared by July 25. On May 11-24, 1993, Peter Metropulos found 12+ nests, many with eggs, in a pond east of Crittenden Marsh[1]. Nests were constructed of emergent vegetation in 2-3 feet of water over *Salicornia*, about 10-15 feet from shore. On July 5, there was no eared grebe activity on the pond, although five pairs and six nearly-fledging young were on Crittenden Marsh. In 1994, as many as 10 adults were seen in the same area, at least six of them obviously paired, but no nesting evidence was obtained[2]. Irregular, but at least sometimes successful nesting is thus demonstrated in a bay-related habitat in our area of interest. Bousman (pers. comm.) also reported that Gloria Heller discovered at the Western Foundation of Vertebrate Zoology (Camarillo, California) a "nest card for eared grebe on an unnamed lake on Stanford University on May 14, 1908 with seven eggs (not collected)." This was apparently the earliest record of breeding anywhere near the Bay. Neither Grinnell and Wythe (1927) nor Grinnell and Miller (1944) mentioned this early record, although they indicated summer occurrence on Lake Merced, San Francisco, as indicative of possible nesting there.

---

[1] This was an out-of-use salt pond, and so may have contained brackish rainwater.
[2] These records were summarized from the Santa Clara County breeding season records of eared grebes, supplied by William Bousman.

Migration Ecology – The Great Salt Lake, Utah, and Mono Lake in central-eastern California are well-known major concentration points for post-breeding migrant eared grebes. Adults engage in a "molt-migration" to reach such areas and begin to put on weight from the abundant food (brine shrimp, etc.) before beginning their annual molt, which involves loss of all flight feathers at the same time. The birds are thus flightless for more than a month. Many aspects of the Mono Lake populations – the weight changes, progress of the molt, mortality, arrival, departure, and distribution on the surface of the lake – are detailed by Jehl (1988). Total eared grebe populations on Mono Lake, per Jehl's extensive sampling and careful analysis, reached peaks of 500,000 to 800,000 in September through October. He also showed a summary map of sizes of populations at this and other (all lesser) migration stopover points for August through October 1985. However, Jehl's work did not include San Francisco Bay salt ponds, despite the fact that they undoubtedly held far more than the median number of grebes (6,000) among his sites from Saskatchewan to southeastern California.

Wintering Ecology – According to Jehl (1988) the only truly major concentrations during mid-winter are on the Salton Sea in southeastern California, and the Gulf of California, Mexico; but small numbers persist through some winters even at Mono Lake and other inland waters not subject to freezing. At Salton Sea, estimates of the total population in February and March have been as high as 205,000 to 700,000 (1977 and 1953 aerial counts; AOU 1998 and *Audubon Field Notes*). Christmas Bird Counts in 1981-82 through 1985-86 for only the south end of the Sea ranged from 3,510 to 24,140 (Jehl 1988).

Distribution and Abundance

North America – The regular breeding range of the eared grebe extends from southwestern Canada to western Minnesota and eastern Illinois south to northwestern Mexico and south-central Texas, with local populations south to central Mexico. In winter, numbers are found regularly along the Pacific Coast from southern British Columbia to Central America, and inland from central California, Utah, and central Texas south. Non-breeding birds of this species occur casually in the eastern United States. In the Old World, the eared or "black-necked" grebe is found locally across central and southern Eurasia and parts of Africa (AOU 1998, map in Palmer 1962). Several closely related species (classified as subspecies of the eared grebe by some authors) are resident in the Andes, high plateaus, or southern part of South America (Sibley and Monroe 1990).

San Francisco Bay Area – Eared grebes occur rather widely as migrants and more narrowly through the winter on waters of many sorts in the Bay Area. They have been seen on lakes, ponds, marsh sloughs, the open bay, and (especially during spring migration) even the ocean as far offshore as the Farallon Islands.

The larger counts or estimates of numbers of eared grebes tallied from published reports or field notes pertaining to San Francisco Bay or vicinity by Cogswell (1977) range from 10 to 170 on freshwater lakes (September through January), five to 50 on brackish lakes (Lake Merritt in Oakland and Berkeley Aquatic Park, October through January), 13 to 90 on eastern mid-San Francisco Bay or harbors connected to it (October through January), and 25 to 600 on the ocean near South Farallon Island (October through May, but mostly Christmas Bird Counts). By comparison, the peak numbers reached on medium-salinity salt evaporators from October through April regularly range in the hundreds or thousands per one to several large ponds. Counts in the southwestern Hayward evaporators were from 113 to 751 in September through December 1965-69, 490 on February 14, 1965, and 7,500 on April 17, 1965 – but only 83 on May 4, 1965 (H. Cogswell, field notes). The 7.5-mile radius Hayward-Fremont Christmas Bird Count circle (centered at Hwy. 880 and Whipple Rd.) includes all of the same salt ponds and others to the south as far as Dumbarton Point. Over 1,000 eared grebes are tallied in many years of that count, nearly all of which are on salt evaporators. The same is probably true for the occasional thousands (max. 13,615 in 1973) on the San Jose Christmas Bird Count, although a smaller area of salt ponds is in that circle.

Habitat Use and Behavior

Eared grebes may occasionally be seen in a variety of habitats within the San Francisco Estuary, but they most frequently are found in medium to high-salinity salt evaporator ponds, where they rest and forage. The decidedly preferred habitat from late August through April or early May is the medium or medium-high salinity ponds, where counts may range up to several thousand birds per pond. These ponds show high concentrations of brine shrimp (*Artemia salina*) and/or water boatmen (Hemiptera: *Corixidae*), which are prime prey for these small grebes. When on fresh water, they also take many kinds of aquatic insects and crustaceans but apparently few fish (Palmer 1962).

Two special studies of the use of salt-pond habitats by birds deserve mention. Anderson (1970) studied the series of ponds lying north of Mowry Slough, which then ranged from low-salinity (intake pond M1) through medium-high salinity. He found a maximum of 6,330 eared grebes in November on his "ponds of high salinity[3]." In a

---

[3] These ponds were actually of lower salinity than two or three other ponds that lay between his study area and the final crystallizers.

more thorough, two-year study of the 11 ponds lying west of Coyote Hills and north of the Dumbarton Bridge approach, Swarth, et al. (1982) reported a maximum count of 5,565 eared grebes in April 1980, but numbers the following spring were below 3,200. They had average counts of 500 and about 1,950 in November of the two successive years, and a very few were found through the summer. The November through April eared grebe numbers per 10 hectares in each of the 11 ponds in the same study were strongly correlated (at p<0.02 level) with the grams dry weight of invertebrate biomass in the same ponds. That biomass was calculated from samples obtained by hundreds of plankton hauls thru the upper ¼ meter of water within three meters of a canoe. Brine shrimp (*Artemia salina*) and water-boatmen (Hemiptera: *Corixidae*) constituted nearly all of these samples. The grebes may, however, also have been eating brine-fly (Diptera: *Ephydra* sp.) larvae and pupae which spend most of the time below the ¼-meter depth, or even adult brine flies on the water surface which are quite able to escape the hauled net.

In the baylands of the San Francisco Estuary, eared grebes will also use subtidal and tidal habitats (including large marsh channels) for foraging and resting, although this is more common on offshore islands during migration than on the Bay proper. A relatively few birds use freshwater marsh for breeding and foraging. Seasonal wetlands are used for foraging and less commonly for breeding, particularly when water ponds for long periods and there is at least some emergent or near-surface vegetation. For the purposes of the Goals Project (and the Project's Habitat Matrix), it should be considered that eared grebes do not significantly use those areas classified by the Project as tidal flats, tidal marsh, riparian woodland, adjacent uplands, unvegetated supratidal shores, rocky islands or cliffs, and towers or other human-built structures.

Conservation and Management

On the South Bay, each set of medium- to medium-high saline salt evaporators presumably hosts numbers of eared grebes similar to those cited above for the Mowry Slough, Coyote Hills, and southwest Hayward areas. Peaks appear to be in October or November on some ponds (at which time Mono Lake still harbors about a half-million or more grebes), while on other ponds the peak does not occur until spring migration in April. For example, during the April migration period in 1980, over 5,000 birds were reported west of Coyote Hills (Swarth et al. 1982), and on April 14, 1996, 2,000 birds were counted on one salt pond (H9) in Hayward (J.& F. Delfino, pers. comm.). There are at least seven sets of such medium-salinity ponds in the South Bay system. If it were estimated that each set of ponds harbors just 3,500 birds (the mean of the two figures cited) during the spring migration and in the fall, then it could be hypothesized that the South Bay salt ponds may support as many as 24,500 eared grebes. This would constitute an additional migration stop for this species that is well above the median for the entire range shown by Jehl. While midwinter numbers here are somewhat lower, there are still thousands of eared grebes to be found on the salt ponds, and the area as a whole may well serve as wintering or migration habitat for 50,000 to 100,000 birds—a significant portion of the total species population, even though far below the major magnets of Mono Lake and Salton Sea.

This species is the most partial to use of the salt-pond habitat of any of the birds found there. It should be recognized in all plans for future habitat management that this species would thus suffer a marked impairment of its total available high-quality habitat if the saline ponds were eliminated or sharply reduced in extent. Nearly the same dependence on saline lakes or salt ponds for migration stopovers is also likely true of the Wilson's and red-necked phalaropes, even though their wintering area is far to the south of that of the eared grebe.

References

American Ornithologists' Union (AOU). 1998. Checklist of North American birds, seventh ed. American Ornithologists Union. Allen Press, Inc. Lawrence, Kansas. 877pp.

Anderson, W. 1970. A preliminary study of the relationship of saltponds and wildlife–South San Francisco Bay. Calif. Fish and Game 56: 240-252.

Cogswell, H.L. 1977. Water birds of California. Univ. of Calif. Press, Berkeley. 399pp.

Grinnell, J. and M.W. Wythe. 1927. Directory to the bird-life of the San Francisco Bay region. Pacific Coast Avifauna no.18. 160pp. (Cooper Ornithological Club, Berkeley, Ca.).

Grinnell, J. and A.H. Miller. 1944. The distribution of the birds of California. Pacific Coast Avifauna no.27. 608pp. (Cooper Ornithological Club, Berkeley, Ca.).

Jehl, J.R. Jr. 1988. Biology of the eared grebe and Wilson's phalarope in the nonbreeding season: A study of adaptations to saline lakes. Studies in Avian Biology no.12. 74pp. (Cooper Ornithological Society).

Palmer, R.S. (ed). 1962. Handbook of North American birds. Volume 1. loons through flamingos. Yale Univ. Press, New Haven Conn. 567pp.

Sibley, C.G. and B.L. Monroe, Jr. 1990. Distribution and taxonomy of birds of the world. Yale Univ. Press, New Haven, Conn. 1111pp.

Swarth, C., C. Akagi and P. Metropulos. 1982. The distribution patterns and ecology of waterbirds using the Coyote Hills salt ponds. Report to San Francisco Bay Natl. Wildlife Refuge. U.S. Fish and Wildl. Serv. 75pp.

Other Birds

Personal Communications

William Bousman, *North American Birds*, Santa Clara County subregional editor. Menlo Park, California.
Janice and Frank Delfino, Castro Valley, California.
Peter Metropulos, *North American Birds,* San Mateo County subregional editor. Belmont, California. Pjmetrop@aol.com.

Western and Clark's Grebes

Aechmophorus occidentalis and *A. clarkii*

David G. Ainley

Introduction

The western and Clark's grebes are very closely related; until recently, the Clark's grebe was thought to be a light morph of the western grebe. Still more recent work indicates that the two soon may be re-merged taxonomically. In the San Francisco Bay region, the western grebe outnumbers the Clark's grebe by at least 9 to 1 (Shuford et al. 1989). The biology of the two species is virtually identical. Unless indicated otherwise, the information elsewhere in this account applies to both species and is from Storer and Nuechterlein (1992).

The western/Clark's grebe is the largest grebe in North America and one of the largest in the world; they are the size of a medium-sized duck (weighing about 1,430 g). These species are basically piscivores and the stiletto-shaped beak is well-suited for spearing fish. The bill also is used like a forceps to grasp fish (and occasionally crustaceans).

Distribution and Abundance

Western/Clark's grebe is found throughout the western portion of North America, except in the deserts and tundra. These grebes frequent lakes, large rivers, tidal sloughs, bays, and coastal marine waters (greater than 15 m deep). They breed on inland bodies of fresh and saline waters or protected tidal waters, from the Pacific Coast east to Colorado and from Saskatchewan south to Colorado. The breeding season extends from February to September (Cogswell 1977), and they vacate inland breeding areas, flying to the west coast, before freeze-up. Wintering birds occur in Pacific Coast waters from British Columbia south to Mexico.

These species do not breed in habitats that are directly part of San Francisco Bay. Around the Bay Area, these grebes breed among the tall emergent vegetation on a number of isolated reservoirs (e.g., Calaveras Reservoir, Santa Clara County: Bousman, pers. comm.; Lake Merced, San Francisco County: Grinnell and Miller 1944). The largest breeding population close to San Francisco Bay is at Clear Lake, Lake County, and at Lake San Antonio, Monterey County.

No area-wide counts for western/Clark's grebes are available either historically or in recent years. The longest records of local censuses come from various Christmas Bird Counts. Counts that have provided data from the late 1960s at localities reporting few grebes (circa five or fewer grebes reported per party-hour) — Crystal Springs Reservoir, Benicia, Oakland, Hayward-Fremont, and Palo Alto — have shown no trends in numbers. The southern Marin County count, however, began at levels of 30-70 grebes/party-hour in the early 1970s, but declined gradually to vary around 10 grebes/party-hour by the late 1980s or early 1990s.

Most of the grebes of these species seen on San Francisco Bay are non-breeding individuals. In the Bay Area, peak numbers occur October through April (Ainley and DeSante 1980, Briggs et al. 1987, Shuford et al. 1989), the non-breeding period. The majority of such wintering birds come from breeding sites well inland (Great Basin, etc.). A few individuals, perhaps including local breeders, can be seen on San Francisco Bay in any month of the year, however.

Habitat Use and Behavior

Within the San Francisco Estuary, western/Clark's grebes can be found in the waters of sheltered coves, and sparsely in sloughs. Rarely are they found in the open Bay, except along tidal rips in the vicinity of Racoon Straits and Angel Island.

Western/Clark's grebes are entirely aquatic and never come to land, unless ill. Their nests float, but are attached to emergent reeds. When foraging, these grebes dive by jumping up and forward. They use their feet for propulsion. Many of the fish consumed are near-bottom dwellers. Herring (*Clupea harengus*) are an important component of the diet of these grebes in bays of the Pacific Coast, such as Puget Sound (Palmer 1962). This fish is likely an important part of the grebe diet in San Francisco Bay.

S. H. Hinshaw

Other Birds

Conservation and Management

The presence of these species in San Francisco Bay is contingent upon the availability of forage fish, such as herring. The decline in grebe numbers in southern Marin may be due to changes in the herring population size or distribution. Herring, which occur most densely in the central and outer part of San Francisco Bay (waters of Marin and San Francisco counties), declined in spawning biomass from the 1960s through the mid-1980s, and during the 1990s, they have shifted somewhat from spawning in waters off Marin to waters off San Francisco (CDFG 1995).

The western/Clark's grebes and other grebe species typically seek sheltered waters, where in San Francisco Bay they are constantly displaced by the boats of human fishers, which also seek these localities. The prohibition of boats in the inner part of Richardson's Bay provides sanctuary. In fact, very large numbers of these grebes occur in Richardson's Bay, which is also in proximity to herring spawning areas.

References

Ainley, D.G. and D.F. DeSante. 1980. The avifauna of the South Farallon Islands, California. Studies in Avian Biol. No. 4.

Briggs, K.T., W.B. Tyler, D.B. Lewis and D.R. Carlson. 1987. Bird communities at sea off California: 1975-1983. Studies Avian Biol. No. 11.

California Department of Fish and Game (CDFG). 1995. Pacific herring commercial fishing regulations, final environmental document. Sacramento, Calif.

Cogswell, H.L. 1977. Water birds of California. Univ. of Calif. Press, Berkeley. 399pp.

Grinnell, J. and A.H. Miller. 1944. The distribution of the birds of California. Pacific Coast Avifauna No. 27.

Palmer, R.S. 1962. Handbook of North American birds, Vol. 1. Yale Univ. Press, New Haven, Conn.

Shuford, W.D., G.W. Page, J.G. Evans and L.E. Stenzel. 1989. Seasonal abundance of waterbirds at Point Reyes: a coastal California perspective. West. Birds 20: 137-265.

Storer, R.W. and G.L. Nuechterlein. 1992. Western and Clark's grebe. *In*: A. Poole, P. Stettenheim and F. Gill (eds). The birds of North America, No. 26. Acad. Natur. Sci., Philadelphia, Penn.

Personal Communications

William Bousman, *North American Birds*, Santa Clara County subregional editor. Menlo Park, California.

American White Pelican

Pelecanus erythrorhynchus

David G. Ainley

Introduction

The American white pelican is one of the larger birds of North America, and certainly the largest piscivore (22-35 kg). The species is very gregarious, being both a colonial breeder and a group-forager.

Distribution and Abundance

The species nests exclusively on islands within large saline lakes in western North America, from just south of the tundra in central Canada to Texas, and from the Pacific Coast to the Mississippi River Valley. During winter, breeding populations move to traditionally established sites in California and Mexico as well as areas along the Gulf of Mexico (Palmer 1962).

Occurrence in the San Francisco Bay Area is very localized and is confined to the non-breeding season, generally from June through December (Shuford et al. 1989, Bousman 1993). The American white pelican frequents very shallow water and is seen (rarely) in the open parts of the Bay only in transit. They are almost exclusively gregarious and roost in flocks on dikes. One wintering population can be found at White's Slough, Contra Costa County (pers. obs.), another in the Hayward area, and another frequents salt evaporation ponds of the South Bay (Bousman 1993).

A few thousand likely spend their non-breeding season in the San Francisco Bay Area. No trend in numbers has been apparent during recent decades (Bousman 1993).

Peter Weber

Other Birds

Habitat Use and Behavior

American white pelicans feed on small, rough fish; in San Francisco Bay this would include sticklebacks (*Gasterosteus lineatus*) (Palmer 1962). They capture prey by swimming in large groups, corralling them, and then scooping them up with their large beaks.

Conservation and Management

The presence of this species in San Francisco Bay results from its well-being at inland breeding sites and the presence of quiet waters, such as salt evaporation ponds.

References

Bousman, B. 1993. The birds of Santa Clara County. Riparia News 8(3): 6-9.

Palmer, R.S. 1962. The handbook of North American birds, Vol. 1. Yale Univ. Press, New Haven, Conn.

Shuford, W.D., G.W. Page, J.G. Evans and L.E. Stenzel. 1989. Seasonal abundance of waterbirds at Point Reyes: a coastal California perspective. West. Birds 20: 137-265.

Brown Pelican

Pelecanus occidentalis

David G. Ainley

Introduction

The brown pelican is one of the largest piscivorous birds of coastal and estuarine waters of North America (weighing about 17 kg). The species breeds colonially, constructing its stick nests on the ground or, more commonly, in trees or shrubs. Pelicans lay two eggs per nesting attempt.

Distribution and Abundance

In western North America, the brown pelican breeds on islands in marine waters on either side of Baja Califor-

Peter Weber

nia, Mexico, north to the Channel Islands of southern California and to Florida. In the West, following the breeding season, many thousands move north to "winter" from central California north to the Columbia River. Peak numbers in central California, including the San Francisco Bay and surrounding area, occur from July through November (Shuford et al. 1989, Bousman 1993, Jacques 1994). During years when pelicans do not breed, such as during El Niño years, large numbers (in the thousands) occur throughout the year in northern California, including San Francisco Bay (Anderson and Anderson 1976). The highest counts in central and northern California occur during those warm-water periods (Ainley and DeSante 1980, Jacques 1994). Choice of wintering areas has to do with the availability of food and to tradition (Jacques 1994).

There are no current or historical Bay-wide censuses of brown pelican. The number of birds found over the waters of San Francisco Bay in a given year varies according to the well being of this species at its breeding grounds and the numbers in coastal waters of central California. In years of high breeding productivity or years of non-breeding, more pelicans can be found here. The fall peak in brown pelican numbers in central California has ranged from about 7,000 (in 1987) to 21,000 (in 1981; Jacques 1994). Currently, on average, several hundred occur within the Bay each summer and fall. As the species recovers from effects of DDT on its breeding productivity in the 1950s and 1960s (Anderson and Gress 1983), numbers seen in the Bay Area have slowly increased (e.g., Ainley 1972, Baldridge 1973).

Habitat Use and Behavior

In San Francisco Bay, brown pelicans frequent all the deeper waters, including some salt evaporation ponds and the mouths of the larger creeks (e.g., Corte Madera Creek, Marin County). Significant numbers are not found much farther inland than San Pablo Bay. They roost in numbers on small islands (e.g., Red Rocks) and breakwaters (e.g., Alameda Naval Air Station).

Brown pelicans feed on schooling fish. In waters of the San Francisco Bay, their diet includes such species as anchovies (*Engraulis mordax*) and smelt (e.g., *Hypomesus* spp.; Pers. obs. and Palmer 1962). Their technique of feeding—plunging beak first from altitude into the water to grasp fish up to a meter or so deep—requires deep water.

Conservation and Management

Except on nesting grounds, brown pelicans are not intimidated by the presence of humans. The species occurs in close proximity to humans and forages very close to human fishers. As long as forage fish are available, the population of brown pelicans will do well. When forage fish are not available, brown pelicans scavenge fish offal discarded by humans.

Because this species is a higher order consumer, populations suffered considerably due to the effects of DDT on breeding productivity in the 1950s and 1960s (Anderson and Gress 1983).

Currently, the California population of this species is listed as endangered on the Federal Endangered Species List, but may (or should) be down-listed or delisted soon (e.g., CEQ 1986, Ainley and Hunt 1990).

References

Ainley, D.G. 1972. Brown pelicans in north-central coastal California. Calif. Birds 3: 59-64.

Ainley, D.G. and D.F. DeSante. 1980. The avifauna of the South Farallon Islands, California. Studies in Avian Biol. No. 4.

Ainley, D.G. and G.L. Hunt Jr. 1990. Status and conservation of seabirds in California. In: J.P. Croxall (ed). Seabird status and conservation: a supplement. Internatl. Council Bird Preserv., Cambridge. Tech. Pub. 11: 103-114

Anderson, D.W. and I.T. Anderson. 1976. Distribution and status of brown pelicans in the California current. Amer. Birds 30: 3-12.

Anderson, D.W. and F. Gress. 1983. Status of a northern population of California brown pelicans. Condor 85: 79-88.

Baldridge, A.B. 1973. The status of the brown pelican in the Monterey region of California: past and present. West. Birds 4: 93-100.

Bousman, B. 1993. The birds of Santa Clara. Riparia News 8(3): 6-9.

Council on Environmental Quality (CEQ). 1986. Environmental quality, 17th annual report. Washington, D.C.

Jacques, D.L. 1994. Range expansion and roosting ecology of non-breeding California brown pelicans. Unpubl. M.S. Thesis, Univ. Calif., Davis.

Palmer, R.S. 1962. Handbook of North American birds, Vol. 1. Yale Univ. Press, New Haven, Conn.

Shuford, W.D., G.W. Page, J.G. Evans and L.E. Stenzel. 1989. Seasonal abundance of waterbirds at Point Reyes: a coastal California perspective. West. Birds 20: 137-265.

Double-Crested Cormorant

Phalacrocorax auritus

David G. Ainley

Introduction

Cormorants are found the world over from the Arctic to the Antarctic. The family is large, and its members are mostly confined, with exception, to coastal marine waters. Cormorants are foot propelled divers and feed mostly on fish, although they take mid-water swimming crustaceans (such as shrimp) as well (Ainley 1984).

Cormorants construct their nests in colonies. Most nest on the ground, although some colonies occur in trees or on man-made structures. Among marine birds, cormorants are the most prolific, with their clutches averaging three to four eggs per nest. The capacity to lay so many eggs (most marine birds lay one egg only) allows their populations to respond positively to periodic conditions of food abundance. On the other hand, having so many chicks to feed often leads to food stress among parents when food is sparse and, consequently, to high mortality of chicks (Ainley 1984).

Distribution and Abundance

In North America, the double-crested cormorant is the only cormorant species associated with inland bodies of fresh, brackish, and saline water. They also occur close to ocean shores in protected waters. All other North American cormorant species are strictly marine, and in San Francisco Bay, except for vagrants, these other species occur only in the vicinity of the Golden Gate and Angel Island.

Don DesJardin

Other Birds

In the early part of the 20th century, almost all double-crested cormorants that occurred in San Francisco Bay likely nested on the offshore Farallon Islands, but commuted to the Bay for foraging. Since the late 1970s, they began to nest in small numbers around the Bay, especially on power transmission towers, bridges and, rarely, trees.

This species now is widespread in San Francisco Bay and the Delta. Since the species is a colonial breeder, breeding birds are concentrated in only a few locations – one major concentration is in the North Bay salt evaporators near Napa, two are in the Central Bay at the Richmond and Oakland-Bay bridges, and another is in the South Bay at the Dumbarton Bridge. The birds radiate outward from these colonies to forage at distances of 20 or more miles away. Double-crested cormorants often forage in flocks (see Barlow 1942, 1943), but also do so singularly.

In the 1800s through the 1940s, many thousands of these birds occurred in San Francisco Bay and were associated with schools of sardines (*Sardinops coerulea*), upon which they fed (Barlow 1942, 1943; Ainley and Lewis 1974). Owing to persecution by humans and perhaps the decline of sardine populations, the numbers of double-crested cormorants in San Francisco Bay declined rapidly, reaching a low during the 1960s and early 1970s (Ainley and Lewis 1974, Carter et al. 1995). Since then populations have been recovering. As of 1991, about 2,800 birds nested around San Francisco Bay in 12 colonies: Russ, Knight, Wheeler, and Donlon islands; San Pablo Bay radar station and beacon; the Richmond, Bay, and San Mateo bridges (and associated electric towers); and electric towers along the very southern shore of the Bay (Carter et al. 1995; SF Bay Bird Observatory, unpubl. data). The largest colonies in the Bay are on the Oakland-San Francisco Bay Bridge and Richmond-San Rafael Bridge (846 and 1,116 birds, respectively, in the mid-1990s; Carter et al. 1995). On the basis of sightings of banded birds, as well as a decline at the Farallones and simultaneous increase on the Richmond Bridge, the Farallon colony has supplied many recruits to these populations (Stenzel et al. 1995). A few pairs also nest at several localities in counties bordering San Francisco Bay; for example, several pairs nest on transmission towers near the mouth of Stevens' Creek, Santa Clara County (Bousman 1993).

This species is most prevalent in waters of the San Francisco Bay and Delta during winter – November through March. The increasing summer breeding population is the result of the arrivals of yearlings from the previous breeding season and birds from the colder, interior parts of North America. Although no Bay-wide census has been conducted during winter, their numbers likely reach 10,000 or more.

Habitat Use and Behavior

Breeding cormorants typically are very sensitive to disturbance from the intrusion of humans. Double-crested cormorants are among the least sensitive among all cormorants, which is not to say, however, that the species is oblivious to the presence of humans. They will flee their nests, leaving the contents to scavenging gulls or corvids when people approach within a couple hundred feet.

The double-crested cormorant forages in shallow waters overlying bottoms of flat relief. Such foraging areas may include rivers and sloughs tributary to San Francisco Bay, as well as salt evaporation ponds and areas such as San Pablo Bay. Large numbers are found in the tidal rips associated with Angel Island and Raccoon Straits. Double-crested cormorants feed mainly on fish. Herring (*Clupea harengus*) is an important prey in many coastal areas, and likely also in San Francisco Bay during winter. Midshipmen (*Porichthys notatus*) are an important food item during spring and summer (Palmer 1962, Ainley et al. 1981, Ainley, pers. obs. for San Francisco Bay).

Conservation and Management

For many years, the species was eradicated throughout North America because it was accused of foraging on favorite sport fishes. Protection from persecution and disturbance, and the increased availability of man-made structures on which to nest, has contributed greatly to the increase in numbers during recent decades. Even today there is pressure to control numbers, especially in cases where they forage on stupid, hatchery raised trout introduced to urban reservoirs (e.g., Lagunitas Reservoir, Marin County). Another factor that may have "allowed" the recent increases has been control of pesticides. This species is particularly sensitive to these compounds (Gress et al. 1973, Fry 1994).

References

Ainley, D.G. 1984 . Cormorants. *In*: D. Haley (ed). Seabirds of the eastern North Pacific and Arctic waters. Pacific Search Press, Seattle, Wash. pp. 92-101.

Ainley, D.G. and T.J. Lewis. 1974. The history of Farallon Island marine bird populations, 1854-1972. Condor 76: 432-446.

Ainley, D.G., D.W. Anderson and P.R. Kelly. 1981. Feeding ecology of marine cormorants in southwestern North America. Condor 83: 120-131.

Barlow, Jr., G.A. 1942. The fishing activities of double-crested cormorants on San Francisco Bay. Condor 44: 13-21.

_____. 1943. The daily movements of cormorants on San Francisco Bay. Condor 45: 3-18.

Bousman, B. 1993. The birds of Santa Clara. Riparia News 8(4): 8-10.

Carter, H.R., A.L. Sowls and M.S. Rodway. 1995. Population size, trends and conservation problems of the double-crested cormorant on the Pacific Coast of North America. Colonial Waterbirds 18 (Special Publ. 1): 189-215.

Fry, D.M. 1994. Injury of seabirds from DDT and PCB residues in the Southern California bight ecosystem. Unpubl. Rept., U.S. Fish Wildl. Serv., Sacramento.

Gress, R., R.W. Risebrough, D.W. Anderson, L.F. Kiff and J.R. Jehl, Jr. 1973. Reproductive failures of double-crested cormorants in southern California and Baja California. Wilson Bull. 85: 197-208.

Palmer, R.S. 1962. Handbook of North American birds, Vol. 1. Yale Univ. Press, New Haven, Conn.

Stenzel, L.E., H. R. Carter and R.P. Henderson. 1995. Breeding success of double-crested cormorants in the San Francisco Bay Area, California. Colonial Waterbirds 18 (Special Publ. 1): 216-224.

Snowy Egret

Egretta thula

William G. Bousman

Introduction

The snowy egret is a member of the family of herons and egrets (Ardeidae) that occur in wetlands throughout the world's avifaunal regions. Within the New World, the snowy egret is widespread in its distribution and is a counterpart of the little egret (*Egretta garzetta*) of the Old World. Two subspecies are recognized (Palmer 1962), *E. t. thula*, that breeds in the eastern United States through Mexico and into South America as far south as Chile and Argentina, and *E. t. brewsteri*, that breeds in the western United States including California south to Baja California and western Mexico. Within its breeding range it is generally common, although strongly dependent upon wetlands for foraging both during and outside of the breeding season. In the San Francisco Bay, it is a resident species.

Snowy egrets are generalists in their feeding habits, foraging on small fishes, frogs, lizards, snakes, crustaceans, worms, snails, and insects. As with most generalists, they are opportunistic in their feeding and benefit from drying periods in seasonal wetlands and fish blooms that occur in salt ponds or other impoundments. Males establish breeding territories, and then, after pair formation, the pair normally defends a smaller nesting territory (Palmer 1962). Foraging territories are also defended. Breeding is normally colonial with one brood per year. Snowy egrets normally lay three to five eggs, but the young hatch asychronously, and the smallest young survive only when food is plentiful. Nests are constructed on the ground, in trees, or marsh vegetation. On West Marin Island, they nest on the ground, in coastal scrub, in buckeye, and in live oaks. Birds that occasionally nest at Audubon Canyon Ranch use redwood trees and nest 60 to 70 feet above the ground (Shuford 1993). In Alviso, they nest in tules along Artesian Slough just barely above the surface of the water.

Distribution and Abundance

Modern Distribution – McCaskie et al. (1979) described the snowy egret as common to abundant in the seashore, coastal, interior, and Great Basin districts in northern California, although they noted that it is much less common inland, as well as on the coast north of Sonoma County. They considered beaches, mudflats, and marshes to be the primary habitat for this egret.

In Southern California, Garrett and Dunn (1981) considered snowy egrets to be common residents at the Salton Sea and along the Colorado River Valley, but only common as a winter visitor along the coastal slope where some birds are found uncommonly in the summer. It has occurred as an uncommon transient anywhere in the region. This species has nested along the Salton Sea, but has declined because of competition with cattle egrets. Along the coastal slope, recent nesting records included Sandyland Slough in Santa Barbara County and Buena Vista Lagoon and the Tijuana River Valley in San Diego County.

Today this species is a common, year-around resident in the San Francisco Bay. Christmas Bird Count (CBC) data from the late 1960s to the present, shown in **Figure 7.1**, indicate that this species is found regularly on the CBCs in Benicia, Oakland, Hayward-Fremont, San Jose, Palo Alto, Crystal Springs Reservoir,

Don DesJardin

Figure 7.1 Christmas Bird Count data for Snowy Egret — Approximate geographic location of Count circles indicated by dashed lines

National Audubon Society's *Audubon Field Notes*, and its successor publications, *American Birds*, and *Field Notes*, Volumes 24-51.

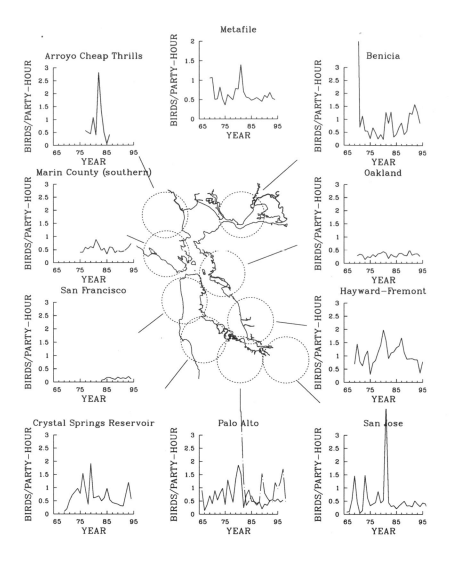

Marin County (southern), and Arroyo Cheap Thrills. For all of these counts, the numbers are comparable and show no substantial changes in the last 25 years. The aggregate number of birds counted in the nine CBC circles shown in **Figure 7.1** can be approximated by summing the mean number recorded on each count. This aggregate mean, 1,112 birds, represents a lower bound of the birds present in San Francisco Bay, as not all estuarine habitats are sampled within these circles, and it is likely that some birds were missed during these counts. Comparisons of Palo Alto CBC and Summer Bird Count (SBC) data obtained in the same count circle allow a comparison of summer and winter numbers using identical census protocols. These data show essentially the same population in both the summer and winter seasons, and it appears that this species is permanently resident in this portion of the Bay.

Historical Distribution – Within California, Grinnell and Miller (1944) considered the snowy egret to be a year-round resident below the 1,000-foot elevation level in the southern three-fourths of the State, which includes the San Francisco Bay Area. Elsewhere it was found only in the summer or as a vagrant. They

described the Sacramento, San Joaquin, and Colorado River valleys as the chief location for this egret, but noted that it was found coastally from Marin County south to San Diego County.

Prior to 1880, this species was considered locally common in the State (Grinnell and Miller 1944). Plume hunting, however, was as devastating to this species on the Pacific Coast as it was in the East, and starting in the 1880s, this species was nearly wiped out in the State. By the early 1900s, it was thought to be extinct within California. By the 1920s, it was considered a rare straggler to the Bay Area with only two locations noted (Grinnell and Wythe 1927). By the early 1940s, however, this species had started to recover and in favored places was locally common. Even by 1940, however, the only known breeding site was in Los Banos (Grinnell and Miller 1944).

By the early 1950s, in the South Bay, this species was considered an uncommon winter visitant (Sibley 1952). Emily Smith (*Audubon Field Notes* 9:51) considered ten birds at Alviso on 30 August 1954 to be notable, and this was the largest number reported for the Middle Pacific Coast Region in that season. A survey of South

Bay breeding birds in 1971 (Gill 1977) recorded 340 pairs on Bair Island, near Redwood City and this colony apparently was first started in 1969. This colony was still active at least through 1975 (Gill 1977), but it is no longer extant, and the reasons for its abandonment have not been described.

The species now appears to have recovered to its carrying capacity in the Bay Area, as noted above by the CBC population trends. It appears that most of this recovery occurred in the period from the mid-1950s to the late 1960s. No census data are available, however, that can accurately characterize the numbers present prior to European settlement.

Habitat Use and Behavior

From Palmer (1962), this species uses fresh, brackish, and salt-water habitats throughout its range. Within the San Francisco Estuary, it uses all of these habitats for foraging, although for breeding, it is rarely far from brackish or salt water. The densest concentrations of snowy egrets are found either where drying ponds concentrate suitable fish species or where fish blooms occur, and by inference, seasonal wetlands and impoundments are an important source of prey. Nonetheless, this species feeds widely along the tidewater margin, in nearby freshwater streams, and in lakes and reservoirs. In all cases, it depends upon healthy fish habitats for its prey base.

It uses a wide variety of substrates for nesting, and it seems clear that the actual substrate is of little importance compared to the security that the nesting locality provides from predation. Nearly 500 pairs have been noted at West Marin Island (Shuford 1993) and this is the largest concentration in the Bay Area. At Alviso, nests are built only slightly above the water in dense tules and 150 pairs were noted here in 1980 (*Am. Birds* 34: 811). Away from the Bay Area, this egret was first found breeding in Sonoma County in 1991 in the midst of an active black-crowned night heron colony in Penngrove. Seven active nests were found that year (Burridge 1995), and this shows the flexibility this species exhibits as long as a satisfactory prey base exists and there are secure nesting sites.

No quantitative data are available on the use of estuarine habitats for foraging by this species, either during the breeding season or at other times of year. In the South Bay, this species is observed in a wide range of habitats; birds leaving the Alviso heronry fan out to forage on the mudflat tidal edge, along streams flowing into the Bay, and the salt ponds. At times, unusual fish concentrations occur in seasonal wetlands or salt ponds, and, at these times, unusual concentrations of herons result. Some representative high counts from the South Bay include 390 counted by Alan M. Eisner in Charleston Slough on 3 August 1992, and 340 censused by Stephen

C. Rottenborn in the vicinity of the Sunnyvale Water Pollution Control Plant ponds on 24 July 1993 (Bousman 1994).

The two breeding population centers of this species in the North and South bays suggest the plasticity of this species in its uses of all major estuarine habitats. South Bay observations clearly indicate the importance of salt pond habitats, as well as the tidal edge of mudflats and riparian areas, whereas in the North Bay, use of salt ponds and other impoundments is less important than foraging in tidal areas.

Conservation and Management

The basic needs of this species are secure areas for nesting, adequate wetlands for foraging, and continued protection from direct persecution by man. However, this species is still vulnerable in its limited nesting colonies as indicated by the killing of snowy egrets, along with many great egrets in the West Marin Island colony in October 1955 (*Audubon Field Notes* 10: 51). The protection of the two large colonies, the one on West Marin Island in the North Bay and the other along Artesian Slough in the South Bay, is the most important need for this species within the estuarine system. As a foraging generalist tied directly to numerous habitats within the Estuary, the continued health of this population depends upon the general health of the Estuary and the various prey stocks.

Population surveys of the West Marin Island colony (Shuford 1993) are shown below in **Table 7.1**. Although these numbers demonstrate fairly wide fluctuations in breeding numbers, they do not indicate any long-term changes. Comparable data from the Alviso heronry have not been published. Both of these major Bay colonies are presently protected, but each is vulnerable to natural hazards, as well as direct and indirect acts of man.

The Bair Island colony near Redwood City was successful from 1969 into the 1980s and was then abandoned. Except for Gill's records (Gill 1977), data documenting the growth and decay of this colony have not been published, and there has been only limited discus-

Table 7.1 Estimated Breeding Pairs of Snowy Egrets on West Marin Island (Shuford 1993)

Year	No. of Birds	Year	No. of Birds
1979	262	1986	126
1980	-	1987	239
1981	325	1988	212
1982	500	1989	245
1983	400	1990	300
1984	400	1991	277
1985	161		

Other Birds

sion of why the colony was abandoned. San Francisco Bay Bird Observatory records indicate that the decline of the colony is probably linked to severe predation by red fox (Cogswell, pers. comm).

The Baire Island colony example of a fairly recent birth, growth, and decay of a major colony within the estuarine system, with little documentation, remains a warning for the stewards of our estuarine system. It is unclear how the Goals Project is to set goals for estuarine health without sufficient data to examine the 'pathology' of specific population failures or shifts.

It is believed that the greatest hazard now for this species is the continuing population increase of the non-native red fox in the South Bay. The Alviso heronry nests are largely in tules slightly above the tidal line, and although the water offers some protection from predators, the red fox has shown in its depredations on the clapper rail its willingness to overcome water barriers. As this population increases it appears only a matter of time before this colony is extirpated. It is possible that colony protection against this predator's burgeoning population could be obtained through a carefully designed barrier that enhances the effect of the present water barrier. It is possible that this colony could be re-established on Bair Island; however, protection of that area may be even more difficult.

References

Bousman, B. 1994. The birds of Santa Clara County, Riparia News, Vol. 9, No. 1.

Burridge, B. 1995. Sonoma County breeding bird Atlas. Madrone Audubon Society.

Garrett, K. and J. Dunn. 1981. Birds of southern California: status and distribution. Los Angeles Audubon Society, Los Angeles.

Gill, Jr., R. 1977. Breeding avifauna of the south San Francisco Bay estuary, W. Birds 8: 1-12.

Grinnell, J. and A.H. Miller. 1944. The distribution of the birds of California. Pacific Coast Avifauna No. 27, Cooper Ornith. Club.

Grinnell, J. and M.W. Wythe. 1927. Directory to the bird-life of the San Francisco Bay region. Pacific Coast Avifauna No. 18, Cooper Ornith. Club.

McCaskie, G., P. De Benedictis, R. Erickson, and J. Morlan. 1979. Birds of Northern California: An annotated field list. Golden Gate Audubon Society, San Francisco.

Palmer, R.S. 1962. Handbook of North American birds, Vol. 1, loons through flamingos. Yale Univ. Press, New Haven, Conn.

Sibley, C.G. 1952. The birds of the south San Francisco Bay region (mimeo).

Shuford, W.D. 1993. The Marin County breeding bird atlas. Bushtit Books, Bolinas, Ca.

Black-Crowned Night Heron

Nycticorax nycticorax

William G. Bousman

Introduction

The black-crowned night heron is a member of the family of herons and egrets (Ardeidae) and is found worldwide. In the New World, the subspecies *N. n. hoactli* is recognized and breeds from Oregon and southern Canada, south to Chile and Argentina. In winter, the northern populations withdraw to the southern United States, although they linger on the West Coast to Oregon and the East Coast to Massachusetts (AOU 1957). Within its breeding range, it is generally common and is dependent largely on wetlands for foraging. It is a resident species in the San Francisco Bay Area.

The black-crowned night heron generally forages at the margins of lakes and streams, on brackish and on salt waters. Its chief prey items are fish, crustaceans, insects, and amphibians normally obtained by stalking or waiting for prey from a stationary position. It normally feeds at night, dawn, or dusk on individual feeding territories and roosts during the day. When trees are available it will frequently use them for roosting, otherwise it uses tules and cattails. It tends to use less open habitats than other egrets and herons (*Egretta* and *Ardea*), but is not so secretive as the bitterns (Palmer 1962, Cramp 1977).

Locally, in the South Bay, this species is nicknamed the "night raven" for its tendencies to prey on recently hatched ducklings. On 26 June 1988, Phyllis Browning (pers. comm.) watched two herons take six Class 1 gadwall ducklings in a half-hour period in the Palo Alto

Doug Rodda

Flood Control Basin. At the same time, a western gull made 17 attempts on a gadwall family without success.

The black-crowned night heron nests in trees and shrubs, or less frequently in tules. Although a solitary feeder, this species is gregarious at roosts and is a colonial breeder. Males establish territories within the breeding colony and will bring twigs to a nesting site as part of advertising displays. Once a pair-bond is established, the male will bring sticks to the site where the female remains. A number of social behaviors are associated with nesting pairs (Palmer 1962, Cramp 1977). The species is single-brooded and will normally lay three to five eggs. The young hatch asynchronously, and the younger (smaller) nestlings will survive only when food is plentiful.

Distribution and Abundance

Modern Distribution – McCaskie et al. (1979) described the black-crowned night heron as uncommon to fairly common in Northern California within the seashore, coastal, interior, and Great Basin districts, but as a vagrant in the mountain district. They characterized its habitat use as beaches, mudflats, marshes, rocky shores, and riparian areas. Garrett and Dunn (1981) noted the species as fairly common in Southern California along the coastal slope, at the Salton Sea, and along the Colorado River Valley. They recorded recent breeding from Morro Bay, Santa Barbara, and San Diego.

Current Christmas Bird Count (CBC) data from the late 1960s to the present, shown in **Figure 7.2**, indicate that this species is found regularly on CBCs in Benicia, Oakland, Hayward-Fremont, San Jose, Palo Alto, Crystal Springs Reservoir, San Francisco, Marin County (southern), and Arroyo Cheap Thrills. For all of these counts, the numbers are comparable. Winter populations in terms of birds/party-hour have increased for Benicia (+6.0%, p<0.005), San Jose (+3.7%, p<0.025), and Arroyo Cheap Thrills (+19.5%, p<0.025), while declines are noted on Crystal Springs Reservoir (-5.8%, p<0.005) and Palo Alto (-3.7%, p<0.025). This species is less common in the Palo Alto count circle during the summer based on Summer Bird Count (SBC) data with a mean of 0.33 birds/party-hour (std. dev.= 0.47, n=15) compared to the winter average of 0.87 birds/party-hour (std. dev.= 0.61, n=27). Interestingly, the Palo Alto SBC also shows a significant decline in the population (-2.6%, p<0.005). The black-crowned night heron appears to be common throughout the Bay Area, and is perhaps best considered a resident species, with some augmentation in winter by non-resident northern or interior birds. The aggregate number of birds counted in the nine CBC circles, calculated by summing the means of the CBCs, is 838 birds. This represents a lower bound on the wintering population of black-crowned night heron in the San Francisco Bay estuarine system.

Doug Rodda

Historical Distribution – Grinnell and Miller (1944) considered the black-crowned night heron to be somewhat common throughout the State in the summer with fewer birds present in the winter. They noted that it occurred on both sides of the Sierran crest and bred from the lower Sonoran to the Transition life zones. They commented that this heron was formerly abundant in some localities, but numbers had been greatly depleted in historical times. Within San Francisco Bay, they cited breeding records from Belvedere Island in Marin County, and Alameda and a location near Alvarado in Alameda County.

Sibley (1952) noted that the Alameda County nesting colonies were no longer active by the 1920s and that there were no longer any active colonies in the South Bay. Emily Smith (*Audubon Field Notes* 8: 359) considered 27 birds counted on 11 July 1954 and 21 on 25 July 1954 at Alviso to be an unusual concentration. A nesting colony was established on Bair Island near Redwood City in 1967, and this included at least 684 nests in 1971 (Gill 1977). This colony was later abandoned because of red fox incursions (H. Cogswell, pers. comm.).

This species has clearly recovered in recent decades to where there are relatively stable populations, although it is unclear whether these are as large as existed prior to European settlement. Unlike the snowy egret, it is not apparent that this bird was hunted for its plumes at the end of the last century, and the down turn in its population must be related to other factors. Without knowing what these factors were, it is difficult to determine with any certainty why the species has recovered. It is possible, however, that the decline of duck hunting in the South Bay has benefited this species, as well as a number of other non-game species that were targets of casual hunters.

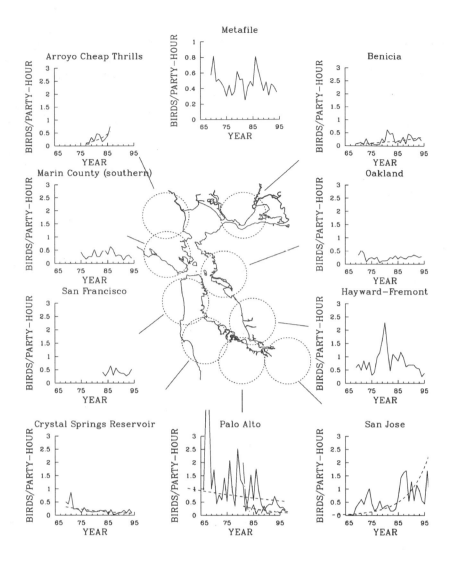

Figure 7.2 Christmas Bird Count data for Black-Crowned Night Heron — Relative geographic location of Count circles indicated by dashed lines

National Audubon Society's *Audubon Field Notes*, and its successor publications, *American Birds*, and *Field Notes*, Volumes 24-51.

Habitat Use and Behavior

The black-crowned night heron is a generalist in its foraging, as with many of the herons, and uses a variety of habitats. Unlike some of the other herons, however, it is a solitary feeder and does not normally concentrate at drying ponds and fish blooms. Suitable habitat requires numerous foraging opportunities in either fresh, brackish, or salt water. A suitable roost site for this crepuscular species is required as well.

The black-crowned night heron uses a variety of substrates for nesting. On West Marin Island, it uses coastal scrub and sometimes buckeye for their nests (Shuford 1993). At Alviso, they nest in tules along Artesian Slough. There is some evidence that introduced eucalyptus provide particularly safe nest locations because of the smooth bark (Roberson and Tenney 1993). The substrate *per se* appears to be relatively unimportant for this species, and the primary need is for a nest site that is safe from predation. Up to 300 pairs have nested on West Marin Island (Shuford 1993), and this is the densest concentration in the Bay Area. Up to 150 pairs were counted nesting in the Artesian Slough colony in

the South Bay in 1980 (Am. Birds 34: 811). Outside of the Bay Area, breeding is less common in coastal areas. A small colony exists in Monterey County at Carmel Point in eucalyptus. A maximum of 13 nests were counted in 1992 (Roberson and Tenney 1993). At least three small colonies are located in Sonoma, largely in urban areas where they create some difficulties for the local (human) residents (Burridge 1995).

Conservation and Management

The basic needs of this species are secure areas for nesting, adequate wetlands for foraging, and the continued protection from direct persecution by man. The protection of the two large colonies, one on West Marin Island in the North Bay and the other along Artesian Slough in the South Bay, is the most important need for this species within the estuarine system. As a foraging generalist tied directly to numerous habitats within the Estuary, the continued health of this population depends upon the general health of the Estuary and the various prey stocks. Population surveys of the West Marin Island colony (Shuford 1993) are shown in **Table 7.2** and,

Table 7.2 Estimated Breeding Pairs of Black-Crowned Night Herons on West Marin Island (Shuford 1993)

Year	No. of Birds	Year	No. of Birds
1979	98	1986	40
1980	-	1987	41
1981	109	1988	35
1982	80	1989	61
1983	89	1990	37
1984	54	1991	45
1985	79		

although these data demonstrate fairly wide fluctuations in breeding numbers, they do not indicate any long-term population changes. Comparable data from the Alviso heronry have not been published. Both of these major San Francisco Bay colonies are presently protected, but each is vulnerable to natural hazards, as well as direct and indirect acts of man. We have, at best, only a poor understanding of the factors that determine whether a nesting colony will succeed or fail. As an example, the Bair Island colony near Redwood City was successful from 1969 into the 1980s and was then abandoned. Except for Gill's records (Gill 1977), data that document the growth and decay of this colony have not been published, nor has there been a detailed discussion as to why the colony was abandoned. The fairly recent history of birth, growth, and decay of a major colony within the estuarine system, with little documentation, remains a warning for the stewards of our estuarine system.

It is believed that the greatest hazard now for the black-crowned night heron is the increasing population of the non-native red fox in the South Bay. The Alviso heronry nests are largely in tules, slightly above the tidal line and, although the water offers some protection from predators, the red fox has shown in its depredations on the clapper rail its willingness to overcome water barriers. As the fox population increases, it appears only a matter of time before this colony is extirpated. It is possible that colony protection against this predator's burgeoning population could be obtained through a carefully designed barrier that enhances the effect of the present water barrier. It is possible that this colony could be re-established on Bair Island; however, protection of that area may be even more difficult.

No quantitative data are available on the use of estuarine habitats for foraging by this species, either during the breeding season or at other times of year. In the South Bay, this species is observed in a wide range of habitats, and birds leaving the Alviso heronry fan out to forage on the mudflat tidal edge, the salt ponds, and along streams flowing into the Bay. This species does not concentrate at prey resources, such as fish blooms or drying ponds as some of the other Ardeids, but it does congregate at secure day roosts. A representative day roost was of 145 birds tallied at the Palo Alto Baylands on a high tide on 22 November 1984 (pers. obs.).

References

American Ornithologists' Union (AOU). 1957. Checklist of North American birds, fifth ed., Amer. Ornith. Union.

Burridge, B. 1995. Sonoma County breeding bird atlas. Madrone Audubon Society.

Cramp, S. 1977. The birds of the western palearctic, Vol. I, ostriches to ducks. Oxford Univ. Press.

Garrett, K. and J. Dunn. 1981. Birds of Southern California: status and distribution. Los Angeles Audubon Society, Los Angeles.

Gill, Jr., R. 1977. Breeding avifauna of the South San Francisco Bay estuary, W. Birds 8: 1-12.

Grinnell, J. and A.H. Miller. 1944. The distribution of the birds of California. Pacific Coast Avifauna No. 27, Cooper Ornith. Club.

McCaskie, G., P. De Benedictis, R. Erickson and J. Morlan. 1979. Birds of northern California: an annotated field list. Golden Gate Audubon Society, San Francisco.

Palmer, R.S. 1962. Handbook of North American birds, Vol. 1, loons through flamingos. Yale Univ. Press, New Haven, Conn.

Roberson, D. and C. Tenney. 1993. Atlas of the breeding birds of Monterey County, California. Monterey Peninsula Audubon Society, Monterey.

Shuford, W.D. 1993. The Marin County breeding bird atlas. Bushtit Books, Bolinas, Ca.

Sibley, C.G. 1952. The birds of the South San Francisco Bay region (mimeo).

Personal Communications

Phyllis Browning, birdwatcher and Santa Clara Valley Audubon member, Palo Alto, California.

Howard Cogswell, Professor Emeritus, California State University, Hayward, California.

California Clapper Rail

Rallus longirostris obsoletus

Joy D. Albertson
Jules G. Evens

Introduction

Populations of clapper rails along the Pacific Coast and the Colorado River have been considered variously as races of *Rallus longirostris*, races of *Rallus elegans*, or separate species (AOU 1983). Currently, *R. longirostris* and *R. elegans* are treated as superspecies (Taylor 1996). Three subspecies of clapper rail (*Rallus longirostris*) occur in California: the 'California' clapper rail (*R. l. obsoletus*), the 'light-footed' clapper rail (*R. l. levipes*), and the 'Yuma' clapper rail (*R. l. yumanensis*) (AOU 1957). Each of the three subspecies is classified as 'endangered' by the U.S. Department of the Interior (Federal Register 50 CFR 17.11; USFWS 1973), primarily due to habitat loss. Both *obsoletus* and *levipes* are listed as 'endangered' by the State of California; *yumanensis* is listed as 'threatened' (CCR Title 14, Section 670.5).

The California clapper rail is a secretive, hen-like waterbird, indigenous to estuarine marshlands in San Francisco Bay (Grinnell and Miller 1944, Gill 1979, AOU 1983). Though *R. l. obsoletus* may still occur as a transient in outer coast marshes, its status there is precarious. No breeding populations have been detected at Morro Bay and Elkhorn Slough in recent years. Comments that *R. l. obsoletus* is "resident at Tomales Bay and Monterey Bay" (AOU 1957) are no longer accurate.

Description

The clapper rail is one of the largest species of the genus *Rallus*, measuring 31-40 cm in length and weighing approximately 250-350 grams, with the males slightly larger (Taylor 1996). It has a rusty or rufous breast, orange bill, white and black feathers on the flanks, as well as white undertail coverts, creating effective cam-

Peter LaTourrette

ouflage within the marsh vegetation (Ridgeway 1880, Grinnell et al. 1918).

Breeding Biology – Clapper rail pairs are monogamous and will fiercely defend overlapping, year-round territories (Applegarth 1938, Massey and Zembal 1987, Zembal et al. 1989, Albertson 1995). Courtship is initiated by the male and involves the male approaching the female with an uplifted tail, pointing his bill to the ground and swinging it from side to side. Courtship feeding of the female is also common. Males normally build the nest, which occurs on or near the ground, usually on a slight rise (Ehrlich et al. 1988). The nest consists of a platform of dead plant material arched over by surrounding live vegetation to form a roof. In the South Bay, nests have primarily been found in gumplant bushes (*Grindelia humilis*), pickleweed clumps (*Salicornia virginica*), cordgrass stands (*Spartina foliosa*), saltgrass patches (*Distichlis spicata)*, and wrack (DeGroot 1927, Applegarth 1938, Zucca 1954, Harvey 1988, Foerster et al. 1990). In the North Bay, nests have been found in *Scirpus robustus*, *Salicornia virginica*, or *Grindelia humilis*. Nests tend to be located less than two meters from first-order channels and at least 100 meters upstream from the marshland shoreline (Evens and Page 1983, Evens and Collins 1992). The marshland beneath the nests ranges in elevation from 15 cm below Mean High Higher Water (MHHW) to about five cm above MHHW, and the nests themselves are constructed entirely above MHHW (Evens and Collins 1992, Collins et al. 1994).

Eggs are laid March through July (DeGroot 1927, Harvey 1980, Evens and Page 1983). A clapper rail can lay between five and 14 eggs, with the average being seven eggs per clutch (DeGroot 1927, Zucca 1954). Incubation is shared by both adults and is variously reported as 23 to 29 days (Applegarth 1938, Zucca 1954) and 18 to 29 days (Taylor 1996). The peak nesting period for clapper rails is April through May, and a majority of hatching occurs mid-April through early June (Applegarth 1938, Zucca 1954, Harvey 1988, Foerster et al. 1990). DeGroot (1927) states that clapper rails may "double clutch," or produce two broods per year. However, Applegarth (1938) attributes late nesting attempts to renesting, occurring when the first nest has failed, rather than to production of a second clutch after a successful hatch.

Clapper rail chicks are precocial and will leave the nest soon after hatching (Applegarth 1938). One adult will tend the newly hatched chicks, while the other parent continues incubation until all eggs have hatched (Applegarth 1938, Meanley 1985). Young rails accompany the parents for approximately eight weeks, learning to forage for food on their own (DeGroot 1927, Zembal 1991). Juveniles fledge at ten weeks (Johnson 1973) and may breed in the spring following hatch.

Survivorship is low, 0.49-0.52 (Albertson 1995), similar to that of the Yuma clapper rail (Eddleman 1989).

Much predation takes place during high winter tides and is likely due to the ease of capture by predators at this time. This increased predation is likely enhanced by the increased movement of rails within this season, similar to other clapper rail subspecies (Eddleman 1989, Zembal et al. 1989). Raptors, in particular, gain advantage during high tide in marshes that do not have sufficient high vegetation to provide aerial cover for rails. In one study, most (64%) of the rails killed were taken by raptors, primarily during the winter season (Albertson 1995). In another study, an estimated 25% of the population of rails in one 35 ha marsh was taken by raptors from April through November; circumstantial evidence indicated that the barn owl (*Tyto alba*) was the primary predator at that site (Evens and Page 1983). In that study, predation of nests and eggs was also attributed to rats, ravens, and high tides (Evens and Page 1983).

Migration Ecology – California clapper rails are considered non-migratory residents of San Francisco Bay salt marshes, but post-breeding dispersal has been documented during the fall and early winter (Orr 1939, Wilber and Tomlinson 1976). Harvey (unpubl. data) reported three of 54 banded birds moving approximately one km across a slough and one moving about 10 km, from Dumbarton Point to Alameda Creek. Most birds, however, did not move from the marsh in which they were banded: 48% were found 100 m or less from the capture sight, and 78% were less than 500 m away. Albertson (1995) reported one of 29 monitored rails moving approximately three kilometers in early breeding season and successfully establishing a breeding territory. Old records from the Farallon Islands, outer coast marshes, and a variety of extralimital locations (Grinnell and Miller 1944; Evens, unpubl. field notes; American Birds notebooks) suggest that there is a fairly regular fall dispersal period from August through November. This dispersal may be irruptive in nature, occurring in some years, not in others.

Food and Feeding – The primary diet of clapper rails consists of various invertebrate species, including mussels, clams, crabs, snails, amphipods, worms, spiders, insects, and fish (Williams 1929, Applegarth 1938, Moffitt 1941). In addition, clapper rails will opportunistically take small birds (Jorgensen and Ferguson 1982) and rodents (pers. obs.), as well as carrion (Moffitt 1941). A majority of foraging occurs during low tide when mudflats and tidal sloughs are exposed, and food is more readily available (Applegarth 1938, Foerster and Takekawa 1991).

Distribution and Abundance

Historical Distribution – The historical distribution of the California clapper rail was restricted to the tidal marshlands of coastal California from Humboldt Bay in the north to Morro Bay in the south (Grinnell 1915, Grinnell and Wythe 1927, Grinnell and Miller 1944, AOU 1957, AOU 1983, Gill 1979). It occurred formerly at Humboldt Bay (Grinnell and Miller 1944); Tomales Bay (Storer 1915, Brooks 1940, Grinnell and Miller 1944, AOU 1957); Elkhorn Slough, Monterey County (Grinnell and Miller 1944, Varoujean 1972); and Morro Bay, San Louis Obispo County (Brooks 1940, AOU 1957). Present distribution is restricted to the tidal marshes of San Francisco Bay (Evens 1985, Baron and Takekawa 1994). Recent records from coastal estuaries outside of San Francisco Bay are sporadic and represent presumed dispersants or vagrants.

The historical distribution within San Francisco Bay was apparently restricted to tidal marshlands downstream from Suisun Bay (Grinnell 1915, DeGroot 1927, Grinnell and Wythe 1927, Moffitt 1941, Grinnell and Miller 1944). The literature suggests that the populations have fluctuated widely in historic times. A decline noted in the 19th century was attributed to depredation by hunters (Taylor 1894). DeGroot (1927) implies that numbers declined around the turn of the century in the North Bay, and Grinnell and Wythe (1927) reported that although still common in the South Bay, they had become rare elsewhere around the Bay. By 1944, Grinnell and Miller stated that clapper rails had recently recolonized former habitat "in marshes on northern and eastern sides [of the Bay] in Marin, Sonoma, Napa, Contra Costa and extreme western Solano counties." This wording, along with a distribution map delimiting the range at Carquinez Strait (Grinnell and Miller 1944), suggests the North Bay population was limited to the shores of San Pablo Bay. It seems clear that, historically, clapper rails were restricted to the tidal marshes of San Francisco and San Pablo bays, but were absent from Suisun Bay and associated marshlands (Collins et al. 1994).

Modern Distribution – Data on current population levels is somewhat equivocal and may indicate fairly wide population fluctuations, or partial knowledge of abundance, among sub-regions of the Bay. Based on surveys conducted from 1971 through 1975, Gill (1979) estimated a population of 4,200-6,000 rails with 55% in the South Bay, 38% in the Napa marshes, and the remaining 8% in other North Bay and outer coast marshes. There is some indication that Gill overestimated; however, the weight of the evidence suggests that the decline in the population has been real, at least since the mid-1980s (J. Takekawa, pers. comm.). By the mid-1980s, on the basis of breeding and winter population estimates, approximately 1,200-1,500 California clapper rails remained, with greater than 80% of the population found in the South Bay (Harvey 1980, Harvey 1988, T. Harvey and P. Kelly, unpubl. data). By 1988, populations were estimated to have declined to 700 rails (Foerster and Takekawa 1991), with one of the primary causes of this decline being predation caused by the introduction of the red fox. One estimate suggested that the South Bay supported up to 90% of the total rail population (SFEP 1992), however, the most recent update suggests a more even distribution between the South and North bays (see below).

In 1990-91, the Bay-wide population was estimated as 300-500 individuals, followed by a rebound in 1993 to over 800 individuals (USFWS unpubl. data). Increases in South Bay rail populations during this time period are largely attributable to ongoing predator management, initiated in 1991 (Harding et al. 1998). Winter surveys conducted in 1997-98 estimated the South Bay populations to be 650-700 individuals (USFWS unpubl. data). The most recent comprehensive surveys (1992-93) in the northern reaches of the Bay (San Pablo and Suisun bays) resulted in conservative estimates of 195-282 breeding pairs, or 390-564 individuals (Collins et al. 1994). Given these data (and their limitations) the most recent estimates indicate a total population of 1,040-1,264 rails in San Francisco Bay. **Figure 7.3** shows the known distribution of California clapper rails around the San Francisco Bay.

Carquinez Strait – Habitat is limited along the Strait, but a small population (estimated at one to three pairs) has persisted at least since 1948 at Southhampton Marsh (Evens and Collins 1992).

Suisun – Clapper rails are scattered at several sites around Suisun Bay and Marsh, with an indication that populations are present some years but not others. Areas where rails have been found with some regularity since 1978 include the shoreline marshes from Martinez east to Point Edith, bayshore marshes near the mouth of Goodyear Slough, the upper portions of Suisun and Hill sloughs (B. Grewell, pers. comm.), and the western reaches of Cutoff Slough and associated tributaries (Harvey 1980). Winter records appear to be more numerous in this region than breeding season records. An apparent range expansion into this area probably indicates habitat changes resulting from conversion of these marshes into more brackish condition with substantial decreases in freshwater flow from the Sacramento-San Joaquin Delta (Rozengurt et al. 1987, Evens and Collins 1992, Leipsic-Baron 1992.)

North Bay – The marshlands along the North Bay shore and associated rivers and sloughs support clapper rails, with concentrations near the mouths of the larger tributaries (e.g., Gallinas Creek, Novato Creek, Petaluma River, Black John Slough, Sonoma Creek, and Napa River). Gill (1979) identified the Napa River as a North Bay population center which supported "40% of the entire population." Subsequent field work (Evens and Collins 1992, Collins et al. 1994) suggests a decline at that site, but concentrations still exist at White Slough (Vallejo) and Coon Island (Evens and Collins 1992).

Central Bay – A relatively small extent of appropriate habitat occurs in the Central Bay. Primary areas that support clapper rails are: Corte Madera (aka 'Heerdt') and Muzzi marshes (30 pair in 1992-93; Collins et al. 1994); San Leandro Area (Arrowhead and Elsie Romer marshes); and inner Richmond Harbor (Collins et al. 1994). Muzzi Marsh is of particular interest because it is a restored marsh that was not colonized until 1984, and the population was estimated at 15 rails in 1987 (Evens and Page 1987). Other sites include Richardson Bay and Creekside Marsh, Marin County.

South Bay – Foerster (1989) indicated that California clapper rail numbers on the western side of the Bay were stable, but the East Bay population (primarily in Ideal, Dumbarton, and Mowry marshes) had decreased substantially during the past decade, from 400-500 individuals in the early 1980s, to 50-60 in 1991-1992 (Harvey 1980, USFWS unpubl. data). Recent surveys show strong recovery of East Bay populations following implementation of a predator management program to control red foxes (Harding et al. 1998), with over 330 counted in 1997-98 winter surveys. Currently, the largest populations of rails occur in Dumbarton and Mowry marshes on the East Bay, and Palo Alto and Greco marshes on the West Bay. The most recent survey data indicate that rail populations on the east and west sides of the South Bay are approximately equal.

Habitat Use and Behavior

Habitat Requirements – The California clapper rail occurs primarily in emergent salt and brackish tidal marshlands of San Francisco Bay. Preferred habitat is subject to direct tidal circulation and is characterized by predominant coverage by pickleweed (*Salicornia virginica*) with extensive stands of Pacific cordgrass (*Spartina foliosa*), and, in the North Bay, *Scirpus robustus*, abundant high marsh cover, and an intricate network of tidal sloughs which provide abundant invertebrate populations (Grinnell et al. 1918, DeGroot 1927, Harvey 1988, Collins et al. 1994) as well as escape routes from predators (Zembal and Massey 1983, Foerster et al. 1990).

Generally, the upper marsh zone is dominated by pickleweed, with saltgrass (*Distichlis spicata*), alkali heath (*Frankenia grandifolia*), and jaumea (*Jaumea carnosa*) occurring at the highest elevations, as well as gumplant (*Grindelia* spp.) along the upper edge of some tidal sloughs. The lower marsh zone along the Bay is dominated by stands of Pacific cordgrass, which also occurs along the banks of tidal sloughs within the marsh (DeGroot 1927, Hinde 1954, Harvey 1988). Low marsh areas with sparse vegetation, mudflats, and tidal sloughs are important foraging areas for rails (Applegarth 1938, Albertson 1995). Higher marsh areas with dense vegetation are used for nesting and high-tide refugia (DeGroot 1927, Harvey 1988, Foerster et al. 1990, Evens and Collins 1992, Collins et al. 1994).

Past studies (Applegarth 1938, Zucca 1954, Jorgensen 1975, Massey et al. 1984, Harvey 1988) re-

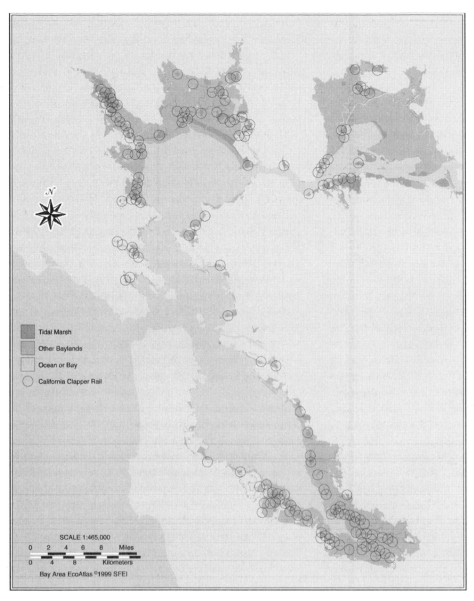

Figure 7.3 Known Distribution of the California Clapper Rail – Each circle represents one or more breeding pairs

Other Baylands Birds Focus Team

Tidal Marsh

Other Baylands

Ocean or Bay

○ California Clapper Rail

SCALE 1:465,000

0   2   4   6   8   Miles

0   4   8   Kilometers

Bay Area EcoAtlas ©1999 SFEI

ported on the importance of cordgrass as a canopy and nesting material. This apparent preference for cordgrass may be tied to the fact that cordgrass grows primarily along tidal sloughs and at the marsh edge, where rails prefer to forage. Weather-influenced changes in *Spartina* biomass and productivity may account for variations in nesting habitat preference (Gill 1979).

California clapper rails also occur in brackish wetlands consisting of bulrush (*Scirpus* spp.) (Gill 1979). In these areas, rails use bulrush plant materials for nest building and cover, but nests are still associated with tidal channels, as in pickleweed dominated marshes (Evens and Collins 1992). This type of habitat occurs along the larger creeks in the South Bay, in some areas of Napa Marsh, Petaluma River, and Sonoma Creek in San Pablo Bay, and in Suisun Bay (Gill 1979).

In the North Bay, natural habitat for *obsoletus* is the saline and marginally brackish tidal marshland with small channels that extend through or into patches of tall monocot vegetation. The ecological functions of salinity and tidal action are unknown. The tidal channels serve an important function as areas for foraging and as protected pathways. The monocot vegetation is used as nesting material. At marshland elevations near Mean High Water (MHW), the vegetation must be at least 50 cm tall to permit the construction of a nest that is low enough to be concealed by the natural plant canopy and yet high enough that it will not be inundated by the maximum high tides of the breeding season. At marshlands of higher elevation, shorter vegetation may be utilized.

Rail density seems to be positively correlated to channel density, although minimum and maximum values of channel density are not obvious from the data collected thus far. Suitable habitat is provided by most of the youthful marshlands that have evolved since the middle of the last century, as well as the remaining fragments of historical, mature marshlands. Local populations of breeding California clapper rails are most dense where patches of habitat are at least 100 ha in size. Such patches typically comprise some historical and youthful marshlands together. These marshlands may support relic populations of *obsoletus*. Fewer than fifteen such patches exist within the northern Estuary. One third of these adjoin the mouths of major tributaries downstream from Carquinez Strait. Small parcels of marshland along the immediate margin of a major tributary seem more likely to support *obsoletus* than similar sized parcels that are more isolated. In general, the density of rails decreased upstream toward the headward extent of the major tributaries of the Estuary (Collins and Evens 1992, Collins et al. 1994).

Other physical attributes of a marsh that influence rail use and may contribute to creating a self sustaining population of rails include size of the marsh, location relative to other marshes, buffer areas between marsh and upland, marsh elevation, and hydrology (Collins et al. 1994, Albertson 1995). These "high quality" characteristics play an integral part in the everyday survival of the clapper rail, providing food resources, cover from predators, breeding and nesting habitat, and refuge areas at high tides. Hence, the quality of a marsh will determine how many rails can be supported in a particular marsh (Garcia 1995, Albertson 1995).

There are few records of breeding rails utilizing diked marshes or other non-tidal habitat, but one observer (K. Rambo, pers. comm., in Orton-Palmer and Takekawa 1992) documented a successful breeding pair in a sewage oxidation pond, and Orton-Palmer and Takekawa (1992) documented use of a diked marsh by a breeding pair at Moffett Field. One pair was noted breeding in a small diked marsh adjacent to a larger undiked wetland at Muzzi Marsh, Marin County in 1992, and a pair apparently bred in a sewage pond adjacent to Richardson Bay in Mill Valley 1n 1997. Close proximity of tidal marshes supporting other breeding rails are thought to contribute to the use of these non-tidal areas.

Movement – Results of recent radio-telemetry studies indicated that most rails showed strong site tenacity, with very little movement between seasons and small core-use area (x=0.87 ha) which was defended throughout the year (Albertson 1995). This same observation has been made for Yuma clapper rails (Todd 1987) which were found to vocalize only in core-use areas, demonstrating probable territorial defense areas. Home ranges sizes varied by individual bird, but significant within-season differences are apparent among marshes, particularly in core-use areas (Albertson 1995). Core-use areas are defined as the highly defended portion of the territory (*per* Hinde 1954) and contain the nest site. Although the basis for differences in rail homerange size between marshes has not been absolutely determined, differences in predation pressure, quality of

habitat, and size/orientation of the marsh may account for most of these differences (Albertson 1995).

Conservation and Management

Numerous human-related factors, including commercial and sport hunting during the late 1800s (DeGroot 1927, Wilber and Tomlinson 1976, Gill 1979), have led to rail population declines over the last 150 years (Harvey 1988, Foerster et al. 1990). The Migratory Bird Treaty Act (1913), which restricted harvest on game species including the clapper rail, is believed to have led to a substantial recovery of populations in many remaining marshes (Bryant 1915, Moffitt 1940, Grinnell and Miller 1944). During the early to mid-1900s, commercial and urban development destroyed over 85% of the primary tidal marshes of San Francisco Bay, resulting in severe rail population declines, range contraction, and fragmented distribution (Gill 1979, USFWS 1984, Nichols et al. 1986, Foerster et al. 1990, Leipsic-Baron 1992).

Presently, California clapper rail populations are restricted to fragmented salt marshes in San Francisco Bay. Remaining marshes are geographically disjunct, and characterized by lack of a significant transition zone to terrestrial habitat, relatively small size, a large edge to area ratio, and close proximity to urban and industrial development. Several factors have previously been identified as negatively affecting current rail populations, including predation by non-native red fox (Foerster et al. 1990, Albertson 1995), contaminants (Ohlendorf and Fleming 1988, Ohlendorf et al. 1989, Lonzarich et al. 1990, Leipsic-Baron 1992), and marsh conversion and degradation (Foerster and Takekawa 1991). Predation is likely their most immediate threat for survival.

Clapper rail (*Rallus* sp.) populations are subject to predation by a number of species. At least ten native and three non-native predators are known to prey on California clapper rails and their eggs (Albertson 1995). However, recent evidence suggests that the non-native red fox may pose the most serious threat to adult clapper rails (USFWS and USN 1990, Foerster et al. 1990, Foerster and Takekawa 1991, Zembal 1992, Albertson 1995).

During the late 1800s, the red fox (*Vulpes fulva*) was introduced to western California by hunters. In addition, some individuals escaped from commercial farms (Lewis et al. 1993). Red foxes are well adapted to urban environments, and thus their populations have rapidly expanded along the coast in such areas as San Francisco Bay (Albertson 1995).

In addition, free-roaming and feral cats (*Felis domesticus*) prey on rails in marshes adjacent to housing and landfill areas (Albertson 1995). The Norway rat (*Rattus norvegicus*), raccoons (*Procyon lotor*), and non-native foxes prey on eggs and may cause low annual recruitment (DeGroot 1927, Applegarth 1938, Harvey 1988, Foerster et al. 1990). Harvey (1980) found that rats took 24% of eggs in 50 nests, and a 1992 study in the South Bay showed that rats preyed on 31% of eggs in 54 monitored nests (USFWS unpubl. data).

Extensive conversion of tidal lands resulting from historic and ongoing pressures of agricultural production, urbanization, and salt production has drastically reduced California clapper rail habitat in the San Francisco Estuary. The remnant tidal marshlands of the Estuary, the largest and last refuge of *obsoletus*, occupy only about 15% of their historic extent (Dedrick 1989), yet even in such diminished capacity comprise greater than 90% of all remaining California tidal marshlands (MacDonald 1977).

Fragmentation of habitat involves the construction of dikes and levees that serve as corridors for terrestrial predators. The devastating effect of red fox on *obsoletus* in the southern reaches of the Estuary is well-documented (Foerster et al.1990, Burkett and Lewis 1992), and has been noted in regard to *R. l. levipes* in southern California (Zembal *in* Foerster et al. 1990). In the northern reaches of the Estuary, the distribution of red fox is disjunct. They are reported west of Benicia and east of Dixon, but not in the Suisun system (Bob Smith, pers. comm.). We observed red fox at Wildcat, Point Pinole, China Camp, Mare Island, Second Napa Slough, and Dutchman Slough. None were detected in the Suisun Marsh, where coyote (*Canis latrans*) was quite common. We also noted sign of raccoon (*Procyon lotor*), striped skunk (*Mephistis mephistis*), feral cat, and rats (*Rattus* spp.). Raccoon sign was noted in virtually every tidal marsh, and we suspect that, as in the southern reach (Foerster et al. 1990), raccoon populations as well as those of other mesopredators have increased dramatically over the last decade. In addition, river otter (*Lutra canadensis*) is quite common in the Suisun Marsh area and should be considered as a potential predator of birds that nest on the ground near water (Ingles 1965).

According to MacArthur (1972), colonization among isolated patches of habitat requires very high fecundity of source populations. Given the effects of fragmentation, increased predation rates, possibly lowered fecundity (Foerster et al. 1990), and a low rate of dispersal, California clapper rails probably can not colonize or survive in all fragments of their habitat. Mortality due to predation could be so severe that immigration from source populations is infrequent, and the rate of survival of pioneering individuals is low. This might explain their absence in ostensibly suitable habitat observed in this study.

As with the California black rail (*Laterallus jamaicensis coturniculus*) and other tidal marsh dependant species (Evens et al. 1991, Nur et al. 1997) subject to similar pressures, simulation models have demonstrated that populations of fewer than 10 pairs (Richter-Dyn and Goel 1972, Roth 1974), or perhaps 25 pairs (Shaffer 1981), are inherently unstable and tend toward extinc-

Peter LaTourrette

tion due to stochastic events. Due to these factors, the persistence of subpopulations may depend on contiguity of marsh parcels and ability of rails to disperse among sites.

In addition to habitat fragmentation and the concomitant threat of predation, other pressures that threaten to alter or degrade the habitat and impact rail populations include: continued diversion of freshwater inflow from the North Bay (Rozengurt et al. 1987, Williams and Josselyn 1987); a progressive rise in sea level (Williams 1985, Moffatt and Nichol et al. 1987); and contamination. Contamination of other species of estuarine birds has been documented in this estuary (Ohlendorf et al. 1986, Ohlendorf and Fleming 1988, Phillips and Spies 1988), and other studies have detected dangerous levels of contaminants in clapper rail eggs (Lonzarich et al. 1990). The threat of toxic contamination of the substrate is ongoing, cumulative, and poorly understood.

Recommendations

The quality of restored habitat will dictate the potential rail population density. High quality habitat should include:

- Direct tidal circulation sufficient to allow the full tidal cycle,
- A predominant pickleweed marsh with cordgrass, gumplant, and other high marsh plants,
- Abundant, dense high marsh cover, and
- An intricate network of tidal sloughs.

In addition to these qualities, other physical characteristics of marshes that should be taken into account when planning a restoration project include size of marsh, location relative to other marshes, buffer area between marsh and upland, and type/extent of interface with humans and human-made structures.

Small sites may not provide enough habitat for a viable population of breeding birds. Ideally, restored areas should be able to potentially support viable rail populations and not be subject to wide population fluc-

Other Birds

tuations. Therefore, marsh restoration sites should be at least as large as existing sites, such as Dumbarton Marsh (118 ha) or Mowry Marsh (164 ha). Marsh restoration should focus on significantly expanding marsh acreages in areas currently supporting high populations of clapper rails, such as the Dumbarton, Mowry, Greco, and Palo Alto areas in the South Bay. In the North Bay, historic wetland acreage in close proximity to rail population centers provide opportunities for restoration, for example White Slough and Coon Island on the Napa River, diked areas adjacent to Sonoma Creek and the Petaluma River, and in large diked areas associated with Suisun Slough in Suisun Bay. This would allow existing populations to increase, reducing the probability of local extinctions.

Location of marshes with respect to one another should also be taken into consideration when planning restoration. Areas to be managed for clapper rails should be in close proximity to facilitate dispersal without risk of excessive predation. Rails have been found to disperse between 1-3 km, therefore primary marshes should be within this distance from one another. Intervening marsh corridors need to be of sufficient quality and width (at least several hundred feet) to provide adequate cover and food resources for dispersing rails.

Buffer areas between marsh and upland are critically important to rails for escape cover from predators during high tides. Absence of higher transitional areas adjacent to a marsh could result in high mortality during periods of tidal inundation. In a telemetry study (Albertson 1995), much of the predation was found to occur during high tides, when cover was scarce and little refugial area was available. Buffer areas need to provide cover of sufficient height and density to protect rails during extreme high tides. Marsh restoration projects should incorporate gradual transition areas from marsh into upland whenever possible, rather than an abrupt elevation change from marsh to levee.

Human-made structures, such as power lines, poles, and buildings, provide raptor perches. If these structures are in close proximity to marshes, predation by raptors can be high (Albertson 1995). Marsh restoration projects should take this into account and plan to remove structures if possible, or plan larger restoration projects to minimize the effects of such structures. Human dwellings, landfills, and rubble piles can harbor Norway rat and feral cat populations, therefore marshes in these areas may be subject to high levels of predation from these species. Human disturbance from recreational use, utilities maintenance, and high-intensity adjacent uses can disturb rails and cause homerange abandonment with subsequent nesting failure. Proposed use of adjacent land and public access to marshes should, therefore, be carefully evaluated prior to being permitted.

Habitat restoration should include management of non-native plant species, such as smooth cordgrass (*Spartina alterniflora*) and pepperweed (*Lepidium* spp.), in order to protect existing and future rail habitat from degradation. In particular, invasion of smooth cordgrass causes excessive sedimentation, which will clog tidal sloughs important to rails for foraging. A Bay-wide effort must be undertaken to control smooth cordgrass.

Continued predator management will be needed to maintain viable clapper rail populations and prevent extinction. Control efforts should target red fox, feral cats, and selected known native predators in areas of prime rail use. Structures and debris that harbor rats (riprap, decrepit buildings and vessels, etc.) should be removed from areas adjacent to rail habitat.

Predator management is not the solution to increasing future populations, however. In the long-term, only restoration of high quality tidal marsh habitat will ensure future survival and recovery of the California clapper rail. The current amount and configuration of suitable habitat is insufficient to substantially increase rail densities and population sizes. Several tidal restoration projects around the Bay are being undertaken by the San Francisco Bay National Wildlife Refuge complex and others. One 1,500 acre parcel, Cullinan Ranch, formerly farmland along the Napa River area of the North Bay is being restored to full tidal action by means of levee breaching and sedimentation. The Knapp property, a 452 acre former salt pond in Alviso and Guadalupe sloughs, will be restored to tidal marsh. Bair Island, a 1,600 acre former salt pond will be restored to tidal action. This area holds much promise for rail recovery due to its large size and close proximity to another fairly large rail population on nearby Greco Island. Additional opportunities exist in San Pablo and Suisun bays.

Recovery of California clapper rail populations will require the preservation of existing habitat and restoration of large acreages of high quality tidal marshes. In order to afford this species the best chance for recovery, restoration of former salt and brackish tidal marsh areas should be maximized in all subregions of San Francisco Bay. Restoration should focus on areas that have the greatest potential for developing into high quality salt marsh habitat.

References

Albertson, J.D. 1995. Ecology of the California clapper rail in South San Francisco Bay. M.S. Thesis, San Francisco State Univ. 200pp.

American Ornithologists' Union (AOU). 1957. Check-list of North American Birds, fifth ed. Amer. Ornith. Union.

_____. 1983. Check-list of North American birds, sixth ed. American Ornithologists Union. Allen Press Inc. Lawrence, Kansas. 877pp.

Applegarth, J.H. 1938. The ecology of the California clapper rail in the south arm of the San Francisco

Bay. M.S. Thesis, Stanford Univ., Palo Alto, Calif. 153pp.

Baron, T. and J. Takekawa. 1994. The California clapper rail. Life of the edge: a guide to California's endangered natural resources. Wildlife. pp. 158-9. Biosystems Books. Santa Cruz, Calif.

Brooks, A. 1940. The clapper rail of Morro Bay. Condor, Vol. 42.

Bryant, H.C. 1915. California clapper rail breeds in Alameda salt marshes. Calif..Fish and Game 1: 192.

Burkett, E.E. and J.C. Lewis. 1992. The spread of the red fox. Outdoor California 53(2): 1-6.

Collins, J. and J. Evens. 1992. Evaluation of impacts of naval riverine forces training operations on nesting habitat of the California clapper rail at Napa river, California. Final Report to Department of Navy, West. Div., from Avocet Research Assocs.

Collins, J., J. Evens and B. Grewell. 1994. A synoptic survey of the distribution and abundance of the California clapper rail (*Rallus longirostris obsoletus*) in the northern reaches of the San Francisco Estuary during the 1992 and 1993 breeding seasons. Draft Tech. Rept. to Ca. Dept. Fish and Game.

Dedrick, K.G. 1989. San Francisco Bay tidal marshland acreages: recent and historic values. Proceedings of the 6th Symposium in Coastal and Ocean Management (Coastal Zone 1989). Am. Soc. of Engineers. pp. 383-398.

DeGroot, D.S. 1927. The California clapper rail: its nesting habits, enemies, and habitat. Condor 29: 259-270.

Eddleman, W.R. 1989. Biology of the Yuma clapper rail in the southwestern United States and northwestern Mexico. Final Rpt. U.S. Bur. Reclam., Yuma Proj. Off., Yuma, Arizona. 127pp.

Ehrlich, P.R., D.S. Dobkin and D. Wheye. 1988. The birder's handbook. Simon and Schuster, Inc.

Evens, J. 1985. Endangered species information system. U.S. Fish Wildl. Serv.

Evens, J. and J. Collins. 1992. Distribution, abundance and habitat affinities of the California clapper rail (*Rallus longirostris obsoletus*) in the northern reaches of the San Francisco Estuary during the 1992 breeding season. Final Rept. to Ca. Dept. Fish and Game.

Evens, J. and G. Page. 1983. The Ecology of rail populations at Corte Madera Ecological Reserve, Marin Co. Rept. to Marin Audubon Society from Point Reyes Bird Observatory.

_____. 1987. The sizes of clapper rail populations at Corte Madera Ecological Reserve, Muzzi Marsh, San Clemente Creek, and Triangle Marsh. Rept. to Marin Audubon Society from Point Reyes Bird Observatory. Apr. 4, 1987.

Evens, J.G., G.W. Page, S.A. Laymon and R.W. Stallcup. 1991. Distribution, relative abundance, and status of the California black rail in western North America. Condor 93: 952-966.

Foerster, K.S. 1989. Summary of California clapper rail winter populations in the San Francisco Bay National Wildlife Refuge, November 1988-January 1989. U.S. Fish Wildl. Serv. 17pp.

Foerster, K.S. and J.E. Takekawa. 1991. San Francisco Bay National Wildlife Refuge predator management plan and final environmental assessment. San Francisco Bay Natl. Widl. Refuge, Fremont, Calif. 54pp.

Foerster, K.S., J.E. Takekawa, and J.D. Albertson. 1990. Breeding density, nesting habitat, and predators of the California clapper rail. Unpubl. Rpt. No. SFBNWR-116400-90-1, prep. for San Francisco Bay Natl. Widl. Refuge, Fremont, Calif. 46pp.

Garcia, E.J. 1995. Conservation of the California clapper rail: an analysis of survey methods and habitat use in Marin County, California.. M.S. Thesis, Univ. of Ca., Davis.

Gill, Jr., R. 1979. Status and distribution of the California clapper rail (*Rallus longirostris obsoletus*). Calif. Fish and Game 65: 36-49.

Grinnell, J. 1915. A distributional list of the birds of California. Pacific Coast Avifauna No. 11.

Grinnell, J. and A. Miller. 1944. The distribution of the birds of California. Pacific Coast Avifauna No. 27. Cooper Ornithological Club.

Grinnell, J. and M.W. Wythe. 1927. Directory to the bird life of the San Francisco Bay region. Pacific Coast Avifauna No. 18. Contribution No. 493 from the Museum of Vertebrate Zoology, Univ. of Calif.

Grinnell, J., H.C. Bryant and T.I. Storer. 1918. California clapper rail. *In*: The gamebirds of California. U.C. Press, Berkeley. pp. 283-291.

Harding, E.K., D.F. Doak, J.D. Albertson and J.E. Takekawa. 1998. Predator management in San Francisco bay wetlands: past trends and future strategies. Report for U.S. Fish and Wildl. Serv. 60pp.

Harvey, T.E. 1980. A breeding season survey of the California clapper rail (*Rallus longirostris obsoletus*) in south San Francisco Bay, California. Unpubl. Final Rpt. prep. for San Francisco Bay Natl. Wildl. Refuge, Fremont, Calif. 45pp.

_____. 1988. Breeding biology of the California clapper rail in South San Francisco Bay. Trans. of Western Sect. of the Wildlife Society 24: 98- 104.

Hinde, H. 1954. The vertical distribution of salt marsh phanaerogams in relation to tide levels. Ecol. Monogr. 24: 209-225.

Ingles, L. 1965. Mammals of the Pacific states. Stanford Univ. Press, Stanford, Calif. 505pp.

Johnson, R.W. 1973. Observations on the ecology and management of the northern clapper rail, *Rallus longirostris crepitans* Gmelin in Nassau County, New York. Ph.D. Thesis, Cornell Univ. 222pp.

Jorgensen, P.D. 1975. Habitat preference of the light-footed clapper rail in Tijuana Marsh, California. M.S. Thesis, San Diego Univ. 84pp.

Jorgensen. P.D. and H.L. Ferguson. 1982. Clapper rail preys on savannah sparrow. Wilson Bull. 94(2): 215.

Leipsic-Baron, T. 1992. Anthropogenic influences on the biogeography of clapper rails in California. M.S. Thesis, Univ. Ca., Los Angeles.

Lewis, J.C., K.L. Sallee and R.T. Golightly, Jr. 1993. Introduced red fox in California. Rpt. 93-10, Ca. Dept. Fish and Game, Nongame Bird and Mammal Sect., Sacramento, Calif.

Lonzarich D.G., T.E. Harvey and J.E. Takekawa. 1990. Trace element and organochlorine concentrations in California clapper rail (*Rallus longirostris obsoletus*) eggs. Arch. Environ. Contam. Toxicol. 23: 147-153.

MacArthur, R.H. 1972. Geographical ecology: patterns in the distribution of species. Princeton Univ. Press. 269pp.

MacDonald, K.B. 1977. Coastal salt marsh. *In*: M.G. Barbour and J. Major (eds). Terrestrial vegetation of California. John Wiley and Sons, New York, NY. pp. 263-294.

Massey, B.W. and R. Zembal. 1987. Vocalizations of the light-footed clapper rail. J. Field Ornith. 58: 32-40.

Massey, B.W., R. Zembal and P.D. Jorgensen. 1984. Nesting habitat of the light-footed clapper rail in Southern California. J. Field. Ornithol. 55(1): 67-80.

Meanley, B.W. 1985. The marsh hen: a natural history of the clapper rail of the Atlantic coast salt marsh. Centreville, MD. Tidewater Publishers. 118pp.

Moffatt and Nichol, Engineers; Wetland Research Associates, Inc.; and San Francisco Bay Conservation and Development Commission Staff. 1987. Future sea level rise: predictions and implications for San Francisco Bay. Report to San Francisco Bay Conservation and Development Commission, San Francisco, Calif.

Moffitt, J. 1940. Clapper rail project. Gull 22: 45.

_____. 1941. Notes on the food of the California clapper rail. Condor 43(6): 270-273.

Nichols, F.H., J.E. Cloern, S.N. Luoma and D.H. Peterson. 1986. The modification of an estuary. Science 231: 567-573.

Nur, N., S. Zack, J. Evens and T. Gardali. 1997. Tidal birds of the San Francisco Bay region: status, distribution, and conservation of five Category 2 taxa. Draft Final Rept. to U.S. Geological Survey-Biol. Res. Div. Point Reyes Bird Observatory.

Ohlendorf, H.M. and W.J. Fleming. 1988. Birds and environmental contaminants in San Francisco and Chesapeake Bays. Marine Pollution Bull. 19: 487-495.

Ohlendorf, H.M., R.H. Lowe, P.R. Kelly, and T.E. Harvey. 1986. Selenium and heavy metals in San Francisco Bay diving ducks. J. Wildlife. Manage. 50: 64-71.

Ohlendorf, H.M., K.C. Marois, R.W. Lowe, T.E. Harvey and P.R. Kelly. 1989. Environmental contaminants and diving ducks in San Francisco Bay. *In*: Selenium and agricultural drainage: proceedings of the fourth selenium symposium, Berkeley, Calif., March 21, 1987. The Bay Institute of San Francisco, Sausalito, Calif. pp. 60-69.

Orr, R.T. 1939. Fall wanderings of clapper rails. Condor 41: 151-152.

Orton-Palmer, A.E. and J.E. Takekawa. 1992. Breeding census for the California clapper rail (*Rallus longirostris obsoletus*) at Naval Air Station Moffett Field and Guadalupe Slough, 1992. Unpubl. Rept., U.S. Fish Wildl. Serv. (for U.S. Dept. Navy, Contract No. N62474-91-M-0604).

Phillips, D.J.H. and R.B. Spies. 1988. Chlorinated hydrocarbons in the San Francisco estuarine ecosystem. Marine Pollution Bull. 19: 445-453.

Richter-Dyn, N. and N.S. Goel. 1972. On the extinction of colonizing species. Theoretical Pop. Biol. 3:406-433.

Ridgeway, R. 1880. On *Rallus longirostris*, Bodd., its geographical races. Bull. NuHall Ornithol. Club 5: 138-140.

Roth, D.A. 1974. The analysis of a population model demonstrating the importance of dispersal in a heterogeneous environment. Oecologia 15: 259-275.

Rozengurt , M.A, M.J Herz, and S. Feld. 1987. Analysis of the difference of water withdrawals on run-off to the Delta, San Francisco Bay (1921-1983). Tiburon Center for Env. Studies. Tiburon, Calif.

San Francisco Estuary Project (SFEP). 1992. Status and trends report on wildlife of the San Francisco Estuary. U.S. Fish Wildl. Serv.

Shaffer, M.L. 1981. Minimum population sizes for species conservation. Bioscience 31: 131-134.

Storer, T. 1915. Additional records of California clapper rail and red phalarope in California. Condor 17: 98.

Taylor, H.R. 1894. Among the California clapper rail. Nidologist 1(10-11): 153-155.

Taylor, P.B. 1996. Clapper rail species account. *In:* Hoyo et al. (eds). Handbook of the birds of the world, Vol. 3. haotizin to auks. Lynx Edicions. Barcelona. p. 167.

Todd, R.I. 1987. A saltwater marsh hen in Arizona. Arizona Game and Fish Dept., Phoenix, Ariz.

U.S. Fish and Wildlife Service (USFWS). 1973. United States list of endangered fauna. U.S. Fish Wildl. Serv., Office of Endangered Species and Internatl. Activities, Washington, D.C.

_____. 1984. The salt marsh harvest mouse/California clapper rail recovery plan. U.S. Fish Wildl. Serv., Region 1, Portland, Oregon.

Other Birds

U.S. Fish and Wildlife Service and U.S. Navy (USFWS and USN). 1990. Final environmental impact statement, endangered species management and protection plan. Naval Weapons Station - Seal Beach and Seal Beach Natl. Wildl. Refuge, Orange County, California. U.S. Fish Wildl. Serv., Reg. 1, Portland, OR.

Varoujean, D.H. 1972. A study of the California clapper rail in Elkhorn Slough, 1972. Report for Ca. Dept. Fish and Game. 9pp.

Wilber, S.R. and R.E. Tomlinson. 1976. The literature of the western clapper rails. Wildl. Res. Rpt. No. 194, U.S. Fish Wildl. Serv., Washington, D.C.

Williams, L. 1929. Notes on the feeding habits and behavior of the California clapper rail. Condor 31: 52-56.

Williams, P.B. 1985. An overview of the impact of accelerated sea level rise on San Francisco Bay. Report to the Bay Conservation and Development Commission, San Francisco.

Williams, P.B. and M. Josselyn. 1987. An overview of flow and salinity standards required to protect the ecosystem of San Francisco Bay. Report to San Francisco Bay Conservation and Development Commission, 19 Sept. 1987. Project #390.

Zembal, R. 1991. Light-footed clapper rail census and study, 1991. Report to Dept. Fish and Game.

_____. 1992. Light-footed clapper rail census and study, 1992. Rpt. 93-8, Ca. Dept. Fish and Game, Nongame Bird and Mammal Sect., Sacramento, Calif.

Zembal, R. and B.W. Massey. 1983. To catch a clapper rail – twice. North American Bird Bander 8(4): 144-148.

Zembal, R., B.W. Massey, and J. M. Fancher. 1989. Movements and activity patterns of the light-footed clapper rail. J. Wildl. Manage. 53: 39-42.

Zucca, J.J. 1954. A study of the California clapper rail. Wasmann J. Biology 12(2): 135-153.

Personal Communications

Robert Smith, California Department of Fish and Game. Shasta Valley Wildlife Area Manager, former Assistant Manager Grizzly Island Refuge, 1987-1992.

John Takekawa, Research Wildlife Biologist, U.S. Geological Survey, Biological Resources Division, San Francisco Bay Estuary Field Station, California.

Brenda Grewell, Department of Environmental Science and Policy, University of California, Davis.

California Black Rail

Laterallus jamaicensis coturniculus

Lynne A. Trulio

Jules G. Evens

Introduction

Two subspecies of the black rail breed in North America, the eastern black rail (*Laterallus jamaicensis jamaicensis*) and the California black rail (*L. j. coturniculus*). The bulk of the population (>90%) is associated with the tidal marshlands of the San Francisco Estuary. The species' reliance on tidally influenced, completely vegetated, high elevation salt marsh habitat makes it a valuable indicator species of mature, upper tidal marsh habitat.

The California subspecies is a sparrow-sized bird, approximately five to six inches long. Cogswell and Christman (1977) note that this secretive bird can be positively identified by its "dark slate color, with faint white bars on the sides and chestnut nape and the prominent white spotted back." The California black rail is found primarily in three locations on the West Coast: the San Francisco Estuary and local coastal marshes, the lower Imperial Valley and the lower Colorado River at the border of California and Arizona, and northwestern Baja California (Eddleman et al. 1994).

The discovery in 1994 of a black rail population in freshwater marsh habitat in the Sierra foothills east of Marysville (Aigner et al. 1995) suggests that other unknown populations also may exist. Indeed, in 1997, systematic surveys of potential habitat in the vicinity of this 1994 site detected small populations scattered throughout the foothills, mostly between 100 and 200 meter elevations. Of more than 100 sites surveyed, approximately one quarter supported black rails in 1997 (J. Tecklin, pers. comm.). Subsequent field work detected rails at 71 sites in the lower foothills of three counties, extending from north of Chico on Butte County, south through Nevada County (J. Tecklin, *in press*)

In the San Francisco Bay Area, this rail is primarily a bird of tidally influenced marshes and is most often seen during very high tides when it is forced out of the lower elevation pickleweed marsh.

Other Birds

Description

Because the California black rail is so furtive, very little is known about its ecological requirements, although recent studies have begun to reveal some of these mysteries (Flores and Eddleman 1993). Old records from San Diego Bay and more recent surveys in San Francisco Bay indicate that birds may begin the breeding season (as evidenced by calling) as early as mid-February at coastal locations, later in the interior. During breeding season, birds call primarily during twilight hours. Males and females are distinguished by their very different calls, although much remains to be learned about the vocalizations of this species.

Breeding Biology – Nesting occurs in tall grasses or marsh vegetation, and nests consist of a small, woven cup of marsh plants, reeds, or grasses constructed by the male and female. In San Francisco Bay, nests with eggs have been found in April (J. Evens, pers. obs.), in San Diego Bay (where the species no longer breeds) in May (Cogswell and Christman 1977). Limited data suggest that San Francisco Bay rails lay 6 $\pm$ 1.4 eggs (Wilbur 1974). Data from non-tidal Arizona habitat showed that both males and females may incubate, that incubation is 17 to 20 days, and that second and replacement clutches are possible (Flores and Eddleman 1993). Behavior in tidal marshes in San Francisco Bay may differ from Arizona, however.

The first known record of the species in California was of a single individual on the Farallon Islands, 48 km west of San Francisco, October 18, 1859 (Brewster 1907). There are no reliable records of birds breeding in San Francisco Bay before 1970 (Evens et al. 1991), but undoubtedly this species has been resident since before European colonization. Recent evidence confirms breeding in the North Bay at China Camp, Black John Slough and Day Island, Marin County, and Sonoma Creek, Sonoma County (J. Evens, 1986-94 unpubl. field notes), however, presence of territorial birds during the breeding season implies breeding throughout the tidal marshlands of San Pablo Bay, Carquinez Strait and Suisun Bay, and at sporadic sites in the Delta and on the outer coast.

Single nest or juvenile observations have been recorded at Alviso, Newark, Richardson Bay, Benicia, and Pinole between 1910 and 1970. Very few nests or juveniles have ever been recorded from the Central or South Bay, none in recent years and breeding status there is uncertain. Records compiled by S. Rottenborn from Santa Clara Valley Audubon Society dating back to 1927 suggest that black rails have been very rare to non-existent outside the winter months in the South Bay during this period. A recent late-season record of a black rail calling was on April 26-27, 1993 at the Palo Alto Baylands. Evens et al. (1991) also report territorial calling at the Dumbarton Bridge in April 1989.

Migration Ecology – Migration is commonly believed to be an autumn (August through October) dispersal, probably comprised mostly of birds of the year (juveniles). Extralimital records support this view. Grinnell and Wythe (1927) noted that this species was a "fairly common fall and winter visitant" in the San Francisco Bay Area. Although black rails winter in the United States, their migration pattern in California is not clear, and the extent of their winter dispersal is not known (Ehrlich et al. 1992). Based on the known distribution within San Francisco Bay, it seems likely that the post-breeding season dispersal from North Bay marshes accounts for winter numbers in the South Bay.

Although there are numerous non-breeding season (August-March) records of black rails in these Central and South Bay marshes, their numbers are apparently not sustained through the spring (Evens et al. 1991). Very little is known, however, about spring movement. Reasons for the breeding season absence in the South Bay may include several interrelated factors, including lower elevation of marshes, less peripheral high marsh or transitional habitat, and increased predation rates (Manolis 1978, Evens et al. 1991).

The recent discovery of numerous populations in freshwater marshes and seepages in the Sierra Foothills (Aigner et al. 1995; J. Tecklin, pers. comm.) indicates that the species has the ability to colonize isolated habitat patches. The Rallidae in general disperse themselves effectively and the colonization of several disparate and isolated sites in California in recent years, some of which are newly created (Evens et al. 1991, Aigner et al. 1995, Nur et al. 1997), points to the importance of any marsh habitat for black rails.

Food and Feeding – This species feeds by ground gleaning on terrestrial insects, aquatic invertebrates, and perhaps seeds. Sampling of rail habitats in North Bay marshes indicate Arachnida and Amphipoda as likely prey items, although these findings are largely speculative (Evens, pers. obs.).

Distribution and Abundance

Historically, the black rail occurred from Central California south to San Diego and Baja. Several breeding season surveys of the bird's distribution in California provide current information on the abundance, distribution, and habitat choice of this species in the San Francisco Bay (Manolis 1978, Evens et al. 1991, Nur et al. 1997). Eddleman et al. (1994) stated that in "coastal California during the breeding season, the California black rail is presently found at Bodega Bay, Tomales Bay, Bolinas Lagoon, San Francisco Estuary, and Morro Bay" Although once more widely distributed, the bulk of the population is "now restricted...to the tidal marshlands of the northern reaches of the San Francisco Estuary (San Pablo Bay)... at relatively few sites" (Evens et al. 1991).

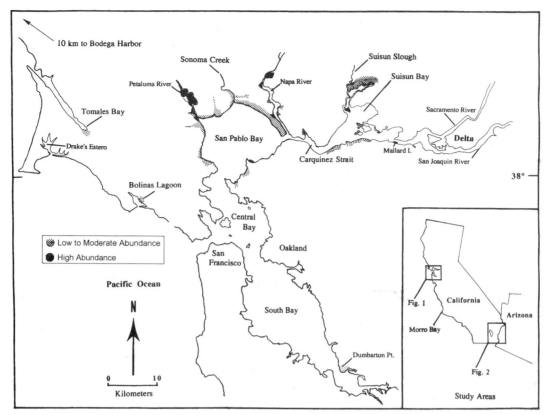

Figure 7.4 Distribution and Relative Abundance of Black Rails (*Laterallus jamaicensis coturniculus*) in the San Francisco Bay Region Point Reyes Bird Observatory breeding season surveys, Evens et al. 1991.

Figure 7.4 shows the approximate current distribution and relative abundance of black rails in the San Francisco Bay region (Evens et al. 1991). Evens et al. (1991) described the species as rare throughout most of its California range, except in those areas noted by Eddleman, where it is fairly common. Currently, the coastal Southern California breeding population is extirpated.

In his spring and summer surveys, Manolis (1978) found no birds in Central and South Bay marshes, but did find them in San Pablo Bay and Suisun marshes. The extensive breeding season survey by Evens et al. (1991) in San Francisco Bay marshes confirmed distributional patterns found by Manolis. The survey also found numbers concentrated in the northern reaches; birds were largely missing from the Central Bay (except Corte Madera marsh) and were very rare in the South Bay.

Areas of highest concentration are "Petaluma River Wildlife Management Area, along Black John and Fagan sloughs and Coon Island in Napa Marsh, and in some bayshore marshes of San Pablo Bay" (Evens et al. 1991, SFEP 1992). "In these northern reaches rail numbers were: much higher in tidal marshes than in marshes with restricted tidal flow, generally higher in marshes along large tributaries than in smaller tributaries or along the bayshore; much higher in bayshore marshes located at the mouths of creeks, rivers, or sloughs than in bayshore marshes not bisected by water courses" (Evens

et al. 1991). Nesting birds are also patchily distributed in Suisun Bay marshes and the Delta (SFEP 1992). Recent field work suggests that black rails are more widely distributed in Suisun Marsh than previously understood, particularly in the northern most undiked marshes (B. Grewell, pers. comm.).

A survey of the entire Estuary, conducted from 1986-1988, detected 608 rails at 1,168 stations (Evens et al. 1991). All but two rail detections occurred in the northern reaches of the Bay, including San Pablo Bay, the Carquinez Strait, Suisun Bay, and the Delta. This survey detected rails at 87% of the San Pablo Bay stations, 20% of the Carquinez Strait and Suisun Bay stations, 5% of the Delta stations, <1% of the South Bay stations, and none of the Central Bay stations. Evens (pers. obs.) notes that the population at the Corte Madera Ecological Reserve is believed to now be extirpated.

A follow-up study in 1996 of those parcels surveyed in 1986-1988 (Nur et al. 1997) found stable populations in San Pablo Bay and Suisun Bay and detected no black rails in the Central and South bays. Although there was no overall trend for decrease in the San Francisco Bay population, in the outer coast marshes (smaller and more isolated than the Bay marshes), numbers of black rails were low and appeared to have decreased over the past decade and are considered in danger of extirpation. While this study found that individual marsh size was

Other Birds

not significantly related to overall black rail density, it did find a significant tendency for black rails to be absent from small marshes.

There are many records of adults and juvenile black rails in Central and South bays during the non-breeding season, but no breeding is known to occur in these areas (SFEP 1992). The lack of high tide refugia for birds and low marsh elevation in the Central and South Bay may explain why breeding populations are not found there.

Rick Stallcup

Habitat Use and Behavior

This species prefers *Salicornia* dominated marsh habitat (Cogswell and Christman 1977). It is also known to occur in fresh, brackish, and salt marshes (Erhlich et al. 1988). In their survey of the San Francisco Bay during breeding seasons from 1986-1988, Evens et al. (1991) found the birds occurred almost exclusively in marshlands with unrestricted tidal influence. This study found very few birds associated with diked, impounded, or partially tidal marshes. Moreover, Evens and his colleagues found that rails during the breeding season were almost exclusively associated with more mature, higher elevation marshes dominated by *Scirpus* and *Salicornia*. Breeding birds were often associated with marshes that had significant amounts of *Scirpus* spp. Subsequent field work indicates that seasonal wetlands with muted tidal flow, especially those adjacent to tidally influenced marshes, may be utilized by rails in "wet" years when precipitation occurs late in the season and hydrates the substrate of marshes isolated from tidal influence, but supporting a dense cover of salt marsh vegetation, i.e., *Salicornia* (J. Evens, pers. obs.).

Newer, younger marshes with *Spartina* were not used by breeding birds, although rails could be found in these areas during the non-breeding season. Subsequent field work indicates that seasonal wetlands with muted tidal flow that are adjacent to fully tidal marsh and have 95-100% vegetative cover of salt marsh vegetation may be occupied in years of high precipitation (J. Evens, pers. obs.).

Josselyn (1983), citing Evens and Page (1983), noted that rails in Corte Madera Ecological Preserve were most commonly associated with areas of 90-97% pickleweed cover with a canopy height of 29 cm. These areas also had a "high degree of understory penetrability" which allowed rails to move easily through the pickleweed.

Evens and Page (1983) found that important components of breeding habitat were a dense pickleweed canopy and open structure below the canopy for nesting and easy movement. During nesting season, rails were associated with nearly solid pickleweed stands. Other important habitat parameters are elevation, timing and degree of flooding, marsh age and size, and proper soil and water salinity (Evens et al. 1991).

Peripheral vegetation at and above mean high higher water is necessary to protect the birds during periods of extremely high tides. They may be able to use a range of cover species; at Corte Madera they used fennel growing at the edge of the marsh (Evens and Page 1983). The birds are very vulnerable at this time and, if not hidden, are subject to predation by northern harriers (*Cirrus cyaneus*), great egrets (*Casmerodius albus*), great blue herons (*Ardea herodias*), and probably many other predators (Evens and Page 1986). Observations at Tomales Bay suggest that bird abundances may be depressed by lack of sufficient, quality upland for refuge during high tides (Evens and Page 1986). Uplands can also be degraded by having pedestrians too close to the marsh, which inhibits the escape of birds to the upland during high tides (Evens and Page 1983).

Conservation and Management

This taxon is acknowledged to be declining (Evens et al. 1991, SFEP 1992) and is listed as threatened and as a 'California Fully-protected Species' under the California Endangered Species Act, and as a 'Species of Special Concern' (formerly 'Category 2 Candidate Species') under the Federal Endangered Species Act. Fragmentation and habitat loss associated with historic and ongoing pressures of agricultural practices, salt production, and urbanization are identified as the primary causes of the decline. The remnant tidal marshlands of San Francisco Bay occupy only 15% or less of their historic area (Dedrick 1989), yet even in this diminished capacity comprise 90% of all remaining California tidal marshes (MacDonald 1977).

Marshlands of San Francisco Bay and the outer coast still occupied by black rails have been degraded by the loss of the zone of peripheral halophytes that form a natural vegetative transition between the marsh and upland and provide high tide refugia for rails. Livestock grazing and diking have reduced or eliminated this transition zone in most of the marshes around the Bay and the outer coast, resulting in rail susceptibility to heavy predation by herons, egrets, and raptors during high tides (Evens and Page 1986). Predation by rats, feral cats, and red foxes are also likely to contribute to the problem (SFEP 1992).

Other pressures that threaten to alter or degrade San Francisco Bay habitat include continued diversion of freshwater inflow from the North Bay, a progressive rise in sea level, and contamination by toxic agents shown to have had adverse biological effects on other birds in the Estuary (Evens et al. 1991). The patchy distribution of black rails makes the population susceptible also to metapopulation dynamics and stochastic variables (Evens et al. 1991, Nur et al. 1997).

Recommendations

Increases in black rail populations will require the protection of existing habitat and the restoration of good quality rail breeding habitat. This habitat should be undiked (fully-tidal) salt marsh, with dense stands of pickleweed, and other halophytes characteristic of the salt marsh community. Upland refugium that provides cover during highest tides is critical. Formerly diked marshes that are restored to tidal influence may provide additional habitat for black rails if they encompass elevations at or above mean high higher water, are adjacent to extensive tidal marshes with full tidal influence, and include high tide refuge.

Control of non-native predators is also expected to benefit the rail. The largest, most resilient rail populations may not occur in newly established marshes, but may require the development of a mature salt marsh community. The age of the marsh necessary to support black rails is unknown. To ensure the continued viability of this taxon, it is critical that, as marshes are restored, current rail habitat be protected, and transitional vegetation be allowed to become established around the perimeter of existing habitat. It may be many years before restored marshes offer ideal habitat for black rails.

Rail habitat shares many similar features with salt marsh harvest mouse (*Reithrodontomys raviventris*) habitat, although the rail occupies a narrower band within the elevational marsh gradient. Whatever habitat improvements benefit the rail are likely to benefit the mouse, and *vise versa*.

References

Aigner, P.A., J. Tecklin, and C.E. Koehler. 1995. Probable breeding population of the black rail in Yuba County, California. Western Birds 26: 157-160.

Cogswell, H. 1977. Water birds of California. Illust. by G. Christman. Univ. of Ca. Press, Berkeley. 399pp.

Dedrick, K. 1989. San Francisco Bay tidal marshland acreages: recent and historic values. Proceedings of the 6th Symposium in Coastal Ocean and Management (Coastal Zone 1989). Am. Soc. of Engineers. pp. 383-398.

Eddleman, W.R., R.E. Flores and L. Legare. 1994. Black rail. The Birds of North America. 123: 1-19.

Erhlich, P., D.S. Dobkin and D. Wheye. 1988. The birder's handbook. Simon and Schuster, Inc., New York. 785 p.

_____. 1992. Birds in jeopardy. Stanford Univ. Press, Palo Alto, Calif.

Evens, J. and G.W. Page. 1983. The ecology of rail populations at Corte Madera Ecological Reserve. Final report to Main Audubon Society by Point Reyes Bird Observatory.

_____. 1986. Predation on black rails during high tides in salt marshes. Condor 88: 107-109.

Evens, J., G.W. Page, S.A. Laymon and R.W. Stallcup. 1991. Distribution, relative abundance and status of the California black rail in western North America. Condor 93: 952-966.

Flores, R.E. and W.R. Eddleman. 1993. Nesting biology of the California black rail in Southwestern Arizona. Western Birds 24: 81-88.

Grinnell, J. and M.W. Wythe. 1927. Directory to the bird-life of the San Francisco Bay region. Pac. Coast Avifauana No. 18.

Josselyn, M. 1983. The ecology of San Francisco Bay tidal marshes: a community profile. U.S. Fish Wildl. Serv., Div. of Biol. Services, Washington, D.C. FWS/OBS-83/23. 102pp.

MacDonald, K.B. 1977. Coastal salt marsh. *In*: M.G. Barbour and J. Major (eds). Terrestrial vegetation of California. John Wiley and Sons. New York. pp. 263-289.

Nur, N., S. Zak, J. Evens and T. Gardali. 1997. Tidal marsh birds of the San Francisco Bay region: status, distribution, and conservation of five Category 2 taxa. Final draft rept. to U.S. Geol. Survey-Biol. Res. Div. Point Reyes Bird Observatory, Calif.

San Francisco Estuary Project (SFEP). 1992. Status and trends report on wildlife of the San Francisco estuary. U. S. Dept. Int., Fish and Wildl. Serv. Sacramento, Calif. 283pp.

U.S. Fish and Wildife Service and California Department of Fish and Game (USFWS and CDFG). 1977. Protection and restoration of San Francisco Bay fish and wildlife habitat, Vol. II. Prepared by Jones and Stokes Assoc. Inc.

Wilbur, S.R. 1974. The literature of the California Black Rail. U.S. Fish and Wildl. Serv., Special Science Rept. Wildl. No. 179. 17pp.

Personal Communications

Jerry Tecklin, Sierra Foothill Research and Extension Center, University of California, Davis.

Brenda Grewell, Department of Environmental Science and Policy, University of California, Davis.

Other Birds

Common Moorhen

Gallinula chloropus

William G. Bousman

Introduction

A member of the rail family (Rallidae), approximately 12 subspecies of common moorhen are found worldwide, ranging through Europe, Asia, Africa, North America, and numerous islands in the Pacific and Indian oceans. The North American subspecies, *G. c. cachinnans*, breeds widely in North America and winters south to Mexico (AOU 1957).

In general, the common moorhen requires open fresh water with plant cover. An omnivorous forager, it consumes varying proportions of plant and animal materials. It feeds while swimming or while walking on land or floating plants (Cramp 1980).

A nest is normally constructed in vegetation above water. The typical clutch size is six to seven eggs; pairs are often double-brooded and experienced birds may even raise three broods in a season (Cramp 1980). Birds defend breeding territories and, where resident, reduced winter territories. Generally, moorhens are monogamous and the pair-bond is normally for just a single year. However, an extended bond may occur for resident birds (Cramp 1980).

Distribution and Abundance

Modern Distribution – McCaskie et al. (1979) reported moorhens to be uncommon to fairly common in the interior (Central Valley) of Northern California and rare to very uncommon along the coast. More birds were reported to occur along the coast in the winter, but only stragglers were found along the northern coast. McCaskie et al. (1979)noted the primary habitats used were lakes and marshes. Garrett and Dunn (1981) reported that in Southern California, moorhens are uncommon to fairly common along the Salton Sea and in the Colorado River Valley, but occur primarily as a winter visitant

Dan Sudia

along the coastal slope. They noted that the moorhen was formerly more common along the coast, but it now breeds there only rarely and is largely extirpated because of the destruction of freshwater marshes.

In the last 25 years, comparable numbers have been found on the Benicia, Hayward-Fremont, and San Jose Christmas Bird Counts (CBCs), as shown in **Figure 7.5**. Elsewhere in the Bay, this species is at best a straggler. Aggregate numbers, based on the means of the nine CBCs shown in **Figure 7.5**, are 48, and this represents a lower bound on the winter population. The Benicia CBC has been showing a long-term decline in numbers (-10.1%, p<0.005), while San Jose CBC has shown an increase (+5.8%, p~0.05). The Palo Alto CBC, on the other hand, reported few birds until about 1980 when the Mountain View Forebay was constructed. Currently, within the Palo Alto count circle, equal numbers of birds are found on the CBC and the Summer Bird Count (SBC), indicating that the species is largely resident. This species is still considered uncommon in the South Bay, although it is regularly found in freshwater areas and is known to breed at the brackish Warm Springs Marsh near Newark. It is much less commonly found on the Marin CBCs and, in this respect, its distribution appears to be little different than that noted by Grinnell and Miller (1944).

Historical Distribution – In the earlier part of the century, Grinnell and Wythe (1927) noted records from San Francisco and Alameda but did not believe that the species bred within the estuarine system. Grinnell and Miller (1944) considered the common moorhen a summer resident of the Sacramento and San Joaquin valleys and the coastal district southwards from Alameda County. They noted that it did not occur north along the coast beyond San Francisco, and some birds were reported to remain through the winter. Within its preferred habitat of freshwater marsh, they considered it to be locally common. They noted a reduction in numbers in direct proportion to the reduction in available habitat, but pointed out that the species does take advantage of habitat created by irrigation, and this has offset the destruction of marshland to some degree.

Sibley (1952) considered this species to be an uncommon summer resident and noted records from W. E. Unglish of eggs taken from "Soap Lake." Sibley's map shows that his "Soap Lake" is what is presently called San Felipe Lake, just south of the Santa Clara line in San Benito County. Ken Schulz (*Audubon Field Notes* 11: 427) reported a high count of six adults and 12 immature birds at a 'colony' near the intersection of Singleton Road and Coyote River [sic] on 4 July 1957. Very small numbers of common moorhens were found throughout the 1970s in various areas along Coyote Creek in the southern Santa Clara Valley, but not in any locations along the Bay. Gill (1977), in his survey of South Bay breeding avifauna, did not include the common moorhen on his

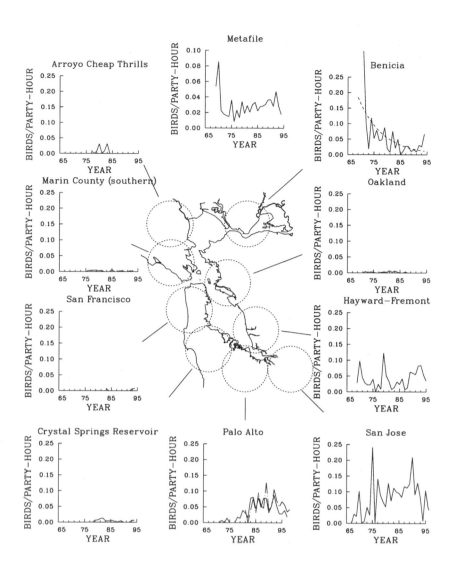

Figure 7.5 Christmas Bird Count data for Common Moorhen — Relative geographic location of Count circles indicated by dashed lines

National Audubon Society's *Audubon Field Notes*, and its successor publications, *American Birds*, and *Field Notes*, Volumes 24-51.

list, suggesting that he failed to find it in any areas he checked, including sites such as Coyote Hills Regional Park.

The historic abundance of the common moorhen is difficult to determine, not only because of the lack of historical data, but also because it appears that the San Francisco Bay estuarine system is near the northern limit of this species' range. The historical atlas clearly shows that there was more freshwater habitat available 200 years ago than there is today and, in the South Bay, there were a number of freshwater marshes associated with willow thickets and natural artesian systems. However, there are no records of moorhens having used these marshes, and it may be that this species is a recent colonizer of man-made freshwater habitats along the Bay edge.

Habitat Use and Behavior

The common moorhen appears to be tied closely to freshwater impoundments within the San Francisco estuarine system and, less often, along freshwater streams. These freshwater areas are usually dominated by cattails. For the most part, these freshwater areas are constructed

for other uses, and the moorhen invades once the vegetation becomes suitable for foraging and breeding.

The species breeds in small numbers in Marin County and was found in two atlas blocks near Novato during that county's breeding bird atlas. There are prior breeding records from Olema Marsh in 1967 as well and recent records from the Bolinas sewage ponds and Novato (Shuford 1993). It nests, as well, on Joice Island (C. Wilcox, pers. comm.) in the Suisun Marsh – this site being more typical of natural sites found in the Sacramento Delta than the highly modified man-made sites which this species uses along the Bay. The common moorhen also breeds in small numbers in Santa Clara County, but it is found more regularly there than in the North Bay. It nests every year in freshwater areas alongside the bay, such as the Mountain View Forebay and the Moffett channel at the Sunnyvale Water Pollution Control Plant. It also uses a number of the freshwater percolation ponds on the upper reaches of the Guadalupe River and, apparently, portions of the river itself. In wetter years, it extends its range to suitable percolation ponds with sufficient growth of cattails and tules, such as the small ponds at Coyote. Draining and maintenance activities along Coyote Creek during the atlas period prevented breeding in a number of areas where the species nested previously (and may still do so in wetter years).

Conservation and Management

The common moorhen, perhaps more than any other single species, is directly tied to freshwater marshes with good cover of cattails. This species is an active prospector for new territories (Cramp 1980) and, in this limited sense, is adaptable to change. Examples of this adaptability include the development of a new breeding population following construction of the Mountain View Forebay in the late 1970s. As cattails started to grow in this freshwater area, birds moved in and breeding was detected by 1983. Peak population counts in this area include 20 birds counted by David Suddjian on 24 November 1985 (pers. comm.) and 20 there as well reported by Peter Metropulos on 13 August 1988 (pers. comm.). Similarly, a suitable freshwater marsh developed at Moffett Field in the early 1980s due to cooling water runoff and a blocked drain, and by 1983 at least three pairs were nesting in this area. With the repair of the drain and a different treatment of the cooling water effluent, this area is no longer suitable for common moorhen and they are not present.

The moorhen's inflexibility in habitat needs is balanced by its adaptability in finding new habitats when and where they occur. In this sense, this species can respond successfully to carefully designed freshwater management programs. At the present time, within the bounds of the San Francisco estuary, almost every location used by this species has been constructed to serve the needs of local communities in one way or another. As a consequence, these habitats are not designed to benefit the common moorhen and, in almost none of these situations, do the agencies that oversee these habitats include within their management plans an oversight and stewardship responsibility for the moorhen. This lack of responsibility by local agencies is regrettable and in most cases where their actions discourage or destroy this species' local populations, alternate approaches can be en-

visioned that would enhance the local population without significantly impacting local agency goals. There are numerous opportunities, both through education and legal mandates, to improve the management of freshwater habitats in the San Francisco Bay Area to benefit this species.

References

American Ornithologists' Union (AOU). 1957. Checklist of North American Birds, fifth ed., Amer. Ornith. Union.

Cramp, S. 1980. The Birds of the Western Palearctic, Vol. II, hawks to bustards, Oxford Univ. Press.

Garrett, K. and J. Dunn. 1981. Birds of Southern California: status and distribution. Los Angeles Audubon Society, Los Angeles, Calif.

Gill, Jr., R. 1977. Breeding avifauna of the South San Francisco Bay estuary, W. Birds 8: 1-12.

Grinnell, J and A.H. Miller. 1944. The distribution of the birds of California, Pacific Coast Avifauna No. 27. Cooper Ornith. Club.

Grinnell, J and M.W. Wythe. 1927. Directory to the bird-life of the San Francisco Bay region. Pacific Coast Avifauna No. 18. Cooper Ornith. Club.

McCaskie, G., P. De Benedictis, R. Erickson and J. Morlan. 1979. Birds of northern California: an annotated field list, Golden Gate Audubon Society, San Francisco, Calif.

Shuford, W.D. 1993. The Marin County breeding bird atlas. Bushtit Books, Bolinas, Calif.

Sibley, C.G. 1952. The birds of the South San Francisco Bay region (mimeo).

Personal Communications

Peter Metropulos, *North American Birds,* San Mateo County subregional editor. Belmont, California. Pjmetrop@aol.com.

David Suddjian, Biological Consulting Services, Capitola, California. Dsuddjian@aol.com.

Carl Wilcox, California Department of Fish and Game, Yountville.

California Gull

Larus californicus

Thomas P. Ryan

Introduction

California gulls are a recent addition to the breeding avifauna of San Francisco Bay, drawn here by the availability of remote nesting grounds and rich food sources provided by the salt ponds and local refuse dumps. They have steadily increased in number since their first breeding attempt in 1980. Associated species which use simialar habitats are Forster's tern (*Sterna forsteri*), Caspian tern (*Sterna caspia*), black-necked stilt (*Himantopus mexicanus*), American avocet (*Recurvirostra americana*), killdeer (*Charadrius vociferus*), and Wilson's phalarope (*Phalaropus tricolor*).

Description

California gulls attain adult plumage in their fourth year. The adult California gull has a white head, chest, and underparts. The mantle (upperwings) is grey, their mantle is darker than similar appearing ring-billed gulls and herring gulls (Garrett 1985). Their wing-tips are black, with white mirrors. In breeding plumage their legs are bright yellow-green, this fades during the winter. Their bill is yellow with black and red subterminal spots (gonys). Juvenile birds are very dark with mottled underparts, pale undertail coverts, and pink legs (Garrett 1985). First year birds are a lighter grey-brown mottled with white, and have dull pink legs. The rump is barred. Second and third year birds have increasingly white underparts and more grey on the mantle, and the bill may have a black ring around it (Garrett 1985). Adult California gulls can be told from western gulls, herring gulls, and glaucous-wing gulls by their smaller size and yellow-green leg color. They can be distinguished from ring-billed gulls by a darker mantle, yellow-green leg color, and black and red subterminal spots.

Breeding Biology – California gulls begin to return to their breeding colonies three to seven weeks prior to breeding (Winkler 1996). The nest is a scrape in the substrate with bones, feathers, and vegetation placed within the cup (Winkler 1996). Nests are sometimes used in subsequent breeding seasons (Winkler 1996). Two to three, and occasionally four eggs are laid at daily intervals approximately one week after nest building begins (Winkler 1996, Baicich and Harrison 1997). Larger clutches (four or more) may be the result of female-female pairs. Eggs are laid in early to mid-May. Eggs at a given colony are laid within 20 days of each other, later clutches are often second attempts (Vermeer 1970, Winkler 1983, Jones 1986). The incubation period lasts 23-27 days (Winkler 1996); Jones (1986) reported a mean of 26.6 days at South Bay colonies. Both parents incubate the eggs (Winkler 1996). Chicks hatch at South Bay colonies in late May to early June. Chicks stay in or near the nest for the first week, from nine to 20 days old they have been found to run as far as seven meters from the nest for cover (Winkler 1996). Most chicks abandon the nest area entirely at 40-60 days, and fledge by 48 days (Winkler 1996). There is little association between adults and juveniles after fledging (Winkler 1996). California gulls are long lived with high survivorship, banded adults of 27 and 30 years of age have been reported (Winkler 1996).

Migration Ecology – California gulls appear to move continuously throughout the fall, winter and spring (Winkler 1996). Younger birds are found farther south in the fall and farther north in the spring. Individuals on the West Coast move farther north after breeding, and are driven farther south as winter storms increase in number and intensity.

Wintering Ecology – California gulls winter from central California, south to Guerrero, Mexico (AOU 1983). In California, concentrations are found in the Central Valley and along the coast. Local populations are found as far north as British Columbia. Birds banded as chicks at San Francisco Bay colonies have been observed at Pismo Beach in San Luis County and at Doheny State Beach and Seal Beach in Orange County.

Distribution and Abundance

In North America, California gulls breed at inland lakes from the Great Basin northward to the Northwest Territories (Canada) and southward to Utah, east to the Dakotas. They winter in smaller numbers in Utah, in Nevada through the Colorado River Valley, and at the Salton Sea in California.

On the Pacific Coast, California gulls breed at inland lakes east of the Sierra-Cascade axis from British Columbia through central California and in San Francisco Bay. The largest breeding population in California is at Mono Lake, Mono County (Winkler 1996).

California gulls winter along the Pacific Coast from British Columbia to Mexico. They are also found in the Central Valley and at the Salton Sea in California. Small numbers are found in the Columbia River Valley of Washington and Oregon and Willamette Valley in Oregon (Winkler 1996).

Approximately 5,000 California gulls nested at six sites in southern San Francisco Bay in 1997 (**Table 7.3**). They breed in the hundreds at Alameda Naval Air Station; this colony has been active since 1992 (L. Collins, pers. comm.). There are no known active colonies in the North Bay. They roost in large numbers during the winter in mixed flocks on the levees and in the salt ponds in the South Bay.

Population Trends – In 1982, Conover (1983) estimated the United States population at 276,000 California gulls. The worldwide population of this species is likely between 500,000 and one million individuals (Winkler 1996). Winkler (1996) notes apparent declines across prairies south and east from Alberta. However, he notes that patchy distribution of this species makes it difficult to determine any actual trend. The overall population appears to be increasing since the turn of the century, although there is debate about the rate of increase (Winkler 1996). This increase has been attributed to an increase in farmlands, increased availability of nesting sites at reservoirs, decreased harvesting of feathers and eggs, and increased winter food availability, especially at refuse dumps (Conover 1983).

California gulls first nested in the San Francisco Estuary in 1980 when 12 nests were encountered at Pond A6, near Alviso in Santa Clara County. We believe this was the first time California gulls nested in a coastal region. This colony grew each year, peaking in 1994 with 4,363 nests. Between 1994 and 1997, nest counts at Pond A6 decreased 26% to 3,241 nests. Beginning in 1984, California gulls began breeding at other sites within the South Bay. At Newark, 22 nests were found in 1984, increasing to 277 in 1985; this site was abandoned in 1989. In 1984, 33 nests were found at Pond A9 near Alviso, 2.2 km from Pond A6. Low numbers of California gulls nested here from 1984 to 1990, except

Table 7.3 California Gull Breeding Sites in the South Bay

Colony Site	Status	1997 Nest Count
Alameda NAS	Active	100+
Pond A1	Active	22
Pond B2	Active	328
Pond A6	Active	3,128
Pond A9/A10 levee	Active	878
Mowry M1/M2 levee	Active	620
Newark	Historic	0

in 1985 when 187 nests were found. In 1991, the colony was abandoned. It was re-established in 1992, but failed in 1994 and 1995. However, in 1996 and 1997 the colony increased to 702 and then to 878 nests. In 1990, a colony established on Pond A1. This colony grew to 86 nests in 1994, and currently has an estimated 40 nests. In 1992, a colony was established near Mowry Slough in Alameda County, 3.5 km from Pond A6. This site has been characterized by year-to-year fluctuations in nest numbers. In 1996, this colony moved to Pond M1/2, 1 km west of the original site. Red fox had been found at Pond M4/5 prior to this move. In 1993, California gulls nested on an attached levee and a series of small dredge spoil islands at Pond B2 near Mountain View, Santa Clara County, 2.4 km from Pond A6. Initially, colony size fluctuated, but increased from 1995 to 1997.

Currently approximately 10,000 California gulls nest in South Bay. California gulls are abundant in the San Francisco Bay in the winter, although no reliable estimates of wintering numbers exist (Harvey et al. 1992).

Habitat Use and Behavior

California gulls are opportunistic feeders, and their diet varies greatly at different locations. In 1983-84, Jones (1986) found the diet at colonies in the South Bay included arthropods (brine fly larvae, brine shrimp, insects, etc), garbage, and fish. California gulls are often seen foraging at garbage dumps, and at the edge of salt ponds on rafts of brine fly larvae and brine flies. They are also observed feeding in fields and schoolyards, presumably on insects and human refuse.

California gulls roost in mixed species flocks on salt pond levees, salt ponds, and schoolyards. There is a large daily movement from the local refuse dumps to the roosting areas on the levees and salt ponds.

Conservation and Management

California gulls are documented to abandon colonies following predation events, and observations of feral cats and red fox in close proximity to their nesting grounds. There have been partial and complete nesting failures at all sites that are attached or become land-bridged to the mainland early in the nesting season.

California gulls in the South Bay require remote, insular, abandoned levees and abandoned islands for nesting. The continued presence of such levees and islands will provide them with adequate nesting grounds. They require high saline salt ponds for their primary natural food source, brine fly larvae, brine flies, and brine shrimp. These are also food sources for many other species that use salt ponds.

The largest colony of California gulls is at the original point of colonization, Pond A6, where in recent years 3,000 to 4,600 pairs have nested annually. These levees should be maintained as nesting habitat for this species. If this colony is flooded as has been suggested, approximately 7,000 adult, breeding California gulls will be displaced. This could also negatively impact the tern populations in the South Bay. It is unknown exactly what the result would be of a major disruption of this colony. The possible consequences should be studied in greater depth before such an action is undertaken.

California gulls provide us with a robust subject to study the reproductive biology of a salt pond associated species. We are studying the effects of predation on species nesting on insular *versus* non-insular levees. We are studying the re-colonization of an area by a colonially nesting species after major predation events. At Pond B2, nesting occurs on a series of different sized islands, providing a natural experiment for studying the effects of island size and colony size on the reproductive success of larids.

In the 1980s, thousands of chicks were banded by San Francisco Bay Bird Observatory. Currently, 20-25% of the adults at these colonies carry U.S. Fish and Wildlife Service bands, and 5-10% carry color bands identifying them to cohort. As these birds are long lived, they provide an excellent subject for studies of survival, population dynamics, fall and winter movements and ecology, and eventually senescence, in addition to other banding related studies.

Acknowledgments

I would like to thank the Peg Woodin, Mike Rigney, and the late Richard Mewaldt for their meticulous efforts in studying the South Bay colonies in their early years; Laura Collins for her information regarding the Alameda Naval Air Station colony; and the many dedicated volunteer observers of the San Francisco Bay Bird Observatory.

References

American Ornithologists' Union (AOU). 1983. Checklist of North American birds, sixth ed. American Ornithologists Union. Allen Press Inc. Lawrence, Kansas. 877pp.

Baicich, P.J. and C.J.O. Harrison. 1997. A guide to the nests, eggs, and nestlings of North American birds. Academic Press. San Diego, Calif. 347pp.

Conover, M.R. 1983. Recent changes in ring-billed and California gull populations in the western United States. Wilson Bull. 95: 362-383.

Garrett, K. 1985. California gull. *In*: J. Ferrand, Jr. (ed). The Audubon Society master guide to birding Vol. 2: gulls to dippers. Alfred A. Knopf, New York, NY.

Harvey, T.E., K.J. Miller, R.L. Hothem, M.J. Rauzon, G.W. Page and R.A. Keck. 1992. Status and trends report on the wildlife of the San Francisco Estuary. San Francisco Estuary Project, U.S. Fish and Wildl. Serv. 283pp. plus appendices.

Jones, P.A. 1986. Aspects of the reproductive biology of the California gull in Alviso, California. M.A. Thesis, San Francisco State Univ., San Francisco, Calif.

Vermeer, K. 1970. Breeding biology of California and ring-billed gulls: a study of ecological adaptation to the inland habitat. Can. Wildl. Serv. Rept. Ser. No. 12.

Winkler, D.W. 1983. Ecological and behavioral determinants of clutch size: the California gull (*Larus californicus*) in the Great Basin. Ph.D. Diss., Univ. of Ca., Berkeley.

_____. 1996. California gull (*Larus californicus*). *In*: A. Poole and F. Gill (eds). The birds of North America, No 259. The Academy of Nat. Sciences, Philadelphia, Penn., and The Amer. Ornith. Union, Washington, D.C.

Personal Communications

Laura Collins, biologist, Berkeley, California.

Forster's Tern

Sterna forsteri

Thomas P. Ryan

Introduction

The Forster's tern is a mid-size tern found in open water, salt pond, marsh, and estuarine habitats within the San Francisco Estuary. It nests and roosts on dredge spoil islands and degraded, insular levees. Forster's terns forage in salt ponds, open bay, slough channels and marshes. Associated species which use similar habitats are California gull (*Larus californicus*), Bonaparte's gull (*Larus philadelphia*), Caspian tern (*Sterna caspia*), American avocet (*Recurvirostra americana*), black-necked stilt (*Himantopus mexicanus*), and killdeer (*Charadrius vociferus*).

Photo by M. Iliff

Marshall Iliff

Other Birds

Description

Forster's terns are a medium-sized tern. In breeding plumage, they have an all white body, a dark cap, black eyes, grey upperwings, orange bill with a black tip, and orange legs. Forster's terns are distinguished from other terns by size, a black cap and nape, deeply forked grey tail with white outer feathers, and uniformly light-colored upperwings (Peterson 1990). In August, they begin to molt into winter plumage: the black cap becomes a mask, with black coloration around and behind the eye. The crown becomes white, the nape varies from grey to black, and the bill turns from a bright orange color to a uniform black (Peterson 1990).

Forster's terns occur in freshwater and salt marshes, seacoast, estuaries, and inland rivers and lakes (AOU 1983). They feed on small fish and arthropods. The call is a harsh, nasal "za-a-ap" and a nasal "kyarr" (Peterson 1990)

Breeding Biology – Forster's terns nest alone and in colonies ranging in size between two and 600 birds. Their breeding season spans from April until August. They usually begin breeding in their second to third year. First year birds remain on their wintering grounds year-round. During courtship, the males pass fish to the females. The pair will remain together for the duration of the breeding season (Bent 1921). The nests are usually scrapes made in the dirt, with vegetation, small stones, sticks, and bones placed in the cup (Baicich and Harrison 1997, SFBBO unpubl. data). They are placed both in vegetation and on bare dirt. Birds at the South Bay colonies lay two to three eggs from mid-May to mid-June. Both parents incubate the eggs; incubation lasts 23 to 25 days (Baicich and Harrison 1997). Chicks begin to appear in mid-June. The young hatch in a semi-precocial state, and fledge at approximately 28 days (Baicich and Harrison 1997). Most young have fledged by the end of August.

Migration Ecology – During September and November, most Forster's terns begin their southward migration to spend the winter in locations from central California to Mexico, and possibly as far south as Costa Rica (Gill and Mewaldt 1979, AOU 1983). Of 2,943 Forster's tern young banded by Gill and Mewaldt (1979) at South Bay colonies, five were recovered during migration in the Los Angeles - San Diego area, and the sixth was recovered in Sinaloa, Mexico. It appears that their migration route follows the coastline of California; whether they cross Baja into the Sea of Cortez or move around the peninsula is unknown.

Wintering Ecology – It is unknown exactly where the San Francisco Bay population of Forster's terns spends the winter. Circumstantially, Forster's terns are common along the coast of western Mexico during the winter months (Arbib 1974, 1975, 1976). These sightings and the six band recoveries noted above led Gill and Mewaldt (1979) to state that, "nearly all Forster's terns leave the San Francisco Bay area each winter and that most juveniles and adults winter from coastal southern California well down the west coast of Mexico." Their habits and ecology are poorly known on their wintering grounds.

Distribution and Abundance

In North America, Forster's terns breed in the interior of the continent from central British Columbia to central Ontario, and south from Oregon to northwest Indiana. Along the East Coast, they breed from southern New York to South Carolina, and along the Gulf Coast from Tamaulipas, Mexico to Alabama. They winter from the Virginia coast to Florida and western Texas south to Mexico, casual to Costa Rica (AOU 1983).

On the Pacific Coast, breeding occurs from the coast of British Columbia south to Baja California. They winter from central California south to Oaxaca and Guatemala, casual to Costa Rica (AOU 1983).

In the North Bay, nesting occurs in the Napa River Marsh salt ponds, but there are no recent population summaries available for all colonies (Carter et al. 1990). Colonies were documented during the Napa County Breeding Bird Atlas Project at Russ Island (1989), Island #2 at the Can Club Duck Club (1989, 1991), Little Isle (1991), Knight Island (1990), and White Slough (1987, 1988, 1989, 1992, 1996) (R. Leong, pers. comm.) (**Table 7.4**). From counts done at these sites in various years, it appears that the total number of nests at these colonies are in the low hundreds in any given year. These colonies should be surveyed more completely to determine their actual size.

In 1997, Forster's terns bred at 21 colonies in the South Bay; two colonies were not surveyed. Since 1992, they have bred at 28 sites. These sites extend from Belmont Slough south to Alviso on the western side of the Bay, and from Baumberg south to Alviso on the eastern side (**Table 7.5**). They breed on dredge spoil islands, and degraded levees in current or former salt ponds, slough channels (Belmont), and diked marshes (Ravenswood).

Small numbers are found locally throughout the winter (W. Bousman, CBC data). Numbers increase during the spring, as migrants begin to arrive in April

Table 7.4 Forster's Tern Breeding Sites in the North Bay

Colony Site	Status
Coburn	Unknown
Island #2	Unknown
Knight Island	Unknown
Little Isle	Unknown
Russ Island	Unknown
White Slough	Unknown

Colony Site	Status	Colony Site	Status
Dumbarton ponds		**Alviso ponds**	
N1 (01)	Active	A5	Historical
N3 (02-04)	Active	A6	Historical
Baumberg ponds		A7	Active
P6 (01)	Active	A8	Active
P14 (02)	Historical	A16	Active
P12 (03)	Active	A17	Not accessible in 1997
P11 (04)	Active	A18	Active
Coyote Hills ponds		A20	Not accessible in 1997
NA2 (02)	Active	**Mountain View ponds**	
Hayward Shoreline ponds		A1	Active
		A2	Historical
HARD	Active	A3	Historical
3A	Active	B2	Active
3B	Active	**Charleston Slough**	Active
Turk Island ponds		**Bair Island ponds**	Active
		Ravenswood	
4C (01)	Active	OSP ponds (R1)	Active
7 (02)	Active	**Belmont Slough**	Active

Table 7.5 Forster's Tern Breeding Sites in the South Bay

(Harvey et al. 1992). Migrants and local breeders are found here until late October through November (Harvey et al. 1992).

Population Trends – Currently there are no estimates available for either the total North American population or the total Pacific Coast population. The only population estimates available from other coastal colonies are from the Bolsa Chica Ecological Reserve, where a colony established in the late 1980s and has increased to over 200 pairs (C. Collins, pers. comm.).

Forster's terns first bred in the San Francisco Estuary in 1948, when roughly 100 nests were found near the eastern end of the San Mateo Bridge (Sibley 1952). Gill (1977) found 935 nesting pairs at six South Bay colonies in 1971; this would be 1,200 nesting pairs if colonies "found outside the study area" were to be included. In 1972, 10 colonies were present, containing an estimated 2,000 pairs (Mansfield *in* Gill 1977). Rigney and Rigney (1981) estimated 2,500 pairs at six sites in 1981. Woodin (1988) summarized San Francisco Bay Bird Observatory data from 1984 to 1988 and reported that counts ranged from 2,183 adults present in 1987 to 3,610 in 1984. In 1988-89, 3,550 breeding birds were estimated at 21 colonies for all Bay Area colonies (Carter et al. 1990). From 1992 to 1997, between 1,842 and 2,365 individuals were observed, and between 1,012 and 1,754 nests were counted at peak breeding season counts at all South Bay colonies. Data collected in 1993 were not used in these figures as surveys were not as thorough as in other years. A decrease from 1,754 nests to 1,012 nests was seen between 1992 and 1994, a 42% decline. The number of nests increased to 1,362 in 1997.

Historically, the largest nesting site was at Pond B2 near Mountain View, with approximately 600 nests. The second largest site was at the Baumberg salt pond islands and the former Knapp Property, near Alviso (Rigney and Rigney 1981, Harvey et al. 1992). In 1997, the largest colony was at Turk Island (300 nests), followed by Hayward Shoreline (226 nests), and Pond B2 (127 nests).

California gulls have colonized both B2 and the Knapp property. At B2, California gulls have expanded from zero to 328 pairs from 1992 to 1997. At the Knapp property, California gulls increased in number from 2,750 pairs to 3,241 pairs between 1992 and 1997. Additionally, since 1992, red fox have been noted predating Forster's tern colonies in both areas.

Forster's tern populations steadily decreased between 1971 and 1997 (the time of this writing). Population estimates place the number of Forster's terns between 1,870 and 5,000 individuals (x=3,623; SD=1,599) between 1971 and 1981; 2,183 and 3,610 (x=2,707; SD=536) between 1984 and 1988; and 1,842 and 2,365 (x=2,137; SD=202.9) between 1992 and 1997. Although the population of Forster's terns in San Francisco Bay decreased across these periods, the large year-to-year fluctuations in the local breeding population make it difficult to determine if any significant trend exists.

Habitat Use and Behavior

Forster's terns forage on the open bay, slough channels, freshwater and salt marshes, and on salt ponds. During the breeding season, they are generally observed foraging singly and in groups. They are occasionally observed foraging with pelicans, egrets, gulls, and other terns in large foraging flocks on certain salt ponds, particularly in the late summer and fall. Forster's terns roost prior to, during, and after breeding on the dredge-spoil islands and levees. They also have been observed on docks,

Archimedes' screws, duck blinds, pilings, algal mats, floating debris, and other suitable structures surrounded by water. During the breeding season Forster's terns move singly and in groups between their nesting sites within the salt ponds and the aforementioned foraging areas throughout the day. Nocturnal movements, if any, are unknown.

Conservation and Management

In the San Francisco Bay Area, feral red fox (*Vulpes vulpes*) and domestic cat (*Felis domesticus*) are known predators of active Forster's tern colonies (SFBBO unpubl. data). Predation by great egrets and other ardeids is likely; other possible avian predators include raven, peregrine falcon, northern harrier, and red-tailed hawk.

It is unknown what effects, if any, contaminants have on Forster's terns in the San Francisco Estuary. Ohlendorf et al. (1988) found measurable levels of mercury, DDE, organochlorines, and PCBs in the eggs of Forster's terns at Bair Island in 1982.

In a few cases, colonies have been abandoned in association with off season levee maintenance and fluctuating water levels within ponds. High water levels can flood islands. Low water levels can land-bridge islands, making them more susceptible to mammalian predation. Most colonies are in areas of restricted human access, and at these colonies, disturbance does not appear to be a significant problem.

The continued presence of isolated, insular islands is crucial to the continued presence of Forster's terns in the San Francisco Estuary. In all cases, colonies are found within or in close proximity to former and current salt ponds. This habitat provides suitable nesting substrate isolated from human disturbance and makes access more difficult for mammalian predators. We recommend the continuation of programs to control mammalian predators, as this will likely decrease the impact of predation on these colonies.

A schedule of levee maintenance that will minimize disturbance to breeding colonies should be implemented. We recommend initiation of a management program that will: 1) minimize work near colonies during the breeding season (April 1 to September 1); 2) maintain islands by placing fresh dredge material on colonies after the breeding season is over (September 1st); 3) minimize the impact to the population in a given area by disturbing as few colonies within a given pond system as possible within a given year; and 4) construct more islands within salt ponds when possible.

The status of North Bay colonies is unknown due to a lack of available surveys, but it is likely that these colonies are still active. It should be noted that when South Bay Caspian terns were predated and disturbed in the South Bay, they shifted their nesting activities to the Central Bay and North Bay. These North Bay colonies could increase in importance in the event of a natural or man-made disturbance at the South Bay colonies. Our recommendations are to maintain or increase local nesting and foraging habitats. These areas include salt ponds, levees and islands associated with salt ponds, lagoons, shallow bay/strait, and marsh.

Research Needs – The reasons behind the decline of the South Bay Forster's tern population requires further study. Possible causes of this decline include encroachment by California gulls, predation by red fox and feral cats, disturbance by levee maintenance, and fluctuating water levels within salt ponds. Continued population monitoring is needed to document future population trends. Studies of reproductive success and fledgling success would be valuable in documenting problems with the year-to-year reproductive effort. Combining these studies with studies of predation, the presence and effects of contaminants would be valuable in detecting causes of the current decline.

Studies of their natural history and ecology on their wintering grounds in southern California and the west coast of Mexico are needed as well. The general decline in the total number of individuals returning and year-to-year fluctuations in the total numbers of individuals present may indicate problems elsewhere.

References

American Ornithologists' Union (AOU). 1983. Checklist of North American birds, sixth ed. American Ornithologists Union. Allen Press, Inc. Lawrence, Kansas. 877pp.

Arbib, R. 1974, 1975, 1976. American Birds. National Audubon Society. Various editions.

Baicich, P.J. and C.J.O. Harrison. 1997. A guide to the nests, eggs, and nestlings of North American birds. Academic Press. San Diego, Calif. 347pp.

Bent, A.C. 1921. Life histories of North American gulls and terns. U.S. Natl. Museum Bull. No. 113. 345 pp.

Carter, H.R., D.L. Jaques, G.J. McChesney, C.S. Strong, M.W. Parker and J.E. Takekawa. 1990. Breeding populations of seabirds on the northern and central California coasts in 1989 and 1990. U.S. Dept. Int., Fish Wildl. Serv., No. 14-12-001-30456. 443pp.

Gill, Jr., R. 1977. Breeding avifauna of the South San Francisco Bay Estuary. Western Birds 8: 1-12.

Gill, Jr., R. and R. Mewaldt. 1979. Dispersal and migratory patterns of San Francisco Bay produced herons, egrets and terns. North American Bird Bander 4: 4-13.

Harvey, T.E., K.J. Miller, R.L. Hothem, M.J. Rauzon, G.W. Page and R.A. Keck. 1992. Status and trends report on the wildlife of the San Francisco Estuary. San Francisco Estuary Project, U.S. Fish Wildl. Serv. 283pp. + appendicies

Ohlendorf, H.M., T.W. Custer, R.W. Lowe, M. Rigney and E. Cromartie. 1988. Organochlorines and mercury in eggs of coastal terns and herons in California, USA. Colonial Waterbirds 11(1): 85-94.

Peterson, R.T. 1990. A field guide to western birds. Houghton Mifflin Co. Boston, Mass. 432pp.

Rigney, M. and T. Rigney. 1981. A breeding bird survey of the South San Francisco Bay salt pond levee system. Rep. for South Bay Institute for Avian Studies.

Sibley, C.G. 1952. Birds of the South San Francisco Bay region. San Jose State College, 44pp. (mimeo.)

Woodin, P. 1988. San Francisco Bay Bird Observatory Unpubl. report.

Personal Communications

Robin Leong, Subregional Editor, *North American Birds*. Vallejo, California. leong@community.net.

Charles T. Collins, Department of Biology, California State University, Long Beach.

Caspian Tern

Sterna caspia

Thomas P. Ryan

Introduction

This large tern forages on the open bay, salt ponds, marshes, freshwater ponds, rivers, reservoirs, and in the open ocean near San Francisco Bay. They nest on sandy beaches and on salt pond levees and islands. The continental and Pacific Coast populations have both increased. However, declines have been seen at southern San Francisco Bay breeding colonies in recent years. Associated species include Forster's tern (*Sterna forsteri*), least tern (*Sterna antillarum*), and California gull (*Larus californicus*).

Description

The Caspian tern is the largest of the North American terns. The body and underwings are white, the under-

side of the tips of the primaries are black, the upperwings are a light silvery-grey, and the crown is black extending below the eye. The tail is shallowly forked. The bill is a deep red to orange-red with black on the tip. The legs are black in adults, and vary between orange, red, and black in the fall immature birds. Immature and winter plumage birds have white streaks in the cap (Peterson 1990).

The Caspian tern is a cosmopolitan species. They occur at lakes, bays, estuaries, marshes, and rivers, on all continents except Antarctica (AOU 1983). They forage by "plunge diving"—the bird hovers over the water before diving to or below the surface to catch their prey. They feed on fish, amphibians, and arthropods. Their call is a hoarse, low "*kraa-uh* or *karr*" (Peterson 1990).

Breeding Biology – Caspian terns breed on sandy beaches, dredge spoil levees, and islands. They are colonial, but will nest singularly (Baicich and Harrison 1997). They often nest with or near other larids. The nest is generally a hollow depression in the substrate, with plant and other debris placed in it (Baicich and Harrison 1997). In the San Francisco Bay Area, eggs are layed from May to July. They lay two to four eggs asynchronously at intervals of two to three days (Soikkeli 1973). Chicks hatch in June and July, and are present through August. The chicks are semi-precocial and move about the nesting colony after a few days; they fledge at 25-30 days (Baicich and Harrison 1997), but many stay near the colony as long as it is active.

Migration Ecology – Caspian terns which breed in San Francisco Bay migrate along the Pacific Coast to and from southern California and western Mexico (Gill and Mewaldt 1979).

Wintering Ecology – During the winter months, Caspian terns are found from central California, southward along the western coast of Mexico, to northern Colombia. Band recoveries indicate that Caspian terns that breed in the Bay Area winter along the west coast of Mexico, going as far south as southern Chiapas (Gill and Mewaldt 1979). Little is known about their winter ecology other than they are found at both coastal and inland sites (Gill and Mewaldt 1979). Christmas Bird Counts indicate that small numbers of Caspian terns winter locally throughout the Bay Area(W. Bousman, pers. comm.).

Distribution and Abundance

In the interior of North America, Caspian terns breed east of the Sierra-Cascade axis in the Great Basin from eastern Washington to California, and from Nevada through Utah to northwestern Wyoming (AOU 1983). In the Mid-West, they breed in northwestern Alberta, and central Saskatchewan east through the Great Lakes region south to North Dakota and central Michigan (AOU 1983). On the East Coast, they breed from Newfoundland to South Carolina. They breed along the Gulf Coast from Texas to Florida (AOU 1983). Caspian terns winter from North Carolina south to Venezuela (AOU 1983).

On the Pacific Coast, Caspian terns breed from British Columbia, Canada south to islands off the coast to Sinaloa, Mexico. They winter from coastal central California to northern Colombia (AOU 1983).

The first breeding accounts in the San Francisco Bay Area are from the South Bay, where the majority of Caspian terns nested prior to 1990. Since 1990, the majority of birds nest at colonies in the Central Bay and North Bay. Former colonies in the South Bay exist at Baumberg, Turk Island, Bair Island, and Drawbridge/ Mowry. Current colonies exist at Pond A7 near Alviso (104 pairs) and Coyote Hills (30 pairs). Single pairs have recently nested among Forster's terns at Ravenswood Open Space Preserve, and Hayward Shoreline.

The only North Bay breeding colony exists at Knight Island at the Napa River Marsh. This colony was first detected in 1989 (R. Leong, pers. comm.). In 1977, a small colony was detected at the Can Club, Island #2 (Gill 1977; R. Leong, pers. comm.).

In the Central Bay, colonies are found at Brooks Island and at the Alameda Naval Air Station (NAS).

Population Trends – The largest continental population of Caspian terns is found in North America, with a minimum of 35,000 pairs nesting throughout North America in the 1980s and 1990s (Cuthbert and Wires 1999). The North American population has steadily increased since at least the 1960s (Cuthbert and Wires 1999).

Prior to 1970, the largest reported breeding colony of Caspian terns on the Pacific Coast was in San Diego, California (Gill and Mewaldt 1983). In the early 1980s, the largest colony was at Gray's Harbor in Washington, where there were 2,157 pairs in 1981 (Gill and Mewaldt 1983). This colony was abandoned in the late 1980s, and relocated at nearby Rice Island, Oregon. Currently, the Rice Island colony is believed to be the largest breeding colony, with 8,000+ pairs (Cuthbert and Wires 1999). Other coastal colonies exist or have existed at Gray's Harbor and Willapa Bay, Washington; Columbia River, Oregon; Humboldt Bay, Elkhorn Slough National Estuarine Research Reserve, Salinas River Mouth, Bolsa Chica Ecological Preserve, Newport Back Bay Ecological Preserve, Salton Sea, and South San Diego Bay, California (Gill and Mewaldt 1983; Cuthbert and Wires 1999); and Laguna Figuroa (Palacios and Alfaro 1992), Scammon's Lagoon (Bancroft 1927), and Laguna San Ignacio (Danemann 1992), Mexico. Overall, the Pacific Coast population has shown an increase from at least 5,661 pairs estimated by Gill and Mewaldt (1983) to at least 12,263 pairs estimated by Cuthbert and Wires (1999). Most of this increase is accounted for in the Gray's Harbor/Rice Island colo-

nies where, roughly 2,300 pairs were estimated in the early 1980s (Gill and Mewaldt 1983), and over 8,000 pairs were estimated in 1996-97 (Cuthbert and Wires 1999).

In 1922, Caspian terns were first documented nesting in San Francisco Bay on a levee near the Dumbarton Bridge in the Coyote Hills salt ponds. This small colony of about seven nests increased over the next two decades, with a total of 287 nests in 1931 (DeGroot 1931), and 378 nests in 1943 (Miller 1943). This colony numbered approximately 299 pairs in 1966; however, because of levee maintenance between 1968-69, the colony was abandoned.

Several new colonies formed and disappeared in other regions of the Bay. A colony established itself in 1968 near the town of Drawbridge, adjacent to Mowry Slough, in Alameda County, which contained over 100 nests; 200 nests were counted in 1971 (Gill 1977). In 1968, colonies were also established at Baumberg and Turk Island. The Turk Island colony rose to 540 nests in 1985, but was abandoned in 1986, after levee maintenance in 1985 (SFBBO 1988). In 1971, a colony was discovered with 304 nests on a salt dike on outer Bair Island. This colony grew to between 500-600 nests by 1975 (Gill 1977) and 800-850 nests by 1981 (Rigney and Rigney 1981).

In the ensuing years, the activity and success at the outer Bair Island colony was erratic. After decreasing to 200 nests in 1983 and being abandoned in 1984 and 1985, the colony was reestablished and included 1,700 adults (850 pairs) by 1988. The colony was again abandoned in 1989 and then re-colonized in 1992 and 1993, but no young were produced. In recent years, both the Turk Island and outer Bair Island colonies have been deserted.

South Bay populations were estimated at 1,000-1,200 individuals in 1971 (Gill 1973) and 2,350 individuals in 1981 (Rigney and Rigney 1981). From 1984 to 1988 South Bay populations ranged from 1,120 to 2,111 adults (Woodin 1988), but in 1990 only 100 pairs were reported (Woodin *in* Harvey et al. 1992). A Bay Area-wide estimation of 2,818 individuals at five colonies in 1989-90 was made by Carter et al. (1990). In 1997, an estimated 1,400 to 1,500 pairs nested in the Bay Area, although only 136 pairs nested in the South Bay.

Nesting colonies have been growing in the Central Bay at Brooks Island and Alameda Naval Air Station (NAS), concurrent with the colony abandonments in the South Bay. The colony at Brooks Island began in the early 1980s, grew to 400 adults (200 nesting pairs) in 1990 (Carter et al. 1990), and had reached 500 nesting pairs in 1997. Six hundred pairs of Caspian terns were recorded at the Alameda NAS colony in the early 1990s (Harvey et al. 1992), and approximately 350 pairs nested there in 1977.

In addition to the colonies at Brooks Island and Alameda NAS, there are two other smaller colonies: one near Alviso with approximately 104 pairs, and one, a recently reoccupied (1997) historical colony at Coyote Hills, with approximately 30 pairs. The overall population of Caspian terns in the San Francisco Estuary has increased in the past 26 years. However, in part due to predation and levee maintenance, the population has decreased in the South Bay. **Table 7.6** shows some of the historic and existing colony locations around the Bay.

The only other nearby colonies are in Monterey County at Elkhorn Slough, which was active until 1995; and the Salinas River Mouth, which was abandoned in 1997 (J. Parkin, pers. comm.).

Habitat Use and Behavior

Caspian terns forage on the open bay, salt ponds, marshes, freshwater ponds, rivers and reservoirs, and at sea (Sibley 1952, SFBBO unpubl. data). They feed on small to medium sized fish, arthropods, and amphibians. In California, they have been reported to feed on fish and crayfish (Horn et al. 1996; Loeffler 1996; J. Parkin, pers. comm). Bent (1921) reported that they feed on shrimp, water mussels, and eggs and young of other birds. Ewins et al. (1994) added insects and larid eggshells from Caspian terns in the Great Lakes region.

Caspian terns roost on salt pond levees, sandy beaches, mudflats, and on islands in salt ponds, slough channels, marshes, and in the Bay. During the breeding season, the majority are observed roosting locally, near nesting colonies, although some are seen at local reservoirs (Almaden Lake Park, Los Gatos Creek Park, Calero Reservoir, Lexington Reservoir, Anderson Reservoir, Stevens Creek Reservoir) and along the outer coast. After breeding season, they disperse and roost in association with each other and with other larids at sites throughout the Bay. The post breeding season aggregations may be augmented by individuals dispersing from colonies elsewhere.

Table 7.6 Caspian Tern Breeding Sites in the San Francisco Bay

Colony	SiteStatus
Knight Island, Napa River Marsh	Active
Brooks Island	Active
Coyote Hills, west levee	Active
Baumberg	Historic
Turk Island	Historic
Drawbridge	Historic
Bair Island	Historic
Alviso, Pond A7	Active
Alviso, Pond A3	Historic
Hayward Shoreline	Active
Ravenswood OSP	Active

The majority of their foraging likely occurs in the Bay and surrounding marshes and salt ponds. However, Caspian terns are occasionally seen over urban areas carrying fish. Presumably, they are hunting in local reservoirs and ponds, bringing this prey to their nesting colonies in the South Bay (Cogswell 1977, SFBBO unpubl. data). A trout tag from a lake 16 miles away was found at a nesting colony in San Francisco Bay (Cogswell 1977). Additionally, local observers have noted small numbers of Caspian terns flying, perhaps daily, on north-south routes over the Santa Cruz Mountains to the Pacific Ocean. In 1987, 64 individuals were observed making such crossings, and 88 were observed in 1988 (W. Bousman, pers. comm.). After breeding, some adults and juveniles remain near the nesting areas, while others disperse within the Bay and beyond. Little is known about these post-breeding movements.

Conservation and Management

Caspian terns numbers have declined in recent years in the South Bay, in part due to predation, flooding, routine levee maintenance, and levee erosion. Routine levee maintenance is a threat to South Bay colonies because of the small number of larger colonies, and because of the tern's tendency to nest on levees rather than on dredge spoil islands. The colonies at Coyote Hills and Turk Island were deserted after levee maintenance. Alviso and Coyote Hills have been subject to flooding.

Their tendency to nest on attached levees also increases their exposure to predation. Predators have been observed to dig under and otherwise defeat barriers erected to protect nesting birds. The desertion of the Drawbridge/Mowry colony was associated with an increase in observations of predators, such as red fox and feral cats, in the area, with direct evidence of predation (SFBBO unpubl. data). At Bair Island, the colony was deserted following episodes of predation and erosion of levees leading to tidal inundation of the colony (SFBBO unpubl. data, Harvey et al. 1992).

Contaminants may also pose a threat to local Caspian tern populations. Ohlendorf et al. (1988) found high levels of DDE, mercury, and PCBs in the eggs of Caspian terns nesting at Bair Island. Additionally, the colony at Brooks Island may be exposed to contaminated prey from the Levin Richmond Terminal Superfund Site (Harvey et al. 1992). The impact of these contaminants on the reproductive success and populations of Caspian terns in the San Francisco Bay is unknown at this time. At Alameda NAS, the current plans for development and usage of the existing runways could adversely impact the nesting colony there.

Human disturbance is a potential threat at Brooks Island. It is important to restrict public access to the site prior to and during the breeding season, which spans from early April to the end of August. Other colonies are in areas of restricted access where human disturbance is minimal, but they should be carefully monitored.

Caspian terns are known to re-occupy historical nesting areas many years after they have been abandoned, as was most recently demonstrated by the re-occupation of the Coyote Hills site. As predation is reduced and levees become suitable again after maintenance, Caspian terns may return to former nesting areas in the South Bay. Therefore, it is important to conserve and protect these areas even though there are no Caspian terns currently occupying them.

Research Needs – Colonies in the South Bay have declined from a mean of 1,626 individuals (SD=491) between 1971 and 1988, to 136 nests in 1997. Possible causes of this decline include predation by red fox and feral cats, disturbance by levee maintenance, flooding, and environmental contamination. Continued population monitoring is needed to document future population trends. Studies of reproductive success and fledgling success would be valuable in documenting problems with year-to-year reproduction. By combining these studies with studies of predation and the presence and effects of contaminants, we may better understand the causes of the current decline. Studies of nest site selection coupled with studies of reproductive success will provide information on which features of the habitat are most important to the reproductive success of these birds. This information can assist in lessening the impact of levee maintenance on the Caspian tern by allowing improved maintenance techniques with more rapid recovery of disturbed nesting areas.

Acknowledgments

I would like to thank Jennifer Parkin for her assistance with the text; Linda Wires for assistance with national and regional population trends; Howard Cogswell for supplying records from his field notes and a helpful review of the text; William Bousman and the Santa Clara County Breeding Bird Atlas for numerous records; and the many dedicated volunteer observers at the San Francisco Bay Bird Observatory.

References

American Ornithologists' Union (AOU). 1983. Check-list of North American birds, sixth ed. American Ornithologists Union. Allen Press, Inc. Lawrence, Kansas. 877pp.

Baicich, P.J. and C.J.O. Harrison. 1997. A guide to the nests, eggs, and nestlings of North American birds. Academic Press. San Diego, Calif. 347pp.

Bent, A.C. 1921. Life histories of North American gulls and terns. Smithsonian Inst., U.S. Nat. Mus. Bull. 113.

Carter, H.R., D.L. Jaques, G.J. McChesney, C.S. Strong, M.W. Parker and J.E. Takekawa. 1990. Breeding populations of seabirds on the northern and central California coasts in 1989 and 1990. U.S. Dept. Int., Fish Wildl. Serv., No. 14-12-001-30456.

Cogswell, H. 1977. Water birds of California. Illust. by G. Christman. Univ. of Ca. Press. Berkeley. 399p.

Cuthbert, F.J. and L.R. Wires. 1999. Caspian tern *In*: A. Poole and F. Gill (eds). Birds of North America No. 403. The Birds of North America, Inc., Philadelphia, PA., 32 pp.

Danemann, G.D. and J.R. Guzman-Poo. 1992. Notes on the birds of San Ignacio Lagoon, Baja California Sur, Mexico. Western Birds 23(1):11-19.

DeGroot, D.S. 1931. History of a nesting colony of Caspian terns on San Francisco Bay. Condor 33: 188-192.

Ewins, P.J., D.V. Weseloh, R.J. Norstrom, K. Legierse, H.J. Auman and J.P. Ludwig. 1994. Caspian terns on the Great Lakes: organochlorine contamination, reproduction, diet and population changes, 1972-*1991*. Canadian Wildl. Serv. Occasional Paper No. 85, 30 pp.

Grinnell, J. and M.W. Wythe. 1927. Directory to the bird-life of the San Francisco Bay region. Pacific Coast Avifauna 18. Cooper Ornithological Club. Berkeley, Calif. 160pp.

Gill, Jr., R.E. 1973. The breeding birds of the South San Francisco Bay Estuary. M. A. Thesis, San Jose State Univ., San Jose, Calif. 145pp.

_____. 1977. Breeding avifauna of the South San Francisco Bay estuary. Western Birds 8: 1-12.

Gill, Jr., R.E. and L.R. Mewaldt. 1979. Dispersal and migratory patterns of San Francisco Bay produced herons, egrets and terns. North American Bird Bander 4: 4-13.

_____. 1983. Pacific Coast Caspian terns: dynamics of an expanding population. Auk 100: 369-381.

Harvey, T.E., K.J. Miller, R.L. Hothem, M.J. Rauzon, G.W. Page and R.A. Keck. 1992. Status and trends report on the wildlife of the San Francisco Estuary. San Francisco Estuary Project, U.S. Fish Wildl. Serv.

Horn, M.H., P.A. Cole and W.E. Loeffler. 1996. Prey resource base of tern and skimmer colonies at the Bolsa Chica Ecological Reserve, Orange County, and the Western Salt Works, South San Diego Bay. Final Rept. to U.S. Fish Wildl. Serv., Carlsbad, Calif.

Loeffler, W.E. 1996. Dietary overlap and its implications for coexistence in a recently established assemblage of nesting seabirds at the Bolsa Chica Ecological Reserve. Unpubl. M.A. Thesis, Ca. State Univ., Fullerton, Calif.

Miller, A.H. 1943. Census of a colony of Caspian terns. Condor 45: 220-225.

Ohlendorf, H.M., T.W. Custer, R.W. Lowe, M. Rigney and E. Cromartie. 1988. Organochlorines and mercury in eggs of coastal terns and herons in California, USA. Colonial Waterbirds 11(1): 85-94.

Peterson, R.T. 1990. A field guide to western birds. Houghton Mifflin Co. Boston, Mass. 432pp.

Rigney, M. and T. Rigney. 1981. A breeding bird survey of the South San Francisco Bay salt pond levee system. Rep. for South Bay Institute for Avian Studies.

Sibley, C.G. 1952. Birds of the South San Francisco Bay region. San Jose State College, 44p.mimeo.

Soikkeli, M. 1973. Breeding success of Caspian terns in Finland. Bird Banding 44: 196-204.

Woodin, P. 1988. San Francisco Bay Bird Observatory. Unpublished report.

Personal Communications

William Bousman, *North American Birds,* Santa Clara County subregional editor. Menlo Park, California.

Charles Collins, Department of Biology, California State University, Long Beach.

Robin Leong, *North American Birds,* Napa and Solano counties subregional editor. Vallejo, California. Leong@community.net.

Jennifer Parkin, San Francisco Bay Bird Observatory, Alviso, California.

California Least Tern

Sterna antillarum browni

Leora Feeney

Introduction

The California least tern was first described from a specimen collected in San Diego County (Mearns 1916). It is currently one of three subspecies of least terns in the United States — *S. antillarum antillarum* is found on the East Coast (Lessons 1847), and *S. antillarum athalassos* is associated with the great interior river systems of the United States (Burleigh and Lowery 1942). The California least tern was listed as an endangered species by the Federal government in 1970 and by the State of California in 1971.

Description

The length of the least tern averages 23 cm. (9 in.), and its wingspan is about 51 cm (20 in.). The rump and upper tail of adults are a pale gray, concolorous with the back and upper wings. The outer primary feathers are black, creating narrow black outer wing edges. The tail is relatively short and forked. During the breeding season, the adult head is crowned in black, with a white triangular patch on the forehead. The bill is yellowish, and tipped in black. The short legs are a varying yellow-orange color. The basic plumage of some adults is sometimes observed in California late in the breeding season. These birds will have dark bills and legs. The definition of the black cap and triangular head patch is lost to a white face with sooty cap. It takes two to three years for least terns to mature. There sub-adult plumages are similar in complexity to other members of the gull group and are therefore not described here. It is impossible, for the most part, to separate least tern subspecies in the field, and races are usually identified by distribution.

The least tern bears a close physical resemblance to the little tern (*Sterna albifrons*), which is found seasonally along coastal waters of Great Britain, Europe, Africa, Asia, and Australia. During a period when combining or "lumping" species was a trend, the two accepted New World least terns, *S. antillarum antillarum* and *S. antillarum browni,* became subspecific (Hartert 1921) to the worldwide species. This was supported later (Peters 1934). Studies defining differences in morphology, behavior, and vocalizations (Massey 1976) provided the foundation needed to support the original separate specification, and in 1983, the American Ornithological Union split the American least tern from the more cosmopolitan little tern; the New World tern was once again *S. antillarum.* The least tern is slightly smaller than the little tern, making it the smallest member of the gull family, Laridae (Olsen and Larsson 1995).

Two other subspecies of least terns are in the literature, but are not found in the United States; *S. a. mexicana* is found along the east coast of the Gulf of California or the Sonoran coast (Van Rossem and Hachisuka 1937) and *S. a. staebleri* is found in southern Chiapas (Brodkorb 1940).

Breeding Biology – Least terns typically arrive at California breeding areas in middle or late April. Courtship is observed from the time birds arrive. Nesting is reported in "two waves," the first from early May through early June, and the second from mid-June through early July. The species is a colonial nester, although single pairs are sometimes found.

Least tern nests are simple depressions in the substrate, called scrapes. One to three (usually two) eggs require about 21 days of incubation. The young are downy and able to walk soon after hatching. Least terns with adequate food resources fledge from about 17 to

21 days. Flight skills that allow young birds to follow their parents to foraging areas typically take longer (Laura Collins, pers. comm.). Both parents tend the young and share at some portion incubating, brooding, and feeding responsibilities. Young, well-fledged, least terns eventually leave breeding sites and disperse to localized post-breeding foraging areas where fish are plentiful and waters are calm. These post-breeding foraging areas, which offer young birds opportunities to develop foraging skills and provide all terns the food to build reserves for migration, are considered by some to be as important to the survival of juvenile terns as the nesting areas (Massey and Atwood 1984). Several post-breeding sites in the Bay Area are located at South Bay "intake" salt ponds. Shallow tidal areas are also used, such as at the E. B. Roemer Bird Sanctuary in Alameda and at Roberts Landing in San Leandro. California least terns most often finish breeding activities by late August and are usually absent from California breeding and post-breeding areas by late September.

Distribution and Abundance

The California least tern is migratory. Winter distribution is largely unknown, although least terns banded as chicks in California have been found as far south as southern Colima (Massey 1981) and Guatemala (Charles Collins, pers. comm.). Least terns have been found along the coast of Peru (Schulenberg et al. 1987), Panama (Vaucher 1988), and Costa Rica (Stiles and Skutch 1989, Barrantes and Pereira 1992), but these accounts do not specify *S. a. browni*. A better knowledge of winter locations and migratory routes for California least terns would greatly improve our understanding of this bird.

During the breeding season (spring and summer), California least terns are found nesting along the Pacific Coast as far north as Pittsburg, Contra Costa County, California (Collins 1988) and as far south as Bahia Magdalena (Palacios and Alfaro 1993). In addition, there are reports of *S. antillarum* nesting at the northern Gulf of California on the Colorado River delta (Palacios and Mellink 1994) and in northwestern Sonora on the Mexican mainland (Mellink and Palacios 1993), without reference to subspecies.

In the State of California, least terns nest annually at about 35 sites from San Diego County to Contra Costa County. Some colonies, though reported separately, are so close as to be considered related sites. For instance, the Mission Bay area in San Diego County has three small colonies. The breeding locations shift somewhat due to annual conditions; nearly 40 colony sites are monitored (Caffrey 1995a).

It was once thought by some that California least terns nested from the Mexican border north only as far as Monterey County (Wilbur 1974). However, records show the bird's presence further north in Santa Cruz County from 1939 through 1954 (Wilbur 1974). Accounts of least tern numbers in California prior to 1970 are sketchy, however, colony numbers described as "abundant," in the "thousands," "good-sized," "1,000," "600 pairs," and "large numbers" were reported at numerous sites along California's coast at the turn of the century (as in Caffrey 1995b). By 1971, Craig (1971) reported less than 300 pairs over only 15 sites. Craig's work was limited and may have overlooked some sites. In 1973, Bender (1973) located 624 pairs statewide. After state and federal listings, recovery efforts and sometimes-intense management strategies were put into place. Recovery efforts succeeded. Surveys in recent years have indicated fluctuating numbers, but in 1995, approximately 2,536 pairs of least terns were estimated to have nested at about 35 California nesting locations (Caffrey 1995a).

Sightings in the San Francisco Bay Area date back to 1927. Curiously, the earliest Bay Area sighting was in the city of Alameda (Grinnell and Miller 1944), where the current largest northern California colony breeds, with over 200 pairs in 1996 (Laura Collins, pers. comm.). Although least terns, including groups with over 50 birds and juveniles, had been sighted in the Bay Area for decades (Allen 1933, Allen 1934, Chase and Paxton 1965), it was not until 1963 that nesting was confirmed at the Oakland Airport (Roemer 1963) and at another Alameda County location soon thereafter (Chandik and Baldridge 1967). These nest sightings caused some to speculate that breeding least terns had expanded their range. However, the fact that California least terns, including young, have been seen in the Bay Area since the 1920s could also support the contention that an infrequently seen population of the bird may have bred undetected here for decades.

At the present time, Alameda's least tern colony and two to three least tern pairs nesting at the Pittsburg Power Plant are the only known Bay Area nesting sites producing fledglings. In 1995, one to six pairs nested at the Oakland Airport, but all failed due to predation (Feeney 1996). In the past, least terns were documented to nest on Bair Island (CDFG 1981, Anderson 1970), and on various salt pond levees (CDFG 1981).

Although the history of the least tern in the San Francisco Bay Area is not clear, the Bay Area birds are today considered a critical population – vital to the statewide species recovery effort. In 1995, California Department of Fish and Game preliminary numbers showed that the Alameda Colony was the State's fourth largest producer of fledglings (CDFG, Unpubl. data).

There are currently large gaps between breeding colonies throughout the modern range of the California least tern, probably due primarily to disturbance and habitat loss. A particularly significant gap of 330 km (178 miles) occurs between the breeding Bay Area least terns and the nearest breeding colony to the south (Pismo Dunes) (Caffrey 1995b).

Habitat Use and Behavior

California least terns forage by hovering over shallow to deep waters and diving or, less often, dipping onto the surface of the water to catch prey. Least terns also make short skimming approaches onto pools of water left on mudflats during low tide to catch trapped prey items. Although California least terns have been known to consume a wide variety of fish species, they appear partial to northern anchovy (*Engraulis mordax*), and silversides (*Atherinidae* sp.) (Atwood and Kelly 1984, Collins 1985). To a much lesser extent there is evidence that least terns may take small invertebrates such as the water borne larvae of drone files, *Eristalis tenax* (Laura Collins, pers. comm.; Leora Feeney, pers. obs.).

For nesting, least terns require tracts of open sand or fine gravel substrate with sparse vegetation. Loss of natural habitat has caused these birds to become opportunistic, using areas such as newly filled or graded lands and airports for nesting. Nesting areas must be located near open water, usually along coastal beaches and estuaries, and they must host adequate numbers of small elongate fishes to sustain adults and growing young.

Conservation and Management

Human development of least tern habitat, highway access to the coast, and summertime beach recreation have caused the destruction of breeding sites and resulted in least tern breeding failures. Although recovery efforts have brought about increased least tern numbers in California, some problems continue to challenge these efforts. It appears that for colonies to have guaranteed successes, they require intense management policies to protect nest sites, including regular monitoring of breeding activities, adequate barriers or supervision to restrict public access, persistent predator control, and vegetation management. These measures can be costly and funds are not always available for known breeding sites to be properly protected.

Predator management has become more difficult due to the recent introduction of red fox (*Vulpes vulpes*) on California's coast. Feral cats and the establishment of cat feeding stations in the State have added to least tern reproductive failures (Edwards 1919, Caffrey 1995b, Feeney 1996). Public support for feral animals has created additional problems with predator management programs. In recent years, there has been concern over reduced fish availability at some sites, which may be related to "El Niño" weather patterns or other phenomena (Caffrey 1995a.).

To assure the future of a healthy least tern population in the San Francisco Bay Area, adequate habitat must be set aside and properly managed to support nesting and post-breeding foraging. These protected areas should be established at several locations around the Bay to allow for alternative safe sites during potential localized habitat crises.

References

Allen, A. 1933. The season: San Francisco Region. Bird-Lore 35:336-337.

_____. 1934. The season: San Francisco Region. Bird-Lore 36:316.

Anderson, W. 1970. The California least tern breeding in Alameda and San Mateo counties. Calif. Fish and Game 56: 136-137.

Atwood, J.L. and P.R. Kelly. 1984. Fish dropped on breeding colonies as indicators of least tern food habits. Wilson Bull. 96(1): 34-47.

Barrantes, G. and A. Pereira. 1992. Abundancia y fluctuaciones de aves limicolas (Charadriiformes) en una playa fangs de Chomps, Costa Rica. Rev. Biol. Trop. 40(3): 303-307.

Bender, K. 1973. California least tern census and nesting survey, 1974. Ca. Dept. Fish and Game, Nongame Wildl. Investigation W-54-R, Progress Rept. 47pp.

Brodkorb, P. 1940. New birds from southern Mexico. Auk 57: 542-549.

Burleigh, T.D. and G. Lowery Jr. 1942. An inland race of *Sterna albifrons*. Occ. Papers of the Mus. of Zool. Louisiana State Univ. 10: 173-177.

Caffrey, C. 1995a. California least tern preliminary nesting records. 1995 Season. Unpubl. report. Ca. Dept. Fish and Game.

_____. 1995b. Characteristics of California least tern nesting sites associated with breeding success or failure with special reference to the site at the Naval Air Station, Alameda. Unpubl. report to Naval Facilities Engr. Command, Western Div., San Bruno, Calif.

California Department of Fish and Game (CDFG). 1981. Unpublished table of California least tern colony estimated pair/fledgling numbers from 1978 through 1981.

Chandik, T. and A. Baldridge. 1967. Nesting season, middle Pacific Coast Region. Audubon Field Notes 21(5): 600-603.

Chase, T. and R.O. Paxton. 1965. Middle Pacific Coast Region. Aud. Field Notes 19:574-576.

Collins, L.D. 1985. California least tern nesting season at the Alameda Naval Air Station, 1985. Appendix 2: Dropped fish collected at the least tern colony, Alameda Naval Air Station, Calif. Rept. prepared for the Ca. Dept. Fish and Game, and the United States Navy.

_____. 1988. The California least tern nesting season at the PG&E Power Plant, Pittsburg, Calif. 1988. Unpubl. Rept. to Ca. Dept. Fish and Game. 66pp.

Craig, A.M. 1971. Survey of California least tern nesting sites. Ca. Dept. Fish and Game Project W-54-

Other Birds

R-4, Job II—5.1. Job Completion Rept. 55pp.

Edwards, H.A. 1919. Losses suffered by breeding birds in Southern California. Condor 21(2): 65-68.

Feeney, L.R. 1996. California least tern breeding season at the Metropolitan Oakland International Airport-1995. Report prepared for the Port of Oakland.

Grinnell, J. and A. Miller. 1944. The distribution of the birds of California. Pacific Coast Avifauna 27: 1-608.

Hartert, E. 1921. Die vogel der palaarktischen fauna. Bd. II und Erganzundshand, Berlin. 1715pp.

Lessons, R. 1847. La Sternule des Antilles. In Compl. Ouevres Buffon. 20: 256.

Massey, B.W. 1976. Vocal differences between American least terns and the European little tern. The Auk 93: 76-773.

_____. 1981. A least tern makes a right turn. Nat. Hist. 90: 62-71.

Massey, B.W. and J.L. Atwood. 1984. Application of ecological information to habitat management for the California least tern. Progress report No. 6. Prepared for the U.S. Fish Wildl. Serv.

Mearns, E.A. 1916. Description of a new subspecies of the American least tern. Proceedings of the Biological Society of Washington. 24: 71-72.

Mellink, E. y E. Palacios. 1993. Status y conservación de la avifauna costera y marina del delta del Río Colorado. Reunión Anual del CIPAMEX sobre el Estudio y la Conservación de las Aves en México. Catemaco, Ver.

Olsen, K.M. and H. Larsson. 1995. Terns of Europe and North America. Princeton Univ. Press. Princeton, New Jersey. 220pp.

Palacios, E. and L. Alfaro. 1991. Breeding birds of Laguna Figueroa and La Pinta Pond, Baja California, Mexico. Western Birds 22:27-32.

Palacios, E. y E. Mellink. 1994. Incremento de las poblaciones de Sterna antillarum en el Alto Golfo de California durante el período mi 1991-1993. V Congreso de la Asociación de Investigadores del Mar de Cortés. La Paz, B.C.S.

Peters, J.L. 1934. Checklist of birds of the world, Vol. II, Harvard Univ. Press, Cambridge, Mass.

Roemer, E.B. 1963. Personal unpublished records.

Schulenberg, T.S., T.A. Parker III, and R.A. Hughes. 1987. First records of least terns, Sterna antillarum for Peru. Le Gerfaut 77: 271-273.

Stiles, G.F. and A.F. Skutch. 1989. A guide to the birds of Costa Rica. Comstock Publ. Co. Cornell Univ., Ithaca, N.Y. pp. 161-162.

Van Rossem, A.J. and the Marquess Hachisuka. 1937. A further report on birds from Sonora, Mexico, with descriptions of two new races. Trans. of the San Diego Society of Natural History 8: 321-326.

Vaucher, G.L. 1988. Christmas count, Pacific Canal Area, R. P. Panama. American Birds 42: 1154-1155.

Wilbur, S.R. 1974. The literature of the California least tern. U.S. Fish Wildl. Serv. Special Scientific report. Wildlife No. 175. 18pp.

Personal Communications

Charles Collins, Department of Biology, California State University, Long Beach.

Laura Collins, biologist, Berkeley, California.

Western Burrowing Owl

Athene (Speotyto) cunicularia hypugaea

Lynne A. Trulio

Introduction

The western burrowing owl is a small, semi-fossorial bird of prairie and grassland habitats. It is the only owl that routinely lives and nests underground. Burrowing owls in the western United States rarely dig their own burrows, but take over burrows dug by ground squirrels (*Spermophilus* spp.), prairie dogs (*Cynomys* spp.), badgers (*Taxida taxidus*) or other burrow digging species (Zarn 1974). The western subspecies of the burrowing owl lives west of the Mississippi to the Pacific Coast and from southern Canada into northern Mexico.

The species was listed by the California Department of Fish and Game as a Species of Special Concern in 1979. In November 1994, the U. S. Fish and Wildlife Service listed the species as a federal Category 2 Candidate for listing as endangered or threatened. The revised and shortened candidate species list in the February 28, 1996 Federal Register does not include the burrowing owl. In California, owl numbers have declined 50-60% in the last 10 years.

Joe DiDonato, bioQuest

Description

The burrowing owl is a small, brown and white mottled owl, approximately 230-280 mm (9-11 inches) tall. It is not easily confused with any other owl due to its semi-fossorial nature. Males and females are often difficult to distinguish in the field and, unlike many other raptors, the male is slightly larger than the female. Adults weigh an average of 150g (Zarn 1974). Chicks less than three months of age are distinguished from adults by their completely buffy breast and white collar. Chicks often emerge from the burrow weighing approximately one-half to two-thirds adult weight, and they reach adult weight within a month of emergence (S. Neudecker, pers. comm.; Trulio, pers. obs.).

Western burrowing owls are migratory throughout much of their U. S. range and leave their breeding grounds in the fall. Owls often return to the same or nearby burrows the next spring. This site fidelity is well documented (Martin 1973, Green 1983). In most parts of its range in central and southern California, the owl is a year-round resident.

Breeding Biology – Burrowing owls are primarily monogamous for the nesting season. They produce one clutch per year, but may lay a second clutch if the first is lost. Burrowing owls lay between two to eleven eggs (average four to six) in a chamber of the nest burrow. Eggs are laid between March and May depending upon location. The female incubates the eggs for approximately 26 to 29 days (S. Neudeker, pers. comm.; Zarn 1974). After the chicks hatch, they remain in the burrow for approximately three weeks. Just before or just after they emerge, chicks lose their natal down and gain juvenile plumage. An average of two to four chicks emerge, although clutches of six or eight are not uncommon. Generally, an average of two to four chicks survive to fledging (age at which they can fly), which occurs about one month post-emergence. Fledglings remain with their parents until fall and then disperse. They molt by this time and gain their adult plumage. Some young remain with their parents through their first winter (P. Delevoryas, pers. comm.).

Demographic parameters and their relationship to populations are not well known. Thomsen (1971) found a juvenile survival rate of 0.3 and an adult survivorship of 0.81 based on two years of study at the Oakland Airport, Alameda County. The longevity of free-living owls has not been documented, although an average of five years is informally used (Priest, pers. comm.). Fecundity is better known. Thomsen found an average of 3.9 chicks survived to fledging. At Moffett Field, Santa Clara County, Trulio (1994) found an average fledging success of 2.6 chicks per reproductive pair (SD=1.4) and an average of 1.8 chicks per pair (SD=1.7). An average of 73% of pairs produced emergent chicks. This level of fledgling success is the second lowest reported in the literature.

Food and Feeding – During the day, owls may be visible at their burrows, but tend to do little hunting. They become active at dusk and do most of their feeding at night (Haug and Oliphant 1990). They use multiple feeding strategies, including running along the ground, but most often they can be seen hovering over fields and diving at prey. Haug and Oliphant (1990) found burrowing owls at their site in Canada had an average home range size of 2.4 sq. km, and owls confined 95% of their movements to within 600 m of their nest burrows.

Burrowing owls are mid-level carnivores preying primarily on large insects and small rodents, but they will take a wide variety of prey. Many studies have found that important food items include vole species (*Lagurus* spp., *Microtus* spp.), mice (*Peromyscus* spp., *Mus* spp., *Reithrodontomys* spp., *Zapus* spp.), pocket mice (*Perognathus* spp.), pocket gophers (*Tomomys* spp.), and young ground squirrels (*Spermophilus* spp.), as well as a wide array of beetles, grasshoppers, crickets, reptiles, amphibians, small birds, fish, and crustaceans (Zarn 1974). They forage in ruderal, manicured, or natural grasslands. Burrowing owl predators include the great horned owl, harrier, and the red fox.

Distribution and Abundance

Burrowing owls inhabit flat, dry, open grasslands in prairie and arid habitats throughout California, exclusive of the humid, northwest coastal areas and the forested and shrub-covered mountains. Burrowing owls are most abundant in wide, low, interior valley bottoms and in flat coastal lowlands (Grinnell and Miller 1944). DeSante and Ruhlen (1995) found that fully 92% of the breeding owls occurred in such lowland areas, generally below 60 to 300 meters in elevation.

Once a widely distributed and relatively common grassland bird, the burrowing owl has been declining significantly in California for at least the last 40 years (Grinnell and Miller 1944). At least 50% of the population has been lost in the last 10 years. DeSante and Ruhlen (1995) estimate that approximately 9,450 pairs of birds remain in the State. Over 71% of these pairs live in the Imperial Valley, an area subject to rapid human population growth and development in the near future (DeSante and Ruhlen 1995). In the San Francisco Bay Area, nearly all the owls, approximately 170 pairs, are found in the South and East Bay between Palo Alto and the Fremont-Newark area.

Researchers have noted burrowing owl declines, especially since the 1950s (Zarn 1974, Arbib 1979, James and Ethier 1989), although there was little quantitative data to support this impression until just recently. The Institute for Bird Populations completed an extensive, cooperative three-year study (1991-1993) of the burrowing owl population in California, exclusive of the Great

Basin and desert areas (DeSante and Ruhlen 1995; DeSante et al., *in press*). Overall, in the entire census area, nearly 60% of the breeding groups of owls known to have existed during the 1980s had disappeared by the early 1990s (DeSante and Ruhlen 1995).

The species has disappeared as a breeding bird from substantial portions of its former range. DeSante and Ruhlen (1995) showed that the burrowing owl apparently has been extirpated as a breeding species within the last 10 to 15 years from Marin, San Francisco, Santa Cruz, Napa, coastal San Luis Obispo, and Ventura counties, as well as from the Coachella Valley. It has been very nearly extirpated from Sonoma, Santa Barbara, Orange, coastal Monterey, and San Mateo counties. Perhaps only one to two breeding pairs still exist in most of these counties.

The basic threat to burrowing owls in California is the annual, methodical loss of breeding and foraging habitat to development by humans. Habitat loss to urban development and destruction of ground squirrels (DeSante and Ruhlen 1995, Trulio 1995) are two primary reasons for the decline. Other factors include soil disturbances such as disking, grading, and blading, vehicular strikes, and predation by non-native or feral species. In agricultural areas, where the majority of owls live, chemical spraying may be contributing to population declines.

Habitat Use and Behavior

Historically, owls were found in natural areas of open prairies or open shrub-steppe habitat (Butts 1971, Coulombe 1971). Human population growth and continuous land use changes have resulted in burrowing owls utilizing human-altered habitats ranging from agricultural irrigation ditches (Coulombe 1971) to urban habitats (Collins and Landry 1977, Trulio 1995, Thomsen 1971). Burrowing owls have become quite tolerant of human presence, as long as suitable nesting and foraging habitat exist. Florida burrowing owls (*S. c. floridiana*) readily use suburban areas up to a density of approximately 60% development; when development densities exceed 60%, owl numbers drop (Wesemann and Rowe 1987).

Good burrowing owl habitat is open, dry, and sparsely vegetated with available burrows (Zarn 1974). However, several other subtle characteristics make some burrows more suitable than others. These characteristics include percent vegetative cover, height of vegetation surrounding the burrow, the presence of colonial fossorial mammals, soil texture, and presence of perches for horizontal visibility.

The California Department of Fish and Game's "Wildlife Habitat Relationships System" database lists 18 major habitat types that support burrowing owls. In most of these habitats, burrowing owls are generally found in open country, where tree or shrub canopies

cover less than 30% of the habitat. Typical habitats include annual and perennial grasslands, open agricultural areas, deserts, and vacant lots.

Burrowing owls are able to adapt to some human-altered landscapes. The land uses of sites where owls live include dry open grassland, the perimeters of agricultural fields, irrigation ditches, fallow agricultural fields, open fields prepared for development, airports, golf courses, military bases, and parks.

These owls can be found adjacent to the San Francisco Bay on levees next to salt ponds, open unmanicured grasslands, or manicured fields near the Bay's edge where ground squirrel numbers and foraging area are adequate. These birds are primarily terrestrial predators and in these locations still focus on mice and insects. However, they are opportunistic and will eat species associated with wetlands, including amphibians and crustaceans (L. Yuen, pers. comm.).

Conservation and Management

Increasing burrowing owl numbers will require adding more nesting and foraging habitat. Burrowing owls are an indicator of the marsh-upland edge of the San Francisco Bay. Within the structure of the San Francisco Estuary Goals Project, burrowing owl habitat may be increased by adding upland transition zones between the high marsh and lands converted to human use. These zones should include short grass habitat capable of supporting a healthy population of ground squirrels. Trees should be kept to a minimum.

Increasing habitat for burrowing owls should also provide upland refugia for marsh species that must escape high tides, such as salt marsh harvest mice, as well as black and clapper rails. Since burrowing owls are predators and since this habitat will also benefit marsh hawks, adequate cover for mice and rails must be provided.

References

Arbib, R. 1979. The blue list for 1980. National Audubon Society. Am. Birds 33: 830-835.

Butts, K.O. 1971. Observations on the ecology of burrowing owls in western Oklahoma. A preliminary report. Proc. Okla. Acad. Sci. 51: 66-74.

Collins, C.T. and R.E. Landry. 1977. Artificial nest burrows for burrowing owls. No. Am. Bird Bander 2: 151-154.

Coulombe, H.N. 1971. Behavior and population ecology of the burrowing owl, *Speotyto cunicularia*, in the Imperial Valley of California. Condor 73: 162-176.

DeSante, D.F. and E. Ruhlen. 1995. A census of burrowing owls in California, 1991- 1993. Institute for Bird Populations. Point Reyes Station, Calif.

DeSante, D.F., E.D. Ruhlen, S.L. Adamany, K.M. Burton and A. Sabrina. 1997. A census of burrowing owls in central California in 1991. *In:* J.L. Lincer and K. Steenhof (eds). The burrowing owl, its biology and management including the proceedings of the first international burrowing owl symposium. Raptor Research Foundation, Inc. Raptor Research Rept. No. 9. pp. 38-48.

Green, G.A. 1983. Ecology of breeding burrowing owls in the Columbia basin, Oregon. M.S. Thesis. Oregon State Univ., Corvallis, Oregon.

Grinnell, J. and A.H. Miller. 1944. The Distribution of the birds of California. Pac. Coast Avif. No. 27. Cooper Ornitholo. Soc., Berkeley, Calif.

Haug, E.A. and L.W. Oliphant. 1990. Movements, activity patterns, and habitat use of burrowing owls in Saskatchewan. J. Wildl. Manage. 54: 27-35.

James P.C. and T.J. Ethier. 1989. Trends in the winter distribution and abundance of burrowing owls in North America. Amer. Birds 43: 1224-1225.

Martin, D.J. 1973. Selected aspects of burrowing owl ecology and behavior. Condor 75: 446-456.

Thomsen, L. 1971. Behavior and ecology of burrowing owls on the Oakland Municipal Airport. Condor 73: 177-192.

Trulio, L.A. 1994. The ecology of a population of burrowing owls at a naval air station in northern California. Dept. of the Navy. San Bruno, Calif.

_____. 1995. Passive relocation: A method to preserve burrowing owls on disturbed sites. J. Field Ornithol. 66: 99-106.

Wesemann, T. and M. Rowe. 1987. Factors influencing the distribution and abundance of burrowing owls in Cape Coral, Florida. *In*: L.W. Adams and D.L. Leedy (eds). Integrating man and nature in the metropolitan environment. Proc. Natl. Symp. on Urban Wildl. Columbia, MD.

Zarn, M. 1974. Burrowing owl. U.S. Dep. Inter. Bur. Land Manage. Tech. Note T-N-250. Denver, Colo. 25pp.

Personal Communications

Penelope Delevoryas, H. T. Harvey and Associates, Alviso, California.

Joan Priest, Silicon Valley Wildlife Rehabilitation, San Jose, California.

Dr. Stephen Neudecker, Chula Vista Nature Center, Chula Vista, California.

Lois Yuen, Berkeley, California.

Other Studies and Information Sources

Clark, R.J., J.L. Lincer, and J.S. Clark. 1994. A bibliography on the burrowing owl (*Athene cunicularia*). Dept. of Biology, York College of Pennsylvania, York, Penn. 51pp.

Delevoryas, P. 1997. Relocation of burrowing owls during courtship period. *In* J.L. Lincer and K. Steenhof (eds). The burrowing owl, its biology and management including the proceedings of the first international burrowing owl symposium. Raptor Research Foundation, Raptor Research Rept. No. 9. pp. 138-144.

Johnson, B. 1992. Effects of demography, mating patterns, and sociality on the population genetics of the burrowing owl, *Athene cunicularia*. Ph.D. Dissertation, Univ. of Calif., Davis. Davis, Calif.

Wyoming Cooperative Fish and Wildlife Research Unit. Burrowing owl citations for the Western U.S. Status Assessment, a complete bibliography. University of Wyoming. http://uwadmnweb.uwyo.edu/fish_wild/buow.

Expert Sources

Jack Barclay, Albion Environmental, Inc., Santa Cruz, California. Jbarclay@albionenvironmental.com.

Janis Buchanan, California Burrowing Owl Consortium, San Jose, California. Jbuchanan@gaia.arc.nasa.gov.

Penelope Delevoryas, H.T. Harvey Associates, Alviso, California.

David DeSante, Institute for Bird Populations, Point Reyes Station, California. Ddesante@birdpop.org.

Brenda Johnson, University of California, Davis. Bjohnson@mother.com.

Joan Priest, Wildlife Center of Silicon Valley, San Jose, California.

Brian Walton, University of California, Santa Cruz, Predatory Bird Group.

Salt Marsh Common Yellowthroat

Geothlypis trichas sinuosa

Scott Terrill

Introduction

The common yellowthroat (*Geothlypis trichas* spp.) is a small, insectivorous warbler common in most of North America. Twelve subspecies of common yellowthroat have been recognized in the United States (AOU 1957), however, yellowthroat taxonomy remains complicated and there is room for further work (e.g., see Howell and Webb 1995). Grinnell and Miller (1944) listed three yellowthroat subspecies that breed in California: the "western yellow-throat" (*G. t. occidentalis*), the "tule yellow-throat" (*G. t. scirpicola*), and the "San Francisco yellowthroat" (*G. t. sinuosa*), currently known as the salt marsh common yellowthroat. Based on Grinnell and Miller (1944), *occidentalis* is the most widespread and breeds over much of California (excluding the higher Sierra Nevada Mountains). The breeding distribution of *occidentalis* surrounds the breeding distribution of *sinuosa*, which is restricted to San Francisco Bay wetlands and adjacent riparian areas. However, the American Ornithologists' Union (AOU) considers *occidentalis* as restricted to central eastern California and considers the subspecies that surrounds *sinuosa* as *G. t. arizela*. Thus, the AOU considers four subspecies to breed in California. The breeding range of *scirpicola* comprises the western portion of southern California and the Imperial and Lower Colorado River valleys. *Arizela* and *occidentalis* occur in the Bay Area in winter (Evens et al. 1997).

The salt marsh common yellowthroat was first identified as a distinct subspecies by Grinnell (1901). He described this subspecies as being darker dorsally and

Les Chibana

laterally and smaller than the other two subspecies of yellowthroats found in the State. Mewaldt and Rigney attempted to repeat Grinnell's results and were unable to do so with respect to coloration (Rigney, pers. comm.), however, size (specifically wing chord) did appear to hold up, and thus small size may be the primary characteristic for distinguishing this taxon (Rigney, pers. comm.). Foster (1977a,b) compared specimens of all three subspecies and found wing length difference to be significant at the 95% confidence level. Raby (1992) found that 81% of *sinuosa* and *arizela* populations were distinguishable from one another by song. Marshall and Dedrick (1994) indicated that *sinuosa* can be distinguished by dark coloration and small size. These authors found that birds in prealternate molt (July through September) can be distinguished by the darker coloration of the emerging feathering on the back and flanks relative to pale "*occidentalis* (often called *arizela*)." Raby (1992) found that the Grizzly Island population represented a zone of intergradation between *sinuosa* and *arizela,* and more work is needed to clarify the taxonomic situation in Suisun Bay.

Associated species that use similar habitats include the marsh wren (*Cistothorus palustris*), red-winged blackbird (*Agelaius phoeniceus*), and the salt marsh song sparrows (*Melospiza melodia samuelis, M. m. pusillula, M. m. maxillaris*).

Description

The name "salt marsh common yellowthroat" is somewhat of a misnomer, since *sinuosa* occurs in salt marsh only in winter (Foster 1977a,b). Rather, this subspecies breeds in fresh and brackish marsh associated with and close to Bay wetlands. Thus, this taxon has also been referred to as San Francisco yellowthroat (Ray 1916, Schussler 1918, Sibley 1952).

Breeding Biology – Male salt marsh common yellowthroats begin establishing territories by mid-March and the nesting season extends from early March through late July (Hobson et al. 1986). Females construct the nest relatively close to the substrate (ground or water). Yellowthroats lay three to five eggs, which are incubated for 12 days. The young remain in the nest for 10 days and are fed by both parents for at least two weeks following fledging (Hobson et al. 1986).

Food and Feeding –Yellowthroats are primarily insectivorous and glean insects on or near the ground (to about five or six feet above the ground or water) from low herbaceous vegetation, bushes, and small trees, or from the surface of mud — although they will forage substantially higher during the non-reproductive period (Shuford 1993). Yellowthroats in California eat 99.8% animal matter (Shuford 1993). The main dietary items in a sample of 114 were ants, wild bees and wasps, true bugs, beetles, caterpillars and moths, flies, grasshoppers, and spiders.

Predators – There is little direct information on predators of salt marsh common yellowthroats. However, likely predators include species that typically prey on passerines, including feral cats, raccoons and red foxes (eggs and nestlings) and raptors such as Cooper's and sharp-shinned hawks.

Distribution and Abundance

Salt marsh common yellowthroats have been collected in San Luis Obispo, Los Angeles, and San Diego counties (Grinnell and Miller 1944). Sibley (1952) referred to *sinuosa* as a resident species, although the collection of specimens outside the breeding range indicates at least a migratory element to the population. It should be added that there is an influx of other races of common yellowthroats into the San Francisco Bay Area during migration and in winter. The relative numbers of "western" common yellowthroats and salt marsh common yellowthroats in Bay wetlands at this time of year is entirely unknown. I assume that some specimens of *sinuosa* were collected from salt marshes during winter and that these specimens provided the basis for the statement that salt marshes provide wintering habitat for salt marsh common yellowthroats (Foster 1977a,b). However, Foster (1977) stated that it seemed *likely* that the birds that winter in *Salicornia* marshes of San Francisco and San Pablo bays breed in adjacent brackish marshes, and Hobson et al. (1986) indicated that some populations (of *sinuosa*) moved from fresh and brackish marshes to the outer margins of the Bay to areas dominated by *Salicornia* or *Spartina*. Because other races could be occurring in salt marshes during the nonbreeding period, and because specimens of migrant *sinuosa* have been collected outside the breeding range, specimen (or individuals captured in mist nests and measured) evidence would be necessary to document this habitat shift in *sinuosa*.

Foster (1977a,b) found populations to be at critically low numbers in the South Bay and Peninsula areas and greatly reduced from historic abundance throughout the breeding range. During the 1975-76 season, Foster identified breeding habitat at Olema Marsh, Limantour Estero, San Pablo Bay, Napa Marsh, Lake Merced, Sharp Park, Searsville Lake, Palo Alto Marsh, "Alviso" Marshes (including the San Francisco Bay National Wildlife Refuge in the vicinity of Artesian Slough), Coyote Hills Regional Park, Alameda Creek, San Gregorio Creek, and Pescadero Marsh. Foster (1977b) estimated that 200 pairs were present in all areas occupied in the 1976 breeding season. This estimate increased to 230 pairs the following year with more thorough coverage. However, 1976 and 1977 were severe drought years with significant impact on marsh vegetation, and it was recognized that Foster's yellowthroat status reports during those years might not have been representative of normal conditions. This assumption was supported by surveys conducted in 1985 in which breeding populations of salt marsh common yellowthroat in many areas were higher than in 1977 (Hobson et al. 1986). Foster (1977b) assumed the density of yellowthroats in suitable habitat was the same before alteration of marsh areas began, and estimated that the population under pristine conditions was probably on the order of 2,000 to 2,300 pairs (but see below for more recent, higher estimates). Finally, Foster (1977b) calculated that the population of salt marsh common yellowthroats had been reduced by 80 to 95% in the past 100 years based on calculated loss of suitable habitat. Hobson et al. (1986) estimated that fewer than 900 breeding birds occurred in all habitats.

The estimates of both Foster (1977b) and Hobson et al. (1986) may have been low. In a very recent study (Evens et al. 1997), 239 pairs were estimated to breed at Point Reyes alone. An earlier study (Hobson et al. 1986) estimated 135 pairs from the Point Reyes Peninsula. Evens et al. (1997) attributed the increase in estimated population size to increased coverage, increased habitat values due to changing land-use practices, and to more favorable weather patterns in 1996 relative to 1986. The most recent estimate on population size in tidal marsh alone, presented in Nur et al. (1997), was 6,000 to 11,000 breeding birds.

No salt marsh common yellowthroats have been collected during the breeding season outside the range described by Grinnell and Miller (1944), which is bounded by Tomales Bay on the north, Carquinez Strait on the east, and Santa Cruz County on the south (Foster 1977a,b). Within this range, all specimens collected between March and August were *sinuosa* (Foster 1977a,b). Sibley (1952, p. v), evidently, erroneously distinguished between common yellowthroats breeding in South Bay freshwater marshes as "yellowthroats," and yellowthroats breeding in salt marshes around the shores of San Francisco Bay as "race *sinuosa.*" There does not appear to be any substantiation that any race other than *sinuosa* breeds in South Bay marshes.

Habitat Use and Behavior

Common yellowthroats form a complex of superspecies and subspecies that inhabit North and Central American dense, brushy habitats, generally associated with wetlands or moist areas. In California, yellowthroats are found in freshwater marshes, coastal swales, swampy riparian thickets, brackish marshes, salt marshes, and the edges of disturbed weed fields and grasslands that border soggy habitats (Shuford 1993). In the San Francisco Bay region as a whole, about 60% breed in brackish marsh, 20% in riparian woodland/swamp, 10% in freshwater marsh, 5% in salt marsh, and 5% in upland vegetation (Hobson et al. 1986, Shuford 1993).

Yellowthroats frequently use borders between these various plant communities, and territories often straddle the interface of riparian corridors and ecotones between freshwater or tidal marsh and the upland vegetation of weedy fields or grassland (Shuford 1993).

Breeding habitat has been divided into three main categories (Foster 1977a,b): (1) woody swamp (e.g., Olema Marsh, Searsville Lake, etc.); (2) brackish marsh (e.g., Napa Marsh); and (3) freshwater marsh (e.g., Coyote Hills Regional Park). Nests are well concealed and are primarily found on or near the ground in grass tussocks, low herbaceous vegetation, cattails, tules, and bushes to approximately five feet above the ground (Kendeigh 1945, Gross 1953, Stewart 1953, Shuford 1993). Breeding generally starts in mid-March to April, and second clutches take the breeding season into August (Foster 1977b).

Conservation and Management

Foster (1977b) attributed an estimated salt marsh common yellowthroat population decline of 80-95% over the past 100 years to increasing urbanization of the Bay Area and consequential loss of habitat.

Based on Foster (1977a), California Department of Fish and Game (Fish and Game) staff recommended that suitable salt marsh common yellowthroat habitat be maintained and protected in parks and refuges. Other specific recommendations included the preparation of a management plan for Olema Marsh and Limantour Estero, development of fresh and brackish water marsh areas in a portion of New Chicago Marsh, protection and enhancment of habitat in Coyote Hills Regional Park, and incorporation of salt marsh common yellowthroat habitat protection into management of Napa Marsh and Skaggs Island Naval Base. The staff report also recommended that planning agencies in Marin, San Francisco, San Mateo, Santa Clara, and Alameda counties, as well as other agencies and entities that manage or otherwise influence yellowthroat breeding habitats, be advised of yellowthroat breeding habitats in their respective counties and be encouraged to assist in efforts to preserve and enhance these areas. Fish and Game staff concluded that further study should be conducted to determine the location, quality, and extent of salt marsh common yellowthroat wintering grounds; seasonal movement patterns; minimum size of marsh habitat that will support breeding birds; and relative productivity of the various marsh habitat types used by breeding yellowthroats.

Foster (1977b) made the following additional management recommendations:

- Purchase (by county, state, or federal agencies) unprotected breeding sites.
- Protect any area that includes yellowthroat breeding habitat from diking, draining, or removal of vegetation. Protection should be extended to include a buffer zone around the actual occupied area.

- Encourage water treatment plant operations that allow treated discharge to flow into the Bay at places where it will support marsh vegetation, rather than discharging it in the deeper parts of the Bay by means of pipes.
- Encourage parks and other agencies that have yellowthroat breeding habitat in their jurisdiction to ensure the water supply to these areas, by artificial flooding if necessary. Foster (1977a) noted that the yellowthroat habitat least affected by a drought (1975-76) was habitat in which water levels were artifically maintained. Such areas included Coyote Hills Regional Park and outfalls of sewage treatment plants.

Research by Hobson et al. (1986) concluded that continued loss of habitat (due primarily to development), poor habitat management, and drought or flood could seriously affect the future of this subspecies. They recommended further study involving systematic banding, recovery, and resighting; a study of dispersal corridors, buffer zones, and nonreproductive season habitat requirements; and more taxonomic work on the Suisun Bay population to determine the eastern boundary of *sinuosa*.

More recently, Nur et al. (1977) recommend extensive surveys of salt marsh common yellowthroats to derive reliable estimates of population densities in a diversity of potential habitats. Nur et al. (1977) also recommend a molecular genetic analysis to clarify the genetic relationship of this "taxon."

References

American Ornithologists' Union (AOU). 1957. Checklist of North American birds. Port City Press, Inc. Baltimore, Maryland. 691pp.

Evens, J., R. Stallcup, G. Grace and S. Small. 1997. Status of the salt marsh common yellowthroat (*Geothlypis trichas sinuosa*). Final report to the Natl. Park Service, Pt. Reyes Natl. Seashore, Pt. Reyes Station, Calif.

Foster, M.L. 1977a. Status of the salt marsh common yellowthroat (*Geothlypis trichas sinuosa*) in the San Francisco Bay Area, California 1975-1976. Ca. Dept. Fish and Game.

_____. 1977b. A breeding season study of the salt marsh yellowthroat (*Geothlypis trichas sinuosa*) of the San Francisco Bay Area, California. M.A. Thesis, San Jose State Univ., San Jose, Calif.

Grinnell, J. 1901. The Pacific Coast yellowthroats. Condor 3: 65-66.

Grinnell. J. and A.H. Miller. 1944. The distribution of the birds of California. Pacific Coast Avifauna No. 27.

Gross, A.O. 1953. Northern and Maryland yellowthroats, Florida yellowthroat, western yellowthroat, and salt marsh yellowthroat. *In*: A.C. Bent (ed). Life histories of North American wood warblers. U. S. Natl. Mus. Bull. 12(203): 542-577.

Hobson, K., P. Perrine, E.B. Roberts, M.L. Foster and P. Woodin. 1986. A breeding season survey of salt marsh yellowthroats (*Geothlypis trichas sinuosa*) in the San Francisco Bay Region. Report of the San Francisco Bay Bird Observatory to U.S. Fish Wildl. Serv.

Howell, S.N.G. and S. Webb. 1995. The birds of Mexico and Northern Central America. Oxford Univ. Press. 849pp.

Kendeigh, S.C. 1945. Community selection by birds on the Helderberg Plateau of new York. Auk 62: 418-436.

Marshall, J.T. and K.G. Dedrick. 1994. Endemic song sparrows and yellowthroats of San Francisco Bay. Studies in Avian Biol. 15: 316-327.

Nur, N., S. Zack, J. Evens and T. Gardali. 1997. Tidal marsh birds of the San Francisco Bay region: status, distribution, and conservation of five Category 2 taxa. Draft Final Rept. of the Point Reyes Bird Observatory to the U.S. Geol. Survey, Biol. Res. Div.

Raby, K.R. 1992. A study in avian biosystematics using the song of male yellowthroats (*Geothlypis trichas*) to discriminate between subspecies. M.A. Thesis, Antioch Univ.

Shuford, W.D. 1993. The Marin County breeding bird atlas. Bushtit Books. Bolinas Calif. 479pp.

Sibley, C.G. 1952. Birds of South San Francisco Bay region. San Jose State College. 44pp. (mimeo).

Stewart, R.M. 1953. A life history of the yellow-throat. Wilson Bull. 65: 99-115.

Personal Communications

Michael Rigney, Coyote Creek Riparian Station, Alviso, California.

Savannah Sparrow

Passerculus sandwichensis

Howard L. Cogswell

Introduction

The savannah sparrow is a small (12-15 cm), inconspicuous, and unobtrusive bird whose usual perch is a weed stalk in a meadow and seldom anything higher than a fence post. Although this bird bears some resemblance to the song sparrow, it is grayer and smaller than its cousin, and its tail is shorter and slightly notched, that of the song sparrow being somewhat rounded. Adults have a dark brown crown with a distinctive pale yellow mark in front of the eye. The savannah sparrow's song is a weak, buzzy trill, preceded by two introductory notes of differing pitches.

Some 17 subspecies of savannah sparrow are currently recognized (Wheelwright and Rising 1993), all of the northern ones being migratory. The southernmost subspecies in the west are all resident or nearly so, including *P. s. beldingi* of the salt marshes from Morro Bay, California, south into northwestern Baja. That subspecies, now officially listed as threatened, occupies a very similar habitat within its range as do the three salt marsh races of the song sparrow in the San Francisco Bay Region (see report on song sparrows, this publication). The "Coast" subspecies of the savannah sparrow, *P. s. alaudinus*, breeds from Humboldt County south to San Luis Obispo County where it intergrades with *beldingi* at Morro Bay. Through much of its range, *alaudinus* occupies some salt marsh areas, but also the more moist sorts of grasslands of the Coast Ranges. Unlike the very

Don DesJardin

Other Birds

dark *beldingi*, which is easily distinguishable in the field from other races, that winter in its range, birds of the *alaudinus* subspecies (which includes the former *P. s. bryanti* of narrower range) are not readily told from those other races except by close comparison and often measurements in hand. So data on relative numbers of birds of the different wintering subspecies within our area of interest are nearly non-existent.

Description

The 28-page account for savannah sparrow in the new "Birds of North America" series (Wheelwright and Rising 1993) should be a primary source for anyone investigating this species. It includes some information about the various subspecies, particularly the "well-marked" ones of southern California and west Mexico, as well as the pale *P. s. princeps* that breeds on one island off Nova Scotia. The account includes distinguishing characteristics, distribution, migration, habitat (but this lacks any quantification – see below), food habits, sounds, behavior, breeding (including development of young, parental care, etc.), demography and populations, conservation and management, appearance (including molts and geographic variation), and measurements. A few items about the species of special interest for resource managers, as gleaned from this account, seem worth mentioning here.

Male savannah sparrows defend territories (announced by song from frequently used perches), which usually include or may be adjusted to include the much smaller territory defended by nesting females. Polygyny has been noted in a number of populations in good habitat (thus, a census of just singing males may under-report the size of a breeding population). Nests are normally on the ground, well hidden under tussocks of grass or low shrubs and often with an approach tunnel of up to several inches.

From studies in eastern Canada and eastern United States to the Great Lakes area, annual survivorship of adults ranges from 28 to 70%, varying both by location and by years. As with most small birds, mortality in the first year is high, but once a savannah sparrow is a year old the rate remains relatively constant for five to six years, after which it rises abruptly. So an expected maximum life span would be about that number of years.

Although the population dynamics of *beldingi* and *alaudinus* seem not to be reported in the literature, studies from other areas may provide some insight. According to the reference by Wheelwright and Rising (1993), young birds from island populations (especially *princeps*) show a much higher natal philopatry (tendency to return to the area where they were hatched/raised) than do the young from mainland areas. The mere fact that *beldingi* is so strongly differentiated in its markings while *alaudinus* is not, would indicate a similar relationship between these races in California.

During the breeding season, savannah sparrows feed primarily on insects of various orders and all stages of development, spiders, and small crustaceans. In the non-breeding period, the diet is predominantly small seeds and fruits gleaned from the ground or low vegetation – the shift occurring as the young sparrows are fledged in mid-summer. Even when breeding, these sparrows do considerable amounts of foraging off their territory. In the non-breeding period, they may appear to be gregarious, but the "flocks" are probably primarily aggregations drawn together by attraction to a good food supply and have no ongoing social structure.

Predators that take savannah sparrows or their eggs and young are extremely varied; an instance of a clapper rail doing so is cited.

Effects of human activity on savannah sparrow populations have probably been beneficial, over-all, due to extensive clearing of forests and maintenance of agriculture and grazing lands. Pesticides applied to habitats occupied by the species are probably detrimental, but this seems not to have been documented. (These authors do not mention filling or draining of wetlands as a factor – perhaps because of the northeastern emphasis in the research that has been carried out on the species.)

Distribution and Abundance

Savannah sparrows are found nearly continent-wide at the appropriate season, wintering commonly from northern California, Missouri, and New Jersey south to Central America, and irregularly or sparsely as far north as New England and coastal British Columbia. The overall breeding range extends from Arctic shores of Alaska and Canada, south to northern Georgia and Illinois to Colorado, northeastern Arizona, and through California west of the southern deserts, with additional populations in western Baja California, Mexico and on the Mexican tableland.

In various parts of its range, the savannah sparrow is found occupying open, mostly un-wooded habitats of many sorts – from arctic tundra and mountain meadows to hayfields (particularly old or unkempt ones) to cultivated croplands, wet (but not flooded) meadows, marsh borders, and near-desert grasslands in some locations. Wintering savannah sparrows of various subspecies are also to be found in any such open habitat in the Bay Area (more on non-breeding numbers, below). However, the habitats selected by the breeding form, *alaudinus*, were summarized by Johnston (1968) as follows. "It maintains populations in two main types of habitat in coastal California: the *Salicornia* association of tidal marshes and the grassland associations of the coastal fog belt." Comparing its habitat niche with that of the salt marsh races of the song sparrow, he also wrote that the savannah "on salt marshes is limited to the broad expanses of low-lying *salicornia* (*Salicornia ambigua*) on the older and higher parts of marshes...[that] lie back of that salt marsh vegetation (cordgrass, *Spartina foliosa*) best suited to frequent submergence by tidal flooding" (Johnston 1968). Eight nests were found in 1971 by Gill (1977) in his survey of breeding birds around the Bay south of San Mateo Bridge, the preferred nesting habitat being "levee tops grown to annual grasses and high pickleweed growing on the levee banks." Gill (1977) further estimated the overall nesting population of savannahs in his study area to be from 800 to 1,000 pairs; but the large size of area he surveyed precluded any calculation of densities for any type of habitat.

Savannah sparrows have been reported in at least 17 breeding-bird censuses[1] on measured plots in California, although on several of these they were listed only as "visitors" to the plots. Five of these censuses were in bayside marsh or adjacent grasslands and, thus, sampled the gradation of habitats – from marsh to unwooded uplands – which this species exemplifies (**Table 7.7**). Only one of the five surveys listed in **Table 7.7**, the San Pablo Creek survey, was from within the geographic limits of the Goals Project. A similar census on a plot of brackish marsh and adjacent grassland at Southhampton Bay did not find any savannah sparrows (Stoner et al. 1963), nor did one of the somewhat brackish "diked

---

[1] A full listing of these California breeding-bird censuses may be obtained from the author at CA BIRDS@aol.com.

coastal saltmarsh" three miles northwest of Alviso (apparently part of what is now called Triangle Marsh) in 1983 (Anderson and Jennings 1981). However, two census plots including habitat of breeding *beldingi* in southern California showed much higher densities for those strictly marsh-inhabiting birds: 60.8 territories per 100 acres along Ballona Creek in western Los Angeles (Dial 1978), and 104 territories per 100 acres in the Bolsa Chica Ecological Reserve in Orange County (Alexander 1974).

Winter population densities of savannah sparrows have been obtained for a few discrete plots on Humboldt Bay, near Marshall on Tomales Bay, and in coastal southern California. However, I know of no winter population counts for San Francisco Bay, except for some of intertidal mudflats that had a remnant bit of marsh at the edge – hardly a useful sampling for this species.

Some indication of typical numbers (subspecies not distinguished) may be gleaned from counts made two or three times a month for one year in the north-Newark and northwest-Fremont area (**Figure 7.6**). In these studies, several assistants and I made counts of all bird species on three properties of the Leslie Salt Company and three other "comparison" plots in the period of October 1984 through October 1985 – although songbirds were not a targeted subject for the counters until March 1985. Some of the plots were too large for the counts to be considered total censuses, thus the numbers counted are very likely well below the true densities.

Table 7.7 Censuses in California Bayside Marsh or Adjacent Grasslands Where Savannah Sparrows Were Reported

Location (all are in California)	Habitat Description	Date	Population Density (territories/acre)	Reference
San Pablo Creek, Contra Costa County	Tidal marsh (*Salicornia, Spartina, Grindelia*, etc.)		5T/70 ac. (=7T/100ac)	Johnston 1952
Humboldt Bay, 3 mi. So. of Eureka, Humboldt County	"marsh" (but with much grass and some subshrubs)		5.5T/26 ac. (=21.2T/100ac)	Sorenson and Springer 1977
Freshwater Slough, <1mi. E. of Eureka, Humboldt County	Diked marsh	(1979)	3T/19.46 ac. (=15.4T/100ac)	Jacobson 1980
	Diked marsh	(1980)	3T/19.46 ac. (=15.4T/100ac)	Jacobson 1981
	Diked marsh with part of plot open to tidal action	(1981)	2+ as visitors only	Jacobson et al. 1983
Humboldt Bay, 1 mi. So. of Eureka, Humboldt County	"marsh" (brackish, with various herbs and coyote bush)	(1980)	1+ as visitor only/20.3ac	Base 1981
		(1981)	1.0T/20.3 ac. (=4.9T/100ac)	Base 1982
Coastal Prarie, Cypress Grove ACR property, Marshall, Marin County	Marine terrace grassland adjacent to bayside freshwater marsh	(1988)	1+ visitor/31.0 ha.	Kelly 1989

Hickory Tract, Newark 65 acres, partly barren old salt ponds, diked pickleweed marsh, old head of Newark Slough, several acre patch of partly filled land with grass and forbs.

| 1-24 on 6 dates | 3-21 on 6 dates | 2-16 on 6 dates 1 bird singing on Apr.17 | 2-5 on 4 dates with 1-4 birds singing | 2-5 on 2 dates and 0 on 4+ others | 2-13 on 6 dates |

Coyote Tract, Newark About 174 acres, only about 60 of which were vegetated, mostly used as pasture.

| 1-9 on 5 dates | 0-8 – sparrows not tallied some dates | 3 & 2 on 2 dates | 0 on 16 coverages, some of them thorough | 3-5 on 4 dates, 0 on 2 |

Coyote Tract, Fremont About 100 acres, some 60 acres being nearly barren former salt ponds, the remainder well vegetated former gun club ponds re-grown to various herbs, including dock, spike-rush, grass, and local cat-tails; two small ponds much enlarged in winter.

| 5-59 on 8 dates | 1-39 on 7 dates | 3-15 on 8 dates, including 2 courting on Ap.4 & 2 scolding and 1 carrying food on Ap.22 | 1-9 on 5 dates, including 1-2 singing and 2 scolding on t dates | 1 on each of 2 dates, 0 on others | 2-82 on 6 dates w/ max on Oct.23. Nearly all in well-vegetated parts of the plot |

Coyote Hills Regional Park 37 acre plot marked off with posts in 209-ft. squares. Seasonal wetlands with *Salicornia, Scirpus robustus, Frankenia,* local *Rumex* and other tall forbs, grasses in western 1/4, a belt of tall *Typha* marsh along a shallow ditch in eastern and northern parts; all in floodwater storage basin with water covering varying parts of the plot shallowly (many plants protruding) in winter.

| (later start than other areas) | 3-54 on 6 dates, 40 in 3 ac. on Dec.6 | 13-42 on 9 dates | 5-59 on 7 dates, including 1-5 singing on 3 dates & 2 chasing on one date | 17-42 on 5 dates, including 1-8 singing on 5 dates; chasing and scolding | 6-22 on 5 dates, including 1-5 singing, but 0 on Aug.25 (why?) | 10-81 on 6 dates |

Don Edwards S.F. Bay National Wildlife Refuge Headquarters Flat (LaRiviere Marsh) Approximately 105 acres west of Thornton Ave. and south of route 84. Former salt crystallizers and ditches and dikes, plus smaller ponds becoming more marsh than barren; western 1/4 opened to tidal action in previous year, and large central part to muted tidal action (or diked off when gate closed) beginning in spring 1985. Dikes in north-central to northeastern and northwestern parts were usually not walked, so some savannah sparrow habitat was missed. *Note: there was no singing or other evidence of breeding in this plot.*

| 2-6 on 5 dates | 1 on 2 dates and 0 on all others | 1-17 on 4 dates and 0 on several others | 1 on May 7 and 0 on all other dates | 2 on Jul. 7 and 0 on all other dates | 3-28 on 7 dates |

Newark Slough Tidal marsh from the southwest corner of the south tip of Coyote Hills to the slough-head at Thornton Ave. Approximately 60 acres, including the main channel, which was here only about 2-10 feet wide. A few old dikes are in the eastern part, including one at the actual Mayhews Landing site that has tall forbs on it, the others fully covered by pickleweed and various high-marsh plants. Many of the savannah sparrows noted were along the levee between the marsh and the adjacent salt evaporator on the southwest, where there was a narrow, interrupted fringe of upland plants. *Note: Larger numbers in Mar.and Oct. '85 were found by walking the very narrow shoulder of Thornton Ave. fringing the marsh.*

| 3-24 on 8 dates | 1-24 on 9 dates | 1-14 on 5 dates and 0 on 1 date. 3 singing on Mar. 20 | 1-2 on 4 dates and 0 on 2 others. 2 singing on May 8 | 2+ on Aug. 16 and 0 on 6 other dates | 4 on Sep. 26 and 23-31 on 3 dates in Oct. |

Figure 7.6 Summary of Data from Six Bird Count Studies Conducted Between Late Fall 1984 and Winter 1985. Data from Cogswell (1986) and author's personal raw data records.

Other Birds

Conservation and Management

The local population data for the savannah sparrow are so meager that they provide no indication of any local historical population changes. For the continent as a whole, there may be notably larger populations now than occurred before European settlement and expansion (Wheelwright and Rising 1993); however, this can be presumed not to be the case on the periphery of San Francisco Bay. The filling in of the upper parts of many tidal marshes and the urban development that has taken place on uplands so created would have decidedly decreased habitat acreage and quality for savannah sparrows, at least in the central section of the Bay. The conversion of tidal marsh to salt evaporators also eliminated much of the marsh areas in the South Bay – particularly when this conversion is considered in combination with the subsequent urban expansion to the very edge of those salt ponds. Only the conversion of former tidal marshes to bayside or near-bay upland fields – such as the diked farmlands near San Pablo Bay and the gun club/grazing lands established years ago around parts of Suisun Bay – may have been favorable to savannah sparrows. Modern data on the distribution and numbers of the species, especially during the breeding season, are sorely needed from those areas. Such data would be of most value to resource managers if they were obtained with reference to the different vegetation and the changes in it emanating from various land-use practices over all seasons and for years of different rainfall patterns.

The savannah sparrow (especially its subspecies *alaudinus*) is an ideal target species to represent those birds dependent upon both Bay-related marshes of most kinds and the adjacent upland grasslands and fields of various sorts. The relative densities of its populations in the grasslands of higher elevations of the Coast Ranges and in the apparently relatively few areas where it breeds in valleys between these ranges are unknown. Maintenance or restoration of as much vegetation that is transitional from marsh to upland, in various parts of the Bay system where it is still possible, should be a goal until the comparison of qualities of this habitat combination to strictly upland types can be made. I suspect that the transitional marsh-upland habitat will be found to support far higher densities.

References

Alexander, J.F. 1974. *Salicornia* salt marsh [BBC #143]. Amer. Birds 28: 1050.

Anderson, J.R. and V.R. Jennings. 1981. Diked coastal salt marsh [BBC #211 – not diked on bayward side]. Amer. Birds 35: 102.

Base, D.L. 1981. Diked coastal brackish marsh [BBC #209]. Amer. Birds 35: 101-2.

_____. 1982. Restored coastal brackish marsh [BBC #198]. Amer. Birds 36: 103.

Cogswell, H.L. 1986. Use of the Coyote Tract, Newark by birds, October 1984 - October 1985. Rept. to Leslie Salt Co. 115pp. plus 10 figs., 68 tables (of original data organized by season, habitats, and type of use).

Dial, K.P. 1978. Disturbed coastal salt marsh [BBC #166]. Amer. Birds 32: 114-5.

Gill, Jr., R. 1977. Breeding avifauna of the South San Francisco Bay Estuary. Western Birds 8: 1-12.

Jacobson, S.L. 1980. Diked coastal salt marsh [BBC #202a+b/data for 1979 and 1980]. Amer. Birds 34: 100-1.

_____. 1981. Diked coastal salt marsh [BBC #210]. Amer. Birds 35: 102.

Jacobson, S.L., J.P. Kelly and D.L. Base. 1983. Restored coastal salt marsh [BBC #189/data for 1981 and 1982]. Amer. Birds 37: 102-3.

Johnston, R.F. 1952. *Salicornia-Spartina* salt marsh [BBC #25]. Audubon Field Notes 6: 316-7.

_____. 1968. *Passerculus sandwichensis alaudinus* Bonaparte/coastal savannah sparrow. *In*: O.L. Austin, Jr.(ed). Life histories of North American cardinals...sparrows and allies. U.S. Natl. Museum Bull. 237(2): 712-714.

Kelly, J.P. 1989. Coastal prairie [BBC #56]. J. Field Ornith. 60(suppl.): 56-7.

Sorensen, P.C. and P.F. Springer. 1977. Diked coastal salt marsh [BBC #150]. Amer. Birds 31: 86.

Stoner, E.A., M.M. Elmore and J.D. Graham. 1963. Brackish marsh and adjacent grassland [BBD #30]. Audubon Field Notes 17: 507.

Wheelwright, H.T. and J.D. Rising. 1993. Savannah sparrow (*Passerculus sandwichensis*) *In*: A. Poole and F. Gill (eds). The birds of North America, No. 45. Acad. of Nat. Sciences, Phila., Penn. and Amer. Ornithologists' Union, Washington D.C. 28pp.

Other Birds

Song Sparrow

Melospiza melodia samuelis
M. m. pusillula
M. m. maxillaris

Howard L. Cogswell

Introduction

As a breeding species, the song sparrow (*Melospiza melodia*; Emberizidae/Emberizinae) is found across North America from southern Alaska and central and eastern Canada to northern Florida and Mexico, in the drier regions being restricted to riparian or other wetland habitats. As of 1957, some 31 subspecies were recognized as valid on morphological grounds (AOU 1957), including a very pale one in the southwestern desert area, and several quite large ones resident along the Aleutian-Alaska coast area. A population of "ordinary" song sparrows (regular-sized at 6.25 inches total length) breeding in Cincinnati, Ohio was the subject of intensive study using colored leg bands for a number of successive years. The resultant monographs (Nice 1937, 1943) made the song sparrow, for many years thereafter, the best known of any species of American song bird. The study provided details on the bird's home range and territory, mating system (mostly monogamous), tendency to migrate (males there included some that left for the winter, but others that stayed), nesting, production, and survival of young, etc. Nice (1937, 1943) also set a high standard for others in her exhaustive search of relevant literature from throughout the world.

Tidal marshlands along the Atlantic Coast from Long Island to Virginia are occupied by a distinct subspecies of song sparrow (*M. m. atlantica*), but it has

Don DesJardin

apparently been little studied. At least the northern populations of that race are migratory (AOU 1957). In the tidal marshlands about San Francisco Bay, however, three distinctly separate subspecies have evolved, and all of them are apparently quite resident year-round within those marshlands or immediate vicinity. These are:

- *Melospiza melodia samuelis* of San Pablo Bay and northern San Francisco Bay (south to Sausalito and north Richmond); it was first recognized as distinct in 1858.
- *Melospiza melodia pusillula* of the balance of San Francisco Bay shores (breeding originally from San Francisco and southeast Richmond south to Alviso); first described in 1899.
- *Melospiza melodia maxillaris* of the Suisun Bay marsh complex and west to include Southhampton Bay; first described in 1909.

Marshall (1948a, 1948b) studied all of these subspecies from the standpoint of the habitats occupied, and the very tenuous connections their populations had with adjacent upland forms of the song sparrow. The gist of his findings was that all are quite distinct in size or proportions of bill, wings, tail (etc.) and/or coloration from the upland subspecies. Only one of these subspecies, *samuelis*, has been studied in detail using banded birds (Johnston 1954, 1956a, 1956b); but findings from that study that pertain to the birds' adaptations for life in an intertidal area have been supported by incidental observations made on both *pusillula* and *maxillaris* and are used in this account as applicable to all three of these forms. The same assumption was a key aspect of the California Department of Fish and Game staff report to the Fish and Game Commission (Larsen 1989) when a petition to list *maxillaris* as Endangered was forwarded with the recommendation that Threatened status was warranted. A general survey of the status of all three San Francisco Bay races of song sparrows was done by Walton (1975), and Marshall and Dedrick (1994) presented an updated review that ties the estimated populations to the acreages of remaining tidal marshes. The last paper also has a color figure that illustrates diagnostic features of each of these subspecies compared to their adjacent upland relatives.

The presence within such a small, overall region of three such narrow endemics is in itself a highly valuable sample of evolution at the critical "not-yet-species" level – the case histories of which serve to illustrate early stages of the gradual process of speciation.

Description

Song sparrows of most of the United States are "typical" Emberizine sparrows about six to 6.5 inches in total length, with rather average body, neck, head, bill, and leg ratios. They have somewhat shorter wings (approximately seven inches spread) and longer tail (2.6 inches) than other species in the subfamily that occupy more open habitats. They are brownish above and whitish below, with darker brown to blackish streaks (varying in marginal hues among the subspecies). On the mid-breast, the dark streaks tend to be grouped, forming an irregular blotch. The tail is even-ended or somewhat rounded (not notched as in many sparrows), and is usually moved up and down as the bird flies from disturbance into cover.

Birds of the *samuelis* race are slightly smaller, and considerably less rusty-toned in dorsal color than *gouldii* of the adjacent Marin and Sonoma County uplands. The South Bay *pusillula* birds are still smaller, especially the bill, and with a tail averaging 10% shorter than the upland form there, *santacruceis* (included in *gouldii* by the AOU). Marshall and Dedrick (1994) show *pusillula* as being generally grayer in background tone, with a distinct light gray collar (but brown-streaked) on the hind-neck; but at the Museum of Vertebrate Zoology in Berkeley, H. Cogswell surveyed over 50 spring-summer specimens of *pusillula* (many collected by Marshall himself) and could not distinguish this grayness on at least half of them. The degree to which differences persist or disappear with wear of the feathers apparently remains to be worked out. The Suisun Bay birds, *maxillaris*, are more nearly equal to typical upland song sparrows in size, and show much rusty coloration in the lighter areas above and on the back of the neck and the tail; but their most distinctive feature is a somewhat swollen basal half or so of the bill (noticeable only on very close inspection). This last feature should be the easiest clue to distinguish them from *mailliardi* of the adjacent Sacramento and lower San Joaquin valleys, but Marshall and Dedrick (1994) do not illustrate that subspecies.

Breeding Phenology – Territories of salt marsh song sparrows are apparently "held" all year, even if not actively defended in fall and early winter. Singing by males is prevalent by February, however, and one of the major adaptations discovered by Johnston (1954, 1956a) for *samuelis* is that the peak date for completion of the first clutch of eggs is more than two weeks earlier than that of song sparrows of the nearby upland race. The mode of this laying comes about March 27 with fair numbers of birds completing first clutches up to mid-April. The advantage of early laying is that the nests are less vulnerable to being flooded by the gradually increasing height of high tides that occurs annually in late April and even more in late May and June, the young of the early nesters fledging before then. In some years, the first clutch layings were delayed by bad weather, and loss of eggs or nestlings to flooding was widespread. Nests are not always placed in the highest vegetation available, a trait that Johnston attributes to the selective pressure of nest-predators. He also found a lower peak of clutch-completion in mid-May and a third small one (seven

nests out of 111 total) in June, when spring-phase high tides would almost certainly flood most of the marsh. These may include re-nestings by birds that lost their first brood, but many were apparent attempts to raise a second brood even if a higher percentage are then flooded out. Indeed Johnston (1968: 1548) says "almost all pairs nest twice in a season. If replacement nests are considered, each pair will nest on the average 2.5 to (rarely) three times each season."

The same seasonal time pattern for clutches of eggs is seen in *pusillula*, of which many sets of eggs were taken by collectors prior to 1940, and presumably also for *maxillaris*, for which relative few data are at hand[1]. Of 80 egg-sets of *pusillula*, 50 were taken in April, 25 in May, five in March, and only one in June. There were 14 sets of *samuelis* eggs, all of which were taken between April 8 and May 7, and seven sets of *maxillaris* eggs, all of which were taken between the first and 23rd of May. Whether there is a difference in timing for individual birds of any of these subspecies that hold territories adjacent to a suitable dike or other bit of upland that permits nesting above the level of the June high high tides has not been investigated. Johnston's study area had a dike only along its northeastern side, with channels attractive to sparrows only at its two ends, so the question was not addressed.

Nests of *samuelis* were found by Johnston (1956a, 1968) to be placed on average 9.5 inches above ground, but averaging 12 inches in the marsh lower in the tide range. Any of the four main marsh plant species (*Salicornia, Spartina, Grindelia, Distichlis*) were used for nest support; but the uppermost parts of the tallest (*Grindelia*) were avoided, which Johnston attributed to the selective effect of predators finding nests there more readily.

Productivity – The mean clutch size of 157 nests found in Johnston's study varied among years from 2.91 to 3.42 eggs, with the mid-season (April 6 to May 25) nests having a slightly larger mean number (3.23) of eggs than the earlier or later ones. However, the mid-season group for 1953, the year with highest success of early nestings, was almost identical to the later nest group which Johnston (1956a: 37) suggests might be a response to the saturated population, including the many juveniles still on hand from the early nests.

Basic natality (number of eggs/pair/year) ranged from 7.5 to 9.1 in the years 1952-55 of Johnston's study (1956b: 260). Since his studies of dispersal (see below) indicate a very strong tendency of the song sparrows to remain in the area where they were hatched and raised, he assumed that a color-banded individual that disap-

[1] This author maintains a database (dBase IV format) containing the data from the egg sets in most museum collections, as well as all other published and many unpublished records of song sparrows of any race in or near the Bayland marshes.

peared had died. Using these data and the ongoing numbers of birds, he also calculated a life-table showing the survivorship for this population. It shows a 26% mortality (=2% per day by my calculation) for the first 13 days of a young bird's life (the nestling period), 30% (3.3% per day) for the next 10 days (fledglings still cared for by adults), and 80% for the balance of the first year (341 days, or ca. 0.23% per day). From age one to age two, his data show a mortality of 43% and the same for age two to age three, and he assumes this rate continues through the several remaining years of the relatively short lives of these birds – a little higher than the 30-35% typical, after their first year, of other sparrows handled in large numbers by banders, e.g., white-crowned and golden-crowned sparrows.

Mortality factors applicable to the egg and nestling phases of the birds in the study by Johnston (1956b: 266) show predation and high tides accounting for 20% and 11%, respectively, of the losses. Storms were irregularly important, as in 1955 for 13% of the deaths. Brood-parasitism by the brown-headed cowbird is listed as a factor in five deaths (5% of the 1955 total of eggs and nestlings), but is not discussed. In more recent years, at least at the Hayward Shoreline, pairs of *pusillula* have been often noted feeding cowbird fledglings, so the increased population size of the cowbird now may be a negative factor of significance for these marsh-inhabiting sparrows. Johnston (1956b) also recorded about 49% mortality of eggs attributable to rodent predation (mostly Norway rats), and 59% loss of nestlings from the same factor. These were higher figures than all losses from high water and desertion. Other predators of minor influence were thought to be northern harriers and short-eared owls – but only four song sparrow skulls were found in 491 pellets he examined from the owls in a four-year period (Johnston 1968: 1550).

Dispersal – Johnston's (1956a) study of the *samuelis* population on San Pablo Creek Marsh in the 1950s included the distances from hatching site to breeding site of 34 juveniles, in 23 of which that being 200 meters or less, and in only four birds was it more than 600 meters. Some authors have objected that his single study area was too small to really check on this. However, there was a pronounced exponential drop-off in distance from the peak at 100-200 meters, and nearly 15% of the 241 nestlings he banded were found subsequently breeding in the study area – a very good number when one takes into account the 50% or higher nestling and early fledgling mortality. Furthermore, the Poisson statistical test for randomness in the observed distances showed that while most birds moved very little, a small percentage of individuals had a tendency to move a distance much greater than the mean – beyond the 500-600 meter distance where none were found. This pattern was true also with Nice's song sparrows in Ohio, so is probably a genetic feature in the species – only the

absolute distance being shorter in *samuelis* and presumably also the other salt marsh subspecies. The significance for conservation of the populations of these subspecies is that *continuity of habitat* is of very great importance in ensuring their ability to repopulate local areas where all or most individuals are eliminated by geographically and time-limited factors, i.e., local ecological disasters.

Trophic Relationships – The salt marsh races of the song sparrow, where present in the fully tidal marshes to which their evolutionary history fits them, are the most abundant of the passerine birds to be found there. Therefore, they must constitute an important segment of the food web in such communities. But just where should that segment be placed? On a year-round basis, they must be classed as omnivores; but in most of their breeding period from March through June or so, their mostly animal food would shift them upward trophically into the carnivore blocks – to some extent even into a secondary or tertiary carnivore position because they eat spiders and many carnivorous insects. But what does one do with the carnivore or omnivore that eats detritus-feeders on a large scale from the intertidal mud, which these birds do at least at times? The simple producer/consumer trophic picture is complicated by large quantities of detritus being recycled into the same trophic chains as are the organic products of green plants. Until a more thorough analysis of the percentages of the various types of food taken by birds of these three subspecies has been done, any detailed diagram could have no quantification of the relative importance of the connections shown.

Nearly the same lack of quantification is true for the known trophic relationships that would show song sparrow biomass passing on into predators, parasites, and scavengers, or for the reduction in the sparrow population success that is attributable to the brood-parasitic brown-headed cowbird. The behavior of the song sparrows on a salt marsh when a northern harrier or short-eared owl flies within its view indicates that these predators do indeed take some of the birds. However, the few song sparrow skulls Johnston (1956a) found in pellets from these owls indicates that the transfer of biomass to that species would be a very minor link in the food web. On a population basis, the most important predators of the salt marsh song sparrows are no doubt the Norway rat (*Rattus norvegicus*) and garter snakes (*Thamnophis* sp.), with now, in recent years, the non-native red fox (*Vulpes fulva*) added to the list, and in the parts of the marsh near a dike or upland, feral cats as well.

Habitat Use and Behavior

Except as otherwise indicated, this section is essentially summarized from Johnston's (1956a,b) results for a population of *samuelis* north of Richmond. He had some difficulty in attracting adults into traps, but was able to color-band 33, plus 13 juveniles; most of his data, however, came from the 241 nestlings that he so marked. The marsh in his whole study area covered about 200 acres in 1950-55, but the song sparrows did not inhabit the bayside one-tenth or so that was dominated by *Spartina*, nor the 60% or so that was relatively unbroken *Salicornia* lacking small curving channels. Instead, they were in the parts of the *Salicornia* zone next above the *Spartina* zone and along Wildcat Creek itself and smaller channels with frequent small branch channels or sloughs where scattered to numerous *Grindelia* subshrub "bushes" provided both song perches and usual nest placement above the level reached by most spring tides. Other plants found in this and the upper marsh zone are also listed by Johnston (1956a: 27). During lower tide periods, the mud along the same small side-channels (areas where marsh plants are typically overhanging) provided primary forage areas for these birds.

The territories of salt marsh song sparrows are much smaller, at least in this optimum habitat, than the average of one acre or a little more found by Nice in Ohio, and by many others elsewhere if one judges from the densities reported in various breeding-bird censuses even in "good" riparian situations. Johnston (1956b: 256) showed the linear arrangement of the 14 to 22 territories along one particular tidal channel through six successive years. He reported (p.254) that "thirty feet represents the average width of territories along sloughs *within which the birds perform practically all their activites* [emphasis added] … With this as definition of the area in which [these] song sparrows live, the actual density in a year of high numbers [1953] is seen to run from 8 to 10 pairs per acre. This is not as unreasonable as it may seem, for 10 pairs of song sparrows per acre would give each pair about 4,350 square feet per territory…" — about a 30- by 150-foot swath along one of the small sloughs, as he in fact found to be true. The density per unit area based on the whole marsh, including the parts not inhabited by song sparrows, would of course be much lower. For example, 74 territorial males were found in 70 acres of this same marsh (105 per 100 acres) and reported by Johnston (1952) in a census that included only two other breeding bird species: five territorial male savannah sparrows and four clapper rails. Year-to-year variation in a 100-acre part of this marsh (presumably including the 70-acre 1953 plot) was estimated to range from 87 to 124 pairs. Four different small sloughs supported song sparrows at "linear" densities along their length of a pair every 130 to 170 feet in 1953. The extremely sedentary nature of the territory holders is shown by data in Johnston (1956a), summarizing those birds with territories mapped in two or more successive years. Of the 48 instances of possible movement (24 birds) where movement could have happened, the only cases where territory centers were more than 16 meters from the previous year were

two for males and three for females, and none was moved more than 35 meters.

Johnston's two papers (1956a,b) contained but the barest mention of what happens to song sparrows that hold territories in the salt marsh when the tides are high enough to flood most of the vegetation in the *Salicornia* zone – as they are on the high high tides of May through June and again in November through December. He stressed the shift in breeding times, but did not report on the behavior of post-breeding birds. A selection of records from my own notebook (unless otherwise indicated) and a few other sources indicate that there is often temporary aggregation at the upper fringe of the marsh and particularly on any adjacent dike or fill with vegetation; for example:

- About 50 (5+ juveniles) were at the upper end of Plummer Creek, south-southwest of Newark, at high water on August 19, 1956;
- A similar number was seen while driving the dikes along Mt. Eden Creek, southwest Hayward, on September 10, 1964;
- Thirty to 50 were seen along the railroad fill that crosses the large Dumbarton Marsh on various summer and fall dates, and 100 or more on October 10, 1953 when the railroad was walked eastbound and the nearby San Francisco Aqueduct back westbound (Cogswell 1953, 1956);
- About 120 were seen from a boat plus a short distance afoot (along the railroad) in this same marsh on October 26, 1969 spanning a 7.5 foot high-water;
- About 185 were estimated in walking from near Dumbarton Bridge to Newark Slough along the railroad on January 27, 1979;
- An estimated 75 were seen in two miles of dike through a salt marsh near Alviso on November 19, 1949 at high water (Sibley 1955);
- From 51 to 86 were counted in the marsh fringes along Alvarado Channel (Old Alameda Creek) and/or the northern side of the new Alameda Creek Channel on Christmas Bird Counts from 1967 to 1981 at various times of tide, including a "flock" of 18 feeding on driftwood massed in a salt pan in the marsh at high water on December 31, 1967.

Elsewhere in the Bay, high estimates have been: 200 along Sears Point Road (=*samuelis*) on January 28, 1938 by Graham and Stoner (publ. in The Gull), and 150 by myself on November 19, 1950, during an Audubon group trip by boat down Suisun Slough with walking about on a part of Joice Island (=*maxillaris*). I believe that these aggregations include many territory holders, perhaps mostly in areas without significant number of *Grindelia* or other plants that would still provide cover at the higher high tides, and that these birds return to their territories as the tide ebbs. Johnston (1968: 1552) later reported some limited investigation of such aggregations during winter high tides, at one time having 17 birds perched on the raft he was using to explore the marsh just after a northern harrier flew by.

Food and Foraging – Johnston (1968: 1551-2) gives considerable detail of the foraging behavior of song sparrows in the salt marshes, presumably based on his four years of study of *samuelis*. Preferred forage sites are the muddy edges of small channels, but they also obtain food on the firmer ground under and from the marsh plant surfaces themselves. While they engage in the double-scratch bouts separating periods of pecking at the ground surface, like other sparrows, they also specialize at times on the small molluscs and other marine invertebrates in this intertidal mud. They also feed at the maturing heads of the *Grindelia* flowers, and in autumn (when fresh water from insect foods is at a low ebb) eat the fleshy fruits and tiny seeds of the *Salicornia*. In winter, after the seeds of the latter have been released from the dried spikes, they are washed up in the drift from high tides, and the salt marsh song sparrows spend much time picking at such accumulations, taking both seeds and various invertebrates. In spring and early summer, the young are fed almost entirely on insects [and other invertebrates], some of which are obtained by short hops or flutters approaching flycatching.

Quantitative study of the diet of these subspecies has been very minimal, although Beal is said in the literature to have reported in 1910 on some stomach contents of *samuelis*. Without regard to subspecies, the varied diet of song sparrows in general as reported in various early accounts is summarized by Nolan (1968).

Quality Habitat – The intensive study of a *samuelis* population by Johnston (1954, 1956a,b), the follow-up surveys of *maxillaris* populations from Southampton Bay through the Suisun Marsh complex as summarized by Marshall and Dedrick (1994), and numerous but more casual observations of *pusillula* populations in the Hayward, Newark, Alviso, Palo Alto, and Redwood City areas all lead to the general picture of highest populations of each of these subspecies being found in fully tidal marshes. This is true even though the vegetation differs very significantly in the marshes about Suisun Bay compared to San Pablo Bay and that in turn differs somewhat from the marshes of the southern arm of San Francisco Bay. The partiality shown for foraging along the banks of the sinuous minor channels within the tidal marsh, and the greater availability of nest sites and song perches in the *Grindelia* "bushes" that tend to grow along these same channels are probably the prime factors in supporting higher populations there. Johnston found no song sparrows with territories in the pure *Spartina* marsh adjacent to the mudflat along the open bay, but at Palo Alto they are moderately numerous in mixed *Salicornia-Spartina* marsh with a channel or adjacent dike and along the boardwalk that traverses

the marsh. Various subsequent searches of open *Salicornia* flats have confirmed Johntson's finding that the two subspecies that inhabit adjacent more complex marshes avoid at least breeding season residence where there are no small channels or adjacent mudflats or dikes.

The extent to which birds of each of these subspecies utilize, and indeed occupy for breeding purposes, the various types of diked marshlands near the tidal marshes is poorly understood. For *maxillaris*, the petition for that race to be listed as Endangered (Marshall and Mewaldt 1988) and the California Department of Fish and Game staff report that accompanied it (Larsen 1989) both indicated that diked-off, managed marshes were not inhabited by birds of that race. However, surveys of many parts of the North Suisun Marsh in 1990 by Marshall and several assistants located 79 pairs in non-tidal situations compared to 334 pairs or singing males on the 621 acres of tidal brackish marsh surveyed. Habitats mentioned for the non-tidal birds included coyote-bush (*Baccharis pilularis*) and roses close to a tidal slough (where those birds might have foraged at times). Seven birds were found in "hedges" of giant *Atriplex* and/or dry grass along a ditch with only water at the ends, and even a few were seen in dry fields with clumps of non-emergent tules. Cogswell's South Bay field notes have for years regularly noted a few *pusillula* living, foraging, and singing along outer-levee rip-rap with only traces of salt marsh vegetation, and others at least foraging frequently in diked-off *Salicornia* with various herbs and sometimes a few shrubs admixed. However, all or most of these sightings were within a few hundred feet from a tidal channel or the outer bayshore. It is not clear from observation with binoculars whether the several birds that regularly sing from coyote-bushes or tall clumps of sweet fennel (*Foeniculum vulgare*) on the western side of Coyote Hills, Fremont, are *pusillula* or upland-race birds. The only mud available to them by May is in the adjacent tidal or diked-off marshes.

Table 7.8 shows the relevant Goals Project "key" habitats, and summarizes their useage by each of the three salt marsh song sparrow races.

Distribution and Abundance

Because there is insufficient data on the actual locations and population sizes of song sparrows, this section outlines the historical changes in the extent (and quality) of suitable habitat, and provides estimates of population sizes based on habitat availability.

M. m. pusillula – Dedrick (1993) measured the total historic (pre-diking) suitable habitat within the range of this subspecies at 65,871 acres and the present habitat area as only 10.2% of that, or 6,678 acres (Marshall and Dedrick 1994: table 1). I performed a separate evaluation to estimate the remaining tidal marsh habitat in the range of *pusillula*, and to rank the quality

Table 7.8 Key Habitats Usage by Three Salt Marsh Song Sparrow Races

	M. m. pusillula	*M. m. samuelis*	*M. m. maxillaris*
Tidal Salt Marsh	Optimum habitat for all life needs provided the marsh has the characteristics detailed in text.	Used for all life needs, with conditions as for *pusillula*. The "magnificent Petaluma Marsh" cited as a stronghold of this form (Marshall and Dedrick 1994).	
Tidal Brackish Marsh	May be used for nesting*.	May have limited use for nesting.	Occupies marsh with often tall to very tall *Scirpus acutus*, shorter *S. robustus*, and local areas of *Salicornia* and *Grindelia*.
Seasonal Wetlands	Used at least for foraging and some singing, provided the wetlands have some of the elements of a salt marsh and adjacent mud for foraging.	Presumably some limited use similar to *pusillula*.	Sometimes found in the diked/ managed marsh of the Suisun complex, but in much lower numbers and with no information on the success of any breeding that may take place there.
Salt Ponds: dikes or levees	Areas adjacent to tidal marshes used for some foraging, or locally even for singing, (hence nesting?) where riprap and herb or shrub vegetation are mixed.	Presumably some limited use similar to *pusillula*.	
Intertidal Mudflats	The upper fringe of open mudflats used for foraging only, where adjacent to any other habitats that support more permanent occupancy.	Presumably some limited use similar to *pusillula*.	
Adjacent Uplands (mixed grass and tall forbs or shrubs)	Used provided they are adjacent to salt marsh or channels. Some nesting may occur in the upland area.	Presumably some limited use similar to *pusillula*.	

* The presence of 17 territories of *M. m. pusillula* in a 14.7 acre plot of tidal salt to brackish marsh (*Spartina foliosa, Salicornia virginica, Scirpus robustus, Frankenia, Distichlis*) NNW of Alviso (Anderson and Jennings 1981) with two nests found in *S. robustus* is the best indication of breeding by this subspecies in brackish tidal marsh.

of this habitat as well. For this work, I measured on 1977-84 aerial photographs (courtesy H. T. Harvey Associates) every habitat block or portion of block that could be classified by close inspection (using some magnification) as of "high," "medium," or "poor" quality for this subspecies. Areas of high quality were those containing tidal marsh with numerous small channels and complex vegetation structure. Areas of medium quality were those with fewer channels or small parcels remote from major parcels. Poor quality was assigned to those tidal marsh areas that did not have the features indicated for high or medium quality. I then considered the position of each habitat block within the landscape and rated each block in overall quality categories of A, A-, A/B, B, B-, B/C, and C quality categories (with a few even of D level). I then summed the total acreage in the highest three categories (A through A/B) and the next three highest categories (B through B/C), and got 3,989 acres and 2,511 acres, respectively. Together these total 6,500 acres, compared to Dedrick's 6,678 total. The acreages of the eight largest single blocks rated as A, A-, or A/B were:

- Dumbarton Marsh (incl. adjacent "Aqueduct Marsh") – 836.9 acres[2]
- Greco Island (Redwood City) – 740.4 acres
- Outer Bair Island (incl. 474.9 ac. reopened to tide) – 603.5 acres
- Mowry Slough mouth to Newark Slough Mouth – 326.1 acres
- Mundy Marsh (Palo Alto) & Faber Tract to Cooley Landing – 316.2 acres
- Whale's Tail Marsh (N&S of Alvarado Channel, Hayward) – 271.1 acres
- Corkscrew Slough (in several segments) – 200.4 acres
- "Ideal Marsh" (Ideal Basic Industries, west of Coyote Hills) – 128.3 acres

[2] Marshall and Dedrick (1994) give the current size of the Dumbarton Marsh as 906.1 acres, but from their text it appears they included all of the marsh belts along Newark Slough up to its head, whereas I kept them separate above the first points where diked salt ponds restrict the marsh to belts along the sloping slough banks.

These blocks are all separated from other sizeable habitat blocks by distances or channels wide enough that they probably constitute a deterrent to free dispersal by the sedentary song sparrows, even though the full-grown birds would have the capability of flying the distance involved. These larger blocks can be grouped with intervening smaller ones to obtain a more geographic comparison. When this is done, the "West Bay" optimum of Bair and Greco islands south through Palo Alto has a total of 1,544.3 acres of "good quality" tidal marsh, while the nearly contiguous marshes in the Dumbarton Point-Newark Slough to Mowry Slough and south to outermost Coyote Creek (where still not very brackish) has 1,719.7 acres.

Using Johnston's (1956b) published population density figures for *samuelis* (1.11 territories per acre), Marshall and Dedrick (1994) estimated the total *pusillula* population to be 7,412 pairs – a little over 10% of that preceding the diking and/or filling of the tidal marshes. Johnston's density figures assumed no song sparrows in those often rather large parts of a tidal marsh more than 10 meters or so distant from a channel. Additional fieldwork is yet to be done to check the actual species population densities at the locations which I quality-rated in my study; until such quantitative checks are completed, no better overall population estimate for *pusillula* than those arrived at by Marshall and Dedrick (1994) can be derived.

M. m. samuelis – Marshall and Dedrick (1994) gave the results of planimeter measurements on the Nichols and Wright (1971) map of historic tidal marshes within the range of this subspecies as 63,690 acres, as well as Dedrick's (1993)1992 measurement of the tidal marshes remaining – 14,060 acres. At 22.1% of the original, this is the best record of marsh retention among the three salt marsh song sparrow ranges, despite the fact that many blocks are narrow and/or isolated about the shores of San Pablo Bay. These authors reported examples of locations where birds of this subspecies were found and some captured in a 1986 survey, also noting that some "verdant marsh" [but diked] areas (e.g., on Tubbs Island) lacked them. Nor were any found in the 2,416-acre bayfront marsh between Sears Point and Mare Island, although Marshall's notes from 1947 indicated they were "abundant" there at that time. Nine birds were caught in November 1986 at Dutchman's Slough off the Napa River, where they used *Baccharis* bushes along the levee (as well as the tidal marsh). By far the largest remaining block of marsh, with an estimated population of 3,548 pairs of bird of this subspecies, is the "magnificent Petaluma Marsh" of 3,196 acres. This is nearly 23% of the admittedly optimistic total of 15,607 pairs estimated by these same authors for the subspecies throughout its estimated 22 square mile (14,080 acre) range.

By rough approximation on 1:24,000 topographic maps of the area, and using Marshall and Dedrick's (1994) figure 3(b) map of present tidal marshlands as a guide, acreages of the next 10 largest blocks are:

- San Pablo Bayfront (Sonoma Creek-Mare Island) – 3,500 acres (expanded over the 1950s topographic map)
- Southwest San Pablo Bayfront – 732 acres
- Coon Island-Fly Bay, 610 acres
- Fagan-Steamboat Slough-Bull's Island – 570 acres (or 112 less if Bull's Island is still diked as shown in 1950s map)
- American Canyon Creek-mouth to Sears Point Road – 550 acres
- Mare Island Bayfront – 400 acres (expanded since 1950s)
- Petaluma River below the large marsh – 400 acres
- Sears Point to lower Tubbs Island – 340 acres
- Wildcat Creek-mouth vicinity – 212 acres
- San Pablo Creek-mouth vicinity – 150 acres
- Muzzi Marsh and nearly contiguous tidal marshes along Corte Madera Creek – 150 acres (approximate)

Most of the blocks from southwest San Pablo Bay (Gallinas Creek vicinity) north to the big marsh near Petaluma and east to Mare Island are connected by at least a narrow bay- or slough-front marsh. Except for the American Canyon to Sears Point Road block, there are also fairly good dispersal corridors along the sloughs from the Napa River to the Petaluma River, although the slough-bank marshes in some cases may be too narrow to be optimum breeding habitat. The smaller blocks on the Contra Costa County shore and in Marin County from San Rafael to Richardson Bay are mostly too isolated for much dispersal among them, except possibly by that small fraction of young that go farther than the limits of Johnston's 1950s study area (the Wildcat Creek-mouth marsh).

An area of 80 ha in the central part of the Petaluma Marsh was surveyed intensively for song sparrows (Collins and Resh 1985). In this study, the vegetation was sampled along transects perpendicular to channels, and the marsh variations grouped into four habitat-types for analysis of the song sparrow data (sloughs, natural channels, mosquito-control ditches, and areas 10 m or more from any channel or ditch). The sparrow's territories were mapped by following the birds and the polygon of each male's mapped song-posts measured. Seven replicate plots in each habitat-type other than the areas beyond 10 m from a waterway (which were found to have no sparrows) were thus surveyed.

In general, territory placement and sizes along natural channels were found by Collins and Resh (1985) to be very similar to that reported by Johnston (1956b), but the plots along the constructed ditches had fewer and larger territories. Collins and Resh (1985) attributed this difference to a lower level of food and nesting-site (and predator-avoidance) resources than was present along the sinuous natural channels with their much greater vegetation diversity. The density of the *samuelis* sparrows was also checked in the non-breeding season during the dispersal phase of the young, thus reflecting the relative attractiveness of each habitat-type. Even then, the natural channel and slough-bank areas were occupied by from 1.5 to three times the number of birds as were found near the ditches. Collins and Resh (1985) concluded "ditches are not preferred habitat for the salt marsh song sparrow, primarily because ditches support shorter and spatially less diverse vegetation than apparently occurs along sloughs and natural channels. However, ditches do provide additional habitat that has increased the carrying capacity of Petaluma Marsh for salt marsh song sparrows…" [because the ditches are better than having no small channels at all]. The amount of marsh along tidal waterways [of any sort] was increased by 300% by such ditches and thus "ditching has added more than two thousand salt marsh sparrow territories to the Petaluma Marsh" (Collins and Resh 1985)

M. m. maxillaris – In their petition to list the Suisun song sparrow as endangered, Marshall and Mewaldt (1988) estimated the 1850s extent of tidal marshes within the range of this subspecies, plus those that developed as a result of sedimentation from placer mining at 66,618 to 73,712 acres. Such marshes, they also estimated, would have supported 69,949 to 77,398 pairs of these birds. These authors also cited a 90.4% reduction in area of such marshes, the total areas they had planimetered being 6,762 acres in 1986, which they estimated then supported about 5,666 pairs. Sizes and estimated populations were given for 10 different blocks of such marsh, and the distinctiveness in morphology and ecology of the taxon is summarized. Sites where previous investigators had conducted special studies or censuses were mapped and their results summarized. The petition included a map showing sectors of the Benicia Christmas Bird Count circle that included any tidal and adjacent marshes, and a graph showing the number of song sparrows (probably most, though not all of this subspecies) recorded in those sectors in the years 1977 through 1986 (compiled by Robin Leong). Year-to-year numbers varied considerably as census effort and methods of access varied. Thus they "do not reflect population changes but they show that the birds were constantly found over the years in optimum habitats" (Marshall and Mewaldt 1988). Michael Rippey's measurements of seeds available to the salt marsh sparrows of San Pablo Bay-Napa River marshes and the Suisun Marsh area were also cited: the largest common seed of Suisun being that of alkali bulrush (*Scirpus robustus*) at 5/32 inch, which is notably larger than seeds of *Distichlis*, *Grindelia*, and *Salicornia* – a food resource feature that may help to explain the advantage for birds of this subspecies in having a swollen bill shape.

A California Department of Fish and Game staff report (Larsen 1989), forwarded to the Commission with the Marshall-Mewaldt petition, cited a number of additional pertinent studies and supported most of the petition's findings, but the petition was rejected by the Commission. Nevertheless, these two reports in combination present an amount of detail for this subspecies not yet attained for the other two salt marsh races, for the details of the ecology of *samuelis* as learned by Johnston (1956a,b) were included as applicable to *maxillaris* as well. Under "Essential Habitat," Larsen (1989) listed many details of the description by Marshall (1948a) for this subspecies. She summarized: "Suisun song sparrows use the tallest *S. acutus* in the centers of patches for song and calling perches, find concealment in the piles of dead stems, and forage on the bare surface of the mud between the stems and along the slough margins at low tide. They do not forage between stems that are only 2.5 to five centimeters (one to two inches) apart, but only forage in areas with stems that are 10 to 15 centimeters (four to six inches) apart. … Thus they are limited to the area covered by tides, where flow is unimpeded by dikes, levees or channels."

Larsen (1989) described marginal use of upland plants along levees by the sparrows, "but their territorial headquarters are always at the slough margins." Their avoidance of diked marsh areas with *Salicornia* and *Grindelia* with no or impeded tidal flow was mentioned, although a few birds were found in such an area, on the eastern side of Cordelia Slough, that drained well through a culvert. [As noted above for *pusillula*, small populations of that subspecies also use such areas.]

Marshall and Dedrick (1994) reported a more recent measuring of the tidal marsh areas of the Suisun to Southhampton Bay marshes, and the surveys of locations where there were still birds of this subspecies found in or near those marshes, its historic range. Of the 64,255 acres of historic tidal marsh, 8,586 acres (13.4%) remained as of 1992, with a total estimated population of 9,530 pairs. Marshall and Dedrick (1994) emphasized the prime habitat as being the fully intertidal brackish marsh, although they did find in a 1990 survey (in just parts of the North Suisun area) some 79 pairs (out of 3,803 total) occupying "non-tidal territories," 30 of them near Roaring River. As mentioned above, Marshall (1948a) found a few of these in territories centered on a "hedge" in dry grass by a ditch with water only at the two ends.

Using sophisticated Geographic Information System (GIS) software, Scollon (1993) carried out the most thorough analysis of the remaining habitat for this subspecies. This study evaluated pertinent data for the tidal marshes, such as block size, distance from neighboring blocks, and availability of suitable habitat for dispersal between blocks, and rated the blocks and to some extent, the corridors, as to numbers of Suisun song sparrows they could support. The rating was based on the pairs-per-acre ranges for five "strata" of habitat quality as given in an unpublished 1992 document by Joshua Collins – the field data in support of which I have not seen. Scollon himself apparently did no field work with the sparrows, but integrated the spatial aspects of the findings of others who have worked with song sparrows in the range of *maxillaris*. For example, in addition to using Collins' "strata" evaluations, the dispersal distances found in one local population by Johnston in the 1950s [of *samuelis*, and cited above], plus a single comment by Larsen (1989) that these birds [*maxillaris*] "will generally not travel more than 50 meters over areas lacking protective cover, such as open water", were the sole basis for his ratings of the suitability of dispersal corridors. Nevertheless, Scollon's (1993) maps of the various blocks of habitats, each with its rating indicated by type of hatching, and the subsequent "linking" of habitat patches [or, alternatively, not linking them] based on the dispersal capabilities as applied to the maps, result in a set of "population patches" for the subspecies. This is the broadest scale approach to a population analysis of any of the tidal marsh subspecies yet performed. Scollon (1993) presented histograms of all the population patches by area (<30, 30-399, and 400-1200 acres) and by four ranges of population size. However, these were all apparently based on the data from quick surveys of singing birds, or possibly in part on data from Johnston's and Collins' separate reports from *samuelis* populations. What is really needed, of course, is to carry out a number of field checks with actual censuses of *maxillaris* population blocks to see whether the basic assumptions underlying all these "What if?" manipulations in the GIS system are borne out. Such field checks should be done with blocks of several different sizes and several different degrees of isolation.

Every ecologically oriented investigation of this subspecies has indicated that its prime habitat is tall brackish marsh with full tidal flows. However, the rating system of habitat strata cited (from Collins) by Scollon indicates considerable difference of populations to be expected even within the intertidal brackish category. In addition, although several authors have stressed that birds of this subspecies "avoid" or "do not use" diked marshlands of various sorts, Larsen (1989), Marshall and Dedrick (1994), and Scollon (1993) all cite instances where smaller populations or limited numbers of *maxillaris* sparrows were indeed using such habitat. It is possible that most or all of such birds in diked (and therefore marginal?) habitat are those excluded by intraspecific competitors already on territory within more optimum habitat, and that their attempts to breed in the marginal situations are doomed to failure or sharply reduced productivity. Field studies are needed to address this critical ecological question, and to determine whether diked marsh could be managed in such a way

as to provide good dispersal corridors, even if not breeding habitat. In the meantime, there is undoubtedly optimum value in fully intertidal brackish marsh with tall *Scirpus* vegetation along channels or sloughs with mud banks not too steep for low-tide foraging, and not too far from overhanging vegetation for protection from predators.

Recommendations for Conservation and Management

This section provides suggested goals for wetlands occurring in the range of each of the three subspecies of salt marsh song sparrow. These goals would be highly beneficial to population success of the target subspecies, while not overly detrimental to the populations of other important wetlands species in these same areas. The proposed goals are listed in order of priority for each subspecies/range.

Range of *M. m. pusillula* (South to Central San Francisco Bay) –

1. Keep inviolate all bayward and slough boundaries of the existing large blocks of intertidal marsh. In the East Bay, this should include Dumbarton Marsh and its connecting "Aqueduct" and Newark Slough marshes, the Mowry Slough marsh and bayside marsh west and south of the slough-mouth, the "Ideal Marsh" (bayfront west of Coyote Hills), and "Whale's Tail Marsh" (south and north of the mouth of Alvarado Channel). In the West Bay, this should include Outer Bair Island plus Corkscrew Slough; Greco Island; and north and south of Cooley Landing through Palo Alto Baylands marshes (nearly contiguous now). In the far-South Bay, this should include Triangle Marsh (NNW of Alviso), Albrae Slough and nearby shores of Coyote "Creek," outer parts of Alviso and Guadalupe sloughs, Stevens Creek, etc. (all somewhat brackish but occupied). Other parts closer to the major sewage effluent outfall in Artesian Slough east of Alviso are of too low salinity to support vegetation that is usually occupied by this subspecies, as are the parts of Coyote Creek and Mud Slough near Newby Island at present.

One recently proposed change in land use across the largest block (Dumbarton Marsh) is to upgrade the railroad right-of-way there as a part of a new high-speed rail route from the Central Valley (and Los Angeles) to San Francisco. The fill along the unused tracks has been, for over 20 years, both a high-tide refugium for sparrows, rails, etc., and an avenue for access to the marsh by red foxes and feral house cats – although this avenue has been interrupted to the west and east in recent years by keeping "open" the bridges over the Dumbarton Strait and Newark Slough.

2. Expand any of the areas listed under the first priority above, especially in directions that would either: (a) provide habitat linkage for breeding populations of *pusillula* in locations between any of these areas, or at least good habitat for dispersal between populations in the event any local population suffers a disastrous decline; or (b) enhances the overall quality of habitat available within or at the edge of the habitat block. Examples of the latter might be to provide additional high-tide refugia where not now adequate, as on Greco Island (birds that use the Pacific Gas and Electric boardwalk are very vulnerable to predators), along various sloughs where the existing marsh is only in the form of a strip between the mudflat and open salt pond levee, or next to diked or industrial development.

   Also in this priority should be the enhancement of habitat values for these birds in existing or planned smaller blocks. Such areas would include: Burlingame Cove, Belmont Slough and nearby Bird Island, inner Steinberger Slough, Ravenswood Slough and shoreline through the newly acquired gun club marsh near Dumbarton Bridge, La Riviere Marsh, and Mayhews Landing Tract of the National Wildlife Refuge, "Pond 3" marsh north of new Alameda Creek, Mt. Eden Creek-Baumberg Tract -Alvarado Channel in Hayward, tidal lagoons in both south and north parts of Hayward Regional Shoreline (plus possibly the adjacent H.A.R.D. marsh), newly tidal south part of San Leandro shore area, Arrowhead Marsh and other smaller marsh bits in the vicinity of San Leandro Bay and Oakland Airport, Emeryville Crescent Marsh, Albany Cove and Hoffman Marsh (in se. Richmond) – the last being very close to the original northernmost point where this subspecies was found.

3. As the opportunities arise, establish new habitat for this subspecies in areas where it does not now exist. This effort should target areas that would add marsh corridors or patches along likely dispersal routes between major blocks of existing good to optimum habitat. Even small blocks would be worthwhile if spaced relatively closely in such areas. Major gaps in habitat acceptable to this form currently occur from the Bay Bridge through the Oakland Estuary/Alameda (except the far eastern part of the south shore), salt pond levees not bordered by marsh though much of Hayward and Fremont, and the shoreline near developed areas through Foster City and San Mateo. It seems unlikely much opportunity will arise to create tidal marshes north of San Francisco Airport, but a 20-acre "marsh" (some to be open tidal flat) is a part of the Golden Gate National Reserve Area Plan for Crissy Field in the Presidio [implementation began in late 1999]. If birds of *pusillula* parentage are to reach it, they would probably have to be introduced there, at what was likely the northwestern-most limit of the range of this subspecies.

4. Restore, to the extent possible, a "natural" range of salt marsh habitats in the location of the operating salt evaporators or diked former salt ponds (e.g., on Bair Island), should any of these areas become available. This would not only greatly benefit the song sparrows of this subspecies, but also the clapper rail, salt marsh harvest mouse, and several other species. The slow development of marsh vegetation on the "scraped" parts of the former salt ponds in the Hayward Regional Shoreline tidal lagoons, and the silting of a number of the too-straight (engineered) channels excavated there, should be compared with the rapid development of salt marsh vegetation on reopened parts of Bair Island when choosing methods for restoration of the desired habitat.

Range of *M. m. samuelis* (North San Francisco Bay through San Pablo Bay) –

1. Keep the present large blocks of high quality habitat in that condition. This includes not ditching the parts that already have adequate small channels with the diverse vegetation the sparrows prefer. The "keeping" also applies to the marsh corridors or small blocks that are spaced to provide dispersal opportunities among the larger blocks.

2. Restore sufficient intervening tidal marsh blocks or strips where there are currently the longest gaps in such. For example, suitable tidal marsh should be restored along the eastern side of the lower Napa River, and wherever possible along the entire Contra Costa County shore from Selby to San Pablo Point (the probable southeastern limit of the original range), as well as from San Rafael through San Quentin Cove. Topography prevents any suitable marsh corridor to Richardson Bay, which has some marsh remaining, but none of these sparrows in it according to Marshall (1948a,b).

3. Expand the tidal marsh area by opening to tide action some of the now disused salt evaporator ponds in the area between Napa River and Sonoma Creek. Since all or most of these ponds are now owned by the State, a truly major addition to the habitat for *samuelis* song sparrows (as well as clapper rails and other tidal marsh inhabitants) could be realized. Since this area adjoins an existing brackish marsh at Fly Bay and fronts on grassy uplands to the north (as does the existing tidal marsh east of the Napa River near Bull's Island), other species requiring the transitional sort of habitat, such as savannah sparrow and black rail, would also be benefited. This tidal marsh to

upland zone is now all but absent in San Francisco Bay proper, so the goals for San Pablo Bay should certainly include a major provision to preserve and extend it.

Range of *M. m. maxillaris* (Suisun Bay marshes and vicinity, west through Southhampton Bay) –

1. Preserve the acreage and quality of existing habitat blocks used by all significant numbers of birds. To preserve quality, prevent further salinity intrusion into the Suisun marsh areas caused by greater diversions of freshwater flow in or above the Delta. With increased salinity, the tall brackish marsh to which this race is adapted would likely be replaced by shorter, more salt-tolerant vegetation, more like that in the range of *samuelis*. Birds of that race would, however, be unlikely to disperse eastward into the Suisun area because of lack of habitat along the Carquinez Strait.

Scollon (1993) modeled two levels of salinity intrusion, based in turn on salinity levels for May 1965 and February 1971, as mapped by Rumboltz (1979). Rumboltz' (1979) 1971map shows a level of 2,500 micromohos along a line extending across the middle of Honker Bay, and also Joice Island. According to Scollon (1993), this is nearly equivalent to the salinity standard of 2 ppt recommended by the San Francisco Estuary Project [for the continued health of the Suisun Marsh?]. At that salinity level, the vegetation, and hence the sparrows, of the marshes along the southern side of Suisun and Honker bays (totaling approximately 1,900 acres) have already suffered heightened salinity impact. However, there is insufficient recent data on *maxillaris* sparrow populations in this area with which to test this hypothesis. If that level of salinity intrusion holds, Scollon's model (case A) predicts that the major populations in the northern part of the Suisun Marsh complex would escape severe impacts. These include the population in the largest block of marsh (1,394 acres) in the Rush Ranch-First Mallard Branch area, as well as that in Hill Slough and vicinity (468 acres). In spring 1990, Marshall found 159 pairs of *maxillaris* in the western 154 acres of the former block and 58 pairs in 130 acres in the latter one (Marshall and Dedrick 1994).

If, however, salt intrusion above the threshold level of major vegetation change extends to east of Chipps Island and includes most of Monetzuma Slough (Scollon's 1993 case B), there would be a major reduction of *maxillaris* populations in these last strongholds of the subspecies, and in all other smaller blocks in the northern Suisun Marsh. Without knowing whether Marshall's 1990 censuses were conducted in average quality habitat within the blocks of marsh he sampled, and

without census data from other blocks, no firm prediction can be made as to the future survival of this critically restricted form. It seems quite possible, however, that this one factor alone could eliminate it.

2. Improve the contiguity of tidal marsh blocks throughout the Suisun complex. Although still retaining a higher percentage of its original extent of such marsh than the range of *pusillula*, the separation of major blocks is more widespread. On the southern side of Suisun Bay, this is due primarily to industrial and small harbor developments along the shore, but also in some locations to old filling alone. North of eastern Suisun Bay and Honker Bay, and particularly throughout the area from near Benicia and Cordelia east to Nurse Slough and Denverton, the whole wetland area is nearly all behind dikes and managed. Most impediments to dispersal of the sparrows between larger blocks of tidal marsh are interruptions in the narrow bands of tidal marsh along the numerous sloughs. Scollon (1993) assumed that the birds would tend to spread more toward their optimum lower salinity, with increasingly saline conditions in the western part of the Bay, and his recommendations of key areas to provide the best routes for such shift of range are:

   • Along the shoreline of Joice Island (both sides) to "provide a critical link between populations along the shoreline of Grizzly Bay and those in the northern reaches of Suisun Marsh;"

   • Along the northern shore of Honker Bay and southern shore of Suisun Bay, to link populations west and east; and

   • Along the eastern reach of Montezuma Slough, to connect the northern populations with those in the eastern Suisun Bay area. Scollon (1993) indicated that a 1991 proposal would have increased tidal marsh in this area, but it was apparently not accomplished, at least by the time of his writing.

3. Evaluate the management practices in the extensive gun club and wildlife agency lands throughout the western and northern parts of the range of *maxillaris*, with a focus on alternative types of vegetation control. Management practices should be sought that would provide corridors of brackish marsh across strategic areas that now act as barriers to these birds. At a minimum, provide reasonably continuous marsh-mud interfaces (even if freshwater) that might also provide for dispersal when it occurs during the late summer period. Such manipulations could be done in different locations (rotated) in different years. The area is noted for its provision of habitat for waterfowl. The recommendation made here is not intended to diminish that

value, and might even be found to enhance it as well as habitat for the sparrows.

References

American Ornithologists' Union (AOU). 1957. Checklist of North American Birds, fifth ed. Prep. by a Committee of the A.O.U.

Anderson, J.R. and V.R. Jennings. 1981. Diked coastal saltmarsh [Breeding Bird Census #211]. Amer. Birds 35: 102. [from the authors' description, the 14.7 acre plot they studied must have been a part of "Triangle Marsh", which is diked off from the adjacent salt ponds but not from the Bay or Coyote Creek.]

Basham, M.P. and L.R. Mewaldt. 1987. Salt water tolerance and the distribution of South San Francisco Bay song sparrows. Condor 89: 697-709.

Cogswell, H.L. 1953. Dumbarton Point salt marshes. The Gull 35: 45-46.

_____. 1956. Maps of the new San Francisco Bay sanctuaries. The Gull 38: 42-45.

Collins, J.N. and V.H. Resh. 1985. Utilization of natural and man-made habitat by the salt marsh song sparrow, *Melospiza melodia samuelis* (Baird). Calif. Fish and Game 71: 40-52.

Dedrick, K.G. 1993. Atlas of present tidal marshland, San Francisco Bay, California. *In*: O.T. Magoon et al. (eds). Proc. Eighth Sympos. Coastal and Ocean Mgmt. (Coastal Zone-93), Amer. Soc. of Civil Engineers, New York, NY. pp.2451-2463. [not seen, but cited by Marshall and Dedrick (1994) and Scollon (1993).]

Johnston, R.F. 1952. *Salicornia-Spartina* salt marsh. No.16 *In*: Sixteenth Breeding Birds Census. Aud. Field Notes 6: 316-317.

_____. 1954. Variation in breeding season and clutch size in song sparrows of the Pacific Coast. Condor 56: 268-273.

_____. 1956a. Population structure in salt marsh song sparrows. Part I. Environment and Annual Cycle. Condor 58: 24-44.

_____. 1956b. Population structure in salt marsh song sparrows. Part II: Density, age structure, and maintenance. Condor 58: 254-272.

_____. 1968. Song sparrow, San Francisco Bay marsh subspecies. *In*: O.L. Austin, Jr. (ed). A.C. Bent and collaborators. Life histories of North American Cardinals...sparrows and Allies. U.S. Natl. Mus. Bull. 237(3): 1547-53.

Larsen, C.J. 1989. A Status review of the Suisun song sparrow (*Melospiza melodia maxillaris*) in California. Report to the Fish and Game Commission, from Wildl. Mngmt. Div., Nongame Bird and Mammal Sec., Dept. Candidate Species Status Report 89-6.

Marshall, J.T. 1948a. Ecologic races of song sparrows in the San Francisco Bay region. Part I. Habitat and abundance. Condor 50: 193-215.

_____. 1948b. Ecologic races of song sparrows in the San Francisco Bay region. Part II. Geographic variation. Condor 50: 233-256.

Marshall, J.T. and K.G. Dedrick. 1994. Endemic song sparrows and yellowthroats of San Francisco Bay. Studies in Avian Biol. 15: 316-327. [publ. by Cooper Ornithological Soc.]

Marshall, J.T. and L.R. Mewaldt. 1988. [Petition to list the Suisun song sparrow as Endangered]. Presented through Coyote Creek Riparian Station to the Ca. Dept. Fish and Game.

Nice, M.M. 1937. Studies in the life history of the song sparrow. I. A population study of the song sparrow. Trans. Linn. Soc. N.Y. 246pp.

_____. 1943. Studies in the life history of the song sparrow. II. The behavior of the song sparrow and other passerines. Trans. Linn. Soc. N.Y. 328pp.

Nichols, D.R. and N.A. Wright. 1971. Preliminary map of historic margins of marshland, San Francisco Bay, California. U.S. Geological Survey, Open File Map.

Nolan, V. Jr. 1968. Eastern song sparrow. *In*: O.L. Austin, Jr. (ed). A.C. Bent and collaborators. Life histories of North American Cardinals...sparrows and Allies. U.S. Natl. Mus. Bull. 237(3): 1492-1512.

Rumboltx, M.C. 1979. Impact of Delta outflow upon salinity and waterfowl in the Suisun Marsh. U.S. Bur. Reclamation. [Map and citation in Scollon 1993.]

Scollon, D.B. 1993. Spatial analysis of the tidal marsh habitat of the Suisun song sparrow. M.A. Thesis, San Francisco State Univ. 145pp.

Sibley, C.G. 1955. The responses of salt-marsh birds to extremely high tides. Condor 57: 242-3.

Walton, B.J. 1975. The status of the salt marsh song sparrows of the San Francisco Bay system, 1974-1975. M.A. Thesis, San Jose State Univ., Avian Biol. Lab. 37pp.+ appendices.

Response of Birds to Managed Water Levels at Charleston Slough – A Case Study

William G. Bousman

Introduction

Charleston Slough is a former tidal estuary at the boundary of Palo Alto and Mountain View. A dike was placed across the outer slough in the 1920s, but a 60-inch pipe in that dike allowed tidal exchange up through the early 1970s, and a healthy salt marsh community of about 40 to 60 acres existed under the muted tidal regime of that period. In the mid-1970s, the 60-inch pipe was replaced with a 48-inch pipe placed higher in the dike, with the result that the tidal flow became highly muted (or non-existent), and the mean water level in the slough increased sufficiently that the salt marsh was inundated and lost.

Based on the destruction of the salt marsh in Charleston Slough, the San Francisco Bay Conservation and Development Commission (BCDC) prepared a Cease and Desist Order for Leslie Salt Company (now Cargill Salt). The company then transferred ownership to Mountain View, leaving that city to comply with the BCDC requirements. These requirements included the development of a new outlet structure in the outer dike that would provide a tidal fluctuation in the slough of 1.0 feet. At this time, the Santa Clara Valley Audubon Society (SCVAS) started a series of weekly censuses of the slough, and these continued through 1995, although the frequency of the censuses was reduced to every two weeks in the early 1980s.

The present case study is based upon a comparison of census data from the fall periods of 1980 and

Les Chibana

1981. This comparison shows species composition and abundance changes that resulted from managed changes of water levels in Charleston Slough.

Methods

In the period from October 1980 through the end of 1981, Charleston Slough was censused on a weekly basis by four to five volunteers. Volunteers were given a one-week window in which to perform their censuses, but otherwise were allowed to select both the day of the census and the time of day. No attempt was made to census the birds in relationship to the tidal cycle. The census was made either on foot or by car using the public levee between Charleston Slough and the Palo Alto Flood Control Basin. Birds were censused within or above the slough to the centerlines of surrounding levees. As essentially all portions of the 109-acre slough were visible from the public levee, the census recorded all birds present. Each census required about two hours. Observers were encouraged to count certain species as groups because of identification difficulties. These groups included greater and lesser scaup and short-billed and long-billed dowitchers. In some censuses, when large numbers of gulls were using the private levees for roosting, not all were identified to species.

Results

Census data show the lowest number of birds and species to occur in the summer, with the greatest number observed during fall, winter, and spring. The initial two years of the census were a time of substantial transition as construction for the new outlet structure was completed in February 1981, substantially changing the water levels in the slough. Prior to the removal of the cofferdam around the outlet structure, the water level was approximately 4.6 feet above Mean Lower Low Water (MLLW) and the entire slough was inundated. With the removal of the cofferdam, the water level dropped by approximately 1.8 feet, and 50 to 60 acres of mudflats were exposed. Very little tidal flow occurred in the slough because of siltation outside of the outer levee.

The water level in the slough started to increase in the winter of 1981-82, and this increase continued in later years so that as of 1996, the slough is largely inundated once again.

A comparison of the census data collected in October and November of 1980 (n=7) and October and November of 1981 (n=6) are shown here as representative of two different water regimes. The 1980 data are for the slough at its maximum water level, with essentially no exposure of mudflats. The 1981 data are for the slough at its minimum water level, with 60-80 acres of mudflats. The census data for the two periods are com-

Other Birds

| Species | October-November | | | |
| | 1980 (n=7) | | 1981 (n=6) | |
	Birds/Cen	Rank	Birds/Cen	Rank
Pied-billed grebe	45.9	10	17.8	18
American white pelican	78.8	7	6.3	20
Double-crested cormorant	8.3	17	0.3	34
Great egret	1.5	28	2.5	30
Snowy egret	5.7	18	2.8	28
Mallard	0.7	30	3.2	26
Northern pintail	224.0	3	24.8	16
Northern shoveler	80.6	6	7.5	19
Gadwall	18.6	15	1.7	31
American wigeon	111.0	4	0.0	35
Canvasback	0.1	32	3.0	27
Bufflehead	10.9	16	0.3	33
Scaup spp.	2.4	26	1.0	32
Ruddy duck	1,221.0	1	103.0	6
American coot	1,066.0	2	26.0	14
Black-billed plover	2.0	27	75.2	8
American avocet	63.3	8	267.7	4
Greater yellowlegs	4.3	20	5.3	22
Willet	2.7	25	25.2	15
Marbled godwit	3.3	23	23.5	17
Western sandpiper	0.0	35	53.8	9
Least sandpiper	3.4	22	48.5	11
Dunlin	0.4	31	53.2	10
Dowitcher spp.	25.7	12	400.0	2
Ring-billed gull	19.4	14	165.0	5
California gull	28.6	11	1,720.0	1
Herring gull	57.9	9	343.0	3
Western gull	99.6	5	41.3	13
Glaucous-winged gull	3.3	24	0.0	36
Forster's tern	21.2	13	75.5	7
European starling	0.1	33	2.8	29
Savannah sparrow	5.2	19	5.8	21
White-crowned sparrow	0.0	36	3.7	24
House finch	4.0	21	4.5	23
Total Birds	3,220.8		3,559.0	

Table 7.9 Census Data from 1980 and 1981 for Charleston Slough

Santa Clara Valley Audubon Society data.

1980 data were collected when the slough was at its maximum water level, with essentially no exposure of mudflats.

1981 data were collected when the slough was at its minimum water level, with 60-80 acres of mudflats.

pared in **Table 7.9** for the 36 species counted and, included with the mean number of birds within each period, is the rank of that species relative to the others censused. **Table 7.9** shows that 33 species were tallied in 1980 and 34 in 1981, while the mean species total for each census in 1980 was 3,221 birds and in 1981 was 3,559 birds.

The species list from **Table 7.9** was sorted by the rank obtained in 1980 and the fifteen most common species in that year are shown in **Table 7.10** in rank order. The species totals and ranks for 1981 are also included in this table, but not in rank order. The percent of the total number of birds for 1980 is shown in the

table as the final column and the cutoff at fifteen species is based on reaching 98% of the total number of birds recorded in all censuses.

The species list from **Table 7.9** was sorted by the rank obtained in 1981 and the eighteen most common species are included in **Table 7.11** by the 1981 rank order where, again, the inclusion of common species is based on reaching 98% of the total number of birds.

Discussion

The total number of birds counted in October and November of 1981 were approximately 10% greater than

Table 7.10 Fifteen Most Common Species Censused at Charleston Slough in 1980 – sorted by 1980 rank order

Santa Clara Valley Audubon Society data.

Data were collected when the slough was at its maximum water level, with essentially no exposure of mudflats.

| Species | October-November Birds/Census | | | | |
| | 1980 | | 1981 | | % 1980 |
	n=7	Rank	n=6	Rank	pop.
Ruddy duck	1,221.0	1	103.0	6	0.38
American coot	1,066.0	2	26.0	14	0.71
Northern pintail	224.0	3	24.8	16	0.78
American wigeon	111.0	4	0.0	35	0.81
Western gull	99.6	5	41.3	13	0.85
Northern shoveler	80.6	6	7.5	19	0.87
American white pelican	78.8	7	6.3	20	0.89
American avocet	63.3	8	267.7	4	0.91
Herring gull	57.9	9	343.0	3	0.93
Pied-billed grebe	45.9	10	17.8	18	0.95
California gull	28.6	11	1,720.0	1	0.96
Dowitcher spp.	25.7	12	400.0	2	0.96
Forster's tern	21.2	13	75.5	7	0.97
Ring-billed gull	19.4	14	165.0	5	0.98
Gadwall	18.6	15	1.7	31	0.98
Total Birds	3,161.6		2,856.6		

Table 7.11 Eighteen Most Common Species Censused at Charleston Slough in 1981 – sorted by 1981 rank order

Santa Clara Valley Audubon Society data.

Data were collected when the slough was at its minimum water level, with 60-80 acres of mudflats.

| Species | October-November Birds/Census | | | | |
| | 1980 | | 1981 | | % 1981 |
	n=7	Rank	n=6	Rank	pop
California gull	28.6	11	1,720.0	1	0.48
Dowitcher spp.	25.7	12	400.0	2	0.60
Herring gull	57.9	9	343.0	3	0.69
American avocet	63.3	8	267.7	4	0.77
Ring-billed gull	19.4	14	165.0	5	0.81
Ruddy duck	1,221.0	1	103.0	6	0.84
Forster's tern	21.2	13	75.5	7	0.86
Black-bellied plover	2.0	27	75.2	8	0.88
Western sandpiper	0.0	35	53.8	9	0.90
Dunlin	0.4	31	53.2	10	0.91
Least sandpiper	3.4	22	48.5	11	0.93
Black-necked stilt	0.9	29	41.5	12	0.94
Western gull	99.6	5	41.3	13	0.95
American coot	1,066.0	2	26.0	14	0.96
Willet	2.7	25	25.2	15	0.97
Northern pintail	224.0	3	24.8	16	0.97
Marbled godwit	3.3	23	23.5	17	0.98
Pied-billed grebe	45.9	10	17.8	18	0.98
Total Birds	2,885.3		3,505.0		

observed in 1980. Although the variance of the data has not been examined, a 10% change in abundance is unlikely to be significant. Similarly, the number of species comprising 98% of the entire bird population increased from 15 to 18 between 1980 to 1981 and, again, changes of this size are not believed to be significant. Thus abundance and diversity, as measured here, did not change substantially between the two different managed water regimes.

The changes that did occur between 1980 and 1981, however, were in species composition. In 1980 just five species comprised 81% of the population: ruddy duck, American coot, northern pintail, American wigeon, and western gull. The first four of these are species that clearly benefit from ponding and inundation. In 1981 censuses, however, these five species represented only 5% of the total population. Similarly, in 1981, a different five species comprised 81% of the population: California gull, dowitcher species, herring gull, American avocet, and ring-billed gull. The gull species appear to have responded to the extensive mudflats as areas secure for loafing, while the two shorebirds species used the slough for foraging, as well as resting. These five species that were most common under the high water regime accounted for only 6% of the local population in the prior year's census data.

The first point from this case study is that the two managed regimes used for this 109-acre former slough resulted in equal numbers of birds and species diversity. The water level between the two years was very different. In 1980, the water level was sufficiently high to inundate the entire slough such that no mudflats were available for foraging or secure roosts. In 1981, the water level had been lowered such that about half the slough's area was available as mudflat for foraging or roosting. The species composition changed drastically between the two managed water levels – but these sort of changes are not quantified by simple ecological measures, such as total abundance (unchanged) or species diversity (unchanged).

A second point to consider is that the potential of Charleston Slough to be productive in terms of species abundance and diversity under two water management regimes is related to its scale compared to the entire estuarine system. Its size, 109 acres, is small compared to the overall South Bay system, and the variety and number of birds that can opportunistically take advantage of changes in such a small area are quite large. Although this case study probably applies to any similarly sized area within the estuarine system, it is not clear that it applies to areas that are substantially larger.

A third point, and one directly related to the first, is that if simple measures of ecological health such as abundance and diversity cannot be used to distinguish between two managed regimes, than what metrics can be used? As a community of individuals, we all may see and voice the need for some sort of balance in our management of estuarine systems. In particular, when we obtain stewardship responsibilities for a new component of the system, we all see the wisdom of studying this component to allow us to make wise and informed decisions. However, in the end, as in this Charleston Slough example, there may be no sound or rational basis for selecting a "correct" management regime. In the absence of sound ecological principals to be used for management, how do we make our choices? Do we use community values? Do we allow some portion of the electorate a vote? Or do we rely upon leaders of the scientifically-informed community to govern our choices?

Epilogue

This case study is concluded by reporting the "final" solution for the management of Charleston Slough, which was achieved recently, twenty years after the original Cease and Desist Order. It was agreed that the former non-functional outlet structure would be replaced with multiple pipes with sufficient tidal capacity, so that with time, a new tidal prism would be established and the blocked outer channel would be opened through scouring. This construction was accomplished during the 1998 summer season. Although there is an increased tidal range in the slough under this new regime, it does not meet the original requirements. The next step will be to assist tidal scouring by removing some of the Bay mud outside the new outlet structure. There is no prediction, presently, as to when a functioning salt-water marsh is likely to be restored.

Les Chibana

Les Chibana

Other Birds

The Use of Salt Ponds by Some Selected Birds Other than Shorebirds and Waterfowl

Howard L. Cogswell

The term "salt ponds" is traditionally used to cover any or all of the saltwater impoundments around the San Francisco Bay that are used in the various evaporation stages leading to final crystallization in the salt company plant-sites (now only one company, Cargill Inc., Salt Division). A number of salt ponds have been taken out of such use by this company and the last other company to operate (Oliver Brothers of Hayward), but many of these remain mostly barren of vegetation. The accumulated salts in their bottoms make the rainwater ponded in them in the winter ecologically somewhat similar to regular evaporators even though the salinity changes over the year are probably greater than in any one pond in the ponds currently in use. I would recommend that all such inoperative saline areas be included in the salt pond habitat category by the Focus Team, as long as they are mostly barren of vegetation, even though they may be completely dry for half or more of the year. I also recommend that they be placed in the "diked seasonal wetlands" habitat category when there has been sufficient growth of vascular plants that birds and such mammals as voles and the salt marsh harvest mouse typical of such "marshes" can be expected to be present in significant number.

South Bay examples of places where such former salt ponds are still mostly barren are on parts of Bair Island, the southernmost and northwestern-most ponds of the sequence west of Alviso Slough (the northwest ponds are the "Knapp Tract," and part of the National Wildlife Refuge (NWR)), parts of the Hickory Tract just west of the head of Newark Slough, and parts of the Baumberg Tract in Hayward. Other parts of Bair Island, and the Hickory and Baumberg tracts have already succeeded to more seasonal marsh than salt pond characteristics. Presumably, the large area of former salt ponds between the lower Napa River and Sonoma Creek also have portions that would fit in each category as well.

As thus restricted, the majority of the salt pond system is heavily used by birds. A large percentage of that use depends on the shoreline of the ponds, as well as the water, and a special value is easily traced to islands and the remote or undisturbed parts of the dikes between the ponds. Such habitat aspects seem inseparable from the ponds themselves for many species, including some of those mentioned below (but especially, of course, the shorebirds – to be addressed by another focus team). For species that nest or roost on these dry land inclusions in the salt ponds, it is the isolated placement of such land within the surrounding water that makes it valuable. A tenth-acre island in a salt pond is far more valuable as bird habitat than an acre of barren ground in an upland situation! In addition, some "Other Birds," such as herons, often use the shoreline or shallower water adjacent to dikes and islands for foraging. Hence, this report in no way avoids consideration of the dry land parts of the system.

Salt Pond Operations

It is important in defining wetlands goals for salt ponds to understand the basics of operation of those ponds still used in the salt-extraction process. Details seem inappropriate here, except that: 1) the ponds are functionally connected into salinity gradient sequences as a result of systematic transfers of water among them; 2) each evaporator pond can thus be classified as a low, medium, or high-salinity pond, these categories having marked differences in forage value for birds; 3) some ponds are occasionally pumped nearly dry, and when this happens, their function in "isolation" from predators of roosts or, in the breeding season, of nests is sharply reduced; 4) the most highly saline ponds (crystallizers and the "pickle" ponds just before them in the sequence) have essentially no organisms suitable as food for birds, but in some locations still provide roosting protection; and 5) the "bittern ponds" (currently large ones at Newark and small ones at Redwood City) are filled with the brine remaining after sodium chloride crystallizes, and seem to provide essentially no wildlife value at all, but are a necessary part of the system since water quality restrictions now prohibit the disposal of that brine in the Bay.

Salt Pond Numbering Systems

Leslie Salt Company (which was bought by Cargill in the late 1980s) assigned numbers to each evaporator in the sequence of the water movement at each of their separate plants: Newark (plants 1 and 2), Mowry, Alviso, Redwood City, Baumberg (in west Hayward), and Napa. In several areas, additional ponds were added to the system at either the beginning or somewhere in the middle of the water-movement sequence, these ponds being distinguished by additional letters usually in suffix position. Except for the San Pablo Bay-Napa unit (sold to the State in the early 1990s), all these pond numbers continue in use by Cargill, even though the Alviso plant was closed long ago, and the Baumberg and Redwood City plants in 1972 (Redwood City being reopened a few years later). Water is no longer moved in sequence of the pond numbers, and old systems are combined with converging flows at several salinity levels.

Because duplicate numbers existed for many ponds in different areas, I came up with prefix letters making all the ponds in the NWR distinctively numbered. These are shown on the map in **Figure 7.7**. I have used "K" instead of "N" as prefix for the Newark system because N could be confused with the abbreviation for "north" when parts of the ponds are to be referenced. For the system of ponds in Hayward (the old Baumberg plant ponds) currently outside the NWR limits, I use the prefix "H" to avoid confusion with ponds B1 and B2 (Leslie's designations) in Mountain View – a part of the old Alviso system.

Current Studies of Salt Pond Ecology

A few studies have analyzed ecological or ornithological aspects of groups of salt evaporators with consideration of the differences among the ponds. The chief ones are:

1. Carpelan (1957), who studied a sequence of ponds in the Alviso area and reported primarily on the water chemistry, algae (including microscopic forms), and invertebrates, but mentioned some birds.

2. Anderson (1970), who studied five ponds south of Mowry Slough east to the Southern Pacific Railroad with respect to their use by birds in relation to different salinities and seasons of the year. However, his study omitted three ponds that were involved in the water-movement sequence from intake to three or four ponds short of the crystallizers, as the system then operated.

3. Gill (1977), essentially a summary of his 1971 survey of all breeding species found in bay-related habitats south of San Mateo Bridge (his M.A. thesis at San Jose State), with updates through 1975 from scattered later observations by him and others. Does mention salt ponds and their dikes as habitat features for many species.

4. Swarth (1981), who reported waterbird numbers pond by pond on the 11 ponds lying west of Coyote Hills between the new Alameda Creek Channel (which obliterated the former Coyote Hills Slough) and the east approach to Dumbarton Bridge.

5. Swarth, Akagi and Metropulos (1982), who incorporated the results from Swarth (1981) and extended counts of birds on the same set of ponds. The bird numbers were also analyzed for correlation with the biomass of major invertebrate populations (chiefly brine shrimp and water boatmen) as determined by hundreds of plankton hauls in the upper ¼ meter of water within three meters of a canoe, as well as to variations in water temperature, salinity, pH and depth and to wind direction and location about the periphery of each pond.

The last is by far the most thorough study of bird use of salt ponds and should be reviewed for information about each species to be considered in developing wetlands goals for this habitat type. Yet both that study

Howard L. Cogswell

Eared Grebes between foraging dives on salt pond K3, January 12, 1989

and the earlier one by Swarth (1981) counted birds only during the four to six hours spanning the high tide point on the adjacent Bay, ostensibly to be able to report the "maximum use" of the ponds by birds. They reported in general terms only, e.g., that most shorebird species were essentially absent from the salt ponds when the nearby tidal flats were exposed. Cogswell (1981) found that exposed tidal flats at the lower tide-levels had a drawing power for shorebirds that even exceeded that of higher level tidal mudflats (that had been created by opening dikes of long-abandoned salt ponds at Hayward). This study included data from all tide levels, but of course none from existing salt ponds.

Another limitation of the studies west of Coyote Hills which was not mentioned by Swarth et al. (1982), is that some or all of the ponds they studied had been receiving water since 1972 from the approximately 20 evaporators that lie to the north of new Alameda Creek. That area is the former Baumberg Unit of the Leslie Salt operation, water from which since that year has been sent by siphon under the new creek channel to merge with that in ponds south of it. So, the Swarth et al. classification of ponds into "low, medium, and high" salinity apparently did not include any that were strictly the lowest or "intake only" salinity. In addition, under the Leslie operation since 1972, ponds K3, K2, and K1 south of the Dumbarton Bridge approach have been the final evaporators in this sequence before the water is pumped to the pickle pond and crystallizers. So Swarth et al. also had no bird data from these highest salinity evaporators, although they did sample invertebrates in the western part of Pond K3 (their Pond 14) and two small "pump donut" ponds close to the bridge.

In 1992-93, I did semi-monthly counts of shorebirds and ardeids, and noted general numbers of other birds on Pond K1 and adjacent Newark Slough as a part of the San Francisco Bay Bird Observatory (SFBBO) Shorebird High-tide Habitat Use Study. Other observers did the same in many units around the South Bay in the same periods. The SFBBO has also implemented (for some 17 years) a Colonial Waterbird Breeding Monitor-

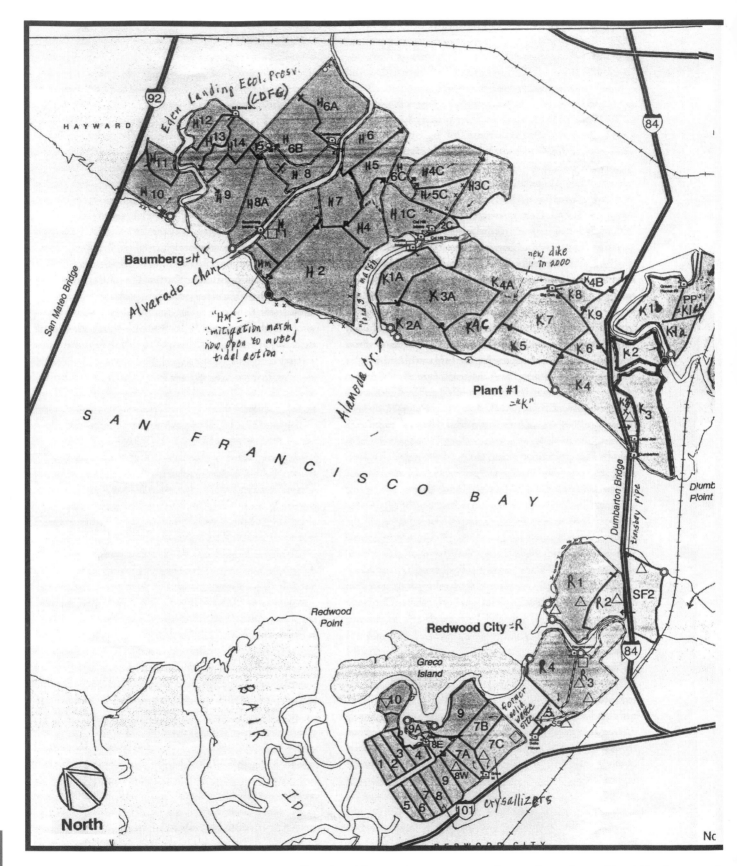

Figure 7.7 Numbering System for the Salt Ponds of South San Francisco Bay.   Developed by H.L. Cogswell

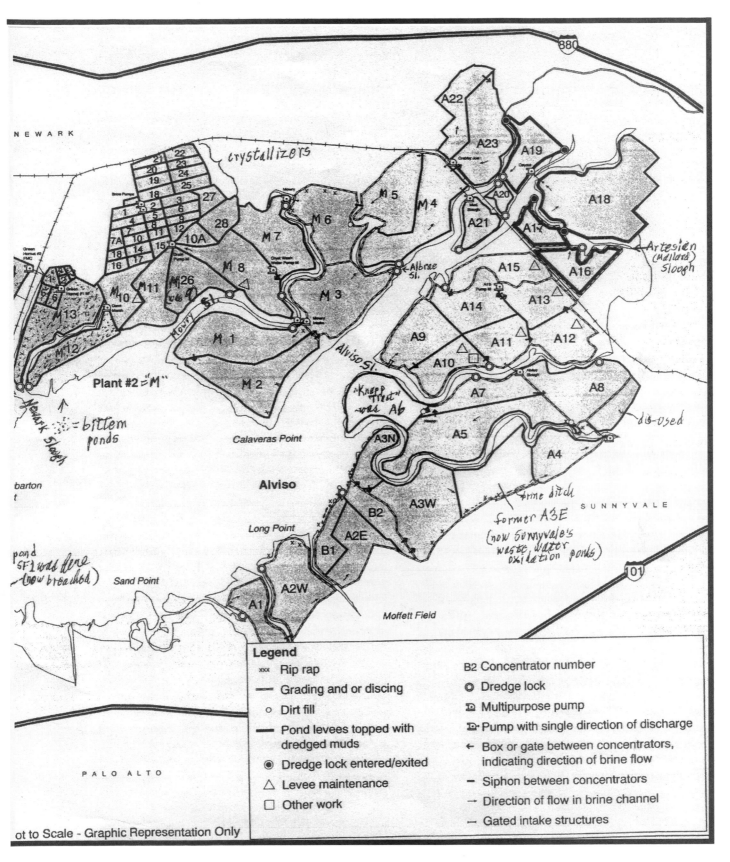

Legend

xxx Rip rap

— Grading and or discing

○ Dirt fill

— Pond levees topped with
    dredged muds

◉ Dredge lock entered/exited

△ Levee maintenance

☐ Other work

B2 Concentrator number

◎ Dredge lock

⊡ Multipurpose pump

⊡ Pump with single direction of discharge

← Box or gate between concentrators,
    indicating direction of brine flow

– Siphon between concentrators

→ Direction of flow in brine channel

⊣ Gated intake structures

ot to Scale - Graphic Representation Only

based on a map from the Cargill Salt 1998-1999 Completion Report.

ing Program. This program encompasses areas around the Bay south of the San Mateo Bridge, and includes all of the nesting herons and egrets (and a few white-faced ibises) and all of the gulls and terns. Yearly reports (e.g., Layne 1995) are made to the NWR as to the locations and numbers of nests or birds in each colony and for some years some data regarding success. Trends in total numbers and some colonies of herons and egrets for the first 15 years were analyzed by Ryan (1998) for all habitats, including the few in salt ponds.

Use of Salt Ponds by Some Key Bird Species

The following sections summarize information on the use of salt ponds by 16 of the 24 bird species that were selected by the "Other Birds" Focus Team as representative of our group of species. The summaries are based on information from each of the above-mentioned reports, plus from my own memory based on over 30 years of experience with birds on salt ponds (mostly in the Hayward to Fremont area). The literature makes frequent reference to "low," "medium," and "high-salinity" evaporators or salt ponds. Herein, I use the terms "salt ponds" and "evaporators" interchangeably, unless specific reference is made to crystallizers or pickle ponds, and I omit bittern ponds entirely because of their exceedingly low habitat value for any birds.

My "low salinity" pond category includes ponds with apparently higher fish populations than any west of Coyote Hills, and thus also encompasses high-fish ponds (intake ponds or the next few in long strings of evaporators), such as those sampled for fish by Lonzarich (1989). The "high-salinity" category also is extended at least by several ponds from what was considered to be that category by Swarth et al. (1982); but my "medium-salinity" ponds encompass the same range as theirs and a bit more on each end. In the future, a thorough analysis of data over the whole range of salinities might justify recognizing as many as five salinity categories rather than three.

Eared Grebe (*Podiceps nigricollis*) – Abundant on medium or medium-high saline evaporators from October through April, and present in lesser numbers in late August through September and in May. Anderson (1970) reported a maximum count of 6,330 in November on his "ponds with high-salinity". Swarth et al. (1982) reported their maximum of 5,565 in April 1980, but numbers the following spring were below 3,200. They had average counts of 500 and about 1,950 in November of the two successive years, and a very few were found through the summer. Correlation of eared grebe November-April numbers per 10 hectares in each of the 11 ponds in the same study was strongly correlated (at $p < 0.02$ level) with the grams dry weight of invertebrate biomass sampled in the same ponds. The brine shrimp and water boatmen that constituted nearly all of these biomass samples are apparently the prime food for this

species during its stay here. Brine fly larvae and pupae, spending most of the time on or near the bottom of the salt ponds, may also be important foods, but were mostly missed in the surface plankton hauls.

There have been an estimated one to several thousand eared grebes on each of several different evaporators in the medium-salinity range in southwest Hayward in the fall of different years, and the same is probably true for each set of salinity-sequence ponds around the South Bay. In some areas, the numbers are higher in the April migration period. The total number may thus be 50,000 to 100,000 or more birds – a significant portion of the species population, although minor by comparison with its concentration in late summer at Mono Lake and the winter numbers on Salton Sea.

In 1983, a nesting colony of 70+ adult eared grebes on abandoned sewage ponds in Pleasanton, eastern Alameda County, produced at least nearly the same number of young before abandoning them still in flightless condition as the pond was drained in July. A smaller colony the same year also produced young in the Crittenden Marsh (brackish?) near Mountain View (W. Bousman, pers. comm.), and some persisted for several years in a nearby area. Swimming invertebrate or fish food resources, plus at least some emergent or submerged vegetation to which floating nests can be anchored, are required for grebe nesting. The salt ponds that supply the former very rarely have any of the latter, so their value as a breeding habitat for this species is very limited.

American *White Pelican* (*Pelecanus erythrorhynchos*) – Present as non-breeding visitors (most probably post-breeding) to the several lowest salinity salt evaporators in most of the intake sequences around the Bay from July through October in considerable numbers. Some 900 or so were regularly in the South Bay from 1965 through about 1980, then somewhat fewer. Numbers diminish through the winter at rates that vary among years (to zero in some years), followed by resurgence in some years in April and early May. There are a few records also through June.

Even in their peak period, local surveys of only one set of low-saline ponds may often reveal no white pelicans, while a few days later (or even later the same day) scores or hundreds may be present. The 900 total estimated above was supported by numerous flights by small airplane which I made in the 1970s and early 1980s, covering most of the salt ponds from Hayward, south to Alviso, and north through Mountain View, and occasionally on through Redwood City. Salt ponds in which white pelicans were seen feeding and/or resting (both activities in many cases) were: H10 and H11 [H10 has been an intake pond since 1973], and H1 and H2 (and sometimes the adjacent H4 and H7) in Hayward, K1A and K2A in northwestern Fremont, M1 and M2 south of Mowry Slough in southwestern Fremont, A9 in Alviso, and A1 and A2W in Mountain View. Flocks have been observed flying on nearly straight-line routes between some of these locations.

Pond K1 south of upper Newark Slough, but visible from the Dumbarton Bridge approach, was for years a major gathering point – and most of the white pelicans in the old "Dumbarton Bridge" records noted in Audubon Field Notes and other publications were probably there. After the closing of the Baumberg Salt Plant, however, and the re-ordering of the water flow in late 1972, this pond became a highly saline pond and has held no white pelicans that I know of, even though it still has the numerous small islands on which they formerly rested. In the fall of 1964 and 1965, the full 900 were estimated on ponds H4 through H7 near Turk Island hill, which should have been medium-salinity ponds in those years. Several color-dyed birds were observed there that had come from marking programs at Great Salt Lake, Utah, and Malheur Lake, Oregon, and as I remember, one from Yellowstone Lake. Small flocks have continued to use the H3C, H4C, and H5C ponds and rest on adjacent dikes in at least some winters since 1985, perhaps only when extended rainy weather dilutes those ponds or when the salt company moves water into them in particularly accelerated fashion so that many fish are included.

The presence of large numbers of small to medium-sized fish in water less than a meter deep, where they are susceptible to ready capture (by the swim-and-scoop method often used in concert by flocks of this species), is undoubtedly the chief factor that controls just which ponds are used by them. Barren islands or remote dikes seldom traveled by any human or large predator are augmenting favorable factors – but such features are sometimes reached by flights from the feeding areas if need be. For example, up to 100 or so white pelicans often come to sit on the dikes between effluent ponds in a fenced-off area of the Hayward Regional Shoreline, where they preen, sleep, and fly away again without (at

least much of the time) swimming on those ponds or attempting to forage. For an account of the variety of fishes [and their relative numbers?] in salt ponds, the research work of David Lonzarich (1989) in the mid-1980s should be reviewed. A short commentary about his findings and enthusiasm for the study appeared in the San Francisco Bay Bird Observatory Newsletter 5(no.8, Sep.1986).

The question of whether white pelicans would ever breed on any islands in the salt pond system if they were located near a favorable food supply should be considered. Perhaps such a situation could be developed at the Napa-Solano County ponds now owned by the State. There were modest size flocks that used the low-salinity ponds there at least at times; but the fish-bearing ponds would have to be maintained as such, which presents an expense and management problem for public agencies not engaged in salt production. There might even be some possibility for a nesting island in a portion of the Baumberg Tract, purchase of which by the Wildlife Conservation Board has just been authorized. This would require maintenance of the site's island characteristic (water all around it wide and deep enough to deter most predators) and continued presence of good fishing nearby – probably depending on Cargill Salt continuing Pond H10 as an intake.

Brown Pelican (*Pelecanus occidentalis*) – This species has been said (in the December 12, 1995 meeting notice for this Focus Team) to be "restricted to Central Bay." This is not completely true. Small numbers frequently reach areas on the open Bay south to Dumbarton Bridge, and occasionally even farther. I recall seeing in late summer or fall up to 30 or 40 on Pond H1, an intake pond in Hayward, where they sat with the white pelicans or fished in their midst. Sometimes these birds would use the same surface-feeding technique as the white pelican, but sometimes it would plunge-dive at a shallow angle obviously designed to avoid striking

White pelicans and ducks on a salt pond west of old Alvarado, September 17, 1964.

Howard L. Cogswell

Chapter 7 — Other Birds of the Baylands Ecosystem   395

Other Birds

the bottom in such shallow water. There is probably little that could be done in operating salt ponds to enhance their value to this species, beyond the provision of some islands in or near the fish-bearing ponds, which would be done for the white pelican or for various terns (see accounts for those species). The northernmost nesting ground for this species, at Point Lobos, Monterey County, has long been abandoned, and there seems little likelihood of any area north of that being chosen. Alcatraz or Red Rock Islands in the Central Bay would be more like their traditional sites, and have been "available" for many years.

Double-Crested Cormorant (*Phalacrocorax auritus*) – Birds of this species use the fish-bearing low-salinity salt ponds all year, but in considerable numbers primarily in the fall. Swarth et al. (1982) found a maximum of 82 (on Pond K2A) in their study area in December 1979 and 79 in late September 1981, although mean numbers were less than half of these figures. Numbers sometimes reach well over 100 in the fish-rich ponds H1 through H4 in southwest Hayward, where they rest on the dikes with pelicans, or on the numerous wooden posts in some of the ponds. In the Central Bay, they have roosted at night on power lines or power-line towers for years, e.g., over 5,000 on the line to Brooks Island in the early 1940s (Bartholomew 1942, 1943a,b) and late 1940s (Cogswell, pers. obs.). That power-line has since been removed.

Gill (1977) did not find double-crested cormorants breeding in the South Bay during his 1971 survey. However, in more recent years, they have increasingly taken to nesting on the platforms or sometimes at junctions of legs and braces of powerline towers, e.g., many such south of the western part of San Mateo Bridge. In the salt ponds west of the Napa River, a few nested for a number of years in eucalyptus trees that had died when one salt pond was formed around them; and in the same general pond system, small numbers nested at least in the early 1980s on powerline towers over some of the salt ponds. I know of no such nesting yet in the South Bay, but there are many places where it might take place. However, the numbers of double-crested cormorants using salt ponds either for foraging and daytime resting or for nesting on structures within the ponds is probably rather small compared to the total number in or near the deeper parts of the Bay.

Snowy Egret (*Egretta thula*) – Although Swarth et al. (1982) reported a maximum count of 16 in their 11-pond study area, there are times in late summer or fall when just ponds H1 and H2, and H4 through H7 in southwest Hayward (at least H1, H2, and H4 having high fish populations) are utilized by over 100 snowy egrets at a time [and at least half to 2/3 that number of great egrets and many great blue herons as well]. There are probably similar large numbers on the low- to medium-salinity salt ponds near the largest nesting colony.

This is in tule marsh within Artesian (Mallard) Slough, east of Alviso, where the tremendous flow of San Jose-northern Santa Clara County sewage effluent has converted the tidal marsh to that type. Snowy egrets formerly nested on outer Bair Island in the upper part of *Salicornia* marsh on and next to the outer levee and later in coyote-bushes (*Baccharis*). Gill (1977) counted 340 and 362 active nests in these areas in 1971 and 1973, respectively. The salt ponds next to this site were taken out of use in the early 1970s, and the colony was decimated by predators (probably red foxes) in subsequent years.

Non-breeding snowy egrets will probably continue to use the low-salinity salt ponds for feeding and resting as long as they continue to have fish within their reach. The numbers foraging during the breeding season does drop in those ponds that are far from the colonies, which could perhaps be improved by providing other tall marsh areas in sloughs or freshwater ponds near those salt ponds. The only example of that known to me is the presence in 1995 of over 100 pairs of snowy egrets nesting (many young being produced successfully) in tall tules planted in effluent ponds at the Hayward Shoreline just three years earlier. A fair number of these birds flew south a mile or so to active salt ponds H10 and H11 and perhaps farther to forage. This colony has continued active at least to 1999.

Black-Crowned Night Heron (*Nycticorax nycticorax*) – Birds of this species use the low-salinity, fish-bearing salt ponds for foraging, but it seems in more localized fashion than the snowy egret. They seem to prefer places where water moves past their still-watch perch, such as gates or siphon-flows between ponds. Partly because they do much of their feeding at night, less is known about all the situations they use. Daytime roosting is usually in trees or within marsh growth, in small to fairly large flocks in the non-breeding season, e.g., in the primarily pickleweed marsh south of the outermost part of Alvarado Channel (old Alameda Creek). This marsh is being expanded eastward by 34 acres by Cargill Salt as mitigation for the impact on tidal marshes around the Bay by their levee-maintenance dredge (terms of the permit issued by the U.S. Corps of Engineers and San Francisco Bay Conservation and Development Commission). Several islands have or will be constructed in that vicinity also, and the attraction of all the diverse habitat may increase for this species.

Nesting colonies of night herons are established in very diverse types of vegetation: tall marsh (as in Artesian Slough, east of Alviso); on the ground or in coyote-bushes as on outer Bair Island [609 nests in 1973 (Gill 1977) but colony later abandoned]; dense-foliaged shrubs and low trees (as on Alcatraz Island); and dense-canopied cypress trees even in urban areas (as for years in the City of Alameda). For this species, and potentially other herons as well, a grove of such trees, or even densely-growing eucalyptus, might be planted on Turk

Island hill, which is surrounded by salt ponds in southwest Hayward. Some type of predator-proof (or strongly deterrent) structure would have to be placed across each of the several levees that tie into the island. Perhaps the species most likely to respond to such trees, however, would be the great blue heron which already nests in salt ponds in that general vicinity on the scattered old duck blinds, Archimedes' screw pumps, and one old gun club building.

Northern Harrier (*Circus cyaneus*) – This species nests in some salt marshes (upper portions, that are not flooded by tides in April or May), as well as in or near freshwater marshes or grassy flats inland. In the non-breeding season around the entire South Bay, and in the breeding period within a probable several-mile radius from their nest sites, they forage frequently over various marshes, fields, roadsides, dikes, and also those salt ponds that have numerous birds. The passage of a harrier in its typical low-level flight is sufficient to cause massed fly-ups of sandpipers and even ducks, and to send sparrows and other songbirds diving into cover. A persistent harrier on the Hayward Shore successfully captured a red phalarope that only flew short distances from the surface of a pond on the predator's first three or four swoops at it. The actual impact on the population of birds using the salt ponds from predation by harriers is unknown, but is probably small for healthy and alert fully grown individuals which see the harrier coming. There might be some serious impact on downy to partly grown young on the open dikes or islands, but I know of no studies addressing this question.

On the other hand, the population levels of the northern harrier itself (and of several other avian predators) are of concern, and should be watched. With reduction of their natural habitats, especially those required for successful nesting, the harrier may be in some trouble where its chief hunting opportunities are over salt ponds. In 1971, Gill (1977) found five nests near the Bay south of San Mateo Bridge, three of them in pickleweed. In 1979 and 1980, a pair nested in "Ideal Marsh" west of the salt pond series studied by Swarth et al. (1982), and in 1985, a pair nested (but doubtfully successfully) in pickleweed marsh of upper Newark Slough close to Coyote Hills. A pair (or two?) nests fairly regularly in or near Coyote Hills Regional Park. North of there, in summer 1999, one female was seen hunting low over a large colony of Forster's terns, from which many young were found (partly to nearly fully eaten) on nearby levees. All of these birds probably foraged for considerable periods over nearby salt ponds. A study of the nesting success of the species in such situations compared to the more extensive habitat combinations of marshy ponds and fields of the Suisun area would be valuable.

Peregrine Falcon (*Falco peregrinus*) [and by implication also the wintering Merlin (*Falco colum- *barius*)]** – Birds of these species forage over any of the salt ponds that harbor many birds of their normally preferred types. Individual peregrines sometimes become specialists and pursue and capture primarily or only ducks, others work on shorebirds, others take readily to rock or mourning doves, etc. Their hunting covers large areas, yet individuals or pairs take up quarters for the winter where there are elevated perches (e.g., powerline towers) to which they return regularly to rest, pluck, and consume their prey, etc. The merlin is from this standpoint a smaller edition of the peregrine, feeding on smaller birds and normally selecting lower perches. Both species forage over salt ponds frequently, but only the peregrine seems susceptible to having its habitat enhanced in the area. This is because more and more of them are now adapting to human structures for nesting (Bay Bridge, high-rise buildings, etc.). Where this is encouraged and protected within the several-mile forage distance from salt ponds having many birds of suitable size, the salt pond resource would contribute to the breeding success of the peregrines.

California Clapper Rail (*Rallus longirostris obsoletus*) – This highly endangered subspecies depends almost entirely on tidal salt marsh for its foraging, retreat from danger, and for nesting. The impact on that habitat by salt-pond maintenance operations, now detailed and avoided or mitigated by the terms of the permit recently issued to Cargill Salt, will require ongoing watch to make sure that such damage does not resume. Clapper rails do occasionally step out into the open on a salt pond dike – but normally only when a super-high tide floods the adjacent marsh. This behavior is more prevalent around the dredge locks that the company builds to move the dredge between the outer ponds and the Bay. The low dikes of these locks soon become covered with pickleweed and other high-marsh plants; are they then a part of the salt marsh habitat, rather than the salt pond?

California Gull (*Larus californicus*) – Traditionally this species was only a non-breeding migrant and winter resident in coastal California, with large numbers beginning to arrive from inland and/or northern breeding areas in late July. Total populations reached 40,000 or more by September or October, the majority gathered for much of each day at or near the numerous solid-waste disposal sites near the Bay (Cogswell 1970, 1974). Numbers of California gulls dwindle somewhat near those sites (except in the Suisun Bay area), as winter numbers of larger gulls (western, and particularly the herring and glaucous-winged) increase; but spring migration of California gulls makes them again the most numerous species in March and early April. Especially in late summer and fall, but to some extent at other seasons also, many California gulls are seen foraging on the surface of medium to medium-high saline salt ponds – pecking here and there at the surface and apparently obtaining brine shrimp as food in the same fashion as they do, for example, on Mono Lake where thousands of these gulls nest. This species, like other medium- to large-size gulls, also forages on open tidal flats, or aerially over many different habitats, including the salt ponds. Gulls of all species (except the smallest, Bonaparte's) also use the salt pond dikes and islands for nighttime roosting or just as a protected place for daytime resting. Some flocks in the 1968-71 period even roosted at night standing in the saturated brine of crystallizers at Newark.

In 1982, about 30 pairs of California gulls were discovered nesting on small islands (old, partly submerged, dikes) in the salt ponds of the Knapp Tract, four miles northwest of Alviso. This was the first known breeding by this species in a coastal situation and the first documented record of nesting west of the Sierra Nevada-Cascade mountain ranges. By 1994, that colony had expanded to nearly 4,000 pairs (Layne 1995). Several smaller "satellite" colonies have also arisen – one on a dike in the crystallizer area in Newark, two others south and north of Mowry Slough (the latter with the Caspian Terns) with a total 471 nests in early June 1994, and a fourth on a salt pond dike near Triangle Marsh north of Alviso, with 490 birds (but only 43 nests in 1994) (Layne 1995). The last-mentioned colony was for several prior years much larger. Some of these satellite colonies have been decimated in some years by red foxes; but the three largest colonies have persisted at least through 1995, and the one south of Mowry Slough through 1999.

For several years (1983-1988), hundreds of the young California gulls were banded by SFBBO teams, mostly at the original Knapp Tract colony, as part of a detailed study of the increase in numbers and production of young within a small part of that colony (Jones 1986). For the past few years, the Knapp area has been cut out of the saltwater movement in the Cargill system, so it largely dries up by mid-summer. Large numbers of gulls have continued to nest there, but nests were disrupted apparently by red foxes in 1994 [and 1995?]. It is obvious that the breeding range expansion by this species now includes San Francisco Bay – in fact, a few pairs have even bred at the Alameda Naval Air Station (NAS).

Elsewhere, nesting gulls have been noted as having negative impacts on the nesting of other waterbirds in their vicinity. Their possible impact through predation on eggs or young of herons, egrets, and terns should be evaluated here – particularly for the Forster's and least terns. If it is decided that management of habitat should be directed toward maintaining the gull populations, as well as the other waterbirds, some decisions on just which areas can be provided or enhanced for the gulls will probably be necessary.

A major paper on the present range and status of California and ring-billed gulls throughout California is in preparation by W. David Shuford of Point Reyes Bird Observatory and Valerie Layne of San Francisco Bay Bird Observatory. A poster summarizing the growth of the California gull colonies around southern San Francisco Bay was presented by Hanson and Ryan, SFBBO staff, at the 1997 meeting of the American Ornithologists' Union.

Western Gull (*Larus occidentalis*) – This is the most "marine" in habits of all the large gulls in the Bay Area. It successfully maintains a more-or-less equal-numbers status through the mid-winter period in the Central Bay, even when large wintering numbers of glaucous-winged and herring gulls are present. Particularly in late summer and fall, considerable numbers of western gulls also spread to the inner reaches of the Bay – south to Alviso and east to at least Antioch. They are always in the minority among gulls in these areas, using the disposal sites, bay and shores, salt ponds, and marsh sloughs as forage areas.

The traditional major nesting grounds of this species, the Farallon Islands, continues to hold by far the largest number of breeding birds, over 10,000 pairs. Some of these nesting birds commute to Bay Area disposal sites for food, as evidenced by market-prepared chop and steak bones regurgitated on the nesting grounds. Nesting colonies existed on several islands in the Central Bay by at least the late 1960s, and on top of Pier 45 in San Francisco by 1971. A few pairs of western gulls also were found nesting amid the California gulls on the Knapp Tract, northwest of Alviso, in the 1980s by SFBBO teams, who banded a few of their young. One nesting pair was there in 1994 (Layne 1995). Thus, the salt pond habitat is at least marginally a breeding habitat for this species, and the remarks pertaining to the California gull (above) also apply to the western gulls, although in lesser degree.

Caspian Tern (*Sterna caspia*) – This largest tern has nested on dikes between or on barren islands within salt evaporators in the South Bay since at least 1922 in a colony that had 287 active nests in 1931 (DeGroot 1931). This colony apparently shifted exact location over the years, but was always near the eastern approach to Dumbarton Bridge. The colony was observed to have 378 nests on 21 May 1943 (Miller 1943), 188 nests plus 202 young out of nests on 21 June 1952 (C. Sather, oral report in my field notes), and 499 active nests (most with eggs, few with young) on 14 May 1954 (personal field notes). At least on these later dates, the colony was on the dike separating salt ponds K5 and K7, north of the bridge approach, and persisted there until at least the mid-1960s.

Anderson (1970) discovered a thriving colony of Caspian terns on the southern part of the curving dike between ponds M4 and M5, east of Albrae Slough. This site continued in use, at least intermittently, to 1996, when it was decimated by red fox predation a second time.

Avocets, Willets, and Marbled Godwits on Oliver Brothers' Salt Ponds During High-tide Period on the Adjacent Bay, December, 1967.

Walt Halland

Large numbers of this species have also nested in the 1970s and 1980s (at each site for a few years only) on the dike between ponds H10 and H11 (and low islands in H10), on the western end of a long peninsular dike between ponds H4 and H7, and on a still barren area of a former salt evaporator on outer Bair Island, Redwood City (estimated 500-600 pairs in July 1975 per Gill 1977). The H10/H11 colony (1969-74) was plagued by salt foam blowing across the nesting birds and was abandoned abruptly. The H4/H7 colony (1976-86?) was perhaps the new location of these same birds and continued expansion to over 100 pairs, including some on the still drivable levee between H4 and H2 – until all the levees in this area were retopped with dredge spoils. The SFBBO observers checking the colony in 1986 (or 1987?) recorded the mostly failed efforts of the terns to nest on the deeply cracked drying mud. Swarth et al. (1982) recorded a maximum of 9 Caspian terns in the salt ponds west of Coyote Hills in 1980 and 1981 – at which time the colony was only a mile or two to the north. The Bair Island colony suffered from probable red fox predation, but some birds continued to gather at the site for several years after any successful nesting. Caspian terns were also regularly seen in the San Pablo Bay-NapaRiver Unit of salt ponds (at least along Highway 37), and probably nested somewhere in that system.

Foraging by birds of this species is wide-ranging, but a majority apparently seeks fish in the open Bay. Certainly, compared to the Forster's terns, relatively few are seen diving over salt ponds, even the fish-rich low-salinity ones. Small numbers of Caspians also appear during the nesting season over reservoirs in the hills quite far from the Bay, and are known to carry fish from such locations back to the colonies (e.g., tags from fish stocked at Del Valle Reservoir have been found on the major South Bay colonies). Hence, the nesting and roosting

safety of islands and remote dikes in the salt pond system are the prime ways in which this species is benefited by this habitat.

Forster's Tern (*Sterna forsteri*) – This species is found mostly from May through September in or near salt pond habitats, when it is nesting or the fledged young are still under intensive care by the adults. A few are present through the winter in favored locations around the Bay, but are seldom seen on salt ponds then. Nesting takes place at numerous locations, mostly on small islands within the low- to medium-low salinity ponds (where fish are abundant, and where the newly fledged young may first try their own plunge-dives). Some colonies, however, are on islands within medium-high to high-salinity ponds, e.g., K1, K2 and K3 just south of the eastern approach to Dumbarton Bridge and Newark Slough. There are no fish in those ponds, and foraging is entirely in the slough or the open Bay. The total number of active nests tallied south of San Mateo Bridge in 1971 by Gill (1977) was 935, while in 1994 somewhat over 1,000 were in 27 colonies there (Layne 1995), nearly all of them on islands or remote dikes in salt ponds. Hence, there is no obvious increase or decrease in the total population in recent years.

Colonies of Forster's terns sometimes persist for many years at the same sites, but in other cases shift to new locations in the same general region. The species seems more able to succeed with smaller colonies than the Caspian, and is thus able to use even quite small islands. However, where these are in salt ponds subject to spring or early summer draw-down by the pond operators, their success is jeopardized by the relatively much easier access to the sites by predators. This took place, for example, in at least two years between the middle and end of May in Pond H8A and a colony of over 100 pairs disappeared. A goal for optimal habitats for this species would certainly include some careful planning and co-operation to keep higher water levels in ponds with nesting islands until the young terns were flying.

California Least Tern (*Sterna antillarum browni*) – This endangered subspecies has its northernmost ongoing breeding colony at Alameda NAS, where they are normally present from May to August. Some pairs with the earlier fledglings apparently move from this colony by mid-August to other sites with abundant small fish and nearby resting sites barren of vegetation and free of most disruption by predators or humans. These post-breeding assembly areas are considered important for the successful maturing of the young birds, including their development of adequate foraging skills. In the salt pond system, the areas most regularly used for this sort of activity are ponds H10 and H11 (resting on the dike between them or on islands), and H1 and H2 in southwest Hayward.

A few late nests of this species, probably by pairs that had nests interrupted at Alameda, have been found (June - August) in both of these areas; but I believe none persisted through hatching of the eggs. For several years small numbers of least terns gathered in summer on barren islands in the experimental ponds (treated sewage effluent) on the Hayward shore; and in 1990 one pair nested there successfully (young fledged) on the one island to which crushed oyster-shells had been added to attract them. There has not been any subsequent nesting there through 1999, however. In 1972-75 (Gill 1977), a small colony with at least 14 active scrapes in 1975 did nest successfully on the barren flat (former salt pond) near the Caspian tern colony on outer Bair Island—the least terns perhaps depending on the vigorous defense by the larger species against predator intrusion into the area. A few pairs also have nested near Pittsburg, on or near industrial wastewater ponds in the marsh zone.

The question of whether some parts of the salt pond system could be managed to provide enhanced habitat for this species is made more difficult to answer by the varying success of the "outliers" from the main Bay Area colony itemized above. The only procedure likely to succeed would be the provision of low, barren islands in or very close to low-salinity (intake) salt ponds and/or large channel-mouths at the bayshore. Elsewhere in its range, the least tern is known to take advantage of new dredge spoil islands (but of <u>sandy</u> spoils), and has done so to some extent in the Alameda–Oakland Airport area. The pervasively muddy nature of the substrate in the salt pond areas, and the vigorous growth of marsh or other halophytic vegetation on islands that are just above the waterline would have to be overcome, since these are ecological features which this species tends to avoid.

Coast Savannah Sparrow (*Passerculus sandwichensis alaudinus*) – Formerly known (at least in part) as the Bryant's marsh sparrow (*P. s. bryanti*), this is the form

of the continent-wide savannah sparrow that breeds in the coastal strip (especially the summer fog belt) of California from Humboldt County south to the vicinity of Morro Bay in San Luis Obispo County. It is somewhat more "marsh-adapted" than most subspecies of savannah sparrows, but notably less so than *beldingi* of southern California. Savannah sparrows of several other subspecies occur in migration or winter in grasslands and weed fields and to some extent in the marshes around the Bay. Many of these are essentially impossible to distinguish from *alaudinus* in the field, so habitat-use differences are very poorly known for these seasons.

The nesting habitat of *bryanti* [now *alaudinus*] was originally described as "tidal marshes" around San Francisco Bay, but gradually the form was found to occupy also the more moist grasslands of nearby valleys and outer Coast Range hills. Johnston (1968) provides the best summary – "It maintains populations in two main types of habitat in coastal California: the *Salicornia* association of tidal marshes and the grassland associations of the coastal fog belt." He gives some details from his own research on San Pablo Marsh and from earlier work elsewhere by Marshall (1948), and further compares the habitat niche of this form with the overlapping salt marsh form of song sparrow: "…on salt marshes [it] is nearly limited to the broad expanses of low-lying salicornia (*Salicornia ambigua*) on the older and higher parts of marshes…[that] lie back of that salt marsh vegetation (cordgrass, *Spartina foliosa*) best suited to frequent submergence by tidal flooding." The song sparrow's favorite forage area is the mud banks of the small channels within the latter type of marsh, but Johnston (1968) does mention that savannah sparrows are occasionally seen in that habitat in the higher marsh.

Eight nests were found in 1971 by Gill (1977) in his intensive survey of breeding birds south of San Mateo Bridge, where he cited the preferred nesting habitat as "levee tops grown to annual grasses and high pickleweed growing on the levee banks." Gill (1977) further estimated the overall nesting population of the area at 800 to 1,000 pairs. How many of these would be within the salt pond zone is unclear.

With respect to the salt pond habitats, savannah sparrows are often seen in winter and migration periods along those dikes that have at least frequent patches of herbaceous vegetation or *salicornia*, sometimes well away from marshes or herblands of greater width. The numbers that use such linear habitat zones are much greater, however, where there is upper-zone tidal marsh or seasonal wetland adjacent across the dike from the salt pond. Presumably, some of these birds are of the breeding form *alaudinus*, but this should be verified by in-hand identification. Where there is as much as an acre or two of mixed herbs and *salicornia*, such as along the Dumbarton Bridge highway fill through the salt pond zones, scattered individual savannah sparrows sing on territory (and are thus presumably *alaudinus*) through May and June. Elsewhere, in my experience, singing savannah sparrows are found in the diked-off "seasonal wetland" habitat as well as in the upper parts of the tidal marshes, and the species appears to be a marginal one with respect to use of even the "upland" bits included in the salt-pond complex.

Alameda Song Sparrow (*Melospiza melodia pusillula*) and Samuel's Song Sparrow (*M. m. samuelis*) – These are two of the three subspecies of song sparrows endemic to the tidal marshes and immediate vicinity in the San Francisco Bay system. The third one is *M. m. maxillaris* of the Suisun Bay area, where there are no salt ponds. All three forms were studied in detail from the standpoint of validity as subspecies, distribution, and habitats by Marshall (1948), and have been further updated with respect to ties to the remaining tidal marshes by Marshall and Dedrick (1994). Only *samuelis*, found in the marshes about San Pablo Bay and the Marin County side of San Francisco Bay, has been studied with respect to its breeding cycle, territory, and foraging habits (Johnston 1956). This involved three years of intensive work with banded birds on the San Pablo Marsh, Contra Costa County, and illuminated several ways, other than morphology, in which birds of that subspecies differ from their upland neighbors: 1) their territories are smaller and usually linearly arranged along the small curving channels in the marsh; 2) birds use the *Grindelia* or other higher plants of the marsh for nesting and/ or high-tide refuge, or even leave their territories for nearby upland edges during the higher high-tides; 3) the peak period of first brood egg-laying is March-April and renesting laying peaks in May, thus most nests avoid being flooded during the extra-high tides of June, whereas the upland song sparrows usually have eggs or nestlings from April to early July; and 4) dispersal of the young birds is much more limited than in the upland song sparrows, averaging only 185 meters from their hatching place. Presumably similar adpatations to the intertidal habitat exist in *pusillula* and *maxillaris*.

In the South Bay, Gill (1977) found 17 nests of *pusillula* in 1971, all between 12 March and 7 May, and estimated the total population south of San Mateo Bridge at 1,800 pairs. Birds of that race are commonly seen using the levees and dikes adjacent to its normal marsh habitats, and presumably *samuelis* in the San Pablo Bay–Napa River salt pond system does the same. No special study of the use of such habitats has been done, so the comments that follow are rather random recollections from my own experience with *pusillula*.

During the higher high tides of spring tide periods, when all the small channels in the tidal salt marsh are flooded, and even much of the *salicornia* zone is underwater, song sparrows that live or forage in such areas at other times of tide move to any nearby "above-water" refugium available. Where that is a salt pond dike, the birds gather and forage in and near the uppermost bits of vegetation – a few sometimes crossing the dike to forage on brine flies, e.g., at the edge of the salt pond itself. Occupancy that is more permanent at all tide levels, even singing on territory, occurs spottily along the bayfront levees of the outermost salt evaporators, even up to a half-mile or so from any real salt marsh. The few birds I have seen in such places forage amid rip-rap and the wisps of *salicornia* and ruderal herbs that grow in such places. This sort of habitat is also occupied where the habitat landward of the levee is seasonal wetland, with at least some "marsh" vegetation. I have also noted several song sparrows (presumably *pusillula*) on the dike with no rip-rap between Pond K1 (or PP1 of Leslie's system) and the former salt ponds of the Hickory Tract in Newark. This dike is now partly covered by *salicornia* and cuts off bits of the original head of Newark Slough, where there is always some residual water. Elsewhere, *pusillula* sparrows (or presumably such) are sometimes seen taking refuge or foraging on small walkways, pump structures, or associated fences within the edges of salt ponds themselves. All of these instances are, however, marginal to the main habitat occupied by these forms – the tidal salt marshes – and these salt marsh song sparrows actually are more restricted to the vicinity of such marshes than are the savannah sparrows. Hence, conservation goals should emphasize that type of habitat for all three endemic salt marsh adapted subspecies of the song sparrow.

References

Anderson, W. 1970. A preliminary study of the relationship of saltponds and wildlife – South San Francisco Bay. Calif. Fish and Game 56:240-252.

Bartholomew, Jr., G.A. 1942. The fishing activities of double-crested cormorants on San Francisco Bay. Condor 44: 13-21.

_____. 1943a. The daily movement of cormorants on San Francisco Bay. Condor 45: 3-18.

_____. 1943b. Contests of double-crested cormorants for perching sites. Condor 45:186-195.

Carpelan, L. 1957. Hydrobiology of the Alviso salt ponds. Ecology 38:382-385.

Cogswell, H.L. 1970. Gulls and solid waste disposal in the San Francisco Bay area, California. Proc. World Conf. on Bird Hazards to Aircraft, Queens Univ., Ontario. (Natl. Res. Council of Canada): 421-438.

_____. 1974. Ecological factors in the hazard of gulls to aircraft in a bayside complex of airports and solid waste sites. *In*: S.A. Gauthreaux, Jr. (ed.) Proc. Conf. Biological Aspects of the Bird/Aircraft Collision Problem, Feb.5-7, 1974, Clemson Univ., So. Carolina: 27-108.

_____. 1981. Populations of birds using new tidal lagoons compared to an outer tide flat on San Francisco Bay at Hayward, California. Tiburon

Ctr. for Envir. Studies, Tech. Rept. No. 1: 67-172,plus refs.

DeGroot, D.S. 1931. History of a nesting colony of Caspian terns on San Francisco Bay. Condor 33:188-192.

Gill, Jr., R. 1977. Breeding avifauna of south San Francisco Bay estuary. Western Birds 8:1-12.

Hanson, J.T. and A.D. Kopec. 1994. Habitat location and utilization by wintering and migrating shorebirds during high tides in South San Francisco Bay. Draft report by San Francisco Bay Bird Observatory for the San Francisco Estuary Project. 83pp.

Johnston, R.F. 1956. Population structure in salt marsh song sparrows. Part I: Environment and annual cycle; Part II: Density, age structure, and maintenance. Condor 58: 24-44, 254-272.

_____. 1968. *Passerculus sandwichensis alaudinus* Bonaparte/coastal savannah sparrow. *In*: O.L. Austin, Jr (ed) - A.C. Bent and collaborators. Life histories of North American Cardinals…sparrows and Allies. U.S. Natl. Mus. Bull. 237(2): 712-714.

Jones, P.A. 1986. Aspects of the reproductive biology of the California gull in Alviso, California. M.A. Thesis, San Francisco State Univ. 96pp. [has data on colony growth, clutch and egg sizes, growth of young in relation to various factors, and nest success compared to that in Mono Lake and Great Salt Lake colonies].

Layne, V. 1995. Colonial waterbird monitoring on South San Francisco Bay, a 1994 summary. San Francisco Bay Bird Observatory report to San Francisco Bay Natl. Wildl. Refuge. 9pp. [Giving for each species the range of observation dates, maximum count of adults and nests and date of such for each of numerous sectors around the South Bay. Comparable reports for prior years also on file at the NWR and at SFBBO.]

Lonzarich, D.G. 1989. Temporal and spatial variation in salt pond environments and implications for fish and invertebrates. M.A. Thesis, San Jose State Univ. 81pp.

Marshall, Jr., J.T. 1948. Ecologic races of song sparrows in the San Francisco Bay region. Part I: Habitat and abundance; Part II: Geographic variation. Condor 50: 193-215, 233-256.

Marshall, J.T. and K.G. Dedrick. 1994. Endemic song sparrows and yellowthroats of San Francisco Bay. Studies in Avian Biol. No.15: 316-327.

Miller, A.H. 1943. Census of a colony of Caspian terns. Condor 45: 220-225 [the same colony as described by DeGroot 1931].

Ryan, T.P. 1998. Population trends of herons and egrets in southern San Francisco Bay. Paper presented at the 1998 North American Ornith. Conf., 11 April, St. Louis, Missouri.

Swarth, C.W. 1981. A study of waterbird abundance and distribution on salt ponds in South San Francisco Bay. M.S. report for independent study class, Calif. State Univ., Dept. of Biol. Sci. 34pp. [pp. 24-34 present the raw data by each pond and census date].

Swarth, C.W., C. Akagi and P. Metropulos. 1982. The distribution patterns and ecology of waterbirds using the Coyote Hills salt ponds. Report to San Francisco Bay Natl. Wildl. Refuge, U.S. Fish Wildl. Serv. 75pp.

Other Birds

Appendix A

Author Contact Information

David G. Ainley
H.T. Harvey and Associates
3150 Almaden Expressway, Suite 145
San Jose, California 95118.
408-448-9450
dainley@harveyecology.com

Joy D. Albertson
Don Edwards SF Bay National Wildlife Refuge
P.O. Box 524
Newark, California 94560-0524
510-792-0222
joy_albertson@fws.gov

Janice M. Alexander
University of California, Berkeley
151 Hilgard Hall
Berkeley, California 94720-3110
510-643-5430
jalexand@nature.berkeley.edu

Peter R. Baye
U.S. Fish and Wildlife Service
Endangered Species Division
P.O. Box 2012
Mare Island, California 94592
707-562-3003
peter_baye@fws.gov

Dennis R. Becker
California Deptartment of Fish and Game
Grizzly Island Refuge
2548 Grizzly Island Road
Suisun, California 94585-9539
707-425-3828
grizzlyisland@dfg.ca.gov

William G. Bousman
321 Arlington Way
Menlo Park, California 94025
650-322-5282

Andrée M. Breaux
SF Bay Regional Water Quality Control Board
1515 Clay Street, Suite 1400
Oakland California 94612
510-622-2324
ab@rb2.swrcb.ca.gov

Michael L. Casazza
U.S. Geological Survey
Western Ecological Research Center
6924 Tremont Road
Dixon, California 95620
707-678-0682 ext.629
mike_casazza@usgs.gov

Steven C. Chappell
Suisun Resource Conservation District
2544 Grizzly Island Road
Suisun, California 94585
707-425-9302
srcd@castles.com

Howard L. Cogswell
1548 East Avenue
Hayward, California 94541-5313
510-581-2201
CABIRDS@aol.com

Ron Duke
H.T. Harvey and Associates
3150 Almaden Expressway, Suite 145
San Jose, California 95118
408-448-9450
rduke@harveyecology.com

Jules G. Evens
Avocet Research Associates
P.O. Box 839
Point Reyes California 94956
415-663-1148
jevens@svn.net

Phyllis M. Faber
212 Del Casa
Mill Valley, California 94941
415-388-6002
pmfaber@aol.com

Leora Feeney
1330 Eighth Street
Alameda, California 95401
510-522-8525

Steve Foreman
LSA Associates, Incorporated
157 Park Place
Point Richmond, California 94801
510-236-6810
steve.foreman@lsa-assoc.com

Stephen L. Granholm
LSA Associates, Incorporated
157 Park Place
Point Richmond, California 94801
510-236-6810
stephen.granholm@lsa-assoc.com

Brenda J. Grewell
University of California, Davis
Environmental Study & Policy Development
Davis, California 95616
530-752-4326
bjgrewell@ucdavis.edu

Janet T. Hanson
San Francisco Bay Bird Observatory
P.O. Box 247
Alviso, California 95002
408-946-6548
jthanson@sfbbo.org

Laura A. Hanson
Hanson and Associates
5686 Lakeville Highway
Petaluma, California 94954
707-747-9659
pipefish@earthlink.net

Elaine K. Harding
University of California, Santa Cruz
Department of Environmental Studies
Santa Cruz, California 95064
831-476-1906
mouser@cats.ucsc.edu

Bruce Herbold
U. S. Environmental Protection Agency-Region 9
75 Hawthorne Street (WTR-3)
San Francisco California 94105-3901
415-744-1992
bherbold@aol.com

Catherine M. Hickey
University of California, Davis
Graduate Group in Ecology
1 Shields Avenue
Davis California 95616
cmhickey@ucdavis.edu

Kathryn A. Hieb
California Department of Fish and Game
4001 North Wilson Way
Stockton, California 95205
209-942-6078
khieb@delta.dfg.ca.gov

Glen Holstein
1509 Pacific Drive
Davis, California 95616
530-758-6787
holstein@pa.mother.com

Mark R. Jennings
U.S. Geological Survey
39913 Sharon Avenue
Davis, California 95616
530-753-2727
RanaResources@aol.com

Michael L. Johnson
University of California, Davis
John Muir Institute of the Environment
1 Shields Avenue
Davis, California 95616
530-752-8837
mbjohnson@ucdavis.edu

Robert E. Jones
Museum of Vertebrate Zoology
University of California, Berkeley
Berkeley, California 94720-3160
510-642-1379

Kurt F. Kline
Advanced Biological Testing
5685 Redwood Drive, Suite 105
Rohnert Park, California 94928
707-588-2880
abt@hooked.net

Brita C. Larsson
Romburg Tiberon Center
P.O. Box 855
Tiburon, California 94920
415-338-3540

Robert A. Leidy
U.S. Environmental Protection Agency-Region 9
75 Hawthorne Street
San Francisco, California 94105
415-744-1970

William Z. Lidicker, Jr.
Museum of Vertebrate Zoology
University of California, Berkeley
Berkeley, California 94720-3160
510-643-7713
lidicker@socrates.berkeley.edu

Kevin MacKay
2880 Zanker Road
San Jose, California 95136
408-434-2244
kevinm@jsanet.com

Wesley A. Maffei
Napa County Mosquito Abatement District
P.O. Box 655
Napa, California 94559
707-258-6044
midge@lanminds.com

Lt. Dante B. Maragni
National Marine Fisheries Service, SW Region
Habitat Conservation Division
777 Sonoma Avenue, Suite 325
Santa Rosa, California 95404
707-575-6050

Carolyn M. Marn
U.S. Geological Survey-Davis Field Station
Western Ecological Research Center
1Shields Avenue, Kerr Hall, Room 278
Davis, California 95616
530-752-9163
carolyn_marn@usgs.gov

Michael F. McGowan
San Francisco State University
Tiburon Center for Environmental Studies
P.O. Box 855
Tiburon, California 94920
415-338-3514
mcgowan@sfsu.edu

A. Keith Miles
U.S. Geological Survey-Davis Field Station
Western Ecological Research Center
Graduate Group in Ecology
1 Shields Avenue, Kerr Hall, Rm 278
Davis, California 95616
530-752-5365
keith_miles@usgs.gov

Michael R. Miller
U.S. Geological Survey-Dixon Field Station,
6924 Tremont Road
Dixon, California 95620
michael_r_miller@usgs.gov

Gary W. Page
Point Reyes Bird Observatory
4990 Shoreline Highway
Stinson Beach, California 94970
415-868-1221 ext.23
gpage@prbo.org

Thomas P. Ryan
San Francisco Bay Bird Observatory
P.O. Box 247
Alviso, California 95002
408-946-6548
wtswift@aol.com

Michael K. Saiki
U.S. Geological Survey-Dixon Field Station
Western Fisheries Research Center
6924 Tremont Road
Dixon, California 95620
707-678-0682 ext.617
michael_saiki@usgs.gov

Howard S. Shellhammer
San Jose State University
Department of Biological Sciences
San Jose, California 95192-0100
408-924-4897
shellham@email.sjsu.edu

Ted R. Sommer
California Department of Water Resources
Environmental Services Office
3251 S Street
Sacramento, California 95816-7017
916-227-7537
tsommer@water.ca.gov

Lynne E. Stenzel
Point Reyes Bird Observatory
4990 Shoreline Highway
Stinson Beach, California 94970
415-858-1221
lstenzel@prbo.org

John Y. Takekawa
U.S. Geological Survey-SF Estuary Field Station
P.O. Box 2012
Vallejo, California 94592
707-562-2000
john_takekawa@usgs.gov

Robert N. Tasto
California Department of Fish and Game
20 Lower Ragsdale Drive, Suite 100
Monterey, California 93940
831-649-7142
btasto@dfg.ca.gov

Scott Terrill
H.T. Harvey and Associates
3150 Almaden Expressway, Suite 145
San Jose, California 95118
408-448-9450
sterrill@harveyecology.com

Lynne A. Trulio
San Jose State University
1 Washington Square
San Jose, California 95192-0116
650-964-5944
ltrulio@email.sjsu.edu

Nils Warnock
Point Reyes Bird Observatory
4990 Shoreline Highway
Stinson Beach, California 94970
415-868-1221 ext.37
nilsw@prbo.org

Sarah E. Warnock
Point Reyes Bird Observatory
4990 Shoreline Highway
Stinson Beach, California 94970
415-868-1221 ext.37

Frank G. Wernette
California Department of Fish and Game
4001 North Wilson Way
Stockton, California 95205
209-948-7800
fwernett@delta.dfg.ca.gov

NOTES

NOTES

NOTES

NOTES